✔ **labels on each tape, tape box and lyric sheet giving your name, address and phone number?**

✔ **a stout self-addressed stamped envelope (SASE) with enough postage to cover the cost of returning your demo to you?**

First impressions are critical. A professionally presented demo package will give you an immediate advantage over most of the competition.

1991
Songwriter's Market

Where & How to Market Your Songs

Edited by
Mark Garvey

Assisted by
Brian C. Rushing

Cincinnati, Ohio

Managing Editor, Market Books Department:
Constance J. Achabal

Songwriter's Market. *Copyright © 1990 by*
Writer's Digest Books. Published by F&W Publi-
cations, 1507 Dana Ave., Cincinnati, Ohio
45207. Printed and bound in the United States of
America. All rights reserved. No part of this book
may be reproduced in any manner whatsoever
without written permission from the publisher, ex-
cept by reviewers who may quote brief passages to
be printed in a magazine or newspaper.

International Standard Serial Number
0161-5971
International Standard Book Number
0-89879-425-0

Contents

Services & Opportunities

From the Editor

If you had the chance to do whatever you wanted with your songwriting talent, what would you choose to do? Many of you might aim immediately for the top of the charts—shooting for the big rock, pop or country hit that would establish your reputation and fatten your bank account. Some of you might have a flair for marketing, which, combined with the ability to write on demand in a wide variety of styles, could make you a formidable jingle writer. Still others might excel at writing music for the theater, symphony or even songs for rock bands in your own hometown. The fact is, whatever style (or styles) of music you write, and whatever your level of ambition, there is a place for you in today's music business. If you don't believe it, just take a quick look through some of the listings in this year's *Songwriter's Market*.

Like the wide variety of choices facing the songwriter, *Songwriter's Market* offers a diverse smorgasbord of people and companies interested in every conceivable style and form of music. No matter what kind of music you write, there is someone listed in this book who is interested in hearing it.

Our goal each year is to bring you the most complete and informative compilation of facts available on over 2,000 music markets. This, the 1991 edition, is no exception. Of this year's listings—which include music publishers, record companies, record producers, managers, advertising agencies, play producers and more—over 850 are new to *Songwriter's Market*. Of those that are repeat listings from last year, 70% indicate some kind of change since the 1990 edition in areas such as music needs, payment policy, address or contact person. All of the listed companies take the time and trouble to carefully describe for you the kinds of music they seek, the projects they've been involved with in the past and the kinds of things they'll be doing in the future. With this information at your fingertips, it's a simple matter to match your ambitions and strengths with those companies whose goals most closely parallel yours.

Valuable contacts aren't all you'll find in *Songwriter's Market*, however. In The Business of Songwriting, you'll learn all the business basics you need to know to start pitching your tunes more professionally *today*. From an expanded explanation of the structure of the music business to contracts, money matters, song shark "rip offs" and more, The Business of Songwriting is your annually updated introduction to the ins and outs of this exciting industry.

Effective demos require a smart combination of appropriate production techniques and savvy salesmanship. This year's Special Business Feature, Fine-Tuning Your Demos, surveys publishing and A&R executives to find out what a demo needs to compete in today's market.

Divining the future of the music industry is no easy task, but author and music publishing executive Randy Poe takes an informed shot at it in his entertaining article, What's Ahead for the Music Industry. From his vantage point at a major West Coast music publishing house, Randy assesses recent changes in musical technology, music publishing and independent record labels and tells how the latest developments in these areas will affect you, the songwriter.

Encouraging, entertaining and informative: those three adjectives aptly describe this year's Close-up interviews with music industry executives and some of today's hottest songwriters. You'll get first-hand advice from publishers, A&R reps and writers of such hits as "I've Had the Time of My Life," "Wind Beneath My Wings," "The Living Years," and "Girl You Know It's True."

Being a successful songwriter in today's music business means nurturing your talent, constantly working to improve your craft, and learning as much as you can about how the business is run. Beyond that, it's up to you to decide which of the many available paths you and your music will take. *Songwriter's Market* is here to help you make the choices that are best for your songwriting career. Good luck!

How to Use Your Songwriter's Market

Before studying the listings and making your marketing plans, read these suggestions for the most productive use of all the features in _Songwriter's Market_. Especially note the explanations of the information given in the sample listing.

Read the section introductions _first_. Each gives a brief overview of the market area and can help you decide if it's a facet of the music industry appropriate for your style of writing and your personal goals.

Keep in mind that the information you are reading in the listings came directly from representatives of the companies listed. It is reported exactly as they gave it to us.

The Glossary in the back of this book will explain unfamiliar terms you might encounter while reading the listings.

For an explanation of the information given in the listings, match the numbered phrases in the sample listing with the corresponding numbers in the copy that follows.

(1) *CHRYSALIS MUSIC GROUP, 645 Madison Ave., New York NY 10222. (212)758-3555. (2) Professional Manager: Michelle Mannies. (3) Music publisher. (4) ASCAP, BMI. (5) Estab. 1972. (6) Publishes 100-150 songs/year; publishes 3-5 new songwriters/year. (7) Hires staff songwriters "in small quantities." Works with composers and lyricists; teams collaborators. (8) Pays royalty "standard in most cases, but negotiable."
Affiliates: (9) Chrysalis Music (ASCAP) and Chrysalis Songs (BMI).
How to Contact: (10) Call first and obtain permission to submit a tape. Prefers cassette with 3-5 songs and lyric sheet. (11) "Quality is stressed instead of quantity." Returns unsolicited material with (12) SASE. (13) Reports in 2 weeks.
Music: (14) Mostly pop/R&B, rock and country. (15) Published "Heart of Stone" (by Hill/Sinfield), recorded by Cher on Geffen Records (single-rock/pop); "Peace in Our Time" (by Hill/Sinfield), recorded by Eddy Money on Columbia Records (single-rock/pop); and "Anything I Want," written and recorded by Kevin Paige on Chrysalis Records (pop/R&B).
Tips: (16) "Be confident, and unique."

(1) **New listing.** An asterisk appears before the names of companies new to this edition.
(2) **Contact.** The name of the contact person(s) is supplied by the company listed. Address all submissions to this person unless otherwise indicated in the submission instructions. If no name is given, it's probably best to make contact by mail or phone, asking who the appropriate contact person is, before submitting a tape.
(3) **Type of company.** Each listing provides a description of the company's function(s).
(4) **Performing rights.** If a company indicated which performing rights societies it is affiliated with, we can include this information. ASCAP, BMI and SESAC are the major U.S. societies. PRO CAN, PRS and SACEM are examples of foreign societies.
(5) **Establishment date.** The year the company was established is given for each company that responded to that question. Sometimes there is a greater risk when dealing with new companies. So far as we know all are reputable, but some are unable to compete with older, larger companies. Many do survive, however, and become very successful. And most new companies are very open to material from new songwriters.
(6) **Size of market.** Figures given (e.g., number of songs published, released or produced per year or number of new songwriters published per year) are approximations to help you determine a market's activity and its openness to material from new songwriters.
(7) **Additional services/activities.** If applicable, the listing specifies that the company

hires staff writers, works with composers and/or lyricists, and helps to team collaborators. Some markets list additional services offered to songwriters.

(8) Payment. Most companies indicate their payment policy. "Standard" royalty means music publishers split royalties received with the songwriter 50-50. Some markets (advertising agencies, audiovisual firms) pay by the job or per hour rather than by royalty. Some markets (play producers, fine arts) are nonprofit and do not pay at all but offer valuable exposure for songs. Some listings in Record Producers and Managers and Booking Agents indicate that they charge a legitimate fee (negotiated in advance) for their services rendered rather than pay money to songwriters. They are still considered "markets" because they are in a position to shop songs to artists and companies for you, and they may be seeking writer/artists to represent.

(9) Affiliates. If a publisher has affiliated companies, they are listed in this special subhead. The affiliates are usually members of a different performing rights society than the main company listed, so they can work with writers who are members of either organization.

(10) How to submit. The types of music, the number of songs you may include in the submission, and the way you should submit your songs are stated in each listing. Failure to follow these instructions could result in your submission being refused or returned. Your close attention to the exact specifications of a particular listing will help assure your success. "Query" means to contact the company by phone or mail *before* submitting anything. "Does not accept unsolicited material" means you should never submit anything before you request and receive permission to submit. Some markets may indicate in their listings that you may send for evaluation a video of your act in performance or a group doing your songs in lieu of a standard cassette or reel-to-reel demo. Most have indicated that a videocassette is not required, but told us the format (Beta or VHS) of their VCR should a songwriter/artist want to send one. If no format is stated it is generally safe to assume that VHS is acceptable, but it is always a good idea to check with the company *first*. Always be sure to include a lyric and/or lead sheet with your video submission as you would with any other. It's always a good idea to write (or call) first for appropriate video format and television system before sending a videocassette as part of an international submission. Be aware that the television system in many foreign countries is different from that in the United States. For example, a Beta or VHS format tape recorded using the U.S. system (called NTSC) will not play back on a standard English VCR (using the PAL system) even if the recorder formats are identical. It is possible to transfer a video demo from one system to another but the expense in both time and money may outweigh its usefulness as opposed to a standard audio demo. Systems for some countries include: NTSC—United States, Canada, and Japan; PAL—United Kingdom (including England), Australia, and West Germany; and SECAM—France.

(11) Additional instructions. Many listings give additional submission instructions. Following these specific requests will increase the chances of your demo being listened to quickly and favorably.

(12) Return envelope. All mail should contain a stamped, self-addressed envelope (SASE); submissions to listings in foreign countries should include a self-addressed envelope (SAE) and International Reply Coupons (IRC) available at most major post offices. Some companies will not even answer a query letter unless you include a reply card or an SASE for their response. Those companies with "SASE" printed in their listing have indicated that they will return submissions if a large enough SASE with sufficient postage is included.

(13) Reporting time. The length of time markets say that they need to report back to songwriters on submissions is approximate. Music professionals go through periods of unbelievably heavy loads of submissions, and sometimes fall behind. Allow extra time for international submissions. If a market doesn't respond within several weeks after the reporting time given in its listing, don't despair. As long as your submission is in the possession of a market there is a chance someone may eventually find the time to review it a second, or even a third time. Every listening your demo gets represents one more chance for it to be picked up. That opportunity ends when your demo is sent back to you. Not receiving your submission back right away doesn't necessarily mean you've been ripped off. If after a reasonable length of time you still haven't received word on your submission, follow up with a *friendly* letter giving detailed information about your submission. Include your name, address and phone number; titles of songs submitted; type of demo submitted; and the date of submission.

(14) Musical styles. The companies listed indicate which types of music they are most interested in. This is very important—do not bother to send inappropriate material. Some of the terminology is standard (for instance, R&B = rhythm and blues) but some of the descriptions are worded exactly the way the company reported it to us.

(15) Examples of work. The published works, releases, and productions given within the Music subhead of each listing represent examples of the companies' accomplishments and not a complete list. In many instances they are not necessarily the companies' most current releases but the ones they feel best represent the kind of music they want to see.

(16) Tips. Many listings share additional information to help you further evaluate their needs and goals. Don't overlook this unique information!

Key to Symbols and Abbreviations

* New listing
SASE self-addressed stamped envelope
SAE self-addressed envelope
IRC International Reply Coupon, for use on reply mail in Canada and foreign markets

(for definitions of terms and abbreviations relating specifically to the music industry, see the glossary in the back of the book)

What's Ahead for the Music Industry

by Randy Poe

If the 1980s were any indication of where the music industry is heading in the 1990s, by the end of the decade there could be only one music publishing company and one record company in the United States, both of which would be owned by a Japanese electronics firm.

Luckily for American songwriters and recording artists, such monopolies aren't supposed to be allowed in this country. However, this doesn't negate the fact that the publishing and recording industries have changed considerably in recent years.

What does the music industry hold in store for you in the 1990s? Let's take a look at three areas that will have the greatest effect on songwriters, lyricists and performer/songwriters in the decade ahead: 1) advances in technology; 2) the cyclical nature of record companies; and 3) the evolution of music publishing.

Advances in technology

When Columbia and RCA Records introduced versions of fine-groove records which rotated at 33⅓ and 45 revolutions per minute, many people argued that they would never become commercially acceptable since the general public would be required to pay higher prices for the records and purchase new equipment to play them on.

Despite the fact that 78 r.p.m. records quickly became passe after the introduction of these two new forms of vinyl records, "experts" recently challenged the commercial viability of compact discs based on the same argument that the general public wouldn't be open to the idea of purchasing new audio equipment or paying substantially more money for CDs than they had been paying for LPs. To paraphrase Santayana, those who aren't aware of earlier goofy predictions are doomed to repeat them.

Of course, not every technological move the music industry made was an ongoing hit with the public. Although the 8-track tape was popular for a season, it was quickly replaced by the prerecorded cassette. This swift change in choice of technological preference by the general public was a sure sign that American society will not hesitate to move on to a more practical, better quality product when that product is introduced and properly marketed.

Based on this premise, my first prediction of what's ahead in the decade of the 1990s is an easy one: In the future the music industry will continue to create new types of phonorecords. (*Phonorecords* are defined by the 1976 Copyright Act as "material objects in which sounds . . . are fixed by any method now known or later developed, and from which the sounds can be perceived, reproduced, or otherwise communicated, either directly or with the aid of a machine or device.") If these devices are more practical and of higher audio quality than those then currently available in the marketplace, the current model will be replaced in a briefer amount of time than the "experts" will predict.

The next obvious wave in the technology of prerecorded music is the digital audio tape,

Randy Poe *is currently executive vice-president and general manager of Leiber & Stoller, a music publishing company whose copyrights include "Jailhouse Rock," "Kansas City" and "Stand By Me." For five years Randy was executive director of the Songwriters Hall of Fame and now serves on that organization's board of trustees. He frequently writes and speaks about music business topics and is the author of* Music Publishing: a Songwriter's Guide *(Writer's Digest Books).*

also known as DAT. If digital audio tapes have better sound quality and are marketed properly, a large number of the population may move on from the compact disc to DAT, while others may bypass CDs altogether. Whatever the outcome of the CD/DAT battle, there is no doubt that the vinyl LP has quickly become a part of the music industry past. The prerecorded cassette which is currently popular will, no doubt, also eventually succumb to the popularity of the CD and/or DAT.

To leap even further into the future, I believe that we are not too far away from a time when the industry will become tied into the personal computer. Although it may be a few years yet, we will probably find ourselves being capable of creating our own personalized compilation tapes much like those of the Personics System which is already on the market. The Personics System allows the public to go into a record store and pick out specific selections which are then automatically recorded onto a cassette tape. In the future, a person will be able to enter his musical selections on his home computer and create a tape which will contain the recordings of his choice.

We are getting very near the point at which we will be able to pay our bills by transferring monies via home computer. With that technology in place, it will be a simple matter for royalties to be paid automatically to record companies and music publishers when the consumer creates his own personalized recordings.

For those who might argue that this isn't probable since people like to go to a store and purchase recordings, I'm not trying to imply that record stores (or whatever they will be called) won't continue to exist in some form. However, it is interesting to note that, since the advent of television—and with the added attraction of the VCR in recent years—American society has shown a pattern of spending more and more time at home. Also, by providing recorded music directly to the consumer, record companies will be able, for the most part, to bypass the middle men (in this case, distributors and record stores) and make higher profits for themselves. There is no safer prediction than to say that, if a record company finds a method of making higher profits, that method will be implemented with great speed.

How advances in technology will affect you

The above-mentioned technological changes in the recording industry will be very good for the songwriter of the 1990s. On a very basic level, the average consumer wants the best possible quality at an affordable price. And, for the present moment, CDs fit those two consumer requisites. Because of this, music lovers are buying CDs at a brisk pace.

One major advantage of the CD for today's songwriters is so obvious that it tends to be overlooked: the amount of music the CD is capable of containing. The LP of earlier days usually had a total of 10 to 12 songs on it (approximately 35 to 45 minutes), whereas today's compact disc is capable of handling up to just over 70 minutes of recorded sound. This means more songs will be recorded for each release. **In the 1990s, then, there will be a greater demand for songs than ever before. That's good news for songwriters and music publishers alike.**

The bad news on the technological front is the increased ease of high quality duplication of copyrighted, pre-recorded music. A few years ago music publishers (and, consequently, songwriters) began to lose large amounts of money on sheet music sales when photocopying became accessible to the general public. The loss of income caused by duplication began to affect record companies and recording artists as well as writers and publishers in the 1970s, when dual cassette decks went on the market.

As the quality of the duplicating equipment has improved, all of the parties in the music industry have lost out on royalties due to what is commonly referred to as "home taping." This loss of income will only become worse in the next few years, as technological improvements make home recording even easier and of higher quality, unless Congress takes action which would make home taping more difficult, or unless a tax is required on blank tapes which would go toward making up for the loss of income to the artistic community.

The cyclical nature of record companies

The modern era of the record industry (beginning in the mid-1950s) has now been in existence long enough that a definite cyclical pattern has begun to emerge. The late 1950s and early '60s were a time when scores of successful smaller independent record companies existed alongside several major recording company empires.

During those years, the major labels slowly began to purchase many of these smaller companies, mainly for the purpose of acquiring the successful acts signed to them. These buyouts also proved to be an effective means of eliminating the competition. Before long, many of the smaller labels were gone, either due to their sale to majors or because they had grown large enough to become major labels themselves.

Since the major labels had their own distribution systems, the independent distributors were left with a much smaller amount of recorded product to distribute. This loss of income forced the indie distributors to hang on to the funds they received from retailers for a longer period of time than had been necessary in the past. The result was a severe lack of the kind of cash flow required to keep most independent record companies afloat.

Once the major labels began to dominate the pop charts in the '70s, many of the independent labels that managed to survive did so mainly because of their extensive back catalog of hits. Other indies managed to stay alive by striking a distribution deal with one of the major labels.

But the major labels found that they were encountering financial problems as well. After over two decades of acquisitions, their rosters were now filled with more artists than they could handle. The rise in recording and manufacturing costs became a great strain. Since many of the artists signed to these companies were not selling enough records to justify the expense of keeping them on the label, the solution was a series of roster cuts by most of the majors, leaving many well-known recording artists without a contract for the first time in their careers.

Luckily, there were some entrepreneurial-minded people around who realized the opportunity at hand. A major label needed each of its artists to sell at least 250,000 records to justify keeping the performer on the roster. But an independent label could turn a healthy profit if it had an artist which sold less than half of that amount.

So, near the end of the 1970s there began a new era of thriving independent labels that specialized in specific types of music. Blues artists who had been dropped by major labels began to find new homes at record labels that specialized in the blues. The same was true of folk artists, soul singers, and others who had been abandoned by the majors.

About the same time, other independent labels cropped up which specialized in punk, rap and other forms of new music which had begun to develop cult followings around the country. These indie labels were the counterpart of the early independent record companies which specialized in rock & roll in the late '50s and early '60s. As the audience for rap music grew, the major labels began buying up the smaller independent labels, just as they had in earlier days. And, the cyclical pattern had started once again.

How the cycle will affect you

There is no denying that getting a song recorded by a superstar on a major label is one of the more difficult tasks anyone could hope to accomplish. Major music publishers in New York, Nashville and Los Angeles attempt this feat everyday, meeting with failure much more often than with success. **Luckily for young songwriters, the independent label is an avenue which could prove to be very rewarding, thanks to the cyclical nature of the record industry.**

In the decade of the '90s, major record labels are going to continue to rely on independent labels as an important resource for new material. **Therefore, one of the more logical**

moves for a young songwriter to make is to get the attention of independent labels. A writer and/or artist who is creating new types of music on an independent label may suddenly find himself involved with a much larger label by virtue of the indie's sale to one of the majors.

Also, many hit songs of the past were originally recorded on small labels by unknown artists, only to be covered later by superstars. This practice will certainly continue in the 1990s — another important reason that songwriters shouldn't ignore the indies.

One of the major disadvantages that often befalls independent labels is a short life span. For every one that is successful or acquired by a major, there are hundreds which are unable to survive financially, or which have no real impact on the music industry. For the previously unrecorded songwriter, however, getting a song cut on *any* label — no matter how large or small — is always a step in the right direction.

The evolution of music publishing

Music publishing has always been an evolving industry. From the beginning, publishers have been forced to keep up with musical, social and technological changes. Before the days of recordings and performance royalties, publishers reaped their profits from the printing and selling of sheet music and song books.

When records caught on with the public, songwriters and music publishers were in constant demand since performers and record companies were in need of new songs. The advent of motion pictures with sound also called for the creation of more songs.

As years went by, times changed, and artists began to record their own material. The publishing companies found themselves banging on the record companies' doors, with each publisher trying to sell record company executives on the idea that their songs were better than their competitors'. As the number of artists recording outside material grew ever smaller, competition among publishers grew stronger.

Eventually music publishers got into the game of artist development, selling the artist/songwriter package to record companies rather than just trying to convince a record company A&R person of the merits of one particular song.

Although the buying and selling of music publishing catalogs is nothing new, beginning in the 1980s a sort of merger fever swept through the publishing industry.

At one time the world of music publishing consisted of several dozen major companies, each of which owned several thousand copyrights, and hundreds of smaller companies which owned anywhere from one to several hundred copyrights. When the Hollywood movie industry began to use songs in films, many of the motion picture companies bought up publishing companies already in existence as a simple way of acquiring a large number of readily available songs.

Since that time, the number of publishing companies in the United States has grown and shrunk like an accordion. While new companies are constantly being formed, new and old companies alike are also being bought and incorporated into larger companies.

In the 1980s there was an unprecedented amount of buying and selling among music publishers. In 1986, for example, music industry veterans Charles Koppelman and Martin Bandier, along with New York-based financier Stephen Swid, purchased the publishing catalogs owned by CBS at a reported cost of $125 million, forming a publishing company called SBK Entertainment World.

The following year, Warner Communications bought the publishing firm of Chappell & Co. for approximately $250 million, merging Warner Bros. Music and Chappell & Co. into a company called Warner/Chappell Music.

In 1989, CBS, now owned by Sony, got back into music publishing by purchasing Tree International, a Nashville-based publishing company, for around $40 million. A few days after CBS acquired Tree, SBK Entertainment World was purchased by Thorn-EMI for just over $300 million.

As one large company has devoured another, the number of major publishers has shrunk to only a handful. The biggest problem these large conglomerate-type publishers will face in the 1990s is a lack of personal contact with the thousands and thousands of songwriters whose songs are signed to these megacompanies. Although smaller publishers may not be able to compete in the area of advances to staff writers, these smaller companies will be able to have a personal relationship with their writers.

Another advantage of the nonconglomerate publisher will be that entrepreneurial spirit which first gave birth to music publishing in America. While the major publishing companies will be run by lawyers and accountants, the smaller companies will be run by real music men and women who got into the business to promote music rather than to constantly worry about numbers and legalese. Like crumbs from the king's table, many opportunities will fall through the cracks of the major publishing companies' operations, and the smaller publishers will be there to pick them up and profit from them.

In the 1990s there will be vast new opportunities for music publishers of all sizes. Not only will new technology create improved products for publishers to profit from, there will also be new avenues for publishers to take for further exploitation of their songs.

In recent years, for instance, the video market has allowed publishers to acquire new royalties on old movies. Musical instrument digital interface (MIDI) software containing compositions protected by copyright have only recently become a viable market for new uses of publishers' catalogs. Other markets of this type will open up to music publishers in the years ahead, causing copyrights to increase even more in value.

How the evolution of music publishing will affect you

As I said earlier, the most radical change of recent vintage in the publishing world has been the remarkable number of mergers between the major players in the industry. Even as I am writing today, there are all sorts of rumors in the air about possible buying and selling which will make the number of major players even smaller. My next prediction, then, is that these mergers and takeovers will continue until there are only two or three major publishing companies in the U.S. **I also believe that these mergers — although financially profitable to the seller in the short term — will cause the industry to become very top-heavy, opening doors for dozens of smaller independent companies to compete on a more active basis. These smaller companies will also provide young songwriters with new possibilities for breaking into the business.**

The indie publishers may not be able to offer the massive advances the major publishers can, but this isn't necessarily a disadvantage to songwriters wishing to break in via the independent route. A major publisher which gives large advances is more likely to demand 100% of the publishing, whereas the smaller independents will be open to offering contracts which are more in the songwriter's favor, even offering co-publishing deals. **Also, as I mentioned previously, the majors now have thousands of songwriters to contend with, while a small company with a handful of songwriters will be able to give each of them the attention they need to grow and succeed.**

To your future

Musical fads will come and go, but there will always be a demand for good songs. As a songwriter, determining where you're going to fit into this constantly changing industry will be up to you, your talent, and a heaping dose of luck.

If you keep up with the changes in the business, work hard at developing your craft, keep having faith in yourself, and keep your fingers crossed, you will succeed. Remember, thousands upon thousands of others have done it. So can you.

The Business of Songwriting

Completing a song can give you a wonderful feeling of accomplishment and pride. Imagine how much greater your pleasure would be if your song were reaching millions of listeners through record sales and/or air play. Of course, you don't need the adulation or attention of millions in order to derive artistic satisfaction from your songwriting, but there is certainly nothing wrong with going after your own slice of the fame and fortune pie. And for many writers or artists, the drive to reach the public ear comes not so much from a desire to reap the praise or money that accompany such success, but from a desire to convey their insights and experience to an ever-wider audience. Whatever your motivation for success in the music business, there are definite steps you can take to bring you closer to your goal.

Those songwriters and performers who have been successful in their careers are those who have taken the time to learn as much as they can about the music business. Such an education can come by study or by experience or (more usually) by some combination of the two. It's best to learn all you can by study, because experience can often be a cruel teacher. As an example, would you rather take the time to learn what "work for hire" means before you sign a contract, or find out afterward that it effectively prohibits you from ever collecting royalties on that song? It is simply good sense to approach the business side of songwriting with as much seriousness and energy as you put into your musical creations.

The music business operates in accord with most of the economic principles of any industry. The law of supply and demand forms the heart of the business. Consumers want to hear music on the radio and buy it for their own use (in the form of records, tapes, CDs, etc.). Record companies attempt to meet that demand by offering musical product that they hope will appeal to enough people to turn a profit. It is a fiercely competitive arena. Consumers don't have unlimited funds to spend on music, and the choices they make can spell success or failure for recording artists and record companies.

The same applies to songs. There is a finite number of artists releasing albums containing just nine or ten songs each, while there are thousands of songwriters trying to get their new songs recorded and their older songs re-recorded. So you can imagine how important it is for songwriters to understand how the business works. It's true that there would be no music industry without songs—the artists, producers, publishers and everyone involved need you. But because of the competition, you *must* understand the business of songwriting and function on a professional level as they do.

Getting started

First you need great songs. You have to write and polish and rewrite, and listen to the radio to learn what types of music are popular and judge how your songs stack up against the hits.

Some songwriters may think their efforts end with writing the song. Others know that it's necessary to go on to get their songs published and recorded, but they think once they sign a publishing contract or record deal, they're home free, waiting for the royalty checks to start rolling in. Unfortunately, that's not the case. Every step along the way to a successful record takes a team effort, and the songwriter needs to be a knowledgeable member of the team.

The structure of the music business

The music industry in the United States traditionally revolves around three hub cities: New York, Los Angeles and Nashville. Power is concentrated in those areas because that is where most of the record companies, publishers, songwriters and performers are. Many people who are trying to break into the music business—in whatever capacity—move to one of those three cities in order to be close to the people and companies they want to contact. From time to time a regional music scene will heat up in a non-hub city such as Austin, Seattle or Minneapolis. When this happens, songwriters and performers in that city experience a kind of musical renaissance complete with better paying gigs, a creatively charged atmosphere in which to work and active interest from the major labels. All this is not to say that a successful career cannot be nurtured from any city in the country. It can be, particularly if you are a songwriter. The disadvantages one faces by not being in a major music center can be offset somewhat by phone and mail contact with industry people and, if possible, occasional trips to the music hub nearest you. For the serious songwriter, a well-planned, once-a-year trip to New York, Los Angeles or Nashville to attend a seminar or to call on record companies and music publishers can be of immense value in expanding music-industry contacts and learning how the business operates. There are, of course, many smaller, independent companies located in cities across the country. A career of international scope can be started on the local level, and some may find a local career more satisfying, in its own way, than the constant striving to gain the attention of a major label.

The perspective of any company, big or small, must begin with the buying public. Their support, in the form of money spent on records and other kinds of musical entertainment, keeps the record companies in business. Because of that, record companies are anxious to give the public what they want. In an attempt to stay one step ahead of public tastes, the record companies hire people who have a facility for spotting musical talent and anticipating trends and put them in charge of finding and developing new recording acts. These talent scouts are called "A&R representatives." "A&R" stands for artist and repertoire, which simply means they are responsible for finding new artists and matching songs to artists. The person responsible for the recording artist's finished product—the record—is called the producer. It is the producer's job to bring the recording artist out of the studio with a good-sounding, saleable product. His duties often involve choosing the songs to be included on the album, so record producers are great contacts for songwriters. Some A&R reps produce the bands they discover.

The A&R reps and the producers are helped in their search for songs (and sometimes artists) by the music publisher. A publisher is really a songwriter's representative who, for a percentage of the profits (typically 50% of all publisher/songwriter earnings), tries to find commercially profitable uses for the songs in his catalog. A good publisher stays in close contact with several A&R reps, trying to find out what kinds of projects are coming up at the record companies and whether any songs in his catalog might be of use.

When a song is recorded and commercially released, the record company, the recording artist, the producer, the publisher and the songwriter all stand to profit. Recording artists earn a negotiated royalty from their record company based on the number of records sold. Publishers and songwriters earn mechanical royalties (based on records sold) and performance royalties (based on radio air play). Producers are usually paid either a negotiated royalty based on sales or a flat fee.

Until you establish relationships with specific professionals in the industry who appreciate your music and are willing to work with you on a regular basis, you should submit your material to as many appropriate contacts as you can find. Based on what we've just discussed, you can see that appropriate contacts would include A&R reps, producers and publishers. You can add managers to that list. Depending on how "big" the artist is, he may have a personal and/or road manager. These people have direct access to the artists they manage, and they're always on the lookout for hit songs for them.

Any method of getting your song heard, published, recorded and released is the best way if it works for you. In this book music publishers, record companies, record producers and managers are listed with specifications on how to submit your material to each. If you can't find the person or company you're looking for, there are other sources of information you can try. Check trade publications such as *Billboard* or *Cash Box*, available at most local libraries. These periodicals list new companies as well as the artists, labels, producers and publishers for each song on the charts. There are several tipsheets available that name producers, managers and artists currently looking for new material. Album covers and cassette j-cards can be excellent sources of information. They give the name of the record company, producer, and usually the manager of the artist or group, and reveal who publishes the songs on the album. Liner notes can be revealing as well, telling how a song came to someone's attention, how a musical style evolved or what changes or new projects lie ahead for the artist. Be creative in your research—any clue you uncover may give you an edge over your competition.

Submitting your songs

When it comes to showing people what you have to offer, the tool of the music industry is a demonstration recording—a demo. Most people prefer cassettes because they're so convenient. Songwriters make demos showcasing their songs and musicians make demos of their performances. These demos are then submitted to various professionals in the industry. It's acceptable to submit your songs to more than one person at a time (this is called simultaneous submission). Most people try their best to return tapes if a self-addressed, stamped envelope is included in the submission, but even with the best intentions in the world sometimes it just doesn't happen. (A person screening tapes might open dozens of packages, take the tapes out and put them all in a bag or box, and listen to them in the car on his way to and from the office, thus separating the tapes from their SASEs. *Always* put your name, address and phone number on every item in your submission package, including the tape itself.)

The one exception to simultaneous submissions is when someone asks if he may put a song of yours on "hold." This means he intends to record it, and he doesn't want you to give the song to anyone else. Sometimes he'll give a song back to you without recording it, even if it's been on hold for months. Sometimes he'll record your song but decide that it's not as strong as his other material and so he won't include your song on his album. If either of these things happens, you're free to pitch that song to other people again. (You can protect yourself from having a song on hold indefinitely. Either establish a deadline for the person who asks for the hold, i.e., "You can put my song on hold for x number of months." Or modify the hold to specify that you will pitch the song to other people, but you will not sign a deal without allowing the person who has the song "on hold" to make you an offer.) When someone publishes your song, you grant that publisher exclusive rights to your song and you may not pitch it to other publishers (though you *may* pitch it to artists or producers who are interested in recording the song without publishing it themselves).

The production quality of demos can vary widely, but even simple demos with just piano/vocal or guitar/vocal need to sound clean, with the instrument in tune and the lyrics sung clearly with no background noise. Many songwriters are investing in equipment such as four- or eight-track recorders, keyboards and drum machines — for recording demos at home. Other writers like to book studio time, use live musicians, and get professional input from an engineer and/or producer. It's also possible to hire a demo service to do it all for you. Ultimately, you'll have to go with what you can afford and what you feel best represents your song. Once you have a master recording of your song, you're ready to make cassette copies and pitch your song to the contacts you've researched. [For more on demos and how to pitch them effectively, see "Fine-Tuning Your Demos" on page 22.]

Submitting by mail

Here are guidelines to follow when submitting material to companies listed in this book:

- Read the listing and submit exactly what a company asks for and exactly how it asks that it be submitted.
- Listen to each demo before submitting to make sure the quality is satisfactory.
- Enclose a brief, neat cover letter of introduction. Indicate the types of songs you're submitting and recording artists you think they might suit. If you are a writer/artist looking for a record deal yourself, or pitching your demo for some reason other than for another artist to record your songs, you should say so in your letter. Be specific about your goals and intentions.
- Include typed or legibly printed lyric sheets. If requested, include a lead sheet. Place your name, address and phone number on each lead or lyric sheet.
- Neatly label each tape and tape box with your name, address, phone number and the names of the songs on the tape in the sequence in which they are recorded.
- Keep a record of the date, the names of the songs and the company to which you are submitting.
- Include an SASE for the return of your material. Your return envelope to companies based in countries other than your own should contain a self-addressed envelope (SAE) and International Reply Coupons (IRC). Be certain the return envelope is large enough to accommodate your material, and include sufficient postage for the weight of the package.
- Wrap the package neatly and write (or type on a shipping label) the company's address and your return address so they are clearly visible. Your package is the first impression a company has of you and your songs, so neatness is very important.
- Mail First Class. Stamp or write "First Class Mail" on the package and on the SASE you enclose. Don't send by registered mail unless the listing specifically requests it. The recipient must interrupt his day to sign for it and many companies refuse all registered mail.

If you are writing to inquire about a company's current needs or to request permission to submit, your query letter should be neat (preferably typed), brief and pleasant. Explain the type of material you have and ask for their needs and current submission policy.

To expedite a reply, you should enclose a self-addressed, stamped postcard asking the information you need to know. Your typed questions (see the Sample Reply Form) should be direct and easy for the receiver to answer. Don't forget to include a line for the respondent's name and title. Also remember to place the company's name and address in the upper lefthand space on the front of the postcard so you'll know which company you queried. Keep a record of queries, like tape submissions, for future reference.

Sample Reply Form

I would like to hear:

(   ) "Name of Song" (   ) "Name of Song" (   ) "Name of Song"

I prefer:

(   ) reel-to-reel (   ) cassette (   ) videocassette

                                                      (   ) Beta (   ) VHS

With:

(   ) lyric sheet (   ) lead sheet (   ) either (   ) both

(   ) I am not looking for material at this time, try me later.

(   ) I am not interested.

_____

Name

                                                               Title

Submitting in person

A trip to Los Angeles, Nashville or New York will give you insight as to how the music industry functions. You should plan ahead and schedule appointments to make the most of your time while you're there. It will be difficult to get in to see some people, as many professionals are extremely busy and may not feel meeting out-of-town writers is their highest priority. Other people are more open to, and even encourage, face-to-face meetings. They may feel that if you take the time to travel to where they are, and you're organized and persistent enough to schedule meetings, you're more advanced and more professional than many aspiring songwriters who blindly submit inappropriate songs through the mail.

You should take several cassette copies and lyric sheets of each of your songs. More than one of the companies you visit may ask that you leave a copy. If the person who's reviewing material likes a song, he may want to play it for someone else. There's also a good chance the person you have the appointment with will have to cancel (expect that occasionally), but wants you to leave a copy of your songs so he can listen and contact you later. *Never* give someone the last or only copy of your material—if it is not returned to you, all the effort and money that went into your demo will be lost.

Many good songs have been rejected simply because they weren't deemed appropriate by one listener at one particular time, so don't take rejection personally. Realize that if one or two people didn't like your songs, they just could have been having a bad day. However, if there seems to be a consensus about your work, like the feel of the song isn't quite right or a lyric needs work, you should probably give the advice some serious thought. Listen attentively to what the reviewers say and summarize their comments when you return home. That information will be invaluable as you continue to submit material to those people who now know you personally.

The money

Songwriters receive money in the form of royalties from five major sources: performance, mechanical, print, synchronization and foreign subpublishing.

Performance royalties are generated when songs are performed. The majority of this income comes from radio and TV. Other sources include live performances by artists or bands in clubs, bars, etc.; and recorded performances played on a jukebox, Muzak, etc. Performing rights societies (ASCAP, BMI and SESAC in the U.S.) collect fees from these various music users and divide the money among publisher and writer members according to formulas based on sales and airplay. You can't affiliate with one of these societies until your song is recorded on a record or for a motion picture soundtrack (or performed on radio or television). A published songwriter *must* belong to the same organization to which the publisher belongs. You'll notice that many publishers listed in this book have affiliate companies belonging to a different performance rights organization. That allows the publisher to deal with writers of each of the various performing rights societies.

Each performance rights organization has its own unique method of determining how many times a year your song is performed during a given period. Their primary difference is *how* they make that determination. ASCAP monitors individual radio and television stations as well as concerts and clubs where music is performed. BMI uses logs sent them from radio and TV stations. SESAC uses the charts of the trade magazines to determine the popularity of individual songs.

The songwriter receives quarterly a statement of performances and a royalty check from his chosen performance rights society. The amount earned depends on how many times the organization determined the song was performed and the kind of performance (e.g. a prime time network TV show vs. a local TV newscast).

ASCAP, BMI and SESAC are highly professional and reputable friends of the songwriter. To look into the specific policies, procedures, benefits and requirements of each before joining, use the addresses given in our Organizations section and write or visit them.

All types of royalties except performance royalties are paid directly to the publisher, who then splits them with the songwriter according to the publishing contract. Mechanical royalties are paid for every copy of your song (record, tape or CD) that is sold and not returned. The statutory rate is the maximum payment allowable by law, and it is currently 5.7 cents per song per record sold or 1.1 cents per minute, whichever is greater. The rate is scheduled to increase every two years based on the consumer price index.

The record company pays the mechanical royalty to the publisher, and the publisher sends the writer his share. Record companies are notorious for not paying on time and not accounting accurately and thoroughly. Many publishers go through the Harry Fox Agency to collect mechanical royalties for them. The Harry Fox Agency will also collect synchronization fees in some cases.

Synchronization fees are generally paid for uses of music in film, videos, television and commercials. If a song or instrumental work is written expressly for a movie or TV show, the writing is sometimes done as "work-for-hire" where the composer receives an initial flat fee and the production company owns all rights to the work. In that case, a synchronization license is unnecessary but the writer may sign a single-song publishing agreement with the production company and remain entitled to the songwriter's share of future royalties.

The songwriter shares 50-50 in any royalties the publisher receives from the foreign subpublisher who collects the publishing monies generated by songs in his territory (for all of the various uses there might be for that song within his territory).

The publisher also pays you a share of the profit from the sale of sheet music, orchestrations, choral arrangements and folio sales. You can earn a flat rate for each sheet of piano music sold and 10-15% of the retail price of orchestrations, choral arrangements and folios. For more information, see the Music Print Publishers section of this book.

A songwriter will sometimes receive a cash advance at the time a publishing contract is signed; an artist may receive an advance when he signs a record deal. These advances are recoupable. If a publisher gives you a $100 advance, and then your song is recorded and released, you won't receive any additional money for the song until the publisher recoups certain expenses, including the $100 he paid you. If the song doesn't earn money, you don't have to pay the $100 back to the publisher. That gamble is just a part of music publishing (and you can bet that if a publisher is willing to give you an advance, he's going to work hard to get your song recorded so that he can recoup his investment). Usually, if a songwriter already has a well-produced, high quality demo and the publisher doesn't have to redemo the song, the publisher will be more likely to give the songwriter an advance.

Staff writers who receive a draw against future royalties are in a similar position. Their publisher pays them a sum of money per week or month. If their songs don't make money, the songwriter does not have to pay the publisher back. But if the songs do earn money, the publisher recovers the advance from royalties that would otherwise be paid the songwriter. (Remember, the songwriter receives performance royalties directly from the performing rights society. The income from which the publisher can deduct is comprised of the other types of royalties: mechanical, print and synchronization.)

Any contract should spell out what payment you will receive, including advances and future royalties.

Contracts

You may encounter several types of contracts as you deal with the business end of songwriting, beginning with a legal agreement between you and a co-writer as to what percentage of the writer's royalties each of you will receive, what you will do if a third party (e.g. a recording artist) wishes to change your song and receive credit as a co-writer, and other things. Usually as long as the issues at stake are simple, and co-writers respect each other and discuss their business philosophy in advance of writing a song, they can reach an agreement verbally. A written contract is not necessary. (A written contract is usually necessary only when one writer wishes to control the rights to the song or one of the writers wants to remove his contribution if no use is made of the song within a certain period of time, e.g., take his lyrics and have them set to different music or vice versa.) In other situations—if a publisher, producer or record company wants to do business with you— you need a contract. You should always have any contract offered to you reviewed by a knowledgeable entertainment attorney.

Single song contracts

Probably the most common type of contract you will encounter at first will be the single song contract. A music publisher offers this type of contract when he wants to sign one (or more) of your songs, but he doesn't want to hire you as a staff writer. This type of agreement rarely includes more than two or three songs. You assign your rights to a particular song to the publisher for an agreed-upon number of years (usually the life of the copyright).

Every contract should contain this basic information: the publisher's name, the writer's name, the song's title, the date, and the purpose of the agreement. The songwriter also declares that the song is an original work and he is the creator of the work. The contract must specify the royalties the songwriter will earn from various uses of the song. These include performance royalties, mechanical, print, synchronization, foreign subpublishing, and an agreement as to what will be paid for any uses not specifically set forth in the wording of the contract. The songwriter should receive no less than 50% of the income his song generates. That means, whatever the song earns in royalties, the publisher and songwriter should split 50/50. The songwriter's half is called the "writer's share" and the publisher's half is called the "publisher's share." If there is more than one songwriter, the songwriters split the "writer's share." Sometimes songwriters will negotiate for a percentage of the "publisher's share"; that is, a copublishing agreement. This is usually feasible only if the songwriter already has some hits and is unlikely for beginning songwriters.

Other issues a contract should address include whether or not an advance will be paid to the songwriter and how much it will be; when the royalties will be paid (quarterly or semi-annually); who will pay for the demos—the publisher, the songwriter or both; how lawsuits against copyright infringement will be handled, including the cost of such lawsuits; what will happen if a dispute over the contract needs arbitration; whether the publisher has the right to sell the song to another publisher without the songwriter's consent; and whether the publisher has the right to make changes in a song or approve of changes written by someone else, without the songwriter's consent. In addition, the songwriter should have the right to audit the publisher's books if the songwriter deems it necessary and gives the publisher reasonable notice.

Songwriters should also negotiate for a reversion clause. This calls for the rights to the song to revert (return) to the songwriter if some provision of the contract is not met. The most common type of reversion clause is for the failure to secure a commercial recording or release of the song. Songwriters fear that a publisher will sign one of their songs and then forget about it while he actively pitches other songs in his catalog. Songwriters want a clause in the contract stating that if the publisher does not secure a commercial release of their song within a specified period of time (usually one or two years) the rights to the song revert back to the songwriter, who can then give the song to a more active publisher if he so chooses. Some publishers will agree to this, figuring that if they don't get some action on the song in the first year, they're not likely to ever get any action on it. Other publishers are reluctant to agree to this clause. They may invest a lot of time and money in a song, redemoing it and pitching it to a number of artists; they may be actively looking for ways to exploit the song. They may have even interested a few artists or producers in the song, but whether the song is recorded or not, and especially whether it's released or not after it's recorded, is usually beyond the publisher's control. If a producer puts a song on hold for a while and goes into a lengthy recording project, by the time the record company (or artist or producer) decides which songs to release as singles, a year can easily go by. That's why it's so important to have a good working relationship with your publisher. You need to trust that he has your best interests in mind. If a song really is on hold you can give him more time and/or know that if your song is recorded but ultimately not released by the artist, it's not your publisher's fault and he'll work just as hard to get another artist to record the song.

The Songwriter's Guild of America (SGA) has drawn up a Popular Songwriter's Contract which it believes to be the best minimum songwriter contract available. The Guild will send a copy of the contract at no charge to any interested songwriter upon request (they do ask that you include a self-addressed stamped envelope with your request). SGA will also review free of charge any contract offered to its members, checking it for fairness and completeness. (See the Guild's listings in the Organizations section.)

The following list, taken from a Songwriter's Guild of America publication entitled "10 Basic Points Your Contract Should Include" enumerates the basic features of an acceptable songwriting contract:

1. Work for Hire. When you receive a contract covering just one composition you should make sure that the phrases "employment for hire" and "exclusive writer agreement" are not included. Also, there should be no options for future songs.

2. Performing Rights Affiliation. If you previously signed publishing contracts, you should be affiliated with either ASCAP, BMI or SESAC. All performance royalties must be received directly by you from your performing rights organization and this should be written into your song contract. (The same goes for any third party licensing organization mutually agreed upon.)

3. Reversion Clause. The contract should include a provision that if the publisher does not secure a release of a commercial sound recording within a specified time (one year - two years, etc.) the contract can be terminated by you.

4. Changes in the Composition. If the contract includes a provision that the publisher can change the title, lyrics or music, this should be amended so that only with your previous consent can such changes be made.

5. Royalty Provisions. Basically, you should receive fifty percent (50%) of all publisher's income on all licenses issued. If the publisher prints and sells his own sheet music and folios, your royalty should be ten percent (10%) of the wholesale selling price. The royalty should not be stated in the contract as a flat rate ($.05, $.07, etc.).

6. Negotiable Deductions. Ideally, demos and all other expenses of publication should be paid 100% by the publisher. The only allowable fee is for the Harry Fox Agency collection fee, whereby the writer pays one half of the amount charged to the publisher. Today's rate charged by the Harry Fox Agency is 4.5%.

7. Royalty Statements and Audit Provision. Once the song is recorded and printed, you are entitled to receive royalty statements at least once every six months. In addition, an audit provision with no time restriction should be included in every contract.

8. Writer's Credit. The publisher should make sure that you receive proper credit on all uses of the composition.

9. Arbitration. In order to avoid large legal fees in case of a dispute with your publisher, the contract should include an arbitration clause.

10. Future Uses. Any use not specifically covered by the contract should be retained by the writer to be negotiated as it comes up.

For a more thorough discussion of the somewhat complicated subject of contracts, see these two books published by Writer's Digest Books: *The Craft and Business of Songwriting*, by John Braheny and *Protecting Your Songs and Yourself*, by Kent Klavens.

Copyright

When you create a song and put it down in some fixed or tangible form it is a property you own, and it is automatically protected by copyright. This protection lasts for your lifetime (or the lifetime of the last surviving author, if you co-wrote the song) plus 50 years. When you prepare demos, lyric sheets and lead sheets of your songs, you should put notification of copyright on all the copies of your song (on the lyric or lead sheet and on the label of a cassette). The notice is simply the word "copyright" or the symbol © followed by the year the song was created (or published) and your name: © 1991 by John L. Public.

For the best protection, you can register your copyright with the Library of Congress. Although a song is copyrighted whether or not it is registered, such registration establishes a public record of your claim to copyright that could prove useful in any future litigation involving the song. Registration also entitles you to a potentially greater settlement in a copyright infringement suit. To register your song(s) send the following to the Register of Copyrights, Library of Congress, Washington, DC 20559:

● a tape or lead sheet of your song(s). Submit one copy if the work has not been published, two if it has been published.

● a government form PA, available on request from the Copyright Office. Call (202)707-9100 to order forms.

● $10 registration fee for each song. It is possible to register groups of songs, with each collection being one title such as "The John L. Public Songbook," for one $10 fee. You will not be able to add future songs to that particular collection.

It may take as long as four months to receive your certificate of registration from the Copyright Office, but your songs are protected from the date of creation, and the date of registration will reflect the date you applied for registration.

If you ever feel that one of your songs has been stolen—that someone has unlawfully infringed on your copyright—you will need to have proof that you were the original creator of the work. Copyright registration is the best method of creating proof of a date of creation. You *must* have your copyright registered in order to file a copyright infringement lawsuit. One important way people prove a work is original is to keep their rough drafts and revisions of songs, either on paper or on tape, if they record different versions of the song as they go along.

True copyright infringement is rarer than many people think. For one thing, a title cannot be copyrighted, nor can an idea, nor can a chord progression. Only specific, fixed melodies and lyrics can be copyrighted. Second, a successful infringement suit would have to prove that another songwriter had access to your completed song and that he deliberately copied it, which is difficult to do and not really worthwhile unless the song is a smash hit. Song theft sometimes happens, but not often enough to allow yourself to become paranoid. Don't be afraid to play your songs for people or worry about creating a song that might sound similar to someone else's. Better to spend your time creating original songs, register the copyrights you intend to actively pitch to music professionals, and go ahead and make contacts to get your material heard.

The ripoffs

As in any other business, the music industry has its share of dishonest, greedy people who try to unfairly exploit the talents and aspirations of others. Most of them employ similar methods of attack which you can learn to recognize and avoid. These "song sharks" prey on beginners—those writers who are unfamiliar with ethical industry standards. Ethical companies hope to earn money with you as your quality songs earn royalties. Song sharks will take any song—quality doesn't count. They don't care about future royalties, because they get their money upfront from songwriters who don't know better.

Here are some guidelines to help you recognize such a person or company:

- Never pay to have your songs published. A reputable company interested in your songs assumes the responsiblity and cost of promoting your material. That company invests in your song because it expects a profit once the song is recorded and released.
- Never pay to have your music "reviewed" by a company that may be interested in publishing, producing or recording it. Reviewing material—free of charge—is the practice of reputable companies looking for hits for their artists or recording projects. (Song critique and consultation by another songwriter or someone not in the market for original material is another matter.)
- Never pay to have your lyrics or poems set to music. "Music mills"—for a price—may use the same melody for hundreds of lyrics and poems, whether it sounds good or not. Publishers recognize one of these melodies as soon as they hear it.
- Read all contracts carefully before signing and don't sign any contract you're unsure about or that you don't understand. Don't assume any contract is better than no contract at all. Remember that it is well worth paying an attorney for the time it takes him to review a contract if you can avoid a bad situation that may cost you thousands of dollars in royalties if your song becomes a hit.
- Don't pay a company to pair you with a collaborator. Better ways include contacting organizations which offer collaboration services to their members. (See Co-writing.)
- Don't sell your songs outright. It's unethical for anyone to offer you such a proposition.
- If you are asked by a record company or some other type of company to pay expenses upfront, beware. Many expenses incurred by the record company on your behalf may be recoupable, but you should not be paying cash out of your pocket to a company that either employs you as an artist or owns your master recording. If someone offers you a "deal" that asks for cash upfront, it's a good idea to ask to speak with other artists who have signed similar contracts with them before signing one yourself. Weigh the expenses and what you have to gain by financing the project yourself, then make your decision. Read the stipulations of the contract carefully, however, and go over them with a music business attorney. Research the company and its track record, and beware of any company that won't answer your questions or let you know what it has done in the past. If it has had successes and good working relationships with other writers and artists, it should be happy to brag about them.
- Before participating in a songwriting contest, read all of the rules closely. Be sure that what you're giving up (in the way of entry fees, publishing rights, etc.) is not greater than what you stand to gain by winning the contest. See the introduction to our Contests and Awards section for more advice on this.
- There is a recent version of the age-old chain letter scheme with a special twist just for songwriters and musicians. The letter names five songwriters whose tapes you are supposed to order. You then add your name to the letter and mail it to five more songwriters who, in turn, send you $7 each for your tape. Besides the fact that such chain letter or "pyramid" schemes generally fail, the five "amateur" songwriters named in the letter are known song sharks. It's simply one more scheme to separate the unwise from their cash. Don't fall for it.
- Verify any situation about an individual or a company if you have doubts. Contact the performance rights organization with which it is affiliated. Check with the Better Business Bureau in the town where it is located or the state's attorney general's office. Contact professional organizations you're a member of (and the national ones listed in the Organization section of this book) and inquire about the reputation of the company.

Record keeping

It is a good idea to keep a ledger or notebook containing all financial transactions related to your songwriting. Your record keeping should include a list of income from royalty checks as well as expenses incurred as a result of your songwriting business: cost of tapes, demo sessions, office supplies, postage, traveling expenses, dues to songwriting organizations, class and workshop fees, and publications of interest. It's also advisable to open a checking account exclusively for your songwriting activities, not only to make record keeping easier, but to establish your identity as a business for tax purposes.

Your royalties will not reflect tax or other mandatory deductions. It is the songwriter's responsibility to keep track of income and file appropriate tax forms. Contact the IRS, or an accountant who serves music industry clients, for specific information.

International markets

Everyone talks about the world getting smaller, and it's true. Modern communication technology has brought us to the point at which media events and information can be transmitted around the globe instantly. No business has enjoyed the fruits of this progress more than the music industry. The music business of the 1990s is truly an international industry. American music is heard in virtually every country in the world, and music from all over the world has taken a firm hold on America's imagination over the past few years.

Those of you who have been buying *Songwriter's Market* over the years may have noticed a steady increase in the number of foreign companies listed. We believe these listings, though they may be a bit more challenging to deal with than domestic companies, provide additional opportunities for songwriters to achieve success with their music, and it is obvious from the response we get to our listing questionnaires that foreign companies are very interested in American music.

If you consider signing a contract with an enthusiastic publisher from a country outside the United States, use the same criteria that we referred to earlier when making a decision as to the acceptability of the contract.

Co-writing

Co-writing affects the creative side of your songwriting, but it also affects the business side. Many songwriters choose to collaborate because they like the instant feedback a writing partner can provide; they feel they are stronger in lyric or music writing skills and they seek someone whose talents will complement their own; they want to write in a style of music somewhat unfamiliar to them and so they seek someone more experienced in that genre. Or they feel the final outcome of two or more writers' experiences and creative input will be greater than the sum of its parts. While co-writing can be a boon to your creative output, you should think about how it will affect your business. You'll have to share the writer's royalties which means less money for you. On the other hand, your co-writer will be pitching your song to people you may not even know, thus expanding your network of contacts and increasing the possibilities for your song to get recorded.

Where do you find collaborators? Check the bulletin board at your local musician's union hall. If you don't see an advertisement that seems suitable for you, ask if you can post your own ad telling what type of writer you're looking for, what styles of music you're interested in, what experience you've had, what your goals are, etc. Other places to advertise are at music stores and college and university music departments, if they allow it.

Professional organizations like The National Academy of Songwriters, The Songwriters Guild of America, The Nashville Songwriters Association International and the Los Angeles Songwriters Showcase offer opportunities to meet collaborators or correspond with them through the mail. Check the Organizations section for addresses. Most local songwriters associations also provide names of potential co-writers. See if there's an organization in your area.

If there's not, why not start one? Having a local songwriting organization can be a great way to pool resources, critique each other's songs, help each other on demos, and cooperate in many other ways. As you use *Songwriter's Market* and learn more about the music industry, you'll have much to share with the songwriters in your area.

Fine-Tuning Your Demos

by Mark Garvey

Though the music business changes from year to year and decade to decade, your calling card as a songwriter or musician continues to be the demo — a demonstration recording that displays your talents as a songwriter or performer. Originally, in order to get your material heard by people in the business, you had to pack up your instrument and take it with you to a record company office or publishing company and give a live performance of your songs in hopes of sparking some interest. Eventually, the live performance gave way to the reel-to-reel demo tape, which has, in turn (with the advent of ever smaller and better recording technologies), given way to the cassette, DAT (Digital Audio Tape), and even CD. For some current feedback about the demo's place in today's music business, and to better equip you, the songwriter, to approach publishers and record label employees as professionally — and successfully — as possible, we surveyed a number of professional managers and A&R representatives for this article. They spoke candidly about demo do's and don'ts, and they came up with plenty of good advice which should come in handy the next time you pitch your tunes.

Presentation

If you've read The Business of Songwriting (page 11) or studied the endleaves, you know the importance of properly presenting your demo. The package should be as professional-looking as you can afford to make it. Include typed lyric sheets and an SASE (self-addressed stamped envelope); also be sure to put your name, address and phone number on every item in your package. Neatness and attention to detail just might be enough to make your submission stand out among the hundreds of submissions that monthly pass across the desks of busy publishers and A&R executives. Sherry Bond of Johnny Bond Publications in Nashville puts it this way: "The more professional it looks the more attractive it is, and that does influence my decision when I am deciding which tape to listen to." Sherry says a handwritten label is an immediate tip-off that the sender is probably an amateur.

Another indicator of nonprofessionalism and a source of annoyance, according to Ralph Johnson of Big Wedge Music, is that "an amateur will wrap everything but the bed sheet around that cassette, and then he'll put forty tons of tape on the envelope like it's gonna go out in space somewhere. I get so aggravated that by the time I get it open, he's lost two points with me before I put his cassette on. A pro makes it simple because he knows your time is important." Brad Edwards of Audioloft Recording Studios suggests "a bubble pack-type mailer — one that's big enough to get the tape in and out of without tearing something up. The return envelope should be just as good. I don't like business-size envelopes for sending things back."

Lack of a proper SASE for return of materials is one problem we frequently hear about from companies listed in *Songwriter's Market*. It's important to include an envelope that is big enough and sturdy enough to carry your tape safely back to you. Be sure the postage on the return envelope is sufficient to cover the weight of the tape and whatever other materials may be returning to you. Publishers and A&R reps don't have the time — nor is it their responsibility—to make sure that each demo being returned to a writer is properly packaged. And of course they cannot be expected to make up the difference on insufficiently posted materials. Sherry Bond's attitude on return envelopes may seem tough, but it's sensible: "SASEs are not a problem for me. I just put them in the mail and if they don't get to the writers, I figure *they* have to worry about that."

Quality

Of course, the packaging is just the sizzle, not the steak. No matter how attractively presented your demo may be, it's all for nothing if the songs don't live up to the promises implied by the wrappings. Most of the professionals interviewed for this article agreed that the two most important ingredients in creating an impressive demo are the vocal performance and the lyric.

"Lousy vocals can ruin a demo," says Barry Bergman of Barry Bergman Management, "and the lyrics have to say something. They shouldn't be mundane. Lyrics have to create some images. When you consider romantic songs, you know everyone is basically singing about the same thing—the trick is to say it a little differently." Mike Whelan of Merit Music, a Nashville publisher, agrees: "Bad lyric content can really just blow it from the first. That's especially true in country music, where the lyric needs to be strong." Again, Sherry Bond: "I listen mostly for lyric content. And if a songwriter is going to put a lot of money into a demo, I think most of the money should be spent on the vocalist—a really good one who sounds as generic as possible, one who doesn't have a whole lot of interpretation but can just deliver the melody very straightforwardly."

Ralph Johnson of Big Wedge advises songwriters to be sure the musical track does not overpower the vocal performance on a demo. "You are selling those words," he says, "and if they can't be heard, then it's going to get thrown in the trash can." Ralph shares his colleagues' concern about the quality of the lyrics: "The main thing I look for is a different philosophy or point of view. And anyone who is successful in this business gets that point of view across in the first four lines; if you don't get it in there you don't need to worry about writing a good second verse because nobody is ever going to listen to it."

Production

One concern shared by all songwriters who are actively pitching demo tapes is the quality or level of production expected by those who are going to be listening to the tapes. Is a simple piano/vocal or guitar/vocal demo OK? Will a publisher, producer or A&R rep be able to look beyond low-tech or no-tech production and see the potential of the song or the performance? Will a more fully-produced (and therefore more expensive) demo increase the chances of success? By "fully produced" I mean a demo that sounds as much like a real record (in terms of arranging, instrumentation and recording quality) as possible. A guitar/vocal or piano/vocal demo is just what the name implies—a person singing the song accompanied by one instrument in an attempt to convey the "bare-bones" structure of the song; the thought is that once such a demo is accepted, the song will be fleshed out by a producer for the final recording.

It is generally true that up-tempo pop, rock and dance demos need to be more fully produced than pop/rock ballads and country demos. But understand that is a generalization. Individual tastes, needs and abilities vary. Mike Whelan, a country music publisher says, "A demo doesn't have to be elaborate, if the song is really there. Most ballads don't need an incredibly well-produced demo. The up-tempo stuff needs a little more sometimes to capture what the song is trying to accomplish. It also depends on the producer who ends up working on the song; some like a straight guitar/vocal so they can create. In country music, if the lyrics are there, the producer can usually create around that." Sherry Bond, also a country music publisher, says, "I really like a very simple guitar or piano/vocal. I don't like full production at all because I think that interferes with the song. I like to produce songs the way that I hear them and want to pitch them. Production pretty much locks it into an idea and it's hard to hear past that once it's already locked in." Rap A&R representative Kevin Maxwell, of Tommy Boy records, says it doesn't matter how elaborately produced a demo is: "A lot of people think they need a 24-track demo, but that's not true. If it's on a 4-track and the quality is good and you have a basic idea of what they're doing, that's all that needs to happen. I've heard great 4-track demos and I've heard poor 24-track demos. It depends on the producer and what his input is."

Now let's hear from some of those who prefer a more finished presentation. "We like a pretty dressed-up sounding demo," says Brad Edwards, a country and gospel producer, "It doesn't have to be a real lavish thing, but something more than a guitar/vocal. If it is a guitar/vocal, we like it to be of enough quality that it isn't an effort to listen to it." Ralph Johnson, who deals with pop, rock and country, agrees. "It makes it easier for us to pitch them when they come in like that [more fully produced]. Producers have been spoiled; they want all their work done for them. The better the demo, the better your chances, that's what it amounts to." "I think everybody should put their best foot forward and give the best presentation possible," says Barry Bergman, who is involved with pop, rock and R&B. "After all, the competition is so fierce out here that the more you have to show, the better off you'll be."

You can see how widely divergent opinions on demo production can be. As a songwriter, your challenge is to balance what you perceive to be the needs of the market against your own production capabilities and budgetary constraints. But you may take it as a general rule that the more your songs lean toward the up-tempo market — whether you're writing country, gospel, pop or rock — the more attention you're going to have to pay to the quality of your demo production. Many of the companies listed in *Songwriter's Market* offer hints (in the "Tips" section of their listings) about what kinds of demos they like to hear. Others may be willing to provide you with that information over the phone.

The song line-up

Everyone interviewed agreed that three songs is about the right number to include on a demo tape. Any more and you're asking for too much of the listener's time, any less and they may not be getting a good sampling of what you have to offer. The first song on the tape should be your best song. Opening with a weak song is the best way to assure that the rest of the songs on your tape will not be heard. If your best song is also up-tempo, it's even more important to put it first, especially if you're writing for the pop or country market. "There is not a company in Nashville that doesn't tell me at least twice a week, 'Send me up-tempo, up-tempo.' Most of the companies cannot get enough of it," says Ralph Johnson. Sherry Bond and Mike Whelan concur. Sherry: "Everybody is always looking for that positive up-tempo song as opposed to the ballad, so if you have a good fast song I would definitely put that first." Mike: "Good up-tempo stuff is hard to find. If you've got something up-tempo that you feel is just a killer song, by all means put it on first."

Preparation for success

Success in the music business is usually dependent on a variety of factors, including talent, luck and preparation. Given that you have the talent to succeed and that luck is beyond anyone's control, preparation is the one factor that is most left up to individual initiative. Preparation means constantly honing your songwriting skills, it means practicing your instrument (if you're a musician), and it means putting together a demo that clearly and effectively showcases your talents. The information in this article, combined with information in The Business of Songwriting (page 11) and hints gleaned from the individual listings in *Songwriter's Market* should help you construct a demo package that will be well received and — more importantly — listened to.

Important information on market listings:

● *Although every listing in* Songwriter's Market *is updated, verified or researched prior to publication, some changes are bound to occur between publication and the time you contact any listing.*

● *Listings are based on interviews and questionnaires. They are not advertisements, nor are markets reported here necessarily endorsed by the editor.*

● *Looking for a particular market? Check the Index. If you don't find it there, it is because 1) It's not interested in receiving material at this time. 2) It's no longer in business or has merged with another company. 3) It charges (counter to our criteria for inclusion) for services a songwriter should receive free. 4) It has failed to verify or update its listing annually. 5) It has requested that it not be listed. 6) We have received reports from songwriters about unresolved problems they've had with the company. Check the '90-91 Changes list at the end of each section to find why markets appearing in the 1990 edition do not appear in this edition.*

● *A word of warning. Don't pay to have your song published and/or recorded or to have your lyrics—or a poem—set to music. Read "Rip offs" in the Business of Songwriting section to learn how to recognize and protect yourself from the "songshark."*

● Songwriter's Market *reserves the right to exclude any listing which does not meet its requirements.*

The Markets

Music Publishers

The job of the music publisher has changed considerably over the years. Originally, a publisher dealt exclusively with the manufacture and sale of printed sheet music. Though the sale of sheet music is still a part of his job, today's music publisher performs a wide variety of duties that mirrors the complex and multi-faceted business which musical entertainment has become.

In simplest terms, a music publisher's job is to match songs to artists and artists to songs. Typically, a songwriter will sign over control of a song's copyright and a percentage of that song's earnings to a publisher — usually because he believes that publisher has the expertise, ambition and contacts to secure a commercially profitable use for the song. Once such a commercial recording takes place, the publisher oversees all monies coming in from all licensed uses of the song, subtracts his percentage (commonly 50% of all earnings) and passes the remaining money (the other 50%) on to the writer or writers.

From the above description, you can see that music publishing involves two distinct facets: the creative side and the business side. Creatively, publishers are constantly looking and listening for hit songs, thinking of artists whom they know are recording or are about to record, and trying to arrange the perfect marriage between song and artist. Many of the larger publishers, over the last few years, have also begun to put together "development deals," in which new bands or artists are taken under the publisher's wing and are nurtured and polished and eventually pitched to a record company in hopes of landing a recording contract. The fact that some publishers now have an "A&R" representative (a title normally given to a record company talent scout) points to a new aggressiveness and commitment to artist development on the part of the publisher. A relationship with an influential publisher could, therefore, be a great help if your eventual goal is to secure a recording contract. [For more information on recent trends in music publishing, see Randy Poe's article, "What's Ahead for the Music Industry" on page 6.]

The business end of publishing involves, among other things, negotiating contracts; handling all pertinent contacts with the agencies that collect and distribute mechanical and performance royalties; filing copyright forms; distributing royalties to writers; and, in general, accounting for all of the money that comes and goes as a result of the creation and use of a song.

The effectiveness of any music publisher is judged by the success he has had finding commercially lucrative uses for songs. There are many ways for a song to make money: sale of records, air play, background music licensing, film and TV licensing, advertising uses, sheet music sales, and more. The ambitious publisher will seek out new and innovative uses for the songs in his catalog. Virtually any conceivable public use of music represents a source of potential profit for the music publisher and the songwriters he represents.

When deciding whether or not to work with a particular publisher you should consider:

● His track record. Has he had success with the kind of music you write? If he has, he should be more than happy to tell you about it. If he is a new publisher, does he have the contacts and drive necessary to get your songs to the right people?

● His personality. Is he the kind of person you feel you can deal with on a long-term basis? Is he sympathetic to your artistic concerns? Does he personally like and believe in your songs?

● His contract. Is it weighted heavily in his favor? Does he claim it is "the standard songwriter's contract" and therefore not open to negotiation? (If he does, don't believe it—all contracts are negotiable. For more on contracts, see The Business of Songwriting, page 11.)

● His honesty. No ethical publisher will ask you to sell your songs to him outright, nor will an ethical publisher ask you to pay for the "privilege" of having your song published. "Publishers" who operate that way are called song sharks, and you can learn more about them in The Business of Songwriting, page 11. To the best of our knowledge, the companies we have selected to be in this year's *Songwriter's Market* are honest companies that are interested in hearing your music.

With whatever companies you choose to submit to, remember that a professional, courteous approach goes a long way in making a good impression. Be aware that you are competing against successful hit songwriters who know how to submit high-quality, attractive demo packages to publishers. You can give yourself an edge by only sending out your best work to appropriate markets in a smartly prepared demo package. (For specific tips on increasing the effectiveness of your demos, see "Fine-Tuning Your Demos," on page 22.)

To increase your chances of success with the companies in *Songwriter's Market*, it is important to look for those who are interested in the kind of music you write and to follow their submission instructions to the letter. The listings in this section are filled with helpful information and reflect a need for every conceivable style of music, from traditional bluegrass to reggae, rap and thrash metal. So jump right in, find those companies that are in need of your songs and start submitting!

You may wish to try dealing with a foreign publisher—a healthy potential market for new material. Listings of companies in foreign countries will have the name of the country in bold type. At the end of the Music Publishers section is a geographical index of publishers in New York, Los Angeles and Nashville that will be helpful in planning a trip to one of these major music centers. You will also find an alphabetical list, by country, of all the foreign publishers in this year's *Songwriter's Market*.

*A. M. PERCUSSION PUBLICATIONS, P.O. Box 436, Lancaster NY 14086. (716)937-3705. Administrative Assistant: Charlene C. Wisner. Music publisher. Works with composers.
How to Contact: Submit a demo tape and sheet music (if possible) by mail—unsolicited submissions are OK. Prefers cassette. SASE.
Music: Only interested in percussion music pieces.

A STREET MUSIC, Suite 9W, 701 7th Ave., New York NY 10036. (212)764-3872. A&R Director: K. Hall. Music publisher, record company (A Street Records) and record producer (A Street Music). ASCAP. Estab. 1986. Publishes 15-20 songs/year; publishes 5 new songwriters/year. Works with composers. Pays standard royalty.
How to Contact: Prefers cassette with 3 songs. "No lyric sheets. SASE *only* will receive reply; for tape return include adequate postage."
Music: Mostly rock (heavy to pop/radio oriented); will listen to R&B (dance-oriented, radio/pop oriented). Published "Out of the Blues" (by Delton Weikie), recorded by Zeudus (heavy rock/fusion); "Edge of Insanity" (by Mark Rohrbach), recorded by Without Warning (radio-oriented rock); and "Dressed to Kill" (by Brian Nicary), recorded by Ripper Jack (A&R rock) all on A Street Records.
Tips: "Don't over-produce your demo; we want to hear the song. A good vocalist will help. Enclose an SASE."

ABIDING LOVE MUSIC PUBLISHING, P.O. Box 09045, Milwaukee WI 53209. (414)442-6500. President: L.L. Russell. Music publisher and record company (Creation Records and Kei Records). BMI. Estab. 1986. Publishes 1-7 songs/year; publishes 1-2 new songwriters/year. Works with composers, lyricists and team collaborators. Pays standard royalty.
Affiliates: La-Net Music, Gospel Music Association, and American Music Network Inc.
How to Contact: Submit a demo tape by mail—unsolicited submissions are O.K.Prefers cassette with 1-4 songs and lyric sheet. "Send a good tape, and make your first impression count." SASE or SAE and IRC. Reports in 1 month.
Music: Mostly gospel, M.O.R., R&B, pop and country/western. Published "There's Only One Way" (by Laf'eet' Russell), recorded by Laf'eet' Russell on Creation Records (gospel); "Jesus, He Always Can" (by Laf'eet' Russell), recorded by Laf'eet' Russell on Creation Records (gospel).
Tips: "Send a good tape. We'll be more active in our quest for musical excellence. Make a good demo and believe in your ability as a writer."

*ABINGDON PRESS, 201 8th Avenue, South, Nashville TN 37202. (615)749-6158. Music Editor: Gary Alan Smith. Music publisher. ASCAP. Re-entered music publishing in 1989. Publishes approximately 100 songs/year; publishes as many new songwriters as possible.
How to Contact: Submit a demo tape by mail—unsolicited submissions are OK. "Unsolicited material must be addressed with Gary Alan Smith's name on the first line." Prefers cassette with no more than 4 songs and lyric sheet. "Please assure name and address are on tapes and/or manuscripts, lyric sheets, etc." SASE. Reports in 1 month.
Music: Mostly "Sacred choral and instrumental; we do not publish separate octavos currently."
Tips: "Focus material on mid-size, volunteer church choirs and musicians."

AFTER YOU PUBLISHING CO., 29903 Harvester Rd., Malibu CA 90265. (213)457-4844. President: Matthew Katz. Music publisher, record company (San Francisco Sound and Malibu Records) and record producer (Matthew Katz Productions). Estab. 1955. BMI. Publishes 10 songs/year; publishes 2 new songwriters/year. Works with composers and lyricists; teams collaborators. Pays standard or negotiable royalty.
How to Contact: Prefers cassette with 3 songs and lead sheet. Does not return unsolicited material.
Music: San Francisco sound, psychedelic rock, 60's style.
Tips: Write songs with an up message.

ALA/BIANCA SRL, Mazzoni 34/36, Modena 41100 **Italy**. Phone: (059)223897. President: Toni Verona. Music publisher, record company (Bravo, Flea, River Nile), record producer (Idem) and video production. S.I.A.E. Estab. 1978. Publishes 200 songs/year; publishes 10 new songwriters/year. Teams collaborators. Pays standard royalty.
How to Contact: Write first to get permission to submit a tape. Prefers cassette with 2-3 songs. Does not return unsolicited material. Reports in 1 month.
Music: Mostly pop, rock and dance; also instrumental. Published "Children of the Sky" (by A. Sorrenti), recorded by Giorgia Morandi on E.M.I. Records (pop); "Freedom Rain" (by G. Romani), recorded by Rocking Chairs on River Nile Records (rock); and "Awaka Boy" (by Farina/Crivellente), recorded by Tatjana on Dureco Records (dance).

ALEXIS, Box 532, Malibu CA 90265. (213)463-5998. President: Lee Magid. Music publisher, record company, personal management firm, and record and video producer. ASCAP. Member AIMP. Estab. 1950. Publishes 50 songs/year; publishes 20-50 new songwriters/year. Works with composers and lyricists; teams collaborators. Pays standard royalty.
Affiliates: Marvelle (BMI), Lou-Lee (BMI) and D.R. Music (ASCAP).
How to Contact: Submit a demo tape—unsolicited submissions are OK. Prefers cassette (or VHS videocassette of writer/artist if available) with 1-3 songs and lyric sheet. "Try to make demo as clear as possible—guitar or piano should be sufficient. A full rhythm and vocal demo is always better." SASE. Reports in 1 month "if interested".

 The asterisk before a listing indicates that the listing is new in this edition. New markets are often the most receptive to unsolicited submissions.

Music: Mostly R&B, jazz, MOR, pop and gospel; also blues, church/religious, country, dance-oriented, folk and Latin. Published "Jesus is Just Alright" (by Art Reynolds), recorded by Doobie Bros. on W/ B Records (R&B/R&R); "What Shall I Do?" (by Quincy Fielding), recorded by Tramaine Hawkins on Sparrow Records (gospel); and "I Played the Fool" (by D. Alexis), recorded by The Clovers on Atlantic Records (R&B).

Tips: "Create a good melody-lyric and a good clean demo tape. A home recording will do."

ALHART MUSIC PUBLISHING CO., P.O. Box 1593, Lakeside CA 92040. (619)443-2170. A&R: Rue Anna Boland. Music publisher and record company (Alhart). BMI. Estab. 1981. Publishes 6-8 new songs/year; publishes 3-6 new songwriters/year. Works with composers and lyricists; teams collaborators. Pays standard royalty.

How to Contact: Write or call first and obtain permission to submit a tape. Prefers cassette with 1-3 songs and lyric sheets. SASE. Reports in 3 months.

Music: Mostly country, R&B and pop. Published "Julie" and "Memories" (by Mike Edwards — pop), and "After All" (by Renay Nelson — country).

ALL ROCK MUSIC, P.O. Box 2296, Rotterdam 3000 CG **Holland**. Phone: (10)4224889. President: Cees Klop. Music publisher, record company (Collector Records) and record producer. Estab. 1967. Publishes 50-60 songs/year; publishes several new songwriters/year. Pays standard royalty.

Affiliates: All Rock Music (England) and All Rock Music (Belgium).

How to Contact: Submit demo tape by mail. Prefers cassette. SAE and IRC. Reports in 4 weeks.

Music: Mostly 50s rock, rockabilly and country rock; also piano boogie woogie. Published "Loving Wanting You," by R. Scott (country rock) and "Ditch Digger" by D. Mote (rock), both recorded by Cees Klop on White Label records; and "Bumper Boogie" (by R. Hoeke), recorded by Cees Klop on Downsouth Records (boogie); "Spring In April" by H. Pepping (rock).

*ALLISONGS INC., 1603 Horton Ave., Nashville TN 37212. (615)292-9899. President: Jim Allison. Music publisher, record company (ARIA Records), record producer (Jim Allison, AlliSongs Inc.) BMI, ASCAP. Estab. 1985. Publishes more than 25 songs/year; approximately 3 new songwriters/year. Works with composers and lyricists; teams collaborators. Pays standard royalty of 50%.

Affiliates: Jims' Allisongs (BMI), d.c. Radio-Active Music (ASCAP) and Annie Green Eyes Music (BMI).

How to Contact: Submit a demo tape by mail — unsolicited submissions are OK. Prefers cassette and lyric sheet. Does not return unsolicited material. Reports in 1-2 months.

Music: Mostly country, pop and R&B. Published "What Am I Gonna Do About You" (by Allison/ Simon/Gilmore), recorded by Reba McEntire on MCA Records (country); "Preservation of the Wild Life" (by Allison/Young), recorded by Earl Thomas Conley on RCA Records (country) and "Hard-Hearted Heart" (by Allison/Chauvin), recorded by Bruce Van Dyke on ARIA Records (country).

ALLORA MUSIC PUBLISHING, Box 153, Sea Isle NJ 08243. (609)263-1777. President: Marc Dicciani. Music publisher and record producer (MJD Productions, Inc.). ASCAP. Estab. 1980. Publishes 15 songs/year; publishes 3 new songwriters/year. Works with composers and lyricists; teams collaborators. Pays standard royalty.

Affiliates: Allora (ASCAP).

How to Contact: Submit a demo tape by mail — unsolicited submissions are O.K. Prefers cassette with 3-4 songs and lyric sheets. SASE. Reports in 3-4 weeks.

Music: Mostly rock, dance, pop and R&B. "You're the First Thing" (by Mary Welch), recorded by Bobby Rydell on Applause (pop); "Dance on Air" (by Bob Pruitt), recorded by R.B. Pruitt on Manhattan (R&B); "It's Alright" (by Anthony Ventura), recorded by Ant on Allora (rock).

Tips: "Keep song demos simple with vocals out front."

ALTERNATIVE DIRECTION MUSIC PUBLISHERS, Box 3278, Station D, Ottawa, Ontario K1P 6H8 **Canada**. (613)225-6100. President and Director of Publishing: David Stein. Music publisher, record company (Parade Records), record producer and management firm (Alternative Direction Management). PROCAN. Estab. 1980. Publishes 5-10 songs/year; publishes 2-3 new songwriters/year. Works with composers; teams collaborators. Pays standard royalty.

"How to Use Your Songwriter's Market" (at the front of this book) contains comments and suggestions to help you understand and use the information in these listings.

How to Contact: Prefers cassette (or Beta videocassette) with 2-4 songs. SASE if sent from within Canada; American songwriters send SAE and $2 for postage and handling. Reports in 6 weeks.
Music: Uptempo rock, uptempo R&B and uptempo pop. Published "Big Kiss" (by David Ray), recorded by Theresa Bazaar on MCA Records (pop/dance) and Cindy Valentine on CBS Records (rock), Kyana on Parade Records (R&B); The edge on Parade Records (rock).
Tips: "Make certain your vocals are up front in the mix in the demos you submit. I am looking only for uptempo R&B and pop songs with a strong chorus and killer hooks. Don't send me any MOR, country, blues or folk music. I don't publish that kind of material."

AMALGAMATED TULIP CORP., 117 W. Rockland Rd., Box 615, Libertyville IL 60048. (708)362-4060. President: Perry Johnson. Music publisher, record company and record producer. BMI. Estab. 1968. Publishes 12 songs/year; publishes 3-6 new songwriters/year. Pays standard royalty.
Affiliate: Mo Fo Music.
How to Contact: Submit a demo tape—unsolicited submissions are OK. Prefers cassette with 3-5 songs and lyric sheet. SASE. Prefers studio produced demos. Reports in 2 months.
Music: Mostly rock, top 40/pop, dance and R&B; also country, MOR, blues, and easy listening progressive. Published "This Feels Like Love to Me" (by Charles Sermay), recorded by Sacha Distel (pop); "Stop Wastin' Time" (by Tom Gallagher), recorded by Orjan (country); and "In the Middle of the Night," recorded by Oh Boy (pop).
Tips: "Send commercial material."

AMBRA MUSIC, Liechtenstein Str.117/17, Vienna A-1090 **Austria**. Phone: (0222)310 9020. Contact: Blacky Schwarz. Music publisher, record company (Ambra) and record producer (Ambra Music). AUME, AKM. Estab. 1988. Publishes 100 songs/year. Works with composers and lyricists. Pays 60% composer/lyricist, 40% publisher (payed by AKM directly) if original rights are by AMBRA Music.
Affiliates: Cebra, Avox, Czech, Daniel, PZ, Timeless Music and Wild Songs (all AKM, AUME).
How to Contact: Submit a demo tape by mail—unsolicited submissions are OK. Prefers cassette or 7.5 ips reel-to-reel with lyric sheets. "Instrumental music (any style) for compilation records (radio/tv/film) welcome."
Music: Mostly pop, rock and new age; also dance/disco. Published "Sehr Aut" (by Scheutz/Scheutz/Spitzer), recorded by Wilfried on Bellaphon Records (pop/rock); "It's Not Easy" (by Fisher, Stocker Kochauf), recorded by El Fisher on CBS Records (mainstream power-rock); and "Die Leut san alle deppert!" (by Georg Danzer), recorded by Georg Danzer on Teldel (rock/pop).

AMIRON MUSIC, 20531 Plummer St., Chatsworth CA 91311. (818)998-0443. Manager: A. Sullivan. Music publisher, record company, record producer and manager. ASCAP. Estab. 1970. Publishes 2-4 songs/year; publishes 1-2 new songwriters/year. Pays standard royalty.
Affiliates: Aztex Productions, and Copan Music (BMI).
How to Contact: Prefers cassette (or Beta or VHS videocassette) with any number songs and lyric sheet. SASE. Reports in 10 weeks.
Music: Easy listening, MOR, progressive, R&B, rock and top 40/pop. Published "Lies in Disguise," "Rapid," and "Let's Work It Out" (by F. Cruz), recorded by Gangs Back; and "Try Me," written and recorded by Sana Christian; all on AKO Records (all pop). Also "Boys Take Your Mind Off Things" (by G. Litvak), recorded by Staunton on Les Disques Records (pop).
Tips: Send songs with "good story-lyrics."

ANGELSONG PUBLISHING CO., 2714 Westwood Dr., Nashville TN 37402. (615)297-2246. President: Mabel Birdsong. BMI, ASCAP. Music publisher and record company (Birdsong Records). Publishes 2 albums/year; publishes 2 new songwriters/year.
How to Contact: Prefers cassette with maximum 4 songs and lyric sheet. Does not return unsolicited material. Reports in 2 weeks, "if requested."
Music: Mostly gospel, country and MOR; also pop. Published *Bless This House* by Junior Rutty; and *Go Where The Peace Is* by the Songwriters.

ANOTHER AMETHYST SONG, 96 McGregor Downs, West Columbia SC 29169-2850. (803)791-4137. Contact: Manager. Music publisher, record company (Amethyst Group), record producer (Jojo St. Mitchell) and management firm. BMI. Estab. 1985. Publishes 40 songs/year; publishes 30 new songwriters/year. Works with composers. Pays standard royalty.
How to Contact: Prefers cassette (or VHS videocassette) with 3-7 songs and lyric sheet; include any photos, biographical information. SASE. Reports in 5 weeks.
Music: Mostly metal, rock, pop, new wave and eclectic styles. Recently published "Complicated Love" (by C. Sargent and C. Hamblin), recorded by True Identity on Antithesis Records; "Back in the Race" (By C. Sargent and C. Hamblin), recorded by True Identity on Antithesis Records; and "If You Had Your Mind Made Up" written and recorded by Kourtesy on Antitesis Records.

Tips: "Simplicity is the key. A hit is a hit regardless of the production. Don't 'overkill' the song! We mainly sign artists/writers. Keep trying."

*ANOTHER EAR MUSIC, Box 110142 Nashville TN 37222-0142. General Manager: T.J. Kirby. BMI, ASCAP. Music publisher, record company (T.J. Records), record producer (T.J. Productions) and management firm (T.J. Productions). Publishes 2 songs/year; publishes 2 new songwriters/year. Works with composers and lyricists; teams collaborators. Pays standard royalty.
Affiliate: Peppermint Rainbow Music/ASCAP.
How to Contact: Submit a demo tape with 1-2 songs (or VHS videocassette) by mail. One song only on video with lyric sheets.
Music: Mostly country/pop and R&B: also gospel, rock and "concept songs." Published "Let it Be Me Tonight" (by Tom Douglas/Bob Lee/T.J. Kirby), recorded by Kathy Ford on Prerie Dust Records; and "Don't Take a Heart" (by Kirby/Lapp/Smith) and "Faster than a Speeding Bullet" (by Paul Hotchkiss), recorded by Deb Merrit on T.J. Records (all country/pop).
Tips: "Videos are great to help present a writer's concept but don't let the ideas of what you would put in a video stand in the way of writing a great song."

ANTIOCH MINISTRIES INTERNATIONAL, INC., Box 11058, Honolulu HI 96828. General Manger: Mike Miyashiro. Music publisher and record company (Bellavia Records). ASCAP. Estab. 1989. Publishes 3-4 songs/year. Works with team collaborators. Pays standard royalty.
How to Contact: Submit a demo tape by mail—unsolicited submissions are O.K. Prefers cassette with 2 songs and lyric sheets. Does not return unsolicited material. Reports in 3-4 weeks. No phone calls.
Music: Mostly pop-R&B, pop-funk, pop-love ballads and pop-rock; also gospel and pop-country. Note: Bellavia has an "in-house" songwriting team now with projects for 1991. New additions at this point are limited. Will consider *only* pop love songs ballads. Published "I Magnify" (by Mark Souza), recorded by Dean Pagan on Bellavia Records (gospel) and "Lock it in" (by Miyashiro Makuakane) recorded by Koa on Bellavia Records (rap).
Tips: "Establish your 'hook' within the first 30 seconds of your song, whether by lyric or instrumental arrangement. A good pop song must get to the point simply and as soon as possible."

APON PUBLISHING CO., Box 3082, Steinway Station, Long Island City, NY 11103. Manager: Don Zemann. Music publisher, record company (Apon, Supraphon, Panton and Love Records) and record producer. ASCAP. Estab. 1957. Publishes 250 songs/year; publishes 50 new songwriters/year. Teams collaborators. Pays standard royalty or by special agreements made with individual songwriters.
How to Contact: Submit a demo tape—unsolicited submissions are OK. Prefers cassette (or VHS Videocassette) with 1-6 songs and lyric sheet. SASE. Reports in 2 months.
Music: New Age, classical, background music, dance-oriented, easy listening, folk and international. Published "Who Knows" (by B. Sedlacek), recorded by BRNO Radio Orchestra on Panton Records (background music); "Operatic Arias" (by Peter Dvorsky), recorded by Slovak Symphony Orchestra; "You Are Everywhere" (by Karel Gott), recorded by J. Staidl Orchestra.
Tips: "We are sub-publishers for pop music from overseas. We publish and record background music for the major background systems operational all over the world. Need only top quality, no synthesizer recordings."

APPLE-GLASS MUSIC, A division of American Music Company, Box 8604, Madison WI 53708. Professional Manager: Daniel W. Miller. Music publisher and recording studio (Legend). BMI. Publishes 10-25 songs/year. Pays standard royalty.
How to Contact: Prefers "professionally produced" 7½ ips reel-to-reel or cassette with 1-3 songs and lyric sheet. "We suggest songwriter's name, address and song titles be typed on labels affixed to tape reel (or cassette) and box for identification." SASE. Reports in 6 months. "Our contracts do not feature reversion clauses or offer advances on unearned royalties. No telephone calls, please."
Music: Country, polka, gospel and top 40/rock.

ARCADE MUSIC CO., Arzee Recording Co., 3010 N. Front St., Philadelphia PA 19133. (215)426-5682. President: Rex Zario. A&R Director: Lucky Taylor. Music publisher, booking agency and record company. ASCAP. Publishes 100-150 songs/year. Pays standard royalty.
Affiliates: Valleybrook (ASCAP), Rex Zario Music (BMI) and Seabreeze Music (BMI).
How to Contact: Prefers cassette with 4-5 songs and lead sheet. SASE. Reports in 5 weeks.
Music: Bluegrass, country, easy listening, folk, gospel, rock (fifties style) and top 40/pop. Published "Why Do I Cry Over You" (by DeKnight and Keefer), recorded by Bill Haley on Arzee Records (country); "Hand Clap For Jesus" (by Rodney Harris), recorded by Gospel Blenders on Arzee Records

(gospel); and "I Couldn't See the Tears" (by Miller and Marcin), recorded by Dee Dee Marcin on Arzee Records (country).

ART AUDIO PUBLISHING COMPANY/TIGHT HI-FI SOUL MUSIC, 9706 Cameron Ave., Detroit MI 48211. (313)893-3406. President: Albert M. Leigh. Professional Manager: Dolores M. Leigh. Music publisher and record company. BMI, ASCAP. Pays standard royalty.
How to Contact: Prefers cassette with 1-3 songs and lyric or lead sheets. SASE. Reports in 2 weeks.
Music: Mostly MOR, R&B, soul and rock; also disco, easy listening, gospel and top 40/pop. Published "Are You An Angel In Disguise" (by Albert M. Leigh), recorded by Willie Jennings on Echoic Hi-Fi Records (rock); "Jesus Showed Us The Way" (by W. Ayers) on X-Tone Records; and "Twon Special," written and recorded by Jesse Taylor on Echoic Hi-Fi Records (R&B).
Tips: "Basically we are interested only in a new product with a strong title, a love story, or an expressive, emotional sound. Arrange your songs to match a professional recording artist and his or her working style and pattern. Our record company must judge your tape according to the preference and demand of the current marketplace to decide if your songs are suitable. Keep lyrics up front on demo—make sure words are clearly understandable."

ASSOCIATED ARTISTS INTERNATIONAL (HOLLAND), Maarschalklaan 47, 3417 SE Montfoort, **The Netherlands.** Phone: (0)3484-2860. FAX: 31-3484-2860. General Manager: Joop Gerrits. Music publisher, record company (Associated Artists Records), record producer (Associated Artists Productions) and radio and TV promotors. BUMA. Estab. 1975. Publishes 200 songs/year; publishes 50 new songwriters/year. In 1987 subpublished more than 70 new songs, 27 local recordings by different record companies such as Phonogram, Polydor and EMJ, released in The Netherlands, Belgium, Germany, Spain, Italy, Denmark and the United Kingdom. Works with composers and lyricists; teams collaborators. Pays by agreement.
Affiliate: BMC Publishing Holland (BUMA); Hilversum Happy Music (BUMA); Intermelodie and Holland Glorie Productions.
How to Contact: Submit demo tape by mail. Prefers compact cassette (or VHS videocassette). SAE and IRC. Reports in 1 month.
Music: Mostly disco, pop and Italian disco; also rock, gospel (evangelic), musicals, MOR and country. Works with "Electra Salsa," who "reached the top 40 in the Benelux countries, and the Disco dance top 50." Older copyrights recorded by the Tremeloes, Whamm, Kayak and John Mackenzie. Published "Stormind," written and recorded by Dan Stevens on AAR Records (MOR); "Hot Line" (by Dan Aaronson), recorded by Laurice on AAR Records (disco); and "Touch Me," (Botolotti), *The Mark Fushere catalogue*-(USA), *The songs of Panfilo Di Matteo*-(Canada), The Berhard Haisch translations of German songs as 'In a Zanzibar Bar' and others.
Tips: "Send good quality demos."

NICHOLAS ASTOR-GROUF ENTERPRISES, P.O. Box 3248, Yale Station, New Haven CT 06520. (212)348-8288. Vice President, A&R Department: Casper Krantz. Music publisher, record company (Nick Nack Paddywack Records) and record producer (Yale Undergraduate's Productions). Estab. 1985. Publishes 30-40 songs/year; publishes 5-10 new songwriters/year. Works with composers and lyricists; teams collaborators. Pays standard royalty. "Charges production fee."
Affiliates: Astor Publishing, No Sweat Records, Chairs for Charity, No Exit Productions, IRS Records, FBI and Warner Bros.
Music: Mostly new rock, pop rock and top 40/pop, jazz and funk; also folk, ethereal new age and classical. Published "Bodies at Night" (by Astor), recorded by Nicky Burns (new rock); "Alone" (by Astor), recorded by Nicky Burns (pop/rock); "Thiongs Got Smaller in the Rear View Mirror" (by Stewart), recorded by Margaret Ensemble (new rock musical); and "Everyday" (by Sal Fourg), recorded by Boogie Boys (tex/mex/funk/punk); all on Nick Nack Paddywack Records.
Tips: "Songs should be both witty and literate, with careful attention to subject matter and motif. We, as an unaffiliated Yale organization, press a number of albums and one double compilation effort which often finds international distribution. We consider all contributions and encourage communication."

Market conditions are constantly changing! If you're still using this book and it is 1992 or later, buy the newest edition of Songwriter's Market at your favorite bookstore or order directly from Writer's Digest Books.

ASTRODISQUE PUBLISHING, Plum Sound and Video, 335 Merrimack St., Newburyport MA 01950. (617)465-5653. President: Richard Tiegen. Music publisher, record company (Plum Records) and record producer (Richard Tiegen/Magic Sound Productions). BMI. Estab. 1980. Publishes 10 songs/year; publishes 10 new songwriters/year. Works with composers and lyricists; teams collaborators. Pays standard royalty. "Charges recording and production fees."
How to Contact: Write or call first to obtain permission to submit. Prefers cassette (or VHS videocassette). Does not return unsolicited material. Reports in 3 weeks.
Music: Rock, R&B and country; also New Age and acoustic. Published "Star Train Express," "Too Hot to Handle" and "I Need Your Love," (all by Letourneau), recorded by Dixie Train on Plum Records (all country singles).

ATTID MUSIC CO., #1 Colony Rd., Gretna LA 70053. President: Carlo Ditta. Music publisher and record company (Orleans Records). ASCAP. Estab. 1986. Publishes 10 songs/year; publishes 5 new songwriters/year. Works with composers and lyricists. Pays standard royalty.
How to Contact: Write first and obtain permission to submit a tape. Prefers cassette with 5 songs and lyric sheets. Does not return unsolicited material. Reports in 6 weeks.
Music: Mostly soul, blues and folk; also gospel, country and R&B. "True Blue" (by C.P. Love), recorded by Carlo Ditta on Orleans (soul); "Pray" (by Carlo Ditta), recorded by Mighty Sam on Orleans (gospel); "Whatever It Takes" (by Jon Aylle and Carlo Ditta), recorded by Mighty Sam on Vivid Sand (inspirational).

AUDIO MUSIC PUBLISHERS, 449 N. Vista St., Los Angeles CA 90036. (213)653-0693. Contact: Ben Weisman. Music publisher, record company and record producer. ASCAP. Estab. 1962. Publishes 25 songs/year; publishes 10-15 new songwriters/year. Works with composers and lyricists; teams collaborators. Pays standard royalty.
How to Contact: Submit a demo tape—unsolicited submissions are OK. Prefers cassette with 3-10 songs and lyric sheet. "We do not return unsolicited material without SASE. Don't query first; just send tape." Reports in 1 month.
Music: Mostly pop, R&B, rap, dance, funk, soul and country; also rock (all types).

AUNTIE ARGON MUSIC, Box 4125, West Hills CA 91308. Director: Steve Hobson. Music publisher. BMI. Estab. 1988. Publishes 2-4 songs/year; 1 new songwriter/year. Works with composers and lyricists. Pays standard royalty.
Affiliates: Mama Freon Music (ASCAP).
How to Contact: Write first and obtain permission to submit a tape. Prefers cassette with 1-3 songs with lyric sheets. Does not return unsolicited material. "Unsolicited material goes directly into the trash!!" Reports in 2 weeks.
Music: Mostly mainstream pop/top 40, country and novelty. Published "City Boy Gone Country" and "Go Mountaineers" (by Steve Hobson), recorded by Daddy Hoedown on Pops Neon Records (country-rock).

*AVATAR PRODUCTIONS, Suite 605, 6290 Sunset Blvd., Los Angeles CA 90028. (213)464-1593. President: Reginald Brown. Music publisher. ASCAP/BMI. Estab. 1985.
How to Contact: Submit demo tape by mail—unsolicited submissions are OK. Prefers cassette with songs and lyric sheets. SASE. Reports in 2 months.
Music: R&B. Published "The Right Stuff" (by Kipper Jones) and "Darlin' I" (by Kenny Harris), recorded by Vanessa Williams on Wing Records (R&B singles) and "Livin' Large" (by Larry Robinson), recorded by E.U. Band on Virgin Records (R&B single).
Tips: "No phone calls, please."

*AVILO MUSIC, 8055 W. 21 Lane, Hialeah FL 33016. (305)822-9701 or (305)822-9708. President: Carlos Oliva. Music publisher, record company and record producer. Estab. 1979. BMI. Member NARM. Publishes 20 songs/year; publishes 2 new songwriters/year. Teams collaborators. Pays standard royalty.
Affiliates: Oliva Music (SESAC) and Santa Clara Music (ASCAP).
How to Contact: Prefers cassette with any number of songs and lyric sheet. SASE. Reports in 2 weeks.
Music: Dance-oriented, Spanish and rock. Published "Iman" (merengue); "No Comprendo" (salsa); and "Pa Que Sufrir" (salsa) all (by Carlos Olivia), recorded by Los Sobrinos Del Juez on Polygram Records.
Tips: "Songs should have a strong hook, simple melody and sense-making lyrics."

AXBAR PRODUCTIONS, Box 12353, San Antonio TX 78212. (512)829-1909. Business Manager: Joe Scates. Music publisher, record company, record producer and record distributors. BMI. Member CMA. Estab. 1978. Publishes 30 songs/year; publishes 10-12 new songwriters/year. Works with composers. Pays standard royalty.
Affiliates: Axbar Productions and Axe Handle Music (ASCAP).
How to Contact: Submit a demo tape—unsolicited submissions are OK. Arrange personal interview. Prefers cassette (or VHS videocassette) with 1-5 songs and lyric sheet. SASE. Reports as soon as possible, but "we hold the better songs for more detailed study."
Music: Mostly country; also country crossover, comedy, blues, MOR and rock (soft). Published "Daylight," written and recorded by Kenny Dale on EMI-NZ (country single); "This Darn Pen" (by E. Lobello), recorded by Billy D. Hunter on Axbar (country ballad); and "Since My Woman Set Me Free," written and recorded by Jackson Boone on Trophy Records (country single).
Tips: "Polish your material. Don't expect us to rework your lyrics. Bad grammar and poor spelling hurt your chances."

B.A.M. MUSIC, 68A Delancey St., London NW1 **England**. Phone: (01)485-3733. A&R Director: André Jacquemin. Music publisher and record producer. PRS. Member MCPS. Estab. 1974. Publishes 10 songs/year; publishes 2 new songwriters/year. Works with composers and lyricists; teams collaborators. Pays standard royalty.
How to Contact: Submit a demo tape—unsolicited submissions are OK. Prefers cassette. SAE and IRC. Reports in 2 months.
Music: Mostly rock, pop; also New Age. Published "The Rumour" (by G. Richards, S. Mills, E. Colerman) recorded by Tubilah Dog (rock); "Out of the Sky" (by S. Mills, G. Richards), recorded by Tubilah Dog (rock); and "When I Woke" (by Johnny Q.), recorded by Bob Gone Crazy (pop) all on B.A.M. Records.

B. SHARP MUSIC, 24 rue Gachard, 1050 Brussels, **Belgium**. Phone: (02)241-41-86. Music publisher, record company (B. Sharp, Selection Records) and record producer (Pletinckx). Estab. 1950. Works with composers and lyricists; teams collaborators. Pays standard royalty.
Affiliates: Prestation Music and Multi Sound.
How to Contact: Write first and obtain permission to submit. Prefers cassette. Does not return unsolicited material. Reports in 2 weeks.
Music: Jazz, rock, instrumental music and music library. Published "Artline" recorded by J. Pirotton; "Lemon Air" recorded by G. Cabay; and "Speed Limit" recorded by M. Verderame, all on B. Sharp Records (instrumentals).

BAD GRAMMAR MUSIC, Suite 306, 35918 Union-Lake Rd. Mt. Clemens MI 48043. Music Director: Joe Trupiano. Music publisher, record company (Rockit Records), record producer (Bad Grammar Enterprises) and management company. Estab. 1982. BMI. Publishes 10-20 songs/year; publishes 10-20 new songwriters/year. Works with composers and lyricists; teams collaborators. Pays standard royalty.
How to Contact: Submit a demo tape—unsolicited submissions are OK if submitting according to listing. Prefers cassette (or VHS videocassette) with 3-4 songs and lyric sheet. Reports in 6 weeks.
Music: Mostly dance-oriented, pop/rock and rock; adult contemporary, top 40/ballads, and country. Published "Nightmares (of Losing You)" (pop/rock), "Living Without You" (ballad) and "Car Crazy" (pop/rock), all written and recorded by Joey Harlow on Rockit Records; also "Red Tape" (rock) by Messenger.
Tips: "We are presently screening material for our 'Power in Numbers' compilation CD, any material sent on 24 track format is given prompt attention and consideration. Be commercial and trendy and keep it hooky, but write from your soul. Listen to what's getting airplay, keep music and lyrics simple, and tell a definite story. We need songs that the public can walk away humming. The biggest sellers in our industry today would have to be white pop/dance, pop/rock and love ballads."

BAGATELLE MUSIC PUBLISHING CO., 400 San Jacinto St., Houston TX 77002. (713)225-6654. President: Byron Benton. BMI. Music publisher, record company and record producer. Publishes 40 songs/year; publishes 2 new songwriters/year. Pays standard royalty.
Affiliate: Floyd Tillman Publishing Co.
How to Contact: Prefers cassette (or videocassette) with any number of songs and lyric sheet.
Music: Mostly country; also gospel and blues. Published "Everything You Touch," written and recorded by Johnny Nelms; "If I Could Do It All Over Again," written and recorded by Floyd Tillman; and "Mona from Daytona" (by Byron Benton), recorded by F. Tillman; all on Bagatelle Records (country).

BAL & BAL MUSIC PUBLISHING CO., P.O. Box 369, LaCanada CA 91012-0369. (818)548-1116. President: Adrian Bal. Music publisher, record company (Bal Records) and record producer. ASCAP. Member AGAC and AIMP. Estab. 1965. Publishes 2-4 songs/year; publishes 2-4 new songwriters/year. Works with composers and lyricists; teams collaborators. Pays standard royalty.
Affiliate: Bal West Music Publishing Co (BMI).
How to Contact: Submit a demo tape—unsolicited submissions are OK. Prefers cassette with 3 songs and lyric sheet. SASE. Reports in 1-3 months.
Music: Mostly MOR, country, rock and gospel; also blues, church/religious, easy listening, jazz, R&B, soul and top 40/pop. Published "Right To Know" and "Fragile" (by James Jackson), recorded by Kathy Simmons; and "You're a Part of Me," "Can't We Have Some Time Together," "You and Me," and "Circles of Time," all written and recorded by Paul Richards on BAL Records (adult contemporary).

*BANNERLEAGUE, LTD. T/A BOLTS MUSIC, 619 Salisbury Prom, Green Lanes, Harringay, London N8 ORX **England**. (01)809-1460. Contact: Nicky Price. Music publisher. Estab. 1987. Publishes 10 songs/year; publishes 2 new songwriters/year. Hires staff songwriters. Works with composers; teams collaborators. Pays 60% royalty to composer.
How to Contact: Submit a demo tape by mail—unsolicited submissions are OK. Prefers cassette or 7½ ips. reel to reel or VHS videocassette (PAL standard) with 1 song and lyric or lead sheet. SASE. Reports in 3 weeks.
Music: Mostly dance; also all types. Published "Don't Stop" (by Darral Tim Mclee), recorded by Dance Addiction on Bolts Records (house); 'Trip on This" (by Asmo), recorded by Asmo on Bolts Records (techno); "Vindiloo Rap" (by Chris Fergason Kelly), recorded by Bagi Jon on Bolts Records (rap comedy).

BARTOW MUSIC, 68 Old Canton Rd N.E., Cartersville GA 30120. (404)382-1442. Publishing Administrator: Jack C. Hill; Producer: Tirus McClendon. Music publisher and record producer (HomeBoy, Ragtime Productions). BMI. Estab. 1988. Publishes 5 songs/year; 5 new songwriters/year. Works with composers and lyricists; teams collaborators. Pays royalty.
How to Contact: Submit a demo tape by mail—unsolicited submissions are O.K. Prefers cassette (or VHS videocassette) with 3 songs and lyric sheets. SASE. Reports in 1 month.
Music: R&B, pop, dance and house. Published"Oh Father" (by Maurice Carroll), recorded by Simply Suave (R&B); "I Need You Tonight" (by Maurice Carroll), recorded by Simply Suave (R&B) dance) and "New Day" (by Tirus McClendon), recorded by Celebrations (R&B dance) all on West View Records.

BAY TONE MUSIC PUBLISHING, 1218 Hollister Ave., San Francisco CA 94124. (415)467-5157. Owner: Bradbury Taylor. Music publisher. BMI. Pays standard royalty.
Affiliates: Bay-Tone and Soul Set Records.
How to Contact: Write or call first and obtain permission to submit. Prefers cassette, 7½ or 15 ips reel-to-reel (or VHS videocassette) with any number of songs and lyric and lead sheets. Does not return unsolicited material. Reporting time varies.
Music: Pop, rock and R&B. Published "Only You," by Elektryk Starr and "No Second Chance" by Mark Taylor, both on Bay Tone Records.
Tips: "Be precise; make sure the story is complete to the music."

BEARSONGS, Box 944, Birmingham, B16 8UT **England**. Phone: 44-021-454-7020. Managing Director: Jim Simpson. Music publisher and record company (Big Bear Records). Member PRS, MCPS. Publishes 25 songs/year; publishes 15-20 new songwriters/year.
How to Contact: Prefers reel-to-reel or cassette. SAE and IRC. Reports in 2-3 weeks.
Music: Blues, jazz and soul.

BECKIE PUBLISHING COMPANY, INC., Box 14671, Memphis TN 38114. (901)272-7039. President: Linda Lucchesi. Music publisher. ASCAP, BMI. Estab. 1965. Publishes 1-5 songs and new songwriters/ year. Works with composers and lyricists; teams collaborators. Pays standard royalty.
Affiliates: Memphis Town Music, Inc. and Simply Grand Music, Inc.
How to Contact: Submit a demo tape—unsolicited submissions are OK. Prefers cassette with 1-3 songs and lyric sheet. SASE. Reports in 3 months.
Music: Mostly pop and soul; also easy listening, MOR, R&B, country and soft rock.
Tips: "We're the publishing home of 'Wooly Bully'!"

*K. BEE PRODUCTIONS INC/BUZZ RECORDS, 8900 N. Central Penthouse 405, Phoenix AZ 85020. (602)678-1444. President: Kenneth D. Belanger. Music publisher, record company (Buzz Records/ Belhap Records), record producer (K. Bee Productions Inc.) ASCAP-BMI. Estab. 1989. Publishes 8-

10 songs/year; 2 new songwriters/year. Hires staff songwriters. Works with composers and lyricists; teams collaborators. Pays varying royalty to artist on contract.

Affiliates: Belhap Music Publishers (ASCAP) and Pahleb Music Publishers (BMI).

How to Contact: Submit a demo tape by mail—unsolicited submissions OK. Prefers cassette (or ½″ videocassette if available) with 1-3 songs and lyric sheet. "No phone calls. We will contact if intereted." Does not return unsolicited material. Reports in 1 month.

Music: Mostly rock, pop, country/R&B; also industrial A.V., novelty and heavy metal. Published "Secret Sea of Storm" recorded by Brats on Buzz Records (metal pop); "Lover Deceiver" (crossover/pop) and "Kinda, Sorta, Maybe" (country) both recorded on Belhap Records all written by Rick Funk and Ken Belanger.

Tips: "Send a good clean, clear tape. We are looking for artists and writers with signature in their style."

EARL BEECHER PUBLISHING, P.O. Box 2111, Huntington Beach CA 92647. (714)842-8635. Owner: Earl Beecher. Music publisher, record company (Outstanding and Morrhythm Records) and record producer (Earl Beecher). BMI. Estab. 1968. Publishes varying number of songs/year. Works with composers. Pays standard royalty.

How to Contact: Submit a demo tape—unsolicited submissions are OK. Prefers cassette. SASE. Reports in 3 months.

Music: Mostly pop, ballads, rock and gospel; also country.

Tips: "I am interested mainly in people who want to perform their songs and release albums on one of my labels."

*BEKOOL MUSIC, Box 31819, Dallas TX 75231-0819. (214)750-0720. A&R: Mike Anthony. Music publisher. ASCAP. Estab. 1987. Publishes 12-20 songs/year. Publishes 3 new songwriters/year. Pays standard royalty. Works with composers.

Affiliates: Forest Creek Music (BMI).

How to Contact: Write first and obtain permission to submit a tape. Prefers cassette with 1-2 songs and lyric sheet. "We do not return unsolicited material but will contact if interested."

Music: Mostly country and gospel. Published "Like Goin' Home" (by Allison Gilliam), recorded by Susie Calvin on Canyon Creek Records (country); "No Room in my Heart" (by Bart Barton and D. Byram), recorded by Susie Calvin on Canyon Creek Records (country); and "I Can Lead You to Love" (by Tom Long and Dellas Pearce), recorded by Audie Henry on Canyon Creek/RCA (country).

BENYARD MUSIC CO., P.O. Box 298, Kew Gardens NY 11415. (516)334-4720. Music publisher: Kevin Benyard. Music publisher. Member Songwriter's Guild of America. Estab. 1987. Publishes 5 songs/year; publishes 3 new songwriters/year. Works with composers and lyricists. Pays standard royalty.

How to Contact: Write first and obtain permission to submit. Prefers cassette with 2-5 songs and lyric sheet. SASE (postcard). Reports in 4 weeks.

Music: Mostly R&B, jazz fusion, rock, rap, top 40; also pop. Published "Better Wait to Know Her," (by Benyard/Danle) and "The Time is Right," (by K. Benyard); both recorded by K. Benyard on Jeannae Records.

Tips: "I'm looking for music and songs that are totally new in approach. I'm interested in releasing the music of the 90's."

BERANDOL MUSIC LTD., 110A Sackville St., Toronto, Ontario M5A 3E7 **Canada**. (416)869-1872. A&R Director: Tony Procewiat. Music publisher, record company (Berandol Records), record producer and distributor. BMI. Member CMPA, CIRPA, CRIA. Estab. 1969. Publishes 20-30 songs/year; publishes 5-10 new songwriters/year. Works with composers. Pays standard royalty.

How to Contact: Submit demo tape with 2-5 songs. Reports in 3 weeks.

Music: Mostly pop, serious, educational, top 40 and dance. Published "In Your Smile" written and recorded by Cyan on Berandol Records (dance); "Cosmic Love" (by Bruce Lord), recorded by Rob Liddell on Berandol (MOR); "Symphonie #3" (by Jacques Hetv), recorded on Centrediscs (serious).

Tips: "Strong melodic choruses and original sounding music receive top consideration."

HAL BERNARD ENTERPRISES, INC., Box 20244, 443 Riddle Rd. #1, Cincinnati OH 45220. (513)861-1500. President: Stan Hertzman. Professional Manager: Paul Myers. Music publisher, record company and management firm. Publishes 20 songs/year; 1-2 new songwriters/year. Teams collaborators. Pays standard royalty.

Affiliates: Sunnyslope Music (ASCAP), Bumpershoot Music (BMI), Apple Butter Music (ASCAP), Carb Music (ASCAP), Saiko Music (ASCAP), TYI Music (ASCAP) and Smorgaschord Music (ASCAP).

Close-up

Andy Partridge
Singer/Songwriter
Swindon, England

Photo by: The Douglas Brothers

"There's always that period for me where I think I can't write another song — it's time to hang up the guitar on the wall for good and put the pen away."

Andy Partridge has become known as a writer of intricate pop melodies, deadly hooks and witty, intelligent lyrics. He writes and sings most of the songs for XTC, one of the most inventive pop bands to emerge from England in the wake of the mid-seventies punk explosion. As prolific as he is, he says the feeling that it might all be over is never far away. "I always get it — and it gets worse and worse each album. But if I dig deep enough, something comes up, and it's usually not very good. And then I dig some more and some more, and suddenly, 'Whoosh,' here comes something quite good. So it seems to be a self-righting, a self-correcting thing."

He claims to be unable to force himself to write good songs, and says it is more a matter of getting into the right frame of mind so the songs can come to him. "I can't squeeze them out. They just have to pop into my head. I have to empty my brain, shut myself away and enter the land of music in some way. I'm having a little studio built at the end of the garden right now; I shall lock myself in there and get myself in a musical frame of mind."

Andy says his songwriting has changed since the early days of XTC. "Early on, the songs would begin with a lyrical phrase first — a couple of words, maybe just one word. Then I would think, 'Ooh, that's nice; how can I musically put a carpet of some sort under this interesting phrase?' I did a lot of tripping up in public, I think, on our first couple of albums; the songs tended to be just masses of fun lyrical ideas that popped little light bulbs in your brain but they were not connected too well with melody. These days it happens at once. Yeah, the music and the lyrics usually come together in one . . . bang. That is to say, the initial keystone comes that way. You know, you get the keystone first and then you build the rest of the arch around it. I'll find a phrase on the keyboard or something and I'll think, 'Oh, that's just like fog,' and then, within a split second, I find some lyrical idea falling out that's drawn out by the chord that has reminded me of fog. And then as I'm mumbling this kind of . . . *intention* that I have in my head, I'll find that my hands are drifting toward other chords to support that. That's how the keystone comes out. And then I'll spend either the rest of the day or the rest of the year trying to finish the song off."

For subject matter, Andy draws on "the everyday sensations, the mundane sensations that eventually filter through and sort of drip right down to the core. Then I find that stuff getting into songs about where I live, the people I know, relatives, kids, whatever. Becoming a father, kids are all over our last album [*Oranges and Lemons*, Geffen]."

Intellectual honesty is an important part of Andy's approach to songwriting. "A lot of songwriters throw flak out that is just distracting. They just pick subjects, pretend subjects — they send out 'song fiction,' and a lot of people don't know that it's fiction and they start taking these . . . fashion statements and rebel ideas as being dead serious.

"It's how high do you want to get on the entertaining ladder, and how high do you want to get on the pleasing yourself ladder? I want to get as high as I can on the pleasing myself ladder, because if I'm not pleased with the stuff, I couldn't live with my conscience. So everything that comes out is really as mean-to-say-it as I can get it."

How does he know when a subject has brewed long enough and it's time to sit down and write a song about it? "Usually, if I'm walking the dog and I'm singing the subject, then I know that the subject is pulling some sort of melody towards me, and the melody is sticking to this subject in some way. It's not so much I'm ready to write a song about a subject as it kind of boils to the top. It's obviously on my mind, you know. The subject matter is plaguing me in some way, and writing a song is kind of like exorcising it."

Andy is an unschooled musician. "In songwriting, there is a lot to be said for intuition and gut feeling. I'm just a Neanderthal on the keyboard. But I find that very inspiring. I can't fall into habits because I don't have any. I don't have any habits because I can't play the thing. So I still get a lot of—for me—very fresh ideas coming out of the keyboard." But his intuition and experimentation are coupled with lots of hard work. "Songwriting for me is not easy. I'm continuously messing around with the lyrics. I rewrite and rewrite and keep thinking, 'No, this could be better lyrically, it could be better rhythmically.' I'll go in and take 'um's and 'ah's out and add in 'it's and 'the's and 'but's, you know, stuff like that—to try and get the rhythm to fit. That's very important to me, the rhythm of the lyrics."

Andy's acid test for a song is whether it can stand up with just one person singing the melody. "Make sure it sounds good when you're just singing it without an instrument. Then, put one instrument with it; if it still sounds as good or even better when you put that one instrument with it, then you're on to a winner. But songwriting does take a lot of mental sweating. I can't think of anything easy about it. I sometimes think I'm totally insane to even be attempting it."

—Mark Garvey

How to Contact: Submit a demo tape—unsolicited submissions are OK. Prefers cassette with 3 songs and lyric sheet. SASE. Reports in 6 weeks.
Music: Rock, R&B and top 40/pop. Published "Lone Rhino" and "Desire Caught By The Tail" (by Adrian Belew), recorded by Belew on Island Records (progressive); "Fear is Never Boring," "Trust" and "Aches and Pains," recorded by The Bears on PMRC/IRS Records (rock); "Oh Daddy," "House of Cards" and "Bad Days," all written and recorded by Adrian Belew on Atlantic Records (progressive pop).
Tips: "Best material should appear first on demo. Cast your demos. If you as the songwriter can't sing it—don't. Get someone who can present your song properly, use a straight rhythm track and keep it as naked as possible. If you think it still needs something else, have a string arranger, etc. help you, but still keep the *voice up* and the *lyrics clear*."

M. BERNSTEIN MUSIC PUBLISHING CO., 2170 S. Parker Rd., Denver CO 80231. (303)755-2613. President: R.J. Bernstein. Music publisher, record company (Finer Arts Records), and record producer (Transworld Records). ASCAP, BMI. Estab. 1960. Publishes 15-25 songs/year; publishes 5-10 new songwriters/year.
How to Contact: Prefers cassette and lyric or lead sheet. Does not return unsolicited material. Reports in 1 month.
Music: Rock, country and jazz. Published "Over and Over" (by Pamela Dawn), recorded by Penda on Finer Arts Records (R&B); and "Dance Baby Dance" (by Pamela Dawn), recorded by Penda on Fine Arts Records (rap).
Tips: "No *phone calls* please."

BEST BUDDIES, INC., , P.O. Box 121738, Nashville TN 37212-1738. (615)383-7664. Contact review committee. Music publisher, record company (X-cuse Me) and record producer (Best Buddies Productions). BMI. Estab. 1981. Publishes 18 songs/year. Publishes 1-2 new songwriters/year. Works with composers and lyricists. Pays standard royalty.
Affiliates : Swing Set Music (ASCAP), Best Buddies Music (BMI).
How to Contact : Write first and obtain permission to submit. Must include SASE with permission letter. Prefers cassette (or VHS videocassette) with maximum 3 songs. SASE. Reports in 8 weeks. Do not call to see if tape received.

Music : Mostly country, rock and roll and pop; also gospel and R&B. Published "Somebody Wrong is Looking Right," (by King/Burkholder), recorded by Bobby Helms; "Give Her Back Her Faith in Me" (by Ray Dean James), recorded by David Speegle on Bitter Creek Records (country); and "I Can't Get Over You Not Loving Me" (by Misty Efron and Bobbie Sallee), recorded by Sandy Garwood on Bitter Creek Records (country).
Tips : "Make a professional presentation. There are no second chances on first impressions."

*BEST WEST PRODUCTIONS, 1301 Morrison, Redlands CA 92374. (714)798-6449 or (714)370-1980. Contact: Deborah Harmon. Music publisher, record company (Best West Records) and record producer (Robert Harmon). BMI. Estab. 1988. Works with composers and teams collaborators. Pays standard royalty.
How to Contact: Submit a demo tape by mail—unsolicited submissions are OK. Prefers cassette (or VHS or Beta videocassette if available) with 3 best songs and lyric sheet. SASE. Reports in 3 weeks.
Music: Mostly country and pop. Published "Trouble" (by R. Harmon), recorded by Bob Harmon on Best West Records (country).
Tips: "Do not worry about elaborate productions. Simple vocal with guitar or piano is preferred."

BEVERLY HILLS MUSIC PUBLISHING, Division of Larrco Industries of Texas, Box 3842, Houston TX 77253-3842. President: Dr. Lawrence Herbst. Music publisher, record company (Best-Way, Beverly Hills, D.T.I., Larr, Lawrence Herbst and Total Sound Records) and record producer (Lawrence Herbst). BMI. Estab. 1966. Publishes 12 songs/year; publishes 3 new songwriters/year. Teams collaborators. Pays standard royalty.
Affiliates: K-Larrco Satellite Radio and TV and K-Larrco Music Publishing.
How to Contact: Prefers cassette (or VHS videocassette), lyric sheet and writer background information. Does not return unsolicited material. Reports in 6 weeks.
Music: Mostly rock; also country, top 40/pop, bluegrass, blues, easy listening, folk, jazz, progressive, R&B, gospel and soul.

*BIG EARS MUSIC LTD., 147, Waller Rd., London SE145LX **England**. Phone: (01)358-0802. Director: Greg Cutler. Music publisher. PRS. Estab. 1985. Publishes 50 songs/year; publishes 2-3 new songwriters/year. Works with composers, teams collaborators and lyricists. Royalty normally higher than 50%.
Affiliate: Uncut Music (PRS).
How to Contact: Write or call first to get permission to sumbit a tape. Prefers cassette with 3 songs maximum and lyric sheet. SAE and IRC. Reports in 1 month.
Music: Mostly R&B, pop and rock; also African music. Published "Shine" (by K. Stevens), recorded by Keni Stevens and "Interval" (by T. Agbethu), recorded by Rosaline Joyce, both on Jam Today Records (R&B); and "Shikisha" (by S. Mabuse), recorded by Sipho Mabuse on Virgin Records (pop).

BIG RON PRODUCTION AND PUBLISHING INC., 440 Fairway Dr., Springboro OH 45066. (513)748-0063. President: Ronald Czarnecki. Music publisher and record producer (RC Enterprises Inc.). BMI. Estab. 1987. Publishes 10 songs/year; 4 new songwriters/year. Works with composers and lyricists; teams collaborators. Pays standard royalty.
How to Contact: Write first and obtain permission to submit a tape. Prefers cassette (or VHS videocassette if available) with 4 songs and lyric sheet. "Please submit a good quality tape. Does not have to be studio recorded but should be clean and clear." SASE. Reports in 1 month.
Music: Mostly country, rock and pop; also gospel, R&B and new age. Published "God Bless America Tonight" by Wayne Barker Jr. (country), and "Carolina Gold" by Joseph Schmitt, Curt Arnspiger (pop); both recorded by Vettz on Fraternity Records.
Tips: "Know your goals, submit a brief resume about yourself and explain what you are looking to accomplish in the music business. Cost of production and promotion of new artists is getting to be a great expense for independent label and record companies. Artists and writers should be willing to invest in their careers and run their careers like a business. There are a lot of opportunities available to them through the independent network of companies."

*BIG SNOW MUSIC, P.O. Box 279, Hopkins MN 55343. (612)942-6119. President: Mitch Viegut. General Manager: Mark Alan. Music publisher. BMI. Estab. 1989. Publishes 30 new songs/year; publishes 5 new songwriters/year. Works with composers and lyricists; team collaborators. Pays standard royalty.
How to Contact: Submit a demo tape by mail—unsolicited submissions are OK. Prefers cassette with 3 songs and lyric sheet. Does not return unsolicited material. Reports in 6 weeks.
Music: Mostly rock, pop and black. Published "Make Believe" (by Mitch Viegut), (pop); "Thief in the Night" (by Doug Dixon/Mitch Viegut), (rock); and "Rock City" (by Mitch Viegut), (rock), all recorded by Airkraft on Premiére Records.

BIG WEDGE MUSIC, P.O. Box 29-0186, Nashville TN 37229-0186. (615)754-2950. President: Ralph Johnson. BMI. Music publisher. Estab. 1960. Pays standard royalty. Publishes 1,000 songs and 200 new songwriters/year.
Affiliates: Wedge Entertainment Group, Wedge Records, Inc., Pro-Star Talent, Inc. and Pro Rite Music (ASCAP).
How to Contact: Prefers cassette (or videocassette) with maximum of 4 songs and lyric sheet or lead sheet. SASE. Reports in 2 weeks.
Music: Mostly country, pop and rock; also gospel and R&B. Published "Not Enough Country" (by Gary Newman); *That Little Green Worm*, (by Dave Martin); "Mr. Blue Eyes" (by Jackie Minarik/Chic Bixby/Billy Lee Napier), recorded by Will Beery (country/pop); and "My Dreams Came True" written and recorded by Stella Parton (country/pop), all on Wedge Records.

BLACK STALLION COUNTRY PUBLISHING, Box 2250, Culver City CA 90230. (213)419-8142. President: Kenn Kingsbury. Music publisher and book publisher (*Who's Who in Country & Western Music*). BMI. Member ACM, CMA, CMF. Publishes 2 songs/year; publishes 1 new songwriter/year. Pays standard royalty.
How to Contact: Prefers 7½ ips reel-to-reel or cassette with 2-4 songs and lyric sheet. SASE. Reports in 1 month.
Music: Bluegrass, country and top 40/pop.
Tips: "Be professional in attitude and presentation. Submit only the material you think is better than anything being played on the radio."

*BLADE TO THE RHYTHM MUSIC, 114-22 116th St., S. Ozone Pk. NY 11420. (718)672-8755 or (718)845-4417. President: Juan Kato Lemus. Music publisher and production company/Producers. ASCAP. Estab. 1990. Publishes 5-10 songs/year; publishes 2-4 new songwriters/year. Hires staff songwriters. "Depending on work." Pays "depending on work to be added or song to be changed."
Affiliates: Piedra Productions Music (ASCAP), Davidson Ospina Music (ASCAP), John Wilson Music (ASCAP) and Pavel De Jesus (ASCAP).
How to Contact: Submit a demo tape by mail—unsolicited submissions are OK. Prefers cassette with 2-4 songs and lyric sheet. "Send photo or bio." Does not return unsolicited material. Reports in 4 weeks.
Music: Mostly dance/pop, house and R&B; also freestyle, rap and ballads. Published "No Para" (by Bladerunners), recorded by Sound Factor on Warlock Records (house).

*BLUE HILL MUSIC/TUTCH MUSIC, 308 Munger Lane, Bethlehem CT 06751. Contact: Paul Hotchkiss. Music publisher, record company (Target Records, Kastle Records) and record producer (Red Kastle Records). BMI. Estab. 1975. Published 15-25 songs/year; publishes 1-5 new songwriters/year. Pays standard royalty.
Affiliates: Blue Hill Music (BMI) and Tutch Music (BMI).
How to Contact: Write or call first and obtain permission to submit a tape. Prefers cassette with 2 songs and lyric sheet. "Demos should be clear with vocals out in front." SASE. Reports in 3 weeks.
Music: Mostly country and country/pop; also MOR and blues. Published "Heart of Luv" (by Hotchkiss/Terry), recorded by "Michael Terry" on Roto Noto Records (country pop); "Under Cover Lovers" (by S. Johnson/P. Hotchkiss), recorded by "Beverlys Hillbilly Band" on Puzzle Records (country); and "My Island" (by Hotchkiss/Terry), recorded by Michael Terry on Target Records (country).
Tips: "Dare to be different; but remember it must have commercial appeal."

BLUE UMBRELLA MUSIC PUBLISHING CO./PARASOL MUSIC PUBLISHING CO., 3011 Beach 40th St., Brooklyn NY 11224. (718)372-6436. Contact: Mr. Kadish Millet. Music publisher. ASCAP, BMI. Estab. 1970. Publishes 15 songs/year; publishes 7 new songwriters/year. Pays standard royalty.
How to Contact: Submit a demo tape—unsolicited submissions are OK. Prefers cassette with 1-10 songs and lead sheet. Prefers studio produced demos. "Wrap cassette well; some cassette boxes have fairly sharp edges and break through envelope. I want a lead sheet and/or lyric sheet and accurate information on who owns the copyright and if it was registered in Washington at the time of submission. Affiliation of writers (ASCAP/BMI) or non-affiliation needed in order to issue proper contract." SASE *"with proper amount of return postage.* What gripes me is the package that comes in with $1.25 in stamps and a SASE with a 25¢ stamp on it." Reports in 2 weeks.
Music: Country. "I want country songs with double entendre (sexy, adult type) lyrics such as 'Behind Closed Doors,' 'Almost Persuaded,' 'Here Comes My Weekend Friend,' 'Help Me Make It Through the Night,' 'Sleepin' Single in a Double Bed,' and 'Teach Me to Cheat,' MOR country/pop crossover as well as novelties."
Tips: "In this day and age of groups and singer/songwriters (who are fortunate enough to have a recording contract) writing, arranging and recording their own songs, the music business has become virtually impossible. There is no room any more for just a 'pretty good song.' It has to be a supersong

or 'blockbuster.' Even then the odds are against getting a song recorded. Be aware of that fact when sending out material."

BLUEFIELD MUSIC, P.O. Box 726, Los Angeles CA 90028. President: David Bluefield. Music publisher and record producer (Rhythm & Bluefield Productions and Dave Bluefield). ASCAP/BMI. Publishes 16 songs/year; publishes 1 new songwriter/year. Hires staff writers. Works with lyricists; teams collaborators. Pays standard royalty.
Affiliate: Pearly Blue (BMI).
How to Contact: "Excellent lyricists welcome" to submit a tape. Prefers cassette with maximum of 5 songs and lyric sheet. Sometimes returns material if accompanied by SASE. "Reports immediately only if interested."
Music: Mostly popular music and power pop. Published "Explosion of Love" and "Good Bad Habit" (by Dave Bluefield/Christi Mottola), recorded by Christi Mottola on D Blue Records (power pop).
Tips: "Get out to the West Coast where the action is. Give yourself one month to shop yourself. Bring different representations of your songs."

*BMG MUSIC PUBLISHING, 8370 Wilshire Blvd., Beverly Hills CA 90211. (213)651-3355. Director, Talent Acquisition: Nanci M. Walker. Professional Manager: Ron Handler. Creative Assistant: Margaret Mittleman. Music publisher and record company (Arista Records, BMG/RCA). BMI, ASCAP.
Affiliates: BMG Songs and Careers.
How to Contact: Write or call first and obtain permission to submit a tape. Does not return unsolicited material. Reports in 2-4 months.
Music: Alternative pop (college and AOR), rock CHR/AOR, pop CHR/AC; also R&B, country and gospel. Published "No Myth," written and recorded by Michael Penn on BMG/RCA Records (CHR/AC/AOR); "Pretending" (by Jerry Williams), recorded by Eric Clapton on Warner Bros. (CHR/AC/AOR); and "Dreams In The Dark," written and recorded by Badlands on Atlantic Records (heavy metal).

*BMG PACIFIC MUSIC PUBLISHING LTD., 58 Pak Tai St., Kai It Bldg., Tokwawan, Kowloon Hong Kong. (852)761-5251. FAX: (852)761-0733. General Manager: Irene Padilla Ho. Music publisher and record company (RCA, Motown, Arista, Current).
How to Contact: Submit demo tape by mail. Unsolicited submissions are okay. Prefers cassette with 10 songs and lead sheet. Does not return unsolicited material. Reports in 3 months.
Music: Mostly pop, ballads and country. Works primarily with vocalists. Current acts include Prudence Liew, Maria Cordero, Frankie Choi, Tommy Sou, Fanny Cheng, Fundamental, Bowie Lam, Rosanne Lui, Vivian Lai and Raymond Choi.

JOHNNY BOND PUBLICATIONS, 1815 Division St., Nashville TN 37203. (615)327-8436. President: Sherry Bond. Music publisher. BMI/ASCAP. Estab. 1955. Publishes 100 songs/year; 1 new songwriter/year. Works with composers. Pays standard royalty.
Affiliates: Red River Songs, Inc. (BMI), Crimson Creek Songs (ASCAP).
How to Contact: Write or call to arrange a personal interview. Prefers cassette with 1 song and lyric sheet. SASE. Reports in 1 month.
Music: Country only. Published "Blues Stay Away From Me" (by The Delmore Bros.), recorded by The Judds and Carl Perkins on Universal Records, K.D. Lang on Sire Records and Chris Austin on Warner Bros. Records (country).
Tips: "Because we receive so many requests to submit songs, we are very selective. Big corporations are buying up small publishing companies, making it more difficult to get songs recorded. Songwriters need to know as much as possible about the publishing companies they approach."

BONNFIRE PUBLISHING, Box 6429, Huntington Beach CA 92615-6429. (714)962-5618. Contact: Eva and Stan Bonn. Music publisher, record company (ESB Records) and record producer. ASCAP, BMI. Estab. 1987. Publishes 2-10 songs/year; publishes 2-10 new songwriters/year. Pays standard royalty.
How to Contact: Submit demo cassette with lyric sheet. Does not return unsolicited material.
Music: Country, country/crossover/pop, Spanish, new age and gospel. Published "Highway 44" (by Bobby Caldwell/Jim Weaver), "She's A Dance Hall Lady" (by Eva Bonn/Nancy Cyril), "She's a Lady By Day, Lover By Night," (by Bobby Caldwell), "Don't Watch Me Fall Apart" (by Bobby Lee Caldwell); "You're Workin' on Leavin Me" (by Eva Bonn, Nancy Cyril, Marda Philpott), recorded by Bobby Lee Caldwell (country); "There's a Memory in My Heart," written and recorded by Bobby Lee Caldwell (country), all on ESB Records; and "The Gold in This Ring" (by Tigg Griffin and Todd Hartman), on OL Records.

BOOGIETUNES MUSIKPRODUKTION GmbH, Seelingstrasse 33, 1000 Berlin 19, **West Germany.** Phone: 030/321 60 47. Managing Director: Timothy E. Green. Music publisher and record company. Estab. 1978. Publishes 100 songs/year; publishes 2 new songwriters/year. Teams collaborators. Pays standard GEMA rate.
How to Contact: Submit a demo tape—unsolicited submissions are OK. Prefers cassette. Does not return unsolicited material. "No cassette returns!"
Music: Mostly disco/dance, electronic, rap and house. Published "Silver Machine," recorded by Acieedo Domingo on TELDEC Records (house); and "¾," recorded by Bass Mental on Dance Street Records (Rave Music); and "Radio Songs," recorded by Hold the Front Page on Up and Down Records (SKA Music)
Tips: "Write good commercial pop."

BOOT SONGS, Box 1065, Stn. B., Mississauga, Ontario L4Y 3W4 **Canada.** (416)238-2783. President: Jury Krytiuk. Music publisher, record company (Boot, Cynda, Generation, Boot Leisure Corp.) and record producer (Jury Krytiuk). CAPAC. Estab. 1987. Publishes 100 songs/year; publishes new song-writers/year. Pays standard royalty.
Affiliates: Boot Tunes (PROCAN), Boot House of Songs (ASCAP), Boot House of Tunes (BMI), and The Musical Boot (PRS).
How to Contact: Prefers cassette and lyric sheet. SAE and IRC. Reports in 2 weeks.
Music: Mostly country, folk and MOR. Published "For We Are the Irish" (by Ray Fynes), recorded by Mary Fynes on Boot Records (Irish); "Love is a Beautiful Song" (by Terry Dempsey), recorded by John McNally on Quality Records (MOR) and "Mama's Fiddle" (by Ray Keating), recorded by Ray Keating on Boot Records (country).

***BRANCH INTERNATIONAL MUSIC,** Box 31819, Dallas TX 75231. (214)750-0720. A&R Director: Mike Anthony. Music publisher. BMI. Publishes 20 songs/year. Pays standard maximum royalty.
How to Contact: Prefers cassette with 1-4 songs and lead or lyric sheet. SASE. Reports in 1 month.
Music: Country and gospel. Published "Too Many Ladies," by David Denman/Kevin Clark/Bart Barton (country); and "Hide Me," by Jess Hudson/Kenny Serrat (uptempo country) both recorded by D. Denman on Yatahey Records (uptempo country).

***BRENTWOOD MUSIC, INC.,** 316 Southgate Ct., Brentwood TN 37027. (615)373-3950. Product Development Department: Melody Blaire. Music publisher and record company (Brentwood Music, Inc.). ASCAP, BMI, SESAC. Estab. 1981. Publishes 50 songs/year; publishes 1-2 new songwriters/year.
Affiliates: New Spring Publishing (ASCAP), Bridge Building Music (BMI), Designer Music (SESAC).
How to Contact: Write first and obtain permission to submit a tape. Prefers cassette with 2 songs and lyric or lead sheets. "Do not send your original copy. We reply only if interested." Reports in 8 months.
Music: Mostly anthems, children's music, worship and praise choruses; also comedy (clean—nothing questionable or vulgar), contemporary Christian, inspirational, pop (Christian or secular). Published "When the Time Comes" (by David Kavich), recorded by Sandi Patti on Benson Records (inspirational); "Though Your Sins Be As Scarlet" (by Wayne Goodine), by Jimmy Swaggart on Jim Records (inspirational); and "Bible Break," written and recorded by Stephen Wiley on Brentwood Records (Christian rap).

BROAD RIVER PUBLISHING, Rt. 4 Box 48, Cowen WV 26206. Music Editor: Gladys Spearmon. Music publisher and record company (New Dawning Records). BMI. Estab. 1973. Publishes 12 songs/year.
How to Contact : Write first and obtain permission to submit. Prefers cassette with 1-3 songs. SASE. Reports in 2 months. Pays 2¢ per song per tape: "We are a small independent trying to help writers, for we are also writers."
Music : Gospel. Published "Let's All Climb the Mountain" (by Muriel Ellis); "Come A Little Closer" (by Angie Sanson); and "It'll Be Worth All My Trials" (by E. and G. Spearman) all country/gospel recorded by The Spearmans on the New Dawning label.
Tips : "We are interested only in southern gospel, country gospel and bluegrass gospel. No songs over 4 minutes long. Base your songs on scripture. Make sure demo has good professional sound music and voice so can send out to artist or other publishers. Also be sure material is copyrighted for protection."

SATCHEL BROWN MUSIC, Box 1611, Greenville MS 38702-1611. (601)332-3746. A&R Director: Sherri S. Allen. Music publisher. BMI. Estab. 1984. Pays standard royalty.
How to Contact: Submit a demo tape by mail—unsolicited submissions are O.K. Prefers cassette with 1-4 songs and lyric sheets. Does not return unsolicited material. Reports in 4 weeks only if interested.

Music: Mostly Gospel (all types), Contemporary Christian and Southern Gospel.
Tips: "We listen to every song we receive."

*BUG MUSIC, 6777 Hollywood, Los Angeles CA 90028. (213)466-4352. Contact: Fred Bourgoise. Music publisher. BMI, ASCAP. Estab. 1975. Hires staff songwriters. We handle administration.
Affiliates: Bughouse (ASCAP).
How to Contact: Prefers cassette. Does not return unsolicited material.
Music: All genres. Published "Angel Eyes" (by John Hiatt), recorded by Jeff Healy on Artista Records; and "Full Moon Full of Love" (by Leroy Preston), recorded by K.D. Lang.

BURIED TREASURE MUSIC, 524 Doral Country Dr., Nashville TN 37221. Executive Producer: Scott Turner. Music publisher and record producer (Aberdeen Productions). ASCAP. Estab. 1972. Publishes 50-75 songs/year; publishes 3-10 new songwriters/year. Pays standard royalty.
Affiliate: Captain Kidd Music (BMI).
How to Contact: Submit a demo tape—unsolicited submissions are OK. Prefers cassette (or VHS videocassette) with 1-4 songs and lead sheet. Reports in 3 weeks. "Always enclose SASE if answer is expected."
Music: Country and country/pop; also rock, MOR and contemporary. Published "I Still Can't Say Goodbye" (by J. Moore and B. Blinn), recorded by Chet Atkins; "You Did it All" (by D. Baumgartner and Scott Turner), recorded by Shelby Lynne on CBS Records (country); "The Presidents' Waltz" (by Audie Murphy and Scott Turner), recorded by Scott Turner (MOR) and "Love Enough" (by Brad Moranz), recorded by L. Greenwood (MOR).
Tips: "*Don't* send songs in envelopes that are 15"x20", or by registered mail. It doesn't help a bit. Say something that's been said a thousand times before . . . only say it differently. A great song doesn't care who sings it. Songs that paint pictures have a better chance of ending up as videos. With artists only recording 10 songs every 18-24 months, the advice is . . . Patience!"

BUTTON MUSIC, 322 Whitchurch Lane, Edgware, Middlesex HA8 6QX, **England**. Phone: (01)952-3551. Director: Helen Holt. PRS. Music publisher and record company. Estab. 1982. Publishes up to 20 songs/year; publishes 5 new songwriters/year. Works with composers; teams collaborators. Pays 60% royalty.
Affiliate: Dingle's Music.
How to Contact: Prefers cassette with 3-4 songs. SAE and IRC. Reports in 6 weeks.
Music: Mostly folk, pop and novelty; also country, gospel and MOR. Published "Captain Pugwash" (by Holt), recorded by QED on Dingle's Records (folk novelty/pop); "Sunny Days" (by QED), recorded by QED on Dingle's Records (pop) and "Hunger in the Soul" by (D. Wheat), on Button Records (pop).
Tips: "Maximum of 3 songs and uncluttered, clear production. It's the *song*, not production sought initially."

*C. P. I. MUSIC, %Franz B. Swegal, P.C., F. B. Swegal, Div. of Centaur®, 12220 Tiara St., N. Hollywood CA 91607. (818)762-7417. Principal: Franz B. Swegal, P.C. Music publisher. ASCAP. Estab. 1984. Works with composers and lyricists; teams collaborators. Pays standard royalty.
How to Contact: Submit a demo tape by mail—unsolicited submissions are OK. "With simple release obviating C.P.I. Music from any liability with reference to copyright infringement." Prefers cassette with 3 songs. SASE. Reports in 3 weeks.
Music: Mostly AOR; also, pop, country, R&B and rap; also jazz and classical.

CACTUS MUSIC AND GIDGET PUBLISHING, 5 Aldom Circle, West Caldwell NJ 07006. Owner: Tar Heel Pete. Music publisher and record company (Dynamite Records). ASCAP, BMI. Estab. 1974. Publishes 5-8 songs/year; publishes 3-5 new songwriters/year. Works with composers. Pays standard royalty.
Affiliate: Jimmy Allison Music (BMI).
How to Contact: Write first and obtain permission to submit. Prefers cassette with 3 songs minimum and lyric sheet. Does not return unsolicited material. Reports in 1 month.
Music: Mostly C&W, R&B and blues; also jazz. Published "Give Me Roses" (by Morris Hall Hellman), recorded by Coleman O'Neal; "Release You" (by Rose), recorded by Coleman O'Neal; "Crazy Over You" (by La Flame), recorded by Tony Ansems on Dynamite Records (C/W); "Cochabamba" (by Hall), recorded by Tony Ansems on Dynamite Records (C/W); and "Days in the Park" (by Bergeron), recorded by Tony Ansems on Dynamite Records (rock).

CALIFORNIA COUNTRY MUSIC (BMI), 112 Widmar Pl., Clayton CA 94517. (415)672-8201. Owner: Edgar. J. Brincat. Music Publisher, record company (Roll On Records). BMI. Estab. 1985. Publishes 10-12 songs/year;. publishes 2-4 new songwriters/year. Works with composers and lyricists; teams collaborators. Pays standard royalty.

Affiliates: Sweet Inspirations Music (ASCAP).
How to Contact: Submit a demo tape by mail—unsolicited submissions are O.K. Prefers cassette with 3 songs and lyric sheet. Any calls will be returned collect to caller. SASE. Reports in 6 weeks.
Music: Mostly MOR, contemporary country and pop; also R&B, gospel and light rock. Published "One Heart At A Time" (by Ann Leisten/John Covert); "Thank God" (by Ann Leisten/Jeff Powell/ Walter Horban); and "The Earth Could Move In California" (by Thomas A. Del Vecchio) all contemporary country recorded by Steve Jordan on Roll On Records.
Tips: "Listen to what we have to say about your product. Be as professional as possible."

CALVARY MUSIC GROUP, INC., 142 8th Ave. N., Nashville TN 37203. (615)244-8800. President: Dr. Nelson S. Parkerson. Music publisher and record company ASCAP, BMI, SESAC. Publishes 30-40 songs/year; publishes 2-3 new songwriters/year. Pays standard royalty.
Affiliates: Songs of Calvary, Music of Calvary and LifeStream Music, Soldier of the Light, Torchbearer Music.
How to Contact: Accepting material at this time.
Music: Church/religious, contemporary Christian, gospel and wedding music.

*GLEN CAMPBELL MUSIC GROUP, Box 158717, Nashville TN 37215. (615)385-9875. Office Manager: Cherie Gamblin. Music publisher. BMI. Estab. 1970. Publishes 25 songs/year; publishes 1 new songwriter/year. Works with composers and lyricists. Pays standard royalty.
Affiliates: Seventh Son (ASCAP), Keytee Kay (ASCAP), Latter End (BMI), Chapter IV (ASCAP), Allanwood (BMI).
How to Contact: Write or call first and obtain permission to submit a tape. "Include an SASE with query." Prefers cassette with 2 songs and lyric sheet. "If more than two are sent we will throw the tape away." Does not return unsolicited material. Reports in 2 months. "We only call if we can use the material."
Music: Mostly country, contemporary or traditional; also female country/pop. Published "Breakin New Ground" (by Carl Jackson), recorded by Wild Rose on Universal Records (country); and "Blue Blooded Woman" and "Here In the Real World," written and recorded by Alan Jackson on Arista Records (country).
Tips: "Be ultra-selective; send only quality songs, as the business is more competitive than it's ever been."

*CAPAQUARIUS PUBLISHING & ARTIST MGT., INC., Suite 1106, 4525 Henry Hudson Parkway, Riverdale NY 10471. (212)549-6318 or 222-2933. Europe: Seeburgerstr 87, 1000 Berlin 20, West Berlin Germany. (030) 331-4568. President: P. Januari Watts. Music publisher, record producer and artist management firm. ASCAP. Publishes 3-4 songs/year; publishes 1 new songwriter/year. Works with composers and lyricists; teams collaborators. Pays standard royalty.
Affiliate: Yanita Music (BMI).
How to Contact: Prefers cassette (or NTSC/PAL/SECAM videocassette) with 2-3 songs and lead sheet. "Video should be 4-5 minutes in duration, black and white or color." SASE. Reports in 3-4 weeks. "We are also accepting material as listed above at our office in Germany, with return postage."
Music: Mostly rock and gospel rock; also top 40, contemporary gospel, R&B, soul and blues. Published "Being with You" and "Yahna's Blues" (blues), written and recorded by Queen Yahna and co-published with Marie-Marie Musikverlag; and "Doesn't Anybody (Wanna Fall in Love)" (by Q. Yahna/Danny Deutschmark), recorded by Q. Yahna for Another Record Company, GmbH.

CAPITOL STAR ARTIST ENTS., INC., 301 W. Ridge Rd., Rochester NY 14615. (716)647-1617. Director: Don Redanz. Associate Director: Tony Powlowski. Music publisher, record company and record producer. BMI. Publishes 20 songs/year; publishes 5 new songwriters/year. Pays standard royalty.
Music: Country, gospel, and pop. Published "Dust on Mother's Bible," and "Away from Home," (by Anthony Powlowski), recorded by Tony Starr on Capitol Star (country); and "V-8 Detroit," by A. Powlowski.
Tips: "We like country songs with a heartwarming story."

*CAPRICORN LTD. (PUBLISHING), Jungstrasse 15A, Zürich CH. 8050 **Switzerland**. Phone: (01)302-74 01 and (01)302-80 11. Professional Manager: Freddy J. Angstmann. Music publisher, record company (Capricorn), record producer (Capricorn), management firm and booking agency. SUISA, SESAC, BMI, ASCAP. Pays standard royalty.
Affiliates: Nadine Music (SESAC), Joecliff Music (BMI) and Lauren Music (ASCAP).
How to Contact: Prefers cassette (or VHS videocassette [PAL]) with lyric and lead sheets. "Clearly label each item you send; include photo and bio if possible." SAE and IRC or does not return unsolicited material. Reports in 6 weeks.

Music: Mostly gospel, blues and jazz; also R&B, country and classical. Published "Who Shall Abide," "Glorious Feeling," and "On My Way To Zion," all by J. Thompson, recorded on Capricorn (gospel).

CARAVELL MAIN SAIL MUSIC, HCR 5, Box 2400, Branson MO 65616. (417)334-7040. President: Keith O'Neil. Music publisher, record producer (Caravell Recording Studio). ASCAP. Estab. 1988; publishes 20 songs/year. Publishes 4 new songwriters/year. Works with composers and lyricists; teams collaborators. Pays standard royalty of 50%.
How to Contact: Submit demo tape by mail—unsolicited submissions are OK. Prefers cassette with 3 songs and lyric sheet. SASE. Reports in 4 weeks.
Music: Mostly country, pop and gospel. Published "Sarah's on the Phone" written and recorded by Lonnie Curtis on Caravell Records (country) and "Gospel Songs and Old Time Recipes" (by Albert E. Brumley, Jr. and Dale G. Vest), recorded by Albert E. Brumley, Jr. on Caravell Records (country).

DON CASALE MUSIC, INC., 377 Plainfield St., Westbury NY 11590. (516)333-7898. President: Don Casale. Record production, music publishing, artist management; affiliated recording studio. Estab. 1979. Deals with artists, songwriters, managers and agents. Fee derived from sales royalty.
Affiliates: ELASAC Music (ASCAP), Don Casale Music (BMI).
How to Contact: "I will accept unsolicited cassettes (except during August and September) with one or two songs and legible, typed lyric sheets (no registered mail). No "lyrics-only" submissions. Please include address and phone number and letter stating exact purpose (publishing deal?; record deal?; etc.) anything else you'd like to say is welcome too (I frown on 'form' letters). Press kit, bio and photo(s) or VHS videocassette are helpful, if available. For return of your material, always include SASE (envelope *must* be large enough to handle contents). If you don't need your material returned, include a *signed* note stating so and only include SASE for my response letter. Sorry, but I will not listen or correspond without SASE. A call first is very welcome (between 12 noon and 12 midnight EST), but not necessary, or you may inquire first by mail (with SASE). I'll listen to every note of your music and respond to you as soon as possible, usually between two weeks and two months, depending on volume of submissions."
Music: Everything but jazz and classical.
Tips: "Submitted songs should have a 'special' nature about them; a different quality and lyric. Melodies should be particularly 'catchy' and memorable. Songs should be in tune with the current radio market. I want only 'career-starting,' top 10 singles; not B sides or album fillers. Please try to be SELECTIVE and send me that ONE SONG you think is a KILLER; that ONE SONG that JUMPS OFF THE TAPE! Don't include a second song just because there's room on the cassette. Songwriters seeking a publishing contract need only a simple, in-tune, clear version of the song(s); a big production and recording, although welcome, is not necessary. Artists seeking a recording contract should submit a 'quality' performance (musically and vocally), incorporating their very best effort and their own, perferably unique, style. Your recording needn't be master quality, but your performance should be. I give extra points for following my instructions to the letter."

*ERNIE CASH MUSIC, INC., P.O. Box 469, Joppa MD 21085. (301)679-2262. President: Ernest W. Cash. Music publisher, record company (Continental Records, Inc.), record producer (Vision Music Group, Inc.) and Vision Video Production, Inc. BMI. Estab. 1987. Publishes 30-60 songs/year; publishes 10-15 new songwriters/year. Works with composers and lyricists; teams collaborators. Pays standard royalty.
Affiliates: Big K Music, Inc. (BMI), Guerriero Music (BMI) and Deb Music (BMI).
How to Contact: Submit a demo tape by mail—unsolicited submissions are OK. Write or call to arrange a personal interview. Prefers cassette (VHS videocassette if available) with 3 songs and lyric sheet. SASE. Reports in 2 weeks.
Music: Mostly country, gospel and pop; also R&B and rock. Published "A Man Called Jones" written and recorded by Jimmy Peppers; "If You're Not Here By Closing Time" (by Pam Hanna), recorded by Pam Bailey; and "Kansas Waltz" (by James Hession), recorded by Doug Lester, all on Go-Records, all country.
Tips: "Give me a call, I will review your material."

CA-SONG MUSIC PUBLISHER, Room 1204, 1650 Broadway, New York NY 10019. (212)586-3700/333-3239. Contact: Mike Cassone. Music publisher, record company, record producer and record promoter. BMI, ASCAP, AGAC. Member CMA, AFM. Publishes varying number of songs/year; "many" new songwriters "under negotiation with demos in process." Pays standard royalty.
Affiliates: Glad-Jack Music Publishers (ASCAP) and Comerc Music Publishers (ASCAP).
How to Contact: Submit demo tape and lyric sheet or arrange personal interview. Prefers cassette or records as demo. "Label all cassettes with your name, phone number (address if it fits) and song titles." Does not return unsolicited material. "If demo has an SASE we will return it after review and decisions have been reached, but prefer no returns." Reports "only if we place a song."

Music: Mostly MOR, easy listening and top 40/pop; also country, dance-oriented, gospel, jazz, progressive, R&B, rock, soul, nostalgia, big band and 50s and 60s. Published "Juke Box Baby" (by Bill Newburg), recorded by Vicki; "Turn Me On" and "Grand Central Breakdown" (written and recorded by Jimmy DeVito); "Nothing New" and "Tell Me Another Story", (written and recorded by Eleanor Tralli; "Someone Greater" (by M. Cassone), recorded by Tiny Tim and Tess Winters.

*CHAPIE MUSIC BMI, 228 West 5th, Kansas City MO 64105. (816)842-6854. Owner: Chuck Chapman. Music publisher, record company (Fifth Street Records(, record producer (Chapman Recording Studios). BMI. Estab. 1977. Publishes 12 songs/year; 12 new songwriters/year. Works with composers; teams collaborators. Pays standard 50% royalty.
Affiliates: Chapie Music, BMI.
How to Contact: Call to get permission to submit tape. Prefers cassette with 1-3 songs and lyric sheet. SASE. Reports in weeks.
Music: Mostly country, pop, gospel; also jazz R&B and New Age. Published "Lonely Country Road" and "Talkin 'Bout" both written and recorded by Mike Eisel and "Sometimes Takes A Woman" (by Greg Camp), recorded by Rick Loveall all recorded on Fifth Street Records (country).
Tips: "Make it commercial—with a twist on the lyrics."

*CHARIS MUSIC, P.O. Box 997, Florida, Transvaal **South Africa** 1710. (001)674-2030 or (001)674-2031. Publishing Department: Mrs. Shelley du Plessis. Music publisher and record producer (Grace Music Pty Ltd). SAMRO/SARRAL. Estab. 1981. Publishes 10-20 songs/year; publishes 10-20 new songwriters/year. Works with composers and lyricists; teams collaborators. "The publisher shall pay to the composer a royalty of 10% of the retail selling price of all printed copies of work sold by or on behalf of the publisher and paid for in all countries, provided that if the publisher arranges any agency for the sale of his edition of the work in any country outside the territory, the royalty payable to the composer in respect of sales in such country shall be 5%."
Affiliates: "We are sub-publishers in South Africa for Word Inc., Tempo, Forefront, Fairhill, Jubilee, Sandy Music, Word Music (UK)."
How to Contact: Submit a demo tape by mail—unsolicited submissions are OK. Prefers cassette with 1 or more songs, lyric sheets and lead sheets. SAE and IRC for return.
Music: Interested in gospel only. Published "Let the Nations Praise the Lord" (by Anamarie Pringle), "I Thank You" (by Nicola Smart) and "Child Be a Song" (by Billy Joubert), all recorded by SABC on Grace Music (all gospel).

CHASANN MUSIC, P.O. Box 12151, Birmingham AL 35202. (205)786-6924. Owner: Charles Hall. Music publisher. BMI. Estab. 1975. Publishes 12 songs/year; publishes 4 new songwriters/year. Hires staff songwriters. Works with composers and lyricists; teams collaborators. Pays standard royalty.
Affiliates: Chasann Music (BMI).
How to Contact: Submit a demo tape by mail—unsolicited submissions are OK. Prefers cassette (videocassette if available) with 2 songs and lyric sheet. SASE. Reports in 3 weeks-1 month.
Music: Mostly pop, R&B and gospel.

*CHERIE MUSIC CO., 3621 Heath Ln., Mesquite TX 75150. (214)279-5858. Contact: Jimmy Fields. Music publisher, record company and record producer. BMI. Publishes 30 songs/year; publishes 10-15 new songwriters/year. Pays standard royalty.
How to Contact: Prefers cassette with 5 songs and lyric sheet. SASE. Does not return material without proper return postage and proper mailing package. Reports in 3 months.
Music: Country only.
Tips: "Do not over produce—let us hear the melody and lyrics."

CHESTLER PUBLISHING CO., 3515 Clovertree Ln., Flint MI 48532. (313)232-0083. Owner: Harry F. Chestler. Music publisher, record company (Tawas Records) and record producer (Harry F. Chestler). BMI. Estab. 1967. Publishes 2 songs/year; publishes 2 new songwriters/year. Pays standard royalty.
How to Contact: Write first and obtain permission to submit. Prefers cassette with 2 songs. Does not return unsolicited material. Reports in 2 weeks.
Music: Mostly rock, country and gospel; also rap. Published "Big Thinker" and "Going to Nashville" (by Harry Chestler), recorded by Hank Chess on Tawas Records (country).

CHINA GROOVE, 404 St. Henri, Montreal Quebec H3C-2P5 **Canada**. (514)871-8481. Publisher: Mario Rubnikowich. Music publisher. SDE, CAPAC. Estab. 1987. Publishes 6-10 songs/year; publishes 3 new songwriters/year. Hires staff songwriters. Works with team collaborators. Pays standard royalty of 50%.

Affiliates: Foxtrot (CPAC).
How to Contact: Submit a demo tape by mail—unsolicited submissions are O.K. Prefers cassette or 15 IPS reel-to-reel with 3 songs and lyric sheet and lead sheet. SASE. Reports in 3-5 weeks.

*CHIP 'N' DALE MUSIC PUBLISHERS, INC., 315 Mt. Juliet Rd., Mt. Juliet TN 37122. (615)754-0417. Contact: Karen Jeglum Kennedy. Music publisher, record company (Door Knob Records, Society Reocrds), record producer (Gene Kennedy Enterprises, Inc.). ASCAP. Estab. 1975. Publishes 20-25 songs/year; publishes 10-15 new songwriters/year. Works with composers and lyricists. Pays standard royalty.
Affiliates: Door Knob Music Publishing, Inc. (BMI), Lodestar Music, A Division of Gene Kennedy Enterprises, Inc. (SESAC).
How to Contact: Submit a demo tape by mail—unsolicited submissions are OK. Prefers cassette with 1-3 songs and lyric sheet. Include SASE for tape return and/or response. Send regular mail. SASE. Reports in 2 weeks.
Music: Mostly country, gospel. Published "I've Had Enough of You" (by Johnette Burton), recorded Debbie Rich; "I Still Love You Babe" (by Linda Easterling), recorded by Marily Mundy; "What Kind of Girl Do You Think I Am" (by Sandy Ellwanger and Ralph Porter), recorded by Sandy Ellwanger; all country on Door Knob Records.
Tips: "Respect our submission policy and keep trying."

CHRIS MUSIC PUBLISHING, 133 Arbutus Ave., P.O. Box 396, Manistique MI 49854-0396. President: Reg B. Christensen. Music publisher and record company (Global Records and Bakersfield Records). BMI. Estab. 1959. Publishes 15-35 songs/year; publishes at least 20 new songwriters/year. Works with lyricists. Pays standard royalty with some exceptions.
Affiliate: Saralee Music Publishing (BMI).
How to Contact: Submit cassette *only* with 2-5 songs and lyric sheet. "No fancy, big band demo necessary; just one instrument with a clean, clear voice. Copyrighted material only. Send registration number. If not registered with Copyright office, let us know what you've done to protect your material." SASE. Reports in 1 month or ASAP.
Music: Mostly teen type novelty, gospel, MOR and novelty rock; also bluegrass, contemporary gospel and soul. Published "Is it Really Christmas in L.A." (by P. and S.Alter) recorded by Destiny; "Cross the Line" (by Destiny) recorded by Destiny; "All Night Long" written and recorded by Dianna Greer. All recorded on Global label.
Tips: "The writer should indicate if he has a certain singer in mind. Keep songs to 2-2½ minutes. Voice on demo should be clear—if one must strain to listen, interest is lost fast. Give us time—publishers put in a lot of time and money and we have to wait to hear back from managers and record companies, too. Songwriters are cautioned to be careful about writing flippant letters like 'answer or else,' which most publishers will ignore and deal no further with the writer."

*CHRYSALIS MUSIC GROUP, 645 Madison Ave., New York NY 10022. (212)758-3555. Professional Manager: Michelle Mannies. Music publisher. ASCAP, BMI. Estab. 1972. Publishes 100-150 songs/year; publishes 3-5 new songwriters/year. Hires staff songwriters "in small quantities." Works with composers and lyricists; teams collaborators. Pays royalty "standard in most cases, but negotiable."
Affiliates: Chrysalis Music (ASCAP) and Chrysalis Songs (BMI).
How to Contact: Call first and obtain permission to submit a tape. Prefers cassette with 3-5 songs and lyric sheet. "Quality is stressed instead of quantity." Returns unsolicited material with SASE. Reports in 2 weeks.
Music: Mostly pop/R&B, rock and country. Published "Heart of Stone" (by Hill/Sinfield), recorded by Cher on Geffen Records (single-rock/pop); "Peace in Our Time" (by Hill/Sinfield), recorded by Eddy Money on Columbia Records (single-rock/pop); and "Anything I Want," written and recorded by Kevin Paige on Chrysalis Records (pop/R&B).
Tips: "Be confident, and unique."

*CINDY JANE MUSIC PUBLISHING (BMI), 4724 Lillian Highway, Pensacola FL 32506. (904)455-1109. Publisher: Fred Everett Sollie, President. Music publisher, record company (Sollie Sunshine Records), record producer (Sollie Sunshine Recordings). BMI. Estab. 1978. Publishes 150 songs/year; publishes 2-12 new songwriters/year; teams collaborators. Pays standard royalty. Pays standard royalty to writers. Statutory rate to publishers each record sold.
Affiliates: Cindy Jane Music (BMI).
How to Contact: Write or call first and obtain permission to submit a tape. Prefers cassette with 1-3 lyric or lead sheet. "Submit only best songs on good quality cassette; no home demos please. Studio demos only." SASE. Reports in 1 month.

Music: Mostly traditional or contemporary country/southern gospel, up-temp duets, c/w ballads; also group songs. Published "Memories of Patsy Cline" (by Carlon Miller, T.D. Bayless, J. Fann), recorded by Jim & Jenny West; "These Old Cigarettes" (by Fred & Rebie Sollie, Ray R. Jones), recorded by Ray R. Jones; and "The Auction" (by Fred Sollie & Ray Jones), recorded by Ray Jones; all country on Sollie Sunshine Records.

Tips: "Write a song many people can identify with. No dirty lyrics, honest feeling, meaningful message and demoed in a professional style on quality tape and clearly written lyric sheet. Trends still leading towards traditional country with higher values and with the European market opening up to Traditional Country as we once knew it and great songs like the old standards of the early 40s and 50s. Ballads that reflect the better qualities of human beings and kindness."

*CISUM, Box 192, Pittsburg KS 66762. (316)231-6443. Partner: Kevin Shawn. Music publisher, record company (Cisum), record producer (Cisum). BMI, SESAC and ASCAP. Estab. 1985. Publishes 100 songs/year. Works with composers and lyricists; teams collaborators. Pays standard royalty.

How to Contact: Write first and obtain permission to submit a tape. Prefers cassette (or VHS videocassette if available) and lyric sheet. "Unpublished, copyrighted, cassette with lyrics. Submit as many as you wish. We listen to everything, allow 3 months. When over 3 weeks please call."

Music: Mostly novelty, country and rock; also pop, gospel and R&B. Published "Angry Gun" (by R. Durst), recorded by Gene Straser on Antique Records (country); "Smooth Talk" (by Rhuems), recorded by Rich Rhuems on Antique Records (country); "Mailman Mailman" (by Strasser), recorded by Willie & Shawn on Cisum Records (novelty).

Tips: "Good demo, great song; always put your best effort on the tape first."

*CITKO-SLOTT PUBLISHING CO., Suite 200 East 100 Merrick Rd., Rockville Centre NY 11570. (516)536-8341. President: James Citkovic. Music publisher and consultants. ASCAP. Estab. 1989. Works with composers and lyricists; teams collaborators.

Affiliates: Citko-Slott Publishing Co. (ASCAP).

How to Contact: Submit a demo tape by mail—unsolicited submissions are OK. Prefers cassette (VHS videocassette if available) with open number of songs and lyric sheet. "Send available information to help evaluate the songwriter/band, i.e., bio, press, pictures, etc." SASE. Reports in 5 weeks.

Music: Mostly pop, rock and dance/R&B; also nu-music, pop/rock and commercial hard rock. Published "Songs I Sing" (by Joe Costanzo, pop ballad).

CITY PUBLISHING CO., 3966 Standish Ave., Cincinnati OH 45213. (513)793-8191. President: Roosevelt Lee. Music publisher, record company and record producer. BMI. Publishes 8 songs/year. Pays standard royalty.

Affiliate: Carriage Publishing Co. (BMI).

How to Contact: Write first about your interest. Prefers cassette with maximum of 4 songs and lyric sheet. SASE. Reports in 1 month.

Music: Mostly country, R&B and soul. Published "Love City Part 1&2" (by Ronald Lee), recorded by Larry Daley on WES World Records (soul); and "Come Home to Me" (by Mike Ellis), recorded by M. Ellis on Key Records (country).

Tips: "I am looking for finished masters."

R.D. CLEVÈRE MUSIKVERLAG, Postfach 2145, D-6078 Neu-Isenburg, **West Germany**. Phone: (6102)52696. Professional Manager: Tony Hermonez. GEMA. Music publisher. Estab. 1967. Publishes 700-900 songs/year; publishes 40 new songwriters/year. Works with composers, lyricists; teams collaborators. Pays standard royalty.

Affiliates: Big Sound Music, Hot Night Music, Lizzy's Blues Music, Max Banana Music, R.D. Clevère-Cocabana-Music, R.D. Clevère-Far East & Orient-Music, and R.D. Clevère-America-Today-Music.

How to Contact: "Do not send advanced letter(s) asking for permission to submit your song material, just send it." Prefers cassette with "no limit" on songs and lyric sheet. SAE and a minimum of two IRCs. Reports in 3 weeks.

Music: Mostly pop, disco, rock, R&B, country and folk; also musicals and classic/opera.

Tips: "If the song submitted is already produced/recorded professionally on 16/24-multitrack-tape and available, we can use this for synchronization with artists of the various record companies/record producers."

CLOTILLE PUBLISHING, Suite 608, 214 St. George St., Toronto Ontario M5R 2N8 **Canada**. (416)964-0695. Manager: Al Kussin. Music publisher, record company (Slak Record), and record producer (Slak Productions). PROCAN. Estab. 1988. Publishes 6 songs/year; publishes 1 new songwriter/year. Teams collaborators. Pays standard royalty of 50%.

How to Contact: Submit a demo tape by mail—unsolicited submissions are O.K. Prefers cassette with 3 songs and lyric sheet. "Recording quality must be sufficient to convey the total impact of song." Reports in 4 weeks.
Music: Mostly pop, R&B and dance. Published "Dangerous" (by L. Scott), (dance); "In Love" (by A. Kussin), (R&B); and "If That Was a Dream" (by A. Kussin and L. Scott) (dance); all recorded by L. Scott on Slak Records.
Tips: "Submit good commercial material with strong hooks and interesting form. On most submissions, lyrics are usually cliched and substandard. Production quality must be adequate to get the song across."

COFFEE AND CREAM PUBLISHING COMPANY, 1138 E. Price St., Philadelphia PA 19138. (215)842-3450. President: Bolden Abrams, Jr.. Music publisher and record producer (Bolden Productions). ASCAP. Publishes 20 songs/year; publishes 4 new songwriters/year. Works with composers and lyricists; teams collaborators. Pays standard royalty.
How to Contact: Prefers cassette (or VHS videocassette) with 1-4 songs and lyric or lead sheets. Does not return unsolicited material. Reports in 2 weeks.
Music: Mostly pop, R&B, gospel and country. Published "Beat Your Feet" (by Peter Crawford) recorded by Gabrielle on Saphire Rose Records (hip hop/dance/house); "No Time for Tears" (by Bolden Abrams/Keith Batts), recorded by Gabrielle (R&B ballad) and "Sly Like a Fox," (by Regine Urbach), recorded by Joy Duncan on Ultimate Records (pop/dance).

CONTINENTAL COMMUNICATIONS CORP., 450 Livingston St., Norwood NJ 07648. (201)767-5551. President: Robert Schwartz. ASCAP, BMI. Estab. 1952. Music publisher and record company (Laurie Records and 3C Records). Publishes 50 songs/year; publishes 5-10 new songwriters/year. Works with composers, lyricists and teams collaborators. Pays standard royalty.
Affiliates: 3 Seas Music (ASCAP) and Northvale Music (BMI).
How to Contact: Prefers cassette. SASE. "Submit only a few of the most commercial songs with lead sheets and demo."
Music: Mostly rock. Published "Because of You" (by B. Sunkel), recorded by B. Sunkel on Laurie Records (pop); "Complicated" (by Allen Bros.), recorded by Allen Bros. on 3C Records (urban); and "Lament 62" (by D. Groom and P. Renari), recorded by D. Groom on Laurie Records (pop).

*CONTINENTAL SOUND MUSIC, Box 81065, Rotterdam 3009GB **Holland.** Phone: (010)4211098. Music publisher. BUMA. Publishes 200-500 songs/year; publishes 5-10 new songwriters/year. Hires staff writers. Works with composers and lyricists; teams collaborators. Royalty varies.
Affiliates: CAmusic, Gordon Thompson, Thank You Music, Ears & Eyes, Word Music, Kingsway, Fairhill, Little Beat, Sorgente, Matterhorn, Scripture in Song, Sullivan Family, Cherith Publishing, Heartcry, New Song Ministries and Opwekking.
How to Contact: Prefers cassette with 5 songs and lyric or lead sheet. SAE and IRC. Reports in 2 months.
Music: Gospel only.

COPPELIA, 21, rue de Pondichéry, 75015 Paris **France.** Phone: 45 67 30 66. FAX: 43 06 30 26. Manager: Jean-Philippe Olivi. Music publisher, record company (Olivi Records), record producer (Coppelia) and music print publisher. SACEM. Publishes 150 songs/year; publishes 80 new songwriters/year. Works with composers and lyricists. Pays standard royalty.
How to Contact: Submit a demo tape—unsolicited submissions are O.K. Prefers cassette (or VHS videocassette). SAE and IRC. Reports in 1 month.
Music: Mostly pop, rock and new age; also background music and movies/series music. Published "A St. Germain de prés" written and recorded by Bodin on Olivi Records (sax); "Sagapo" recorded by Ferchit on Olivi Records (accordion); and "Ambitions" (by Remt), recorded by Ferchit on Olivi Records (pop).

THE CORNELIUS COMPANIES, 803 18th Ave. South, Nashville TN 37203. (615)321-5333. Owner/Manager: Ron Cornelius. Music publisher and record producer (The Cornelius Companies, Ron Cornelius). BMI, ASCAP. Estab. 1987. Publishes "as many as possible" songs/year; publishes 2-3 new songwriters/year. Occasionally hires staff writers. Works with composers and lyricists; teams collaborators. Pays standard royalty.
Affiliate: RobinSparrow Music (BMI).
How to Contact: Write first and obtain permission to submit a tape. Prefers cassette with 2-3 songs. SASE. Reports in 2 months.
Music: Mostly country and pop. Published "Time Off for Bad Behavior" (by Larry Latimer), recorded by David Allen Coe; and "You're Slowly Going Out of My Mind" (by Gordon Dee), recorded by Southern Tracks; both on CBS Records.

CORNISH LEGEND MUSIC, 12 East St., Stonehouse, Plymouth PL1 3NU **England**. Phone: (0752)66 71 00. FAX: (0752)22 42 81. Partners: Nick Strachan and Rob Hancock. Music publisher. PRS. Member Music Publishers Association. Estab. 1987. Publishes 1 song/year. Plans to publish 2 new songwriters/year minimum. Works with composers. Pays 50-60% royalty.
How to Contact: Prefers cassette or 3¾ or 7½ IPS reel-to-reel with 1-4 songs and lyric sheet. SAE and IRC. Reports in 2 weeks.
Music: Mostly commercial material, pop, disco, ballads; anything commercially acceptable. Published "Your Fool" (by Rob Hancock), recorded by Roger Whittaker on Tembo Records (pop ballad).

*COSMOTONE MUSIC, P.O. Box 71988, Los Angeles CA 90071-0988. President: Rafael Brom. Music publisher, record company (Cosmotone Records, Cosmotone Studios) and record producer. ASCAP. Estab. 1984. Publishes 10 new songs/year; publishes 2 new songwriters/year. Works with lyricists; teams collaborators. Pays standard royalty.
How to Contact: Write first and obtain permission to submit a tape. Prefers cassette (VHS videocassette if available) with all songs and lyric sheet. "Will respond only if interested."
Music: All types. Published "Padre Pio"; "Sonnet XVIII"; and "O Let Me Be" all written and recorded by Lord Hamilton on Cosmotone Records (Christian/rock pop).

COTTAGE BLUE MUSIC, P.O. Box 121626, Nashville TN 37212. (615)726-3556. Contact: Neal James. Music publisher, record company (Kottage Records) and record producer (Neal James Productions). BMI. Estab. 1971. Publishes 30 songs/year; publishes 3 new songwriters/year. Works with composers and lyricists; teams collaborators. Pays standard royalty of 50%.
Affiliates: James & Lee (BMI) and Neal James Music (ASCAP).
How to Contact: Write first and obtain permission to submit a tape. Prefers cassette with 2 songs and lyric sheet. SASE. Reports in 4 weeks.
Music: Mostly country, gospel and rock/pop; also R&B. Published "22" (by Neal James), recorded by Jeremiah Hedge on Kottage Records (pop/rock); "Love Don't Lie" (by Neal James and Larry Lee), recorded by Ted Yost on Kottage Records (pop); and "The Lips that Say I Love You" (by Neal James and Ted Yost), recorded by Ted Yost on Kottage Records (country/pop).
Tips: "Screen material carefully. We are looking for hits."

COUNTRY BREEZE MUSIC, 1715 Marty, Kansas City KS 66103. (913)384-4454 or 384-1020. President: Ed Morgan. Music publisher and record company (Country Breeze Records and Walkin' Hat Records). BMI, ASCAP. Estab. 1984. Publishes 50-75 songs/year; publishes 25-30 new songwriters/year. Teams collaborators. Pays standard royalty.
Affiliate: Walkin' Hat Music (ASCAP).
How to Contact: Submit a demo tape—unsolicited submissions are OK. Prefers cassette (or VHS videocassette) with 4-5 songs and lyric sheet. "The songwriter/artist should perform on the video as though on stage giving a sold-out performance. In other words put heart and soul into the project. Submit in strong mailing envelopes." Reports in 2 weeks.
Music: Mostly country (rock/pop/traditional), gospel (southern/bluegrass and black) and rock. Published "Shatter Me" (by E. Morgan/C. Owens/L. Thomas), recorded by Dianne Elliott on Puzzle Records (country); "Angel is her Name," written and recorded by Jamie Mitchell on Country Breeze Records (country); "Rainbow's End" (by D. Ashton and J. Benjamin), recorded by Edging West on Country Breeze Records (country rock).
Tips: "Make sure your song is strong in both lyrics and melody and have vocal out front. Also if a writer believes they have a good song, put it on a good tape. A good tape makes a lot of difference in the sound. NO SASE, NO RETURNS!!!!"

COUNTRY CLASSICS MUSIC PUBLISHING CO., Box 15222, Oklahoma City OK 73115. (405)677-6448. General Manager: Sonny Lane. Music publisher and record company (Compo Records). BMI. Estab. 1972. Publishes 4-6 songs/year; publishes 2 new songwriters/year. Works with composers and lyricists; teams collaborators. Pays standard royalty.
How to Contact: Submit a demo tape—unsolicited submissions are O.K. Prefers cassette with 2-4 songs and lyric sheet. SASE. Reports in 3 weeks.
Music: Mostly country western, gospel and MOR. Published "Wine From My Table" (by Yvonne DeVaney), recorded by Bonnie Guitar on Playback Records; "Yodel Waltz"; and "Lover's Waltz" (by Yvonne DeVaney), recorded by Yvonne DeVaney and Wes Onley on Compo Records (country duet).
Tips: "We like simple melodies with strong lyrics."

COUNTRY STAR MUSIC, 439 Wiley Ave., Franklin PA 16323. (814)432-4633. President: Norman Kelly. Music publisher, record company (Country Star, Process, Mersey and CSI) and record producer (Country Star Productions). ASCAP. Estab. 1970. Publishes 10-20 songs/year; publishes 2-3 new song-

writers/year. Works with composers and lyricists; teams collaborators. Pays standard royalty.
Affiliates: Kelly Music Publications (BMI) and Process Music Publications (BMI).
How to Contact: Prefers cassette with 1-4 songs and lyric or lead sheet. SASE. Reports in 2 weeks.
Music: Mostly country (80%); also rock, gospel, MOR and R&B (5% each). Published "Pardon Me for Loving You" (by Robert Nailor), recorded by Tara Bailey on Country Star (country); "Time Between the Teardrops" (by Doog Davis), recorded by Junie Lou on Country Star Records (country); and "Every Bird's Gotta Fly" written and recorded by Ron Lauer on Country Star Records (country).
Tips: "Send only your best songs—ones you feel are equal to or better than current hits."

COUSINS MUSIC, 836 Darwin St., Charleston, SC 29412. (803)795-5612. President: Lou Cicchetti. Music publisher, record company (Cousins, Daisy, and Westend) and record producer. BMI, ASCAP. Estab. 1948. Publishes 2-3 songs/year; publishes maybe 2 new songwriters/year. Pays standard royalty.
Affiliate: Neems (ASCAP).
How to Contact: Submit a demo tape—unsolicited submissions are O.K. Prefers cassette with 3 songs and lyric sheet. SASE. Reports in 2 weeks.
Music: "We are interested in 50s and 60s type group songs (the hand-clappers) and good country. Published "Ticket To Home" (by J.O'Daniel T. Percoco), recorded by COCO on Cousins Records (country); and "Need Some Release" (by Jimmy Soul), recorded by In Progress (soul).
Tips: "Remember a song is not a song without a strong melody. A good lyric is only a poem unless you can hang it on strong sounds to color it."

COWABONGA MUSIC, INC., P.O. Box 630755, Miami FL 33163. (305)935-4880. A&R Director: Jack Gale. Music Publisher, record company (Playback Records, Gallery 11 Records, Inc., Ridgewood Records and Caramba! Records) and record producer (Jack Gale). ASCAP. Estab. 1983. Publishes 50 songs/year; publishes 12 new songwriters/year. Pays standard royalty.
Affiliate: Lovey Music Inc. (BMI).
How to Contact: Submit a demo tape—unsolicited submissions are O.K. Prefers cassette (or VHS vidoecassette) with maximum of 2 songs and lyric sheet. Does not return unsolicited material. Reports in 2 weeks.
Music: Mostly contemporary country and pop. Published "Hard Times Come Easy to Me" (by Ann Leisten) recorded by Terry Smith on Ridgewood Records (country); "Touch .. Don't Look" (by Horowitz and Spectue), recorded by Sylvie on Playback Records (country) and "After Hours" (by Nissenson and Lifton), recorded by Carol Persell on Ridgewood Records (country).
Tips: "Write it for play on radio. The song is more important than ever."

COWBOY JUNCTION FLEA MARKET AND PUBLISHING CO., Highway 44 West, Junction 490, Lecanto FL 32661. (904)746-4754. President: Elizabeth Thompson. Music publisher (Cowboy Junction Publishing Co.), record company (Cowboy Junction Records) and record producer. BMI. Estab. 1957. Publishes 2-3 songs/year. Pays standard royalty or other amount.
How to Contact: Submit demo tape (or VHS videocassette) by mail. SASE. Reports as soon as possible.
Music: Country, western, bluegrass and gospel. Published "Little Circle B" (by Boris Max Pastuch), recorded by Buddy Max (country); "Little Band of Gold" (by Boris Max Pastuch), recorded by Buddy Max (country); "Cedar Chips" recorded by Leo Vargason (blugrass); and "Thank You Lord" written and recorded by Wally Jones, all on Cowboy Junction Records.

***CPA RECORDS & PUBLISHING CO.**, 135 Lassiter Dr., #19, Hampton VA 23668. (804)838-8866. CEO: Christopher C. Carter. Music publisher and record company (CPA Records and Publishing Co.). BMI. Estab. 1989. Publishes 10 songs/year; publishes 5 new songwriters/year. Hires staff songwriters. Works with composers and lyricists; teams collaborators. Pays standard royalty.
How to Contract: Write first and obtain permission to submit a tape. Prefers cassette (VHS videocassette if available) with 3 or more songs. SASE. Reports in 1 month.
Music: Mostly R&B, rap and gospel; also country and pop. Published "Why Take a Chance" written and recorded by Lameatha Reed; "Tell Me Why" written and recorded by Chris Carter; and "Perfect Love" written and recorded by Lameatha Reed, all on CPA Records (R&B).

CREEKSIDE MUSIC, 100 Labon St., Tabor City NC 28463. (919)653-2546. Owner: Elson H. Stevens. Music publisher, record company (Seaside Records) and record producer (Southern Sound Productions). BMI. Estab. 1978. Publishes 30 songs/year; publishes 5 new songwriters/year. Works with composers, lyricists; teams collaborators. Pays 25-50% royalty from record sales.

How to Contact: Write or call first and obtain permission to submit. Prefers cassette with 3 songs and lead sheets. SASE. Reports in 1 month.
Music: Mostly country, rock and gospel; also "beach music." Published "Once in a Lifetime" (by Jeff Knight), recorded by Angela on SeaSide Records (country); "When the Feeling is Gone" (by G. Todd), recorded by T.J. Gibson on SeaSide Records (country); and "On the Down Side" written and recorded by T.J. Gibson on SeaSide Records (country).
Tips: "Be original—search for 'the hook'."

CSB KAMINSKY GMBH, Wilhelmstrasse 10, 2407 Bad Schwartau, **West Germany**. Phone: (0451)21530. General Manager: Pia Kaminsky. GEMA, PRS. Music publisher and collecting agency. Estab. 1978. Publishes 2-4 songs/year; 1 new songwriter/year. Teams collaborators. Pays 50% if releasing a record; 85% if only collecting royalties.
Affiliate: Leosong Copyright Service, Ltd., London, United Kingdom, and Sydney, Australia.
How to Contact: Write and submit material. Prefers cassette or VHS videocassette. Does not return unsolicited material. Reports in 4 weeks.
Music: Mostly pop; also rock, country and reggae.

CUDE & PICKENS PUBLISHING, 519 N. Halifax Ave., Daytona Beach FL 32118. (904)252-0381. A&R Director: Bobby Lee Cude. Music publisher, record company and record producer. BMI. Estab. 1978. Publishes 12 songs/year. Pays standard royalty.
How to Contact: "We are not accepting any new writers at this time."
Music: Mostly country; also easy listening, gospel, MOR, top 40/pop and Broadway show. Published "Tennessee's on My Mind" (country); "Texas Red, White and Blue Step" (country); "Who's Lovin You" (pop); and Shot in the Dark" (pop), all by Caz Allen.

*CURRENT MUSICAL ENTERPRISES, INC., 366 Adelaide St. East, Suite #437, Toronto ON M5A 3X9 **Canada**. (416)361-1101. A&R, New Projects: Trevor G. Shelton. Music publisher, record company (Current Records, Rammit Records) and record producer (Trevor G. Shelton). CAPAC, PROCAN. Estab. 1983. Publishes 50 songs/year; publishes 2 new songwriters/year. Pays standard royalty.
Affiliates: Brand New Sounds Music (PROCAN), Current Sounds (CAPAC).
How to Contact: Submit a demo tape by mail—unsolicited submissions are OK. Prefers cassette with 4 songs and lyric sheet. "Please make sure that you include contact information (address and telephone number) and information on yourself." SASE. Reports in 2 weeks.
Music: Mostly rock, pop and dance; also acid, hip hop and rap. Published "Julian" (by Johnson/Orenstein), recorded by Alta Moda (dance/rock); "Love Becomes Electric" (by Kromm), recorded by strange advance (rock); and "So Far Away" (by Scullion), recorded by Mystery Romance (pop); all on Current Records.
Tips: "We understand that you, as a songwriter might not be able to present your material with pleasant vocals. We are interested in your ability to write good music. Please note: if you have material to be compared with the likes of The Jackson Five please by all means, send it in."

D.S.M. PRODUCERS ENT. PUBLISHING CO., 161 W. 54th, New York NY 10019. (212)245-0006. Producer: Suzan Bader. Music publisher, record producer and management firm (Ameircan Steel Management Co.). ASCAP. Estab. 1979. Publishes 30 songs/year; publishes 10 new songwriters/year. Works with composers and lyricists; teams collaborators. Pays standard royalty.
How to Contact: Write or call first and obtain permission to submit. Prefers cassette (or VHS videocassette) and lyric or lead sheet. SASE. "Include SASE or we do not review nor respond to material." Reports in 4 weeks.
Music: Mostly top 40, R&B/dance, CHR and rock; also jazz, country and instrumental tracks for background music. Published "On the Town (by Frank Lakewood), recorded by Frank Lakewood on AACL Records (jazz); "Welcome Home" (by Hal Gold/Mike Fink), recorded by Hal Gold/Mike Fink on AACL Records (pop); and "The Fields" (by Rick Resnick), recorded by Rick Resnick on AACL Records (AOR).
Tips: "Listen to the hits—old and new. There's a reason why they were hits. Study your craft."

*DAGENE MUSIC, P.O. Box 410851, San Francisco CA 94141. (415)822-1530. President: David Alston. Music publisher, record company (Cabletown Corp.) and record producer (Classic Disc. Production). ASCAP. Estab. 1986. Hires staff songwriters. Works with composers; teams collaborators. Pays standard royalty.
Affiliates: Dagene Music, 1956 Music.
How to Contact: Write or call first and obtain permission to submit a tape. Prefers cassette with 2 songs and lyric sheet. "Be sure to obtain permission before sending any material." Does not return unsolicited material. Reports in 1 month.

Music: Mostly R&B/rap, dance and pop. Published "Visions" (by Marcus Justice), recorded by 2-Dominatorz on Dagene Records; "Serving 'Em" (by Rafael Bazile), recorded by Frisco Kid on Dagene Records; and "Started Life" (by David/M. Campbell), recorded by Primo on Cabletown Records (all rap).
Tips: "Keep an ear and eye to the street."

*DAN THE MAN MUSIC, P.O. Box 612, Delbarton WV 25670-0612. President: Daniel L. Bischoff. Music publisher (ASCAP & BMI), record company (Dan the Man Records), and management firm (Dan the Man Management Co.). Publishes approximately 4 songs/year. "Have some major label connections." Pays standard royalty.
Affiliate: Bischoff Music Publishing Co. (BMI).
How to Contact: Please send cassette or VHS tape and lyrics. "We are looking for good country and pop/rock songs. Also, when sending material to us please send a SASE with proper postage for return."
Music: Country, pop/rock. Published "Forget Him" written and recorded by Ted Makse (country); "Interview with Michael Jackson" written and recorded by Dan the Man (pop); and "The King Went on a Journey" (by Lambert Massey), recorded by Johnny Wright (country), all recorded on the Dan the Man label.

*DANA PUBLISHING CO., 824 83rd St., Miami Beach FL 33141. (305)865-8960. President: Walter Dana. Music publisher, record company (Asdan Records) and record producer. BMI. Pays standard royalty.
Music: Classical and ethnic (Polish).

DARBONNE PUBLISHING CO., Route 3, Box 172, Haynesville LA 71038. (318)927-5253. President: Edward N. Dettenheim. Music publisher and record company (Wings Record Co.). BMI. Estab. 1987. Publishes 50 songs/year; publishes 8-10 new songwriters/year. Works with composers and lyricists; teams collaborators. Pays standard royalty.
How to Contact: Submit a demo tape—unsolicited submissions are O.K. Prefers cassette or 7½ ips reel-to-reel with up to 12 songs and lyric sheet. SASE. Reports in 6 weeks.
Music: Mostly country and gospel. Published "Bitter Taste of Leaving" written and recorded by T.J. Lynn on Wings Records (country); "Mama" (by E. Dettenheim), recorded by Donna Ray on Wings Records (country); and "Turner Hotel" (by E. Dettenheim), recorded by T.J. Lynn on Wings Records (country).
Tips: "The better the demo—the better your chances of interesting your listener."

DARK HEART MUSIC, 1236 S. Staples, Corpus Christi TX 78404. (512)882-7066. Music publisher, record company (Dark Heart Records) and record producer. Estab. 1984. BMI. Publishes 10-50 songs/year; publishes varying number of new songwriters/year. Pays standard royalty.
Affiliates: Roland Garcia Music, El Palacio Music, Dillettante Music and Alpen Glow Music.
How to Contact: Prefers cassette. Submissions must include complete name, address and phone number. Does not return unsolicited material. Reporting time varies.
Music: Mostly rock, Spanish and country; also gospel. Published "Ready as Hell," (by Jim Dandy), recorded by Black Oak Arkansas on Hacienda (rock); and "Time of Your Life" by Head East on Dark Heart Records (rock).

DATA PROCESSING MUSIC, 2155 Bennett Creek Rd., Cottage Grove OR 97424. (503)942-5877. President: Jimmy Blue. Music publishers, record company (Data Records, Blue Movies Records) and film studio (motion picture). BMI. Estab. 1983. Publishes 10-25 songs/year; publishes 2 new songwriters/year. Works with composers; teams collaborators. Pays standard royalty.
How to Contact: Submit a demo tape by mail—unsolicited submissions are O.K. Prefers cassette or 15-7½ ips reel-to-reel or videocassette with 3 songs and lyric sheets. "Be as thorough as possible when submitting." SASE. Reports in 2 weeks.

 The asterisk before a listing indicates that the listing is new in this edition. New markets are often the most receptive to unsolicited submissions.

Music: Mostly new age, pop and movie soundtracks; also sound effects and holophonics. Published "Girl Gone Wrong" on Data Records (rock); "Minus the Money" on Data Records (rock); and "Data Turns Your World Around" on Blue Movies Records (movie soundtrack) written and recorded by Jimmy Blues.
Tips: "Don't listen to what MTV says. Always question music authority. It's such a competitive market, put all your efforts into what you do best, don't let anyone tell you it's not marketable, don't let anyone charge you to publish your music, fall in love with your work or get out of the business (you'll save everyone and yourself a lot of trouble and costly time)."

THE EDWARD DE MILES MUSIC COMPANY, 4475 Allisonville Rd., 8th Fl., Indianapolis IN 46205. (317)545-0221 or 549-9006. Attn: Professional Manager. Music publisher, record company (Sahara Records), management,bookings and promotions. BMI. Estab. 1984. Publishes 50-75 songs/year; publishes 5 new songwriters/year. Hires staff songwriters. Works with composers and lyricists; teams collaborators. Pays standard royalty of 50%.
How to Contact: Write or call first and obtain permission to submit a tape. Prefers cassette with 1-3 songs and a lyric sheet,SASE. Does not return unsolicited material. Reports in 1 month.
Music: Mostly top 40 pop/rock, R&B/dance and C&W; also musical scores for TV, radio, films and jingles. Published "The Girl for Me" (by S. Lynn), recorded by Steve Lynn on Sahara Records (ballad); "Need a Lover" (by S. Lynn), recorded by Steve Lynn on Sahara Records (dance) and "High Off Rhymes" (by D. Evans and A. Mitchell), recorded by Multiple Choice on Sahara Records (rap).
Tips: "Copyright all songs before submitting to us."

JASON DEE MUSIC, INC., 44 Music Sq. East, Nashville TN 37203. (615)255-2175. President: Charlie Fields. Music publisher, record company (Charta Records/Delux Records) and record producer (Charlie Fields). BMI. Estab. 1977. Publishes 15 or more songs and new songwriters/year. Works with composers. Pays standard royalty.
Affiliates: Jason Dee Music, Inc.(BMI), Mr. Mort Music, Inc. (ASCAP).
How to Contact: Submit a demo tape by mail—unsolicited submissions are OK. Prefers cassette with 3-4 songs. SASE. Reports in 4 weeks.
Music: Mostly country and country MOR. Published "You Won the Battle" (by J. Walker/D. Erickson), recorded by Eddie Rivers (country); "Somewhere in Canada" (by P. Monette/D. Walsh/J. Loielle), recorded by David Walsh (MOR); and "After the Passion Leaves" (by B.J. Solleberger), recorded by Nina Wyatt (country); all on Charta Records.

DELEV MUSIC COMPANY, 7231 Mansfield Ave., Philadelphia PA 19138-1620. (215)276-8861. President: W. Lloyd Lucas. Music publisher, record company (Surprize Records, Inc.), record producer and management, independently and with Growth Management, of Mt. Holly, New Jersey. BMI, ASCAP, SGA, NAS and CMA. Publishes 6-10 songs/year; publishes 6-10 new songwriters/year. Pays standard royalty.
Affiliate: Sign of the Ram Music (ASCAP).
How to Contact: Write first about your interest. Prefers cassette (or VHS videocassette) with 1-3 songs and lyric sheet. "Video must be of VHS format and as professionally done as possible. It does not necessarily have to be done at a professional video studio, but should be a very good quality production showcasing artist's performance." SASE. "We will not accept certified mail." Reports in 3 weeks.
Music: R&B ballad and dance-oriented, contemporary Christian/gospel, pop ballads, crossover and country/western. Published "We Don't Love Anymore", "You're A Hit With Me", "Burned Out On Love" and "Guilty Of Loving You", all of which are musical works of Tim & Cindy Shafer, Robert Eagleman, Brian Glenn and Chad Fukuda. Also "Michael", a tribute to Michael Jackson by Andy Kouts, "I Believe In Us" by William Heaton and Robert LePree, and "Hang On To Your Dreams" by Tyler O. Sterrett. Country/Western songs include "Old King Love" by Joey Katsos and Mark McLelland. "All of the songs mentioned are very strong in message and melody and we are seeking artists in the area of Philadelphia, PA to record them. We have very strong contemporary gospel material penned by Wayne Graber and Larry A. Stephens, two very prolific writers of religious music and are seeking artists for their material. We are seeking exceptional male vocalists, female vocalists and a male vocal group who can both sing and dance."
Tips: "Songs submitted must be lyrically and melodically strong with good strong hook lines, and tell a story that will appeal to and be related to by the radio-listening and record-buying public. Most important is that the demo be a clear quality product with understandable vocal and lyrics out front."

DEMERIE MUSIC, 708 N 1st St., #135, Minneapolis MN 55401. (612)339-9880. Contact: Don Powell. Music publisher. ASCAP. Estab. 1984. Publishes 20 songs/year; publishes 2 new songwriters/year. Pays 50% royalty.

How to Contact: Submit a demo tape by mail—unsolicited submissions are O.K. Prefers cassette with 3 songs and lyric sheets. SASE. Reports in 6 weeks.
Music: Mostly R&B dance music, R&B ballads and pop. Published "Make It Real" (by D. Powell, R. Kelly and L. Mallan), recorded by The Jets on MCA Records (ballad); "You've Got Another Boyfriend" (by S. Lobelle and G. Felicetta), recorded by The Jets on MCA Records (R&B dance); and "Do You Remember" (by L. Wolfgromm and G. Hunt), recorded by The Jets on MCA Records (R&B ballad).
Tips: "Send me a hit!! Keep it simple."

DEMI MONDE RECORDS & PUBLISHING LTD., Foel Studio, Llanfair Caereinion, POWYS, **Wales**. Phone: (0938)810758 and (0952)883962. Managing Director: Dave Anderson. Music publisher, record company (Demi Monde Records & Publishing Ltd.), record producer (Dave Anderson). Member MCPS. Estab. 1983. Publishes 50-70 songs/year; publishes 10-15 new songwriters/year. Works with composers and lyricists; teams collaborators. Pays standard royalty.
How to Contact: Submit a demo tape—unsolicited submissions are O.K. Prefers cassette (or VHS videocassette) with 3-4 songs. SAE and IRC. Reports in 1 month.
Music: Mostly rock, R&B and pop. Published "I Feel So Lazy" (by D. Allen), recorded by Gong on Demi Monde Records (rock); "Phalarn Dawn" (by E. Wynne), recorded by Ozric Tentacles on Demi Monde Records (rock); and "Pioneer" (by D. Anderson), recorded by Amon Dual on Demi Monde Records (rock).

DENNY MUSIC GROUP, 3325 Fairmont Dr., Nashville TN 37203-1004. (615)269-4847. Chief Executive Officer: John E. Denny. ASCAP, BMI, SESAC. Estab. 1983. Music publisher, record company (Dollie Record Co., Jed Record Production) and record producer. Publishes 100 songs/year; 20 new songwriters/year. Works with composer and lyricists; teams collaborators. Pays standard royalty.
How to Contact: Write or call first and obtain permission to submit. Prefers cassette with 1 song and lyric sheet. Reports in 6 weeks.
Music: Mostly country, gospel and MOR. Published "Cashmere Cowboy" (by F. Hannaway, country); "Inside Information" (by J. Martin, R&B); and "Closer to You" (by T. Rooney, pop).

*DIFFERENT STOKES PUBLISHING, P.O. Box 691068, Los Angeles CA 90069. (213)274-1900. Manager: Michele Elyzabeth. Music publisher. ASCAP. Estab. 1988. Publishes 12 songs/year. Teams collaborators.
Affiliates: Otis Stokes Publishing (ASCAP).
How to Contact: Submit a demo tape by mail—unsolicited submissions OK. Prefers cassette with 4 songs and lyric sheet. SASE. Reports in 1 month.
Music: Mostly R&B, pop and rock; also gospel. Published "Don't Make Me Want" recorded by Jermaine Jackson on Arista Records; "Happy Feeling" and "A Woman Like You" recorded by Otis Stokes on Curb Records, (all written by Otis Stokes, all R&B).

DILEO MUSIC GROUP, 1111 17th Ave. S., Nashville TN 37212. (615)329-1100. President: Frank M. Dileo; Director of Creative Services: Richard Butler. Music publisher. ASCAP/BMI. Publishes 125 songs/year; publishes 3 new songwriters/year. Hires staff writers. Works with composers. Pays standard royalty.
Affiliates: Tioga Street Music (BMI), Clover Street Music (ASCAP), I've Got The Music Co. (ASCAP), Song Tailors Music Co. (BMI), Creative Source Music (BMI), Jam-In-The-Box Music (BMI), Hear No Evil Music (BMI) and See No Evil Music (ASCAP).
How to Contact: Prefers cassette with 2 songs and lyric sheet. SASE. Reports in 2 months. Submit a demo tape. Submissions must be addressed to the attention of Richard Butler or they will be returned "unsolicited material."
Music: Mostly country, pop, rock and R&B; also blues. Published "If I Had You" (by Kerry Chater/Danny Mayo), recorded by Alabama on RCA Records (country); "If I Knew Then What I Know Now" (by Richard Butler/Robert Byrne), recorded by Kenny Rogers and Gladys Knight on Warner Bros. Records (A/C); "I Can't Love You Baby" (by Kerry Chater/Tommy Rocco/Jesse Read), recorded by Highway 101 on Warner Bros. Records (country); "Same Old Heart" (by Mac McAnally), recorded by Mac McAnally on Geffen/Warner Bros. Records (A/C); "Mary Lou" (by Young Jesse/Sam Ling), recorded by Southern Pacific on Warner Bros. Records (country) and "It Ain't Nobody's Business (by Jimmy Witherspoon), recorded by Hank Williams, Jr. on Warner/Curb Records (country).
Tips: "Submit only top drawer, quality material. Be aware of artist's current style and direction."

*DINGO MUSIC, 4, Galleria Del Corso, Milan **Italy** 20122. (02)791141. Managing Director: Guido Palma. Music publisher and record company (Top Records). SIAE. Estab. 1977. Publishes 30-35 songs/year; publishes 5 new songwriters/year. Hires staff writers. Works with composers and lyricists. Pays standard royalty of 50% and 10% on printed copies.

Affiliates: U.C.P. (Ging).
How to Contact: Submit demo tape by mail-unsolicited submissions are OK. Prefers cassette with 2 songs. SAE and IRC. Reports in 2 weeks.
Music: Mostly interested in rock, pop and R&B (pop); also new age and gospel. Published "Lambada" (by Do Berman) on Top Records; "Per Un Po" (by Palma) on Dingo Records (pop); and "La Vita di un Uomo" (by Caminiti) on Kiwi Records (pop).

*DIRECTIONS, 6 Rue Laurencin, Lyon **France** 69002. (32)7240-9212. Managing Director: Andre. Music Publisher, record company (Lucky French Records). SACEM. Estab. 1988. Publishes 200 songs/year; 200 new songwriters/year. Works with composers; teams collaborators. Pays standard royalty.
Affiliates: Andre Records (SACEM).
How to Contact: Write or call to arrange an interview. Prefers cassette with 3 songs and lyric sheets. SAE and IRC. Reports in 2 weeks.
Music: Interested in rock and pop; also classical. Published "Dolly" (by Deux) on Lucky French (rock); "Lyonnais/Lyonnaid" (by D. Guerci) on Directions Records (pop); and "Anita" (by Ambiance Trep) on Andre Records (folk), all recorded by Directions.

DISCAPON PUBLISHING CO., Box 3082, Lic NY 11103. (718)721-5599. Contact: Discapon. Music publisher (Discapon). ASCAP. Estab. 1980. Publishes 100 songs/year. Works with composers. Pays standard royalty.
How to Contact: Submit a demo tape by mail—unsolicited submissions are OK. Prefers cassette with 2-6 songs. SASE. Reports in 2 months.
Music: Mostly background music without words; also classical.

*DISCOVERING MUSIC LTD., Haven Commercial Bldg. 24/F, Room A, Tsing Fung St., **Hong Kong**. Phone: (852)8071297. General Manager: Keith Yip. Music publisher. C.A.S.H. Estab. 1986. Publishes 20-30 songs/year; publishes 2-3 new songwriters/year. Pays standard royalty.
How to Contact: Submit a demo tape by mail—unsolicited submissions are OK. Prefers cassette. SASE. Reports in 2 weeks.
Music: Mostly pop, R&B and rock.

*TOMY DON PUBLISHING, 3608 Harrogate Rd., Cola SC 29210. (803)798-7298. Owner: Tommy Greene. Music publisher and record producer. ASCAP, BMI. Estab. 1985. Publishes 200 songs/year; publishes 10-20 new songwriters/year. Hires staff songwriters. Works with composers and lyricists; teams collaborators. Pays standard royalty.
How to Contact: Write or call first and obtain permission to submit a tape. Prefers cassette (VHS videocassette if available) with 1-3 songs and lyric or lead sheet. SASE. Reports in 1 month.
Music: Mostly country, country gospel and folk.
Tips: "Send good country (traditional) or traditional country with 'gospel feel.'"

DON'T CALL ME (D.C.M.) MUSIC, Agmerhurst House, Kitchenham Rd., Ashburnham, Nr. Battle, Sussex TN33 9NB **England**. M. Director: Mr. Bickersteth. Music publisher. P.R.S. Estab. 1986. Publishes 50 songs/year; 2 new songwriters/year. Sometimes hires staff writers. Teams collaborators. Pays 50-70% depending·upon establishment.
How to Contact: Submit a demo tape by mail—unsolicited submissions are OK. Prefers cassette (or VHS videocassette) with 3-5 songs and lyric or lead sheets. "Submissions should be clearly marked with name, address and telephone number." SASE. Reports in 2 weeks.
Music: Mostly rock; also inspirational, folk and blends/fusions. Published "Brian" (by Silas Crawley), recorded by Fat and Frantic (rock skiffle); "Wake Up!" (by V. Strachan), recorded by Mind the Gap (gospel); and "Mystery of Universe" recorded by Clarinet Connection; all on I'll Call You Records.
Tips: "Will consider most styles of music especially acoustic songs at this time."

*DOOR KNOB MUSIC PUBLISHING, INC., 315 Mt. Juliet Rd., Mt. Juliet TN 37122. (615)754-0417. Contact: Karen Jeglum Kennedy. Music publisher, record company (Door Knob Records, Society Records), record producer (Gene Kennedy Enterprises, Inc.). BMI. Estab. 1975. Publishes 20-25 songs/year; publishes 10-15 new songwriters/year. Works with composers and lyricists. Pays standard royalty.
Affiliates: Chip 'n' Dale Music Publishers, Inc. (ASCAP), Lodestar Music, A Division of Gĕne Kennedy Enterprises, Inc. (SESAC).
How to Contact: Submit a demo tape by mail—unsolicited submissions are OK. Prefers cassette with 1-3 songs and lyric sheet. Include SASE for tape return and/or response. Send regular mail. SASE. Reports in 2 weeks.

Music: Mostly country and gospel. Published "I Just Came In Here To Let a Little Hurt Out" (by Mac Phillips and Doug Zepp), recorded by Sandy Ellwanger; "Let Your Love Take Hold Of Me" (by Ray Sanders and Ann Tygert), recorded by Marily Mundy; "Feelings for Each Other" (by Marion Walton, Jr. and Henry Gray), recorded by Marily Mundy; all country on Door Knob Records.
Tips: "Respect our submission policy and keep trying."

BUSTER DOSS MUSIC, Box 13, Estill Springs TN 37330. (615)649-2577. President: Buster Doss. Music publisher and record company (Stardust). BMI. Estab. 1959. Publishes 500 songs/year; publishes 50 new songwriters/year. Teams collaborators. Pays standard royalty.
How to Contact: Write or call first and obtain permission to submit a tape. Prefers cassette with 2 songs and lyric sheets. SASE. Reports in 1 week.
Music: Mostly country; also rock. Published "What Th' Big Boys Do" (by Buster Doss), recorded by Cliff Archer on Wizard Records; "Small Town Country Girl" (by R.B. Stone) recorded by R.B. Stone on Stardust Records; and "A Little While" written and recorded by Rooster Quantrell on Stardust Records.

DUANE MUSIC, INC., 382 Clarence Ave., Sunnyvale CA 94086. (408)739-6133. President: Garrie Thompson. Music publisher. BMI. Publishes 10-20 songs/year; publishes 1 new songwriter/year. Pays standard royalty.
Affiliate: Morhits Publishing (BMI).
How to Contact: Prefers cassette with 1-2 songs. SASE. Reports in 1 month.
Music: Blues, country, disco, easy listening, rock, soul and top 40/pop. Published "Little Girl," recorded by The Syndicate of Sound & Ban (rock); "Warm Tender Love," recorded by Percy Sledge (soul); and "My Adorable One," recorded by Joe Simon (blues).

DUPUY RECORDS/PRODUCTIONS/PUBLISHING, INC., 10960 Ventura Blvd., Studio City CA 91604. (818)980-6412. President: Pedro Dupuy. Music publisher, record company and record producer. ASCAP. Songwriters Guild. Estab. 1980. Publishes 50 songs/year; publishes 4 new songwriters/year. Works with composers and lyricists; teams collaborators. Hires staff writers. Pays standard royalty.
How to Contact: Write or call first about your interest or arrange personal interview. Prefers cassette with 2-4 songs and lyric sheet. SASE. Reports in 1 month.
Music: Mostly R&B and pop; also easy listening, jazz, MOR, soul and top 40. Published "Find a Way," "I Don't Wanna Know," and "Precious Love," written and recorded by Gordon Gilman. Other artists include David Daymon, Joe Trammel, James G. Sobo and Jon Rider.
Tips: "Songs should have very definitive lyrics with hook."

*E. MINOR MUSIC, (formerly Carene Music), 310 B S. Gallatin Rd., Madison TN 37115. (615)860-2545. Owner: Carl Motsinger. Music publisher. BMI. Estab. 1987. Works with composers. Pays standard royalty.
How to Contact: Submit a demo tap by mail—unsolicited submissions are O.K. Write first and obtain permission to submit a tape. Prefers cassette with 1 song and lyric sheets. Does not return unsolicited material.
Music: Mostly country and gospel.
Tips: "We need great songs. We have plenty of good ones. Small publishers and independents will see a bigger part of the market due to the fact that only they will present new country material."

*EARTH AND SKY MUSIC PUBLISHING INC., P.O. Box 4157, Winter Park FL 32793. (407)657-6016. President: Ernest Hatton. Music publisher, record company (Earth and Sky Records) and record producer (Hatton & Associates, Inc.). BMI. Estab. 1977. Publishes 100 songs/year; publishes 10-15 new songwriters/year. Works with composers and lyricists; teams collaborators. Pays standard royalty.
How to Contact: Submit a demo tape by mail—unsolicited submissions are OK. Prefers cassette (VHS videocassette if available) with 3 songs and lyric sheet. SASE. Reports in 2 months.
Music: Mostly pop/uptempo, pop ballads and rock (soft); also country. Published "All The Seasons" (by Hatton-Hurley), recorded by Sandy Contella (pop ballad); "With My Last Breath" (by Hatton-Contella), recorded by Sandy Contella (pop ballad); and "Catch a Snowflake" (by Hatton-Scott), recorded by Janet O. Neale (Christmas pop), all on E & S Records.
Tips: "We are looking *very hard* for uptempo songs—good lyrics for a young Debbie Gibson type. Have a great young gal but need some material—suggest sending demo with vocal and also without (just tracks) with lyric sheet."

EARTHSCREAM MUSIC PUBLISHING CO., Suite A, 2036 Pasket, Houston TX 77092. (713)688-8067. Contact: Jeff Johnson. Music publisher, record company and record producer. Estab. 1975. BMI. Publishes 12 songs/year; publishes 4 new songwriters/year. Pays standard royalty.

How to Contact: Prefers cassette (or videocassette) with 2-5 songs and lyric sheet. SASE. Reports in 1 month.
Music: New rock and top 40/pop. Published "Always Happens" (by Pennington/Smith), recorded by Barbara Pennington; "Show Me Reaction" (by Wells), recorded by Rick Bardon; and "New Guy" (by Wells), recorded by Valerie Starr (all pop/rock).

*EDICIONES MUSICALES PHONOGRAM S.A., Av. Belgrano 1670-6°piso, Buenos Aires 1093 **Argentina**. (54)38-0665. Publishing Manager: Andrea G. Vardakas. Music publisher. SADAIC. Publishes 100 songs/year; publishes 5 new songwriters/year. Works with composers and lyricists.
Affiliates: "We belong to the Polygram Music Group and our catalogues include: Island Music, Dick James Music, Welk Music Group, Sweden Music.
How to Contact: Write first and obtain permission to submit a tape. Prefers cassette with 2-3 songs and lyric or lead sheets. Always specify: "Sample Without Commercial Value." Does not return unsolicited material. Reports in 4 weeks.
Music: Mostly strong ballads, pop; incidental. No country or gospel. Published "Vas A Salir," written and recorded by Manuel Wirzt on Mercury Records (pop); "Castigo" (by Almafuerte/Cortez), recorded by Alberto Cortez on Philips Records(ballad); "El Sueno De La Gitana" (by W. Giardino), recorded by Rata Blanca on Vertigo Records (metal).

EDITION MUSICA, Webgasse 43, Vienna A-1060 **Austria**. Phone: (1)597-56-46. Publishing Manager: Manfred Blaschko. Music publisher and record company (OK-Musica). AKM. Estab. 1982. Works with composers and lyricists; teams collaborators.
How to Contact: Submit a demo tape by mail—unsolicited submissions are OK or call first and obtain permission to submit. Prefers cassette with 4-6 songs. Does not return unsolicited material. Reports in 4 weeks.
Music: Mostly rock, pop and dance.
Tips: "Send us a demo. If we have an artist for it we will release it."

EGGINK PUBLISHING, 150 5th Ave., New York NY 10011. (212)691-5630. General Manager: Abigail Storm. Music publisher. ASCAP. Estab. 1985. Works with composers and lyricists; teams collaborators. Pays standard royalty. Publishes 3 songs/year (1 new songwriter/year).
How to Contact: Submit a demo tape by mail—unsolicited submissions are O.K. Prefers cassette with 2 songs and lyric or lead sheets. SASE. Reports in 2 months.

*EKG MUSIC, P.O. Box 577, Waterloo Ontario N2J 4B8 Canada. (519)744-4350. President: Eric Gillespie. Music publisher, record producer. PROCAN. Estab. 1988. Publishes 20-30 songs/year; publishes 5 new songwriters/year. Works with composers and lyricists; teams collaborators. Pays standard royalty.
How to Contact: Submit a demo tape by mail—unsolicited submissions are OK. Prefers cassette (VHS videocassette if available) with 3 songs and lyric sheet. SASE. Reports in 4-6 weeks.
Music: Mostly rock and pop. Published "You Never Looked Back," "Say Hi" and "Flaunt It," all (by Syre), all recorded by EKG on A&M Records (rock).
Tips: "Please make sure all submissions are commercially accessible rock or pop, suited for radio airplay."

*ELEMENT MOVIE AND MUSIC, Box 30260, Bakersfield CA 93385. Producer: Jar the Superstar. Music publisher, record company and record producer. BMI. Publishes 2 songs/year; publishes 2 new songwriters/year. Hires staff writers. Pays standard royalty.
How to Contact: Write first about your interest or arrange personal interview. "Query with resume of credits. Do not mail songs without permission! We are taking interviews only." Prefers 15 ips reel-to-reel or cassette with 1-3 songs. Does not return unsolicited material. Reports in 3 months.
Music: Mostly R&B, rock, soul, gospel, jazz, progressive, easy listening and top 40/pop; also blues, children's, choral, church/religious, classical, country, dance-oriented, MOR, Spanish and music for feature films. Published "He's Only There for One Thing" (pop), and "The Way I Am" (funk), recorded on Element Records; "Build Up Your Character for Jesus" (church rock); and "Burning in the Lake of Fire" (Christian rock).

ELLYMAX MUSIC CO., 2555 East 12 St., Brooklyn NY 11235. Owner: Barry Bergman. BMI. Estab. 1985. Publishes 20 songs/year; publishes 2 new songwriters. Works with composers. Pays standard royalty; depends on level of writer. Hires staff writers. "We have 4 staff writers. Depends on level of writer and track record."
Affiliates: Wood Monkey Music (ASCAP).
How to Contact: Prefers cassette with 3 songs and lyric sheets. "We only report back to writers if we are interested." Does not return unsolicited material. Reports in 1 month. "We only accept artist and band tapes. We can no longer accept writer's tapes."

Music: Mostly rock, pop and R&B; also gospel. Published "Still in Love with You" (by Halligan/Bolton), recorded by Cher on Geffen Records (pop rock); "Don't Close Your Eyes" (by Halligan/Purnell), recorded by Kix on Atlantic (rock); and "Forever Eyes," recorded by Michael Bolton on Columbia Records.

Tips: "The song should be from the heart and the lyrics should create strong images. With the big publishing companys acquiring the smaller ones, it is making it easier for independent companies to do a better job for the writers. The writers are not getting lost with us as they are with the majors."

EMANDELL TUNES, 10220 Glade Ave., Chatsworth CA 91311. (818)341-2264. President/Administrator: Leroy C. Lovett Jr. Estab. 1979. Publishes 10-12 songs/year; 3-4 new songwriters. Pays standard royalty "twice a year."

Affiliates: Ben-Lee Music (BMI), Birthright Music (ASCAP), Northworth Songs (SESAC), Chinwah Songs, Gertrude Music (SESAC), LMS Print/Publishing Co. and Nadine Music International in Zurich, Switzerland.

How to Contact: Write first to get permission to submit tape. Prefers cassette (or videocassette) with 4-5 songs and lead or lyric sheet. Include information about writer, singer or group. SASE. Reports in 5-6 weeks.

Music: Inspirational, contemporary and traditional gospel and chorals. Published "High Places," (by Kevin Gaston); and "Surely Goodness and Mercy" (by Kevin Allen and Peppy Smith), both recorded by the Elect on WFL Records (urban contemporary); "Troubled Life" and "He Watches Over Me" (by Leonard Lothlen), recorded by "Infinity" on WFL Records (rock-gospel); "Use Me" and "Something Within" (by Earl W. Woods), recorded by Ricky Womack and New Age Singers on WFL Records. All above are SESAC selections.

Tips: "Submit high quality demos but keep it simple – no production extras."

*EMMELL MUSIC INC., 322 Kentish Town Rd., London NW5 2TH **England**. (01)482-5272. M.P.: Marilyn Levett. Music publisher, record company and record producer. PRS. Estab. 1979. Publishes over 20 songs/year; publishes more than 5 new songwriters/year. Teams collaborators.

How to Contact: Submit a demo tape by mail – unsolicited submissions are OK. Prefers cassette. SASE. Reports in 4 weeks.

Music: Mostly dance, pop and rock.

ESCHENBACH EDITIONS, 28 Dalrymple Crescent, Edinburgh EH9 2NX **Great Britain**. Phone: (031)667-3633. A&R Manager: James Douglas. Music publisher, record company (Caritas Records), record producer and video producer. PRS, MCPS, PPL. Estab. 1985. Publishes 60 songs/year; publishes 10-12 new songwriters/year. Works with composers and lyricists; teams collaborators. Pays negotiable royalty, 6½-12%.

How to Contact: Write first and obtain permission to submit. Prefers cassette, 7½ ips reel-to-reel (or VHS videocassette) with 6 songs and lyric or lead sheet. SAE and IRCs. Reports in 6 weeks.

Music: Mostly rock, jazz and pop; also folk, instrumental and "serious music." Published "Ice Breaker (by G. Johnstone), on Caritas Records; "Show Me" recorded by Jo Gilly (pop); "Full Circle" recorded by Jo Gilly (pop); and "Catridiag's Song" recorded by J. Douglas (instrumental); all on Caritas Records. Also instrumental library music required including ethnic library music.

Tips: "Aim for an international market."

*ESSEX MUSIC OF AUSTRALIA PTY. LTD., 5 Northcliff St., Milsons Point, Sydney NSW 2061 **Australia**. Phone: (02)9224100. Managing Director: Bruce Powell. Music publisher. APRA. Estab. 1957. Publishes 50 songs/year; publishes 2 new songwriters/year. Works with composers; teams collaborators. "Royalties are negotiable depending on prior success of composer."

Affiliates: Cromwell Music of Australia, Buckwood Music, Arwin Music, Essex Music of Australia (all APRA).

How to Contact: Submit a demo tape by mail – unsolicited submissions are OK. Prefers cassette with 3-4 songs and lyric sheet. Does not return unsolicited material. Reports in 3 weeks.

Music: Mostly pop, country and rock; also AOR. Published "Summer" (by Marc Hunter), recorded by Dragon on BMG Records (pop/rock); "Losing One" (by Wayne Gillespie), recorded by Wayne Gillespie on CBS Records (pop/rock); and "Along the Way" (by John Hanlon), recorded by John Hanlon on BMG Records (AOR).

Tips: "Listen to the radio and write with a commercial flair."

EVER-OPEN-EYE MUSIC, Wern Fawr Farm, Pencoed, MID, Glam CF356NB **United Kingdom**. Phone: (0656)860041. Managing Director: M.R. Blanche. Music publisher and record company (Red-Eye Records). PRS. Member PPL and MCPS. Estab. 1980. Publishes 6 songs/year. Works with composers and lyricists; teams collaborators. Pays negotiable amount.

How to Contact: Submit a demo tape —unsolicited submissions are OK. Prefers cassette (or VHS videocassette). SAE and IRC.
Music: Mostly R&B, gospel and pop; also swing. Published "Rumba Time" (by G. Williams), on Red Eye Records,(R&B); "For Ronnie", "Night Stick" (by S. Campbell), on Red Eye Records (R&B); "Night Trains" (by I. Yandell), on Red Eye Records (ballad).

EXPRESS MUSIC (LONDON) LTD., Yew Tree Studio, Charing Heath, Kent TN27 OAU **England**. President: Siggy Jackson. Music publisher, record company (Spectrum Records) and record producer (Siggy Jackson Productions, Ltd.). PRS, MRS, MCPS. Estab. 1967. Publishes 10 songs/year; publishes 2-3 new songwriters/year. Pays standard royalty.
Affiliate: Tempo Music Ltd.
How to Contact: Submit a demo tape — unsolicited submissions are OK. Prefers cassette (or videocassette) and lyric and lead sheet. SAE and IRC.
Music: Mostly country, rock, pop; also jazz. Published "I Can't Feel Feelings" (by Kelsey-Flick), recorded by Vic on Spectrum (pop); "Too Much" (by H. Joseph), recorded by Blue River on Bold Reprieve (reggae); and "Oh Judy" by the Firestone on Bold Reprieve (reggae).

*DOUG FAIELLA PUBLISHING, 16591 County Home Rd., Marysville OH 43040. (513)644-8295. President: Doug Faiella. Music publisher, record company (Studio 7 Records) and recording studio. BMI. Estab. 1984. Publishes 25 songs/year; publishes 5 new songwriters/year. Works with composers and teams collaborators. Pays standard royalty.
How to Contact: Write or call first and obtain permission to submit a tape. Prefers cassette with 3 songs and lyric sheets. Does not return unsolicited material. Reports in 4 weeks.
Music: Mostly country, gospel and rock.

F&J MUSIC. 23, Thrayle House, Stockwell Road, London SW9 0XU **England**. (01)274-9533 or (01)274-7996. Managing Director: Errol Jones.Music publisher and record company (Leopard Music/Jet Set International Records). PRS, BMI. Estab. 1978. Publishes 75 songs/year. Publishes 35 new songwriters/year. Works with composers and lyricists; teams collaborators. Pays standard royalty.
Affiliates : EURUSA Worldwide Publishing Affiliate (BMI).
How to Contact : Write first and obtain permission to submit. Prefers cassette (or VHS PAL videocassette) with 3 songs, lyric sheet and lead sheet. Include biography, resume and picture. SASE. Reports in 2 weeks.
Music : Mostly dance, soul and pop; also ballads, reggae and gospel. Published "Time After Time," (by Guy Spell), recorded by Rico J. on Leopard Music/Jet Set International Records (disco/soul); "I Need You," (by F. Campbell/E. North Jr.), recorded by Big Africa (soul/reggae); and "God is Beauty," written and recorded by Evelyn Ladimeji (gospel); both on Leopard Music.

*FEZSONGS, 252 Mennonite Rd., Collegeville PA 19426. (215)489-8810. President: Jim Femino. Music publisher, record company (Road Records) and record producer (Independent). ASCAP. Estab. 1970. Publishes 12-15 songs/year; publishes 1-2 new songwriters/year. Works with composers and lyricists; teams collaborators. Pays standard royalty. "Charges in advance for demo recording services, only if needed."
Affiliates: Fezsongs (ASCAP).
How to Contact: Submit a demo tape by mail—unsolicited submissions are OK. Prefers cassette (or VHS videocassette) with 3-4 songs and lyric sheet. Does not return unsolicited material. Reports in 6 weeks.
Music: Mostly rock, country and cross-over. Published "All I Want" (written and recorded by Jim Femino on Road Records (country); "Six O'Clock Rise" (by Femino, Bricklin, Bricklin and Meyer), recorded by Jim Femino on Road Records (rock).

FIRST MILLION MUSIC, INC., 50 Music Square West, #207, Nashville TN 37203. (615)329-2591. Vice President: Peggy Bradley. Music publisher. ASCAP. Estab. 1983. Publishes 4 songs/year; 2 new songwriters/year. Pays standard royalty.
Affiliates: Old Guide Music (BMI).
How to Contact: Submit a demo tape by mail—unsolicited submissions are OK. Prefers cassette with 3 songs and lyric sheet. SASE. Reports in 2 weeks.
Music: Mostly country, pop and R&B. Published "Love (by Ruddy), recorded by Jill Jordan on Maxx Records (country/uptempo); and "Jewel of the Mississippi" (by Lips Prat), recorded by Don Juan on Maxx Records (country/ballad).

FIRST TIME MUSIC (PUBLISHING) U.K. LTD., Sovereign House, 12 Trewartha Road, Praa Sands, Penzance, Cornwall TR20 9ST **England**. Phone: (0736)762826. FAX: (0736)763328. Managing Director: Roderick G. Jones. Music publisher, record company (First Time Records, licensed and subsidiary labels), record producer and management firm (First Time Management and Production Co.), and commissioned writers. PRS. Member of MCPS. Estab. 1986. Publishes 500-750 songs/year; 20-50 new songwriters/year. Hires staff writers. Works with composers and lyricists; teams collaborators. Pays standard royalty; "50-60% to established and up-and-coming writers with the right attitude."

Affiliates: Subsidiary and administered catalogues. Sub-publishing worldwide (new associations welcome).

How to Contact: Submit a demo tape—unsolicited submissions are OK. Prefers cassette, 1⅛ ips cassette (or VHS videocassette "of professional quality") with unlimited number of songs and lyric or lead sheets, but not necessary. Reports in 4-10 weeks. SASE in U.K.—SAE and IRC if outside U.K. "Postal costs in the U.K. are much higher than the U.S.—one IRC doesn't even cover the cost of a letter to the U.S., let alone the return of cassettes. Enclose the correct amount for return and contact as stated."

Music: Mostly country and folk, pop/soul/top 20/rock, country with an Irish/Scottish crossover; also gospel/Christian. Published "The Greenhills are Rolling Still" (by Charlie Landsborough), recorded by Dominic Kirwan on Ritz Records (country); "The Land That is Known As Wales" (by R. Cass and C. James), recorded by Sir Harry Secombe on Word Records (male voice choir); and "Jazz" (by D. Lockwood and R. Posey), recorded by Fader Master and The Beat on Digimix International Records (dance).

Tips: "Have a professional approach—present well produced demo's. First impressions are important and may be the only chance you get. Remember that you as a writer/artiste are in a competitive market. As an active independent -international publisher we require good writers/artistes and product. As a company we seek to work with writers who do and do not perform. If the product is good then we generally come up with something in the way of covers. Writers are advised to join the Society of International Songwriters and Composers in the United Kingdom."

FIVE ROSES PUBLISHING COMPANY, Twin Bridge Rd., Liberty NY 12754. (914)292-4042. President: Sammie Lee Marler. Music publisher. Consultant, management. BMI. Estab. 1989. Publishes 100 songs/year; 75 new songwriters/year. Works with composers and lyricists; teams collaborators. Pays standard royalty.

How to Contact: Submit a demo tape by mail—unsolicited submissions are OK. Prefers cassette with 5 songs. SASE. Reports in 2 weeks.

Music: Mostly country and western, bluegrass, country rock, country gospel, light pop, rhythm and blues, Christmas and novelty. Published "Takin' Part" by R. Geddes and S. Marler (C&W); "Cowboy and the Kid" by K. Dooley and S. Marler (C&W); and "Gone But Not Forgotten" by L. Levay and S. Marler (country crossover).

Tips: "We care about the songwriter and keep in personal contact with them. We are one happy family at Five Roses."

*FLANARY PUBLISHING CO., Box 371, La Mirada CA 90637-0371. (213)696-4941. Director of Submissions: Alicia Flanary. Music publisher. Estab. 1988. Hires staff writers for TV and film. Works with composers and lyricists; teams collaborators. Pays standard royalty or open to negotiation.

How to Contact: Submit a demo tape by mail—unsolicited submissions are OK. Prefers cassette with 3 songs and lyric or lead sheets. SASE, otherwise does not return unsolicited material.

Music: Mostly pop/rock and country.

FOCAL POINT MUSIC PUBLISHERS, 920 McArthur Blvd., Warner Robins GA 31093. (912)923-6533. Manager: Ray Melton. Music publisher and record company. BMI. Estab. 1964. Publishes 4 songs/year; publishes 1 new songwriter/year. Works with composers. Pays standard royalty. "Songwriters must have BMI affiliation."

How to Contact: Write first to get permission to send a tape. Prefers cassette with 2-4 songs and lead sheet. Prefers studio produced demos. SASE.

Music: Mostly country and gospel; also "old-style pop and humor". Published "Walk Away" (by Bill Arwood), recorded by Bill Arwood on Bob Grady Records (country); "Troubles" (by Kenny Arledge) recorded by Kenny Arledge on Club 45 (country); and "Band of Gold" by (Bill Arwood) recorded by Bill Arwood on Bob Grady Records (country).

*FOUR NEWTON PUBLISHING, Rt. 1 Box 187-A, Whitney TX 76692. (817)694-4047. President: Allen Newton. Music publisher, record company (Pristine Records, Pleasure Records, Cactus Flats, MFN). BMI. Estab. 1980. Publishes 10-12 songs/year; publishes about 10 new songwriters/year. Works with composers and lyricists; teams collaborators. Pays standard royalty.

How to Contact: Submit a demo tape by mail—unsolicited submissions are OK. Prefers cassette with 3 songs and lyric sheets. SASE. Reports in 3 weeks.

Music: Mostly country, rock and R&B; also pop, gospel and new age. Published "Cold Hearted Woman" (by Felix Van Slyke), recorded by Felix Van Slyke on Pleasure Records (coutry/western); "Concrete Queen" (by J. Jaramillo and Tony Rivera), recorded by Blessed Carrion on Pristine Records (rock); and "Styllin" (by Adre), recorded by Stylle on Pristine Records (R&R).

FOX FARM RECORDING, (formerly The Demo Farm), 2731 Saundersville Ferry Rd., Mt. Juliet TN 37122. (615)754-2444. President: Kent Fox. Music publisher and record producer and Demo Production Recording Studio. BMI, ASCAP. Publishes 20 songs/year; publishes 5 new songwriters/year. Works with composers and lyricists; teams collaborators. Pays standard royalty.
Affiliates: Blueford Music (ASCAP) and Mercantile Music (BMI).
How to Contact: SASE. Prefers cassette with 4 songs and lyric sheet. Reports in 1 month.
Music: Country, bluegrass and gospel.
Tips: "If your song is good enough to become a hit its worth, investing money for a good demo: drums, bass, guitar, keyboard, fiddle, sax, vocals etc."

FOXWORTHY MUSIC, 4002 Liggatt Dr., San Diego CA 92106. (619)226-4152. Vice President: Dottye Foxworthy. Music publisher, record company (Foxworthy Records) and record producer (Foxworthy Productions). BMI. Estab. 1982. Publishes 20 songs/year; publishes 1 new songwriter/year. Teams collaborators. Pays standard royalty.
Affiliates: Foxworthy Music (BMI), Expanding Universe Music (BMI).
How to Contact: Submit a demo tape by mail—unsolicited submissions are O.K. Prefers cassette with 3 songs and lyric or lead sheets. Does not return unsolicited material. Reports in 4 weeks.
Music: Mostly pop, rock and R&B; also rap and new age. Published "Black and White", "Mixed Emotions" and "CA" (by Mike Redmond), recorded by Street Poet Ray on Foxworthy (rap).

FRADALE SONGS, P.O. Box 121015, Nashville TN 37212. Professional Manager: David Leone. BMI. Estab. 1981. Publishes 5 songs/year; publishes 1 new songwriter/year. Pays standard royalty.
Affiliate: Reesha Music (BMI).
How to Contact: Unsolicited submissions are not OK. Does not return unsolicited material. "We strongly suggest that developing writers contact us about critiquing their material—much of successful writing can be learned and Fradale offers workshops and correspondence courses for talented writers."
Music: Country and gospel. Published "My Heartache is Here To Stay" (by R. ALscomb), recorded by Pending (country); "Open to Your Love" (by R. Field), recorded by Cheri Lynn on Classic Records (country/pop); and "Red Beans and Rice," written and recorded by B. Slater on Classic Records (country).

*FRETBOARD PUBLISHING, Box 40013, Nashville TN 37204. (615)292-2047. Contact: A&R Department. Music publisher, record company (Mosrite Records), record producer (Mark Moseley). BMI. Estab. 1963. Publishes 25 songs/year; publishes 3 new songwriters/year. Works with composers and lyricists. Pays standard royalty.
Affiliates: Woodgrain Publishing Co. (ASCAP).
How to Contact: Submit a demo tape by mail. Prefers cassette with 2 songs and lyric sheets. Does not return unsolicited material. Reports in 6 weeks "only if we want to hear more."
Music: Mostly country, rock (not heavy), southern gospel. Published "Even Now" (by Mark Moseley), recorded by Marie Lester (country); "Mommies Playing Santa Claus" (by Maurice Brandon), recorded by Marie Lester (Christmas); and "Queen For a Day" (by Billy Mize), recorded by Barbara Mandrell (country); all on Mosrite Records.
Tips: "Give us time to get to your songs before you make another contact."

FRICK MUSIC PUBLISHING CO., 404 Bluegrass Ave., Madison TN 37115. (615)865-6380. Contact: Bob Frick. Music publisher, record company and record producer. BMI. Publishes 50 songs/year; publishes 2 new songwriters/year. Works with lyricists. Pays standard royalty.
How to Contact: Call first. Prefers 7½ ips reel-to-reel or cassette (or videocassette) with 2-10 songs and lyric sheet. SASE. Reports in 1 month.
Music: Mostly gospel; also country, rock and top 40/pop. Published "Follow Where He Leads" by Christine Starling; "I Found Jesus in Nashville" by Lin Butler; and "I Held Up My Hands" by Frank Conrad; all recorded by Bob Scott Frick on R. Records (gospel).

FYDAQ MUSIC, 240 E. Radcliffe Dr., Claremont CA 91711. (714)624-0677. President: Gary Buckley. Music publisher, record company (Majega Records), record producer and production company. Estab. 1970. BMI. Member ACM, CMA, GMA, NARAS, Audio Engineering. Publishes 30-40 songs/year; publishes 10-20 new songwriters/year. Pays standard royalty.

Affiliate: Jubilation Music (BMI).
How to Contact: Write first; "we'll provide information on our current material needs." Prefers cassette (or VHS videocassette) with 1-3 songs and lead or lyric sheet. SASE. Reports in 3 weeks.
Music: Country, country/pop crossover, easy listening, MOR, rock (country) and top 40/pop. Published "My Only Love" (by T. DeSanto and G. Buckley), recorded by Dusk on Fubar Records (pop); "Used to Be's (Ain't What They Used To Be)" (by S. Brinton), recorded by Will Moore on Fairlane 500 Records (pop).
Tips: "The writer needs to work and refine the song before submitting it. Once completed, a clear single instrumental and vocal demo is more than adequate. Too many submissions are good ideas, but not refined or completed."

*GALAXIA MUSICAL S.A. De C.V., Leibnitz 130, Mexico, D.F. 11590. (905)511-6684. Managing Director: Arq. Jose G. Cruz. Music publisher. SACM. Pays standard royalty.
How to Contact: Write first and obtain permission to submit. "Will only accept submissions from writers who are familiar with type of music currently being produced in Mexico and Spanish speaking territories." Prefers cassette (or VHS videocassette) with 1-5 songs. SAE and IRC. Reports in 2 weeks.
Music: Pop ballads and rock.
Tips: "A well-prepared demo signals good craftmanship."

*GALLO MUSIC PUBLISHERS, A Division of Gallo Africa (PTY) Ltd., P.O. Box 6216, Johannesburg 2000 **South Africa**. Phone: (011)788-0400. Managing Director: Geoff Paynter. Music publisher and record company (Gallo Record Co., Teal Trutone Records and RPM Records.) SAMRO. Estab. 1920. Publishes 500-1,000 songs/year; publishes 10-20 new songwriters/year. Works with composers; teams collaborators. Pays negotiable percentage.
Affiliates: Music Publishing Co. of Africa (SAMRO), Laetrec Music (SAMRO) and Clan Music (SAMRO).
How to Contact: Submit a demo tape by mail—unsolicited submissions are OK. Prefers cassette (PAL 625 videocassette) with 4-6 songs and lyric sheet. "We do not return unsolicited material, but will contact if interested." Reports in 1 month.
Music: Mostly pop, R&B and rock; also country and gospel. Published "Rain Rain Beautiful Rain" (by J. Shabalala), recorded by Ladysmith Black Mambazo on WB Records (A Capella trad.); "Passengers" (Co-Pub) (by E. John/P.Mkhize), recorded by Elton John on Polygram Records (pop); and "Homeless" (Co-Pub) (by Simon/Shabalala), recorded by Paul Simon on WB Records (pop).
Tips: "Be original and concentrate on strong chorus melodies. Also looking for co-composers to work on African originated works (as with Paul Simon on Graceland)."

GEIMSTEINN HF, Skolaveg 12, Keflavik 230 **Iceland**. Phone: 354-2-12717. Manager: Runar Juliusson. Music publisher, record company and record producer. STEF-FTT-GEMA. Estab. 1976. Publishes 1-20 songs/year; publishes 1-10 new songwriters/year. Works with composers and lyricists; teams collaborators. Pays standard royalty (Europe standards).
How to Contact: Submit a demo tape—unsolicited submissions are OK. Write or call first to arrange personal interview. Prefers cassette (or VHS videocassette) with 2-3 songs and lyric sheet. Does not return unsolicited material.
Music: Mostly pop, rock and country; also R&B, jazz and gospel. Published: "Litla Lina," written and recorded by Bjorn Thoroddsen (jazz); "All That I Wanna Do" (by Gp Mk. RJ), recorded by Rúnar Juliuss (pop); "Where" written and recorded by Thor B (MOR); all on Geimsteinn Records.

*LARRY GENE MUSIC, 435 Main St., Johnson City NY 13790. (607)729-2291. Owners: Larry Lupole and Mike English. Music publisher, record company (Ice Records, Inc.) and record producer (Larry Lupole, Ice Records, Inc.). BMI. Estab. 1980. Publishes 2-3 songs/year; publishes 1-2 new songwriters/year. Hires staff writers. Teams collaborators. Pays standard royalty.
How to Contact: Write first and obtain permission to submit. Prefers cassette with 5 songs and lead sheet. SASE. Reports in 2 months.
Music: Mostly pop, rock and country; also R&B, gospel and new age. Published "Classic Fantasy" and "My Love," written and recorded by Larry Lupole; and "Zero Gravity," "Gardens in Orbit," and "Deep Space," written and recorded by David Sweet, all on Ice Records (all rock).

GENETIC MUSIC PUBLISHING, 10 Church Rd., Merchantville NJ 08109. (609)662-4428. Contact: Whey Cooler or Jade Starling. Music publisher, record company (Svengali) and record producer (Whey Cooler Production). ASCAP. Estab. 1982. Publishes 5-10 songs/year; publishes 4 new songwriters/year. Works with composers, lyricists; teams collaborators. Pays standard royalty.

How to Contact: Write or call first and obtain permission to submit a tape. Prefers cassette or VHS videocassette with songs. SASE. Reports in 2 weeks.

Music: Mostly dance, R&B and pop; also rock and jazz. Published "Catch Me I'm Falling", "Nightime" and "When I Look Into U'r Eyes" (by Starling/Cooler), recorded by Pretty Poison on Virgin (dance pop).

Tips: "Just submit it, if we think we can place it we'll hold it on file and submit it to projects as they arise. Should a song be chosen for a given project, we'll then publish the song."

*GET A HIT PUBLISHING, 13611 Chancellor Blvd., Port Charlotte FL 33952. (813)627-9047. President: Alice Jankowski. Music publisher. BMI. Estab. 1989. Publishes 1-2 songs/year; publishes 1-2 new songwriters/year. Pays standard royalty.

How to Contact: Submit a demo tape by mail—unsolicited submissions are OK. Prefers cassette with 2-3 songs and lyric sheets. SASE. Reports in 3 weeks.

Music: Mostly C/W and gospel. Published "What's This Place Like Called Heaven?" (by A. Jankowski), recorded by Heather Lee on Palm Records (C/W).

Tips: "Good, clean professional demos—no kitchen demos."

GIBSON DAVIDSONG PUBLISHING, Box 1150-SM91, Buna TX 77612. (409)423-2521. Owner/Manager: James Gibson. Music publisher. ASCAP. Estab. 1985. Publishes 5-10 songs/year; publishes 2-3 new songwriters/year. Works with composers, lyricists; teams collaborators. Pays standard royalty.

Affiliate: Rushwin Publishing (BMI) and Rushwin Productions.

How to Contact: Prefers cassette with 1-4 songs and typed lyric sheet. "Clearly label each item sent." SASE (6x9 or larger). Reports ASAP.

Music: Southern/country gospel. Published "Running Back to You," (by Eva Bonn/Nancy Cyril), recorded by The Harbingers on Gold Street Records; and "I Am the Life," written and recorded by David Bush on Custom Records (both gospel).

Tip: "We are interested in material suited for the recording artists that appear on the music charts published by *The Gospel Voice* and *The Singing News.*"

*GIFTNESS ENTERPRISE, 3542 Garfield Way SE, Atlanta GA 30354. (404)642-2645. Contact: New Song Department. Music publisher. BMI. Publishes 30 songs/year; publishes 15 new songwriters/year. Employs songwriters on a salary basis. Works with composers and lyricsts; teams collaborators. Pays standard royalty.

Affiliate: Hserf Music (ASCAP).

How to Contact: Prefers cassette with 4 songs and lyric or lead sheet. SASE. Reports in 3 weeks.

Music: Mostly R&B, pop and rock; also country, gospel and jazz. Published "Vicious Rap," written and recorded by Eze T on Northwest Records (dance); "Only in America" (by E. Lyons), recorded by Mojo on Gold Key Records (dance); and "You're So Fine," written and recorded by Cirocco on Geffen Records (R&B).

*GIL CON MUSIC, P.O. Box 57, La Grange IL 60525. (708)759-4271. President: Cornell Ward. Music publisher, record producer and arranger. BMI. Estab. 1983. Publishes 8-20 songs/year; publishes 1-2 new songwriters/year. Works with composers and lyricists; teams collaborators. Pays standard royalty. "Does not charge for services to produce demo of songs published."

Affiliates: Gil Con Music—(BMI).

How to Contact: Submit a demo tape by mail—unsolicited submissions are OK. Prefers cassette (or VHS videocassette if available) with 3-5 song, lyric sheet and lead sheet if available. "Absolutely *no phone calls*!! Will contact if interested. SASE. Reports in 1 month.

Music: Mostly pop, top 40, R&B, easy listening, country, MOR and soft rock; also New Age vocal only, gospel and rap. Published "Thought of You A Little Too Much" (by C. Ward, A. Miller, N. Corrington, O. Laville) and "No Win Situation" (by C. Ward, A. Miller), both recorded by The Dells on King Records-Japan and Veteran Records-USA (R&B/pop); and "Your Sweetness" (by C. Ward, A. Miller), recorded by Willie Clayton on Timeless Records-England (R&B/pop).

Tips: "Submit your best! Let your songs be your calling card. Rewrite, rewrite, rewrite . . . until the song tells a convincing story . . . until you actually believe someone can live the story . . . paint a picture with words."

*GIL-GAD MUSIC, 6015 Troost, Kansas City MO 64110. (816)361-8455. General Manager/Publisher: Eugene Gold. ASCAP, BMI. Estab. 1969. Music publisher and record producer. Publishes 30 or more songs/year; publishes 10 or more new songwriters/year. Teams collaborators. Pays standard royalty.

Affiliates: 3G's Music Co., Eugene Gold Music.
How to Contact: Prefers cassette (or videocassette) with 4-6 songs and lyric sheet. SASE. Reports in 2 months.
Music: Mostly R&B, rock and top 40 pop; also disco/dance, gospel and jazz. Published "Magic," (by Cal-Green, Ronnie & Vicky), recorded by Suspension on 3G's (R&B/top pop); "Bootie Cutie," written and recorded by Robert Newsome on 3G's (R&B); and "Diamond Feather," (by M. Murf), recorded by Bad News Band on NMI (R&B).

*GIZZARD, 265 W. 37th St., New York NY 10018. (212)704-9626. Publishing Director: Andrew Lasseter. Music publisher, record producer (Calliope Productions). ASCAP. Estab. 1985. Pubilshes 100 songs/year; publishes 10 new songwriters/year. Hires staff songwriters. Works with composers and lyricists; teams collaborators. Fee derived from percentage of publishing.
Affiliates: Calliope Productions.
How to Contact: Write or call first and obtain permission to submit a tape. Prefers cassette (or ½" VHS or ¾" videocassette if available) with up to 4 songs and lyric sheet. SASE. Reports in 6 weeks.
Music: Mostly rock, pop and R&B; also hip-hop, New Jack swing and house.
Tips: "Quality of demos getting better—needs to sound like a complete production."

*GLOBEART PUBLISHING, A Division of GlobeArt Inc., Suite 21F, 1755 York Ave., New York NY 10028. (212)860-3023. President: Jane Peterer. Music publisher. BMI, ASCAP. Estab. 1989. Publishes 30 songs/year; publishes 2 new songwriters/year. Works with composers and lyricists. Pays standard royalty.
Affiliates: GlobeSound Publishing (ASCAP).
How to Contact: Submit a demo tape by mail—unsolicited submissions are OK. Prefers cassette (or videocassette) with 3-5 songs and lyric or lead sheet. SASE. Reports in 6 weeks.
Music: Mostly pop/R&B, jazz and gospel; also new age and country. Published "Jamaica" (by Muralidhar), recorded by Muralidhar on AJ Records (pop); "Beautiful Morning" (by Herbert Rehbein and his Orchestra) on Pick Records (MOR); and "I Don't Want to Loose" (by M.L. Bryant), recorded by Muralidhar on AJ Records (pop).

*GO STAR MUSIC, 3345 Hollins Ferry Rd., Baltimore MD 21227. (301)247-7447. Owner: William E. Baker. Music publisher, record company (Go Records) and record producer (International Music). Estab. 1988. Publishes 100 songs/year; 50 new songwriters/year. Pays standard royalty.
Affiliates: Billy Baker and Associates, Go Records, Infinity Productions and Independent International Music Associates.
How to Contact: Write or call for an interview. Prefers cassette and lyric or lead sheet. SASE. Reports in 3 weeks.
Music: Mostly rock, pop, country, R&B, New Age and gospel.

S.M. GOLD MUSIC, INC., % Turney and Gold Artists, Inc., Suite 202, 246 Fifth Ave., New York NY 10001. President: Steven M. Gold. Music publisher and jingle/TV score producer. ASCAP. Publishes 10 songs/year; publishes 3 new songwriters/year. Hires staff writers. "We employ freelance and staff songwriters who are well-versed in all styles of popular music." Pays standard royalty or cash advance (buy-out).
How to Contact: Prefers cassette with 1 song. Does not return unsolicited material. No calls please.
Music: Mainstream pop, R&B and dance/pop.
Tips: "We're not looking for 'album tracks' or 'B sides.' Hits only!"

GORDON MUSIC CO., INC., P.O. Box 2250, Canoga Park CA 91306. (818)883-8224. Owner: Jeff Gordon. Music publisher, record company (Paris Records). ASCAP/BMI. Estab. 1950. Publishes 10-20 songs/year. Works with composers and lyricists; teams collaborators. Pays standard royalty or arrangements of many kinds can be made between author and publisher.
Affiliates: Marlen Music (ASCAP), Sunshine Music (BMI).
How to Contact: Call first and obtain permission to submit a tape or to arrange a personal interview. Prefers cassette or VHS videocassette with 3-4 songs and lyric or lead sheets. Does not return unsolicited material.
Music: Mostly pop, children's and rock; also jazz. Published "New Leave It to Beaver Theme" (by D. Kahn, M. Lenard and M. Greene), recorded by Cabo Frio on MCA Records (jazz); "Jump Bop" and "Big Town" (by T. Lloyd and T. Mockler), recorded by Failsafe on Paris Records (pop-children's).

RICHARD E. GOWELL MUSIC, 45 7th St., Auburn ME 04210. (207)784-7975. Professional Manager: Rich Gowell. Music publisher and record company (Allagash Country Records/Allagash R&B Records/Gowell Records). BMI. Estab. 1978. Publishes 10-30 songs/year; 5-10 new songwriters/year. Works with composers and lyricists. Pays standard royalty.

How to Contact: Submit a demo tape by mail—unsolicited submissions are OK. Prefers cassette with 2-4 songs and lyric sheets. SASE. Reports in 2 months.

Music: Mostly country, pop and R&B. Published "It'll Be a Cold Day" (by L/ Pritchett, R. Sanders), recorded by Ray Sanders on Allagash Country (country); "Workin' Overtime" (by R.E. Gowell), recorded by Phil Coley on Allagash Country Records (country); and "You Know I Have to Have Your Love" (by W. Stevenson), recorded by Tina Meeks on Allagash R&B Records (R&B).

Tips: "Have a great song with a professional demo and keep plugging to the right people."

GRACENOTE MUSIC PUBLISHING COMPANY, INC., Suite 3G, 225 St. Paul's Ave., Jersey City NJ 07306. (201)714-9533. Professional Manager: Isaac Jeret. Music publisher. BMI, ASCAP, SESAC. Estab. 1987. Publishes 20-30 songs/year; publishes 5 new songwriters/year. Hires staff writers. Works with composers and lyricists; "we specialize in teaming collaborators." Pays standard royalty.

Affiliates: Little Gracenote (BMI); Lonely Gracenote (SESAC); and Lingering Gracenote (ASCAP).

How to Contact: Write or call first for permission to submit. Prefers cassette with a maximum of 3 songs and lyric sheet. SASE. Reports in 6-8 weeks.

Music: Mostly country—all types; also R&B/dance, pop/top 40 and rock.

Tips: "Call before submitting for personalized advice. We help songwriters, but only those who work diligently at their craft and have natural ability."

GRADUATE MUSIC LTD., 12, Sansome Pl., Worcester WR1 1UA **United Kingdom**. Phone: (0905)20882. Managing Director: David Virr. Music publisher and record company (Graduate Records Ltd.). PRS and MCPS. Estab. 1980. Publishes approx. 25 songs/year; 2 new songwriters/year. Works with composers and lyricists. Pays standard royalty.

How to Contact: Submit a demo tape by mail—unsolicited submissions are OK. Prefers cassette (or VHS videocassette) with 3 songs. SASE. Reports in 2 weeks.

Music: Mostly rock, pop and new age; also country and anything original. Published "Heartache Avenue" (by Tibenham/Mason), recorded by The Maisonettes on Ready, Steady, Go! Records (60's pop); "Who Is Innocent" (by George Borowski), recorded by Guitar George on Graduate Records (rock); and "The Earth Dies Screaming," by UB40 on Graduate Records (reggae).

*JODY GRENIER WORDS & MUSIC LTD., 600 Bear Street E., Syracuse NY 13208. (315)428-9730. President: Jody Grenier. Music publisher. BMI. Estab. 1990. Publishes 15-30 songs/year; 3 new songwriters. Works with composers and lyricists; teams collaborators. Pays standard 50% royalty.

How to Contact: Write or call first and obtain permission to submit a tape. Prefers cassette cassette (or VHS videocassette if available) with 1-5 songs and lyric sheet and "lead sheets if available." Reports in 2-4 weeks.

Music: Mostly Top 40, rock ballads, jazz ballads, country; also dance, swing and MOR. Published "Dance New York Away" (jazz ballad) and "Hush My Baby" (swing) written and recorded by M. Grenier and J. Grenier and "The Only Thing Missing is You" (rock ballad) written and recorded by J. Grenier and M. Grenier.

Tips: "I am very dedicated to songwriters and great songs whatever style. Please, before you send any song to anybody copyright it now. Then I'll do my very best to find your song a home to grow. I believe the days of the dime store songwriter is over, no more hiding behind a producer. They have beendominating the charts for the past 3 years. The world needs expert lyric writing, such as that of Taupin, Henley, Joel. And the melodies of Gershwin, Wonder, McCartney. Let your imagination take you to worlds never explored by any other writer."

FRANK GUBALA MUSIC, Hillside Rd., Cumberland RI 02864. (401)333-6097. Contact: Frank Gubala. Music publisher and booking agency.

How to Contact: Prefers cassette and lead sheet. Does not return unsolicited material. Reports in 3 months.

Music: Blues, disco, easy listening, MOR, top 40/pop, rock and country.

HAMMER MUSIK GMBH, Christophstr. 38, 7000 Stuttgart 1, **West Germany**. Phone: (0711)6487620-27; FAX: (0711)6487629. Manager: Ingo Kleinhammer. GEMA. Estab. 1982. Music publisher and record company (Avenue and Boulevard). Publishes 100 songs/year; publishes 5 new songwriters/year. Works with composers and lyricists; teams collaborators. Pays standard royalty.

Affiliates: Belmont, Vertex, Sound of the Future and Music Avenue, Westside.

How to Contact: Submit a demo tape—unsolicited submissions are OK. Prefers cassette or VHS videocassette. SAE and IRC.

Music: Mostly dance and disco; also jazz, rock and pop. Published "Perfect," written and recorded by Boys from Brazil on Ariola Records (disco); and "Passion and Pain" (by A. Henningo), recorded by Deborah Sasson on Eighty Eight Records (pop).

MARK HANNAH MUSIC GROUP, 1075 NW Murray Road, Suite 250, Portland OR 97229. (503)642-4201. Owner: Mark Hannah. Music publisher, record company (Radioactive Records), record producer (Mark Hannah Productions) and Mark Hannah Management/Personal Management. BMI. Estab. 1988. Publishes 5-10 songs/year; publishes 1-3 new songwriters/year. Works with composers and lyricists; team collaborators. Pays standard royalty.
How to Contact: Write first and obtain permission to submit a tape. Prefers cassette or 15 ips reel-to-reel (or VHS videocassette) with 1-3 songs and lyric or lead sheets. "The more professional the package and presentation, the better." SASE. Reports in 1 month.
Music: Mostly rock, pop and country; also fusion, new age and jazz. Published "You Stole My Heart Away" (by P. Witt), recorded by P. Witt (pop/rock single); "Forced to Have Sex with an Alien" (by M. Harrop), recorded by M. Harrop (comedy single); and "Desert Moon" (by M. Hannah), recorded by M. Hannah (new age lp). All on Radioactive.

HAPPY DAY MUSIC CO., Box 602, Kennett MO 63857. President: Joe Keene. BMI. Publishes 12-20 songs/year; publishes 3-4 new songwriters/year. Pays standard royalty.
Affiliate: Lincoln Road Music (BMI).
How to Contact: Prefers reel-to-reel or cassette and lead sheet. SASE. Reports in 2 weeks.
Music: Gospel and religious. Published "I'm Going Up," recorded by the Inspirations (gospel); "Glory Bound," recorded by the Lewis Family (gospel); and "Keep Holding On" (by Jans Johnson/Joe Keene) on Cone Records.

*HAPPY HOUR MUSIC, 5206 Benito St., Montclair CA 91763. (714)621-9903. FAX: (714)621-2412. President: Judith M. Wahnon. Music publisher and record company (Happy Hour Music). BMI. Estab. 1985. Publishes 5 songs/year; publishes 3 new songwriters/year. Works with composers.
How to Contact: Write first and obtain permission to submit a tape. Prefers cassette. SASE. Reports in 3 weeks.
Music: Mostly jazz and Brazilian contemporary. Published "The New Lambadas" (by Loão Parahyba); "Alemão Bem Brasileiro" (by Olmir Stocker); and "Hermeto Pascoal Egrupo" (by Hermeto Pascoal), all on Happy Hour Records (Brazilian).

*HAPPY NOTE MUSIC, Box 12444, Fresno CA 93777-2444. (209)266-8066. Owners: Robby Roberson and Karla Farrar. Music publisher. BMI. Publishes 60 songs/year; publishes 20 new songwriters/year. Hires staff songwriters. Works with composers. Pays standard royalty.
How to Contact: Prefers cassette with 3 songs and lyric sheet. "Vocals must be clear." SASE. Reports in 6 weeks.
Music: Mostly country, pop and gospel. Published *There* (by A. Sanifar), recorded by Oh Lamour on Top Secret Records (dance LP); *Angel's Face* (by N. Holley/R. Roberson) and *Walkin* (by Richard Laws/Steve Frye), both recorded by Nick Holley on Lana Records (pop LPs).

*HARRIS-RICHARDSON MUSIC GROUP, 1107 17th Av. S., Nashville TN 37212. (615)329-0603. Creative Director: Rob Henson. Music publisher. ASCAP, BMI, SESAC. Estab. 1987. Publishes 100-150 songs/year. Hires staff writers; "currently have 4 on staff." Works with composers and lyricists; teams collaborators. Pays standard royalty.
Affiliates: Ha-Deb Music (ASCAP), Debarris Music (BMI), J-Deb Music (SESAC), Rice & Rice Music (ASCAP), Shobi Music (BMI), Swallowfork Music (ASCAP), Dunegrass Music (ASCAP), Glass Horse Music (SESAC), Allapattah Music (SESAC).
How to Contact: Submit a demo tape by mail—unsolicited submissions are OK. Prefers cassette with 2 songs and lyric sheets. "Will contact writer if we have interest." Does not return unsolicited material.
Music: Mostly country; also pop, R&B and gospel. Published "What's Going On In Your World" (by Royce Porter and David Chamberlain), recorded by George Strait on MCA Records; "Out of Your Shoes" (by Patti Ryan, Jill Wood, Sharon Spivey), recorded by Lorrie Morgan on RCA Records; and "High Cotton" (by Roger Murrah and Scott Anders), recorded by Alabama on RCA Records; all country.
Tips: "If it's not the best song you've got, don't send it."

HEAVEN SONGS, C-300, 16776 Lakeshore Dr., Lake Elsinore CA 92330. Contact: Dave Paton. Music publisher, record company and record producer. BMI. Publishes 30-50 songs/year; publishes 10 new songwriters/year. Pays standard royalty.
How to Contact: Prefers 7½ ips reel-to-reel or cassette with 3-6 songs and lyric sheet. SASE. Reports in 2 weeks.
Music: Country, dance-oriented, easy listening, folk, jazz, MOR, progressive, R&B, rock, soul and top 40/pop.
Tips: Looking for "better quality demos."

HEAVY JAMIN' MUSIC, Box 4740, Nashville TN 37216. (615)865-4740. Manager: S.D. Neal. Music publisher. BMI, ASCAP. Estab. 1970. Publishes 10 songs/year; publishes 4-10 new songwriters/year. Works with composers. Pays standard royalty.
Affiliates: Sus-Den (ASCAP) and Valynn (BMI).
How to Contact: Submit a demo tape—unsolicited submissions are OK. Prefers 7½ ips reel-to-reel or cassette (or VHS videocassette) with 2-6 songs and lyric sheet. SASE. Reports in 3 weeks.
Music: Mostly rock and country; also bluegrass, blues, easy listening, folk, gospel, jazz, MOR, progressive, Spanish, R&B, soul, top 40/pop and rock-a-billy. Published "Bright Lights" (by D. Derwald), recorded by Dixie Dee on Terock Records (rock-a-billy); "Home Again" (by L. Lynde), recorded by Linda Lynn on Terock Records (country); and "Lonesome and Blue" (by W. Curtiss), recorded by Wade Curtiss on Lee Records (R&B).

JAMES HENDRIX, COMPOSER AND PUBLISHER, Box 90639, Nashville TN 37209. (615)321-3319. Music publisher and record company. Estab. 1940. Publishes 30 songs/year; publishes 6 new songwriters/year. Works with composers. Pays standard royalty.
Affiliates: Mester Music, Jimerlean Music (BMI), and Carrie Records Co.
How to Contact: Submit a demo tape—unsolicited submissions O.K. Prefers cassette (or videocassette) with 3-4 songs and lyric sheet. SASE. Reports in one month.
Music: Church/religious, gospel, hymns and anthems. "What Blood Is This" (by Mrs. B. Lawrence/Lois Giles) (Gospel); "Everyday, Praise The Lord" (by Robt. Shackleford), recorded by The Family (Gospel); and "From Here To Eternity" (by J. Aiken), recorded by Rev. Jerry Aiken C#1600 Records (Gospel).
Tips: "Place a greater emphasis on the value of wards or message directive and try to create that melodic line that will adequately enhance the message."

HEUPFERD MUSIK VERLAG GmbH, Box 30 11 28, Ringwaldstr. 18, Dreieich D-6072 **West Germany**. Phone: (06103)86970. General Manager: Christian Winkelmann. Music publisher. GEMA. Publishes 60-100 songs/year; publishes 2-3 new songwriters/year. Works with composers and lyricists. Pays "royalties after GEMA distribution plan."
Affiliates: Edition Payador (GEMA) and Song Bücherei (book series).
How to Contact: Write first and obtain permission to submit. Prefers cassette and lead sheet. SAE and IRC. Reports in 1 month.
Music: Mostly folk, jazz, fusion; also new age, rock and ethnic music. Published "Fantasia Y Conografica" (by Wolfgang Stute), recorded by Tierra on Castor Records (ibero song); "Valse Mélancolique," written and recorded by Rüdiger Oppermann on Wuntertüte Records (new age); and "A Different Kind of Lovesong" (by Dick Gaughan), recorded by Dick Gaughan and others on Folk Freak Records (folk song).

HICKORY VALLEY MUSIC, 10303 Hickory Valley, Ft. Wayne IN 46835. President: Allan Straten. Music publisher, record company (Yellow-Jacket Records) and record producer (Al Straten Productions). ASCAP. Estab. 1988. Publishes 5 songs/year; publishes 2 new songwriters/year. Works with composers and lyricists; teams collabotators. Pays standard royalty.
How to Contact: Submit a demo tape by mail—unsolicited submissions are O.K. Prefers cassette with 3-4 songs and lyric sheets. SASE. Reports in 4 weeks.
Music: Mostly country and MOR. "Countin' Down to Love" (by April), recorded by April on Yellow-Jacket Records (country); and "Call Me Each Evening" (by Grogg Straten), recorded by April on Yellow-Jacket Records (country).
Tips: "Accept suggestions and be prepared to rewrite."

*HICKY'S MUSIC BMI, 2540 Woodburn Ave., Cincinnati OH 45206. (513)681-5436 or 559-3999. A&R Director: Smiley Hicks. Music publisher. BMI. Estab. 1985. Publishes 8 songs/year; publishes 4 new songwriters/year. Works with composers and lyricists; teams collaborators. Pays royalty.
How to Contact: Write first to get permission to submit a tape. Prefers cassette with 4 songs and lyric sheets. No porno or dirty lyrics, please. SASE. Reports in 4 weeks.
Music: Mostly R&B, gospel and danceable pop; also rap. Published "Stingy" (by Wavier, Hickland), recorded on Vibe Records (dance); and "Heartbeat" (by Barber, Hickland), recorded on Vibe Records (dance).
Tips: "Keep it clean."

*HIGH DESERT MUSIC CO/BMI, 29512 Peoria Rd., Halsey OR 97348-9742. (503)491-3524. A/R: Karl V. Black. Music publisher, record company (Awsome Record). BMI. Estab. 1976. Publishes 20 songs/year. Works with composers and lyricists; teams collaborators. Pays standard royalty.

Affiliates: High Desert Music Co—BMI.
How to Contact: Submit a demo tape by mail—unsolicited submissions are OK. Prefers cassette with 1 song and lyric sheet. "Be sure name is on everything submitted." Does not return unsolicited material.
Music: Mostly holiday music; also gospel. "Xmas in Heaven" (by T.D. Bayless), "High Desert Lullaby" (by Don McHan) and "We Know How Love Should Be" (by Higginbotham) all recorded by Higginbotham on Awsome Records (MOR).

*HIGH-MINDED MOMA PUBLISHING & PRODUCTIONS, Empire Ranch, 2329 Empire Grade, Santa Cruz CA 95060. (408)427-1248. Contact: Kai Moore Snyder. Music publisher and production company. BMI. Pays standard royalty.
How to Contact: Prefers 7½ ips reel-to-reel or cassette with 4-8 songs and lyric sheet. SASE. Reports in 1 month.
Music: Country, MOR, rock (country) and top 40/pop.
Tips: "We have just started to accept outside material."

HISTORY PUBLISHING CO., Box 7-11, Macks Creek MO 65786. (314)363-5432. President: B.J. Carnahan. Music publisher, record company (BOC, History) and record producer (AudioLoft Recording Studios). BMI. Estab. 1977. Publishes 10-15 songs/year; 2 new songwriters/year. Works with composer and lyricists. Pays standard royalty.
How to Contact: Write first and obtain permission to submit a tape. Prefers cassette with 2 songs and lyric sheets. "We prefer not to keep songs on file. Send a good, clean demo with vocal up front." SASE. Reports in 1 month.
Music: Mostly country and gospel. Published "Big Texas Waltz" (by G. Terry), recorded by Merle Haggard on Curb Records (country); "Remember the Alimony" (by J.B. Haynes), recorded by Bill and Roy on Gallery II Records (country); and "Grovespring Swing" (by F. Stowe), recorded by F. Stowe on History Records (country).

HIT & RUN MUSIC PUBLISHING INC., 1841 Broadway, Suite 411, New York NY 10023. Professional Manager: Joey Gmerek. Assistant: Michael Closter. Music publisher. ASCAP. Publishes 20-30 songs/year; publishes 2-4 new songwriters/year. Hires staff writers. Works with composers and lyricists; teams collaborators. Pays standard royalty.
Affiliates: Charisma Music Publishing USA Inc. (ASCAP), Hidden Pun Music Publishing Inc. (BMI).
How to Contact: Write or call first and obtain permission to submit a tape. Prefers cassette (or VHS videocassette) with lyric sheet. Does not return unsolicited material.
Music: Mostly pop, rock and R&B; also dance. Published "The Flame" (by Nick Graham & Bob Mitchell), recorded by Cheap Trick on Epic (power ballad pop); "The Living Years" (by Mike Rutherford & B.A. Robertson), recorded by Mike & The Mechanics on Atlantic (pop); and "Two Hearts" (by Phil Collins & Lamont Dozier), recorded by Phil Collins on Atlantic (pop).

HITSBURGH MUSIC CO., Box 1431, 157 Ford Ave., Gallatin TN 37066. (615)452-0324. President/General Manager: Harold Gilbert. Music publisher. BMI. Estab. 1964. Publishes 24 songs/year; publishes 14 new songwriters/year. Pays standard royalty.
Affiliate: 7th Day Music (BMI).
How to Contact: Prefers cassette (or quality videocassette) with 2-4 songs and lead sheet. Prefers studio produced demos. Does not return unsolicited material. Reports in 3 weeks.
Music: Country and MOR. Published "Make Me Yours" (by K'leetha Megal), recorded by Kim Gilbert (pop); "I'll Be Hurting" (by Hal Gilbert), recorded by Damon King (pop); and "One Step Away," recorded by Keith Walls (country) all on Southern City Records.

HITSOURCE PUBLISHING, INC., 606 Mulford, Evanston IL 60202. (708)328-4203. President: Alan J. Goldberg. Music publisher. BMI. Estab. 1986. Publishes 12-24 songs/year; publishes 3-6 new songwriters/year. Works with composers. Pays standard royalty.
How to Contact: Write or call first and obtain permission to submit. Prefers cassette with 2 songs and lyric sheet. SASE. Reports in 10 weeks.
Music: Country, pop, R&B and dance. Published "Right Lane Man" (by Tom Dundee), recorded by Tom Dundee on Flight Records (country); "Daddy Smoked His Life Away" (by Brian Gill), recorded by Brian Gill (country). "Evolution" (by Howard Berkman), recorded by Howard Berkman on Man-Hole Records (rock).
Also publishes material by T.S. Henry Webb, Maurice Irby, Rokko Jans, June Shellene, Dallas Wayne, Charles Stewart and John Sink.
Tips: "Use vocalists and musicians that can sing and play, not only well, but on key, so that the idea of the song is expressed as it should be."

Close-up

B.A. Robertson
Songwriter
Burbank, California

"Great collaboration is when it sounds to the listener as if all the elements of a song are of one voice," says journeyman songwriter and soundtrack composer B.A. Robertson.

More often known by his words and music than by his name, this 15-year veteran of the music industry has collaborated on many occasions. Among the primarily European songwriters the Scottish-born Robertson has teamed with are Phil Pickett, Tim Rice, Albert Hammond and Terry Britten. Nearly 20 of his songs have placed on either European or international charts as well as some U.S. charts. To date, these have earned him more than 30 silver, gold and platinum record awards.

Most recently and notably, he has authored songs with musician/composer Mike Rutherford for the first two albums by Rutherford's group, Mike & the Mechanics. Interestingly, the songs "Silent Running" and "The Living Years," despite somewhat atypical songforms and subject matter for popular radio formats, turned into major hits for the songwriting team.

As Robertson explains, he and Rutherford each brought something of their own to the songs. "Because I don't have rock 'n' roll 'chops' or heritage, I find I can't write rock 'n' roll records by myself," the 39-year-old Robertson admits, recalling his early formal study and involvement with music for the theater, as well as his more recent work in television and motion pictures. As he also notes, it was Rutherford, better known for his 20-plus years of work with the English rock group, Genesis, who supplied some of the missing ingredients. "I need someone like Mike, who's a little more mainstream and can play the groove, to collaborate with on the music. Then I go off by myself to write the lyric." When he comes back with the words, he adds, Rutherford or another partner will help to fine-tune them.

"It's a very organic process for Mike and me," Robertson continues. "We sit down with nothing . . . a bit of a line, maybe. Mike will set the drum machine and get the groove. Then, I'll play some changes on the keyboard and he'll play guitar and get the 'pocket,' and we'll work it together. For the first album, we had written some songs together, and Mike had some other 'bits.' Then, the producer, Chris Neil, wrote some songs with him and stepped in as the doctor, the 'Mr. Fix-it.' It was sort of cobbled together."

Remarking on the benefit of their first experience of writing together, Robertson claims they had more of a vision of what they wanted to accomplish with the second album. "When we started on the song, 'The Living Years,' we knew roughly what we were doing, but it still only came together in the studio."

In this song, the pair explored a nontraditional subject in pop music: mixed feelings about the death of a parent and missed opportunities for intimacy. And though it may sound to the average listener that the song was written around the dramatic, final verse ("I wasn't there that morning/when my father passed away . . . "), as Robertson points out, that verse was the last element to go into the song. "Everyone assumes that the idea of that verse came early," he says, explaining how the diminuendo in the music of the final verse adds to the impact of the story. "But the track was already recorded that way before we had any idea of what lyric was going in there, least of all me."

With a firm nod of the head to spontaneity in songwriting, Robertson recalls a similar serendipity which the Beatles experienced in the recording of "Strawberry Fields Forever." *That* was an immaculate stumble," he says admiringly. "I'm a great believer in that . . . it's what pop music's all about. Some of the best exponents of pop music are really conscious of it. Someone with natural ability, be it a Bruce Springsteen or an Irving Berlin or a garage band, is more likely to write successful songs than someone with formal training. It's expressing some wonderful human emotion in the simplest way, yet with a sense of originality which is what makes millions of people love it."

As Robertson points out, this lack of self-consciousness is no less true for him and Rutherford. "We're supposed to be grown up, conceptual and know what we're doing. But of course," he adds, chuckling, "we haven't got a clue."

This is far from unusual for most songwriters, Robertson wagers, adding that creativity actually thrives in such a vacuum. "It's a good thing because creative people usually don't know what it is that they're good at or how they do it. We must always remain in awe, in wonderment of what we do. And certainly, no one's more in awe of himself than Springsteen. Even he says: 'Don't ask me why it works. I don't know.' "

What seems to work for Robertson as he chalks up more and more successes is to keep to the basics. "I've become more and more of a traditional songwriter as my career has gone on. I'm interested in isolating the emotion and finding that unique combination between the words and music. You have to get the emotion and feel of the words and music right first, then layer the rest of it on top."

In pursuit of more consistently original compositions, Robertson has also returned to traditional instruments. "If I'm writing on my own, I now write almost exclusively on piano. I found I was writing a really great drum sound and not a very good tune. I became afraid that I was discarding emotion for the benefit of technology. Now a lot of people are coming around to this point of view. Ultimately, it works on the piano or in my head. But it works differently for everybody, and I don't have any secret that way. My only secret is that I try to work harder. I really don't think I work hard enough."

So, as Robertson sees it, working is the end *and* means of songwriting. "It doesn't matter what I or anyone else says, really. All the people who think someone just doesn't have it will never dissuade them if they really want to write songs. They'll just go and do it anyway, just in spite of everybody. I think that attitude, that determination is necessary just to succeed. It's hip to go out and find your own path."

— Sam A. Marshall

---

*HOBO RAILWAYS (MUSIC PUBLISHING) LTD., 14-16 Brewer St., London W1R 3FS **United Kingdom**. Phone: (071)734-1452. FAX: (071)437-9984. Professional Manager: Ron Buzzard. Music publisher. PRS, MCPS. Publishes 25 songs/year; publishes 5-10 new songwriters/year. Works with composers and lyricists; teams collaborators. Pays 60-40% royalty, 70-30% royalty (standard for U.K.).
How to Contact: Prefers cassette (or VHS videocassette [PAL]). SAE and IRC. Reports in 2 weeks.
Music: Mostly rock, pop and jazz. Published "Rules," by Anita Baker; "Almost Certainly," by Gordon Haskell (country); and "I Wanna Walk Out with You," by Judy Boucher (Reggae).

HOLY GRAIL PUBLISHING, 12609 Dessau Rd., Ste. A222, Austin TX 78753. (512)251-0375. Vice President/A&R: Gary A. Coll. Music publisher and record company (Pendragon Records). BMI. Estab. 1987. Publishes 50 songs/year; 5-10 new songwriters/year. Works with composers. Pays standard royalty.
How to Contact: Write or call first and obtain permission to submit a tape. Prefers cassette with 3 songs and lyric sheet. "Include a self-addressed stamped envelope." Does not return unsolicited material. Reports in 2 weeks. "We now (freelance) produce for artists in the Texas area. Please write for terms and prices."

Music: Mostly jazz, rock and pop; also gospel. Published "Leather Lord" (by Tom Kross), recorded by Young Thunder on Pendragon Records (metal); "Wish A Day" (by J. Cook), recorded by Go Dog Go on Pendragon (pop-rock); and "Lion's Creed" (by Tom Kross and S. Wilcox), recorded by Young Thunder on Pendragon Records (metal).

*HOLY SPIRIT MUSIC, Box 31, Edmonton KY 42129. (502)432-3183. President: W. Junior Lawson. Music publisher and record company. BMI. Member GMA, International Association of Gospel Music Publishers. Estab. 1973. Publishes 4 songs/year; publishes 2 new songwriters/year. Pays standard royalty. Works with composers.
How to Contact: Call first. Prefers 7½ ips reel-to-reel or cassette with any number of songs and lyric sheet. SASE. Reports in 3 weeks.
Music: Mostly Southern gospel; also MOR, progressive and top 40/pop. Published "I Went to Jesus," recorded by The Servants; "Excuses," recorded by The Kingsmen; and "Canaanland Is Just in Sight" (by Jeff Gibson), recorded by The Florida Boys (Southern gospel).
Tips: Send "good clear cut tape with typed or printed copy of lyrics."

HOME KEY MUSIC, 15533 Jacana Dr., La Mirada CA 90638. A&R Manager: Jacqueline Casey. Music publisher, record company (Time Capsule Records) and record producer (Time Capsule Productions). BMI. Estab. 1988. Publishes 10-20 songs/year; publishes 2-3 new songwriters/year. Works with composers and lyricists; teams collaborators. Pays standard royalty.
Affiliates: Home Key Music (BMI).
How to Contact: Write first and obtain permission to submit a tape. Prefers cassette or 15 ips reel-to-reel with 3-5 songs and lyric sheets. Does not return unsolicited material. Reports in 4 weeks.
Music: Mostly blues (electric); also delta blues. Published "Lamont's Blues" (by Bruce King), recorded by "2120" on Time Capsule (blues); "Brand New Girlfriend" (by Herb Young), recorded by "2120" on Time Capsule (blues); and "Downtown Shuffle" (by Mark Goldberg), recorded by Back Pocket Blues Band on Time Capsule (blues).
Tips: "Make sure the material is strong and authentic blues. No 'Hybrids.' The artist as songwriter and independent songwriters are gradually increasing; large in-house staffs are becoming less predominant."

*HOPSACK AND SILK PRODUCTIONS INC., Suite 1A, 254 W. 72nd St., New York NY 10023. (212)873-2272. Associate Director: Ms. Tee Alston. Music publisher (Nick-O-Val Music). Estab. 1976. Deals with artists and songwriters.
How to Contact: Call first to get permission to submit a tape.
Music: R&B. Published "Hungry for Me Again" written and recorded by Ashford & Simpson on the Orpheus label (ballad).

HUMANFORM PUBLISHING COMPANY, Box 158486, Nashville TN 37215. (615)373-9312. Publisher: Kevin Nairon. BMI. Music publisher. Pays standard royalty.
How to Contact: Prefers cassette with 4 songs and lyric and lead sheets. SASE. Reports in 4 weeks.
Music: Mostly pop-oriented country, rock, jazz, blues and progressive rock.
Tips: "Please strive for maximum quality when making your demo."

*THE IMAGE MUSIC GROUP PTY., LTD., 137 Moray St., South Melbourne, Victoria, 3205, **Australia.** 61-3-699-9999. US: Mason & Sloane, 1299 Ocean Ave., Santa Monica CA 90401. Director: John McDonald. Music publisher, record company and record producer. APRA, AMCOS, Phonographic Performance Co. of Australia Ltd. Member AMPAL. Publishes 30-40 songs/year; publishes 8 new songwriters/year. Pays standard royalty; royalties paid directly to US songwriters ("if signed to our Australian company"), or through US publishing affiliate ("if songwriter is signed to our US company").
Affiliates: Affiliates/Australia: Rainbird Music (APRA) and Haven Music (APRA). Affiliates/US: American Image Music (BMI) and American Rainbird Music (ASCAP).
How to Contact: Prefers cassette with 3-6 songs and lyric sheet. Submit directly to Australian office. "Concentrate on quality rather than quantity: strong melodic hooks (choruses) and meaningful lyrics that tell a story. Forget obvious rhymes. Make good demos—pay attention to playing and singing. We will not return material unless instructed to do so. Foreign submissions will not be returned unless postage is paid in advance." SAE and IRC. Reports in 1 week.
Music: Dance-oriented, MOR, rock (all kinds) and top 40/pop. Published "Oh How She Loves Me" (by Richard Bennett/Larry Williams), recorded by Bluestone on Avenue Records, Australia (top 40/pop); "Thinking of You" (by Lee Conway), recorded by Gary Holton & Casino Steel on Polygram Records, Europe (top 40/pop); and "Coleraine" (by David Hampson), recorded by the Cobbers on Festival Records, Australia and New Zealand (country).

IMAGINARY MUSIC, 332 N. Dean Rd., Auburn AL 36830. (205)821-JASS. Publisher: Lloyd Townsend, Jr. Music publisher, record company (Imaginary Records) and record producer (Mood Swing Productions). Estab. 1982. Publishes 3-5 songs/year; publishes 1-2 new songwriters/year. Works principally with composer/performers recording for Imaginary Records. Pays standard royalty.
How to Contact: Submit a demo tape—unsolicited submissions are OK. Prefers cassette or 7½ ips reel-to-reel with 4 songs and lyric and lead sheets. "We do not return submissions unless accompanied by proper return envelope and postage." Reports in 3 months.
Music: Classical, Jazz and blues. Published "Hexaphony" (by Somtow Sucharitkul), recorded by Bruce Gaston and Somtow Sucharitkul (improvisational world fusion); and "The Wanderer" (by Les and Mark Lyden), recorded by Nothing Personal (rock); both on Imaginary Records.
Tips: "Know music! How to write it, and how to present it (whether you play it yourself or have another band record it for you)."

IN THE STUDIO PUBLISHING, 5209 Indian Head Hwy., Oxon Hill MD 20745. (301)839-6567. President: Steven Franco. Music publisher. BMI, ASCAP. Estab. 1983. Publishes 12 songs/year; 4-10 new songwriters/year. Hires staff writers. Works with composers and lyricists; teams collaborators.
How to Contact: Submit a demo tape by mail—unsolicited submissions are OK. Prefers cassette with 3 songs. Does not return unsolicited material. Reports in 2 weeks.
Music: Mostly pop, R&B and gospel. Published "Girl You Know It's True" recorded by Milli Vinilli on Arista Records (pop.

INSURANCE MUSIC PUBLISHING, Box 288571, Chicago IL 60628. (312)326-5270. President: Bill Tyson. Music publisher. BMI. Publishes 20 songs/year. Pays standard royalty.
How to Contact: Prefers cassette with 2-4 songs and lyric sheet. Does not return unsolicited material. Reports in 1 month.
Music: Blues, black church/religious/gospel, and R&B.

INTERPLANETARY MUSIC, 7901 S. La Salle St., Chicago IL 60620. (312)962-0130 and (312)886-2003. President: James R. Hall III. Music publisher, record company (Interplanetary Records), record producer and booking agency. Estab. 1972. BMI. Publishes 10 songs/year; publishes 4 new songwriters/year. Works with composers and teams collaborators. Pays standard royalty.
How to Contact: Call or write to arrange personal interview. Prefers cassette. SASE. Reports in 3 weeks.
Music: R&B, top 40/urban contemporary. Published "Make It Last" (by James R. Hall/Lamont Robin) and "No Love" (by James R. Hall/K. Henry), both recorded by Carolyn Hall on Interplanetary Records (pop/R&B).

*IRISH INDIAN MUSIC (BMI), 609A Rosebank Ave., Nashville TN 37206. (615)226-8438. Professional Manager: Alice Rye. Music publisher. BMI. Estab. 1989. Publishes 100 songs/year; publishes 10 new songwriters/year. Works with composers and lyricists; teams collaborators. Pays standard royalty.
Affiliates: Anybody's Music (ASCAP), Group Miracle Music (ASCAP), Wooden Lady Music (ASCAP), F. Spats Music (BMI).
How to Contact: Submit a demo tape by mail—unsolicited submissions are OK. Prefers cassette with 3 songs and lyric sheets. "Audible vocals are more important than hot tracks." SASE. Reports in 1 month.
Music: Mostly pop/rock, country and folk; also new age. Published "Just Say No!" (by Alice Rye, Albert Kennedy Williams and Wayne Osnoe), recorded by Alice and Albert on Pholk Records (pop); "Let's Make Time" (by Albert Kennedy Williams), recorded by T.C. Cantrell on MCR Records (country); "Only A Memory Away" (by Steven Matthew West, Albert Kennedy Williams), recorded by Julie Rowan on BOC Records (country).
Tips: "Heart is more important than art. We are not interested in well-crafted songs that say nothing."

ISBA MUSIC PUBLISHING, INC., 1327 Boul, St. Joseph Est, Montreal, Quebec H2J 1M1 **Canada**. (514)522-4722. General Manager: Maurice Velenosi. Music publisher, record company (ISBA) and record producer. SOCAN. Estab. 1983. Publishes 50 songs/year; publishes 10 new songwriters/year. Works with composers and lyricists. Pays standard royalty.
How to Contact: Write first and obtain permission to submit a tape. Prefers cassette with 3 songs and lyric sheets. Does not return unsolicited material. Reports in 3 weeks.
Music: Mostly pop, rock and dance; also new age, R&B and jazz. Published "Bye Bye Mon Cowboy" (by J.P. Isaac), recorded by Mitsou on BMG/ISBA Records (pop-dance); "Coming Back for More" (by Diodati), recorded by Diodati on ISBA/CBS Records (pop); and "Fait Attention" (by Les. B.B.), recorded by Les. B.B. on ISBA/CBS Records (pop). Also represents HDV, Laymen Twaist, Paris Black, Les B.B. and Revolver.
Tips: "Prepare a good quality demo and work with a singer."

IZA MUSIC CORP., Box 325, Englewood NJ 07631. (201)567-7538. Contact: Professional Dept. Music publisher. BMI, ASCAP. Estab. 1960. Publishes 10-50 songs/year; publishes 8-10 new songwriters/year. Pays standard royalty.
Affiliates: Eden Music Corp (BMI); Prentice Music Inc., and Vanessa Music Corp. (ASCAP).
How to Contact: Write first to obtain permission to send a tape. Prefers cassette with maximum 2 songs and lyric sheet. Prefers studio produced demos. Does not return unsolicited material. Reports in 3 weeks "if time permits."
Music: All kinds; mostly rock, country and R&B. "We have many standards." Published "It's Just a Matter of Time," recorded by Glen Campbell on Atlantic Records; "I Can't Take It Anymore" (by Brook Berton/Clyde Otis), recorded by Billy Joe Royal on Atlantic Records (country); and "A Lover's Question" (by Berton/Williams), recorded by Ben E. King on EMI Records (R&B).

JACLYN MUSIC, 351 Millwood Dr., Nashville TN 37217-1609. (615)366-9999. President: Jack Lynch. Music publisher, producer, recording company (Jaclyn, Nashville Bluegrass and Nashville Country, Recording Companies) and distributor (Nashville Music Sales). BMI. Estab. 1967. Publishes 50-100 songs/year; 25-50 new songwriters/year. Works with composers and lyricists. Pays standard royalties.
Affiliates: Jack Lynch Enterprises (parent company) and Nashville Country Productions.
How to Contact: Submit a demo tape—unsolicited submissions are OK. Send good quality cassette recording, neat lyric sheets and SASE. Prefers 1-4 selections per tape. Reports in 2 weeks.
Music: Country, bluegrass, gospel and MOR. Published "Adieu False Heart" (by Ray Cline), recorded by Ralph Stanley (bluegrass); "Now She's Gone" (by Richard), recorded by Lynch (country); and "Goldmine of Love" (by J. Lynch and M. Adkins), recorded by Jack Lynch (bluegrass); all on Nashville Country Records.

JANA JAE MUSIC, P.O. Box 35726, Tulsa OK 74153. (918)749-1647. Secretary: Sue Teaff. Music publisher, record company (Lark Records) and record producer. BMI. Estab. 1977. Publishes 5-10 songs/year; publishes 1-2 new songwriters/year. Pays standard royalty.
How to Contact : Submit demo tape by mail—unsolicted submissions OK. Prefers cassette (or VHS videocassette) with 4-5 songs and lyric and lead sheet if possible. Does not return unsolicited material.
Music : Country, pop and instrumentals (classical or country). Published "Fiddlesticks," "Mayonnaise," "Bus 'n'Ditty" (by Steven Upfold), and "Let the Bible be Your Roadmap," (by Irene Elliot), all recorded by Jana Jae on Lark Records.

JAMMY MUSIC PUBLISHERS LTD., The Beeches, 244 Anniesland Rd., Glasgow G13 1XA, **Scotland**. Phone: (041)954-1873. Managing Director: John D. R. MacCalman. Music publisher and record company. PRS. Estab. 1977. Publishes 40 songs/year; publishes 2 new songwriters/year. Pays royalty "in excess of 50%."
How to Contact: "We are not currently auditioning."
Music: Mostly rock, pop, country and instrumental; also Scottish. Published "The Wedding Song," (by Bill Padley/Grant Mitchell), recorded by True Love Orchestra on BBC Records (pop); "The Sheep Song" (by Craig Ferguson) recorded on Polydor Records; and "Glasgow" (by Forbes Masson & Alan Cumming), recorded on Jammy Records. "We also specialize in comedy material with artists Bing Hitler, Craig Ferguson, and Victor and Barry."
Tips: "We are now working with a small writers' roster and it's unlikely we would be able to take new writers in the future. We are now specialising in needledrop music."

JA/NEIN MUSIKVERLAG GMBH, Hallerstr. 72, D-2000 Hamburg 13, **West Germany**. Phone: (40)4102161. General Manager: Mary Dostal. Music publisher, record company and record producer. GEMA. Publishes 50 songs/year; publishes 50 new songwriters/year. Works with composers and lyricists; teams collaborators. Pays 50-60% royalty.
Affiliates: Pinorrekk Mv., Star-Club Mv., Big Note Mv and Wunderbar Mv. (GEMA).
How to Contact: Submit a demo tape—unsolicited submissions are OK. Prefers cassette (or VHS videocassette) and lyric sheet. SAE and IRC. Reports in 6 weeks.
Music: Mostly rock, pop, MOR and blues. Published "Lambada-Anstalt" (by H. Bauer), recorded by Helga Feddersen on CBS Records (comic-pop); "Champ's Housewarming" written and recorded by Champ Jack Dupree on Vagabond Records (boogie-blues LP).
Tips: "Send single (A-side) material only, plus photos (if artist). We only send negative reply if SAE and IRC are included."

Listings of companies in foreign countries have the name of the country in boldface type.

JANELL MUSIC, 195 S. 26th St., San Jose CA 95116. (408)286-9840. Owner: Gradie O'Neal. Music publisher. BMI. Estab 1960. Publishes 30-50 songs/year; 20-40 new songwriters/year. Works with composers; teams collaborators. Pays standard royalty.
Affiliates: O'Neal and Friend (ASCAP), Tooter Scooter (BMI).
How to Contact: Submit a demo tape by mail—unsolicited submissions are OK. Prefers cassette with 4 songs and lyric sheets. SASE. Reports in 2 weeks.
Music: Mostly top 40 pop, country and rock; also R&B, gospel and new age. Published "Before and After" (by J. O'Neal), recorded by Sister Suffragette on Rowena (rap); "Texas in Your Eyes" (by S. Ellwanger), Johnny Gitar on Rowena Records (country); and "Where Are You Now That I Need You" (by C. Friend), recorded by Mel Tillis on Mercury Records (country).

*JASPER STONE MUSIC (ASCAP)/JSM SONGS (BMI), Box 24, Armonk NY 10504. President: Chris Jasper. Vice President: Margie Jasper. Music publisher. ASCAP, BMI. Estab. 1986. Publishes 20-25 songs/year. Works with composers; teams collaborators. Each contract is worked out individually and negotiated depending on terms.
How to Contact: Submit a demo tape by mail—unsolicited submissions are OK. Prefers cassette with maximum of 3 songs and lyric sheets. SASE. Reports in 6 weeks.
Music: Mostly R&B/pop, rap and rock. Published "Make It Last," recorded by Chaka Khan on Warner Bros. Records; "The First Time," recorded by Chris Jasper on Gold City/CBS Records; and "Dream Lover," recorded by Liz Hogue on Gold City/CBS Records; all written by C. and M. Jasper (R&B).
Tips: "Keep writing. Keep submitting tapes. Be persistent. Don't give it up."

JAY JAY PUBLISHING, 35 NE 62nd St., Miami FL 33138. (305)758-0000. Contact: Walter Jagiello. Music publisher, record company (Jay Jay Publishing) and record producer. BMI. Estab. 1958. One of the founders of NARAS. Publishes 30 songs/year. Pays standard royalty.
How to Contact: Submit a demo tape—unsolicited submissions are OK. Prefers 15 ips reel-to-reel (or VHS videocassette) with 2-6 songs and lyric sheet. SASE. Reports in 2 months.
Music: Mostly popular, country, polkas, waltzes and comedy. "The type of songs that were made in the 50's and 60's. No rock and roll." Published "Sexy Annie" (by W. Jagiello), recorded by Li'l Wally (polka); "Rainbow Polka," written and recorded by C. Siewierski (polka); "How I Love You Darlin" (by W. Jagiello), recorded by Li'l Wally on Jay Jay Records (waltz); "I'd Love To Call You My Sweetheart" (by W. Jagiello), recorded by Li'L Wally on Jay Jay Records (polka) and "Thrill On The Hill" (by W. Jagiello), recorded by Li'l Wally on Jay Jay Records (polka).
Tips: "Make songs simple lyrics, simple melody, true to life! Send audio demo, sheet music with lyrics."

*JAY-TAM PUBLISHING COMPANY, 676 Pittsburgh Rd., Butler PA 16001. (412)586-6552. Owner: Paul Taimuty. Music publisher. BMI. Estab. 1969. Publishes 15 songs/year; 2 new songwriters/year. Works with composers and lyricists; teams collaborators. Pays standard royalty.
Affiliates: Tigerbabe Music (BMI).
How to Contact: Submit a demo tape by mail-unsolicited submissions are OK. Prefers cassette (or 7½ or 15 IPS reel-to-reel, VHS, Beta or ¾″ videocassette) with 3 songs and lyrics and lead sheets. SASE. Reports in 6-8 weeks.
Music: Interested in "positive lyric rock" and contemporary gospel; also rap, jazz and progressive country. Published "Forged By Fire", written and recorded by Sanxtion on Trope Records (metal gospel); "I Cross My Heart" (by Taimuty/Nelson), recorded by Melissa Anne on Phunn! Records (dance); and "Fight the Fight", written and recorded by M.J. Nelson on Trope Records (dance gospel).
Tips: "Due to recent move to rate records, positive lyric songs are going to be in great demand."

JELLEE WORKS MUSIC, P.O. Box 16572, Kansas City MO 64133 and P.O. Box 247, New York NY 11501. President: Jimmy Lee. Music publisher, record company (Heart Land Records), record producer (Jellee Works Productions) and songwriter recording services. ASCAP, BMI. Estab. 1983. Publishes 24-36 songs/year; publishes 12-15 new songwriters/year. "Will work one on one with select songwriters to help them get started." Works with composers and lyricists; teams collaborators. Pays standard royalty.
Affiliates: Jellee Works Music (BMI) and Jellee Music Works (ASCAP).
How to Contact: Write first to get permission to submit a tape. Prefers cassette with no more than 2 songs per tape (or VHS videocassette) and lyric sheet. SASE. Reports in 6 weeks.
Music: Mostly country, gospel and MOR; also country crossover, rock-a-billy and pop. Published "Roland Was a Nerd," written and recorded by Joe Donovan (folk); "Singing Mama's Songs" (by Kaye Sykes), recorded by Kevin Eason (country); and "I Wanta Touch You Again" (by Jack Lawrence and Jimmy Lee), recorded by Greg Wheelen (country); all on Heart Land Records.

Tips: "Submit only your best work. Demos may be simple (guitar/vocal). If contracted, a studio demo may be required. My best advice for songwriters is to keep writing and listen to the advice and comments others make on your work. Don't give up, and be professional."

JERJOY MUSIC, Box 1264, Peoria IL 61654-1264. (309)673-5755. Professional Manager: Jerry Hanlon. Music publisher. BMI. Estab. 1978. Publishes 4 songs/year; publishes 2 new songwriters/year. Pays standard royalty.
How to Contact: Submit a demo tape—unsolicited submissions are OK. Prefers cassette with 4-8 songs and lyric sheet. SASE. Reports in 2 weeks.
Music: Country (modern or traditional). Published "E.T. We're Missing You," and "Scarlet Woman" (by Jerry Hanlon), recorded by Jerry Hanlon; "Rainy Nights and Honky Tonks" written and recorded by Jerry Hanlon; and "Fast Women and Expensive Toupes" (by Rodger and Jerry Hanlon), recorded by Jerry Hanlon; all on UAR Records (all country singles).

*JIMCO RECORD, a Division of JimCo Japan, JimCo House 4-7-7, Kachidoki, Chuo-Ku Tokyo 104 **Japan**. Phone (03)534-8771. A&R Manager: Eugene Otsuka. Music publisher, record company (Mad About Dance, College Music, Motor-City) and record producer (Ian Levine). JASRAC. Estab. 1989. Publishes 20 songs/year. Pays standard royalty.
Affiliates: M.P.N. Production.
How to Contact: Submit a demo tape by mail—unsolicited submissions are OK. Prefers cassette with 10 songs. SASE. Reports 1 month.
Music: Mostly dance, heavy metal and R&B; also rock and jazz.

*JIMERLEAN MUSIC, P.O. Box 90639, Nashville TN 37209. (615)321-3319. Director: James Hendrix. Music Publisher and record company (Carrie/Tribal). BMI. Estab. 1963. Publishes 6 songs/year; publishes 3 new songwriters/year. Hires staff writers if necessary. Pays standard royalty.
Affiliates: Mester Music (independent).
How to Contact: Submit a demo tape by mail—unsolicited submissions O.K. Prefers cassette with 2 songs. SASE. Reports in 1 month.
Music: Mostly R&B and gospel; also hymns, anthems and seasonal songs.

*JODUNN MUSIC, %Music Cafe New York NY, 7 Kilfoyle Ave., Fords NJ 08863. Owner: Joseph Porrello. Music publisher and record producer (Music Cafe Productions). ASCAP. Estab. 1986. Publishes 25-40 songs/year; publishes 2-5 new songwriters/year. Teams collaborators. Pays standard royalty.
Affiliates: Mighty Matthew (BMI) and Sweet Bernadette (ASCAP).
How to Contact: Submit a demo tape by mail—unsolicited submissions are OK. Prefers cassette with 4 songs and lyric sheet. SASE. Reports in 2 months.
Music: Mostly R&B, pop and rock. Published "Go For The Gusto", "Love Me All Night" and "Lovely Lady" (by J. Porrello/D. Pearson), recorded by Dunn Pearson, Jr. on Compose Records (R&B).

LITTLE RICHIE JOHNSON MUSIC, 1700 Plunket, Belen NM 87002. (505)864-7441. Manager: Tony Palmer. Music publisher, record company (LRJ Records) and record producer. BMI. Estab. 1959. Publishes 50 songs/year; publishes 10 new songwriters/year. Works with composers. Pays standard royalty.
Affiliate: Little Cowboy Music (ASCAP).
How to Contact: Submit a demo tape—unsolicited submissions are O.K. SASE. Reports in 1 month.
Music: Country, gospel and Spanish. Published "Lisa," "Mona," and "June's Back in Town" (by Jerry Jaramilk), recorded by Jerry Jaramillo on LRJ Records (C&W).

AL JOLSON'S BLACK & WHITE MUSIC, 114 175th Ave. South, Nashville TN 37203. (615)244-5656. President: Albert Jolson. Music Publisher. BMI. Estab. 1981. Publishes 65 songs/year; 50 new songwriters/year. Works with composers and lyricists; teams collaborators. Pays standard royalty.
Affiliate: Jolie House Music (ASCAP).
How to Contact: Submit a demo tape—unsolicited submissions are OK. Prefers cassette with 3 songs and lyric sheet. Send: Attn. Ray Richardson. SASE. Reports in 6 weeks.
Music: Mostly country crossover, light rock and pop. "Welcome Home To West Virginia" (by Scott Phelps), recorded by Kathy Mattea; "Ten Tiny Fingers Ten Tiny Toes" (by David John Hanley), recorded by Kelly Dawn on ASA Jolson Records (country); and "Indiana Highway" recorded by Staggerlee on ASA Jolson Records (country).
Tips: "Make sure it has a strong hook. Ask yourself if it is something you would hear on the radio 5 times a day. Have good audible vocals on demo tape."

JONDI MUSIC, #1106, 130 W. 42nd St., New York NY 10036. (212)819-0920. Contact: President. Music publisher, record company and record producer. BMI. Pays standard royalty.
How to Contact: Prefers cassette (or VHS or ¾" U-matic videocassette) with 3 songs and lyric sheet. Reports in 2 weeks only if SASE is included.
Music: Mostly country, top 40/pop, and gospel.

JONGLEUR MUSIC, 9015 Owensmouth Ave., #106, Canoga Park CA 91304. (818)341-4766. Contact: Review Manager. Music publisher. ASCAP. Estab. 1985. Publishes 8 songs/year; 2-4 new songwriters/ year. Works with composers and lyricists; teams collaborators. Pays standard royalty.
Affiliates: Gary Revel Music (ASCAP).
How to Contact: Write first and obtain permission to submit a tape. Does not return unsolicited material.
Music: Mostly country, pop and rock; also gospel and R&B. Published "Maria" (by G. Revel, A. Meza, D. Tuttle), recorded by Dale Tuttle (country); "Hollywood Star" written and recorded by Gary Revel (rock); and "Treat America Like a Lady" (by Gary Revel, Jerry Guthrie), recorded by Hal Jon Norman (pop); all on Top's Records.

*JOSENA MUSIC, P.O. Box 566, Los Altos CA 94022. (408)746-3555. President: Joe Nardone. Music publisher. SESAC. Estab. 1983. Publishes 30-40 songs/year; publishes 1-2 new songwriters/year. Hires staff songwriters. Works with composers and lyricists. Pays standard royalty.
Affiliates: Reign in Me Music (SESAC).
How to Contact: Write first and obtain permission to submit a tape. Prefers cassette with 3 songs and lyric sheet. Does not return unsolicited material. Reports in 1 month.
Music: Mostly Christian rock/pop, pop and gospel; also modern rock. Published "Hold On" (by Joe Nardone/Kevin Phillips); "This is the Day" (by Joe Nardone/Mike Palos); and "By His Stripes" (by Dean Adams), all recorded by Joe Nardone on Latter Rain Records (Christian rock).
Tips: "Be persistent and send commercial material only."

JUMP MUSIC, Langemunt 71, 9460 Erpe-Mere **Belgium.** Phone: (053)62-73-77. General Manager: Eddy Van Mouffaert. Music publisher, record company (Jump Records) and record producer. Member of SABAM S.V., Brussels. Publishes 100 songs/year; publishes 8 new songwriters/year. Works with composers and lyricists; teams collaborators. Pays via SABAM S.V.
How to Contact: Submit demo tape by mail. Prefers cassette. Does not return unsolicited material. Reports in 2 weeks.
Music: Mostly easy listening, disco and light pop; also instrumentals. Published "Feelin' Down" (by Eddy Govert), recorded by Richie, both on Scorpion Records; and "Don Bosco" (by Eddy Govert), recorded by Eigentydse Jeugd on Yeah Songs Records (all ballads).
Tips: "Music wanted with easy, catchy melodies (very commercial songs)."

JUST A NOTE, 1058 E. Saint Catherine, Louisville KY 40204. (503)637-2877. General Partner: John V. Heath. Music publisher (Two John's Music), record companies (Hillview, Estate) and record producer (MVT Productions). ASCAP and BMI. Estab. 1979. Publishes 20-30 songs/year; publishes 10-15 new songwriters/year. Works with composers and lyricists. Pays standard royalty.
Affiliates: Just a Note (BMI) and Two John's Music (ASCAP).
How to Contact: Submit a demo tape by mail—unsolicited submissions are O.K. Prefers cassette, 7½ ips reel-to-reel or VHS videocassette with 3 song and lead sheet. SASE. Reports in 2 weeks.
Music: Mostly pop, country, R&B and MOR; also gospel. Published "Country Music Memories" (by Cece Whittaker), recorded by Cece Whittaker on EOP Records (country); "Night Visions" (by Adonis), recorded by Adonis on Estate Records (rock); and "Heartbreak Tears" (by Herbert Family), recorded by Herbert Family on Hillview Records (country).

*KAMISHI PUBLISHING/A DIVISION OF ARWAY RECORDS, P.O. Box 584, Marion AR 72364. (501)732-6454. President: Mrs. Mikii Hooper. Music publisher and record company (Arway Records and RAJ Records). ASCAP. Estab. 1989. Publishes 25-30 songs/year; publishes 3 new songwriters/ year. Works with composers and lyricists; teams collaborators. Pays standard royalty.
How to Contact: Submit a demo tape by mail—unsolicited submissions are OK. Prefers cassette with 3 songs and lyric sheet. "Send copyright protected submissions only. Furnish copyright registration number, date and ownership." SASE. Reports in 2 months.
Music: Mostly R&B, pop and country; also gospel and blues. Published "Cole-Cashe" (R&B); "Suicide" (soft rock); and "What About Us" (R&B), all written by Cleo Cashe/E & J Coleman, all recorded by Cole-Cashe on Arway Records.
Tips: Submit bio-sketch, expectations, goals. Be artist-composer."

*KARLAMOR MUSIC PUBLISHING, 50 Music Square W., #207, Nashville TN 37203. (615)329-2592. Prof. Manager: Karen Morris. Music publisher. BMI. Estab. 1984. Publishes 20 songs/year; publishes 3 new songwriters/year. Teams collaborators. Pays standard royalty.
How to Contact: Submit a demo tape by mail—unsolicited submissions are OK. Prefers cassette with 3 songs and lyric sheet. SASE. Reports in 2 weeks.
Music: Mostly country, pop and R&B; also rock. Published "All My Life" (by May); "I Never Could Say No" (by Rager); and "You Must Have Been Reading By Heart" (by Westberry), all recorded by Jill Jordan on Maxy Records (country ballad).

K-C PUBLISHING CO., 2525 East 12th St., Cheyenne WY 82001. (307)638-9894. A&R Manager: Gary J. Kelley. Music publisher, record company (Rough Cut Records) and record producer (Rough Cut Records). ASCAP. Estab. 1989. Publishes 5 songs/year; 5 new songwriters/year. Works with team collaborators. Pays standard royalty.
Affiliates: Kelley-Kool Music (BMI).
How to Contact: Submit a demo tape by mail—unsolicited submissions are O.K. Prefers cassette (or VHS videocassette) with 3 songs and lyric sheets. "Guitar/piano demo with "words up front" is sufficient." SASE. Reports in 2 weeks.
Music: Mostly pop, soul and light-rock; also country, R&B and jazz-rock. Published "Just Say No" and "We Got Soul" (by G.J. Kelley & R.P. Creswell), on Rough Cut Records (rock).
Tips: "Be original. Don't copy someone else. We are a brand new company looking for new style songs. It's time record companies quit putting out albums and tapes with B songs (fill songs, junk songs) and only one or two hits. We want to help pave the way for the cassingle (cassette tape with only two hit songs). Don't be afraid to rewrite your songs."

JOE KEENE MUSIC CO., P.O. Box 602, Kennett MO 63857. (314)888-2995. President: Joe Keene. Music publisher. BMI. Estab. 1968. Publishes 15-20 songs/year; 3-4 new songwriters/year. Pays standard royalty.
Affiliates: Lincoln Road Music Co. (BMI), Happy Day Music Co. (BMI); Cone Music Co. (BMI), Smooth Flight Music Co. (BMI).
How to Contact: Write first and obtain permission to submit a tape. Prefers cassette with 3-4 songs and lyric sheets. SASE. Reports in 2 weeks.
Music: Mostly country, gospel and rock. Published "One Old Guitar Man" (by Gill Blankenship) On KSS Records; "Scars On My Heart" (by Joe Jeene), on Texas Gold Records; and "Goodbyes Are All The Same" (by Gill Blankenship), on KSS Records.
Tips: "Pay attention to the market: write for it."

KEENY-YORK PUBLISHING, 29 S. Erie, Toledo OH 43602. Contact: Michael Drew Shaw. Music publisher, record company, record producer and film producer. BMI. Publishes 50 songs/year; publishes 4 new songwriters/year. Pays standard royalty.
Affiliates: Park J. Tunes (ASCAP) and Newstar International Records.
How to Contact: Prefers cassette with 3 songs maximum and lyric sheet. SASE. Reports in 2 months.
Music: Mostly top 40/pop; also country, easy listening and MOR. Published "Distant Shores," (tribute to challenger astronauts), by Mick Payne; and *Moonshine*, by Tanguerey, (LP); both on Newstar Records; *Devil's Lake* LP on Newstar, narrative album performed by Michael DeBrakistar; "Place to Hide," by Rococo on Newstar.

BUTCH KELLY PRODUCTIONS AND PUBLISHING, 11 Shady Oak Trail, Charlotte NC 28210. (704) 554-1162. Manager: Butch Kelly. Music publisher, record company (KAM Executive Records, Fresh Avenue Records and Executive Records), record producer (Butch Kelly Productions), and songwriter. ASCAP, BMI. Estab. 1982. Publishes 6 songs/year; publishes 3 new songwriters/year. Teams collaborators. Pays standard royalty.
Affiliate: Music by Butch Kelly.
How to Contact: Write first and obtain permission to submit. Prefers cassette (or VHS videocassette) with 1-6 songs and lyric or lead sheet."Include bio, and photo if possible." SASE. Reports in 4 months.
Music: Mostly R&B, pop, rap, gospel and rock; also dance oriented, easy listening, jazz, soul and top 40. Published "Miss You" (by Greg Johnson), recorded Fresh Air on Fresh Avenue Records (R&B); "Fantasy," written and recorded by Wylie on KAM Records (R&B); and "Super Star" (by Dinnes Jones), recorded by L.A. Star on KAM Records (rap).
Tips: "Send songs on Maxell UDS II tapes only."

GENE KENNEDY ENTERPRISES, INC., 315 Mt. Juliet Rd., Mt. Juliet TN 37122. (615)754-0417. President: Gene Kennedy. Vice President: Karen Jeglum Kennedy. Music publisher, record company (Door Knob Records), record producer, distributor and promoter. ASCAP, BMI, SESAC. Estab. 1975.

Publishes 30-40 songs/year; publishes 15-20 new songwriters/year. Works with composers and lyricists. Pays standard royalty.

Affiliates: Chip 'n Dale Music Publishers (ASCAP), Door Knob Music Publishing (BMI) and Lodestar Music (SESAC).

How to Contact: Prefers cassette or 7½ ips reel-to-reel with 1-3 songs and lyric sheet. "We will not accept anything we have to sign for." SASE. Reports in 3 weeks.

Music: Country and gospel. Published "Praise Ye The Lord" (by Linda Almond), recorded by Dave Jeglum (gospel); "Open For Suggestions" (by Wyndi Harp), recorded by Perry La Pointe (country); and "I've Had Enough of You" (by Johnette Burton), recorded by Debbie Rich (country); all on Door Knob Records.

KENNING PRODUCTIONS, Box 1084, Newark DE 19715. (302)737-4278. President: Kenneth Mullins. Music publisher and record company (Kenning Records). BMI. Publishes 30-40 songs/year.

How to Contact: Prefers cassette. Does not return unsolicited material.

Music: Mostly rock, new wave and country; also blues, jazz and bluegrass. Published "Crazy Mama," written and recorded by K. Mullins; and "Work Me Over," (by J. Lehane/K. Mullins), recorded by K. Mullins, both on Kenning Records (both rock); and "This Time," (by K. Mullins).

*KICKING MULE PUBLISHING/DESK DRAWER PUBLISHING, Box 158, Alderpoint CA 95411. (707)926-5312. Manager: Ed Denson. Music publisher and record company. BMI and ASCAP. Member NAIRD. Publishes 120 songs/year; publishes 7 new songwriters/year. Pays standard royalties.

How to Contact: Write first. Prefers cassette with 1-3 songs. Does not return unsolicited material. Reports "as soon as possible."

Music: Blues (fingerpicking); and folk (guitar/banjo only). Published "The Sweeper," written and recorded by George Gritzbach on KM Records (folk); "Thunder On The Run" written and recorded Stefan Grossman on KM Records (guitar instrumental); and "Pokerface Smile" (by Robert Force), recorded by Force & D'Ossche (country).

Tips: "We publish only material released on our albums. Since we record virtuoso guitar and banjo players, virtually the only way to get a tune published with us is to be such a player, or to have such a player record your song. We don't publish many 'songs' per se, our entire catalog is devoted 95% to instrumentals and 5% to songs with lyrics. As publishers we are not in the market for new songs. This listing is more of a hope that people will not waste their time and ours sending us blue-sky demos of material that does not relate to our very specialized business."

KIMTRA MUSIC, Sound 70 Inc., 1808 West End Ave., Nashville TN 37203. (615)327-1711. Music publisher. Publishes 75 songs/year; publishes 5 new songwriters/year. Teams collaborators.

How to Contact: Prefers cassette with 1 "great" song and typed lyric sheet. Will not return any material. "Do not enclose SASE. Will contact only if interested."

Music: Country, rock and top 40/pop.

*KINGSPORT CREEK MUSIC PUBLISHING, P.O. Box 6085, Burbank CA 91510. Contact: Vice President. BMI. Music publisher and record company (Cowgirl Records). Estab. 1980. Works with composers, lyricists; teams collaborators. Pays standard royalty.

How to Contact: Prefers cassette (or VHS videocassette) with any number of songs and lyric sheet. Does not return unsolicited material. "Include photos and bio if possible."

Music: Mostly country and gospel; also R&B, and MOR. Published "1st Man" (country); "I Do" (MOR); and "Jesus Is Guiding Me" (gospel). All written and recorded by Melvena Kaye on the Cowgirl label.

Tips: "Videocassettes are advantageous."

*KITTY GROUP INC., (formerly Kitty Music Corporation), 1-8-4 Ohashi, Meguro-ku, Tokyo 153 **Japan**. Phone: (03)499-4711. Manager of International Division: Kazuo Munakata. Music publisher and record company (Kitty Records, Inc.). JASRAC. Estab. 1972. Publishes 400 songs/year; publishes 20 new songwriters/year. Employs songwriters on a salary basis. Works with composers and lyricists; teams collaborators. Pays standard royalty.

How to Contact: Prefers cassette with 5 songs and lyric sheet. "Include pictures and a personal history if you can." SAE and IRC. Reports in 1 month.

Music: Mostly rock and pop; also New Age (instrumental). Published "Dance if You Want It" (by Toshinobu Kubota and Masumi Kawamura), recorded by Toshinobu Kubota on CBS Records (R&B); "Mewo Tojite Oideyo" (by Tomotaka Imamichi); recorded by Barbee Boys on Epic Records (rock); and "Paya Paya" (by Kyoichi Sugimoto and Magumi), recorded by Lä-Ppisch on Victor Records (rock).

*KOCH MUSIC PUBLISHING, A-6652 Elibenalp 91, 05634/6444 **Austria**. Publishing Manager: Rudy Schedler. Music publisher, record company (Koch Records International), record producer (Koch Records). AKM, AUME, GEMA, SUISA. Estab. 1975. Publishes 100 songs/year; publishes 10 new songwriters/year. Works with composers and lyricists. Pays standard royalty.
Affiliates: Koch Records Gmbh (GEMA), Koch Records AG (SUISA).
How to Contact: Submit a demo tape by mail—unsolicited submissions are OK. Prefers cassette with 3 songs and lyric sheets. Does not return unsolicited material. Reports back in 4 weeks.
Music; Mostly pop, rock and R&B; also new age and country. Published "Tell Me That You Lo . ." (by Michael Ernst), recorded on Koch Records (pop, slow); "Yiasou" (by Roland Gutsch), recorded on Koch Records (disco-pop); and "J ai faim de toi" (by A. Moustrou), recorded by Careere, France on Koch Records (pop).

*KOKE, MOKE & NOKE MUSIC, Box 724677, Atlanta GA 30339. (404)355-0909. General Manager: Bryan Cole. Music publisher, record company (Ichiban). BMI. Estab. 1986. Publishes "at least 50" songs/year. Works with composers and lyricists; teams collaborators. Pays standard royalty.
How to Contact: Submit a demo tape by mail—unsolicited submissions are OK. Prefers cassette with 4 or 5 songs and lyric sheets. "Put contact name and number on the tape." Does not return unsolicited material. Reports back in 2 weeks.
Music: Mostly blues, R&B old style, urban contemporary (dance, rap); also gospel, pop and country. Published "I'd Rather Be Alone" (by Buzz Amato), recorded by Billy Paul on Ichiban Records (R&B); "Straight From Heaven" (by Mark Ford, Joey Johnson), recorded by Rev. Charles McLean on Miracle Records (gospel); "What's the Name of That Thing?" (by Gary "B.B." Coleman), recorded on Ichiban Records (blues).
Tips: "Write from the heart and soul, not the head. Listen to some of our records for direction."

KOZKEEOZKO MUSIC, Suite 602, 928 Broadway, New York NY 10010. (212)505-7332. Professional Managers: Ted Lehrman and Libby Bush. Music publisher, record company (Silverado Records), record producer and management firm (Landslide Management). ASCAP. Estab. 1978. Publishes 5 songs/year; publishes 3 new songwriters/year. Works with composers and lyricists; teams collaborators. Pays standard royalty.
How to Contact: Write first and obtain permission to submit. Cassettes (or VHS ½" videocassettes) with 2 songs maximum and typwritten lyric sheet for each song. SASE. Reports in 2 months.
Music: Mostly soul/pop, dance, pop/rock (no heavy metal), adult contemporary, and country. Published "Love Put Some Danger In Me," (Muzak, heavy rotation); "Video! TV-oh!," recorded by Scarlett on Coast-to-Coast Records; "Radio Free Nashville" and "Fool's Mountain," recorded by Jackie Cook on Silverado Records; and "This Heart's Gonna Heal" recorded by Deborah Dotson Livering on Triple R Records.
Tips: "Songs with hooky memorable melodies and lyrics that say something in an original way are what we're looking for. Potential hit singles only; no album cuts, please. A well produced demo gives a submitted song an edge. Communicate with us personally—no form letters."

RALF KRUEGER MUSIKVERLAG, Leopold St. 11-13, 4000 Dusseldorf NRW **Germany** 0211 364545. Director: Ralf Krueger. Music publisher and record company (AIA, BS Modern Music). GEMA. Estab. 1984. Publishes 10 songs/year; publishes 2 new songwriters/year. Works with composers and lyricists; teams collaborators.
How to Contact: Submit a demo tape by mail—unsolicited submissions are O.K. Prefers cassette with lyric sheets. SASE. Reports in 1 month.
Music: Mostly new pop, funk/soul and dance, new house; also stylistic fusion. Published "Milky Way Kiss" (by Bop Whopper/Sira Ain), recorded by Frank Ananda on AIA (soul-pop-rap); and "Violins" (by George Rockwood, Victor Lovera, Sira Ain, Arna Donya), recorded by Frank Ananda on AIA (new pop).

L.S. RECORDS, 120 Hickory St., Madison TN 37115. (615)868-7171. Publisher: Kevin L. Stoller. Music publisher and record company (L.S. Records). ASCAP, SESAC, BMI. Estab. 1972. Publishes 15 songs/year; 3 new songwriters/year. Works with composers. Pays standard royalty.
Affiliates: Cristy Lane Music (ASCAP), L.S. Music (ASCAP), Harvey Wallbanger Music (ASCAP), Kevin Lee Music (BMI), Tammy Lee Music (BMI), Pathfinder Music (BMI), Cindy Lee Music (SESAC).
How to Contact: Write first and obtain permission to submit a tape. Prefers cassette with 1 song and lyric or lead sheet. SASE.
Music: Mostly gospel, country and pop; also rock and rap. Published "All In His Hands" (by Jimmie Young), "How Great Thou Art" (public domain) and "He Sees My Heart" (by Jimmie Young); all recorded by Cristy Lane on L.S. Records (gospel).

*L TRAIN PUBLISHERS, Suite 470, 410 S. Michigan, Chicago IL 60605. (312)939-5581. President: Frederick S. Koger. Music publisher and record company. ASCAP. Estab. 1987. Publishes 6 songs/year; publishes 2 new songwriters/year. Hires staff writers. Pays standard royalty.
How to Contact: Write or call to arrange a personal interview. Prefers cassette, 7½ IPS reel-to-reel with 3-5 songs and lyric or lead sheets. SASE. Reports in 3 weeks.
Music: Mostly R&B, rap and pop; also rock and gospel. Published "Love Quarrel" (by Frederick S. Koger), recorded by Virgik/Rozlyn on Nickle Plat Records (single); and "Stop Watch" (by Jam 200 Derick), recorded by Jam & Derick on Nickle Plate Records (house dance).

*LANSDOWNE AND WINSTON MUSIC PUBLISHERS, 1680 Vine St., #912, Hollywood CA 90028. (213)462-2848. Vice President/Professional Manager: Lynne Robin Green. Music publisher. ASCAP, BMI. Estab. 1958. Publishes 20 songs/year; publishes 10 new songwriters/year. Works with composers and lyricists. Pays standard royalty.
Affiliates: Bloor Music Publishers (BMI); Ben Ross Music (ASCAP); Hoffman House Music Publisher (BMI).
How to Contact: Submit a demo tape by mail—unsolicited submissions are OK. Prefers cassette with 1-3 songs and lyric sheets. SASE. Reports back in 3 weeks.
Music: Mostly R&B (dance and ballads), hip hop, pop-rock; also alternative. Published "The Roach Dance" (by Alonzo Willis and Steve Venet), recorded by Gene and Wendell and The Sweethearts on MCA Soundtrack from the movie, Hairspray (R&B); "Dooley" (by The Dillards), recorded by Porter Wagoner on RCA/Ariola Records (bluegrass); and "Stomp, Look and Listen" (by Porrazzo-Wright), recorded by Be-2 on Victor Japan Records (pop rock).
Tips: "Write from real life, touch the 'head', 'heart' or 'erogenous zone' with a solid story, and a melody that everyone can recall after a few plays. Be selective. A great, memorable melody and lyric will always be the vehicle into tomorrow's music, no matter what genre . . .'"

LANTANA, 9430 Live Oak Pl., #308, Ft. Lauderdale FL 33324. (305)472-7757. President: Jack Bluestein. Music publisher, record company (Twister Records, Quadraphonic Records), and record producer (Quadraphonic Talent - Records). BMI. Estab. 1974. Publishes 10-50 songs/year. Publishes 10 or more new songwriters/year. Works with composers and lyricists; teams collaborators. Pays standard royalty.
Affiliates: Pine Island Music (BMI) and Twister Music (ASCAP).
How to Contact: Write first and obtain permission to submit. Prefers cassette or 7½ ips. reel to reel with 3-6 songs and lyric sheet and/or lead sheet. SASE. Reports in 4 weeks.
Music: Country, country pop, R&B and gospel.

*LARI-JON PUBLISHING, 627 Country View, Columbus NE 68601. (402)564-7034. Owner:Larry Good. Music publisher, record company (Lari-Jon Records) and record producer (Lari Jon Productions). BMI. Estab. 1967. Publishes 20 songs/year; publishes 2-3 new songwriters/year. Teams collaborators. Pays standard royalty.
How to Contact: Submit a demo tape by mail—unsolicited submissions are O.K. Prefers cassette with 5 songs and lyric sheet. "Be professional." SASE. Reports in 2 months.
Music: Mostly country, gospel—Southern and '50's rock. Published "Nebraska Land" (by Larry Good), recorded by Larry Good on Lari-Jon Records (country); "Rock & Rollin' Memories" (by Larry Good), recorded by Larry Good on Hornet Records (country.

*LARRIKIN MUSIC, Box Q78, 72 Bathurst St, Sydney NSW 2000 **Australia**. Phone: (02)267-7433. Professional Manager: John Boughtwood. Music publisher. APRA. Works with composers and lyricists.
Affiliates: Happy Valley Music (USA), Sleeping Giant (UK), Campbell Connelly (UK) and G. Schirmer (USA).
How to Contact: Write or call to arrange a personal interview. Prefers cassette with 3-4 songs and lyric sheet. SASE. Reports in 3 weeks.
Music: All types.

 The asterisk before a listing indicates that the listing is new in this edition. New markets are often the most receptive to unsolicited submissions.

LAYMOND PUBLISHING CO., INC., Box 25371, Charlotte NC 28229. (704)537-0133. A&R Director: Trent Moody. Music publisher, record company (Panhandle Records, Lamon Records) and record producer (David and Carlton Moody). BMI, ASCAP. Publishes 45 songs/year; publishes 20 new songwriters/year. Works with composers. Pays standard royalty.
Affiliates: CDT Productions and Laymond Publishing Co.
How to Contact: Write first and obtain permission to submit. Prefers cassette. Does not return unsolicited material. Reports in 10 weeks.
Music: Mostly country, R&B and rock; also gospel. Published "Too Good To Turn Back Now" (by Rick Bowles), recorded by Vannesa Parker (pop); "You Turn The Light On" (by Shackford), recorded by Moody Bros. (country); and "I'm Through" (by Mildred Beard), recorded by Shedanes (R&B); all on Lamon Records.

*LCS MUSIC GROUP, INC., P.O. Box 7409, Dallas TX 75209. (214)353-0472. Contact: Publishing Assistant. Music publisher. BMI, ASCAP and SESAC. Works with composers. Pays standard royalty.
Affiliates: Bug and Bear Music (ASCAP), Chris Christian Music (BMI), Court and Case Music (ASCAP), Home Sweet Home Music (ASCAP) and Monk and Tid Music (SESAC).
How to Contact: Submit a demo tape by mail—unsolicited submissions are OK. Prefers cassette with lyric sheet (only necessary if the words are difficult to understand) "Put all pertinent information on the tape itself. Such as how to reach the writer." Does not return unsolicited material.
Music: Mostly contemporary Christian and inspirational. Published "Thy Word" and "Find A Way" (by Amy Grant/M.W. Smith), recorded by Amy Grant on Myrrh Records (contemporary Christian); and "Hosanna" (by Mark Gersmehl/Billy Smiley), recorded by Sandi Patti on Word Records (inspirational).

*LE MATT MUSIC, LTD., %Stewart House, Hillbottom Rd., Highwycombe, Buckinghamshire **England** HP124HJ. Phone: (0494)-436301 or 436401. FAX: 0494 461832. Telex 837173. Art Director: Xavier Lee. Music publisher, record company and record producer. MCPS, PRS. Member MPA, PPL. Estab. 1971. Publishes 30 songs/year; publishes 10 new songwriters/year. Works with composers, lyricists; teams collaborators. Pays standard royalty.
Affiliates: Lee Music, Ltd., Swoop Records, Grenoville Records, Check Records, Zarg Records, Pogo Records, Ltd., R.T.F.M., R.T.L. Music.
How to Contact: Prefers 7½ or 15 ips reel-to-reel or cassette (or VHS/Beta 625/PAL system videocassette) with 1-3 songs and lyric and lead sheets. "Make sure name and address are on reel or cassette." SAE and IRC. Reports in 6 weeks.
Music: All types. Published "Hit Man" (by M. J. Lawson), recorded by Emmit Till (rock); "Rock 'n Roll Revival" (by Tyer), recorded by Elmer Goodbody Jr. (rock); "Mood Music" (by R.C. Bowman), recorded by R.C.B. Band (Library Music); "I Want You" (by D. Pritchard), recorded by Mr. Wonderful on Swoop Records (country rock); "What's the Name" (by J. Hoo), recorded by Hoo Bawd on Check Records (disco); and "Don't Leave Me" (by Gary Piper), recorded by Sight'n'Sound on Check Records (pop).

*TY LEMLEY MUSIC (TYMENA MUSIC), 100 S. Crestline Dr., #47, Las Vegas NV 89107. (702)878-3476. President: Ty Lemley. Music publisher (Tymena). ASCAP, BMI. Estab. 1967. Pays standard royalty.
How to Contact: Submit a demo tape by mail—unsolicited submissions are OK. Prefers cassette with lyric or lead sheet. SASE. Reports in 1 month.
Music: Mostly country and pop. Published "Ramblin' Ways" (by Ty Lemley) (country); "1 Day at Time" (by Bassett) (country); and "Offer Me Love" (by Ty Lemley) (pop), all recorded by Ty Lemley on Tymena Records.

"How to Use Your Songwriter's Market" (at the front of this book) contains comments and suggestions to help you understand and use the information in these listings.

LEMMEL MUSIC LTD., Cray Ave., Orpington, Kent BR5 3QP **England**. Music Director: Ron Smith. Head of Documents: Miss Sheelagh Gudgeon. Music publisher. PRS. Estab. 1960. Publishes 200-300 songs/year; publishes 5 new songwriters/year. Works with composers and lyricists. Pays standard royalty.
Affiliates: Rim Music (PRS), Mason Music Limited (PRS) and Lemmel Music.
How to Contact: Submit a demo tape—unsolicited submissions are OK. Prefers cassette and lead sheet. SAE and IRC.
Music: Mostly orchestral; also MOR, instrumental and pop. Published "Another 12 Minutes," written and recorded by Rigby on Rim Records (pop); "Time and Tide" (by Smith), recorded by Lennox on Headline Records (pop); and "Oh Lonely Me," written and recorded by Redway on Redrock Records.

*LEMON SQUARE MUSIC, Box 31819, Dallas TX 75231-0819. (214)750-0720. A&R: Mike Anthony. Music publisher. ASCAP. Estab. 1979. Publishes 10 songs/year. Teams collaborators. Pays standard royalty.
Affiliates: Friends of the General Music (BMI).
How to Contact: Write first and obtain permission to submit a tape. Prefers cassette with 1-2 songs and lyric sheets. "We do not return unsolicited material. Will contact only if interested." Reports in 6 weeks.
Music: Mostly country and gospel. Published "He's My Gentleman" (by Stan Ratlift), recorded by Audie Henry on RCA Records (country); "Like Goin' Home" (by Allison Gilliam), recorded by Susie Calvin on Canyon Creek Records (pop-country).

LEXINGTON ALABAMA MUSIC PUBLISHING CO., Rt. 1, Box 40, Lexington AL 35648. President: Darrell Glover. Music publisher, record company (Lamp Records), and record producer (Lamp Production Co.). BMI. Estab. 1981. Publishes 30 songs/year; publishes 3-5 new songwriters/year. Pays standard royalty.
How to Contact: Prefers cassette with 3 songs and lyric sheet. Does not return unsolicited material. Reports in 1 month "only if material can be used by company."
Music: Mostly country, pop and R&B; also rock and gospel. Published "Off The Wall" (by Curtis Hall), recorded by Apul on Lamp Records (southern rock); "Whoa" (by Jeff Quillen, C. Hall), recorded by Apul on Lamp Records (rock); and "You Are To Me" (by Curtis Hall), recorded by Apul on Lamp Records (pop).
Tips: "We want strong hooks, unusual ideas, and a new way of expressing old ideas."

*LIFT HIM UP MUSIC, 150 Fifth Ave., #1103, New York NY 10011. (212)691-5631. President: Paul Ferrar. Music publisher and record company. (Praise). ASCAP. Estab. 1983. Publishes 6 songs/year; publishes 2 new songwriters/year. Works with composers and lyricists; teams collaborators. Pays standard royalty.
How to Contact: Submit a demo tape by mail—unsolicited submissions are OK. Prefers cassette with 6 songs and lyric or lead sheet. SASE. Reports in 1 month.
Music: Mostly gospel, pop and A.C.; also jazz and blues.

*LIGHT FORCE MUSIC, P.O. Box 858, Sonoma CA 95476. (707)762-4858. Director of A&R: Shelly Trumbo. Music publisher (Victory, Bay City) and record producer (Victory Media Group). ASCAP. Estab. 1987. Publishes 30 songs/year; publishes 4 new songwriters/year. Works with composers; teams collaborators. Pays standard royalty.
Affiliates: Bay City Music (ASCAP).
How to Contact: Write first and obtain permission to submit a tape. Prefers cassette with 3 songs. Does not return unsolicited material. Reports in 3 months.
Music: Mostly rock, pop and Christian rock; also dance and folk/rock. Published "Tambla" (by S. Trumbo); and "Stars in Their Eyes" (by J. Raupp), both recorded by Shelly T. on Victory Records (rock).

LINEAGE PUBLISHING CO., Box 211, East Prairie MO 63845. (314)649-2211. (Nashville branch: 38 Music Sq. E., Nashville TN 37203. (615)255-8005.) Professional Manager: Tommy Loomas. Staff: Alan Carter and Joe Silver. Music publisher, record producer and record company. BMI. Pays standard royalty.
How to Contact: Query first. Prefers cassette with 2-4 songs and lyric sheet; include bio and photo if possible. SASE. Reports in 1 month.
Music: Country, easy listening, MOR, country rock, and top 40/pop. Published "Yesterdays Teardrops," and "Round & Round," (by Phil and Larry Burchett), recorded by the Burchetts on Capstan Records (country).

*LION HILL MUSIC PUBLISHING CO. (BMI), Box 110983, Nashville TN 37222-0983. (615)731-6640. Publisher: Wayne G. Leinsz. Music publisher. BMI. Estab. 1988. Publishes 10-20 songs/year; publishes a few new songwriters/year. Works with composers; teams collaborators. Pays standard royalty.
How to Contact: Submit a demo tape by mail—unsolicited submissions are OK. Prefers cassette with 3 songs and lead sheets. SASE. Reports back in 4 weeks.
Music: Mostly country, pop, humorous; also easy rock, gospel and bluegrass. Published "Your Old Cold Shoulder" (by Chris Caldwell), recorded by Chris Caldwell on Sebert Records (country); "Lisa's Dream (by Bonnie Hind), recorded by Bonnie Hind on Portland Records (country); and "The Best Years After All" (by Bonnie Hind), recorded by Bonnie Hind on Portland Records (country).

LISTEN AGAIN MUSIC, P.O. Box 463, Beaver PA 15009. Owner: William E. Watson. Music publisher. BMI. Estab. 1986. Publishes 10 songs/year; publishes 6 new songwriters/year. Works with composers and lyricists; teams collaborators occasionally. Pays standard royalty; pays cash advances on all songs signed.
How to Contact: Submit a demo tape—unsolicited submissions are OK. Prefers cassette with 2 songs and lyric sheet. "Must have lyric sheet and SASE." Reports in 6 weeks.
Music: Mostly country, top-40, rock; also R&B and MOR. Published "One Step Further," (by B. Watson), recorded by C.R. Band on 7 City Records (country).
Tips: "Submit only your best work; it should have a well conceived title. Concentrate on the lyric— we receive a lot of well produced tapes with weak lyrics. We also publish a monthly newsletter and give free listings to musicians seeking work, bands seeking musicians, or songwriters seeking collaborators."

LITA MUSIC, 3609 Donna Kay Dr., Nashville TN 37211. (615)331-6056. Owner and President: Justin Peters. Music publisher. ASCAP. Estab. 1986.
How to Contact: Submit a demo tape by mail—unsolicited submissions are OK. Prefers cassette with 10 or less songs and lyric or lead sheets. Does not return unsolicited material.
Music: Mostly pop, gospel and country; also reggae music. Published "We Can Make A Difference" (by Brett Perry), recorded by Al Denson on Celebration Records (pop); "No Other Like You" (by Mark Comden and Paula Carpenter), recorded by Twila Paris and Tony Melendez on StarSong Records (gospel); "From the Depths of My Soul" (by John Miller), recorded by Enoch Rich, on Revive Records (gospel); "El Shaddai" (by Michael Card/John Thompson), recorded by Amy Grant and Imperials on Word Records and 'Sanctuary" (by J. Thompson and R. Scruggs), recorded by Continental Singers on Christian Artists records.

LITTLE, BITTY, MIDI CITY MUSIC COMMITTY, P.O. Box 897, Hartford CT 06120. (203)548-0212. Director: Silver Sargent. Music publisher, record company (S.O.C., Silsar and Blue Wave Records), record producer (Silsar Music), management firm (Artist Collective Management and Tri-Sarge Productions). BMI. Estab. 1984. Publishes 13 songs/year; publishes 4 new songwriters/year. Works with composers; teams collaborators. Pays standard royalty.
Affiliate: Silsar Music (BMI).
How to Contact: Write first and obtain permission to submit. Prefers cassette (or VHS videocassette) with 4-6 songs and lyric or lead sheet. "Include a resume." SASE. Reports in 6 weeks.
Music: Mostly funk, soul and R&B; also gospel, jazz and light rock. Published "Keepers of the Dream"; "Handwriting on the Wall"; "Jesus Is Real" all gospel written by Silver and recorded by Silsar on S.O.C. Records; and "Hang Tuff" (by Maurice Starr), recorded by New Kids on the Block on CBS Records (rap).
Tips: "Put your strongest songs at the beginning of the tape."

*LIVE NOTE PUBLISHING (BMI), P.O. Box 16, Hampton Va 23669. (804)838-6930. A&R: Tom or Fonda Breeden. Music publisher. BMI. Estab. 1981. Publishes 20 songs/year; publishes 10 new songwriters/year. Works with composers and lyricists; teams collaborators. Pays standard royalty of 50%.
How to Contact: Submit a demo tape by mail—unsolicited submissions are OK. Prefers cassette with 2-3 songs and lyric sheets. SASE. Reports back in 4 weeks.
Music: Mostly country, rock and pop; also reviewing all types. Published "You Never Told Me" (by Doc Holiday and Tom Breeden), recorded by Savannah Ashley on Tug Boat Records (country); "It's The Music" (by Judith Guthro and Tom Breeden), recorded by Ronn Craddock on Door Knob Records (country); "Juke Box King" (by E. Wohanka, J. Guthro and T. Breeden), recorded by Kevin Irwin on Door Knob Records (country); and "But I Lie," written and recorded by Richie Balin on Door Knob Records (country).
Tips: "Send good quality tapes and typed lyric sheets, and always be sure to include address and phone numbers to contact."

*LO PINE MUSIC, P.O. Box 444, Taylor MI 48180. (313)942-0634. President: John D. Lollio. BMI. Music publisher. Estab. 1980. Publishes 3 songs/year; publishes 2 new songwriters/year. Pays standard royalty.

Affiliate: Carrie-Lynn.
How to Contact: Prefers cassette and lyric or lead sheet. SASE. Reports in 2 weeks.
Music: Mostly country and gospel. Published "Sweetest Worlds," written and recorded by Johni Dee on Ace (country); "If That's What Makes You Crazy," written and recorded by Marty Parker on Mystery Train (country); "After the Pain," (by Jim W. Rice), recorded by Johni Dee on Ace (country); and "Jesus, I Love You," by J.D. Lollio on Ace Records (contemporary Christian).

*LODESTAR MUSIC, A DIVISION OF GENE KENNEDY ENTERPRISES, INC., 315 Mt. Juliet Rd., Mt. Juliet TN 37122. (615)754-0417. Contact: Karen Jeglum Kennedy. Music publisher, record company (Door Knob Records, Society Records), record producer (Gene Kennedy Enterprises, Inc.). SESAC. Estab. 1978. Publishes 5-10 songs/year; publishes 1-3 new songwriters/year. Works with composers and lyricists. Pays standard royalty.
Affiliates: Chip 'n' Dale Music Publishers, Inc. (ASCAP), Door Knob Music Publishing, Inc. (BMI).
How to Contact: Submit a demo tape by mail—unsolicited submissions are OK. Prefers cassette with 1-3 songs and lyric sheet. Include SASE for tape return and/or response. Send regular mail. SASE. Reports in 2 weeks.
Music: Mostly country and gospel. Published "Me Without You" (by Lance Middlebrook), recorded by Debbie Rich; "How I Love You In The Morning" (by Ed Jones and Elaine Jones), recorded by Joann Wintermute; both country, recorded on Door Knob Records.
Tips: "Respect our submission policy and keep trying."

*LOMAN CRAIG MUSIC, P.O. Box 2955, Nashville TN 37219. (615)331-1219 or (615)331-3703. President: Loman Craig. Music publisher, record company (Bandit Records), record producer (Loman Craig Productions). BMI, ASCAP, SESAC. Estab. 1979. Publishes 15 songs/year; publishes 5 new songwriters/year. Works with composers and lyricists. Pays standard royalty.
Affiliates: Outlaw Music of Memphis (BMI), Doulikit Music (SESAC).
How to Contact: Submit a demo tape by mail—unsolicited submissions are OK. Prefers cassette with 2-3 songs and lyric sheet. "Does not have to be a full production demo. Can be guitar/piano vocal demo." SASE. Reports in 3 weeks.
Music: Mostly country and pop; also bluegrass. Published "Love Me As Long" (by Craig-Craig), recorded by The Arbuckles on Bandit Records (bluegrass); "Mansion-Mind," written and recorded by Pat Riley on Bandit Records (pop); and "High on Music," written and recorded by Allen Gray on Bandit Records (country rock).

LONNY TUNES BMI, (formerly Schonfeld Companies), P.O. Box 460086, Garland TX 75046. President: Lonny Schonfeld. Music publisher, record company (KAOS Records). BMI. Estab. 1988. Publishes 6-8 songs/year; publishes 2-3 new songwriters/year. Works with composers and lyricists; teams collaborators. Pays standard royalty.
How to Contact: Submit a demo tape by mail—unsolicited submissions are O.K. Prefers cassette with 3-5 songs and lyric sheets. Expensive demos are not necessary, but please don't send "garage" tapes either. Make sure lyric and melody stand out. SASE. Reports in 6-8 weeks.
Music: Mostly pop, rock, children's and country. Published "Burning Bright" written and recorded by John Megert (pop); "Living For Love" (by John Megert), recorded by Paul McCarthy (pop), both on Puzzle Records; and "The Little Bitty Chicken" (by Charles Goodman) (children's).
Tips: "Don't worry about market trends—a good song is a good song. Finding a market for a song is our job. Many artists are looking for outside material again. The songwriter is again becoming the backbone of the music industry. Send us your best. If you don't think it's great no one else will either."

LOOKING GOOD MUSIC, P.O. Box 56631, Sherman Oaks CA 91413. (818)781-1037. Chairman: Michael D'Anna. Music publisher. ASCAP. Estab. 1980. Member of Harry Fox Agency, CMRRA. Publishes 3-10 songs/year; publishes 1-3 new songwriters/year. Works with complete songs only. Pays standard royalty.
How to Contact: Prefers cassette with 1-3 songs and lyric sheet. SASE required. Does not return unsolicited material. Reports in 2 months.
Music: Mostly pop and rock; also R&B. Published "Me and You" (pop/Top 40) and "Out to You" (AOR-A/C); all written and recorded by Mickey Dee on Rock City Records.

*THE LORENZ CORPORATION, 501 E. Third St., Dayton OH 45401-0802. (513)228-6118. Corp. Vice President: Larry F. Pugh. Music Publisher. ASCAP, BMI. Estab. 1890. Publishes 500 songs/year; 10 new songwriters/year. Hires staff writers. Works with composers and lyricists; teams collaborators. Pays standard royalty.
How to Contact: Submit manuscript (completely arranged); tape not necessary. SASE. Reports in 4 months.
Music: Interested in religious/Christian, high school choral and organ/piano music; also band music.

LOUIE B. PUBLISHING, Box 15117, Kansas City MO 64106. General Manager: Marion Brown. Music publisher, record company (Quinton Productions and QP Records) and record producer. BMI. Estab. 1967. Publishes 10-20 songs/year; publishes 10-12 new songwriters/year. Works with composers and lyricists. Pays standard royalty.
How to Contact: Write first to get permission to submit a tape. Prefers cassette (or VHS videocassette if possible) with maximum 3 songs and lyric sheet or lead sheet. SASE required for return of material. Reports 1-8 weeks.
Music: Top 40, R&B, gospel, country and "crossover." Published "Paradise" (dance); "Shake Me Up" (ballad) (both by C. Bristow/L.Brown), recorded by Demetrios; and "You're So Cold" (by C. Bristow), recorded by L. Brown (dance), all on Paradise Records.
Tips: "We are reviewing material for record production so material should be hit single quality with strong hook. Write about real life situations."

*LOUX MUSIC PUBLISHING CO., 2 Hawley Lane, Hannacroix NY 12087-0034. (518)756-2273. Contact: Editorial Review Committee. Music publisher. ASCAP. Estab. 1976. Publishes 40 songs/year; publishes varying number of new songwriters/year. Works with composers. Pays 5-10%.
How to Contact: Call first and obtain permission to submit a tape. Prefers cassette. SASE. Reports in 4 months.
Music: Mostly classical, Medieval and Renaissance.
Tips: We are publishers of music for early instruments, recorder and/or voice.

*LOVE DOVE PRODUCTIONS, 811 Crotonia Pk .N., Bronx NY 10460. (212)294-6112. Music publisher and record company (Love Dove Music, New Vibe Records) and record producer (New Vibe Records). BMI. Estab. 1989. Publishes 2-4 new songwriters/year. Works with composers and/or lyricists; teams collaborators. Pays standard royalty.
Affiliates: Love Dove Music (BMI).
How to Contact: Submit a demo tape by mail—unsolicited submissions are O.K. Prefers cassette (or VHS & BETA videocassette if available) with a minimum of 4 songs. SASE. Reports in 5 weeks.
Music: Mostly R&B, house, gospel. Published "It's You" (by Leslia Dove), recorded on New Vibe Records (house); "You Changed Me" (by Lesia Dove/A. DeVeaux), recorded on New Vibe Records (R&B); and "In the Breeze" (by Gerald Trottmen) recorded on New Vibe records (jazz).
Tips: "Be dedicated, work hard and keep trying. House music should be the next revolution in the business."

LOVEFORCE INTERNATIONAL, Box 241648, Los Angeles CA 90024. Submissions Manager: T. Wilkins. Music publishers, record company and international record promotion company. BMI. Estab. 1979. Publishes 5-10 songs/year; publishes 2 new songwriters/year. Pays standard royalty.
How to Contact: Write first and obtain permission to submit. Prefers cassette (or VHS videocassette) with 2 songs maximum and lyric sheet. "SASE a must." Reports in 6 weeks.
Music: Mostly pop, rock and R&B; also ballads, country and gospel. Published "One World One People," (reggae); "The Skids," "Blue Rock," and "Godfather of Love" recorded by Bandit on Loveforce International Records (soul/rap).
Tips: "We prefer Master quality demos and working with writer/artists who put their own records out. If you want a response, enclose a SASE."

LOVEY MUSIC, INC., P.O. Box 630755, Miami FL 33163. (305)935-4880. President: Jack Gale. Music publisher. BMI. Estab. 1981. Publishes 50 songs/year; publishes 10 new songwriters/year. Pays standard royalty.
Affiliates: Cowabonga Music, Inc. (ASCAP) and Lovey Music, Inc. (BMI).
How to Contact: Submit a demo tape by mail—unsolicited submissions are O.K. Prefers cassette or VHS videocassette with 1-2 songs and lyric sheets. Does not return unsolicited material. "We report only if we can use a song."
Music: Mostly country crossover and country. Published "Southern Belle" (by Helms and Hall), recorded by Bobby Helms on Playback Records (country); "One Night A Week" (by Paul Hotchkiss), recorded by Robin Right on Roto Noto Records (country); and "Here We Lie" (by Gary Adams), recorded by Bonnie Guitar on Playback Records (country).

THE LOWERY GROUP of Music Publishing Companies, 3051 Clairmont Rd. NE, Atlanta GA 30329. (404)325-0832. General Professional Manager: Cotton Carrier. Music publisher. ASCAP, BMI. Estab. 1953. Publishes 100 songs/year; publishes varying number of new songwriters/year. Works with composers and lyricists. Pays standard royalty.
Affiliates: Lowery Music Co., Inc. (BMI); Low-Sal, Inc. (BMI); Low-Twi, Inc. (BMI); Low-Ab Music (BMI); Low-Bam Music (BMI); Low-Ja Music (BMI); Low-Rico Music (BMI); Low-Thom Music (BMI); Eufaula Music (BMI); Steel City Music (BMI); Wonder Music (BMI); Eternal Gold Music

(BMI); New Testament Music (BMI); Songs of Faith (BMI); Brother Bill's Music (ASCAP); Miss Delta Music (ASCAP); Terri Music (ASCAP); and Holy Ground Music (ASCAP).

How to Contact: Prefers cassette with 3 songs and lyric sheet. Does not return unsolicited material. "No response unless we wish to publish the song."

Music: Mostly country, MOR and pop; also gospel, rock and New Age. Published "I Beg Your Pardon (I Never Promised You A Rose Garden)" (by Joe South, Barry Harris), recorded by Kon Kan on Atlantic Records (pop); "Every Time You Go Outside I Hope It Rains," by The Burch Sisters on Mercury Records; "Old Bridges Burn Slow" (by Joe South/Jerry Meaders/Sanford Brown), recorded by Billy Joe Royal on Atlantic American Records; "Don't It Make You Wanta Go Home" (by Joe South), recorded by Butch Baker on Mercury Records; "Most of All" (by Buddy Buie/J. R. Cobb), recorded by Leon Raines on Southern Tracks Records; and "Sad Cliches" (by Buddy Buie/Ronnie Hammond), recorded by Atlanta on Southern Tracks Records (all country). Copublished "I Still Believe," recorded by Lee Greenwood.

LUCKY'S KUM-BA-YA PUBLISHING CO., Box 6-9283 Evergreen, Brohman MI 49312. (616)745-2270. President: Ross "Lucky" Fulton. Music publisher and record company. ASCAP. Estab. 1976. Publishes 20 songs/year. Works with composers.

How to Contact: Write first and obtain permission to submit. Prefers cassette.

Music: Country, gospel and pop/light rock. Published "Thanks I Needed That" (light rock); "Rocking in the Potato Patch" (light rock); and "Girls, Women and Loving" (country), all written by R. Fulton.

HAROLD LUICK & ASSOCIATES MUSIC PUBLISHER, Box B, Carlisle IA 50047. (515)989-3679. President: Harold L. Luick. Music publisher, record company, record producer and music industry consultant. BMI. Publishes 25-30 songs/year; publishes 5-10 new songwriters/year. Pays standard royalty or will negotiate with established writer.

How to Contact: Write or call first about your interest or arrange personal interview. Prefers cassette with 3-5 songs and lyric sheet. SASE. Reports in 3 weeks.

Music: Traditional country and hard core country. Published "It Must Be Love," (by Roger and Sandra Davis), recorded by Bobbie Brown on Footstomper Records; "Cheese and Butter," written and recorded by Darrell C. Thomas on Footstomper Records; and "Waylon Sing To Mama," written and recorded by Darrell C. Thomas on Ozark Opry Records, (all country).

Tips: "Ask yourself these questions: Does my song have simplicity of lyric and melody? Good flow and feeling? A strong story line? Natural dialogue? Hook chorus, lyric hooks, melody hooks? If it doesn't, then why should a publisher or A&R person take the time to listen to it?"

*MAC-ATTACK PUBLISHING, 14699 NE 18th Ave. #6J, N. Miami FL 33181. (305)947-8315. President: Michael J. McNamee. Music publisher and record producer (Mac-Attack Prod., Inc.). ASCAP. Estab. 1988. Publishes 3-10 songs/year; publishes 1-5 new songwriters/year. Works with composers and lyricists. Pays standard royalty.

How to Contact: Submit a demo tape by mail—unsolicited submissions are OK. Prefers cassette and VHS videocassete with a maximum of 3 songs and lyric sheet. SASE. Reports in 1-2 months.

Music: Mostly pop, rock, alternative; also R&B, New Age and new contemporary. Published "It's Just Like You," and "This Fligan Icehole," (by M. McNamee) recorded by The Maxxturs on Pisces Records (progressive rock and dance) and "What Time Is It?" (by R. Rodriguez), recorded by Don't Know Yet on Dial Records (rereleased on Epic Records).

Tips: "Less is more and simple is better. Great songs can usually be accompanied by just a guitar or a piano—think about it."

JIM McCOY MUSIC, Rt. 2, Box 114 H, Berkeley Springs WV 25411. Owners: Bertha or Jim McCoy. Music publisher, record company (Winchester Records) and record producer (Jim McCoy Productions). BMI. Estab. 1973. Publishes 18 songs/year; publishes 3-5 new songwriters/year. Pays standard royalty.

Affiliates: Alear Music and New Edition Music (BMI).

How to Contact: Submit a demo tape—unsolicited submissions are OK. Prefers cassette, 7½ or 15 ips reel-to-reel (or VHS or Beta videocassette) with 6 songs. Does not return unsolicited material. Reports in 1 month.

Music: Mostly country, country/rock and rock; also bluegrass and gospel. Published "This Woman" (by J. McCoy), recorded by Ronnie Flook; and "She Loved Me Out of My Mind" written and recorded by D.Campbell; both on Winchester Records (country).

MAGIC MESSAGE MUSIC, Box 8734, Incline Village NV 89450. (202)831-9116. Owner: Alan Redstone. Music publisher and record company (Sureshot Records). ASCAP. Estab. 1979. Publishes 6 songs/year; publishes 1 new songwriter/year. Pays standard royalty.

How to Contact: Submit a demo tape by mail—unsolicited submissions are OK. Prefers cassette with 2 songs and lyric sheets. SASE. Reports in 1 week.
Music: Mostly country, ballads and rock. Published "This Time Around," "Salomé" and "Cars Girls Dreams," all written and recorded by Alan Redstone on Sureshot Records (country rock).
Tips: "Best two songs only. Have professional presentation and SASE."

MAINE-LY COUNTRY MUSIC, 212 Stillwater Ave., Old Town ME 04468. (207)827-2185. Owner: Jeff Simon. Music publisher, record company and record producer (Maine-ly Country Records). SESAC. Estab. 1988. Publishes 1-5 songs/year; publishes 2 new songwriters/year. Works with lyricists. Pays standard royalty.
How to Contact: Submit a demo tape by mail—unsolicited submissions are OK. Prefers VHS video-cassette with 1-3 songs and lyric or lead sheets. SASE. Reports in 1 month.
Affiliates: Maine-ly Music (BMI).
Music: Mostly country and country-rock. Published "Goin' Back to Bein' Me" (by J. Simon), recorded by Jeff Simon; "Song of Yesterday" (by G. Willette and A. Ames), recorded by Allison Ames; and "You Know You're On My Mind"(by A. Ames), recorded by Allison Ames, all recorded on Maine-ly Country Records (country).
Tips: "Have a good hook within your song. Keep song length 3½ minutes or less. Be original and have positive message and tell a story."

*****MAKIN TRACKS MUSIC**, 17 Water St., Dracut MA 01826. (508)957-5781. Publisher: Henry Rowe. Music publisher, record company (Hazardous Records) and record producer (Henry Rowe). ASCAP. Estab. 1986. Publishes 4 songs/year; publishes 2 new songwriters/year. Works with composers and lyricists; teams collaborators. Pays standard royalty.
How to Contact: Submit a demo tape by mail—unsolicited submissions are OK. Prefers cassette (VHS videocassette if available) with 4-6 songs and lyric sheet. Does not return unsolicited material. Reports in 2 months.
Music: Mostly metal, rock and pop; also fusion, fazz and new age. Published "Half Life" and "Danger Zone" (by Hazardous Waste) (metal); and "Candle to the Magic" (by Johann Smith) (rock), all recorded by Makin Tracks on Hazardous Records.
Tips: "Have a solid sound and good production."

MANAPRO (MANAGEMENT ARTIST PRODUCTIONS), 82 Sherman St., Passaic NJ 07055. (201)777-6109. Executive Producer: Tomasito Bobadilla. Production company. ASCAP, BMI. Estab. 1987. Publishes 2 songs/year; publishes 3-4 songwriters/year. Hires staff songwriters. Works with lyricists; teams collaborators. Pays standard royalty.
Affiliates: No Mas (BMI), In Che (ASCAP), Step on My Head (BMI).
How to Contact: Submit a demo tape by mail—unsolicited submissions are OK. Prefers cassette with 2 songs and lyric sheet. SASE. Reports in 1 month.
Music: Mostly pop, dance and rock; also R&B and new age. Published "Toss of a Dime" (by S. Lanni, R.Nissen), recorded by Fear of Falling on Emergency Records (rock/pop) and *Sin Syndicate* (by Chein Garcia), recorded by Sin Syndicate on Trumpet Records (dance)
Tips: "Songs should have very catchy hooks, must also be very instrumental."

THE MARCO MUSIC GROUP INC., P.O. Box 24454, Nashville TN 37202. (615)269-7074; FAX: (615)269-0131. General Manager: Terri Walker. Music publisher. Estab. 1988. Publishes approximately 50-75 songs/year; 14-15 new songwriters/year. Pays standard royalty.
Affiliates: Goodland Publishing Company (ASCAP), Marc Isle Music (BMI) and Gulf Bay Publishing (SESAC).
How to Contact: Call first to get permission to send a tape. Prefers cassette (or VHS videocassette) with 1-2 songs and lyric sheet. SASE.
Music: Country, MOR and contemporary.
Tips: "Only send your best 2 or 3 songs with lyrics accompanying. Expect a reply within 4 weeks."

*****MARKS CENTRAL PUBLISHING UNIT**, P.O. Box 540, Dearborn Heights MI 48127. (313)278-6068. President: Mark S. Shearer. Music publisher. BMI. Estab. 1989. Publishes 10 songs/year; 5-10 new songwriters/year. Pays standard 50% royalty.
How to Contact: Call first and obtain permission to submit a tape. Prefers cassette (or VHS videocassette if available) with 3-5 songs. "Promo pack with all submissions." Does not return unsolicited material. Reports in 3 weeks.
Music: Mostly hard rock/heavy metal, alternative and pop. Published "Dangerous Love" (by L. Crystal), recorded by Crystal Rose, "Loves on The Line" written and recorded by B. Glastetter and "Bad Luck" (by R. Miller), recorded by Mad Hatter all on Hardway Records (hard rock).
Tips: "Send strong songs; complete promo pack."

MARULLO MUSIC PUBLISHERS, 1121 Market St., Galveston TX 77550. (409)762-4590. President: A.W. Marullo Sr. Music publisher, record company (Red Dot) and record producer (A.W. Marullo Productions). BMI, SESAC. Estab. 1952. Publishes 27-37 songs/year; publishes 7-14 songwriters/year. Sometimes hires staff writers. Pays standard royalty.
Affiliates: Marullo Music (BMI), Don & Willie Music (SESAC).
How to Contact: Submit a demo tape by mail—unsolicited submissions are O.K. Cassette with only 4 songs. SASE. Reports in 7 weeks.
Music: Mostly country, pop and R&B; also rock, top 40 rock, country and dance songs. Published "Do You Feel Sexy" (by T. Pindrock), recorded by Flach Point on Puzzle Red Dot Records (top 40 rock); "Love Machine" (by T. Pindrock), recorded by Susan Moninger on Puzzle Red Dot Records (top 40 rock); and "You Put the Merry in My Christmas" (by E. Dunn), recorded by Mary Craig on Puzzle Red Dot Records (country and top 40 rock).
Tips: "Send only your best songs. The songwriter with a *new* idea is a crank, until the idea succeeds."

ANDY MARVEL MUSIC, P.O. Box 181, Holbrook NY 11741. President: Andy Marvel. Music publisher, record company (Alyssa Records), and record producer (Marvel Productions and Ricochet Records). ASCAP. Estab. 1981. Publishes 30 songs/year; publishes 10 new songwriters/year. Works with composers and lyricists; teams collaborators. Pays standard royalty.
Affiliates: Andysongs (BMI) and Bing, Bing, Bing Music (ASCAP).
How to Contact: Prefers cassette (or VHS videocassette) with 3 songs and lyric sheet. Reports in 3 weeks only with SASE. "No need for permission."
Music: Mostly pop, R&B and top 40; also country. Published "Learning to Live with a Heartache," (by Andy Marvel/Sheree Sano), recorded by Andy Marvel on Alyssa Records (pop); and "Love Will Never Be the Same Without You," (by Andy Marvel/Don Levy), recorded by John Wesley Shipp on Jamie Records (pop).
Tips: "Be patient. Your tape will be listened to. It helps if your song is produced, but it's not necessary."

MASTER AUDIO, INC./MASTER SOUND, INC./LYRESONG, INC., 1227 Spring St. NW, Atlanta GA 30309. (404)873-6425. Contact: Babs Richardson. Music publisher and recording studio. BMI, ASCAP. Estab. 1960. Publishes 1-2 songs/year. Pays standard royalty.
Affiliates: Paydirt Music (ASCAP), Legal Tender (ASCAP) and Seyah Music (BMI).
How to Contact: Write or call first to get permission to send a tape. Prefers cassette with 2-3 songs. SASE. Reports in 1 month.
Music: Country, disco, gospel, R&B, soul and top 40/pop. Published *Great News*, (by Troy Ramey), recorded by T. Ramey and the Soul Searchers on Nashboro Records (black gospel); "Try Jesus, " recorded by T. Ramey (gospel); "Tea Cups and Doilies," (by Mac Frampton), recorded by M. Frampton on Triumvirate Records (Broadway show type); and "Double Shot (of My Baby's Love)," recorded by Joe Stampley (country); and "Forget The Man" (by Celia Lipton) on IRC Label.
Tips: "After submitting a requested tape, please allow us time to listen and allow us to contact the writer."

MASTER'S COLLECTION PUBLISHING & T.M.C. PUBLISHING, P.O. Box 362, Station A, Rexdale, Ontario M9W 5L3 **Canada**. (416)746-1991. President: Paul J. Young. Music publisher and record company. PROCAN, CAPAC. Member CIRPA. Estab. 1977. Publishes 12 songs/year; publishes 3 new songwriters/year. Pays standard royalty.
How to Contact: Submit a demo tape—unsolicited submissions are OK. Prefers cassette (or VHS videocassette) with 3-6 songs. Does not return unsolicited material. Reports in 1 month.
Music: Christian/religious. Published "Line of Vision" and "Friends," written and recorded by Martin Barrett on The Master's Collection Label (Christian religious); and "One City Stands," (by Andrew Donaldson), recorded on The Master's Collection Records.

*THE MATHES COMPANY, P.O. Box 22653, Nashville TN 37202. Owner: David W. Mathes. Music publisher, record company Star Image, Heirborn, King David), record producer (The Mathes Company) and music industry consultant. BMI, ASCAP, SESAC. Estab. 1962. Publishes 30-50 songs/year; publishes 10-30 new songwriters/year. Pays standard royalty.
Affiliates: Sweet Singer Music (BMI), Sing Sweeter Music (ASCAP) and Star of David (SESAC).
How to Contact: Submit a demo tape by mail—unsolicited submissions are OK. Prefers cassette 7½-15 IPS reel-to-reel (VHS/BETA videocassette) with maximum of 3 songs and lyric sheet. "Only positive country songs (not controversial, political, demeaning or sex oriented). Only gospel songs that are not rock contemporary, and no new age music." SASE. Reports in 2 weeks.
Music: Mostly gospel (country), country and instrumental; also jingle ideas. Published "I'm in Ohio Now (with Georgia on My Mind)" (by C. Donald Frost), recorded by Johnny Newman on Star Image Records; and "My Love For You" (by David Mathes/DeAnna Mathes), recorded by Warner Mack on Sapphire Records (both country).

Tips: "Submit only your best songs and follow submission requirements."

*MAYHEM MUSIC/BUGTUSSLE RECORDING CO., Box 277, Weymouth MA 02190. (617)293-5671. "Poobah": Paul R. Santo. Music publisher, record company (Bugtussle Recording Co.) and record producer. ASCAP. Estab. 1986. Publishes 5 songs/year; published "1 or 2 new songwriters in 1989, more in 1990." Teams collaborators. Pays standard royalty of 50%.
Affiliates: Mayhem Music (ASCAP).
How to Contact: Write first and obtain permission to submit a tape. Prefers cassette (VHS videocassette if available) with 3 songs. "Keep bios short and sweet, but include info on personal goals." Does not return unsolicited material. Reports in 1 month.
Music: Mostly rock, metal-rap, pop; also jazz, thrash and easy listening. Published "Her Eyes" (by James Given), recorded by Jim & I on Bugtussle Records (pop); "World of Your Own" (by Paul Santo), recorded by Paul Santo on Bugtussle Records (rock); and "Please Come Back" (by John D.), recorded by Johnny D on Ground Zero Records (hard rock).
Tips: "Cohesive conceptual continuity."

*MCR RECORDS, Box 7500, Red Bush KY 41219. (606)265-3688. Owner: T.C. Cantrell. Record company (MCR Records), record producer. BMI. Estab. 1980. Pays standard royalty.
How to Contact: Submit a demo tape by mail—unsolicited submissions are OK. Prefers cassette with 2 songs. SASE.
Music: Mostly country.

*MDM PRODUCTIONS, 117 W. 8th, Hays KS 67601. (913)625-9634. President: Mark Meckel. Music publisher, record company (M.D.M. Records), record producer (Sunset Productions), and management firm. BMI. Member CASK and SRS. Estab. 1978. Publishes 20 songs/year; publishes 3-4 new songwriters/year. Works with composers and lyricists; teams collaborators. Pays standard royalty. Sales royalty when song or artist is recorded, outright fee from recording artist, outright fee from record company.
Affiliate: Street Singer Music (BMI).
How to Contact: Prefers cassette with minimum 3 songs and lyric sheet. SASE.
Music: Mostly pop, country rock, 50s rock, Christian rock, R&B and Christmas; also MOR, gospel, blues and dance-oriented. Published "Angel" (by C. Connelly), recorded by C. Connelly (pop rock); "You Inspire Me" (by M Selby), recorded by M. Selby (R&B); and "Shot Gun Wedding" (by M. Benish), recorded by M. Benish (country), all on M.D.M. Records.
Tips: "Be willing to change and work with a producer."

MEGA-STAR MUSIC, 248 W. 5th St., Deer Park NY 11729. (212)713-5229. General Manager: Barry Yearwood. Music publisher, record producer (Barry Yearwood) and management firm (Power Brokerage Management). Estab. 1984. Publishes 4 songs/year; publishes 4 new songwriters/year. Pays standard royalty.
How to Contact: Prefers cassette with 4 songs. Does not return unsolicited material. Reports in 1 month.
Music: Mostly dance and R&B; also pop. Published "Dancing to the Beat," written and recorded by Henderson and Whitfield on Park Place Records; "Solar Flight," written and recorded by Richard Bush on Island Records; and "Mind Your Own Business," written and recorded by R. Bush on Laser-7 Records.

MERTIS MUSIC CO. INC., P.O. Box 21748, Detroit MI 48221-1843. (313)862-5880. President: Mertis John. Music publisher and record company (Meda Records Inc.). BMI. Publishing company estab. 1961; record company estab. 1981. Publishes 40 songs/year; publishes 8-10 new songwriters/year. Works with composers and teams collaborators. Pays standard royalty.
Affiliate: Otis Music Publishing Co.
How to Contact: Prefers cassette (or VHS videocassette) with 4-8 songs and lyric and lead sheet. SASE. Reports in 1 month or ASAP.
Music: Mostly pop and R&B; also country and gospel. Published "Jesus Is Mine," and "When I Got Saved," both written and recorded by Lessie Williams (both gospel); "Why Did You Leave Me," (by M. John), recorded by Chicago Pete (R&B); "Traffic Mania" (by M. John), recorded by Joe Hunter, all on Meda Records.

MICAH MUSIC, 43 Applemore Rd., Scarborough ON M1B 1R7 **Canada**. (416)298-3108. President: Oswald L. Burke. Music publisher and record company (Micah Records). CAPAC. Estab. 1985. Publishes 15 songs/year; 3 new songwriters/year. Teams collaborators. Pays standard royalty.

Affiliates: Job Music (PROCAN).
How to Contact: Submit a demo tape by mail—no unsolicited material. Prefers cassette with 2-3 songs and lyric sheets. SASE. Reports in 8 weeks.
Music: Gospel. Published "Make Us Better" (by E. Haughton); "I Wanna Be More" (by Elvis Boddie); and "One Day" (by K. Burke), all recorded by Sweet Sound on Micah Records (gospel).

MIGHTY TWINNS MUSIC, 9134 S. Indiana Ave., Chicago IL 60619. (312)737-4348. General Manager: Ron Scott. Music publisher and record producer. BMI. Member NMPA, Midwest Inspirational Writers Association. Estab. 1977. Publishes 4-10 songs/year; publishes 5 new songwriters/year. Works with composers and lyricists; teams collaborators. Pays standard royalty.
How to Contact: Submit a demo tape—unsolicited submissions are OK. Prefers cassette with 2-4 songs and lyric sheet. SASE "only if you want material returned." Reports in 2 months.
Music: Mostly top 40, R&B, "hot" inspirational and gospel; also children's. Published "I Really Want You," (by E.Z. Kimball), and "Dreams," (by R. Scott), both recorded by Smoke City on Epic Records (top 40/R&B); "Patches," (recorded on Columbia Records); and "I'm Gonna Miss You," by the Artistics.
Tips: Looking for "good hot songs with hot hooks. Please have tapes cued up. *Do not write for permission!* Submit a cued up cassette and wait for our response. No materials returned without proper postage. Take the time to write and re-write to get the song in its best form; then make a good clear/audible demo."

*MILLHOUSE MUSIC, 1710 Roy Acuff Pl., Nashville TN 37203. (615)255-0428. Professional Manager: Steve Dukes. Music publisher. BMI. Estab. 1978. Publishes 150 songs/year; publishes 10 new songwriters/year. Hires staff writers. Works with composers and lyricists; teams collaborators. Pays standard royalty.
Affiliates: Sheddhouse Music (ASCAP), Wooden Wonder Music (SESAC).
How to Contact: Write or call first and obtain permission to submit a tape. Prefers cassette with 3-5 songs and lyric sheet. Does not return unsolicited material. Reports in 3 weeks.
Music: Mostly country, pop and rock. Published "It Ain't Nothin" (by Tony Haselden), recorded by Keith Whitley on RCA Records (country); "80s Ladies," written and recorded by K.T. Oslin on RCA Records (country); and "Checkmate" (by Keith Hinton), recorded by Paul Rodgers on Atlantic Records (rock).

MIMIC MUSIC, Box 201, Smyrna GA 30081. (404)432-2454. Manager: Tom Hodges. Music publisher, record producer, record company (Trend Records, Stepping Stones, BOAM, Trend/Side Records, Trendsetter Records and Atlanta Records) and management company. BMI, ASCAP. Estab. 1965. Publishes 40 songs/year; publishes 7 new songwriters/year. Works with composers and lyricists; teams collaborators. Pays standard royalty.
Affiliates: Skipjack Music (BMI), Stepping Stone (BMI), and British Overseas Airways Music/BOAM (ASCAP).
How to Contact: Submit a demo tape—unsolicited submissions are OK. Prefers cassette (or VHS videocassette) with 3-10 songs and lyric sheet. "Open to VHS and also for distribution on accepted videos." SASE. Reports in 2 weeks.
Music: Mostly country; also bluegrass, blues, church/religious, easy listening, gospel, MOR, R&B, rock, soul and top 40/pop. Published "Follow You Home" (by Wood/Resua), recorded by Wood/Resua on Trend Records (country); "The Things You Took" (by R. Hullet), recorded by Marlon Frizzell on Trend Records (country); and "Road Lovin' Man" (by D. Ray), recorded by Jerry Wright on Rising Star Records (country). "I also have Keith Bradford, Bill Price, Dell Wood, Lin Butler, Tara Bailey, Deb Watson and Frank Brannon on a mixed artists cassette album."

*MODERN ATTACK PUBLISHING, 61 Palm St., Hartford CT 06112. Director, Marketing: R. Coley. Music publisher. BMI. Estab. 1987. Publishes 12 songs/year; publishes 3 new songwriters/year. Works with lyricists; teams collaborators. Pays standard royalty.
How to Contact: Prefers cassette with 3 songs. "Include biographic information, photos." Does not return unsolicited material. Reports in 3 weeks.
Music: Mostly rap and club. Published "Soft Like Margarine," by M.C. Kapre; "Smiling Faces" and "Srictly For the Jeeps" by Mellow G-Man and "Expressions."

MONTINA MUSIC, P.O. Box 702, Snowdon Station, Montreal, Quebec H3X 3X8 **Canada**. Professional General Manager: David P. Leonard. Music publisher. SOCAN. Estab. 1963. Pays standard royalty. Works with composers, lyricists; teams collaborators.

Affiliate: Sabre Music (SOCAN).
How to Contact: Submit a demo tape—unsolicited submissions are OK. Prefers cassette, phonograph record (or VHS videocasette) and lyric sheet. Does not return unsolicited material.
Music: Mostly top 40; also bluegrass, blues, country, dance-oriented, easy listening, folk, gospel, jazz, MOR, progressive, R&B, rock and soul.
Tips: "Maintain awareness of styles and trends of your peers who have succeeded professionally. Understand the markets to which you are pitching your material. Persevere at marketing your talents. Develop a network of industry contacts, first locally, then regionally, nationally."

MOON JUNE MUSIC, 4233 SW. Marigold, Portland OR 97219. President: Bob Stoutenburg. Music publisher. Estab. 1971. Pays standard royalty.
How to Contact: Prefers cassette (or VHS videocassette) with 2-10 songs. SASE.
Music: Country.

*MORE OF THE SAME (BMI), 1000 Alabama, Sheffield AL 35660. (205)381-2060. President: Butch McGhee. Music publisher, record company (Ameika Records, MSSG Records). BMI, ASCAP, SESAC. Estab. 1985. Publishes 10-12 songs/year; publishes 3 new songwriters/year. Hires staff writers. Teams collaborators. Pays standard royalty.
Affiliates: Poncho Case Music (ASCAP), Music and More (SESAC).
How to Contact: Write or call first and obtain permission to submit a tape. Prefers cassette or VHS videocassette with 4 songs and lyric sheets. Does not return unsolicited material. Reports in 6-8 weeks.
Music: Mostly gospel, R&B and pop; also country. Published "Help Me Praise The Lord" (by Butch McGhee and Frank Williams), recorded by The Christianaires on MSSG Records; "Home Someday" (by Butch McGhee, Shawn Lee, Sr. and Harvey Thompson), recorded by Loretta Handy on Ameika Records; and "In the Midst Of It All" (by Butch McGhee), recorded by Charles Fold and the Fold Singers on MSSG Records; all gospel.

THE FRED MORRIS MUSIC GROUP, Suite 207, 50 Music Sq. West, Nashville TN 37203. (615)329-2591. Publishing Manager: Karen Morris. Music publisher and record company (Maxx Records). Publishes 10-15 songs/year; publishes 2-3 new songwriters/year. Pays standard royalty.
Affiliates: Karefree Music (BMI), Karlamor Music (ASCAP), Old Guide Music (BMI), First Million Music (ASCAP), and Two Bees Music (SESAC).
How to Contact: Submit a demo tape—unsolicited submissions are OK. Prefers cassette (or VHS videocassette) with 3-5 songs and lyric sheet. SASE. Reports in 1 month.
Music: Country, country/rock, pop and rock. No gospel. Published "Family Choir" (by Dolberg Blazy), recorded by Denise Reanhold on Echo Records (country); "All Dressed Up" (by Hotchkiss, Dulberg), recorded by Lorie Ann on Sing Me Records (country); and "You've Must Have Been Reading My Heart" (by Westberg), recorded by Jill Jordan on Maxx Records (country).

MOTHER BERTHA MUSIC PUBLISHING CO., INC., Penthouse Suite, 686 S. Arroyo Pkwy., Pasadena CA 91105. Administrative Director: Harold Esposito. Music publisher, record company (Phil Spector International) and record producer (Phil Spector Productions). BMI.
How to Contact: "We are not accepting or reviewing any new material or artists. Any unsolicited correspondence or material will not be returned."

*MOTHER MUSIC LTD., 30/32 Sir John Rogersons Quay, Dublin 2 **Ireland.** Contact: Barbara Galavan. Music publisher. PRS. Estab. 1984. works with composers. Pays negotiable royalty.
Affiliates: McGuinness Whelan Music Ltd.
How to Contact: Submit a demo tape by mail-unsolicited submissions are OK. Prefers cassette. SASE. Reports in 4-6 weeks.
Music: Interested in rock, pop and country; also folk. Published "Kiss the Ground" (by R. O'Hanlon), recorded by The Word; "I Have Fun" (by N. Toner), recorded by The Dixons; and "100 Boys" (by S. Carmody), recorded by The Golden Horde, all on Mother Records (all rock).

MOUNT SCOTT MUSIC, Box 105, Cooper TX 75432. Professional Manager: Jim Brewer. Music publisher, record company (MSM Records, Hālo Records, Bronco Records), record producer; artists signed to labels only. BMI. Estab. 1979. Publishes 3-4 songs/year. Works with composers and lyricists; teams collaborators. Pays standard royalty.
Affiliates: Pick the Hits Music.
How to Contact: Write first and obtain permission to submit a tape. Prefers cassette with 2 songs and lyric sheets. SASE. Reports in 4 weeks.
Music: Mostly contemporary country, traditional country and pop-rock. Published "Lovers Mountain" (by J. Brewer); "Angels Ain't Supposed to Cry" (by K. and J. Brewer); and "I'm A Believer" (by J. Brewer); all recorded by J. Lewis Brewer on MSM Records (traditional/country); and "Soft Touch"

(by M. Fox & J. Cross), recorded by Gwen Newton on Hālo Records (contemporary country).
Tips: "Submit only material that you truly believe is worth an artist/label spending several thousand dollars on, other—it's probably not good enough. While the market for writers/publishers getting a song recorded by a major artist/label is still tight and very hard to break into, more and more independents are getting records on the chart."

MOUNTAIN HERITAGE MUSIC CO., Rt. 3, Box 280, Galax VA 24333. (703)236-9249. Owner: Bobby Patterson. Music publisher and record company (Heritage Records, Frontier Productions and Mountain Records). BMI. Publishes 14 songs/year; publishes 2 new songwriters/year. Works with composers and lyricists. Pays standard royalty.
How to Contact: Prefers cassette with 3 songs and lyric sheet. SASE. Reports in 6 months.
Music: Mostly bluegrass, gospel and Christmas. Published "King of Kings" (by John R. Shaw); "Sing A Song For Jesus" (by Johnny Jackson), and "That's When He Carries You" (by Cullen Galyean) all recorded by The Christian Quartet on Heritage Records (bluegrass/gospel).
Tips: "Words must tell a complete story within 2½-3 minutes."

MR. MORT MUSIC, 44 Music Square E., Nashville TN 37203. (615)255-2175. President: Charles Fields. Music publisher, record company (Charta Records and Delux Records), and record producer (Charlie Fields). ASCAP. Estab. 1977. Publishes 50 songs/year; publishes 8 new songwriters/year. Pays standard royalty.
Affiliate: Jason Dee Music (BMI).
How to Contact: Prefers cassette with 1-4 songs and lead sheet. SASE. Reports in 2 weeks.
Music: Mostly MOR, easy listening and country; also blues and top 40/pop. Published "Carnival Carousel Horse" (by D. Walsh, J. Loiselle), Recorded by David Walsh on Charta Records (country); "Stranger" (by Fields, Walsh, Loiselle), recorded by Eddie Rivers on Charta (country); and "Just Play Me A Hurting Song" (by F. Nickins), recorded by Fran Nickens on Delux Records (country).

MSM MUSIKVERLAG WIEN, Zollergasse 13, Vienna A-1070 **Austria.** Music publisher. AKM, AUME. Estab. 1985. Works with composers and lyricists; teams collaborators. Publishes 40 songs/year; publishes 10 new songwriters/year. Pays standard royalty.
How to Contact: Submit a demo tape by mail—unsolicited submissions are OK. Prefers cassette with lyric sheet. SASE. Reports in 8 weeks.
Music: Mostly pop, dance and instrumental music; also new age.

*MUNIFICENT MUSIC, P.O. Box 2512, Austin TX 78768. (512)444-4666. Owner: Cass Hook. Music publisher, record company (Amazing Records) and record producer (Branch Productions). BMI. Estab. 1985. Publishes 10-20 songs/year; publishes 1 or 2 new songwriters/year.
How to Contact: Write to arrange a personal interview. Prefers cassette with at least 3 songs and lyric sheet. Does not return unsolicited material.
Music: Mostly rock n' roll, country rock and rhythm 'n' blues; also jazz, folk and reggae. Published "Lookin' for Fun" (by Ty Gavin/E. Cute/G. Howell); "No More Flamingos" (by Gavin/Jarmon/Howell); and "Share" (by Ty Gavin), all recorded by Hunt Sales on Amazing Records (rock).
Tips: "We are doing mostly artists who we record for release on Amazing Records."

*MUSIC AS SOFTWARE, INC., 175 Dolphin Cove Quay, Stamford CT 06902. (203)327-3800. Director of Marketing: Paul Jung. Music publisher. BMI. Estab. 1983. Publishes 35-40 songs/year; publishes 35-40 new songwriters/year. Works with composers. Pays standard royalty.
Affiliates: DMP Publishing, Inc. (ASCAP).
How to Contact: Write or call first and obtain permission to submit a tape. Prefers cassette. SASE. Reports in 2 months.
Music: Mostly jazz. Published "Moon Over Venice" (written and recorded by Thom Rotella); "See You at the Diner" (by Bob Smith), recorded by Bob's Diner; and "Jungle Cat" (written and recorded by Manfredo Fest), all on DMP Records (jazz).

*MUSIC BY BUTCH KELLY, 11 Shady Oak Trail, Charlotte NC 28210. (704)554-1162. Director: Butch Kelly. Music publisher, record company (Kam Executive, Fresh Avenue) and record producer (Butch Kelly Productions. BMI and ASCAP. Estab. 1985. Publishes 4 songs/year; publishes 4 new songwriters/year. Works with team collaborators. Pays standard royalty.
How to Contact: Write first and obtain permission to submit a tape. Prefers cassette (VHS videocassette if available) with 3 songs and lyric sheet. SASE. Reports in 1 month.
Music: Mostly pop, R&B and rock; also rap. Published "Tell Me" (by Butch Kelly), recorded by A. Brown on Kam Records (R&B); "Stumping Blues" (by Butch Kelly), recorded by Caro on Kam Records (R&B, pop); and "Where You Been" (by Butch Kelly), recorded by A. Brown on Kam Records (R&B).

*MUSIC CITY MUSIC (AUSTRALIA), Box 1200, Tamworth NSW 2340 **Australia**. Phone: (067)66-3566. Managing Director: Ed Matzenik. Music publisher. APRA. Estab. 1988. Publishes 20 songs/year; publishes 4-5 new songwriters/year. Works with composers; teams collaborators. "Pays 50% royalty or as negotiated."
How to Contact: Submit a demo tape by mail—unsolicited submissions are OK. Prefers cassette with lyric or lead sheet. "Mark address of writer clearly on cassette." Does not return unsolicited material. Reports in 1 month.
Music: Mostly country, rock and pop; also blues. Published "Heartache For You" (by P. Hotchkiss), recorded by Tony Worsley on Enrec Records (country); "Big Shot" (by D. Craswell), recorded by The Craz on Big Shot (pop); and "Dingo" (by C. Jansen), recorded by Lloyd Jansen on Gidgee Records (country).

MUSICLAND PRODUCTIONS, Suite C, 1627 E. Silver Springs, Ocala FL 32670. (904)622-5599 and 1-800-330-1627 (Florida residents). Contact: Bobby Land. Music publisher, recording studio and printing shop. BMI. Estab. 1987. Publishes 12 songs/year; publishes 4 new songwriters/year. Works with composers. Pays 6% royalty.
Affiliate: Big Sun Music (BMI).
How to Contact: Submit a demo tape—unsolicited submissions are OK. Prefers cassette with 4 songs and lyric sheet. If possible come in person. SASE. Reports in 1 week.
Music: Mostly rock, pop and gospel; also country. Published "Sold Out Of Love" (by B.L. & D.B.), recorded by David Mathis on Musicland Records (country); "20 to Life" (by R.S. BL. J.W.), recorded by Ron Stephens on Musicland Records (country) and "Standing In My Shoes" (by R.S. B.L. J.W.), recorded by Ron Stephens on Musicland Records (country).
Tips: "Stick with one type of music and do it well."

MYKO MUSIC, 1312 S. Avenida #A8, Tucson AZ 85710. (602)885-5931. President: James M. Gasper. Music publisher, record company (Ariana Records) and record producer (Future 1 Productions). BMI. Estab. 1980. Publishes 4 songs/year; publishes 2 new songwriters/year. Works with composers, teams collaborators. Royalty depends on arrangement with songwriter.
How to Contact: Write first and obtain permission to submit. Prefers cassette (or ½″ VHS videocassette or super 8 film) with 3 songs and lyric sheet. SASE Reports in 5 weeks.
Music: Top 40, dance rock, AOR, R&B, ballads and pop/rock. Published "Longer Look" (by Jim Gasper, Tom Priuett, Mike Adair), recorded by Sketches; "Rock N' Roll Surgery" (by The Dead Doners), recorded by The Dead Doners and "Big Girl, Big Love" (by Sonny Moon), recorded by Biff Turbo. All on Ariana Records.
Tips: "If the song's not there, no amount of production is going to make it work. Start with the words and music, worry about production later."

NASHVILLE SOUND MUSIC PUBLISHING CO., P.O. Box 728, Peterborough, Ontario K9J 6Z8 **Canada**. (705)742-2381. President: Andrew Wilson Jr. Music publisher. PRO Canada, CAPAC. Estab. 1985. Publishes 10 songs/year; publishes 5 new songwriters/year. Pays standard royalty.
Affiliate: Northern Sound Publishing Co. (CAPAC).
How to Contact: Submit a demo tape—unsolicited submissions are OK. Prefers cassette or 7½ ips reel-to-reel with 2-4 songs and lyric sheet. "Please send only material you do not want returned. We have an open door policy. We will contact a writer if we hear something of interest."
Music: Mostly country, country/pop and crossover country; also MOR, top 40, pop/rock and gospel. Published "Leave Me the Memory," by I.M. South/A. Wilson Jr./L. Payne; "I'm Not a Fool" (by L. Payne), recorded by Wendy Tibbits; "Twin Fiddles Turn Me On" (by Mel Holt), recorded by Faron Young on Payne Records (country); and "A Hard Bridge to Cross" (by Frank H. Stanton, Ginni D. Johnson, Curtis Young and Andrew Wilson Jr.), recorded by Faron Young on Step One Records.
Tips: "Professional demos, strong lyrics and a memorable melody will greatly increase a songwriter's chances."

NAUTICAL MUSIC CO., Box 120675, Nashville TN 37212. (615)255-1068. Owner: Ray McGinnis. Music publisher and record company (Orbit Records, Ray McGinnis). BMI. Estab. 1965. Publishes 25 songs/year; 10 new songwriters/year. Works with composers. Pays standard royalty.
How to Contact: Submit a demo tape by mail—unsolicited submissions are OK. Prefers cassette with 4 songs and lyric sheets. SASE. Reports in 6-8 weeks.
Music: Mostly country ballads and country rock. Published "I Need The Real Thing" (by D. Acuff), recorded by Kim Tsoy (country); "Baby I've Got to Hand it to You" (by L. Vaughan), recorded by LeRoy Steele (country rock); and "I'm In the Yellow Pages Under Blue" recorded by Kim Tsoy (country); all on Orbit Records.
Tips: "Submit a first class demo, it will get first priority. The trend is back to traditional country music with songs that tell a story."

NEBO RIDGE PUBLISHING COMPANY, P.O. Box 194 or 457, New Hope AL 35760. President: Walker Ikard. Manager: Jim Lewis. Music publisher, promotions firm, record producer, record company (Nebo Record Company), management firm (Nebo Management) and booking agency (Nebo Booking Agency). ASCAP. Estab. 1985. Works with composers and lyricists; teams collaborators. Pays standard royalty.
How to Contact: Submit a demo tape—unsolicited submissions are OK. Prefers cassette demo tape (or VHS videocassette) with 1 song and lyric sheet. "A VHS video of a song would be helpful but not absolutely necessary." SASE always. Reports as soon as possible.
Music: Mostly modern and traditional country, modern and traditional gospel, country/rock, rock and roll, pop, MOR and bluegrass. Published "Nothin' Without You" (by Walker Ikard), recorded by Walker Ikard and Anita Biss (modern country); "Friend, About Jesus," written and recorded by Charles W. Cooper (gospel-modern); and "Blessin' Money Can't Buy," written and recorded by Osie W. Ikard (traditional gospel); all on Nebo Records.
Tips: "Submit in neat form with clear lyrics. Be original; send songs that produce a feeling or effect."

NEON NOTES, 2729 Westwood Dr., Nashville TN 37204. (615)297-2329. President: Roy Yeager. Music publisher and record producer (Rumble Productions). ASCAP, BMI. Estab. 1987. Works with composers; teams collaborators. Pays standard royalty.
Affiliates: Yeager Master (BMI).
How to Contact: Submit a demo tape by mail—unsolicited submissions are OK. Prefers cassette with 3-4 songs and lyric sheets. SASE. Reports in 1 month.
Music: Mostly rock, pop and country; also new age.

NETWORK SOUND MUSIC PUBLISHING INC., 119 Peachwood Dr., Swedesboro NJ 08085. (609)467-1682. President, A&R: Vito Fera. Music publisher, record company (S.P.I.N. Records), record producer (Network Sound Productions) and songwriting organization. ASCAP. Estab. 1980. Publishes 10 songs/year. Hires staff writers "on agreement terms." Pays standard royalty. Publishes 6 new songwriters/year.
Affiliates: Fera Music Publishing (BMI).
How to Contact: Submit a demo tape by mail or UPS with 3 songs maximum and lyric sheet. "Package song material carefully. Always label (name, address and phone) both cassette and lyric sheet. Copyright songs." SASE. Reports in 4 weeks. Unsolicited submissions are OK. Prefers cassette (or VHS videocassette).
Music: Mostly dance/pop/disco, R&B/funk, rock/medium and adult contemporary. Published "Come Back" and "Day by Day" (by Steve Clarke), recorded by CHILL on S.P.I.N. Records; "Can't Wait" and "Jenny, Video Girl" (by Vito Fera), recorded by Vincent James on DiPop Records; also "You Make Me Burn" and "Real Man," written and recorded by Kathy Lamborn on S.P.I.N. Records.
Tips: "The 1990s are on their way to exhibiting the highest standards in music technology ever. Consequently, submitting music, especially in dance/pop, in "raw or unpolished" form makes it somewhat more difficult to recognize the song's potential. The competition is stiff in the music industry and it's time to listen to the songs getting airplay, sharpen your writing skills, feel the "hook line" and pay more attention to production. Record the best commercial demo you can afford with the lyrics clear and upfront. Best of Luck!"

NEW MUSIC ENTERPRISES, "Meredale," The Dell, Reach Lane, Near Leighton Buzzard Beds, **United Kingdom**. Phone: 052523-7700. Manager: Paul Davis. Music publisher and record company. MCPS, PRS. Publishes 20 songs/year. Pays standard royalty; royalties to US songwriters paid through US affiliate.
Affiliates: Wilhelm Music, Arhelger Music, Silhouette Music, Bridge Music, Eric Anders Music, Sherebiah Music, Clancy Music and Jimmy Payne Music.
How to Contact: Write first. Prefers cassette with any number of songs and lyric sheet. SAE and IRC. Reports in 3 weeks.
Music: All forms of contemporary Christian music (bluegrass, children's, gospel, country, MOR and soul). Published "God Specializes," written and recorded by Candi Staton, on Berachah Records (black gospel); and "Today I Followed Jesus," recorded by Bryn Yemm and "Rock of Ages/Alleluia," recorded by George Hamilton IV, both on Word Records (both by Erv Lewis).
Tips: "Songs should have good Christian message and be relevant to everyday living."

NEWCREATURE MUSIC, Box 148296, Nashville TN 37214-8296. President: Bill Anderson Jr. Music publisher, record company, record producer and radio and TV syndicator. BMI. Publishes 5 songs/year; publishes 2 new songwriters/year. Pays standard royalty.

How to Contact: Prefers 7½ ips reel-to-reel or cassette (or videocassette) with 4-10 songs and lyric sheet. SASE. Reports in 1 month.
Music: Country, gospel, jazz, R&B, rock and top 40/pop. Published "Cotton, Popcorn, Peanuts and Jesus" (by H. Yates), recorded by Jeanne Cash on Jana Records (gospel); "His Love Is the Reason," written and recorded by Danny Vance on Livingsong Records (gospel); and "Ragged Ole Memory" (by J. Jerigan), recorded by Jim Chute on Cootico Records (country).

*NEXT TO IMPOSSIBLE MUSIC, Rt. 2, 47 Colonial Estates, Belden MS 38826. (601)840-2006. President: Ronnie Hughes. Music publisher, record company (Angela Records), record producer (Angela Productions), Next To Impossible Music BMI. BMI. Estab. 1986. Publishes 2-5 songs/year; publishes 2 new songwriters/year. Works with composers and lyricists; teams collaborators. Pays standard royalty.
Affiliates: Next To Impossible Music BMI.
How to Contact: Submit a demo tape by mail—unsolicited submissions are OK. Prefers cassette with 3-5 songs and lyric sheet. SASE. Reports in 4 weeks.
Music: Mostly country and gospel; also rock, pop and R&B. Published "One Sided Love Affair," "Rainy Day Morning," and "Something I Don't See" (by Ronnie Hughes), recorded by Ron Lee on Ron Records (country).
Tips: "Send me a great song and I'll do my best to get you a cut."

*NIGHTFLITE MUSIC PUBLISHING, Suite 210, 1209 King St. W., Toronto ON M6K 1G2 **Canada**. (416)820-6400. President: Joey Cee. Music publisher, record company (Nightflite), record producer (Joey Cee Organization). CAPAC, PROCAN. Estab. 1981. Publishes 6-10 songs/year; publishes 2-3 new songwriters/year. Works with composers and teams collaborators. Pays 50% of song or full publishing.
Affiliates: Sagitar Music (CAPAC), Cee Sharp Music (CAPAC), All Day Music (PROCAN).
How to Contact: Submit a demo tape by mail—unsolicited submissions are OK. Prefers cassette with 4-6 songs and lyric or lead sheets. "Doesn't have to be professional recording." Does not return unsolicited material. Reports in 2 months.
Music: Mostly dance/urban, top 40, new age; also rock, country and R&B. Published "Touched By The Sun" (by Joey Cee), recorded by Ron Victors on Nightlife Records (MOR).

NORTHCOTT MUSIC/TANCOT MUSIC, 972 Lexington Ave., New York NY 10021. (212)472-7972. FAX: (212)904-1737. President: Silvio Tancreni. A&R: Tom Musto. Production company, music publisher, record company, remix services, management. Estab. 1980. Publishes 25-30 songs/year; 5-10 new songwriters/year. Hires staff writers "if I could find good ones." Works with composers and lyricists; teams collaborators. Pays standard royalty.
How to Contact: Submit a demo cassette by mail with 3 songs. Unsolicited submissions are OK. Include SASE. Reports in 2-4 weeks. Send tapes to: Tom Musto, 419 Elverton Ave., Staten Island, NY 10308-1552.
Music: Dance, pop, R&B, house, rap, freestyle and ballads. Published "Dangerous" (by P.C.P.), recorded by Musto/Bones on Beggars Banquet (rap); "Time is Running" (by S. Parris), recorded by Carrochia/Musto/Bones on Beggars Banquet (dance); and "Come a Little Closer" (by F. Bones), recorded by Midnight Fantasy on 4th Floor (dance).

*NOVELTY POWER INC., (formerly Jay Gold Music), P.O. Box 409, East Meadow NY 11554-0409. (516)486-8699. President: Jay Gold. Music publisher. BMI. Estab. 1981. Publishes 25 songs/year; 1-2 new songwriters/year. Works with composers and lyricists; teams collaborators. Pays standard royalty.
How to Contact: Submit a demo tape by mail—unsolicited submissions are OK. Prefers cassette with 3 songs and lyric sheets. Reports in 6 weeks.
Music: Mostly pop, rock and country. Published "Tough Guy" (by Jay Gold), recorded by Jail Bait on Star Search T.V. Show (pop); "All the Wrong Reasons," written and recorded by Jay Gold on Turbo Records (pop); and "Radio Riot" (by R. Freeman/J. Gold), recorded by Queen City Kids (rock).
Tips: "Make the best demo you can afford. It's better to have a small publisher pushing your songs than a large one keeping them on the shelf."

NRP MUSIC GROUP, 10 Pebblewood, Irvine CA 92714. (714)552-5231. Vice-President: Fred Bailin. Music publisher. BMI, ASCAP. Estab. 1975. Publishes 5-6 songs/year; 2 new songwriters/year. Works with composers; teams collaborators. Pays standard royalty.
Affiliates: New Ideas Music Co. (BMI), Simma Music Co. Division (ASCAP), Perspective Music Co. (BMI).
How to Contact: Submit a demo tape by mail—unsolicited submissions are OK. Prefers cassette with lead sheets. SASE. Reports in 2 weeks.
Music: Mostly R&B, pop and rock; also rap.

NU-TRAYL PUBLISHING CO., 10015 W. 8 Mile Rd., Franksville WI 53126. (414)835-4622. Contact: Tommy O'Day. Music publisher, record company and record producer. ASCAP. Estab. 1969. Publishes 7-10 songs/year; publishes 2-6 new songwriters/year. Pays standard royalty.
How to Contact: Prefers 7½ ips reel-to-reel or cassette with 1-3 songs and lyric sheet. SASE. Reports in 1 month.
Music: Country, MOR, rock and top 40/pop. Published "I Wrote This Song For You" (by Bob Perice), recorded by Bruce Russell; "Anna" (by Bob Perice), recorded by Kathie Dalely; and "The Haircut," written and recorded by Marvin Rainwater; all on Nu-Trayl Records (country).

OBH MUSIKVERLAG OTTO B. HARTMANN, Box 2691, Ch-6901 Lugano **Switzerland**. Phone: 0041(91)685586. President: Otto B. Hartmann. Music publisher, record company (Kick/OBH) and record producer. Estab. 1968. Publishes 100 songs/year; publishes 2 songwriters/year. Hires staff writers. Works with composers and lyricists. Pays standard royalty.
Affiliates: Edition Plural (classical).
Music: Mostly rock, jazz, folk, pop and R&B; also classical.

***OCEAN WALK MUSIC**, 13159 Glenoaks Blvd., Sylmar CA 91342. (818)364-2464. Owner: Mark Thornton. Music Publisher, record company and record producer (Tommark Records). BMI. Estab. 1989. Publishes 3-6 songs/year; publishes 2-4 new songwriters/year. Works with composers and lyricists. Pays standard royalty.
How to Contact: Submit a demo tape by mail—unsolicited submissions are O.K. Prefers cassette (or VHS videocassette if available) with 4 songs and lyric and lead sheet. SASE. Reports in 2-4 weeks.
Music: Mostly country, western and instrumental; also novelty, R&B and gospel bluegrass. Published "Red Snappers", "Christmas Will be Blue in California" and "Traffic Jam" (by Mark Thornton), recorded on Tommark Records (country).

***OLD EMPRESS MUSIC/DOGHOUSE PRODUCTIONS**, 1226 17th Ave. S., Suite 3, Nashville TN 37212. Professional Manager: Maurice Godwin/Hal Godwin. Music publisher. BMI, ASCAP. Estab. 1987. Publishes 25-30 songs/year; publishes 5 new songwriters/year. Works with composers and lyricists; teams collaborators. Pays standard royalty.
Affiliate: Dish Bowl Music (ASCAP), UN-DER 16 Songs (SESAC).
How to Contact: Submit a demo tape by mail—unsolicited submissions are OK. Prefers cassette with 4 songs and lyric sheets. "Use chrome tape only." SASE. Reports in 3 weeks.
Music: Mostly dance, rock and pop; also country and R&B. Published "Real" (by Roy Cathey Jr.), recorded by Mickey Dee on Rock City Records (rock); "Sheila Likes Hollywood," written and recorded by Bruce McMaster on Black Gold Records (rock); and "In the Beginning" recorded by Eric McClure on Black Gold Records (Philippines).
Tips: "Looking for completed masters for overseas releases. Know the norms about publishing contracts."

O'LYRIC MUSIC, Suite 1, 1837 Eleventh St., Santa Monica CA 90404. (213)452-0815. President: J. O'Loughlin. Creative Director: Kathryn Haddock. Music publisher, manager (O'Lyric Music Management) and production company. BMI. ASCAP. Member California Copyright Conference. Estab. 1980. Publishes 50-75 songs/year; publishes 10-15 new songwriters/year. Hires staff writers; pays $20,000/year—"only duty expected is songwriting. Writers paid by royalties earned and by advances." Pays standard royalty to outside writers.
Affiliate: O'Lyrical Music (ASCAP).
How to Contact: Prefers cassette with 1-3 songs and lyric sheet. Does not return materials. Reports as soon as possible. Send 25 cent SASE or postcard for reply. Please no phone calls.
Music: Mostly R&B, rock, top 40, dance and country; also contemporary jazz and soul. Published "I Live for Your Love" (by P. Reswick/S. Werfil/A. Rich), recorded by Natalie Cole on Manhattan Records (R&B/crossover); "Mr. Right" (by T. Shapiro/M. Garvin), recorded by Smokey Robinson on Motown Records (R&B/crossover); and "I've Still Got the Love We Made" (by Shapiro/Garvin/Waters), recorded by Reba McEntire (country/crossover). Production company works with Double T (Next Plateau Records) and Smoke Tree (country).
Tips: "Please follow our policy without exception."

***OMNI RECORDS, INC.**, P.O. Box 917, Bala Cynwyd PA 19004. (215)828-7030. President: Steven Bernstein. Music publisher and record company. Estab. 1973. BMI. Publishes 50 songs/year; publishes 3-4 new songwriters/year. Employs songwriters on a salary basis. Teams collaborators.
How to Contact: Prefers cassette. Does not return unsolicited material.
Music: R&B and dance ONLY. Published "Closer than Close" (by Terri Price), recorded by Jean Carne; and "Lonely Road" (by Bryan Williams), recorded by Rose Royce, both on Omni Records (both R&B); and "Love Won't Let Me Wait" by Luther Vandross.

ONE HUNDRED GRAND MUSIC, 11 Norton St., Newburgh NY 12550. (914)561-4483. President: Gregg Bauer. Music publisher, record company (100 Grand Records) and record producer. Estab. 1983. Publishes 10 songs/year; publishes 2 new songwriters/year. Teams collaborators. Pays standard royalty.
How to Contact: Write or call first and obtain permission to submit. Prefers cassette (or VHS videocassette) with 3-5 songs and lyric sheet. Submit videocassette "if it has a good story line and good audio." SASE. Reports in 1 month.
Music: Mostly rock, dance and R&B; dance-oriented, MOR, progressive and soul. Published "Feeling Blue" (by P. Otero and G. Bauer) (rock); "Heart in Distress" (by P. Otero) (rock); and "Taste" (by L. Pedroza and P. Coromelas); all on 100 Grand Records.

OPERATION PERFECTION, Suite 206, 6245 Bristol Pkwy,. Culver City CA 90230. Contact: Larry McGee. Vice-President: Darryl McCorkle. Music publisher. BMI. Estab. 1976. Publishes 1-5 songs/ year; publishes 1-2 new songwriters/year. Works with composers and lyricists; teams collaborators. Pays standard royalty.
How to Contact: Submit a demo tape—unsolicited submissions OK. Prefers cassette (or VHS video-cassette) with 1-4 songs and lyric sheet. "Please only send professional quality material!" Does not return unsolicited material. Reports in 8 weeks.
Music: Rock, rap, pop, MOR/adult contemporary and R&B. Published "We're Number One," (by Liz Davis), recorded by The Saxon Sisters on Boogie Band (rock); "Captain Freedom," (by Kenny Sims), recorded by Sheena Kriss on Mega Star (R&B); and "I Feel Good With You," written and recorded by Bill Sawyer on Dollar-Bill (R&B).
Tips: "Make sure your song is in current market or sound."

ORCHID PUBLISHING, Bouquet-Orchid Enterprises, Box 11686, Atlanta GA 30355. (404)355-7635. President: Bill Bohannon. Music publisher, record company, record producer (Bouquet-orchid Enter-prises) and artist management. BMI. Member CMA, AFM. Publishes 10-12 songs/year; publishes 3 new songwriters/year. Works with composers and lyricists; teams collaborators. Pays standard royalty.
How to Contact: Prefers cassette with 3-5 songs and lyric sheet. "Send biographical information if possible—even a photo helps." SASE. Reports in 1 month.
Music: Religious ("Amy Grant, etc., contemporary gospel"); country ("George Strait, The Judds type material"); and top 100/pop ("Peter Cetera & Whitney Houston type material"). Published "Good Loving" (by Ralph Cherry), recorded by the Bandoleers; and "Let Me Be Your Lover" (by Clayton Russ), recorded by Susan Spencer.

*ORDER PUBLISHING, 6503 York Rd., Baltimore MD 21212. (301)377-2270. President: Jeff Order. Music publisher and record producer (Jeff Order/Order Productions). ASCAP. Estab. 1986. Publishes 30-40 songs/year; publishes 3-4 new songwriters/year. Works with composers and lyricists. Pays stan-dard royalty.
How to Contact: Submit a demo tape by mail—unsolicited submissions are O.K. Prefers cassette with 4 songs. Does not return unsolicited material. Reports in 1 month.
Music: All types. Published "OH!", recorded by J. Order & Hiram Bullock (rock); "Won't You Dance With Me", recorded by Tiny Tim (dance); and "Rejoyce", recorded by Jeff Order (New Age), all written by Jeff Order and recorded on Order Productions Records.
Tips: "Submit high-quality, well-recorded and produced material."

OTTO PUBLISHING CO., P.O. Box 16540, Plantation FL 33318. (305)741-7766. President: Frank X. Loconto. Music publisher, record company (FXL Records) and record producer (Loconto Produc-tions). ASCAP. Estab. 1978. Publishes 100 songs/year; publishes 1-10 new songwriters/year. Works with composers. Pays standard royalty.
Affiliates: Betty Brown Music Co. (BMI), and Clara Church Music Co. (SESAC), True Friends Music (BMI).
How to Contact: Call first and obtain permission to submit. Prefers cassette with 1-4 songs and lyric sheet. SASE. Reports in 1 month.
Music: Mostly country, MOR, religious and gospel. Published "Minnie Song" (special); "Family of God" (gospel); and "Drug Free Society" (special), all by Frank X. Loconto, recorded by Loconto Productions on FXL Records. Theme Song "Nightly Business Reports" National Syndicated TV show written and recorded by Frank X. Loconto.

*PALMETTO PRODUCTIONS, Box 1376, Pickens SC 29671. (803)859-9614. FAX: (803)859-3814. Pres-ident: Brian E. Raines. Music publisher, record company (Palmetto Records), record producer and artist management/booking (Palmetto Productions). ASCAP. Publishes 10 songs/year; publishes 5 new songwriters/year. Works with composers and lyricists; teams collaborators. Pays standard royalty.

Affiliates: Brian Raines Music Co. (ASCAP) and Brian Song Music Co. (BMI).
How to Contact: Write first and obtain permission to submit. Prefers cassette (or VHS videocassette) with 2-3 songs and lyric sheet. "All demos are listened to whether professionally recorded or done at home." SASE. Reports "at earliest convenience."
Music: Country, gospel and Top 40. Published "Since I Met You," written and recorded by Brian Raines on Palmetto Records (country); "It Makes Me Glad" (by Jim Hubbard), recorded by Joe Russell on White Line Records (gospel); "Take It To Jesus" (by Dale Cassell), recorded by Trinity on Mark Five Records (gospel).
Tips: "Send good chart material, we also like a biography of writer with a photo if possible. Try to send material that has been recorded by 'local' artists, or that is currently being performed on a local level. SASE required!"

J.S. PALUCH COMPANY, INC./WORLD LIBRARY PUBLICATIONS, INC., 3825 N. Willow Rd., P.O. Box 2703, Schiller Park IL 60176-0703. Music Editors: Mark G. Rachelski, Nicholas T. Freund, Betty Z. Reiber. Music publisher. SESAC. Estab. 1913. Publishes 50 or more songs/year; publishes varying number of new songwriters/year; recordings. Works with composers and lyricists; teams collaborators.
How to Contact: Submit demo tape by mail—unsolicited submissions are OK. Prefers cassette with any number of songs, lyric sheet and lead sheet. SASE. Reports in 3 months.
Music: Sacred music, songs, hymns, choral settings descants, psalm settings; also children's sacred music. Published "Justice Shall Flourish," (by Marchionda); "Whom Shall I Send?" (by Rachelski); and "Mass: Sing Praise and Thanksgiving," (by Michael Joncas).
Tips: "Make your manuscript as legible as possible, with clear ideas regarding tempo, etc. Base the text upon scripture."

PAMSCO INTERNATIONAL INC., 1022 NW Potee Ave., Hipleob Gardens FL 33016. (305)823-8167. Manager: Norbert L. Selasco. Music publisher, record company (Music Hall/Can Records/Sazam Records) and record producer (Sicamericana S.A.C.I.F.I.). SADAIC. Estab. 1950. Publishes 200 songs/year; 10 new songwriters/year. Pays standard royalty.
How to Contact: Write or call first and obtain permission to submit a tape. Prefers cassette with 8 songs and lead sheets. Does not return unsolicited material. Reports in 1½ months.
Music: Mostly pop and rock; also local and tango. Published "Cuando Yo Amo," written and recorded by A. Vezzani; "Enterate Ya," written and recorded by Ian Simmons; and "Que Puedo Hacer Por Ti" (by Valeria Lynch), recorded by Marcelo Alejandro; all on Music Hall Records (ballad).

PANCHO'S MUSIC CO., 3121 29th Ave., Sacramento CA 95820. (916)455-5278. Contact: Frank Lizarraga. Music publisher, record company (Israfel Records) and record producer (Israfel Production and Recording Service). BMI. Estab. 1980. Publishes 3 songs/year; publishes 1 new songwriter/year. Works with lyricists. Pays standard royalty.
How to Contact: Write or call first and obtain permission to submit. Prefers cassette (or VHS videocassette) with 3 songs, lyric sheet and brief resume/fact sheet. SASE. Reports in 2 months.
Music: Mostly Latin, pop and rock; also gospel, country and blues. Published "Lonely Child" (by F. Lizarraca), recorded by Julia (pop); "Sin of Love" (by A. Lizarraga), recorded by A.D. (pop/rock); and "Mis Suénos" (by J. Marin), recorded by Julia (Spanish), all on Israfel Records.
Tips: "We specialize in Latin music and prefer bilingual songwriters."

*PANDISC RECORDS, 38 NE 167 St., Miami FL 33162. (305)948-6466. President: Bo Crane. Music publisher and record company (Pandisc, Jamarc). ASCAP, BMI. Estab. 1979. Publishes 50 songs/year; publishes 3-6 new songwriters/year. Works with composers and lyricists; teams collaborators. Pays standard royalty.
Affiliates: Whooping Crane Music (BMI) and Hombre Del Mundo (ASCAP).
How to Contact: Submit a demo tape by mail—unsolicited submissions are OK. Prefers cassette with 3 songs and lyric sheet. Does not return unsolicited material.
Music: Mostly rap and R&B. Published "B Girls" (by C. Trahan/L. Johnson), recorded by Young & Restless (rap); and "I Can't Let Go" (by Y. Israel), recorded by Joey Gilmore (blues), both on Pandisc Records.

PAPE PUBLISHING, 7 Tansley Ave., Scarborough ON M1J 1P2 **Canada**. Phone: (416)267-7482. President: Peter Panayotu. Music publisher. CAPAC. Estab. 1980. Publishes 3 songs/year; 1 new songwriter/year. Works with composers; teams collaborators. Pays standard royalty.
How to Contact: Write first and obtain permission to submit a tape. Prefers cassette with 1-2 songs and lyric sheets. Does not return unsolicited material. Reports in 2 months.
Music: Mostly pop, country and R&B; also new age, rock and ethnic. Published "Don't Stop This Feeling" (by Morrison/Panayotu), recorded by Pape Gang on Ravin' Records (pop); "What About Me?" (by Bleakley/Panayotu), recorded by Bobby Blake on Pape Records; and "Cool in Grade 10," written and recorded by Sean Lynch on Pape Records (country).

PARK J. TUNES, 29 S. Erie, Toledo OH 43602. Contact: Michael Drew Shaw. Music publisher, record company and record producer. ASCAP. Publishes 25 songs/year; publishes 5 new songwriters/year. Pays standard royalty.
Affiliates: Keeny/York (BMI), Newstar International Records.
How to Contact: Prefers cassette with 3 songs maximum and lyric sheet. SASE. Reports in 2 months.
Music: Country and top 40/pop. Published "Wherever You Are," recorded by MDS Studio Band; "We Are the Future," recorded by Kerry Clark; "Take a Ride," recorded by Mick Payne; and Michael Drew Shaw's *Devil Lake,* recorded by Michael Drew Shaw, on Newstar International Records (LP).

*PATHETIC MUSIC, South: 940 NE 27th Ave., Hallandale FL 33009. (305)454-7044. North: 7808 Green Lake Rd., Fayetteville NY 13066. (315)637-6656. S. Producer Chris Horvath. N. Producer: Matt Tucker. Music publisher. BMI. Estab. 1989. Publishes 5-15 songs/year; publishes 1-2 new songwriters/year. Works with composers; teams collaborators. Pays standard royalty.
How to Contact: Submit a demo tape by mail—unsolicited submissions are OK. Prefers cassette (VHS videocassette if available) with up to 5 songs and lyric sheet. "Send photo, press kit or bio if available. No calls." SASE. Reports in 6 weeks.
Music: Mostly top 40/pop, dance and rock; also rap and R&B. Published "Baha Your Body" recorded by Jodi Bilotti (dance); "How Can I Forget You" recorded by Blue Steel (pop); and "For Us" recorded by Blue Steel (rock), all (by Horvath/Tucker), on CCD Records.
Tips: "If you think your music is 'pathetic,' send it to us."

*PDS MUSIC PUBLISHING, P.O. Box 412477, Kansas City MO 64141-2477. Contact: Dept. 100 submissions. Music publisher and record company (PDS Records, Universal Jazz, PDS Associated labels). ASCAP, BMI. Estab. 1988. Publishes 30 songs/year; publishes 3-4 new songwriters/year. Does not hire staff songwriters. Works with composers and lyricists.
Affiliates: PDS Universal (ASCAP), PDS Worldwide (BMI).
How to Contact: Write first and obtain permission to submit a tape. Prefers cassette with 5-10 songs and lyric sheet. Does not return unsolicited material. Reports in 2 months.

*PECOS VALLEY PUBLISHING, P.O. Box 8248, Roswell NM 88201. (505)622-0244. President: Ray Willmon. Music publisher. BMI. Estab. 1989. Publishes 25 songs/year; publishes 3-4 new songwriters/year. Works with composers and lyricists; teams collaborators. Pays standard royalty.
How to Contact: Submit a demo tape by mail—unsolicited submissions are OK. Prefers cassette (or VHS cassette if available) with 2-4 songs and lyric sheet. SASE. Reports in 2 weeks.
Music: Mostly country, pop and rock. Published "Lifetime Guarantee" (by Ray Willmon), "And Took Your Love Away" (by Ron Ritzwater) and "You Don't Owe Me a Thing" by (Ray Willmon) (country).
Tips: "Good clear recorded lyrics with typed lyric sheet. Record companies seem to listen more these days to traditional country music."

*PEERMUSIC, 8159 Hollywood Blvd., Los Angeles CA 90069. (213)656-0364. Director of Creative Services: Steven Rosen. Music publisher and artist development promotional label. ASCAP, BMI. Estab. 1928. Publishes 40 songs/year; publishes 2-5 new songwriters/year. Hires staff songwriters. Works with self-contained artists.
Affiliates: P.S.O. LTD (ASCAP).
How to Contact: Write first and obtain permission to submit a tape. Prefers cassette (VHS videocassette if available) with 2 songs and lyric sheet. Does not return unsolicited material. Reports in 1 month.
Music: Mostly R&B, pop and rock; also all types. Published "I Don't Have the Heart" (by Jud Friedman/Allan Rich), recorded by James Ingram on W.B. Records (R&B/ballad); "Child Bride" (by Marvin Etzioni), recorded by Katy Moffatt on Philo/Rounder Records (blues rock); and "Metropolis" (by The Church), recorded by The Church on Arista Records (rock).

PEGASUS MUSIC, 27 Bayside Ave., Te Atatu, Auckland 8, **New Zealand**. Professional Manager: Errol Peters. Music publisher and record company. APRA. Estab. 1981. Publishes 20-30 songs/year; publishes 5 new songwriters/year. Works with composers and lyricists; teams collaborators. Pays 3-5% to artists on contract and standard royalty to songwriters; royalties paid directly to US songwriters.
How to Contact: Submit a demo tape—unsolicited submissions are OK. Prefers cassette with 3-5 songs and lyric sheet. SAE and IRC. Reports in 1 month.
Music: Mostly country; also bluegrass, easy listening and top 40/pop. Published "It's Alright," recorded by Sally Burgess on Ode Records; "I Only See You," recorded by Dennis Marsh on Ode Records; and "If This Is Right," recorded by Ginny Peters on Kiwi Pacific Records; all written by Ginny Peters (country).
Tips: "Be fresh and original. We prefer direct lyrics."

PENNY THOUGHTS MUSIC, 484 Lexington St., Waltham MA 02154. (617)891-7800. President: John Penny. Music publisher, record company (Belmont Records and Waverly Records) and record producer. BMI. Publishes 12 songs/year. Pays standard royalty.
How to Contact: Write first to get permission to submit a tape. SASE. Reports in 2 weeks. Not accepting material at this time.
Music: Mostly country; also contemporary and rock (country). Published "Give It Away," written and recorded by Stan Anderson Jr. on Belmont Records (country) and "The Hurt That Hurts Me" and "You're the Right Love," by Mike Cummings (country).

PENTACHORD/PENTARCH MUSIC, 406-68 Water St., Vancouver, British Columbia V6B 1A4 **Canada**. (604)688-0077. Contact: Cliff Jones. Music publisher and record company (Penta Records). Estab. 1987. Publishes 30-40 songs/year; publishes 3 new songwriters/year. "We currently have 4 writers." Works with composers and lyricists; teams collaborators. Pays standard or negotiable royalty.
How to Contact: Submit a demo tape — unsolicited submissions are OK. Prefers cassette (or VHS videocassette) with 4 songs and lyric sheet. Does not return unsolicited material. Reports in 1 month.
Music: Mostly pop, rock and country. Published "Lesson in Love" (by J. Neill), on Geffen Records (rock); "Never Give Up" (Holden M.), recorded by Gould R. on MCA Records (pop); and "Ain't Good Lovin" (by Harnett) on Virgin Records (pop).

PHILIPPOPOLIS MUSIC, 12027 Califa St., North Hollywood CA 91607. President: Milcho Leviev. Music publisher. BMI. Member GEMA, NARAS. Estab. 1975. Publishes 3-5 songs/year; publishes 1-2 new songwriters/year. Works with composers and lyricists; teams collaborators. Pays standard royalty.
How to Contact: Query. Prefers cassette with 1-3 songs. Prefers studio produced demos. SASE. Reports in 1 month.
Music: Jazz and classical fusion. Published "King Basie," "4 + 3," and "N.H." (by Milcho Leviev), recorded by Milcho Leviev on M.A. Records (Japan) (jazz).

***PIN PUBLISHING**, 11 Shady Oak Trail, Charlotte NC 28210. (704)554-1162. Director: Butch Kelly. Music publisher, record company (Kam Executive, Fresh Aire, New Town Records) and record producer (Butch Kelly Productions). ASCAP, BMI. Estab. 1981. Publishes 4 songs/year; publishes 3 new songwriters/year. Teams collaborators. Pays standard royalty.
Affiliates: Pin Publishing (ASCAP), Music by Butch Kelly (BMI).
How to Contact: Write first and obtain permission to submit a tape. Prefers cassette (VHS videocassette) with 3 songs and 3 lyric sheets. SASE. Reports in 2 months.
Music: Mostly pop, R&B and rock; also rap. Published "Waiting" and "Tell Me" (by Butch Kelly), recorded by A. Brown on Kam Records (R&B); and "Stumping Blues" (by Kelly Montgomery), recorded by Caro on Fresh Ave Records (pop).

PINE ISLAND MUSIC, #308, 9430 Live Oak Place, Ft. Lauderdale FL 33324. (305)472-7757. President: Jack P. Bluestein. Music publisher, record company and record producer. BMI, ASCAP. Estab. 1973-1974. Publishes 50-75 songs/year; publishes 25-30 new songwriters/year. Works with composers, lyricists; teams collaborators. Pays standard royalty.
Affiliates: Lantana Music (BMI) and Twister Music (ASCAP).
How to Contact: Submit a demo tape — unsolicited submissions OK. Prefers cassette or 7½ ips reel-to-reel (or VHS videocassette) with 3 songs and lyric sheet. SASE. Reports in 2-4 months.
Music: Mostly country and pop; also gospel, soft rock and contemporary. Published "The Painted Pony" and "Everybody Listens to the Music" (by Ann Leysten), recorded by Gary Oakes and Lou Garcia on Twister (country/pop); "Please Forgive Me," (by Ronnie Lynn), recorded by Julie Lendon on Twister (country); and "I Made It" (by David Berger/David Lipshutz) on Twisted Records.

PLACER PUBLISHING, Box 11301, Kansas City KS 66111. (913)287-3495 (night). Owner: Steve Vail. Music publisher, record company (System Records) and record producer. ASCAP. Estab. 1980. Publishes 2 songs/year; publishes 1 new songwriter/year. Works with composers and lyricists. Pays standard royalty.
How to Contact: Submit a demo tape — unsolicited submissions are OK. Prefers cassette (or VHS or Beta ½" videocassette) with 10-12 songs. Does not return unsolicited material. Reports in 6 weeks.
Music: Mostly classical rock, new age and jazz. Published "Atlantis," "Mind's Eye" and "Above and Below" (all by Vail), recorded by Realm on System Records (progressive).

PLANET DALLAS, P.O. Box 191447, Dallas TX 75219. (214)521-2216. Producer, Music publisher, record producer (Rick Rooney) and recording studio (Planet Dallas). BMI. ASCAP. Estab. 1985. Publishes 5-15 songs/year; 2-3 new songwriters/year. Works with composers and lyricists; teams collaborators. Pays standard royalty; also depends on deal/studio involvement.

Affiliate: Stoli Music (ASCAP).
How to Contact: Write or call first and obtain permission to submit. Prefers cassette with 1-3 songs and lyric sheet. SASE for reply. Reports in 4-6 weeks.
Music: Mostly modern rock and %90 40. Published "This Property is Condemned" (by P. Sugg), recorded by Maria McKee on Geffen Records (pop); "Tickle" (by U Know Who), recorded by U Know Who on WE–Mix Records (rap); and "Hydrogen City" (by Hydrogen City), recorded by Hydrogen City on H1 Records (rock).

PLATINUM BOULEVARD PUBLISHING, 650 Greenbrae Dr., Reno NV 89431. (702)358-7484. President: Lawrence Davis. Music publisher. BMI. Estab. 1984. Publishes 12 songs/year; 1 new songwriter/year. Works with composers and lyricists; teams collaborators. Pays standard royalty, but will negotiate.
How to Contact: Submit a demo tape by mail–unsolicited submissions are OK. Prefers cassette (or VHS videocassette), with unlimited songs and lyric or lead sheets. "Songs must be in English." Does not return unsolicited material. "We report only if interested."
Music: Mostly rock, pop and R&B; also country, jazz and new age. Published "The Future's Always Blind," "You'll Never Know" and "When We Met," all written and recorded by Lawrence Davis on Platinum Boulevard Records (AOR).
Tips: "Be willing to be flexible in understanding the possible placement for your music."

PLUTO MUSIC LTD., Hulgrave Hall, Tiverton, Tarporley, Cheshire, CW6 9UQ **England.** Phone: (0829)3-2427. Managing Director: Keith Hopwood. Music publisher. PRS. Estab. 1976. Publishes 6 songs/year; publishes 1 new songwriter/year. Works with lyricists. Pays standard royalty.
How to Contact: Submit a demo tape–unsolicited submissions OK. Prefers cassette with 3 songs and lyric sheet. SAE and IRC. Reports in 1 month.
Music: Mostly rock/pop and ballads. Published "You're Not the Rule" (rock/single) and *Blue Slipper* (rock/LP), by Watson/McGrath, recorded by Helen Watson on EMI Records.

*PORTAGE MUSIC, 16634 Gannon W., Rosemont MN 55068. (612)432-5737. President: Larry LaPole. Music publisher. BMI. Publishes 5-20 songs/year. Pays standard royalty.
How to Contact: Prefers cassette with 3 songs and lyric sheet.
Music: Mostly country and country rock.
Tips: "Keep songs short, simple and upbeat with positive theme."

*PPI/PETER PAN INDUSTRIES, 88 St. Francis St., Newark NJ 07105. (201)344-4214. Product Manager: Marianne Eggleston. Music publisher, record company (Compose Records; Current Records; Parade Video, Ironbound Publishing, Compose), record producer (Dunn Pearson, Jr.); also outside producers. ASCAP and BMI. Estab. 1928. Publishes over 100 songs/year; publishes over 100 new songwriters/year. Hires staff songwriters. Will hire more in 1990. Works with composers and lyricists; teams collaborators. Pays standard royalty "based on agreements."
Affiliates: Ironbound Publishing (ASCAP).
How to Contact: Submit a demo tape by mail–unsolicited submissions are O.K. Prefers cassette (or VHS videocassette if available) with 3-5 songs and lyric sheet. "Please include name, address and phone numbers on all materials, along with picture, bio and contact information. SASE. Reports in 1-2 months.
Music: Mostly children's–audio, R&B and jazzy; also exercise–video, rock and classical. Pubilshed "Go For The Gusto" (R&B), "Programmed For Love" (jazz) and "Color Tapestry" (jazz), all written and recorded by Dunn Pearson on Compose Records.

*PRATT AND MCCLAIN MUSIC (ASCAP), Box 842, Beverly Hills CA 90213. (818)769-2842. President: Jeremy McClain. Music Publisher (Happy Days Music) and record producer. Deals with artists and songwriters. Voting member of NARAS. Gold record on "Happy Days" (theme from TV show).
How to Contact: Prefers cassettes, video or audio.
Music Mostly pop, rock and some progressive gospel.
Tips: "Direct access to Donna Summer, Christopher Cross, Debbie Boone and Michael Omartian."

PRESCRIPTION COMPANY, 70 Murray Ave., Port Washington NY 11050. (516)767-1929. President: David F. Gasman. Music publisher and record producer. BMI. Pays standard royalty.
How to Contact: Call or write first about your interest. Prefers cassette with any number of songs and lyric sheet. "Send all submissions with SASE (or no returns)." Reports in 1 month.
Music: Bluegrass, blues, children's, country, dance-oriented, easy listening, folk, jazz, MOR, progressive, R&B, rock, soul and top 40/pop. Published "You Came In," "Rock 'n' Roll Blues," and "Seasons," (by D.F. Gasman), all recorded by Medicine Mike on Prescription Records.

Tips: "Songs should be good and written to last. Forget fads—we want songs that'll sound as good in 10 years as they do today. Organization, communication, and exploration of form is as essential as message (and sincerity matters, too)."

*PRESTATION MUSIC, 24 Gachard St., Brussels **Belgium** 1050. (02)6492847. General Manager: Pierre Pletinckx. Music publisher, record company (B. Sharp Selection Multi Sound Music). SABAM. Works with composers; teams collaborators. Pays standard royalty 50%.
How to Contact: Submit a demo tape by mail—unsolicited submission are OK. Prefers cassette. SASE. Reports in 1 month.
Music: Mostly instrumental, jazz and New Age.

JIMMY PRICE MUSIC PUBLISHER, Sun-Ray Production Company, 1662 Wyatt Parkway, Lexington KY 40505. (606)254-7474. Owner: Jimmy Price. Music publisher, record company (Sun-Ray, Sky-Vue) and record producer (Jimmy Price Music Publisher). BMI. Estab. 1950. Works with composers and lyricists. Pays standard royalty.
Affiliates: Jimmy Price Productions (BMI).
How to Contact: Submit a demo tape by mail—unsolicited submissions are O.K. Prefers cassette or track ½ or Full 7½ ips reel-to-reel with 3-7 songs and lyric sheet. SASE. Reports in 1½ months.
Music: Mostly country, gospel and bluegrass. Published "My High Country" written and recorded by Charles Stephens (country); "Walk with Jesus" (by Jimmy Price), recorded by Charles Stephens (gospel), all on Sun-Ray.
Tips: "I must have the lyrics to meter. If a person does not know what I mean about bringing lyrics to meter, please check a gospel hymn song book. You will see in each and every staff there is a music note for each and every word or syllable. This way, should I want to add a composition in print I can do so."

*PRIMAL VISIONS MUSIC, 3701 Inglewood Ave., Suite 133, Redondo Beach CA 90278. (213)214-0370. Creative Director: Jeffrey Howard. Music publisher, record company (Primal Records) and record producer (Primal Productions, Inc.). BMI. Estab. 1989. Publishes 6 songs/year; publishes 3 new songwriters/year. Works with composers and lyricists; teams collaborators. Pays standard royalty or other amount "depending on the deal per artist or writer."
How to Contact: Write or call to arrange a personal interview. Prefers cassette (or DAT or VHS videocassette if available) with 1-5 songs and lyric sheet. SASE. Reports in 6 weeks.
Music: Mostly pop/rock, rock and dance/R&B; also rap, hard rock and country. Published "Mirror, Mirror" (written and recorded by Jeffrey Howard); and "Nightmares" (written and recorded by Jeffrey Howard) all on Primal Records (rock).

PRIMAVERA SOUND PRODUCTIONS, 6283-3410 Shelbourne St., Victoria, British Columbia V8P 5L5 **Canada.** Professional Manager/Producer: Eduardo Pereira. Music publishers and record company (PSP Records). PROCAN, CAPAC. Estab. 1986. Publishes 5-10 songs/year; publishes 1-2 new songwriters/year. Works with composers. Pays standard royalty.
How to Contact: Prefers cassette (or Beta videocassette) with 3 songs. Unsolicited material OK. Does not return material but we keep it on file. Reports in 6 weeks.
Music: Mostly pop, rock; also Latin Jazz, Salsa, Merengue, Cumbia. Published "Papa Nicolas" (by Hugo Beltran), recorded by Hugo Beltran (merengue); "Let Me Know" (by DeGrassi/Walker), recorded by Julie Coy (top 40/rock); and "Pienso Tanto En Ti" (by Ruben Zunica), recorded by Yizeth.

PRITCHETT PUBLICATION (Branch), P.O. Box 725, Daytona Beach FL 32014-0725. (904)252-4848. Vice President: Charles Vickers. Music publisher and record company. (Main office in California.) BMI. Estab. 1975. Publishes 21 songs/year; publishes 12 new songwriters/year. Works with composers and lyricists; teams collaborators. Pays standard royalty.
Affiliate: Alison Music (ASCAP).
How to Contact: Write first and obtain permission to submit. Prefers cassette with 6 songs and lyric or lead sheet. SASE.
Music: Gospel, rock-disco and country. Published *Walkin On The Water* (by Charles Vickers), recorded by Charles Vickers on King of Kings Records (gospel); and "It'll Be A Cold Day" (by Leroy Pritchett), recorded by Ray Sanders on Alagash Country Records (country).

*PROMOTORA COLOMBIA NA DE MUSICA LTDA, "PRODEMUS", CRA.43A 11A 40, Medellin **Colombia,** 14-28. (574)2660341. Manager: Sylvia Arango. Music publisher. Estab. 1974. Publishes 200 songs/year; publishes 50 new songwriters/year. Works with composers. Pays 33.3% royalty.

How To Contact: Submit demo tape by mail—unsolicited submissions are OK. Prefers cassette. Does not return unsolicited material. Reports in 3 months.
Music: Interested in tropical, merengue and salsa. Published "Patacon Pisao" (by Ramon Chaverra), recorded by Juan Carlos Coronel; "Cali Pachanguer" (by Jairo Varela), recorded by Grupo Niche; and "Mi Vecina" (by Diego Gale), recorded by Grupo Gale, all on Codiscos Records.

PROPHECY PUBLISHING, INC., Box 4945, Austin TX 78765. (512)452-9412. President: T. White. Music publisher. ASCAP. Pays standard royalty, less expenses; "expenses such as tape duplicating, photocopying and long distance phone calls are recouped from the writer's earnings."
Affiliate: Black Coffee Music (BMI).
How to Contact: "We now only accept songs which are currently on the charts or have a very good chance of entering them next week."
Music: Published "The Sun and Moon and Stars" (by Vince Bell).

PUBLISHING CENTRAL, (formerly Alltold Music Publishing), 7251 Lowell Dr., Overland Park KS 66204. (913)384-6688. Director of Publishing: Mark David Pine. Music publisher. "We are also a theatrical agency." SAG, ITAA. Estab. 1961. Publishes 5 songs/year; publishes 3 new songwriter/year. Teams collaborators. Pays standard royalty.
Affiliates: Jac-Zang (ASCAP), Bunion (BMI).
How to Contact: Submit a demo tape by mail—unsolicited submissions are O.K. Prefers cassette with 1-3 songs and lead sheets. Does not return unsolicited material. Reports in 2 months.
Music: Mostly country rock, pop and rock; also gospel reggae, alternative, cutting edge and soul (southern). Published "It Did Me In" (by Mark Baysinger), recorded by Brewer/Shipley on Capitol (country/rock).
Tips: "There is a trend toward more professionalism. More songwriters can actually write music. They provide lead sheets and not just lyrics and tapes. Take advantage of the advances in music technology and put a part of your soul in your composition."

PURPLE HAZE MUSIC, P.O. Box 1243, Beckley WV 25802. (304)252-4836. A & R: Carol Lee. Music publisher. BMI. Estab. 1968. Publishes 3-5 songs/year; publishes 3-4 new songwriters/year. Works with composers and lyricists; teams collaborators. Pays standard royalty.
How to Contact: Prefers cassette with 3-5 songs and lyric sheet. SASE. Reports in 4 weeks.
Music: Country, pop/top 40 and R&B/crossover. Published "Keep Movin' " (by Chuck Paul), recorded by Chuck Paul on Rising Sun Records (chr); "A Little Night Lovin' " (by Carol Lee), recorded by Victor Jackson on Rising Sun Records (R&B); and "Blue Kentucky Boy" (by Ron Miller/Don Ma-Clean), recorded by Cypress Creek on Country Road Records (country).
Tips: "Songs should be well thought out with clever hooks and lines. We now only accept a professional demo. All songs should be typed up neatly! We have a Nashville songwriters program for those who qualify."

*PUSTAKA MUZIK EMI (Malaysia) SDN. BHD., No. 8, Jalan Murai Dua, Batu Kompleks, Batu Tiga, Jalan Ipoh, Kuala Lumpur **Malaysia**. 03-6277511. Contact: A&R Manager. Music publisher and record company. Publishes 50 songs/year; publishes 15 new songwriters/year.
How to Contact: Prefers cassette and lyric or lead sheet. Does not return unsolicited material.
Music: Mostly MOR, country and commercial jazz; also blues and rock. Published "Pusara Di Lebuh-raya" (by Fauzi Marzuki), recorded by Ekamatra on EMI Records (commercial rock); "Resah Ku" (by A. Ali), recorded by Rohana on NSR Records (MOR); and "Ke Akhirnya" (by Othman Mohamed), recorded by Freedom on EMI Records (MOR).

*QUARK, INC., #1212, 1650 Broadway, New York NY 10019. (212)489-7260. Manager: Fuschia. Music publisher, record company (Quark Records and Q-Rap Records), record producer (Curtis Urbina). Estab. 1986. Publishes 12fififf/year; 2 new songwriters/year. Teams collaborators. Pays standard royalty of 50%.
Affiliates: Quarkette Music (BMI) and Freedurb Music (ASCAP).
How to Contact: Write first and obtain permission to submit a tape. Prefers cassette with 2 songs and lyric sheet. Does not return unsolicited material. Reports in 2 weeks.
Music: Mostly pop, R&B and New Age. Published "Love Me True" (by G. Louvis), recorded by K. Holmes (R&B); "Hip This House" (by L. Lee), recorded by Shadows J (dance); and "I Like" (by G. Hughes), recorded by Bluejean (dance) all on Quark Records.

R. J. MUSIC, 10A Margaret Rd., Barnet, Herts. EN4 9NP **England**. Phone: (01)440-9788. Managing Directors: Roger James and Laura Skuce. Music publisher and management firm (Roger James Management). PRS. Pays negotiable royalty (up to 75%).

How to Contact: Prefers cassette with 1 song and lyric or lead sheet. Does not return material.
Music: Mostly MOR, blues, country and rock; also disco and chart material.

*R.T.L. MUSIC, LEE MUSIC, LE MATTE MUSIC, POSO RECORDS, Stewart House, Hill Bottom Road, Sands-Ind. Est., Highwycome, Buckinghamshire HP12 4HJ **England**. 0494-36301-36401. FAX: 0494-461832. TELEX: 837173. A&R: Xavier Lee. Music publisher. PRS (UK). Estab. 1971. Works with composers and lyricists; teams collaborators. Pays standard royalty. Publishes 120 songs/year; publishes 50 new songwriters/year.
How to Contact: Submit a demo tape by mail—unsolicited submissions are OK. Prefers cassette, VHS or BETA videocassette with 3 songs and lyric or lead sheets. SASE. Reports in 6 weeks.
Music: Mostly all types. Published "X-R-L" (by Row Lee), recorded by XAV.L. on Swoop Records (r.r); "Rock and Roll Does" and "Circus Freaks" (by R.T. Dickson), recorded by Nightmare on Zarg Records (shock rock).

RAGLAND PUBLICATIONS, Box 43659, Las Vegas NV 89116. (702)794-4588. President: Lou Ragland. Music publisher, record company (Casino Records Inc., Spirit Records of Nevada) record producer (Ragland Enterprises). BMI. Estab. 1962. Publishes 10 songs/year; 2 new songwriters/year. Hires staff writers. Works with composers and lyricists; teams collaborators. Pays standard royalty.
How to Contact: Submit a demo tape by mail-unsolicited submissions are OK. Prefers cassette with 4 songs and lyric sheets. SASE. Does not return unsolicited material. Reports in 2½ months.
Music: Mostly pop, R&B and all gospel; also rock. Published "Welcome to Heaven" (by The First Light), on Casino Records (gospel); "In the Hours of Darkness" (by Lou Ragland), on Casino Records (R&B); and "Shelter of God's Love" (by Ron Paris), on Spirit Records (gospel); all recorded by ATP.
Tips: "Type lyrics always. Copyright all material you can. Write as many songs and styles as you can."

RAINBARREL MUSIC COMPANY, Box 292101, Nashville TN 37229-2101. Director: Teresa Parks Bernard. BMI. Estab. 1972. Music publisher, record company (Paragold Records) and record producer. Publishes 5 songs/year; publishes 2 new songwriter/year. Teams collaborators. Pays standard royalty.
How to Contact: Write first. Prefers cassette with 2 songs and lyric and lead sheets. SASE. Reports in 6 weeks.
Music: Mostly country; also top 40. Published "Devil's Guitar" (by J. Bernard), recorded by Johnny Bernard on Paragold Records; "Muddy Mississippi" (by J. Bernard/Julie Jones), recorded by Reba McEntire on Mercury Records; and "Love," (by J. Bernard/J. Jones), recorded by Johnny Bernard/Julia Jones on Paragold Records (all country).
Tips: "Send only the most outstanding material you have."

RANDOM IMAGE MUSIC, 209 Madison Avenue, Toronto, Ontario MSR 2S6 **Canada**. (416)929-2349. Professional Manager: Peter Randall. Music publisher, record company (Random Records) and record producer (Random Image Productions). PROCAN. Estab. 1986. Publishes 10-12 songs/year; publishes 2-3 new songwriters/year. Works with composers and lyricists; teams collaborators. Pays standard royalty.
How to Contact: Submit a demo tape—unsolicited submissions are OK. Prefers cassette (or VHS videocassette) with 2-3 songs and lyric sheets (lead sheets optional). SAE and IRC. Reports back in several weeks.
Music: Rock, pop and new age only. Published "What Do You Want" (by Shaun Firth), recorded by Peter Randall; "Fool For You," written and recorded by Steven Long (pop); "One Is a Thousand" (by S. Winter), recorded by Winter Heat (rock); and "Indecisions" (by Burlovich, Doucet, Mead), recorded by The Fact (roots rock); all on Random Records.
Tips: "Production, fashion and technology are sadly becoming much more important than the music; at Random Image, the music still matters. A song is never finished, keep writing and rewriting it. It can be improved, think about it carefully, take your time."

*REATA MUSIC, 3800 W. Alameda, Burbank CA 91505. (818)954-0619. Creative Assistant: Mark Friedman. Music Publisher. BMI, ASCAP. Estab. 1988. Publishes 40 songs/year; publishes 2 new songwriters/year. Hires staff writers. Works with composers and lyricists; teams collaborators.
How to Contact: Submit a demo tape—unsolicited submissions are OK. Prefers cassette with 1 song and lyric sheet. SASE. Reports in 1 month. "Do not call."
Music: Mostly pop, rock and R&B; also country. Published "What Goes Around" (by Carolyn Mitchell), recorded by Regina Bell on CBS Records (R&B).
Tips: "Only submit songs that are your best work and will be competitive in today's market."

Close-up

Carla Berkowitz
Reata Music
Burbank, California

Carla Berkowitz began her careeer in the music business as
an independent song plugger, pushing a friend's songs to
anyone who would listen. "All I knew was that my friend
had songs that should be on the radio and I had to get them
there." From that ambitious start, Carla has gone on to
build a successful career for herself in the world of music
publishing. After stints in the creative departments of
Creative Entertainment Music and Chrysalis Music, she is now creative director for Reata
Music in Burbank, California, which is administered worldwide by Warner Music.

A typical day for Carla consists mostly of meetings. "I'll try to go to all the labels—at
least one label a week. For example, I'll go to Warner Bros. and see the entire staff: all of
the pop A&R, the rock A&R, the R&B A&R, the alternative A&R, staff producers—and
I'll set up other appointments while I'm there. Of course, I also meet with writers. So I do
those kinds of meetings, and then I have down time where I close my door and I concentrate
on the artists that need material. I'll do it two ways: either I'll try to find a song for the
artist or I'll try to find an artist for a particular song. If I have one song I particularly love,
I'll play it over and over and read my *Billboard* and get some ideas about who might do it.
I do that kind of 'casting' every day."

Carla advises songwriters to pay close attention to pop song structure. "For example,
some of the songs I hear might not have a chorus. They'll be just verse, verse, verse. Like
somebody wrote a poem and put some music to it. That's not writing a song; that's putting
music to a poem, and that's not going to get placed. Structure is really important. Think
of it like building a house; without a foundation, a house is not going to stand. *I* could write
a song that doesn't have a chorus, and that's fine if I want to write it to my mother or my
dog or my boyfriend or whoever, but I'm not going to try to sell it to someone. The thing
is, if you're in the business of songwriting and you want other people to record your music
then you have to follow the rules. Many people ignore that. They don't realize that the
moment they pitch a song to someone it becomes a business transaction."

To familiarize yourself with current pop song structure Carla suggests this exercise:
"Study the charts and buy some of the top new singles every week for, say, a month. Then
take these songs and copy them in your home studio or on your own instrument. Get a feel
for the chord changes and where the chorus comes in and how it builds. Copy the lyrics to
get a sense of how these professionals are writing; actually write them out, as if you were
writing the song. Do that with five or ten songs, and when you write your next song it will
be better—closer to the real thing."

Once your songs are the best they can be, Carla says don't waste your time by trying to
get someone on the phone or by sending endless letters asking permission to submit your
songs. "Just send the tape!", she says. "These people might not have time to talk on the
phone or answer letters, but they have time to pop in a cassette. We all need and are
looking for the next great writer. Our ears and eyes are wide open."

—Mark Garvey

RED RIVER SONGS/CRIMSON CREEK SONGS, 1815 Division St., Nashville TN 37203. (615)327-8436. President: Sherry Bond. Music publisher. BMI, ASCAP. Publishes 50 songs/year. Works with composers. Pays standard royalty.
Affiliate: Vidor Publications (BMI).
How to Contact: Prefers cassette with lyric sheet. SASE. Reports in 1 month.
Music: Mostly country. Published "Goin' By the Book" (by Chester Lester), recorded by Johnny Cash on Polygram Records (gospel); "I Wonder Where You Are Tonight" (by Johnny Bond), recorded by Keith Whitley on RCA Records (country); and "Lovin' in Vain" (by Freddie Hart), recorded by Rosie Flores on Warner Records (country).
Tips: "Send a very simple guitar/vocal that allows the song to speak for itself. Submit an original idea."

*JACK REDICK MUSIC, Rt. 1, Box 85, Georgetown SC 29440. Manager: Jack Redick. Works with composers and lyricists. Pays standard royalty.
Affiliate: Wagon Wheel Records.
How to Contact: Prefers cassette (or VHS videocassette) with 1-6 songs, plus typed lyrics; also photo, bio, and credits if possible. SASE. "Never send your original master tape of anything, make copies to mail out. We're mostly interested in unpublished material; indicate if it's copyrighted. Also willing to co-write with lyricists or composers with 50-50, collaboration contract. On lyrics for co-write, send only material that's clear (not tied up with anyone) and that you're the sole writer on."
Music: Mostly traditional country and country gospel,some crossover,rockabilly, humorous and tribute styles. Published "WhataChange in My World," "What Must I Do (to prove my love for you)," "Devil in Disguise," and "Imagine the Bitter Tears." Also won 'Songwriter of the Year' award.
Tips: "Lyrics should be over music. Tell a new story, or an old story with a new twist. Hooks (attention grabbers) should be in title, and in 'MEAT' of song. DON'T BE A DREAMER, CAUSE WHEN A DREAMER AWAKES THE DREAM IS GONE. BE A WORKER, AND MAKE YOUR DREAMS HAPPEN."

*REID PUBLISHING INTERNATIONAL, Box 431, Cornwall, Ontario K6H 5T2 **Canada**. (514)264-4473. Manager: Tara Stevens. Music publisher, record company (Colt Records) and record producer (Gilles Godard). PROCAN. Estab. 1987. Publishes more than 3 songs/year; publishes more than 3 new songwriters/year. Works with lyricists; teams collaborators. Pays standard royalty.
How to Contact: Submit a demo tape, unsolicited submissions are OK. Prefers cassette (or VHS videocassette) with up to 4 songs and lyric sheet. SASE and IRC are required. Reports in 3 weeks.
Music: Mostly country, rock and pop; also R&B and new age. Published *Rage Rain* (by Boni Fon), recorded by Boni Fon on Colt Records (rock); "After You Call" (by Eddy Rivette), recorded by Eddy Rivette on Colt Records (country); and *Sub-Storms* (by Eclipse), recorded by Eclipse on Colt Records (pop).
Tips: "If you want your material returned, pay for it. If you want a reply, enclose a stamped envelope. If you want us to read it, type it. Be professional, it shows maturity."

*REN MAUR MUSIC CORP., 521 5th Ave., New York NY 10175. (212)757-3638. President: Rena L. Feeney. Music publisher and record company. BMI. Member AGAC and NARAS. Publishes 6-8 songs/year. Pays 4-8% royalty.
Affiliate: R.R. Music (ASCAP).
How to Contact: Prefers cassette with 2-4 songs and lead sheet. SASE. Reports in 1 month.
Music: R&B, rock, soul and top 40/pop. Published "Same Language," "Do It to Me and I'll Do It to You," and "Once You Fall in Love," (by Billy Nichols), recorded by Rena; and "Lead Me to Love," (by Brad Smiley), recorded by Carmen John (ballad/dance) all on Factory Beat Records.
Tips: "Send lead sheets and a good, almost finished cassette ready for producing or remixing."

RHYTHMS PRODUCTIONS, Whitney Bldg., Box 34485, Los Angeles CA 90034. President: Ruth White. Music publisher and record company (Tom Thumb Records). ASCAP. Member NARAS. Publishes 10 cassettes/year. Pays negotiable royalty.
Affiliate: Tom Thumb Music.
How to Contact: Submit tape with letter outlining background in educational children's music. SASE. Reports in 1 month.
Music: "We're only interested in children's songs that have educational value. Our materials are sold in schools and homes, so artists/writers with a teaching background would be most likely to understand our requirements." Published "Watch Me Grow," (cassette series for children). "We buy completed master tapes."

RIC RAC MUSIC, Ric Rac Inc., Box 712, Nashville IN 47448. (812)837-9569. Professional Manager: Sue Hanson. Music publisher, record company (Ric Rac Records and Country Bump Records), record producer (Rich Hanson Productions) and Ric Rac Inc. (marketing and promotion). ASCAP. Publishes

10-15 songs/year; publishes 5-10 new songwriters/year. Works with composers and lyricists; teams collaborators. Pays standard royalty.
Affiliate: Rick Hanson Music (BMI).
How to Contact: Write first and obtain permission to submit. Prefers cassette (or VHS videocassette) with 1-4 songs and lyric sheet. SASE. Reports in 8 weeks.
Music: Mostly country; also pop/rock, rock, gospel, folk, pop, jazz, R&B, easy listening instrumental. Published "Same Old Barroom Melody," written and recorded by Rick Hanson; and "My Love is Safe With You" (by Hanson/Harland), recorded by Rick Hanson; both on Ric Rac Records (country).
Tips: "Be as professional as possible. Get involved with local and regional songwriting workshops and/ or music associations in your area."

*RIDGE MUSIC CORP., 38 Laurel Ledge Ct., Stamford CT 06903. President/General Manager: Paul Tannen. Music publisher and manager. Estab. 1961. BMI, ASCAP. Member CMA. Pays standard royalty.
Affiliates: Tannen Music Inc. and Deshufflin, Inc.
How to Contact: Prefers cassette with 3 songs and lyric sheet. SASE. Reports in 1 month.
Music: Country, rock, top 40/pop, and jazz.

*RIGHTEOUS RECORDS, P.O. Box 289, B.U. Station, Boston MA 02215. (617)787-3615. A&R: Randy Frisch. Music publisher and record company (Righteous Records). Estab. 1985. Publishes 15 songs/ year; 2-3 new songwriters/year. Works with composers and lyricists; teams collaborators. Pays standard royalty.
How to Contact: Submit demo tape-unsolicited submissions are OK. Prefers cassette or VHS video-cassette with 2-4 songs and lyric sheets. SASE. Reports in 2 weeks.
Music: Interested in rock, rap and R&B. Published "About My Old Girlfriend" (by Frisch/Wechsler), recorded by The McGuires on I Wanna Records (rock) and "I've Got So Many Dreams" (by Frisch/ Wechsler), recorded by Pat Thomas on Heyday Records (rock).
Tips: "Try us!"

*RIGO MUSIC ENTERPRISES/MEDIA CONCEPTS MUSIC, 57 N. Perkins Ave., Elmsford NY 10523. (914)592-2563. Professional Manager: Michael Berman. President: Chip Rigo. Music publisher and record producer. Estab. 1981. BMI, ASCAP. Publishes 20 songs/year; publishes 10 new songwriters/ year. Pays standard royalty; co-publishing deals available for established writers.
Affiliate: Sunsongs Music (BMI).
How to Contact: Prefers cassette with 3-4 songs and lyric sheet. SASE. Reports in 5 weeks.
Music: Dance-oriented, techno-pop, R&B, rock (all styles) and top 40/pop. Published "Big Girl" (by Michael Christian), "What You Get Is What You See," (Etoll/Kalem), and "Nothing But Trouble," (by Robbie Rigo), recorded by Jailbait and performed on Star Search '85 (pop/rock; Jailbait was a finalist and was recently signed to Atlantic Records).

*RISSON MUSIC (PUBLISHING) UK, 127 Aldersgate St., London EC1A 4JQ **England**. Phone: (44)71-2501910. Contact: A&R Department. Music publisher, record company (Presidential; XXI St. Century, record producer. PRS. Estab. 1987. Publishes 20-30 songs/year; 4-5 new songwriters/year. Works with composers and lyricists. Pays 60% to writers and 40% to publisher.
How to Contact: Write or call first and obtain permission to submit a tape. Prefers cassette with 2-5 songs and lyric sheet. Does not return unsolicited material. Reports in 2 weeks.
Music: Mostly house and hip-hop. Pubilshed "Hit The Bit" (by Bellini); "The Riot" (by Tubemaster); and "Do It (In The Mix)" (by Garbelli) all recorded by P.E.L. on Presidential Records (house).

FREDDIE ROBERTS MUSIC, P.O. Box 203, Rougemont NC 27572. (919)477-4077. Manager: Freddie Roberts. Music publisher, record company, record producer (Carolina Pride Productions), and management firm and booking agency. Estab. 1967. BMI. Publishes 45 songs/year; publishes 15 new songwriters/year. Works with composers, lyricists; teams collaborators. Pays standard royalty.

 The asterisk before a listing indicates that the listing is new in this edition. New markets are often the most receptive to unsolicited submissions.

How to Contact: Write first about your interest or arrange personal interview. Prefers 7½ ips reel-to-reel or cassette with 1-5 songs and lyric sheet. SASE.

Music: Mostly country, MOR and top 40/pop; also bluegrass, church/religious, gospel and southern rock (country). Published "Any Way You Want It" (by B. Fann), recorded by Sleepy Creek (southern rock) on Bull City Records; "Just A Little" (by C. Justis), recorded by Dean Phillips (country) on Ardon Records; and "He Knows What I Need" (by J. Dobbs), recorded by the Roberts Family (gospel) on Bull City Records.

Tips: "Write songs, whatever type, to fit today's market. Send good, clear demos, no matter how simple."

ROCKER MUSIC/HAPPY MAN MUSIC, 26082 Princess Lane, Bonita Sprs, FL 33923-6637. (813)947-6978. Executive Producer: Dick O'Bitts. BMI, ASCAP. Estab. 1960. Music publisher, record company (Happy Man Records, Condor Records and Air Corp Records), record producer (Rainbow Collections Ltd.) and management firm (Gemini Complex). Publishes 50 songs/year; publishes 8-10 new songwriters/year. Works with composers; teams collaborators. Pays standard royalty.

Affiliate: Happy Man Music.

How to Contact: Submit a demo tape—unsolicited submissions are OK. Prefers cassette (or VHS videocassette if possible) with 4 songs and lyric sheet or lead sheet. SASE. Do not call. "You don't need consent to send material."

Music: Country, rock, pop and off-the-wall. Published "Can We Talk" (by Chris and Bob Thompson), recorded by Chris and Lenny; and "When Daddy Did the Driving" (by Chris Thompson), recorded by Chris and Lenny; all on Happy Man Records (country).

Tips: "For speedier response send material to be reviewed to Bonita Springs address."

ROCKFORD MUSIC CO., Suite 6-D, 150 West End Ave., New York NY 10023. Manager: Danny Darrow. Music publisher, record company (Mighty Records), record and video tape producer. BMI, ASCAP. Publishes 1-3 songs/year; publishes 1-3 new songwriters/year. Teams collaborators. Pays standard royalty.

Affiliates: Corporate Music Publishing Company (ASCAP) and Stateside Music Company (BMI).

How to Contact: Submit a demo tape—unsolicited submissions are OK. Prefers cassette with 3 songs and lyric sheet. "SASE a must!" Reports in 2 weeks. No phone calls.

Music: Mostly MOR and top 40/pop; also adult pop, country, adult rock, dance-oriented, easy listening, folk and jazz. Published "Falling in Love," (by Brian Downen) and "A Part of You" (by B. Downen/Randy Lakeman), both recorded by D. Darrow on Mighty Records (rock ballad and blues); *Doomsday* (by various songwriters), recorded by Danny Darrow on Colley Records (Euro disco LP); and *Great Folk Songs* (by various songwriters), recorded by Danny Darrow on Mighty Records (folk LP).

Tips: "Listen to top 40 and write current lyrics and music."

ROCKSONG MUSIC PUBLISHING LTD., 152 Goldthorn Hill, Penn., Wolverhampton WV2 3JA **England.** Phone: (902)345345. A&R Manager: David Roberts. Music publisher, record company (FM-Revolver Records and labels in United Kingdom, Japan, Canada and Europe) and record producer. PRS. Estab. 1980. Member MCPS, MRS, MPA. Publishes 100 songs/year; publishes 5 new songwriters/year. Works with composers. Pays negotiable royalty.

Affiliates: Heavy Metal Music and Andersong Music.

How to Contact: Prefers cassette (or VHS PAL System videocassette) with 3 songs. "Send photos and bios if also an artist." Does not return unsolicited material. Reports in 1 month.

Music: Heavy Metal, hard rock, "chart-oriented material" and AOR. Published "Rock & Roll Lady" (by Marino/Dominique), recorded by Lisa Dominique (pop/rock) on FM Records; "Mean Machine" (by Dirk Schneider), recorded by UDO (heavy metal) on RCA Records; and "No Getting Over You" (by Carnochan), recorded by Vibrators (indie pop) on Revolver Records.

Tips: Submit "solid, killer songs that have international chart potential."

*ROLLIN' IN THE DOUGH, BRO MUSIC (BMI), % Irish Indian Music, 609A Rosebank Ave., Nashville TN 37206. (615)226-8438. Professional Manager/Administrator: Albert Kennedy Williams. Music publisher. BMI. Estab. 1988. Publishes 24 songs/year; publishes 3 new songwriters/year. Works with composers. Pays standard royalty.

How to Contact: Submit a demo tape by mail—unsolicited submissions are OK. Prefers cassette with 5 songs and lead sheet. "A lead sheet or chord chart is important, as we only publish instrumentals at this time." SASE. Reports in 1 month.

Music: Mostly New Age, light jazz and progressive bluegrass. Published "This Smile" (New Age), "White Sugar Blues" (New Age) and "Northern Lights" (progressive bluegrass), all written and recorded by Johnny Bellar on Miracle Records.

Tips: "We only publish music written specifically for dobro or guitar."

ROOTS MUSIC, Box 111, Sea Bright NJ 07760. President: Robert Bowden. Music publisher, record company (Nucleus Records) and record producer (Robert Bowden). BMI. Estab. 1979. Publishes 2 songs/year; publishes 1 new songwriter/year. Works with composers and lyricists. Pays standard royalty.
How to Contact: Submit a demo tape. Prefers cassette (or VHS videocassette) with 3 songs and lyric sheet; include photo and bio. "I only want inspired songs written by talented writers." SASE. Reports in 1 month.
Music: Mostly country and pop; also church/religious, classical, folk, MOR, progressive, rock (soft, mellow) and top 40. Published "Pressure Cooker," written and recorded by Jean Schweitzer (country); "Always," written and recorded by Marco Sision (pop); and "Selfish Heart," written and recorded by Robert Bowden (country); all recorded on Nucleus Records.

STEPHEN C. ROSE, 81 Mt. Vernon St., Boston MA 02108. (617)723-5621. Manager: Stephen C. Rose. Songwriter/Music Publisher/Talent Development. Larry Lee: Song plugger. Steve Cooper: Demos/Nashville Representative. Cooperative relationships with LA publishers. Estab. 1988. Publishes 150 songs/year; works with any number of new songwriters/year. Uses Songwriter's Guild Contract, shares 50% net publishing with writers.
Affiliates: Keep on Comin' (ASCAP), Just Hits Music (BMI).
How to Contact: Call first. Unsolicited OK, but SASE utterly essential for a reply. Type one lyric per sheet. Send up to five songs. Responds ASAP.
Music: Only interested in songs that compete with what is top ten on the Billboard pop and country charts. Our emphasis is on discovering a singer/songwriter who can go all the way to the top, pop or country, and helping her/him musically and promotionally. We are also interested in good song ideas from any source.
Tips: "We are a writer-friendly company that believes music row is anywhere the hit song is and that you can write one if you're willing to collaborate and to accept criticism. We vigorously pitch all songs we take to major artists and producers. If your strength is not in original composition, listen to the radio two hours and search for titles two hours for every hour you spend writing. Write with a groove in mind, make the song move and focus on I-you love songs."

ROWILCO, Box 8135, Chicago IL 60680. (312)224-5612. Professional Manager: R.C. Hillsman. Music publisher. BMI. Publishes 8-20 songs/year.
How to Contact: Arrange personal interview. Prefers cassettes or 7½ or 15 ips ¼" reel-to-reel with 4-6 songs (on VHS or Beta Videocassette) and lyric sheet. Submissions should be sent via registered mail. SASE. Reports in 3 weeks.
Music: Blues, church/religious, country, disco, easy listening, gospel, jazz, MOR, rock and top 40/pop.

ROYAL FLAIR PUBLISHING, Box 438, Walnut IA 51577. (712)366-1136. President: Bob Everhart. Music publisher and record producer. BMI. Estab. 1967. Publishes 5-10 songs/year; publishes 1-2 new songwriters/year. Works with composers and lyricists. Pays standard royalty.
How to Contact: Submit a demo tape—unsolicited submissions are OK with SASE. Prefers cassette with 2-6 songs. SASE. Reports in 9 weeks.
Music: Traditional country, bluegrass and folk. Published "Hero of Gringo Trail," "Time After Time," and "None Come Near," written and recorded by R. Everhart on Folkways; and "Smoky Mountain Heartbreak," written and recorded by Bonnie Sanford (all country).
Tips: "Song definitely has to have old-time country flavor with all the traditional values of country music. No sex, outlandish swearing, or drugs-booze type songs accepted. We have an annual Hank Williams Songwriting Contest over Labor Day weekend and winners are granted publishing."

RUSHWIN PUBLISHING, Box 1150-SM91, Buna TX 77612. (409)423-2521.Owner/General Manager: James L. Gibson. Music publisher and record producer (James L. Gibson/Rushwin Productions). BMI. Estab. 1985. Publishes 5-10 songs/year and 1-2 new songwriters/year. Works with composers and lyricists; teams collaborators. Pays standard royalty. Member GMA.
Affiliates: Gibson Davidsong (ASCAP), Rushwin Productions.
How to Contact: Submit a demo tape by mail—unsolicited submissions O.K. Prefers cassette with 1-4 songs and typed lyric sheet. Clearly label each item sent. SASE (6x9 or larger). Reports ASAP.
Music: Southern/Country Gospel. Published "Holy Rolling" (by Ronald T. Sparks), recorded by the Helmsmen (southern gospel) on Morning Star Records; "You're a Saint or You Ain't" (by Randy Lawrence/Bill Fisher), recorded by the Harbingers (southern gospel) on Gold Street Records; and "The Third Day" (by Stephen Mattox), recorded by The Third Day (contemporary southern gospel) on New Breeze Records.
Tips: We are interested in the type material suited for the recording artist that appear in the music charts published by *The Gospel Voice* and *The Singing News*."

RUSTRON MUSIC PUBLISHERS, 1156 Park Lane, West Palm Beach FL 33417. (407)-686-1354. Professional Managers: Rusty Gordon and Ron Caruso. Music publisher and record producer (Rustron Music Productions). BMI. Estab. 1974. Publishes 20-40 songs/year; publishes 4-10 new songwriters/year. Works with composers and lyricists; teams collaborators. Pays standard royalty.
How to Contact: Submit a demo tape (cassette)—unsolicited submissions are OK, or write or call first to get permission to submit a tape. Prefers cassette with 1-3 songs and lyric or lead sheet. "Clearly label your tape and container. Include cover letter." Must include SASE. Reports in 1 month.
Music: Mostly pop (ballads, blues, theatrical, cabaret), progressive country, folk/rock; also R&B and new age. Published "Song For Pedro" and "I Don't Want To Lose You" written and recorded by Marian Joy Ring on Black Dog Records (fusion, jazz/folk); "Shores of Mexico" and "La Lucha" written and recorded by Janet Bratter on Rustron Records, "Appalachian Wind" and "Ellen's Song" (by Sue Massek) recorded by The Reel World String Band on Flying Fish Records (country/bluegrass) and "Rockabye Railroad" (by Jayne Reby) and "Zen Lovesong" (by Bonnie Pedicord) both songs recorded by Jayne Reby and Bonnie Pedicord on Circle and Star Records (folk/rock).
Tips: "Write strong hooks. Keep song length 3½ minutes or less. Avoid predictability—create original lyric themes. Tell a story."

S.M.C.L. PRODUCTIONS, INC., P.O. Box 84, Boucherville, Quebec J4B 5E6 **Canada**. (514)641-2266. President: Christian Lefort. Music publisher and record company. CAPAC. Estab. 1968. Publishes 70-90 songs/year; publishes 15-20 new songwriters/year.
Affiliates: A.Q.E.M. Ltee (CAPAC), Bag Enrg. (CAPAC), C.F. Music (CAPAC), Big Bazaar Music (CAPAC), Sunrise Music (CAPAC), Stage One Music (CAPAC), L.M.S. Ltee (CAPAC), ITT Music (CAPAC), Machine Music (CAPAC), Dynamite Music (CAPAC), Danava Music (PRO/SDE), Coincidence Music (PRO/SDE), Music and Music (CAPAC), Cinemusic Inc. (CAPAC), Cinafilm (PRO/SDE). Editions La Fete Inc. (CAPAC), Groupe Concept Musique (CAPAC) and Editions Dorimen (CAPAC).
How to Contact: Write first to get permission to submit a tape. Prefers cassette with 4-12 songs and lead sheet. SAE and IRC. Reports in 1 month.
Music: Dance, easy listening, MOR, top 40/pop and TV and movie soundtracks. Published "Where Is My Man," recorded by the Eartha Kitt on Able Records (dance); and "Sex Over the Phone," recorded by Village People on Celsius Records (dance), Kaschtin (12 songs on Trans-Canada in Canada and BMG in Europe) Nathalie Carsen (13 songs on Kebec Disc in Canada and Flarenasch in Europe) music soundtracks of: "He Shoots, He Scores" on WEA Records, The Great Land of Small/The Tadpole and the Whale and many soundtracks of French-Canadian T.V. series.

S.U.Y.T. PUBLISHING, P.O. Box 1384, Mobile AL 36633. (205)432-7827. Co-Owner: Kirk Weinacker. Music publisher and record company (Psychotronic Records). BMI. Estab. 1987. Publishes 15-25 songs/year; publishes "all new songwriters." Works with composers and lyricists; teams collaborators. Pays standard royalty.
Affiliates: S.U.Y.T. Publishing (BMI) and Lawsonsongs Music Ltd. (BMI).
How to Contact: Submit a demo tape by mail—unsolicited submissions are O.K. Prefers cassette (or VHS videocassette if available) with 3-5 songs and lyric sheet. SASE. Reports in 6 weeks.
Music: Mostly folk rock, progressive rock and R&B; also country, pop and alternative music. Published "Underground," "It's a Cruel, Cruel World" and "I Got You" all (by M. Lawson), recorded by Mike Lawson on Psychotronic Records (folk rock).
Tips: "Submit a clear demo, even if it's done on a boom box, with a lyric sheet. Don't overproduce demos; allow the song to stand on its own."

SABRE MUSIC, P.O. Box 702, Snowdon Station, Montreal, Quebec H3X 3X8 **Canada**. Professional General Manager: D. Leonard. Music publisher. SOCAN. Estab. 1963. Works with composers and lyricists; teams collaborators. Pays standard royalty.
Affiliate: Montina Music (SOCAN).
How to Contact: Submit a demo tape—unsolicited submissions are OK. Prefers cassette or record (or VHS videocassette) and lyric sheet. Does not return unsolicited material.
Music: Mostly top 40; also blues, country, dance-oriented, easy listening, folk, gospel, jazz, MOR, progressive, R&B, rock, soul and pop.

SABTECA MUSIC CO., Box 10286, Oakland CA 94610. (415)465-2805. President: Duane Herring. Music publisher and record company (Sabteca Record Co.). ASCAP, BMI. Estab. 1980. Publishes 3-5 songs/year; 1 new songwriter/year. Pays standard royalty.
How to Contact: Write first and obtain permission to submit a tape. Prefers cassette. SASE. Reports in 3 weeks.
Music: Mostly R&B, pop and country. Published "Come Into My Arms" and "I Dare You" (by Duane Herring), recorded by Johnny B and the Rhythm Method (rock) on Sabteca Records; and "Make Love Stay" (by Walter Coleman), recorded by Lois Shayne (R&B) on Sabteca Records.

Tips: "Improve your writing skills. Keep up with music trends."

*SADHANA MUSIC PUBLISHING, Suite B, 2113 Elliott Ave., Nashville TN 37204. (615)297-6939. A&R Director: Wesley Bulla. Music publisher and record producer (More Coffee Productions). AS-CAP. Estab. 1981. Publishes 10 songs/year. Works with composers and lyricists; teams collaborators. Pays standard royalty of 50%.
How to Contact: Submit a demo tape by mail—unsolicited submissions are OK. Write first and obtain permission to submit a tape. Prefers cassette with 3 songs and lyric sheet. SASE.
Music: Mostly pop/rock, country and jazz; also gospel.
Tips: "The music business is a personal, one-to-one business. Make personal contacts."

*SAFE RETURN MUSIC, P.O. Box 7032, Marietta GA 30065. (404)436-8631. President: Jeff Higgins. Music publisher and record company (Survival Records). BMI. Estab. 1986. Publishes 8-10 songs/year; publishes 1 new songwriter/year.
How to Contact: Write first and obtain permission to submit. Prefers cassette with 3 songs. Does not return unsolicited material. Reports "if we decide to use it."
Music: Mostly blues rock and southern rock. Published "Honest Man" (by Jeff Higgins), recorded by Reddog on Survival Records (ballad); "Turn Me Baby" (by Chris Long), recorded by Reddod on Survival Records (blues); and "Was It You" (by Jeff Higgins), recorded by Reddog on Survival Records (blues).

*TRACY SANDS MUSIC, Suite 119, 2166 W. Broadway, Anaheim CA 92804-2446. (714)525-5223. Vice President, A&R: Harold Shmoduquet. Music publisher, record company (Orange Records, Beet Records), record producer (Orange Productions). BMI. Estab. 1977. Publishes 12 songs/year; publishes 4 new songwriters/year. Pays standard royalty of 50%.
Affiliates: Fat Cat Music (BMI), Lipstick Traces Music (BMI) and Bastion Music (BMI).
How to Contact: Submit a demo tape by mail—unsolicited submissions are OK. Prefers cassette with 2-3 songs and lyric sheet. SASE. Reports in 2 months.
Music: All types. Published "Hot Summer Days" (by Daniel Dailey and Ted Greenberg), recorded by Wilson Dailey on Orange Records; "Dinah Wants Religion" (by Ellis, Clark, Cammack), recorded by The Fabs on Swak Records and "We're Not What We Are" (by Robert Wahlsteen), recorded by Jubal's Children on Swak Records (all rock).

SARISER MUSIC, Box 211, Westfield MA 01086. (413)783-8386. Operations Manager: Virginia L. Stewart. Music publisher and record company (Sweet Talk Records). BMI. Publishes 6-12 songs/year; publishes 1-2 new songwriters/year. Works with composers and lyricists; teams collaborators. Pays standard royalty.
How to Contact: Write first and obtain permission to submit. No calls. Prefers cassette or 7½ IPS reel-to-reel with 3-4 songs and lyric or lead sheet. "Lyrics should be typed; clear vocal on demo." SASE. Reports in 6 weeks.
Music: Mostly country/pop, country/rock and educational material; also soft rock and rockabilly. "We're interested in 50s/60s style 4-part harmony." Published "One Last Kiss" (by Sparkie Allison) recorded by Moore Twinz on MMT Records (country); "Sweet Talk" (by Sparkie Allison), recorded by Sparkie Allison on Sweet Talk Records (country rock); and "Ride A Rainbow" (by Sparkie Allison), recorded by Sparkie Allison and Ginny Cooper on Sweet Talk Records (country/pop).
Tips: "Lyrics must have positive message. No cheatin' songs. Be unique. Try something different."

SCHMERDLEY MUSIC, 7560 Woodman Pl., #G3, Van Nuys CA 91405. (818)994-4862. Owner: Tom Willett. Music publisher, record company (Tomark Records) and record producer (Tomark Records). BMI. Estab. 1969. Publishes 10 songs/year; 2-4 new songwriters/year. Pays standard royalty.
How to Contact: Submit a demo tape by mail—unsolicited submissions are OK. Prefers cassette (or VHS videocassette). SASE. Reports in 4 weeks.
Music: Mostly country and novelty; also rock. Published "Rockin Rasputin" (by Tom Willett) recorded by Tom Willett on Gong Show (novelty); "My Ex-Wife" (by Tom Willett), recorded by Tom Willett on Tomark Records (country novelty); and "Please Don't Play My Record" (by Tom Willett), recorded by Tom Willett on Tomark Records (country/novelty).
Tips: "Don't send a song which is very meaningful to you. Send something that the masses want to buy."

SCI-FI MUSIC, P.O. Box 941, N.D.G., Montreal Quebec H4A 3S3 **Canada.** (514)487-4551. President: Gary Moffet. Music publisher. PROCAN. Estab. 1984. Publishes 5 songs/year; publishes 2 new songwriters/year. Works with composers; teams collaborators. Pays standard royalty of 50%.

How to Contact: Write or call first and obtain permission to submit a tape. Submit cassette with 3-10 songs and lyric sheet. Returns unsolicited submissions if accompanied by SASE. Reports in 1 month.
Music: Mostly rock, pop and metal. Published "Wedlock Headlock," "Gina" and "Black Cat" (all by Sneaky James) and recorded by SCI on In Negotiations Records (rock); also "It's A Pleasure To See You Again" (by Gary Moffet), recorded by April Wine on Capitol Records (rock).

SCOTTI BROTHERS MUSIC PUBLISHING, 2114 Pico Blvd., Santa Monica CA 90405. (213)450-4143. Professional Manager: Richie Wise. Music publisher and record company. BMI, ASCAP. Member NMPA, AIMP, RIAA and CMA. Publishes 40 songs/year; publishes 2 new songwriters/year. Pays standard royalty.
Affiliates: Flowering Stone and Holy Moley.
How to Contact: Prefers cassette with 1-2 songs and lyric sheet. Does not return unsolicited material; "we report only if we're interested."
Music: Mostly top 40/pop and country; also easy listening, MOR and rock. Published "Eye of the Tiger" (by J. Peterick/F. Sullivan), recorded by Survivor on Scotti Bros.-CBS Records (rock); "How Do You Fall Out of Love," recorded by Janie Fricke on CBS Records (country-pop); and "Them Good Ol' Boys Are Bad" (J. Harrington/J. Pennig), recorded by John Schneider on Scotti Bros.-CBS Records (country).

SCRAMROCK MUSIC CO., 139 E. Harding Rd., Springfield OH 45504. (513)399-6708. Professional Manager: Robert T. "Dusty" Jones. Music publisher, record company (War Minister Records Spike Opera, Paragon, and Scram Records) and management firm ("Dusty" Jones). BMI. Estab. 1980. Publishes 15-20 songs/year; publishes 14-15 new songwriters/year. Works with composers "having full bands only." Pays standard royalty.
How to Contact: Prefers cassette (or VHS videocassette – high energy showmanship-stage clothes). "Include photo of artist or group." SASE. Reports in 2 days.
Music: Mostly heavy metal, thrash metal, hard rock and speed metal. Published "With You All Along" (by Chris Weiser) and "We Rock to Rock" and "Out of the Ashes" (by S. Wallace/B. Bodine/ C. Weiser), all recorded by War Minister on War Minister Records (heavy metal); "My Final Words," "Heed the Prophecy" and "Under Siege" (by J. Faber, K. Wood, D. Bowden, N. Mitchell, and S. Smith), recorded by Paragon on Paragon Records (progressive metal).
Tips: Submit "hard driving, high energy tunes with good catchy hooks and melodies. Have a full band whose music is hard driving with high energy with good catchy hooks and melodies and whose band has super high energy showmanship with a killer look, stage clothes, etc."

*SCRUTCHINGS MUSIC, 429 Homestead St., Akron OH 44306. (216)773-8529. Owner/President: Walter E.L. Scrutchings. Music publisher. BMI. Estab. 1980. Publishes 50-75 songs/year; publishes 10-20 new songwriters/year. Hires staff songwriters. Works with composers and lyricists; teams collaborators. Pays standard royalty of 50%. "Songwriters pay production costs of songs."
How to Contact: Submit a demo tape by mail – unsolicited submissions are OK. Prefers cassette (or videocassette if available) with 2 songs, lyric and lead sheet. Does not return unsolicited material. Reports in 4-6 weeks.
Music: Mostly gospel; also contemporary.

SEA DREAM MUSIC, 236 Sebert Rd., Forest Gate, London E7 0NP **England**. Phone: (081)534-8500. Senior Partner: Simon Law. PRS. Music publisher and record company (Plankton Records, Embryo Arts (Belgium) and Radio Records). Estab. 1976. Publishes 50 songs/year; publishes 2 new songwriters/ year. Works with composers and lyricists; teams collaborators. Pays 66⅔% royalty.
Affiliates: Scarf Music Publishing, Really Free Music, Ernvik Musik (Sweden) and Light Factory Productions.
How to Contact: Submit a demo tape – unsolicited submissions are OK. Prefers cassette with 3 songs and lyric sheet. "Technical information about the recording is useful, as are the songwriter's expectations of the company – i.e., what they want us to do for them." SAE and IRC. Reports in 6 weeks.
Music: Mostly funk/rock, rock and blues; also gospel. Published "Kid In a Hostile World" (by Paul Crick/Greg Nash/Keith Dixon), recorded by Medals (jazz/rock); "Pictures of You" (by Rue Randall), recorded by Solid Air (rock); and "A Choice of Shadows" (by Simon Law), recorded by Fresh Claim (blues/rock), all on Plankton Records.
Tips: "We are specifically interested in material with a Christian bias to the lyrics."

SEGAL'S PUBLICATIONS, Box 507, Newton MA 02159. (617)969-6196. Contact: Charles Segal. Music publisher and record producer (Segal's Productions). BMI, SAMRO. Estab. 1963. Publishes 80 songs/ year; publishes 6 new songwriters/year. Works with composers and lyricists. Pays standard royalty.

Affilates: Charles Segals Publications (BMI).

How to Contact: Call first and obtain permission to submit or to arrange a personal interview. Prefers cassette (or VHS videocassette) with 3 songs and lyric or lead sheet. Does not return unsolicited material.

Music: Mostly rock, pop and country; also R&B, MOR and children's songs. Musicals published include "Everyday Things" and "Magical Mystery Man" as well as traditional children's stories on EMI records (children's); "Forste Saga" (by Segal), recorded by the SABC Orchestra on Decca (ballad); "You're Not Alone" (by Brilliant), recorded by Bibby Stewart on Spin Records (rock).

Tips: "Listen to what is going on in the music business via TV and radio. Write for a specific artist. Do a simple demo cassette, voice/keyboard; write a clean lead sheet."

WILLIAM SEIP MUSIC INCORPORATED, Box 515, Waterloo, Ontario N2J 4A9 **Canada**. (519)741-1252. President: William Seip. Music publisher, record company (H&S Records) and management firm (William Seip Management Inc.). CAPAC. Estab. 1987. Publishes 10-30 songs/year; publishes 1-3 new songwriters/year. Works with composers; teams collaborators. Pays per negotiated contract.

Affiliate: Lyell Communications.

How to Contact: Submit a demo tape — unsolicited submissions are OK. Prefers cassette with 3 songs. SAE and IRC. Reports in 1 month.

Music: Mostly rock and pop. Published "The Storm" (by Vollmer/Hackman), recorded by Helix on Capitol-Can (rock); "Carry Me" (by Lyell), recorded by Ray Lyell on Spy-Can (CHR); and "Another Man's Gun" (by Lyell), recorded by Ray Lyell on Spy-Can (CHR).

SELLWOOD PUBLISHING, 170 N. Maple, Fresno CA 93702. (209)255-1717. Owner: Stan Anderson. Music publisher, record company (Trac Record Co.) and record producer. BMI. Estab. 1972. Publishes 10 songs/year; publishes 3 new songwriters/year. Pays standard royalty.

How to Contact: Submit a demo tape. Unsolicited submissions are OK. Prefers cassette (or VHS videocassette) with 2 songs and lyric sheet. SASE. Reports in 2 weeks.

Music: Mostly country, gospel, pop and rock. Published "Don't Walk Away" (by B.G. White), (country); "Overnight Sensation" and "Mama She Don' Know" (by Ric Blake), (Top 40) all recorded on Trac Records.

*SEYCHELLES MUSIC, Box 13 01 44, Cologne 1 D-5000 **West Germany**. (0221)72 01 79. FAX: (0221)73 93 476. Managing Director: Walther Kahl. Music publisher. GEMA. Estab. 1977. Publishes 40-50 songs/year; publishes 2-3 new songwriters/year. Pays standard royalty. Works with composers; teams collaborators.

How to Contact: Prefers cassette and lyric sheet. Reports in 3 weeks.

Music: MOR, rock and country.

*SHAN-DARLYN PUBLISHING CO., HCR-1-Box 732, Banning CA 92220. (714)849-6064. Owner: Darlene Shanklin. Music publisher. ASCAP. Estab. 1989. Publishes 3 songs/year; 3 new songwriters/year. Pays standard royalty of 50%.

How to Contact: Submit a demo tape by mail — unsolicited submissions are OK. Prefers cassette with 2 songs and lyric sheet. SASE. Reports in 1 month.

Music: Mostly cross-over-country and country. Published "The Greener Years" (by Frank Loren) and "Thats What a Woman Can Do" (by Wayne Shanklin, published by Music Productions) both recorded by Frank Loren on Blue Gem Records (cross-over-country) and "The Lottery Song" (or "I Won the Lottery") (by Jr. Shanklin and Tony Pappas), recorded by Rick Thomas on Southwind Records (country); and "La Loteria" (or "Me Saque La Loteria"), recorded by Lalo Guerrero on Southwind Records (Latin).

SHAOLIN MUSIC, P.O. Box 387, Hollywood CA 90078. (818)506-8660. President: Richard Del Connor. Vice President, A&R: Michelle McCarty. Music publisher, record company (Shaolin Film and Records) and record producer (The Coyote). ASCAP. Estab. 1984. Works with composers, lyricists; teams collaborators. Pays standard royalty.

How to Contact: Prefers cassette with 3-4 songs and lyric sheet. Does not return unsolicited material. Reports in 3 months.

Music: Mostly rock, hard rock and pop; also soundtracks. Published "Show Girls," recorded by The Rich; "Coyote Graveyard" and Out of My Mind" (by Coyote), recorded by Coyote on Shaolin Records (rock).

SIEGEL MUSIC COMPANIES, 2 Hochlstr, 80 Munich 8000 **West Germany**. Phone: 089-984926. Managing Director: Joachim Neubauer. Music publisher, record company, (Jupiter Records and Zip Records) and record producer. Estab. 1948. GEMA. Publishes 2,000-3,000 songs/year; publishes 50 new songwriters/year. Hires staff songwriters. Works with composers and lyricists. Pays standard royalty according to individual society.

Affiliates: Ed. Meridian, Old Friends/Golden Bridge (Nashville), Sound of Jupiter Ltd. (England), Sounds of Jupiter, Inc. (USA), Step Two (Austria), Step One (Holland), Step Two (Austria), Step Four (France), Step Five (Brazil), Step Six (Scandinavia), Step Seven (Australia), Step Eight (Belgium) and Yellowbird (Switzerland).

How to Contact: Prefers cassette (or VHS videocassette, but not necessary). Reports in 8 weeks.

Music: Mostly pop, disco and MOR; also country and soul. Published "So Many People," written and recorded by Hirschburger Hubert on Kah Curb Records (pop); "Let There Be House" (by West Bam), recorded by Deskee on RCA Records (dancehouse); and "Still Beatin' " (by Schudde), recorded by World on Edge on Virgin Records (pop rock).

Tips: "Submit songs with good melody lines, catchy refrains and new arrangements."

SILICON MUSIC PUBLISHING CO., Ridgewood Park Estates, 222 Tulane St., Garland TX 75043. President: Gene Summers. Vice President: Deanna L. Summers. Public Relations: Steve Summers. Music publisher and record company (Domino Records, Ltd. and Front Row Records). BMI. Publishes 10-20 songs/year; publishes 2-3 new songwriters/year. Pays standard royalty.

How to Contact: Prefers cassette with 1-2 songs. Does not return unsolicited material. "We are usually slow in answering due to overseas tours."

Music: Mostly rockabilly and 50s material; also old-time blues country and MOR. Published "Ready to Ride/Ode to a Stuntman" (from the HBO presentation "Backlot"), written and recorded by Pat Minter on Domino Records; "Loco Cat," (by Eddie Hill/Tom Toms), recorded by Gene Summers on White Label; and "Love Me Til I Do," written and recorded by Joe Hardin Brown on Domino Records; and "Rockaboogie Shake" (by James McClung), recorded by Gene Summers on Jan Records (Sweden).

Tips: "We are very interested in 50s rock and rockabilly *original masters* for release through overseas affiliates. If you are the owner of any 50s masters, contact us first! We have releases in Holland, Switzerland, England, Belgium, France, Sweden, Norway and Australia. We have the market if you have the tapes!"

SILVERFOOT PUBLISHING, 4225 Palm St., Baton Rouge LA 70808. (504)383-7885. President: Barrie Edgar. BMI. Music publisher, record company (Gulfstream Records) and record producer (Hogar Musical Productions). Estab. 1977. Publishes 10-30 songs/year; publishes 8-20 new songwriters/year. Pays standard royalty.

How to Contact: Submit a demo tape—unsolicited submissions are OK. Prefers cassette with maximum 4 songs and lyric sheet. "Patience required on reporting time." SASE.

Music: Mostly rock, pop, blues ("not soul") and country. Published "Night Life," "Spirit of Humanity" and "Without Your Love"; all written and recorded by David Hentosh (pop/rock).

*SINGING ROADIE MUSIC, 342 Ogle St., Costa Mesa CA 92627. (714)548-1908. General Manager: Garth Shaw. Music publisher, member of ACM and CMA. ASCAP. Estab. 1984. Publishes 3-10 songs/year; publishes 1-3 new songwriters/year. Pays standard royalty.

Affiliates: Singing Roadie Music (ASCAP), Helioplane Music (BMI).

How to Contact: Submit a demo tape by mail—unsolicited submissions are OK. Prefers cassette with 1-3 songs and lyric sheets. SASE. Reports in 3 months.

Music: Mostly country, folk and rock. Co-published "Follow the Path" (by Garth Shaw, Jim Turner), recorded by Jim Turner on Earthtone Records (gospel); "Rescue Me" (by Paul Hotchkiss), recorded by Pam Rogers on Trophy Records (country); "Bed of Roses" (by Rex Benson, Steve Gillette), recorded by The Oak Ridge Boys on MCA Records (country).

Tips: "If you're a great writer and a terrible singer, find a great demo singer!"

*SINGLE PHASE MUSIC, Box 67, Covina CA 91723. (714)592-3098. President: Steve Mortensen. Music publisher, record company (Blue Sun), record producer (Blue Sun Productions). BMI. Estab. 1986. Publishes 15-20 songs/year; publishes 1-5 new songwriters/year. Works with composers and lyricists; teams collaborators. Pays standard royalty.

Affiliates: Single Phase Music (BMI).

How to Contact: Submit a demo tape by mail—unsolicited submissions are OK. Prefers cassette wityh 2-3 songs and lyric sheet. Does not return unsolicited material. Reports in 1-2 months.

Music: Mostly pop-European, rock and R&B. Published "Off and On" (by Basque), recorded by single phase; "Private Masquerade" (by Basque), recorded by Single Phase; "She's a Beauty" (by Mortensen/Amato), recorded by Emotion; all pop on Blue Sun Records.

Tips: "Specify major recording artists who you feel the song could best be done by."

*SINGNORBERT MUSICHOUSE, 400 Ensley Dr., Knoxville TN 37920. (615)577-5597. President: Norbert Stovall. Music publisher, record company (Unity Records). ASCAP. Estab. 1985. Publishes 100 songs/year; 3 new songwriters/year. Works with composers. Pays standard 50% royalty.
Affiliates: Highlandview Song Co. (BMI).
How to Contact: Submit a demo tape by mail—unsolicited submissions are OK. Prefers cassette (or VHS videocassette if available) with 3 songs and lyric sheet. SASE. Reports in 2 months.
Music: Mostly gospel, country, rock; also dance. Published "What I've Learned From the Cross" written and recorded by Jerry Arhelger on Unity Records (gospel); "Feel So Good Hurt So Bad" written and recorded by Jesse James on Top Records (country); and "Do the Come" (by Vic Ackers, Jr.), recorded by Bruno on Miami International Records (dance).

SIVATT MUSIC PUBLISHING CO., P.O. Box 1913, Easley SC 29641. (803) 295-3177. President: Jesse B. Evatte. Music publisher. BMI. Estab. 1972. Publishes 20 songs/year; publishes 4 new songwriters/year. Works with composers. Pays standard royalty.
How to Contact: Submit a demo tape—unsolicited submissions OK. Prefers cassette with 3-4 songs and lyric sheet. SASE. Reports in 6 weeks.
Music: Gospel. Published "Blessed Are the Meek" (by Kelly Lynch), recorded by Gloryland Singers on Sivatt Records (gospel); "City Heart" (by Casandra Bryan), recorded by Candance Bryan on Sivatt Records (country); and "You're Not Alone" (by Abner Clark), recorded by New Life Choir on Tribute Records (gospel).

SIZEMORE MUSIC, P.O. Box 130441, Birmingham AL 35213. (205)951-3717. Contact: Gary Sizemore. Music publisher, record company (The Gas Co.) and record producer (Gary Sizemore). BMI. Estab. 1960. Publishes 5 songs/year; 1 new songwriter/year. Works with composers and lyricists; teams collaborators. Pays standard royalty.
How to Contact: Submit a demo tape by mail—unsolicited submissions are O.K. Prefers cassette (or VHS videocassette) with lyric sheets. SASE.
Music: Mostly soul and R&B; also blues, pop and country. Published "Liquor and Wine" and "The Wind," written and recorded by K. Shackleford on Heart Records (country); and "She's Tuff" (by Jerry McCain), recorded by The Fabulous Thunderbirds on Chrysalis Records (blues).

*SLEEPING GIANT MUSIC INTERNATIONAL LTD., 34 Great James Street, London WC1N 3HB United Kingdom. Phone: (01)405-3786. Managing Director: Keith C. Thomas. A&R Director: Taylor King. Promotions Director: Danny Curtis. Administration Director: John Beattie. Music publisher and record producer (Keith C. Thomas, Blade Hunter). PRS. Publishes 1,000 songs/year; publishes 100 new songwriters/year. Works with composers and lyricists. Payment depends on strength of material or artist.
Affiliates: Tamara Music (SABAM), Trix Music (SABAM), Bucks Music (SABAM), New York Performance Direction (ASCAP), Six Star Music (SABAM), Street Korner (BMI), Skirt Music (ASCAP), Lowy & Lowy (SABAM) and Plantinum Pyramid Publishing (ASCAP).
How to Contact: Prefers cassette, lyric and lead sheets (if possible). If an artist/writer, send bio and photos. Reports in 2 weeks.
Music: Mostly rock, pop, R&B; also soul, dance/disco, classical/country. Published "Out On The Floor" (by Carl Todd/Kevin Davis), recorded by Porscha (soul); and "Angel Divine" (by Herb Miller), recorded by Herb Miller orchestra (jazz).
Tips: "To work a song or songs on behalf of a writer takes time but inevitably if it's a good song the wait can be very rewarding."

SOMETIMES Y PUBLISHING, P.O. Box 803, Austin TX 78767. (214)969-2766 or 969-2799. Partners: Jim Witcher or Jeff Glass. Music publisher, record company (Sometimes Y Music) and record producer (Sometimes Y Music). BMI. Estab. 1988. Publishes 10 songs/year; publishes 1-5 new songwriters/year. Works with composers and lyricists; teams collaborators. Pays standard royalty.
How to Contact: Submt a demo tape by mail—unsolicited submissions are O.K. Prefers cassette with lyric or lead sheets. SASE. Reports in 3-6 weeks.
Music: Mostly post modern, original rock/jazz. Any new and unique music. Published "Sunday Morning," "Ice Monkey" and "Roses" (by Kevin Taylor), recorded on Sometimes Y (modern).

SONG FARM MUSIC, P.O. Box 24561, Nashville TN 37202. (615)321-4875. President: Tom Pallardy. Music publisher and record producer (T.P. Productions). BMI. Member NSAI. Estab. 1980. Publishes 2-5 songs/year; publishes 1-2 new songwriters/year. Teams collaborators. Pays standard royalty.

How to Contact: Submit a demo tape—unsolicited submissions are OK. Prefers cassette with maximum 2 songs and lyric or lead sheet. SASE required. Reports in 1 month.
Music: Mostly country, R&B and pop; also crossover and top 40. Published "Mississippi River Rat" (by J. Hall, R. Hall, E. Dickey), recorded by Tom Powers on Fountain Records (Cajun country) and "One Time Too Many" (by E. Dickey, R. Hall, H. Norrid), recorded by Tom Powers on Fountain Records (country ballad).
Tips: "Material should be submitted neatly and professionally with as good quality demo as possible. Songs need not be elaborately produced (voice and guitar/piano are fine) but they should be clear. Songs must be well constructed, lyrically tight, good strong hook, interesting melody, easily remembered; i.e., commercial!"

SONGFINDER MUSIC, 4 Reina Lane, Valley Cottage NY 10989. (914)268-7711. Owner: Frank Longo. Music publisher. ASCAP. Estab. 1987. Publishes 20 songs/year; publishes 5-10 new songwriters/year. Works with composers and lyricists; teams collaborators. Pays standard royalty.
Affiliates: Spring Rose Music (BMI).
How to Contact: Submit a demo tape by mail—unsolicited submissions are O.K. Prefers cassette with 2 songs and lyric sheets. SASE. "No SASE—no returns." Reports in 4 weeks.
Music: Mostly MOR, top 40, soft rock, country/pop and uptempo country. Published "The Best Man" (by F. Longo), recorded by Tony Sands on Lost-Gold Records (country); "We Don't Keep In Touch Anymore" (by F. Longo/F. Krejci), recorded by Lyndia Reynolds on Lost-Gold Records (country); and "There's No Easy Way To Forget You" (by Jimmy Crane), recorded by Kimberly Carter on KRC Records.
Tips: "Listen to whats being played on the radio. Be professional. Good demos get good results. Up tempo positive lyrics are always wanted. Success needs no apology—Failure provides no alibi."

SONGWRITERS' NETWORK MUSIC PUBLISHING, P.O. Box 190446, Dallas TX 75219. (214)823-1113. President: Phil Ayliffe. Music publisher and record company (Songwriters' Network Records, Meridian Records). ASCAP. Estab. 1983. Publishes 3 songs/year. Works with composers and lyricists; teams collaborators. Pays standard royalty.
How to Contact: Write first to get permission to submit a tape. Prefers cassette with 3 songs and lyric sheets. SASE. Reports in 6 weeks.
Music: Mostly pop, MOR and adult contemporary country.

*SOTEX MUSIC, (formerly Rooster Music), Box 27, Converse TX 78109. (512)658-2795. Partner: Frank Willson. Music publisher (BSW Records). BMI. Estab. 1989. Publishes 9 songs/year; publishes 6-15 new songwriters/year. Works with composers and lyricists; teams collaborators. Pays standard royalty.
How to Contact: Submit a demo tape by mail—unsolicited submissions are OK. Prefers cassette or ½" VHS videocassette with 3 songs and lyric sheets.
Music: Mostly country, rock and R&B. Published "Last Song" (by B. Dees and Roy Orbison), recorded by Mike Lord; "Memory of a Memory" (by J. Paycheck), recorded by Bobby Lloyd; "Just Try Texas" (by Dave Kinby, W. Robb), recorded by Mike Lord; and "I'll Be Home When I Get There" (by Barry Roberts), recorded by Lost Prairie; all on BSW Records (country western).

*SOUND ACHIEVEMENT GROUP, P.O. Box 24625, Nashville TN 37202. (615)883-2600. President: Royce B. Gray. Music publisher. Estab. 1985. Publishes 150 songs/year; publishes 4 new songwriters/year. Works with composers and lyricists; teams collaborators. Pays standard royalty.
Affiliates: Song Palace Music (ASCAP) and Emerald Stream Music (BMI).
How to Contact: Submit a demo tape by mail—unsolicited submissions are O.K. Prefers cassette (or VHS videocassette if available) with 3 songs and lyric sheet. SASE. Reports in 2 months.
Music: Gospel. Published "I Feel Like Runnin" (by Kenneth Tanner), recorded by Singing Reps on Sugar Mountain Records; "Running" (by Jerry Hurd), recorded by Jerry and Linda Hurd on Candle Records and "Heaven's Bearing Heavy" (by Ricky Medlock), recorded by Medlock's on New Wind Records, (all gospel).

SOUND IMAGE PUBLISHING, 6556 Wilkinson, North Hollywood CA 91606. (818)762-8881. President: Marty Eberhardt. Vice President and General Manager: David Chatfield. Music publisher, record company, record producer and video company. BMI. Member NARAS. Publishes 160 songs/year; publishes 10 new songwriters/year. Pays standard royalty.
How to Contact: Prefers cassette (or VHS videocassette) with 3 songs and lyric sheet. Does not return unsolicited material. Reports in 2 months.
Music: Mostly rock; also dance, R&B.
Tips: "Demos should be professionally recorded. We suggest 16-24 track recording on cassette submissions."

SOUND SPECTRA MUSIC, P.O. Box 2474, Auburn AL 36831-2474. (205)821-4876. President: Larry L. Barker. Music publisher, record company (Rainbow River Records) and record producer (Spectra Productions). BMI. Estab. 1978. Publishes 15-30 songs/year; 3-5 new songwriters/year. Works with composers and lyricists. Pays standard royalty.
How to Contact: Write first and obtain permission to submit a tape. Prefers cassette with 3-4 songs and lyric sheets. Include SASE for reply. Does not return unsolicited submissions. Reports in 6 weeks.
Music: Mostly rock, R&B and new age; also jazz, gospel and country. Published "Don't Hold Back" (by Ronald La Pread and Larry Barker), recorded by Ronald La Pread on Little Records (R&B); "It's Not Easy" (by Larry Barker), recorded by Lennie Hartzog on Rainbow River Records (pop); and "The Trash Bag's Been Ripped" (by Bruce Yandle), recorded by Mr. Resistor on Rainbow River Records (rock).
Tips: "Write first to determine current needs—then send only your tightest material."

*SOUNDTRAX RECORDING, Rt. 2 Box 435, Johnson City TN 37601. (800)552-2576 or (615)926-3986. FAX: (615)926-6392. Owner: Rick Monday or Richard Hinchman. Music publisher and record company (Sunshine, Cameroon). BMI. Estab. 1977. Publishes 100-150 songs/year; publishes 25-50 new songwriters/year. Hires staff writers. Works with composers and lyricists; teams collaborators. Pays standard royalty or salary for on the spot production.
Affiliates: Croaky Frog Music Publishing, and Sunshine Music Publishing and Productions.
How to Contact: Write or call to arrange a personal interview. Prefers cassette (or PCM digital, VHS, SVHS, ¾" video) with 2 songs, lyric sheet and lead sheet. "All songs must be copyrighted!!" SASE. Reports in 2 weeks.
Music: Mostly country, rock and gospel. Published "I Believe", "Tenn Line" (by Brian Gary Blankenbeckler), recorded by Brain Dolp on Cameron Records (country); and "Touch and Go" (by Cecil Null), recorded by Tim Malone on Cameron Records (country).
Tips: "Be ready to work, and go the limit!"

SOUTHERN MOST PUBLISHING CO., 6219 Lathrop, Kansas City KS 66104. (913)229-8107. President: Dann E. Haworth. Music publisher and record producer (Haworth Productions). BMI. Estab. 1985. Publishes 10 songs/year; publishes 3 new songwriters/year. Works with composers and lyricists; teams collaborators. Pays standard royalty.
How to Contact: Prefers cassette or 7½ or 15 ips reel-to-reel with 5-6 songs and lyric or lead sheets. SASE. Reports in 1 month.
Music: Mostly rock (no heavy metal), country and gospel; also blues, jazz and folk. Published "Mary" and "Christian Friends," written and recorded by Tony Glise (classical gospel); and "Ask Her To Dance," written and recorded by Kerry Z. Drake and Debra Wikstrom (country).

THE SPARTA FLORIDA MUSIC GROUP, LTD., 34 Great James St., London WC1N 3HB **England.** (01)823-8524. FAX: (01)581-5855. Managing Director: Stella Groves. Music publisher and record company (Prestige Records). PRS. Estab. 1964. Publishes between 250-500 songs/year. "Always on the lookout for new material and master recordings of either hit or standard quality. Also a major publisher of standard works."
How to Contact: Submit a demo tape by mail—unsolicited submissions are O.K. Prefers cassette with 3 songs and lyric sheets. SAE and IRCs. Reports in 2 weeks.
Music: Mostly pop and rock. Standards include "The Tide is High" (by John Holt), recorded by Blondie on Chrysalis (pop); "Push the Beat" (by ML-K. Kkoshi), recorded by Mirage (pop); and "Lonely Boy" (by Paul Anka), recorded by Nick Kamen (soundtrack LP from *Shag*). "Pop hits 1990 include six cuts on UB40's *Labour of Love II*. Also active in major films (First Blood, Moonstruck, Dinosaurs, etc.)"
Tips: "Try to make demos as close to masters as possible. Also suggest who you think the song would be good for; and always, always, enclose a copy of the lyrics."

SPEEDSTER MUSIC, 6621 N 59th Ave., Glendale AZ 85301. (602)435-0314. Owner: Frank E. Koehl. Music publisher, record company (Auburn Records and Tapes). BMI. Estab. 1988. Publishes 4 songs/year; 2 new songwriters/year. Works with composers. Pays standard royalty.
How to Contact: Submit a demo tape by mail—unsolicited submissions are O.K. Prefers cassette with 2-4 songs and lyric sheets. "Send only traditional, acoustic country music." SASE. Reports 3 weeks.
Music: Mostly country, traditional and bluegrass. Published "Shade Tree" and "Lottery Fever" (by Troy McCourt), recorded by Troy McCourt on Auburn (traditional country); and "Gonna Go To Houston" written and recorded by Frank Koehl on Auburn Records (country).
Tips: "Keep it country and acoustic. Tell a story simply."

SPHEMUSATIONS, 12 Northfield Rd., Onehouse, Stowmarket Suffolk 1P14 3HR **England**. Phone: 0449-613388. General Manager: James Butt. Music publisher. Estab. 1963. Publishes 200 songs/year; publishes 6 new songwriters/year. Works with lyricists; teams collaborators. Pays standard royalty.
How to Contact: Submit demo tape—unsolicited submissions are OK, or write or call first to get permission to submit a tape. Prefers cassette (or VHS or BETA videocassette). SAE and IRC. Reports in 3 months.
Music: Mostly country, blues and jazz, also "serious modern music." Published "Satyr's Song" (by J. Playford, J. Butt), "The Weeper" (by J. Playford, J. Butt); and "O. Moon" (by J. Keats, J. Butt), all on Sphemusations (light).

*SPRADLIN/GLEICH PUBLISHING, P.O. Box 80083, Phoenix AZ 85060. (602)840-8466. Manager: Lee Gleich. Music publisher. BMI. Estab. 1988. Publishes 4-10 songs/year; 2-4 new songwriters. Works with composers and lyricists; teams collatorators. Pays standard 50% royalty.
Affiliates: "We work very closely with Country Cornor Record Co., Pott Pirie, Austrailia."
How to Contact: Submit a demo tape by mail—unsolicited submissions OK. Prefers cassette with 3 songs and lyric sheet or lead sheet. "It must be very good material, I only have time for promoting songwriters who really care."
SASE. Reports in 3 weeks.
Music: Mostly country in the U.S. and Australian country markets, pop, gospel (all types; also rock, theme music and piano jazz. Published "Tommy's Song" and "Friends Like These" (by Lorri Rizzo), recorded by Lorri Rizzo on RTF Records.
Tips: "Don't use me for a sounding board only. I will comment on every tape submitted, if you send postage. I want good, clean lyrics, with something to say. Statement songs are coming in again. (Country music leaning to its roots but lyrics are better than ever!)."

SRSF RECORDINGS/ENTERTAINMENTS ENTERPRISES PUBLISHING®, P.O. Box 14131, Denver CO 80214. President: Sharon R. Smith-Fliesher. Music publisher, record company (SRSF Recordings/ Entertainments Enterprises ® and record producer (SRSF Recordings/Entertainments Enterprises®). ASCAP. Estab. 1980. Pays standard royalty of 50%.
How to Contact: Submit a demo tape—unsolicited submissions are O.K. Prefers cassette with 3 songs and lyric or lead sheet. "For our protection please enclose a signed and dated statement with your submissions stating you are enclosing 'title of song #1, #2, #3, no others follow.' Submissions without this statement will be disposed. Professional multitrack demo, with media kit a must." SASE. Reports in 6 weeks.
Music: Mostly folk and country. "White Light" (by Sharon Soria), recorded by Sharon Soria on SRSF Records® (instrumental); "Hold On" (by Sharon Smith), recorded by Sharon Smith on SRSF Records® (MOR); and "Mother Earth" (by Barbara La Bonne) recorded by Smith and La Bonne on SRSF Records® (folk).
Tips: "We have changed our policy to cater only to the lesbian community working in conjunction with the Lambda Performing Arts Guild of America®. We encourage all interested to contact us. Our purpose is to legitimize and recognize lesbian artists.

STANG MUSIC INC., 753 Capitol Ave., Hartford CT 06106. (203)951-8175. Producer: Jack Stang. Music publisher, record company (Nickel Records) and record producer (Jack Stang). BMI. Estab. 1970. Publishes 20 songs/year; publishes 2 new songwriters/year. Hires staff writers. Works with composers; teams collaborators. Pays standard royalty.
How to Contact: Submit a demo tape by mail—unsolicited submissions are O.K. Prefers cassette with 3 songs and lyric sheets. SASE. Reports in 3 weeks.
Music: Mostly rock, pop, top 40 and R&B; also country. Published "Rage"(by John Bolduc), recorded by John Bolduc (rock); "Can't Believe" (by Billy Chapin), recorded by Billy Chapin (pop); and "Crazy Old Soldier" (by Moshe/Frezzel), recorded by Desert Sky (country); all on Nickel.

*JAMES LEE STANLEY MUSIC, #810, 6253 Hollywood Blvd., Los Angeles CA 90028. (213)461-1008. Manager: Stephen Chandler. Music publisher, record company (Beachwood Records), record producer (Beachwood Productions), Beachwood Recording Studio. BMI, ASCAP. Estab. 1985. Publishes 20 songs/year; 3-6 new songwriters/year. Works with composers and lyricists; teams collaborators. Pays "percentage depends on input/collaboration or straight submission."
Affiliates: James Lee Stanley Music (BMI), Wordsend Music (BMI), Hashram Music (ASCAP).
How to Contact: Write or call first and obtain permission to submit a tape. Prefers cassette with up to 3 songs and lyric sheet. Does not return unsolicited material. Reports in 1 month.
Music: Mostly pop, jazz and New Age; also new country, rock and dance. Published "Coming out of Hiding" (by J.L. Stanley and V. Melamed), recorded by Pamela Stanley on TSR Records (dance); "Same Olde Samba" (by J.L. Stanley and L. Kunkel) and "The Dancer" (by J.L. Stanley) both recorded by James Lee Stanley on Beachwood Records (jazz, pop).

Tips: "Have a strong melodic line and intelligent lyrics."

*STAR INTERNATIONAL, INC., Suite A, 4305 S. Mingo, Tulsa OK 74146. (918)663-7700. President: MaryNell Jetton. Sr. Vice President: Michael Brown. Music publisher. ASCAP. Estab. 1989. Publishes 1-20 songs/year. Works with composers and lyricists; teams collaborators. Pays standard 50% royalty.
How to Contact: Submit a demo tape by mail—unsolicited submissions are OK. Prefers cassette (or VHS videocassette if available) with 1-2 songs and lyric sheet. "If we are interested in your first two songs, we will request more of your material. We respond only if we're interested."
Music: "We accept any type of music material, if it's professional."
Tips: "We are looking for new talent and are interested in songwriters who have material suitable for today's top recording artists in all music categories. We are also interested in new singer/songwriters."

STONEHAND PUBLISHING, P.O. Box 895, Station E, Victoria BC V8W 2R9 **Canada**. (604)386-0507. Project Director: Linda Ehlers. Music publisher, record companies (Stonehand Records). SOCAN, CMRRA. Estab. 1984. Publishes 15 songs/year; publishes 2-3 new songwriters/year. Pays standard royalty.
How to Contact: Submit a demo tape by mail—unsolicited submissions are O.K. Prefers cassette or VHS videocassette with 3 songs and lyric sheets. SASE with IRC. Reports in 6 weeks.
Music: Mostly pop/rock, AOR/MOR and country; also folk. Published "Let Christmas Be Forever" (by Mark Franklin and Kin Cain). Released *Band in Canada* E.P. by Kin Cain on Stonehand Records.
Tips: "Develop strong, visual lyrics, imaginative musical ideas and a persistent belief in yourself."

*STORZ GROUP OF COMPANIES, Box 1670, Hauptstr. 114, 3360 Osterode, **West Germany**. Phone: (05522)73041. Music publisher, record company (Catena Vision, Arminia) and record distributor.
Affiliates: Musikverlag Storz KG and Edition Catena.
How to Contact: Prefers cassette or reel-to-reel (or VHS videocassette).

*STRAWBERRY SODA PUBLISHING, 15 Exeter Rd., Kingston NH 03848. (603)642-8493. Coordinator: Harry Manu. Music publisher. ASCAP. Estab. 1988. Publishes 10-12 songs/year. Publishes 2-4 new songwriters/year. Works with composers and lyricists. Pays standard royalty.
How to Contact: Submit a demo tape by mail—unsolicited submissions are OK. Prefers cassette, 15 IPS reel-to-reel, or VCR videocassette with 3 songs and lyric sheets. SASE. Reports in 6-8 weeks.
Music: Mostly rock, country and pop; "no heavy metal." Published "5¢ Strawberry Soda" (by Doug Mitchell), recorded by Doug Mitchell and Co. (country rock LP); "Message to You" (by Doug Mitchell), recorded by D. Mitchell and Co. (ballad-rock single); and "Songs Piped from the Moon," written and recorded by S. Pappas (avante-guard ballads LP); all recorded on Kingston Records.
Tips: "Simple, understandable lyrics with a flow. Sequenced, electronic music is going too far. I think the acoustic sound might be ready for a comeback."

*STRAWBOSS MUSIC BMI, 101 Hurts Ln., Hendersonville TN 37075. (615)824-5900. FAX: (615)824-8800. President: Jim Pierce. Music publisher and record company (Round Robin Records) and record producer (Jim Pierce). BMI. Estab. 1974. Publishes 25 songs/year; publishes 5 or 6 new songwriters/year. Pays standard royalty.
How to Contact: Submit a demo tape by mail—unsolicited submissions are OK. Prefers cassette with any number of songs and lyric sheet. Does not return unsolicited submission.
Music: Mostly country, country/pop and traditional country. Published "Don't Call Us We'll Call You," "Touch of Your Love," (by Harlen Helgeson) and "Clouds" written and recorded by Barbara Carter, all on Round Robin Records (country).
Music: Commercial rock and pop.

*STREET SINGER MUSIC, 117 W. 8th, Hays KS 67601. (913)625-9634. President: Mark Meckel. BMI. Music publisher, record company (MDM Records) and record producer (MDM productions). Estab. 1980. Publishes 15 songs/year; publishes 4 new songwriters/year. Works with composers and lyricists; teams collaborators. Pays standard royalty.
How to Contact: Prefers cassette with 2-4 songs and lyric or lead sheet.
Music: Mostly pop/rock; also country swing, country rock, 50s rock, Christmas, R&B, country, gospel and country R&B. Published "Tone" (by C. Connelly), recorded by ConLee on M.D.M. Records (rock); "Freedom to Believe" (by M. Selby), recorded by Selby on M.D.M. Records (slow rock) and

"How to Use Your Songwriter's Market" (at the front of this book) contains comments and suggestions to help you understand and use the information in these listings.

"Shot Gun Wedding" (by M. Benish), recorded by Benish on M.D.M. Records (country).
Tips: "Be willing to make changes and work with a producer."

JEB STUART MUSIC CO., Box 6032, Station B, Miami FL 33123. (305)547-1424. President: Jeb Stuart. Music publisher, record producer and management firm. BMI. Estab. 1975. Publishes 4-6 songs/year. Teams collaborators. Pays standard royalty.
How to Contact: Submit a demo tape—unsolicited submissions are O.K. Prefers cassette or disc with 2-4 songs and lead sheet. SASE. Reports in 1 month.
Music: Mostly gospel, jazz/rock, pop, R&B and rap; also blues, church/religious, country, disco, and soul. Published "Saucy Music," written and recorded by Jeboria Stuart on Esquire (jazz/pop/R&B); "Maxie-D" (by Stuart, Shapiro), recorded by J. Stuart on Esquire Records (rap); and "Have a Party Tonight" (by Stuart, Shapiro), recorded by J. Stuart on Esquire Records (R&B).

STYLECRAFT MUSIC CO. INC., 217 Highway 51 S., P.O. Box 802, Madison MS 39110. (601)856-7468. Professional Manager: Style Wooten. Music publisher, record company (Style Records, Styleway Records and Good News Records), record producer, and booking agency (Style Wooten Inc.). BMI. Estab. 1964. Publishes 15-30 songs/year; publishes 10 new songwriters/year. Pays standard royalty.
How to Contact: Write or call first. Prefers cassette with 2-4 songs and "typewritten words." SASE. Reports in 1 month.
Music: Country, R&B and black gospel."Published "Trouble Don't Last Always" (by Benard Franklin), performed by Ted & Spiritial Wonders on Four Winds Records (black gospel); "God Is The Answer" (by Eddie Bentley), performed by Ted & Spiritial Wonders on Four Winds Records (black gospel); and "A City Called Glory" (by Archie Mitchell), performed by Archie Mitchell on Four Winds Records (black gospel).

SUBAR MUSIC PUBLISHING CO. LTD., 21, Any Ma'amin St., Ramat-Hasharon 47212 **Israel**. Phone: (03)5491323. FAX: (3) 5403490. TELEX: (3)32353. Manager: Dr. Ophira Bar-Elan. Music publisher. ACUM Ltd. Estab. 1961. Publishes 20-25 songs/year; publishes 2-3 new songwriters/year. Works with composers and lyricists. Pays standard royalty.
Affiliates: Sharon Music Publishing (ACUM Ltd.), Pa'amonim Music Publishers (ACUM Ltd.).
How to Contact: Write first to get permission to submit a tape. Prefers cassette and lyric or lead sheet. Does not return unsolicited material. Reports in 1 month.
Music: Mostly pop, rock and country.

SUGAR MAMA MUSIC, #805, 4545 Connecticut Ave. NW, Washington DC 20008. (202)362-2286. President: Jonathan Strong. Music publisher, record company (Ripsaw Records) and record producer (Ripsaw Productions). BMI. Estab. 1983. Publishes 3-5 songs/year; publishes 2 new songwriters/year. Works with composers and lyricists. Pays standard royalty.
Affiliates: Neck Bone Music (BMI) and Southern Crescent Publishing (BMI).
How to Contact: Prefers cassette and lyric sheet. SASE. Reports in 1 month.
Music: Mostly rockabilly and traditional rock. Published "No Use Knockin'," "Let Me Give You Lovin'," and "I'm Gonna Have to Send You Back," all written by Arthur Gerstein and recorded by the Uptown Rhythm Kings (jump blues).

SUGARBAKERS MUSIC, 404 Bluegrass Ave., Madison TN 37115. (615)865-6380. President: Bob Frick. Music publisher. ASCAP. Estab. 1988. Publishes 20 songs/year; publishes 5 new songwriters/year. Works with composers and lyricists. Pays standard royalty.
How to Contact: Submit a demo tape by mail—unsolicited submissions are O.K. Prefers cassette with 2 songs and lyric sheets. Does not return unsolicited material. Reports in 2 weeks.
Music: Mostly gospel, country and pop. Published "Follow Where he Leads" (by Christine Starling); "Jesus is the Answer" (by Esther Stewart); and "Peace Within My Heart" (by Katz/Hopwood); all recorded by Bob Scott Frick on R.E.F. (gospel).

*SUGARFOOT PRODUCTIONS, P.O. Box 1065, Joshua Tree CA 92252. (619)366-9539. A&R Director: Sheila Dobson. Music publisher, record company (Sugarfoot, Babydoll, Durban), record producer (Sugarfoot Records). ASCAP. Estab. 1987. Publishes 10-15 songs/year; publishes 4 new songwriters/year. Works with composers and lyricists; teams collaborators. Pays negotiable royalty; statutory rate per song on records.
How to Contact: Submit a demo tape by mail—unsolicited submissions are OK. Prefers cassette with 3 songs and lyric sheet. "Make sure tape and vocal are clear." SASE. Reports in 4 weeks.
Music: Mostly jazz, blues, swing, country (Tex) and (GA), R&B, salsa, dance; also bassas, conga; Cuban, easy listening. Published "Matter of Time," recorded by Smoothies on Sugarfoot Records (country); "If I Knew Then," recorded by Dewey's Group on Sugarfoot Records (jazz); "Sheila's Her Name," recorded by Virgo on Durban Records (easy listening); all written by D. Dobson.

Tips: "I like to hear a melody move and balance with the lyrics. Write for honesty - not a hit! Then rewrite again and again!"

SULTAN MUSIC PUBLISHING, P.O. Box 461892, Garland TX 75046. (214)271-8098. President: Don Ferguson. Music publisher, record company (Puzzle Records), record producer and booking agency (Don Ferguson Agency). BMI. Publishes 15 songs/year including some new songwriters. Works with composers and lyricists; teams collaborators. Pays standard royalty.
Affiliate: Illustrions Sultan (ASCAP).
How to Contact: Prefers cassette with 3 songs and lyric sheet. SASE. Reports in 3 weeks.
Music: Mostly country; also MOR. Published "Leave Me Right Now" written and recorded by Bobby Teesdale (MOR); "Apple Jack" written and recorded by Phil Rodgers (jazz); and "Rhythm of the Night" (by J.Caldwell), recorded by Mary Craig (C&W), all on Puzzle Records.
Tips: "The best quality demo makes the listener more receptive."

*SULZER MUSIC BMI, 3104 "G" St., Philadelphia PA 19134. (215)634-5965. President: Dave Wilson. BMI. Estab. 1965. Publishes 30 songs/year; publishes 20 new songwriters/year. Works with composers and lyricists and teams collaborators. Pays standard royalty.
How to Contact: Submit a demo tape by mail—unsolicited submissions are OK. Prefers cassette (or VHS videocassette if available) with lyric sheet and lead sheet. SASE. Reports in 1 month.
Music: Mostly country, country rock and soft rock; also big band, gospel and R&B. Published "Something Special" (by Mike Dineen), recorded by John Mendell (country), "I Loved You The First time I Saw You" written and recorded by John Mendell (country) and "The Lottery Song" (by Eugene Schrader) recorded by Schrader all on Regime Records (MOR/country).

*SUNDANCE MUSIC, Gammel Kongevej 47B, Copenhagen **Denmark** 1610. (45)31 22 60 80. Managing Director: Dietmar Schmidt. Music publisher, record company (Sundance Records, Stunt Records). GEMA/NCB. Estab. 1981. Publishes 100 songs/year; 20 new songwriters/year. Works with composers and lyricists; teams collaborators. Payment varies with individual contracts. Normal rate is 60%; 67% Skandinavia.
Affiliates: Sundance Music, Germany (GEMA); Sundance Music, Canada (C.M.R.R.A.); Sundance Music, Denmark (NCB).
How to Contact: Submit a demo tape by mail—unsolicited submissions are OK. Prefers cassette with 3 songs. "Send any available press material." SASE. Reports in 1 month.
Music: Mostly jazz, rock and pop. Published "Out in Left Field" (by Jukkis Uomla), recorded by Werner Studio on Stunt Records (jazz); "Shadowman" (by Aja Puurmnen/Esa Kuloniemi), recorded by Sundance Studios on Sundance Records (rock); and "High Spirit" (by Till Barmeyer), recorded by Sundance Studios on Sundance Records (fusion).

SUPER RAPP PUBLISHING, Rt. 16, Box 560 Cain Cr., Gainesville GA 30506. (404)889-8624. President: Ron Dennis Wheeler. Music publisher, record company (Rapp Records, Ready Records, Rapture and Y'Shua Records) and record producer (Ron Dennis Wheeler). BMI. Estab. 1964. Publishes 100 songs/year; publishes 20-50 new songwriters/year. Sometimes hires staff writers. Works with composers and lyricists; teams collaborators. Pays standard royalty; "some projects varied." Charges production fee "if I independently produce without publishing."
How to Contact: Submit a demo tape—unsolicited submissions are O.K. Prefers cassette and 15 ips reel-to-reel (or VHS videocassette) *with lyric sheet, lead sheet, and chords.* "Send recording of *music tracks* and both *vocal or lead with accompaniment.*" SASE. Reports in 3 months. "I will respond with comments."
Music: Mostly gospel, rock and pop; also country and R&B. "No new age." Published "Rode It To The Top" (by Stephen Condon) (country pop); "Silent Night" (by Paul von Thau) (heavy metal rock); and "Songs for Human Beings Movin' Mountains" (pop/jazz) all on RR&R Records.
Tips: "Songs must be melodic and convey positive statements or message. Get emotionally unattached from the song."

*SWEET SINGER MUSIC, The Mathes Company, Box 22653, Nashville TN 37202. President: Dave Mathes. BMI. Member CMA, GMA, NMPA, NARAS and AFM. Publishes 30-100 songs/year; publishes 10-30 new songwriters/year. Pays standard royalty.
Affiliates: Star of David (SESAC) and Sing Sweeter Music (ASCAP).
How to Contact: Accepts "any tape configuration, including videos. Full music demos are unnecessary, but we would like material to be well-performed and extremely well-written." Prefers cassette with 1-3 songs and lyric sheet. SASE.
Music: Mostly country and gospel; also contemporary Christian and MOR. Published "My Love For You" (by David and Deanna Mathes), recorded by Warner Mack on Sapphire Records (country/MOR); "Dreamer" (by Glen Bates), recorded by Jimmy Gateley on Sapphire Records (country); and

"Baby You Know (How I Love You)" (by Larry Coen, Jr./Helen Cornelius), recorded by Jim Ed Brown and Helen Cornelius on RCA Records (country).
Tips: Needs "well-thought out lyrics, resulting from rewriting until satisfied that the song is as good as the top ten songs on the chart. We avoid controversial, political or demoralizing songs. Traditional country songs are making a comeback. Positive songs are 'in' once again. Duets and group songs are in demand. We will comment on material and we listen to every song submitted."

SYNCHRO SOUND MUSIC AB, P.O. Box 1049, Sundbyberg 172 21 **Sweden**. Phone: (46)8-28 13 46. Publishing Manager: Douglas E. Lawton. Music publisher, record company (Synchro Sound Records) and record producer (Synchro Sound Records). STIM (Sweden). Estab. 1986. Publishes 50-75 songs/year; publishes 10-15 new songwriters/year. Hires staff writers. Works with composers and lyricists; teams collaborators. Pays standard royalty.
Affiliates: Desert Music AB, Midnight Sun Music AB, and Coste Apetrea Music AB.
How to Contact: Submit a demo tape—unsolicited submissions are O.K. Prefers cassette or 15" ips reel to reel (or videocassette) with 4 songs and lyric sheet. Does not return unsolicited material. Reports in 6 weeks.
Music: Mostly pop, rock, classical and new-age; also R&B, country and gospel. Published "Angels" written and recorded by M. Siverling on Airplay Records (MOR); "Aliens" written and recorded by D. Saxon on Elektra Records (soul); and "The Way That I Did" (by Bacal), recorded by Sulphuric Sister on Vinyl Mania Records (soul).

*TANGER-MUSIC PUBLISHING CO., INC., % British Record Corp., 1015 Gayley Ave,. Los Angeles CA 90024. Contact: A&R Department. Music publisher. ASCAP, BMI. Estab. 1981. Publishes 20 new songwriters/year. Works with composers and lyricists; teams collaborators. Pays standard royalty 50%.
Affiliates: AKA Music (ASCAP) and Michelina's High Notes.
How to Contact: Submit a demo tape by mail—unsolicited submissions are OK. Prefers cassette with 3-4 songs and lyric and lead sheet. Does not return unsolicited material.
Music: Mostly rock, heavy metal and pop; also blues, folk and R&B.

*TECHNICAL SOUNDS INC., 4220 Broadway, Denver CO 80216. (303)292-2115. A & R: Terry Lynn McMurtry. Music publisher. BMI. Estab. 1981. Publishes 10 songs/year; publishes 1 new songwriter/year. Works with composers and lyricists; teams collaborators. Pays standard royalty.
Affiliations: Technical Sounds Inc. (BMI).
How to Contact: Submit a demo tape by mail—unsolicited submissions are O.K. Prefers cassette with 3-5 songs and lyric sheet. Does not return unsolicited material. Reports in 3 months.
Music: Mostly gospel, rock and pop; also country, R&B and "all others." Published "Two Hands" (by E. Randle Jr.), recorded by Buttercup on Fast Track Records (blues); "C.O.D." (by D. Farivar), recorded by David, John & Steele on Blue Steele Records (rock); and "I'm Not Your Puppet" (by B. Fenton), recorded by Tarah on Fast Track Records (rock).

DALE TEDESCO MUSIC CO., 16020 Lahey St., Granada Hills CA 91344. (818)360-7329. President: Dale T. Tedesco. General Manager: Betty Lou Tedesco. Music publisher. BMI, ASCAP. Estab. 1981. Publishes 20-40 songs/year; publishes 20-30 new songwriters/year. Works with composers and lyricists; teams collaborators. Pays standard royalty.
Affiliates: Dale Tedesco Music (BMI) and Tedesco Tunes (ASCAP).
How to Contact: Submit a demo tape—unsolicited submissions are O.K. Prefers cassette with 1-2 songs and lyric sheet. SASE. Reports in 2 weeks.
Music: Mostly pop, R&B and AC; also dance-oriented, R&B, instrumentals, jazz, MOR, rock and soul.
Tips: "We want a very commerical vehicle with excellent lyrics and melodies."

TENALINA MUSIC, 1609 Congress, Eastover SC 29044. (803)776-8397. President: Howard A. Knight, Jr. Music publisher, record company (Pegasus Records, Boss Records and Wago Records), record producer (Howard Knight Enterprises) and public relations firm (Telstar Productions). ASCAP, SESAC and BMI. Publishes 300 songs/year; publishes 40 new songwriters/year. Works with composers and lyricists; teams collaborators. Pays standard royalty.
Affiliates: Howard Knight Music (SESAC) and Music West of the Pecos (BMI).
How to Contact: Prefers cassette with 4 songs and lyric sheet. Does not return any material. Reports only if interested in song.
Music: Mostly country, pop and rock; also gospel. Published "Texas on a Saturday Night" (by Mundo Earwood), recorded by Willie Nelson on CBS Records (country); and "Wadda You Done With My Heart" (by Lance Middlebrook), recorded by Mark Alan; "Still Missing You" (by Jesse Blevins), recorded by Bandit Band; and "Airwaves of Love" (by John Joslin), recorded by Bandit Band, all on Pegasus Records.

Tips: "We have increased our publishing efforts for 1990-91 and are putting a lot more emphasis on this branch of our company. We are making frequent trips to Nashville to personally pitch our catalogues."

*MIKE THEODORE MUSIC, P.O. Box 841, Montclair NJ 07042. Contact: Mike Theodore. Music publisher and record producer. BMI and ASCAP. Estab. 1970. Publishes 20 songs/year; publishes 10 new songwriters/year. Works with composers and lyricists; teams collaborators. Pays standard royalty.
How to Contact: Submit a demo tape by mail — unsolicited submissions are O.K. Prefers cassette. SASE. Reports in 2 weeks.
Music: Mostly R&B and pop.

THIRD MILLENNIUM MUSIC, 301 Exhibition, Guelph, Ontario N1H-4R8 **Canada**. (519)821-3701. President: John Gandor. Music publisher. ASCAP. Estab. 1988. Publishes 15 songs/year; publishes 2-5 new songwriters/year. Pays standard royalty.
How to Contact: Submit a demo tape by mail — unsolicited submissions are O.K. Prefers cassette (or VHS videocassette) with 1-3 songs and lyric sheets. "Only send material that you feel can compete with the best!" SASE. Reports in 4 weeks.
Music: Mostly pop, rock and country.
Tips: "We are looking for "radio-oriented" hit singles."

TIKI ENTERPRISES, INC., 195 S. 26th St., San Jose CA 95116. (408)286-9840. President: Gradie O'Neal. Music publisher, record company (Rowena Records) and record producer (Jeannine O'Neal and Gradie O'Neal). BMI, ASCAP. Estab. 1967. Publishes 40 songs/year; publishes 12 new songwriters/year. Works with composers. Pays standard royalty.
Affiliates: Tooter Scooter Music (BMI), Rememberance Music (ASCAP), and Janell Music (BMI).
How to Contact: Submit a demo tape — unsolicited submissions are O.K. Prefers cassette with 3 songs and lyric or lead sheets. SASE. Reports in 3 weeks.
Music: Mostly rock/pop, country and gospel; also international, jazz/fusion, rock, R&B and new age. Published "New American Music" written and recorded by Jeannine O'Neal (country); "Bad Attitude, Dude" written and recorded by Sister Suffragette (rap/Top 40); and "On the Road Again Without You" and "Heartbeat" recorded by The Reed Sisters, all on Rowena Records.

TOMPAUL MUSIC CO., 628 South St., Mount Airy NC 27030. (919)786-2865. Owner: Paul E. Johnson. Music publisher, record company, record producer and record and tape distributor. BMI. Estab. 1960. Publishes 100 songs/year; publishes 50 new songwriters/year. Works with composers. Pays standard royalty.
How to Contact: Submit a demo tape — unsolicited submissions are OK. Prefers cassette tapes with 4-6 songs and lyric or lead sheet. SASE. Reports in 2 months.
Music: Mostly country, bluegrass and gospel; also church/religious, easy listening, folk, MOR, rock, soul and top 40. Published "I'm Ready To Go," "It's Alright," "It Won't Be Long," and "Except These Days Be Shortened" all written and recorded by Early Upchurch on Heritage Records (bluegrass/gospel).
Tips: "Try to write good, commercial songs. The lyrics should match the music. Use new ideas; don't try to make alterations in a song that is already established."

*TONE SCIENCE MUSIC, P.O. Box 874, Belmont CA 94002. (415)391-9861. Owner: Cookie Mareno. Music publisher. BMI. Estab. 1984. Works with composers, lyricists; teams collaborators.
How to Contact: Write first and obtain permission to submit a tape. Prefers cassette with 8 songs and lyric and lead sheet. Does not return unsolicited material.
Music: Mostly ethnic, R&B dance and instrumental; also avant-garde.

*TOOTER SCOOTER MUSIC B.M.I., 195 S. 26th St., San Jose CA 95116. (408)286-9840. Owner: Gradie J. O'Neal. Music publisher. BMI. Estab. 1985. Publishes 15 or more songs/year; 6 or more new songwriters/year. Works with composers and lyricists. Pays standard 50% royalty.
Affiliates: Janell Music (BMI) O'Neal & Friend (ASCAP). Remembrance Music (ASCAP).
How to Contact: Submit a demo tape by mail — unsolicited submissions are OK. Prefers cassette with 2-4 songs and lyric sheet. SASE. Reports in 3 weeks.
Music: Country, gospel, pop/rock, Mexican. Published "Before, After" (by Jeannine O'Neal), recorded by Sister Suffragette (pop/rap); "Battle Cry" written and recorded by Scottie Martin (gospel); "On the Road Again Without You" (by J. O'Neal), recorded by the Reed Sisters (country); and

"Reaching Out"(by David Near), recorded by Resounding Joy (gospel).

TOPOMIC MUSIC, 105 Rue de Normandie, Courbevoie 92400 **France**. (1)4333 6515. President: Pierre Jaubert. Music publisher and record producer. SACEM, ASCAP. Estab. 1974. Publishes 60 songs/year; publishes 10 new songwriters/year. works with composers and lyricists; teams collaborators. Pays SACEM royalty which is usually 50/50.
How to Contact: Submit demo tape by mail.
Music: "Looks for new songs for movie soundtrack. Also needs top 40 style singers for movie soundtracks and dance records productions. Topomic Music is looking for new lyricists in English, to write words on compositions already published by Topomic. Writer will receive writer shares only, no publisher share, and lyrics will be published by Topomic for the world." Published "You Call It Love" movie soundtrack performed by Norwegian singer Karoline Kruger.

TORO'NA MUSIC, Box 88022, Indianapolis IN 46208. Contact: A&R Director. Music publisher (Toro'na Music) and record producer (I. McDaniel). Broadcast Music. Estab. 1987. Publishes 3 songs/year; publishes 1 new songwriter/year. Hires independent staff writers. Pays standard royalty.
Affiliates: Broadcast Music Inc.
How to Contact: Write first and obtain permission to submit a tape. Direct all correspondence to A&R department. Prefers cassette with 3 songs and lyric sheets. Does not return unsolicited material. Reports in 8 weeks.
Music: Mostly top 40, R&B and gospel; also rap. Published "Second Chance" (ballad-LP) and "Freestyle" (jazz) (by I. McDaniel), recorded by I. McDaniel on Toro'na Records; and "Don't Say No" (by I. McDaniel), recorded by Payage on Brendo Kent Pub (ballad LP).
Tips: "Write first about your interests. No phone calls please."

TOULOUSE MUSIC PUBLISHING CO., INC., Box 96, El Cerrito CA 94530. Executive Vice President: James Bronson, Jr. Music publisher, record company and record producer. BMI. Member AIMP. Publishes 1 new songwriter/year. Hires staff writers. Pays standard royalty.
How to Contact: Prefers cassette with 2-4 songs and lyric sheet. SASE. Reports in 1 month.
Music: Bluegrass, gospel, jazz, R&B and soul.

*TREASURE TROVE MUSIC, P.O. Box 48864, Los Angeles CA 90048. (213)739-4824. Contact Professional Manager. Music publisher and record company (L.S. Disc). BMI. Estab. 1987. Publishes 3-15 songs/year. publishes 1-5 new songwriters/year. Works with composers and lyricists; teams collaborators. Pays standard royalty.
Affiliates: Treasure Trove Music (BMI).
How to Contact: Submit a demo tape by mail—unsolicited submissions are O.K. Prefers cassette (or VHS videocassette) with 1-10 songs and lyric sheet. SASE. Reports in 2 months.
Music: Mostly rock, pop and folk rock; also unique crossover, novelty and new age. Published "Kathleen" (rock), "More Than Friends" (pop), and "Never Gonna Work" (novelty punk) all written and recorded by Larry Rosenblum on L.S. Disc Records.
Tips: "Nobody really knows where music will be 2 years down the road. Anything can be a hit in the 1990's. So if you believe in your songs, keep on plugging. I can see folk music making a major comeback, especially on environmental issues. I also think people are getting a little bored with the current marketing and labeling. Music should be more than 'just entertainment.' "

*TRI-SHE KIETA PUBLISHERS, INC., #825, 122 W. Monroe, Chicago IL 60603. President: John Bellamy. Music publisher, record company (Source Records), record producer (Anthony Stephens). BMI. Estab. 1974. Publishes 4 new songs/year; 1-2 new songwriters/year. Works with composers and lyricists; teams collaborators. Pays standard royalty of 50%.
Affiliates: Light & Sound Music, Inc. (ASCAP).
How to Contact: Submit demo tape by mail—unsolicited submissions are OK. Prefers cssette (or VHS videocassette if available) with 3 songs and lyric sheet. Does not return unsolicited material. Reports in 3 weeks.
Music: Mostly R&B, pop and gospel. Published "You Got The Love" (by A. Stephens), recorded by Candi Staton (inspiration); "Everybody Dance" written and recorded by Darnell Owens (R&B); and "Keeper of the Dream" (by M. Hughes), recorded by Clear Vision (rap) all on Source Records.

TRUSTY PUBLICATIONS, Rt. 1, Box 100, Nebo KY 42441. (502)249-3194. President: Elsie Childers. Music publisher, record company (Trusty Records) and record producer. BMI. Member CMA, NAS. Estab. 1960. Publishes 5-6 songs/year; publishes 2 new songwriters/year. Works with composers. Pays standard royalty.

Affiliates: Sub-publishers: Sunset Music (Italy) and White Label (Holland).
How to Contact: Submit a demo tape—unsolicited submissions are OK. Prefers cassette (or VHS videocassette) with 2-4 songs and lead sheet. SASE. Reports in 1 month.
Music: Mostly country/blues, contemporary Christian, Southern gospel and dance tunes; some rap. Published "You Make My Bad Days Good" (by E. Childers); "I'm Not A Cheatin' Games Man" (by J. Massey), recorded by Noah Williams; and "Mystical Magic" (by E.Childers), recorded by Noah Williams. All on Trusty Records (country).
Tips: "We consider songwriters who are also on the road with a band, or as a single act, before we consider just songwriters."

21st CENTURY SPIRITUALS, Box 48661, St. Petersburg FL 33743. Coordinator: Pamela Krizmanich. Music publisher. ASCAP. Estab. 1989. Publishes 25 songs/year; 10 new songwriters/year. Works with composers. Pays standard royalty.
How to Contact: Submit a demo tape by mail—unsolicited submissions are OK. Prefers cassette with 1-3 songs and lyric sheets. "Be professional. We prefer typed lyric sheet and studio production." SASE. Reports in 4 weeks.
Music: Mostly new age, pop and modern jazz; also folk-rock. Published "States of Grace," "Between Life & Living," and "Lost in the Hurrah." All written and recorded by Michael Kris on Dustco Records (new age).
Tips: "Sometimes success can be only three minutes away. We prefer the music to speak through the person not the person to speak through the music. There are enough people trying to be somebody else."

*TWL PUBLISHING GROUP, P.O. Box 11227, Detroit MI 48211-0227. Attention: A&R Department. ASCAP, BMI, SESAC. Music publisher and management firm (L2 Management). Estab. 1982. Publishes 10-15 songs/year; publishes 1-2 new songwriters/year. Works with composers and lyricists. Pays standard royalty; negotiates foreign subpublishing..
Affiliates: Lady Marion, Isle Cay Music, Sunscape Publishing and The Clearwind Publishing Group.
How to Contact: "Solicited submissions only!" Write and obtain permission to submit. Prefers cassette with 2 songs and typed lyric sheet. SASE. Reports in 12 weeks.
Music: "Highly commercial" pop/dance, pop/rock and R&B. Published "Don't Stop," (by M. Grabowski), recorded by Cerberus on Starstream (rock); *Champion*, and "What a Friend," written and recorded by Ron Moore on Morada (pop); and "Crazy in Your Ways," written and recorded by R.R. Jackson on Windguest Records (pop).
Tips: "The writer must be flexible and have the (obvious) potential to write not just one commercial success but many. The writer must also have a great amount of persistence, patience, and perseverance."

TWO & TWO PUBLISHING, 2305 Dickey Ave., N. Chicago IL 60064. (312)689-2726. Vice President: Walter T. Barnett. Music publisher, record company (WMB Records, Two & Two Publishing) and record producer (Barnett Productions). BMI. Estab. 1980. Publishes 5 songs/year; 4 new songwriters/year. Hires staff writers occassionally. Works with composers and lyricists; teams collaborators. Pays standard royalty.
How to Contact: Submit a demo tape by mail—unsolicited submissions are OK. Prefers cassette with 4 songs and lyric sheets. SASE. Reports in 1 month.
Music: Mostly R&B, rock and rap; also house, reggae and soul. Published "Emotional Man" (by W. Barnett, M. Gordon), recorded by Shibeli on WMB Records (ballad); "Get Next To You" (by W. Barnett, M. Gordon), recorded by Shibeli on WMB Records (R&B/dance); and "Do You Wanna Party" (by Fulldeck), recorded by Fulldeck on WMB Records (rap/dance).
Tips: "Make sure you have your song put together as close as you would want it to be heard. If you don't sing, have a singer do it."

UMPIRE ENTERPRIZE, Box 6119, Longview TX 75608. (214)759-2054. Owner: Jerry Haymes. Music publisher, record company (Enterprize Records), record producer (Umpire Enterprize) and show promoters. BMI. Estab. 1969. Publishes 6-8 songs/year. Works with composer and lyricists; teams collaborators. Pays standard royalty.
Affiliates: Golden Guitar (BMI), Enterprise Music (BMI).
How to Contact: Submit a demo tape by mail—unsolicited submissions are O.K. Prefers cassette or videocassette (if possible) with lead sheet. SASE. Reports in 6 weeks.
Music: Mostly country, gospel and pop. Published "Get My Hands On You" (by Abbott), recorded by Margaret Ann on Texan Records (country); *Hayloft Saturday Night* (by Haymes/S. Busch), recorded by Show Cast on GM Records (country crossover); and "Smile of a Clown" written and recorded by Jerry Haymes on Enterprize Records (country).

*UNCLE RIKKI'S MUSIC PROJECT, P.O. Box 290786, Nashville TN 37229. (615)885-4733. Professional Manager: Ashley Butler. President: Richard Butler. Music publisher. BMI. Estab. 1989. Publishes 40 songs/year; publishes 1-2 new songwriters/year. Hires staff writers. Works with composers. Pays standard royalty.

How to Contact: Submit a demo tape by mail—unsolicited submissions are OK. Prefers cassette or VHS videocassette with 3 songs and lyric sheets. SASE. Reports in 1 month.

Music: Mostly rock, country and pop. Published "Baby Guccione" and "Passin Thru Glass" (by R. Butler/J. Hannon), recorded by The Binge on Spike Records (rock).

*UNDERCOVER MUSIC, 4919 Murietta Ave., Sherwood Oaks CA 91423. (818)995-1474. Managing Director: Jeff Gordon. Music publisher (Gordon Records), record company, management company. Estab. 1985. Publishes 10-20 songs/year. Works with lyricists; teams collaborators. Pay negotiable.

Affiliates: Fun House Music (BMI).

How to Contact: Submit a demo tape by mail—unsolicited submissions are O.K. Prefers cassette (or VHS videocassette if available) with 2 or more songs and lyric sheet. SASE, "make sure to include phone number." Reports in 1 month.

Music: Mostly hard rock, dance and straight ahead rock; also pop, R&B and comedy.

Tips: "Accept constructive advice; do not give up. Don't be afraid to be adventurous. Example: Rap band doing a hard rock song."

*UNIMUSICA INC., Suite 110, 3191 Coral Way, Miami FL 33145. Manager: Maria Flores. Music publisher, record company (TH/Rodven Records Inc.). ASCAP. Estab. 1981. Publishes 200 songs/ year; 20 new songwriters/year. Works with composers. Pays standard royalty of 50%.

Affiliates: Musica Unica Publishing (BMI).

How to Contact: Write or call first and obtain permission to submit a tape. Prefers cassette and lyric sheet. Does not return unsolicited material. Reports back in 2 months.

Music: Mostly Baladas (pop), salsa and lambada. Published "Ven devorame otra vez" (by Palmer Hernández), recorded by Lalo Rodriguez (salsa); "Tueres" (by Chein Garcia Alonso), recorded by Frankie Ruiz (salsa); and "Solo con um beso" (by F. Osorio), recorded by Ricardo Montaneo (Balada/ pop) all on TH/Rodven Records.

UNIVERSAL STARS MUSIC, INC., HC-80, Box 5B, Leesville LA 71446. National Representative: Sherree Stephens. Music publisher and record company (Robbins Records). BMI. Publishes 12-24 songs/year; publishes 1 new songwriter/year. Pays standard royalty.

Affiliate: Headliner Stars Music Inc.

How to Contact: Prefers cassette with 1-6 songs and lyric or lead sheets. Does not return unsolicited material. Reports in 1 month, if interested.

Music: Mostly religious; also bluegrass, church, country, folk, gospel and top 40/pop. Published "Jesus, You're Everywhere," "I Can Depend On You," and "I Just Came to Thank You Lord," (all by Sherree Stephens), all recorded by J.J. and S. Stephens on Robbins Records (religious).

UTTER NONSENSE PUBLISHERS, Box 1583, Brantford Ontario N3T 5V6 **Canada**. Phone: (519)753-2081. President: John Mars. Music publisher, record company (Ugly Dog Records) and record producer. CAPAC. Estab. 1979. Publishes 2-5 songs/year; publishes 1 new songwriter/year. Works with composers and lyricists; teams collaborators. Pays standard royalty.

How to Contact: Submit a demo tape by mail—unsolicited submissions are OK. Prefers cassette (or BETA videocassette if available) with lyric or lead sheet. "Send picture of artist(s)." SASE. Reports in 1 month.

Music: Mostly rock & roll, also new jazz and R&B. Published "Be My Guest," (by Mars/Lanzalone/ Sinkowski); "Friday Night Gig," and "(This Time) Take Me All The Way" (by Mars/Lanzalone/ Sinkowski/Tremblay); all recorded by The Children on Ugly Dog Records (rock & roll).

VAAM MUSIC GROUP, P.O. Box 29688, Hollywood CA 90029-0688. (213)664-7765. President: Pete Martin. Music publisher and record producer. ASCAP, BMI. Estab. 1967. Publishes 9-24 new songs/ year; varying number of new songwriters per year. Pays standard royalty.

Affiliate: Pete Martin Music.

How to Contact: Prefers cassette with maximum 2 songs and lyric sheet. SASE. Reports in 1 month. "Small packages only."

Music: Top 40/pop, country and R&B. "Submitted material must have potential of reaching top 5 on charts." Published "Good Girls" (by Kevin Bird), recorded by Valerie Canon on Carrere/CBS Records (R&B dance); "The Greener Years," recorded by Frank Loren on Blue Gem Records (country/ MOR); "Bar Stool Rider" (by Peggy Hackworth) and "I Love a Cowboy" written and performed by Sherry Weston in the feature film "Far Out Man" Tommy Chong (of Cheech & Chong comedy team) and also co-starring Martin Mull.

VALANCE ENTERPRISES, 2210 Raper Blvd., Arlington TX 76013. (817)461-8481. President: Jerry Abbott. Music publisher and record company (CCR Records). BMI. Estab. 1962. Publishes 25-30 songs/year; publishes 2-5 new songwriters/year. Works with composers and lyricists; teams collaborators. Pays standard royalty.
Affiliates: Abadaba Music (ASCAP), Power Metal Music (BMI), Valance Enterprises (BMI).
How to Contact: Submit a demo tape by mail—unsolicited submissions are O.K. Prefers cassette with 5 songs and lyric sheets. SASE. Reports in 6 weeks.
Music: Mostly country, rock and pop. Published "Dreamer" (by Abbott/Jackson), recorded by Dow Jones on CCR (country); "When It Comes To Cowgirls" (by Abbott/Jackson), recorded by Moe & Joe on Columbia (country); "Half As Good As Hank" (by J. Abbott), recorded by Jay Rob on CCR (country).
Tips: "Album filler quality songs don't work anymore. Songs must have a single potential or not worth time and effort."

*TOMMY VALANDO PUBLISHING GROUP, Suite 2110, 1270 Avenue of the Americas, New York NY 10020. (212)489-9696. President: Tommy Valando. General Manager: Arthur Valando. Director of Publications: Paul McKibbins. Music publisher. BMI, ASCAP. Member NMPA. Publishes varying number of songs/year. Pays standard royalty. Printed material percentage—rate varies.
Affiliates: Revelation Music Publishing Corp. (ASCAP) and Fiddleback Music Publishing Co., Inc. (BMI).
How to Contact: Call first. Prefers cassette with 1-3 "clear" songs. SASE. Reports "as quickly as possible."
Music: Musical theater scores primarlly; occasionally pop and country.
Tips: "We prefer writer to perform own song to give a true idea of what he or she is trying to convey. Demo does not have to be elaborate."

VALENTINE MUSIKVERLAG, Box 203312, D-2000 Hamburg 20 **West Germany**. Phone: (040) 4300339. FAX: (040)439 65 87.General Manager: Arno H. van Vught. GEMA. Music publisher, record company (Bandleader Records, Range Records) and record producer. Estab. 1973. Publishes 350 songs/year; publishes 50 new songwriters/year. Pays standard royalty.
Affiliates: Mento Music Group KG, Edition RCP Music and Auteursunie.
How to Contact: Write or call first to arrange personal interview. Prefers cassette (or VHS videocassette) and lyric sheet and lead sheet. SAE and IRC. Reports in 2 weeks.
Music: Mostly country, jazz, big band, background music and MOR; also film music. Published "JAZZ" and "Harmony" (by Kammler), recorded by TSS (instrumentals) on Playbones Records; and "Das lachen" (by Reifeg), recorded by Peter R. on DA Records (rock/pop).
Tips: "Send full lead sheet and information about the writer(s)."

VALET PUBLISHING CO., 2442 N.W. Market #273, Seattle WA 98107. (206)524-1020; FAX: (206)524-1102. Publishing Director: Buck Ormsby. Music publisher and record company (Etiquette/Suspicious Records). BMI. Estab. 1961. Publishes 50 songs/year; publishes 10-15 new songwriters/year. Hires staff songwriters. Pays standard royalty.
How to Contact: Submit a demo tape—unsolicited submissions O.K. Prefers cassette or VHS videocassette with 3-4 songs, lyric sheets. SASE. Reports in 1 month.
Music: Mostly R&B, rock, pop; also dance and country. Published "Black Lace" (by Roger Rogers), recorded by Kinetics on Etiquette Records (rock); "Hunger and Emotion" (by Rogers/Caldwell), recorded by Kinetics on Etiquette Records (pop); and "One More Time" (by Morrill/French), recorded by Kent Morrill on Suspicious Records (R&B).
Tips: "Production of tape must be top quality; or lyric sheets professional."

VIN-JOY MUSIC, 872 Morris Park Ave., Bronx NY 10462. (212)792-2198. Contact: Vice President. Music publisher, record company (Dragon Records) and record producer. BMI, ASCAP. Estab. 1960. Publishes 14-16 new songs/year; publishes 3-4 new songwriters/year. Works with composers, lyricists; teams collaborators. Pays negotiable amount.
How to Contact: "We accept material by recommendation only." Write or call first to get permission to submit a tape.
Music: Easy listening, MOR, top 40/pop, and country. Published "Promise Me" (by Heath), recorded by Smokey on Agon Records (country); "Cousins," written and recorded by Badale (mood-background); and "Letters" (by Gagliano), recorded by Smokey Heath on Dragon Records (country).
Tips: "Material has to be exceptional—not amateurish."

*VOICE NOTES PUBLISHING, 1611 Hickory Valley Rd., Chattanooga TN 37421. (615)899-9685. President: B.J. Keener. Music publisher, record company (Go-Roc-Co-Pop Records, War Records). ASCAP. Estab. 1984. Publishes 20 songs/year; publishes 1-5 new songwriters/year. Works with composers and lyricists; teams collaborators. Pays standard royalty.

Affiliates: Voice Score Publishing (BMI).
How to Contact: Submit a demo tape by mail—unsolicited submissions are OK. Prefers cassette with 3 songs and lyric or lead sheets. "Have melody out front, words and diction clear, not a lot of music." SASE. Reports in 3 months.
Music: Mostly traditional country, traditional gospel, southern, contemporary gospel; also R&B, new age. Published "Hey Babe" (by Stan Ramey), recorded by Tim Whalen (pop); "Ballad of a Coal Miner," written and recorded by Tim Whalen (country); and "His Cross Won't Decay" (by Ramey Cunningham), recorded by Tammy Rena (gospel); all recorded on Go-Roc-Co-Pop Records.

VOKES MUSIC PUBLISHING, Box 12, New Kensington PA 15068-0012. (412)335-2775. President: Howard Vokes. Music publisher, record company, booking agency and promotion company. BMI.
How to Contact: Submit cassette (3 songs only), lyric or lead sheet OK. SASE. Reports within a week.
Music: Traditional country-bluegrass and gospel. Published "The Howard Vokes Yodel," "When You Meet Your Lord," "Judge of Hearts," "Your Kisses and Lies" and "If This World Wants Peace."

*W/A MUSIC CORPORATION, (formerly West Hill Music Publishing), Box 9, Station O, Toronto, Ontario M4A 2M9 **Canada**. (416)299-2222. Manager: Joyce Matheson. Music company. PROCAN. Works with composers and lyricists; teams collaborators.
How to Contact: Write first and obtain permission to submit. Prefers cassette with 3-4 songs and lyric or lead sheet. "We are looking for original music for television and film." Does not return unsolicited material. Reports in 1 month.
Music: All types, but mainly instrumental.

WARNER/CHAPPELL MUSIKVERLAG GESELLSCHAFT m.b.H., (formerly Chappell—Intersong Musikverlag GmbH) Diefenbachgasse 35, Vienna A 1150 **Austria**. Phone: (0222) 894 19 20; FAX: (0222) 894 16 15. Contact: Franz Handler. Music publisher. AKM. Works with composers and lyricists; teams collaborators.
Affiliates: Schneider Musikverlag, Gloria Musikverlag, Aberbach Musikverlag and Jonny Musikverlag.
How to Contact: Prefers cassette (or VHS videocassette). SAE and IRC. Reports in 3 months.
Music: Mostly pop, rock and country; also musicals.

*WARNER/CHAPPELL MUSIC, INC., 1290 6th Ave., New York NY 10019. (212)399-6910. Creative Manager: Jon Bonci. Music publisher. ASCAP, BMI. Estab. 1811. Publishes hundreds of songs/year; publishes hundreds of new songwriters/year. Hires staff songwriters. Works with composers and lyricists; teams collaborators.
Affiliates: WB Music Corp. (ASCAP), Warner Tamerlane Publishing Corp. (BMI), W.B.M. Music Corp. (SESAC), Warner/Elektra/Asylum Music Inc. (BMI), Warner/Refuge Music Inc. (ASCAP), Warner/Noreale Music Inc. (SESAC), Chappell & Co. (ASCAP), Intersong U.S.A. Inc. (ASCAP), Rightsong Music Inc. (BMI), Unichappell Music Inc. (BMI), Tri-Chappell Music, Inc. (SESAC), Lorimar Music A Corp (ASCAP), Lorimar Music B Corp (BMI), Roliram Lorimar Music (BMI), Marilor Music (ASCAP), Goldline Music (ASCAP) Silverline Music (BMI) and Oakline Music (SESAC).
How to Contact: "Must be solicited by an attorney or management firm." Company policy prohibits unsolicited submissions.
Music: Mostly pop, rock, R&B and country; also rap, jazz and new music. Published "Don't Wanna Fall in Love" (by Jane Child) on Warner Records (pop/dance); "I'll Be Your Everything" (by Tommy Page) on Sire Records (pop); and "Dr. Feel Good" (by Motley Crew) on Elektra Records (rock).
Tips: "Submit your best song because sometimes you only get to make a first impression. Submit a song you feel most comfortable writing regardless of style."

WATCHESGRO MUSIC, P.O. Box 1794, Big Bear City CA 92314. (714)585-4645. President: Eddie Carr. Music publisher. BMI. Estab. 1987. Publishes 160 songs/year; publishes 5 new songwriters/year. Teams collaborators. Pays standard royalty.
How to Contact: Submit a demo tape by mail—unsolicited submissions are O.K. Prefers cassette. Does not return unsolicted material. Reports in 1 week.

*WAVEWORKS, 2000 P. St. NW, Washington DC 20036. (202)861-0560. Contact: Patrick Smith. Music publisher. BMI. Estab. 1987. Produces and publishes 20 songs/year; publishes 1 new songwriter/year. Hires staff writers. Works with composers and lyricists; teams collaborators.
How to Contact: Submit a demo tape by mail—unsolicited submissions are O.K. Prefers cassette (or ¾" videocassette if available). Does not return unsolicited material.

*WAYNE AND LACEY, 4305 So. 70th St., Tampa FL 33619. (813)621-7055. Publisher: Wayne Lacey. Music publisher, record company (Music City Records) and record producer (Music City Records). BMI. Estab. 1982. Publishes 50 songs/year; publishes 10-15 new songwriters/year. Works with composers. Pays standard royalty.
How to Contact: Prefers cassette with 4 songs. Does not return unsolicited material. Reports in 1 month.
Music: Mostly gospel. Published "Wonderful Place" (by Wayne Lacey), recorded by The Laceys on Music City Records (sourthern); "Washed Up, Cleaned Up" (by Sandra Martin), recorded by Floyd Family on Music City (southern); and "Sing the Glory Down" (by Dave McMullin), recorded by The Laceys on Music City Records (southern).
Tips: "Be sincere and have a message."

WEAVER WORDS OF MUSIC, P.O. Box 803, Tazewell VA 24651. (703)988-6267. President: H. R. Cook. Music publisher and record company (Fireball Records). BMI. Estab. 1978. Publishes 12 songs/year; varying number of new songwriters/year. Works with composers and lyricists; teams collaborators. Pays standard royalty.
How to Contact: Submit a demo tape by mail—unsolicited submissions are O.K. Prefers cassette with 3 songs and lyric or lead sheets. SASE. Reports in 1 month.
Music: Mostly country. Published "Winds of Change," written and recorded by Cecil Surrett; "Texas Saturday Night" and "Old Flame Burning," written and recorded by H.R. Cook; all on Fireball Records (country).

WEEDHOPPER MUSIC, 1916 28th Ave. S., Birmingham AL 35209-2605. (205)942-3222. President: Michael Panepento. BMI. Estab. 1985. Music publisher and record company (Pandem Records, Inc.). Publishes 4 songs/year; publishes 3 new songwriters/year. Works with composers and lyricists. Pays standard royalty.
Affiliate: Panepentunes (ASCAP).
How to Contact: Submit a demo tape—unsolicited submissions are OK. Prefers cassette or 15 ips reel-to-reel with 3 songs. SASE. Reports in 3 weeks.
Music: Mostly pop/rock, AOR, R&B/jazz and rock; also all others. Published "Kings of Steel," (by J. Batton/D. White), recorded by Assault (heavy metal); "Dancin in the Wrong Shoes," (by S. McDavid), recorded by Jan Hunter (AOR); and "Who's Been Sleeping in My Bed," (by S. McDavid), recorded by Scotti (AOR), all on Polymusic Records. Also "Paris" (rock) on Pandem Records Inc., and "I am the One" by (Phillips/Panepento on Pandem Records (soundtrack).
Tips: "Send us the best possible demo/example of your work."

BERTHOLD WENGERT (MUSIKVERLAG), Hauptstrasse 100, D-7507 Pfinztal-Soellingen, **West Germany.** Contact: Berthold Wengert. Music publisher. Teams collaborators. Pays standard GEMA royalty.
How to Contact: Prefers cassette and complete score for piano. SAE and IRC. Reports in 4 weeks.
Music: Mostly light music and pop.

WESTUNES MUSIC PUBLISHING CO., Suite 127 1692 Oak Tree Rd., Edison NJ 08820. (201)548-6700. A&R Director: Kevin McCabe. Music publisher and management firm (Westwood Entertainment Group). ASCAP. Publishes 50 songs/year; publishes 2 new songwriters/year. Works with composers and lyricists. Pays standard royalty.
How to Contact: Write first and obtain permission to submit. Prefers cassette with 3 songs and lyric sheet. SASE. Reports in 6 weeks.
Music: Mostly rock; also pop. Published *Greetings From New Jersey* (various artists) on Westwood Records.
Tips: Submit a "neat promotional package; attach biography of the songwriter."

*WHITE CAR MUSIC (BMI), 11724 Industriplex, Baton Rouge LA 70809. (504)295-1400. Contact: Nelson Blanchard. Music publisher, record company (White Car Records/Techno Sound Records), record producer. BMI, ASCAP. Estab. 1988. Publishes 6 songs/year; publishes 2 new songwriters/year. Works with composers and lyricists; teams collaborators. Pays standard royalty.
Affiliates: Char Blanche Music (ASCAP).
How to Contact: Submit a demo tape by mail—unsolicited submissions are OK. Prefers cassette with 4 songs. Does not return unsolicited material. Reports in 2 weeks.
Music: Mostly country, rock and pop; also R&B. Published "Leading Man" (by Butch Reine), recorded by Atchafalaya on White Car Records (country); "Sail On" (by Blanchard, Watts, Bullion), recorded by Johnsteve on Stebu Records (rock); and "Crazy Bound" (by Blanchard), recorded by Tareva on White Car Records (country).

WHITE CAT MUSIC, 10603 N. Hayden Rd., Suite 114, Scottsdale AZ 85260. (602)951-3115. Professional Manager: Frank Fara. Producer: Patty Parker. Music publisher. Member CMA, CARAS, CCMA, BCCMA and BBB. Estab. 1978. Publishes 30 songs/year; publishes 20 new songwriters/year. "50% of our published songs are from non-charted and developing writers." Pays standard royalty. **Affiliate:** Rocky Bell Music (BMI).
How to Contact: Submit a demo tape—unsolicited submissions are OK. Cassettes only with 1-4 songs and lyric or lead sheet. SASE. Reports in 2 weeks.
Music: Mostly adult contemporary, traditional country and contemporary country; also contemporary gospel. Published "By Your Side (by Richard Schrum), recorded by Jess Owen (contemporary country); "Don't You Worry Darlin' " (by Harrison Lloyd), recorded by Harrison Lloyd (country); and "Your Daddy Would Be Proud" (by Paul Gibson), recorded by Paul Gibson (country), all on Comstock Records.
Tips: "Send only two songs—they will be heard faster and listened to more intently!"

*DON WHITE PUBLISHING/DEW MUSIC, 2020 Ridge Ave., Philadelphia PA 19121. (215)765-4889. Contact: P. Donald White. Music publisher, record company and record producer. ASCAP, BMI. Pays standard royalty.
How to Contact: Prefers cassette and lyric sheet. SASE. Reports in 3 weeks.
Music: Country.

WHITEWING MUSIC, 413 N Parkerson Ave., Crowley LA 70526. (318)783-1601. Owner: Jay Miller. Music publisher, record company (Master-Trak, Showtime, Par T, MTE, Blues Unlimited, Kajun, Cajun Classics) and record producer (Master-Trak Productions). BMI. Estab. 1969. Publishes 25 songs/year. Works with composers and lyricists. Pays standard royalty.
Affiliates: Jamil Music (BMI), Whitewing Music (BMI).
How to Contact: Submit a demo tape by mail—unsolicited submissions are O.K. Prefers cassette with 3-4 songs and lyric sheets. Does not return unsolicited material.
Music: Mostly country, rock & roll and novelty; also blues, party and cajun. Published "Johnny Can't Dance" (by Mike Doucet, Wayne Toups), recorded by Wayne Toups on Master-Trak (rock).

*WILCOX MUSIC ORGANIZATION, 1099A Finchley Rd., London NW11 **England.** Phone: (01)455-6620. Managing Director: Herb W. Wilcox. PRS, MCPS, SGGB. Music publisher, record company (Zodiac Records) and record producer (Zodiac-Wilcox). Publishes 10 songs/year; publishes 6 new songwriters/year. Pays negotiable royalty.
How to Contact: Prefers cassette and lyric sheet. Reports in 1 month.
Music: Mostly jazz, rock and blues; also ballads, instrumentals and gospel.

WILD WEST MUSIC OF CANADA LTD., Box 1500, Edmonton, Alberta T5J 2M7 **Canada.** (403)486-1386. Director of Songwriters: Rita Miller. Music publisher and record company (Disc Records). CAPAC. Publishes 10-20 songs/year; publishes 2-3 new songwriters/year. Works with composers and lyricists; teams collaborators. Pays standard royalty.
Affiliate: Wilder Yet Music (PRO).
How to Contact: Prefers cassette with maximum of 3 songs and lyric or lead sheet. "We would also appreciate biographical material and photos if available." SAE and IRC. Reports in 2 months.
Music: Mostly top 40, rock and pop; also MOR (easy listening), country and R&B/jazz. Published "Love in the Big City" (by G. Sinclair), recorded by Kim Kastle on Disc Records (pop); "Need to Feel," written and recorded by Thunderfoot on Boiler Records (rock); and "You & I," written and recorded by R. Miller on Theta Records (pop).

SHANE WILDER MUSIC, Box 3503, Hollywood CA 90078. (818)508-1433. President: Shane Wilder. Music publisher, record producer (Shane Wilder Productions) and management firm (Shane Wilder Artists Management). BMI. Estab. 1960. Publishes 50-100 songs/year; publishes 15-20 new songwriters/year. Pays standard royalty.
How to Contact: Prefers cassette (or VHS videocassette) with 3 songs and lyric sheet. "Include SASE if you wish tape returned. Photo and resume should be sent if you're looking for a producer." Reports in 1 month.
Music: Mostly country-traditional and crossover. Published "Are There Any Angels in Nashville," "I'm Not Cookin' Your Eggs No More" and "I Just Love A Good Story" by Jane Tyler; and a duet with Jane Tyler and Eddie Campbell "Love Takes All You Can Give" due for release in 1990.
Tips: "Have strong lyrics with a good story line and a good hook in the song."

*MAURIC WILSON'S MUSIC CO., Suite 55-D, 200 S. Glenn Dr., Cumarillo CA 93010. (805)987-3058. President: Morris Lee Wilson. Music publisher, record company (Wilson Records) and record producer (Wilson Music Co.). BMI. Estab. 1978. Publishes 20 new songs/year; publishes 1-20 new songwriters/year. Hires staff writers. Works with composers and lyricists; teams collaborators. Pays standard royalty.

Affiliates: Wilson's Music Co., Kat and Morris Wilson Publications, Jack of Diamond Publishing, Country Creations.

How to Contact: Submit a demo tape by mail—unsolicited submissions are O.K. Prefers cassette (or VHS videocassette) with any number of songs and lyric and lead sheet. SASE "but we prefer to keep it on file." Reports in 2 weeks.

Music: Mostly easy listening, country and MOR; also R&B, jazz and children's. Published "Special Lady" (by Alex Zaneztis and Morris Wilson), recorded by Matt Vincent on Jack of Diamonds (country); "Freedom Man" (by Bonnie Lee Young and Morris Wilson), recorded by Matt Vincent on Jack of Diamonds (country); and "Burning Bridges" (by Maurine Moore and Morris Wilson), recorded by Morris Wilson on Wilson's Records (MOR).

Tips: "We look for songs that have a good hook line, have something to say and are different from the norm. Publishers are looking for songs that will sound as good in 20 years as they do today."

*WONDERWAX PUBLISHING, P.O. Box 4641, Estes Park CO 80517. (303)586-9005. President: James Haber. Music publisher, record company (DG Records; ? Records). BMI. Estab. 1983. Publishes 5 songs/year; publishes 5 new songwriters/year. Works with composer and lyricists; teams collaborators. Pays standard royalty.

How to Contact: Submit a demo tape by mail—unsolicited submissions are OK. Prefers cassette with 4 songs and lyric sheets. "Listen to your submitted cassette beforehand—check for clarity." SASE. Reports in 4-6 weeks.

Music: Mostly rock, pop and R&B; also British 60s rock, novelty and folk. Published "Holy Crow" (by S. Roberts), recorded by Grand Dad on DG Records (60s folk/rock LP); "Music Removed from This Machine Daily," written and recorded by James Halex on DG Records (60s rock LP); and "Only LP" (by Slash Blitz Dr. Meat), recorded by Degenerates on ? Records (folk/thrash).

Tips: "Understated intelligence; I need a 'point of view' and subject matter not usually touched on, presented in a commercially acceptable vien. A 60s sound gets noticed here. Also looking to purchase British 60s rock publishing rights (62-66). Restrictions have freed up, almost any genre of music has the capability (if presented correctly) of being the next thing. Songwriters should listen to the hits—listen for the common thread—and incorporate it into their own vision."

WOOD MONKEY MUSIC, 2555 East 12 St., Brooklyn NY 11235. (718)332-8500. Owner: Barry Bergman. ASCAP. Estab. 1987. Publishes 20 songs/year; publishes 1-2 new songwriters/year. Hires staff writers. "We have 3 staff writers." Works with composers. Pays standard royalty. "Depends on level of writer and track record."

Affiliates: Ellymax Music Co. (BMI).

How to Contact: Prefers cassette with 3 songs and lyric sheets. "We will report back to writers if we are interested." Does not return unsolicited material. Reports in 1 month. "We will only accept artist or band tapes. We no longer are interested in pure writers."

Music: Mostly rock, pop and R&B; also gospel. Published "Don't Shed a Tear" (by Friedman/Schwartz), recorded by Paul Carrack on Chrysalis (pop rock); "Won't Go Wasted" (by Friedman/DeYoung), recorded by Dennis DeYoung on MCA (pop); and "Dreams of You" (by Friedman/Zanes), recorded by Del Fuegos on RCA (rock).

Tips: "Writers today are better off with small independent companys that are active and aggressive."

*WOODEN IRON MUSIC, 601 NW 80th St., Seattle WA 98117. (206)789-7569. President: Paul Scoles. Music publisher, record company (Ironwood Records) and record producer (Ironwood Productions). BMI. Estab. 1978. Publishes 25 songs/year; publishes 1-2 new songwriters/year. Works with composers and lyricists and teams collaborators. Pays standard royalty.

How to Contact: Write or call first and obtain permission to submit a tape. Prefers cassette (or VHS videocassette if available) with 3 songs and lyric sheet. "Good quality demos are a must." Reoprts in 1 month.

Music: Mostly rock, pop and country; also New Age and jazz. Published "In Your Face" written and recorded by Steve Adamek on North Coast Productions Records (film theme song, rock), "Poco Loco" (by Paul Scoles), recorded by The IRS on North Coast Productions Records (film score, rock) and "Neptune's Garden" written and recorded by Michael Lynch on MNTEX (New Age).

WOODRICH PUBLISHING CO., Box 38, Lexington AL 35648. (205)247-3983. President: Woody Richardson. Music publisher and record company (Woodrich Records) and record producer. BMI. Estab. 1959. Publishes 25 songs/year; publishes 12 new songwriters/year. Works with composers; teams collaborators. Pays 50% royalty less expenses.

Affiliates: Mernee Music (ASCAP) and Tennesse Valley Music (SESAC).
How to Contact: Submit a demo tape—unsolicited submissions are OK. Prefers cassette with 2-4 songs. Prefers studio produced demos. SASE. Reports in 1 month.
Music: Mostly country and gospel; also bluegrass, blues, choral, church/religious, easy listening, folk, jazz, MOR, progressive, rock, soul and top 40/pop. Published "Take Your Burdens to the Lord" written and recorded by Wanda Chibuye on Climb Records (Black gospel);"Riding on the AMTRAK Train" (by Adie Grey), on Mayhams Collegiate Records (soul).
Tips: "Use a studio demo if possible. If not, be sure the lyrics are extremely clear. Be sure to include a SASE with *sufficient* return postage."

WORD MUSIC, Division of Word, Inc., Suite 1000, 5221 N.O'Connor Blvd., Los Colnas TX 75039. (214)556-1900. Creative Director: Debbie Atkins, Word Records: Suite 110, 33 Music Square W., Nashville TN 37203. Music publisher and record company. ASCAP. Member GMA. Publishes 200 songs/year; publishes 1-2 new songwriters/year. Teams collaborators. Pays standard royalty.
Affiliates: Rodeheaver (ASCAP), Dayspring (BMI), The Norman Clayton Publishing Co. (SESAC), Word Music (ASCAP), and 1st Monday (ASCAP).
How to Contact: Write or call first to get permission to submit a tape. Prefers cassette (or VHS videocassette) with 1-3 songs and lead sheet. SASE. "Please send a demonstration tape of a choir singing your anthem to Ken Barker, Print Director." Reports in 10 weeks.
Music: Mostly contemporary Christian, Southern gospel, Black gospel, inspiration. Published "Make His Praise Glorious," recorded by Sandi Patti on Word Records (inspirational) and "Watercoloured Ponies," written and recorded by Wayne Watson on Dayspring Records.
Tips: "Lead sheets, or final form—anything submitted—should be legible and understandable. The care that a writer extends in the works he submits reflects the work he'll submit if a working relationship is started. First impressions are important."

*WORLD FAMOUS MUSIC CO., 1830 Spruce Ave., Highland Park IL 60035. (708)831-4162. President: Chip Altholz. Music publisher, record producer. ASCAP. Estab. 1986. Publishes 25 songs/year; 3-4 new songwriters/year. Works with composers and lyricists. Pays standard royalty of 50%.
How to Contact: Submit a demo tape by mail-unsolicited submissions are OK. Prefers cassette with 3 songs and lyric sheet. Does not return unsolicited material. Reports in 1 month.
Music: Mostly pop, R&B and rock. Published "Let Me Show You Love" and "OO LA LA" recorded by Ten-28 on Pink Street Records (pop/dance).

*WW MUSIC, Box 201, Wageningen NL, 6700 AE **Holland.** Music publisher, record company (Timeless, Timeless Traditional Records) and record producer (Timeless Records BV). STEMRA. Publishes 10 songs/year. Works with composers.
How to Contact: Write first and obtain permission to submit. Does not return unsolicited material.
Music: Mostly jazz and blues.

WYOMING BRAND MUSIC, Rt. 7, Box 220, Mt. Juliet TN 37122. (615)444-8431. Chief Executive Officer: Alfred H. LeDoux. Music publisher and record company (American Cowboy Songs, Inc.). BMI. Estab. 1972. Publishes 10-12 songs/year; 1-2 new songwriters/year. Pays standard royalty.
How to Contact: Submit a demo tape by mail—unsolicited submissions are OK. Prefers cassette with 1-3 songs and lyric sheets. SASE. Reports in 2 weeks.
Music: Country only. Published "Look at You Girl" (by Lanty Ross); "Seventeen" (by Chris Le Doux); and "I Do It For Me" (by Steve Buttel), all recorded by Chris LeDoux on ACS, Inc. Records (country).
Tips: "We need country with an authentic American western theme. No Gene Autry, Roy Rogers or Will Carter 'Hollywood country.' "

*YORGO MUSIC, 615 Valley Rd., Up. Montclair NJ 07043. (201)746-2359. President: George Louvis. Music publisher. BMI. Estab. 1987. Publishes 5-10 songs/year; publishes 3-5 new songwriters/year. Works with composers and lyricists; teams collaborators. Pays standard royalty.

The asterisk before a listing indicates that the listing is new in this edition. New markets are often the most receptive to unsolicited submissions.

Close-up

Larry Henley
Songwriter
Nashville, Tennessee

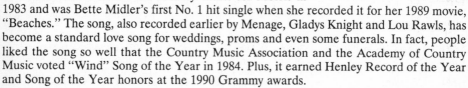

Country artist Gary Morris brought in the new decade for millions of partying TV viewers by singing "The Wind Beneath My Wings" from the stage of the Waldorf Astoria Hotel. But that wasn't the first time Americans had heard this amazingly popular crossover hit, co-written by Nashville songwriter Larry Henley.

"Wind" was a hit on the country charts for Morris in 1983 and was Bette Midler's first No. 1 hit single when she recorded it for her 1989 movie, "Beaches." The song, also recorded earlier by Menage, Gladys Knight and Lou Rawls, has become a standard love song for weddings, proms and even some funerals. In fact, people liked the song so well that the Country Music Association and the Academy of Country Music voted "Wind" Song of the Year in 1984. Plus, it earned Henley Record of the Year and Song of the Year honors at the 1990 Grammy awards.

"I've written big songs before, but this song is bigger than all of my other big hits put together," says Henley. "I'm not surprised that it's a success; I really thought it was a successful song when I wrote it. But I'm really shocked that it's the big success that it is. It feels wonderful and very awesome."

Henley says his inspiration for "Wings" grew out of a love poem he wrote years ago and from an airport scene where his friend, Don Pfrimmer, put his wife, Gail, on a plane to Alaska, where she had never been. As Henley recalls, "She was going up there by herself to get things settled before they moved there, and I thought that was one of the bravest things I'd ever seen anybody do. It was so painful to see them torn apart and for her to have to go without him that I thought to myself what an inspiration it was for that song, for that idea. Because that's exactly what she appeared to be for him."

Henley, a lifelong friend of the late Roy Orbison, used to perform songs before he began writing them. He played with The Newbeats, "white guys doing black voices" in a rhythm and blues rock 'n' roll style. The Newbeats were Orbison's opening act for several years and had a huge hit, "Bread and Butter." It was after his years with The Newbeats that Henley's songwriting career blossomed.

In addition to "Wind" Henley has written or co-written hits such as "Is It Still Over," a hit for Randy Travis, and "He's a Heartache (Looking for a Place to Happen)," one of Janie Fricke's hits. He says success in writing country songs can come from making a serious commitment to your craft and getting closer to the business by moving to Nashville for a few years.

"If you really want it bad enough," he says, "I think the only way you're really ever gonna truly get it — unless you're real lucky — is to come to Nashville and live on those streets with those writers and write those songs, 'cause that's where the heart of it all comes from: all of that electric energy that's in that Music Row area. There's so much vibration going on there from all this creative energy that you can feel it in the air. It just trickles up and down your arm!"

— Tyler Cox

How to Contact: Write or call first and obtain permission to submit a tape. Prefers cassette with 1-3 songs and lyric or lead sheets. "Specify if you are a writer/artist or just a writer." Does not return unsolicited material. Reports in 8 weeks.
Music: Mostly R&B, dance and pop; also ballads and pop metal. Published "To the Maximum" (by S. Stone, S. McGhee, G. Louvis), recorded by Steve D the Destroyer on Q-Rap Records (rap); "Love Me True" (by G. Louvis), recorded by Kimiesha Holmes on Quark Records (dance).
Tips: "We also own two production companies and have access to quite a few artists and labels. Be honest about your material; if you wouldn't buy it, don't send it. We are looking for songs and artists."

YOUNG BOB PUBLISHING CO., 841 Sunrise Hwy., W. Babylon NY 11704. (516)669-1872. President: Steve Young. Music publisher. BMI. Estab. 1988. Publishes 20 songs/year; publishes 2-3 new songwriters/year. Hires staff writers. Works with composers; teams collaborators. Pays standard royalty.
Affiliates: Young Steve Publishing (ASCAP).
How to Contact: Prefers cassette, 15 ips reel-to-reel or ¾-VHS videocassette with 4 songs and lyric or lead sheets. Does not return unsolicited material. Reports in 4 weeks.
Music: Mostly dance, R&B and rock-pop. Published "I Burn" (by Jones), recorded by M. Jones on Profile (dance); and "Time is Right" (by Padova), recorded by Sassa on Profile (dance).

*YOUNG GRAHAM MUSIC (BMI), 50 Music Square W., Nashville TN 27203. (615)320-5707. Vice President: Valerie Graham. Music publisher, record company (Bear Records) and record producer (Bear Records). BMI. Estab. 1989. Publishes 10 songs/year; publishes 4-5 new songwriters/year. Works with composers and lyricists; teams collaborators. Pays standard royalty.
How to Contact: Submit a demo tape by mail—unsolicited submissions are OK. Prefers cassette with 3 songs and lyric sheet. SASE. Reports in 2 weeks.
Music: Mostly country and traditional. "Red Neck" (by Sanger Shafer), recorded by J. Wright; "Michael's" (by T. McClendon), recorded by D. Brannen; and "Girls Like Her" (by Wimberly-Hart), recorded by J. Wright; all country on Bear Records.

REX ZARIO MUSIC, 3010 N. Front St., Philadelphia PA 19133. (215)426-5682. Production Manager: Lucky Taylor. Music publisher, record company and record producer. BMI. Publishes 15-25 songs/year. Pays standard royalty.
Affiliates: Jack Howard Publishing (BMI), Seabreeze Music (BMI), Valley Brook Publishing (ASCAP), Arcade Music Co. (ASCAP).
How to Contact: Prefers 7½ ips reel-to-reel or cassette with 4-6 songs and lyric sheet. SASE. Reports in 1 month.
Music: Country, MOR, rock and bluegrass. Published "Night Wind," (by Lucky Taylor/Doris Frye/Rex Zario/Jesse Rogers), recorded by J.Rogers on Arcade Records (MOR); "Go Man Go, Get Gone," (by L. Taylor/D. Frye/R. Zario), recorded by R. Zario on Rollercoaster Records in England (country); and "Worlds Apart," (by Ray Whitley/R. Zario), recorded by R. Whitley on Arzee (country).

*ZIP KID PUBLISHING, Suite 8M, 377 Rector Pl., New York NY 10280. (212)945-9108. Product Manager: Jacques Battel. Music publisher. BMI. Estab. 1985. Publishes 2 songs/year; 1 new songwriter/year. Pays standard royalty of 50%.
How to Contact: Submit a demo tape by mail—unsolicited submissions are OK. Prefers cassette (or VHS videocassette if available) with 2 songs. "Material will be kept on file. If needed, artist will be contacted."
Music: Mostly R&B, pop, and rock; also country. Published "90 Theme" (by James Duck), on Zip Kid Records (R&B).

Geographic Index
Music Publishers

The U.S. section of this handy geographic index will quickly give you the names of music publishers located in the music centers of Los Angeles, New York and Nashville. Of course, there are many valuable contacts to be made in other cities, but you will probably want to plan a trip to one of these established music centers at some point in your career and try to visit as many of these companies as you think appropriate. The International section lists, geographically, markets for your songs in foreign countries.

Find the names of companies in this index, and then check listings within the Music Publishers section for addresses, phone numbers and submission details.

United States

Los Angeles
Audio Music Publishers
Avatar Productions
Bluefield Music
Bug Music
Cosmotone
Different Stokes Publishing
Loveforce International
Peermusic
Rhythms Production
James Lee Stanley Music
Tanger-Music Publishing Co., Inc.
Treasure Trove Music

Nashville
Abingdon Press
Al Jolson's Black & White Music
Angelsong Publishing Co.
Another Ear Music
Best Buddies, Inc.
Big Wedge Music
Johnny Bond Publications
Buried Treasure Music
Calvary Music Group, Inc.
Glen Campbell Music Group
The Cornelius Companies
Cottage Blue Music
Jason Dee Music, Inc.
Denny Music Group
Dileo Music Group
First Million Music, Inc.
Fradale Songs
Fretboard Publishing
Harris-Richardson Music Group
Heavy Jammin' Music
James Hendrix, Composer & Publisher
Humanform Publishing Company
Irish Indian Music (BMI)

Jaclyn Music
Jimerlean Music
Karlamor Music Publishing
Kimtra Music
Lion Hill Music Publishing Co. (BMI)
Lita Music
Loman Craig Music
The Marco Music Group Inc.
The Mathes Company
Millhouse Music
The Fred Morris Music Group
Mr. Mort Music
Nautical Music Co.
Neon Notes
Newcreature Music
Old Empress Music/Doghouse Productions
Rainbarrel Music Company
Red River Songs/Crimson Creek Songs
Rollin' in the Dough, Bro Music (BMI)
Sadhana Music Publishing
Songfarm Music
Sound Achievment Group
Sweet Singer Music
Uncle Rikki's Music Project
Young Graham Music (BMI)

New York
A Street Music
Ca-Song Music Publisher
Chrysalis Music Group
D.S.M. Producers Ent. Publishing Co.
Eggink Publishing
Gizzard
Globeart Publishing
S.M. Gold Music, Inc.
Hit & Run Music Publishing Inc.
Hopsack and Silk Productions Inc.
Jodunn Music

Jondi Music
Kozkeeozko Music
Lift Him Up Music
Northcott Music/Tancot Music
Quark, Inc.
Ren Maur Music Corp.
Rockford Music Co.
Tommy Valando Publishing Group
Warner/Chappell Music, Inc.
Zip Kid Publishing

International

Argentina
Ediciones Musicales Phonogram S.A.

Australia
Essex Music of Australia Pty. Ltd.
The Image Music Group Pty. Ltd.
Larrikin Music
Music City Music (Australia)

Austria
Ambra Music
Edition Musica
Koch Music Publishing
MSM Musikverlag Wien
Warner/Chappell Musikverlag Gesellschaft m.b.H.

Belgium
B. Sharp Music
Jump Music
Prestation Music

Canada
Alternative Direction Music Publishers
Berandol Music Ltd.
Boot Songs
China Groove

Clotille Publishing
Current Musical Enterprises, Inc.
EKG Music
ISBA Music Publishing, Inc.
Master's Collection Publishing & T.M.C. Publishing
Micah Music
Montina Music
Nashville Sound Music Publishing Co.
Nightflite Music Publishing
Pape Publishing
Pentachord/Pentarch Music
Primavera Sound Productions
Random Image Music
Reid Publishing International
S.M.C.L. Productions, Inc.
Sabre Music
Sci-Fi Music
William Seip Music Incorporated
Stonehand Publishing
Third Millennium Music
Utter Nonsense Publishers
W/A Music Corporation
Wild West Music of Canada Ltd.

Colombia
Promotora Colombia Na De Musica LTDA, "Prodemus"

Denmark
Sundance Music

England
B.A.M. Music
Bannerleague, Ltd. T/A Bolts Music
Bearsongs
Big Ears Music Ltd.
Button Music
Cornish Legend Music
Don't Call Me (D.C.M.) Music
Emmell Music Inc.
Aschenbach Editions
Ever-Open-Eye Music
Express Music (London) Ltd.
F&J Music
First Time Music (Publishing)

U.K. Ltd.
Graduate Music Ltd.
Hobo Railways (Music Publishing) Ltd.
Lematt Music, Ltd.
Lemmel Music Ltd.
New Music Enterprises
Pluto Music Ltd.
R.J. Music
R.T.L. Music, Lee Music, Le Matte Music, Poso Records
Risson Music (Publishing) UK
Rocksong Music Publishing Ltd.
Sea Dream Music
Sleeping Giant Music International Ltd.
The Sparta Florida Music Group Ltd.
Sphemusations
Wilcox Music Organization

France
Coppelia Directions

Germany
Boogietunes Musikproduktion Gmbh
R.D. Clevere Musikverlag
CSB Kaminsky Gmbh
Hammer Musik Gmbh
Heupferd Musik Verlag Gmbh
Ja/Nein Musikverlag Gmbh
Ralf Krueger Musikverlag
Seychelles Music
Siegel Music Companies
Storz Group of Companies
Valentine Musikverlag
Berthold Wengert (Musikverlag)

Holland
All Rock Music
Continental Sound Music
WW Music

Hong Kong
BMG Pacific Music Publishing Ltd.
Discovering Music Ltd.

Iceland
Geimsteinn HF

Ireland
Mother Music Ltd.

Israel
Subar Music Publishing Co. Ltd.

Italy
Ala/Bianca SRL
Dingo Music

Japan
Jimco Record
Kitty Group Inc.

Malaysia
Pustaka Muzik EMI (Malaysia) Sdn. Bhd.

Mexico
Galaxia Musical S.A. De C.V.

The Netherlands
Associated Artists International (Holland)
SE Montfoort

New Zealand
Pegasus Music

Scotland
Jammy Music Publishers Ltd.

South Africa
Charis Music
Gallo Music Publishers

Sweden
Synchro Sound Music AB

Switzerland
Capricorn Ltd. (Publishing)
OBH Musikverlag Otto B. Hartmann

Wales
Demi Monde Records & Publishing Ltd.

Music Publishers/'90-'91 Changes

The following markets appeared in the 1990 edition of *Songwriter's Market* but do not appear in the 1991 edition. Those companies that did not respond to our request for an update of their listing may not have done so for a variety of reasons — they may be out of business, for example, or they may be overstocked with submissions.

Abraxax (did not respond)
Ace Adams (moved; no forwarding address)
Air Manuovres Publishing (out of business)
Americatone Music Publisher (did not respond)
Americus Music (did not respond)
Amokshasongs (did not respond)
Anthem Entertainment (did not respond)
Anti-Conscious Music (moved; no forwarding address)
Ash Music (did not respond)
Associated Music Productions (did not respond)
Baby Raquel Music (did not respond)
Barefoot Lady Music Publishing (asked to be deleted)
Bee Ray Music (did not respond)
Beet Enterprises, Inc. (did not respond)
Beth-Ridge Music Publishing Co. (did not respond)
Betty Jane/Josie Jane Music Publishers (C.E.R. Records) (moved; no forwarding address)
Big State Music Publishing (did not respond)
Blackheart Music (moved; no forwarding address)
Blue August Music Publishing (did not respond)
BMG Ariola Belgium N.V. Publishing (did not respond)
Bolnik Music (did not respond)
Bristol Music Co. (did not respond)
Catherine Courage Music Ltd. (did not respond)
The Cave, Inc. (moved; no forwarding address)
CBS Music Publishing/Canada (asked to be deleted)
CBS Songs/Brazil (did not respond)
Chappell-Intersong Musikverlag Gmbh (did not respond)
The Chu Yeko Musical Foundation (did not respond)
Ciano Publishing (deleted)
Creative Entertainment Music (did not respond)
Crystal Ram Publishing (did not respond)
Dancin Machine Music (asked to be deleted)

Davike Music Co. (did not respond)
D'Lisa Music (did not respond)
Doc Publishing (did not respond)
Eagle Rock Music Co. (asked to be deleted)
Earza Music (did not respond)
Editio Musica Budapest (did not respond)
Editora Presenca Ltda. (did not respond)
Epoch Universal Publications, Inc. (asked to be deleted)
Fairwood Music Limited (did not respond)
Fan Jet Music, Inc. (did not respond)
Bobby Farrell Music Publishing (deleted)
Fazer Music Inc. (did not respond)
Fearless Fidelity Music (moved; no forwarding address)
Fiesta City Publishers (deleted)
First Release Music Publishing (did not respond)
Flaming Star West (asked to be deleted)
4-Frucht Gmbh Musikverlag (did not respond)
Friends/Romans Music (out of business)
Frog and Moose Music (did not respond)
Future Step Sirkle (did not respond)
Geffen Music (asked to be deleted)
General Jones Music (did not respond)
Gold Hill Music, Inc. (asked to be deleted)
Golden Apple Productions (did not respond)
Goldrose Music (did not respond)
Goodsound Sdn. Bhd. (did not respond)
Gotown Publishing Company (did not respond)
Greenaway (did not respond)
Grian Music (did not respond)
Groove & Move Music (did not respond)
Gule Record (did not respond)
Geoffrey Hansen Ents., Ltd. (did not respond)
Johann Hartel Musikverlag (did not respond)
John Harvey Publishing Co. (did not respond)

Hectic House Publishing (did not respond)
High Pockets Publishing (did not respond)
Ho-Hum Music Publishing (did not respond)
Hot Knobs Music (did not respond)
House of Reeds Publishing Co. (did not respond)
Hummingbird Recording Co. International Inc. (did not respond)
Intermedia KG (did not respond)
Ivory Palaces Music (did not respond)
J.L.I. Music (did not respond)
Jackpot Music (did not respond)
Dick James Organizations (moved; no forwarding address)
Janken Music (did not respond)
Jaylo-Bellsar Music Co. (did not respond)
Jewish Family Production Music (did not respond)
Joeyboy Publishing Co. (did not respond)
Jon Music (did not respond)
Johann Kaplan Music Group (did not respond)
Kaspersin Music Publishing Co. (did not respond)
Kayday Music (did not respond)
Keep Calm Music Limited (did not respond)
King Creole, Inc. (did not respond)
Jimmy Kish Music Publishing Co. (did not respond)
Koma Publishing (did not respond)
Leosong Copyright Service Pty. Ltd. (did not respond)
Doris Lindsay Publishing (ASCAP) (did not respond)
Lizard Licks Music (did not respond)
Lorenz Creative Services (asked to be deleted)
Ray Mack Music (did not respond)
Majoga Music (did not respond)
Manhattan Country, Inc. (did not respond)
Memory Lane Music Corp. (asked to be deleted)
Merit Music Corp. (asked to be

deleted)

Merry Marilyn Music Publishing (did not respond)

Mike Music Limited (did not respond)

Mister Sunshine Music, Inc. (did not respond)

MMA Music (did not respond)

MMV Publishing Companies (did not respond)

Modern World Music (did not respond)

MOFO Music (did not respond)

Mike Montgomery Music (did not respond)

Doug Moody Music (did not respond)

Moona Music Co. (did not respond)

MPM Many Productions & Music Publishing GMBH (LTD.) (did not respond)

Munchy Music (did not respond)

Music General Corp/Rosey Red Music (did not respond)

Music Line International Inc. (moved; no forwarding address)

Music Umbrella and Music Umbrella Marketing Services (did not respond)

Musinfo Publishing Group, Inc. (did not respond)

Nasetan Publishing (did not respond)

National Academy of Composers (moved; no forwarding address)

Nervous Publishing (did not respond)

New Clarion Music Group (did not respond)

New Memphis Music (did not respond)

Next Wave Music (did not respond)

Nise Productions Inc. (did not respond)

North Star Music Co., Inc. (did not respond)

North Yonge Publishing (did not respond)

Okisher Music (did not respond)

Old Boston Publishing (did not respond)

The Other Eye Publishing (did not respond)

Peaceable Kingdom Publishing (asked to be deleted)

Peer-Talbot Music Group (asked to be deleted)

Per Productions (did not respond)

Pitman Music (moved; no

forwarding address)

Poca River Music (moved; no forwarding address)

Pollybyrd Publications Limited (did not respond)

The PRI Music Publishing Companies (asked to be deleted)

Prism Music (did not respond)

Radio Tele Music S.A. (did not respond)

The Rainbow Collection Ltd. (asked to be deleted)

Raybird Music (did not respond)

Red Bus Music International Ltd. (did not respond)

Rhythms Productions (did not respond)

Rita (Publishing) Limited (did not respond)

Roba Music (did not respond)

Rob-Lee Music (did not respond)

Rock Solid Songs (moved; no forwarding address)

Rockland Music, Inc. (did not respond)

Rose Hill Group (did not respond)

Rosemark Publishing (did not respond)

Royton Music APS. (did not respond)

S & R Music Publishing Co. (did not respond)

S.M.G. Music Publishing (did not respond)

Score Productions, Inc. (did not respond)

Screen Gems/EMI Music, Inc. (did not respond)

Seaside Music Ltd./The Designer Music Company (did not respond)

Shapes of Things Music (did not respond)

Larry Shayne Enterprises (out of business)

Sidewalk Sailor Music (moved; no forwarding address)

Siebenpunkt Verlags Gmbh (did not respond)

Sin-Drome Music (asked to be deleted)

Sinus Musik Produktion, Ulli Weigel (did not respond)

Slater Pichinson Music, Inc. (moved; no forwarding address)

Societe D'Editions Musicales Et Artistiques "Esperance" (did not respond)

Sometimes Y Publishing (did not respond)

The Sound Box, Inc. (did not respond)

Sound Column Companies

(did not respond)

Spectrum One Music (did not respond)

Terry Stafford Music (did not respond)

Stanton Music (did not respond)

Starbound Publishing Co. (did not respond)

Steeplechase Music (did not respond)

Stonebess Music Co. (did not respond)

Sultry Lady Music (did not respond)

Summerwind Music (did not respond)

Sweet Tooth Music Publishing (deleted)

Tandem Tunes, Inc. (did not respond)

Texas Crude Publishing Co., Inc. (did not respond)

Thema-Verlag (did not respond)

Gordon V. Thompson Music (did not respond)

Time Minstrel Music (did not respond)

Totsiturra Publishing (did not respond)

Toulouse Music Publishing Co., Inc. (did not respond)

Tourmaline Music, Inc. (asked to be deleted)

Tree International (did not respond)

Treehouse Music (did not respond)

Trouble Boy Music (deleted)

Tumac Music Publishing (did not respond)

Twin Towers Publishing Co. (did not respond)

UBM (did not respond)

Udder Publishing (did not respond)

United Entertainment Music (did not respond)

Walk on Water Music (did not respond)

Warner/Chappell Music Canada, Ltd. (asked to be deleted)

Bobe Wes Music (did not respond)

Luther Wilson Music Co. (did not respond)

Lori Lee Woods Music (did not respond)

World Music Group/Bizet P&P (did not respond)

World Wide Music, Inc. (did not respond)

Wunschklang Music Publishing (did not respond)

_____ Music Print Publishers

Originally, the term "music publisher" meant *sheet* music publisher. Today, music print publishing is just one part of the overall music publishing industry. The print publisher's goal is to exploit all of the print possibilities of a copyright. Most of the larger music publishers have print divisions to handle their sheet music publishing and administration, but others often choose to license that responsibility to companies that specialize in print.

Most songs and compositions fall into one of two general categories: popular or educational music. Popular songs are the pop, rock, adult contemporary, country and other hits you hear on the radio. They are printed as sheet music (for single songs) and folios (collections of songs based on a theme, a personality, a specific album or a time period). Educational material includes pieces for chorus, band, orchestra, instrumental solos and methods (instructional) books. In addition to publishing original compositions for chorus, band, etc., publishers will sometimes print arrangements of popular songs for them. So there really are many print options to explore.

Some music print publishers print both pop and educational music, others specialize in one or the other. Most of the major publishers of pop music won't print sheet music for a song until a popular recording of the song has become a hit single, or at least is on *Billboard*'s Hot 100 chart. Most of the companies listed here indicate the lowest chart position held by a song they've printed sheet music for, or say they will print music for songs not even on the charts.

Chart action is obviously not a factor for original educational material. What those print publishers look for is quality work that fits into their publishing program and is appropriate for the people who use their music, i.e., church choirs, grade school bands or high school orchestras.

When dealing with sheet music publishers, it is generally unacceptable to send out simultaneous submissions — sending identical material at the same time to several different publishers. Since most of the submissions they receive involve written music, whether simple lead sheets or entire orchestrations, the time they invest in evaluating each submission is considerable — much greater than the two or three minutes it takes to listen to a tape. It would be discourteous and unprofessional to ask a music print publisher to invest a lot of time in evaluating your work and then possibly have the deal pulled out from under him before he has given you an answer.

Writers' royalties for music in print range from 10-15% of the retail selling price. For educational material that would be a percent of the price of the whole set (score and parts). For a book the 10-15% would be pro-rated to the number of songs in the book. Royalties for sheet music are paid on a flat rate per sheet, which is usually about one-fifth of the retail price. If a music publisher licenses print publishing to a different music print publisher, print royalties are usually split between the music publisher and songwriter 50/50, but it can vary. You should read any publishing contract carefully to see how print deals fit in, and consult your attorney if you have any questions.

A & C BLACK (PUBLISHERS) LTD., 35 Bedford Row, London WC1R 4JH **England**. Phone: (071)242-0946. Commissioning Editors: Sheena Roberts and Brian Hunt. Publishes educational material. Prints 6 items/year. Pays a fee per 1,000 copies printed. Query with complete score and tape of piece. Prefers cassette. SASE. Reports in 4-8 weeks.
How to Contact: Query or write and obtain permission to submit first.
Music: Methods books and children's songs/musicals. Published "Phantasmagoria," by Kaye Umansky (children's songbook); "Abracadabra Clarinet," (graded pieces for clarinet); and "Birds and Beasts," (children's song compilation).

Tips: "We keep a list of good children's songwriters whom we commission to write songs that fit the needs of our compilations. A compilation may consist of around 30-50% commissioned songs. Look at our children's catalogue (available on request) to see what sort of books we publish."

*BLUE UMBRELLA MUSIC PUBLISHING COMPANY (ASCAP), 3011 Beach 40th St., Brooklyn NY 11224. (718)372-6436. President: Kadish Millet. Prints 10 songs/year, mostly individual songs. Pays 6¢/song to songwriter for each sheet sold.
Affiliate: Parasol Music Publishing Company (BMI).
How to Contact: Prefers cassette and lead sheet (lyric sheet if lead sheet is not available). SASE. "If you want your material returned make absolutely certain the SASE has the proper return postage in stamps." Reports in 3 weeks. "State whether you're ASCAP, BMI, SESAC or unaffiliated."
Music: Country and/or anything truly superior. "Although there's no accounting for taste, you can't fool publishers and A&R personnel. Your song has to be memorable, unique, different in some way that makes the listener say, 'Wow! That's incredible!' Otherwise, forget it."

BOSTON MUSIC CO., 116 Boylston, Boston MA 02116. (617)426-5100. Contact: Editorial Department. Prints 100 pieces/year, both individual pieces and music books. Pays standard royalty.
How to Contact: Submit "legible manuscript." Do not send tapes. Reports in 6 months.
Music: Choral pieces, educational material, instrumental solo pieces, methods book and "piano instructional materials that piano teachers would be interested in."

BOURNE COMPANY, 5 W. 37th St., New York NY 10018. (212)391-4300. Contact: Editorial Department. Estab. 1917. Publishes education material and popular music. Prints 50 pieces/year, mostly individual pieces.
How to Contact: Submit unsolicited demo tape, lead sheet, complete score.
Music: Band pieces, choral pieces and handbell pieces.

C. CHASE MUSIC PRODUCTIONS, Division of Chase Dominion Limited, 83 Kneeland Ave., Binghamton NY 13905. (607)797-1190. ASCAP affiliate. Director: Dr. Clarence W. Chase. Estab. 1972. Music publisher and music engraver specializing in hymns; gospel, popular and vocal music; children's songs and lead sheets. Publishes educational material and popular music. Publishes 5 songs/year; publishes 2-3 new songwriters/year. Works with lyricists. Pays minimum standard royalty.
How to Contact: Write first about your interest. Prefers cassette with 1-3 songs and lead sheet. Does not return unsolicited material. Reports "as time allows."
Music: Band pieces and choral pieces. Instrumental solo pieces, instrumental ensemble pieces, methods books in pop style. Children's, traditional hymns and country. Published "Col. Roop," by Robert Lewis (march); and "When Lions Roar," by C.W. Chase (march).
Tips: "Hymns must be a marriage of words and music—use words embodying ideas that will stimulate the imagination. Don't just write poetry—make your hymns 'sing.' Query first!"

*DAVIKE MUSIC CO., P.O. Box 8842, Los Angeles CA 90008. (213)296-2302. Owner: Isaiah Jones, Jr. Estab. 1965. Prints 4 songs/year, mostly individual songs. Publishes 3 new songwriters/year. Pays 50% royalty. Works with composers and lyricists; team collaborators.
How to Contact: Prefers cassette and lead and lyric sheets or complete score. SASE.
Music: Mostly gospel, pop, R&B and inspirational; also folk and country. Published "Great and Wondrous," by I. Jones Jr. (gospel); "Never Be the Same Again," by I. Jones/G. McKinnie (gospel); and "Loving, Caring," by I. Jones (pop).

EMANDELL TUNES, 10220 Glade Ave., Chatsworth CA 91311. (818)341-2264. SESAC affiliate. Administrator: Leroy C. Lovett Jr. Prints 15-20 songs/year, both individual songs and folios. Lowest chart position held by song published in sheet form is 36. Pays statutory royalty or 15¢/song to songwriter for each sheet sold or parts thereof for folios.
Affiliates: Birthright Music (ASCAP), Fair Oaks Music (ASCAP), and Oakfair Music (SESAC).
How to Contact: Write and obtain permission to submit. Prefers cassette (or videocassette showing performance—will return) and lyric and lead sheets. SASE. Reports in 6 weeks.
Music: Inspirational, contemporary and traditional gospel, and chorals. Published "I Love You" (by Ricky Womack), recorded by Womack and the Christian Essence; and "Excitement" (by Brenda Townsend), recorded by Brenda and Linda—Voices of Faith on Marada Records.

GENEVOX MUSIC GROUP, 127 9th Ave. N., Nashville TN 37234. (615)251-3770. SESAC, ASCAP and BMI affiliate. Estab. 1986. Music Production Manager: Fes Robertson. Prints 75-100 songs/year; publishes 10 new songwriters/year. Pays 10% royalty.

How to Contact: Submit demo tape and choral arrangement, lead sheet or complete score. Prefers cassette with 1-5 songs. SASE. Reports in 2 months.

Music: Choral, orchestral, instrumental solo and intrumental ensemble pieces. "We publish all forms of sacred music including solo/choral for all ages, and instrumental for handbell, organ, piano and orchestra." Published "Little People" (by Mark Lanier), recorded by Jake Hess (southern gospel); "Celebrate Today," by Dennis and Nan Allen (children's music); and "Arise, Your Light Has Come," by David Danner (traditional anthem).

Tips: "Most of what we publish is designed for use by church choirs and instrumentalists. Middle-of-the-road, traditional anthems or hymn arrangements in an SATB/keyboard choral format stand the best chance for serious consideration."

*HAMMER MUSIK GMBH, Christophstr. 38, 7000 Stuttgart 1, **West Germany**. Phone: (0711)6487620-7. FAX: (0711)6487269. Contact: Ingo Kleinhammer. Prints mostly individual songs. Interested in receiving band pieces, choral pieces and orchestral pieces. Pays 10% royalty/song to songwriter for each sheet sold. Publishes 100 original songs/year.

How to Contact: Prefers cassette. SAE and IRC. Reports in 2 weeks.

Music: Mostly dance, disco and pop; also rock and jazz. Published "Hit You" (by Volker Barber), "Stop The World" (by Jerome Des Arts and Deborah Sasson), and "I'll Be Forever Your Man" (by Jerome Des Arts and Maria Monrose), all recorded by Oh Well (all dance/just released).

HINSHAW MUSIC, INC., Box 470, Chapel Hill NC 27514-0470. (919)933-1691. ASCAP affiliate. Editors: Don Hinshaw, Richard Thorne. Estab. 1975. Prints 100 pieces/year, both individual pieces and music books. Publishes educational material. Pays 10% royalty.

Affiliates: Hindon Publications (BMI) and Chapel Hill Music (SESAC).

How to Contact: "Send the complete score. Lyric sheets and/or tapes alone are not acceptable. We do not review lyrics alone. Cassette tapes may be sent in addition to the written manuscript. Send clear, legible photocopies, *not* the original. Submit only 2 or 3 manuscripts at a time that are representative of your work. An arrangement of a copyrighted work will not be considered unless copy of written permission from copyright owner(s) is attached. We are unable to return submitted manuscripts. Once a manuscript has been submitted, do not telephone or write for a 'progress report.' Be patient." Does not return unsolicited material. Reports in 3 months.

Music: Choral pieces and piano, organ and instrumental music. Published "Reluctant Dragon" (by John Rutter), recorded by The King Singers; "Zigeunerleder" (by Brahms ed. Neuen), recorded by The Eastman Choral; and "Four New England Pieces" (by Dave Brubeck).

Tips: "Submit your manuscript to only one publisher at a time. It requires considerable time and expense for us to thoroughly review a work, so we want the assurance that if accepted, the manuscript is available for publication. We are unable to 'critique' rejected works. A pamphlet, 'Submitting Music for Publication' is available with SASE."

IVORY PALACES MUSIC, 3141 Spottswood Ave., Memphis TN 38111. (901)323-3509. Estab. 1978. President: Jack Abell. Publishes educational material. Prints 5 songs/year, mostly book/tape combinations. Pays 10% retail price or 50% license income.

How to Contact: Write first and obtain permission to submit. Prefers cassette and lyric sheet. SASE. Reports in 2 months.

Music: Orchestral pieces, instrumental solo pieces, instrumental ensemble pieces, methods books and religious songs. Published "Sonatina Concertata" (by Joe McSpadden), recorded by Linda Jackson and Strings by Archive (classical); "Chamber Music Primer" (by Taylor), recorded by Abell/Jackson/Long (classical); and "Sonatina Concertata 2" (by McSpadden), recorded by Jackson (classical).

JUMP MUSIC, Langemunt 71, 9460 Erpe-Mere, **Belgium**. Phone: (053)62-73-77. Estab. 1976. General Manager: Eddy Van Mouffaert. Publishes educational material and popular music. Prints 150 songs/year, mostly individual songs. Pays 5% royalty.

How to Contact: Prefers cassette and lead sheet or complete score. Does not return unsolicited material. Reports in 2 weeks.

Music: Pop, ballads, band pieces and instrumental. Published "In Jouw Armen," written and recorded by Eddy Govert (ballad); "Niet Met Jij" (by Henry Spider), recorded by Samantha (Flemish); and "Do the Twist" (by Eddy Govert), recorded by Rudy Silvester (Flemish popular).

LANTANA MUSIC, 9430 Live Oak Place, #308, Ft. Lauderdale FL 33324. (305)472-7757. President: Jack P. Bluestein.

How to Contact: Query with complete score and tape of piece or submit demo tape (unsolicited submissions are OK). Prefers cassette or 7½ ips reel-to-reel. SASE. Reports in 4 weeks.

Music: Pop, country and gospel.

*THE LORENZ CORPORATION, P.O. Box 802, Dayton OH 45401. ASCAP, BMI and SESAC affiliate. Member NMPA, MPA and CMPA. Publishes approximately 250 songs/year; publishes 10 new songwriters/year. Pays standard royalty or outright purchase.
Affiliates: Lorenz Publishing Company (publishes easy sacred music for youth and adult choirs as well as for hand bells, piano and organ); Sacred Music Press (publishes "traditional sacred choral and keyboard music for church"); Heritage Music Press (school music); and Roger Dean Publishing Co. ("sophisticated sacred and secular music"),Triune Music, Inc. (traditional to contemporary Christian), Kirkland House (Childrens sacred music), Sunshine Productions (Evangelica Music) and Laurel Press (contemporary Christian).
How to Contact: Send manuscripts only—"no demo tapes." SASE. Reports in 1 month.
Music: Church music publisher. Most interested in band pieces, choral pieces and method books (except Heritage).
Tips: "Send to an appropriate publisher for the style in readable format and persevere."

HAROLD LUICK & ASSOCIATES, Box B, Carlisle IA 50047. (515)989-3679. BMI affiliate. President: Harold Luick. Prints 4-5 songs/year, mostly individual songs. Lowest chart position held by a song published in sheet form is 98. Pays 4% royalty.
How to Contact: Write and obtain permission to submit or submit through publisher or attorney. Prefers cassette or reel-to-reel and lyric sheet. SASE. Reports in 3 weeks.
Music: Mostly traditional country; also novelty songs. Published "Waylon Sing to Mama," written and recorded by Darrell C. Thomas (country, #78 on charts when music was printed).

MUSIC SALES CORP., 5 Bellvale Rd., Chester NY 10918. (914)469-2271. Send material to Attn: Sales Dept. Publishes both educational material and popular music. Prints 100-200 pieces/year, mostly music books; and 50-100 songs/year, mostly in folios. Lowest chart position held by a song published in sheet music form was "at least in the Hot 100."
How to Contact: Query or write and obtain permission to submit first. Submit unsolicited demo tape or complete score. SASE. Reports in 2 months.
Music: Instrumental solo books and methods books; technical reference books; folk, children's and ethnic songbooks; picture books of popular artists, etc. Published *Learning to Play Piano* and *Joy of Children's Favorites*, by Denes Agay (piano methods books); and *Classical Riffs for Guitar* by Jesse Gress. Also handles the catalogs of Paul Simon, Cat Stevens, Bob Dylan, Pink Floyd and Depeche Mode, among others.

PLYMOUTH MUSIC CO., INC., 170 NE 33rd St., Ft. Lauderdale FL 33334. (305)563-1844. General Manager: Bernard Fisher. Prints 50-60 pieces/year: individual pieces, individual songs, music books and folios. Pays 10% of list price to composer per sheet or book sold.
How to Contact: Prefers cassette and lead sheet or complete score. SASE. Reports in 1 month.
Music: Choral pieces and methods books.

THEODORE PRESSER CO., Presser Place, Bryn Mawr PA 19010. (215)525-3636. ASCAP, BMI and SESAC affiliate. Contact: Editorial Committee. Member MPA. Publishes 90 works/year. Works with composers. Pays varying royalty.
Affiliates: Merion Music (BMI); Elkan Vogel, Inc. (ASCAP); and Mercury Music Corp. (SESAC).
How to Contact: Prefers cassette with 1-2 works and score. "Include return label" and postage. Reports in 1 month.
Music: Serious, educational and choral music. "We primarily publish serious music by emerging and established composers, and vocal/choral music which is likely to be accepted in the church and educational markets, as well as gospel chorals of high musical quality. We are *not* primarily a publisher of song sheets or pop songs."

*R.T.F.M., % Stewart House, Hillbottom Rd., Highwycombe Buckinghamshire, **England**. Phone: (0494) 436301 or 36401. FAX: (0494) 461832. Telex: 837137. A&R: Xavier Lee. Publishes educational material and popular music. Prints 40 songs/year, mostly individual songs. Lowest chart position held by a song published in sheet form is 140. Royalty varies.
Affiliates: Lee Music Ltd., Pogo Records Ltd. and R.T.L. Music.
How to Contact: Prefers cassette or 7½ or 15 ips reel-to-reel and lyric and lead sheets or complete score. SAE and IRC. Reports in 6 weeks.
Music: All types: band, orchestral, instrumental solo and instrumental ensemble pieces. Published "Groovin" (15), "Wish You Well" (90) and "Alligator Man" (27) all (by M.I. Lawson), recorded by Till Band.

*BRIAN RAINES MUSIC CO., Box 1376, Pickens SC 29671. (803)859-9614. FAX: (803)859-3814. President: Brian E. Raines. Prints 2-3 songs/year, mostly individual songs. Lowest chart position held by a song published in sheet form is 40. Pays 10% royalty or 10-20¢/song to songwriter for each sheet sold.
How to Contact: Prefers cassette and lyric sheet. SASE. Reports at earliest convenience.
Music: Mostly country, gospel, top 40.

SEA DREAM MUSIC, 236 Sebert Rd., London E7 ONP **England**. Phone: (081)534-8500. Senior Partner: Simon Law. Publishes educational material and popular music. Estab. 1976. Prints 20 songs/year, mostly individual songs. Has printed sheet music for uncharted songs. Pays 10% royalty per sheet sold.
How to Contact: Prefers cassette and lyric sheet. SAE and IRC. Reports in 6 weeks.
Music: Band and choral pieces. Mostly funk/rock, rock, blues and gospel; also "music with a Christian bias to the lyrics." Published "Shipshapes Song" (pop), "Everyone Matters to Jesus" (rock 'n' roll) (both by Derek & Jackie Llewellyn) and "God Loves You So Much" (rock) (by Derek Llewellyn) all recorded by Fresh Claim and all uncharted.

WILLIAM GRANT STILL MUSIC, Suite 422, 22 S. San Francisco St., Flagstaff AZ 86001-5737. (602)526-9355. ASCAP affiliate. Estab. 1983. Manager: Judith Anne Still. Publishes educational material and popular music. Prints 2-3 arrangements/year; 2-3 new arrangers/year. Works with arrangers only. Pays 10% royalty for arrangements sold. "We publish arrangements of works by William Grant Still. This year we are especially interested in developing a catalog of guitar arrangements, though other sorts of arrangements may be considered."
How to Contact: Query. Does not return unsolicited material. Reports in 1 month.
Music: Mostly instrumental solo pieces. Published "Mother and Child" by Timothy Holley; "Memphis Man" by Bert Coleman, for organ (classical); and "Coquette," by Anthony Griggs (classical).
Tips: "We suggest that the prospective arranger familiarize himself with the music of William Grant Still, prepare a sample arrangement and submit it after having been given permission to do so."

3 SEAS MUSIC/NORTHVALE MUSIC, 450 Livingston St., Norwood NJ 07648. (201)767-5551. Vice President: Gene Schwartz. Prints mostly individual songs. Lowest chart position held by a song published in sheet form is 20. Pays 14¢/song to songwriter for each sheet sold.
How to Contact: Prefers cassette and lead sheet or complete score. SASE. Reports in 1 month.
Music: Rock.

TOPOMIC MUSIC, 105, Rue de Normandie, Courbevoie 92400, **France**. Phone: (1)43-33-65-15. President: Pierre Jaubert. Estab. 1974. Prints 60 songs/year, mostly individual songs. Has printed music for uncharted songs.
How to Contact: Submit unsolicited demo tape. Prefers cassette and lead sheet. Does not return unsolicited material. Reports in 2 weeks.
Music: Mostly top 40, film soundtracks, pop and rock; also dance music. Published "Get Another Love" (by D. Donable), recorded by Farid Fedjer (disco #31). Lowest chart position held: #49.

THE WILLIS MUSIC COMPANY, 7380 Industrial Rd., Florence KY 41042. (606)283-2050. SESAC affiliate. Estab. 1899. Editor: David B. Engle. Publishes educational material. Prints 100 publications/year; "no charted songs in our catalog." Pays 5-10% of retail price or outright purchase.
How to Contact: Prefers fully notated score. SASE. Reports in 3 months.
Music: Mostly early level piano teaching material; also instrumental solo pieces, methods books and "supplementary materials-educational material only."

Music Print Publishers/'90-'91 Changes

The following markets appeared in the 1990 edition of *Songwriter's Market* but do not appear in the 1991 edition. Those companies that did not respond to our request for an update of their listing may not have done so for a variety of reasons—they may be out of business, for example, or they may be overstocked with submissions.

Alfred Publishing Co., Inc.
(asked to be deleted)
Another Ear Music (moved; no forwarding address)
Cherry Lane Music Co., Inc. (did not respond)

Gwynn Publishing Co. (did not respond)
Ja/Nein Musikverlag Gmbh (asked to be deleted)
Jenson Publications Inc. (moved; no forwarding

address)
Larry Shayne Enterprises (deleted)
Weyand Music Publishing (moved; no forwarding address)

Record Companies

The record company, or "label," is the hub around which all other players in the music industry revolve. Without the record companies' constant output of new product, in the form of vinyl LPs, cassettes, CDs and DATs, there would be no need for the music publisher, the record producer, the recording artist, or you, the songwriter. Happily for everyone concerned, the record business is a thriving, billion-dollar industry that continuously needs a fresh supply of one very important commodity: songs.

Record company executives are gamblers. Their challenge is to anticipate public opinion by signing artists and songs that the public will like—and seek out in a record store. They base their predictions (and their signings) partly on what has worked before, partly on what they believe to be artistic merit, and partly on what they think they can accomplish through marketing.

Because of the heavy financial risks involved in putting out an album, record companies are cautious in taking on new artists or songs; they tend to consider only those with hit potential. A&R (artist & repertoire) representatives are the record company executives in charge of finding new artists to add to the companies' rosters. They are also often involved in selecting songs for their acts to record and, in many cases, producing their acts' albums. Since they have such an intimate involvement with the artists and songs featured by their labels, A&R reps are the most important record company contacts and allies a songwriter can have.

What is the best way to get your material to a record company A&R executive? The unfortunate truth is that most of the *major* record labels, on the advice of their attorneys, do not accept unsolicited submissions. They accept tapes only from industry people (publishers, managers, entertainment lawyers, etc.) whom they know and whose judgment they respect. You could ignore the "no unsolicited submissions" policy and mail tapes to those companies anyway—with the sort of blind faith of the desert island castaway who scrawls a note on a scrap of paper, seals it in a bottle and hurls it into the sea. But your chances of success by such a thoughtless method are even worse than those of the hopeful castaway. The good news is that there are two strategies that can help you get around the roadblocks thrown up by the major record companies: 1) networking and 2) building your career with or through an independent record label.

Networking is the process of building an interconnecting web of acquaintances within the music business. The more industry people you meet, the broader becomes your network, and the greater become your chances of befriending someone who has the clout to get your demo heard by the right people. Talent is the first prerequisite, but after that, success in the music business is largely a matter of contacts. Networking can begin on the local level, with the musicians and songwriters who live in your hometown. Each of them will know people in the business that you *don't* know; ask them for introductions—then ask *those* people for introductions to the people *they* know, and soon your circle of acquaintances will expand. *Songwriter's Market* is a very effective networking tool; as you deal with the companies in this book, keep good notes about the people you talk to. Make a point to remember names; pay special attention to the secretaries and assistants who surround the people you are trying to reach. If you deal with them professionally and courteously, they will, if they believe in your material, gladly become a part of your network as you become a part of theirs. Music conferences and seminars offer tremendous opportunities for meeting new people and establishing professional relationships. If you can afford to attend one or two national music conferences each year, you will benefit from an immediate increase in the size and quality of your music industry network.

The majority of the record companies that are listed in *Songwriter's Market* are independent labels (indies). Since, as mentioned above, most of the major record labels do not accept unsolicited material, many of them choose not to have a listing in our book. Indies are simply record companies that are smaller and less affluent than the majors. They are, as a general rule, more receptive to new material than the major labels. Many successful acts owe their careers to independent labels — small companies who believed in them enough to give them their first break. Some of these acts go on to major labels when success comes, but some choose to remain with the independent label for their entire careers. (For an encouraging portrait of independent labels in the 90s, see Randy Poe's article, "What's Ahead for the Music Industry," on page 6.)

When submitting material to a record company, be very specific about what you are submitting and what your goals are. If you are hoping to be signed as an artist, say that in your cover letter and submit a demo that showcases your talents as a performer. If you are submitting songs with the intention of their being covered by artists already signed to the label, state that. In either case, be sure to follow closely the submission guidelines that each company lays out for you in its listing. First impressions are important, and with the companies listed in *Songwriter's Market*, their first impression of you and your work is based on how well you read and follow their instructions.

A word about companies who charge. Generally speaking, it is up to the record company that wants to use your songs or sign you as an artist to assume the risk inherent in such a venture. Many smaller companies—many independent labels—will ask the artist to cover some expenses out of his own pocket. While some up-front charging might be expected (*reasonable* producers' expenses, for example), some companies will ask the artist to pay for everything connected to the record deal—production, promotion, distribution, etc. It is our feeling that a record "deal" that requires you to pay for every aspect of making and selling your record is really not much of a deal. A record company is not doing you a favor by signing you to their roster; they are entering into a business arrangement that they hope will be profitable—using you and your talents as a source of income for their company. There is simply no reason for you to assume all of the risks involved. The record company stands to gain a great deal if your record takes off; they should be willing to share the risks. Before you sign any recording contract, consult an attorney familiar with entertainment law to make sure the deal is a fair one.

At the end of this section, you will find a Geographic Index listing alphabetically the record companies in the major music centers—New York, Los Angeles and Nashville—in order to help you plan a trip to one or more of those cities in the future.

A&M RECORDS, INC., 1416 N. La Brea, Hollywood CA 90028. (213)469-2411. Record company and music publisher (Almo Irving Music). Releases 100 singles and 50-60 LPs/year. Works with artists and songwriters on contract.

*AARSON RECORDS %Entertainment Management Enterprises, 454 Alps Rd., Wayne NJ 07470. (201)694-3333. President: Richard Zielinski. Labels include Aarson Records and Unicorn Records. Record company and manager. Estab. 1983. Works with musicians/artists on contract.
How to Contact: Submit demo tape by mail. Unsolicited submissions are OK. Prefers cassette (or VHS videocassette) with 4 songs and lyric sheet. SASE. Reports in 1 month.
Music: Mostly rock, metal and urban. Artists include Mirror's Image and Sinful.

ABACUS, Box 186, Cedarburg WI 53012. (414)375-1482. Producer: Bob Wiegert. Record company, record producer and music publisher (RobJen Music). Works with musicians/artists on contract and musicians on salary for in-house studio work. Pays negotiable royalty to artists on contract; statutory rate to publishers for each record sold.

How to Contact: Write first about your interest. Submit cassette only with 1-3 songs and lyric sheet. Does not return unsolicited material. Reports in 1 month.
Music: New Age, soundtrack productions and fine arts.
Tips: "We are always on the lookout for a talented composer, but would advise all to write first. Unsolicited material will not be sent back."

AIA RECORDS, Leopold Str. 11-13, 4000 Dusseldorf NRW **Germany**. Phone: (0211)364545. Director: Ralf Krueger. Labels include AIA and BS Modern Music. Record company, music publisher (Ralf Krueger Musikverlag) and record producer (Sira Ain/Trance Palace Productions). Estab. 1984. Releases 2 12" singles, 2 LPs and 1 CD/year. Works with musicians/artists and songwriters on contract and hires musicians for in-house studio work.
How to Contact: Submit demo tape by mail. Unsolicited submissions are okay. Prefers cassette with lyric sheet. SASE. Reports in 1 month.
Music: Mostly new pop, funk/soul and dance/new house; also stylistic fusion. Released "Milky Way Kiss" (by Bop Whopper/Sira Ain), recorded by Frank Ananda on AIA (soul-pop-rap); and "Violins" (by Georgie Rockwood, Victor Lovesa, Sira Ain, Ama Donya), recorded by Frank Ananda on AIA (new pop). Other artists include S.A., FreeDome, The Soul and Female Invasion.

AKO RECORDS, 20531 Plummer, Chatsworth CA 91311. (818)998-0443. President: A.E. Sullivan. Labels include Dorn Records and Aztec Records. Record company, music publisher (Amiron Music) and record producer (AKO Productions). Estab. 1980. Releases 2 singles/year. Works with musicians/artists and songwriters on contract. Pays negotiable royalty to artists on contract. Pays statutory rate.
How to Contact: Write first and obtain permission to submit. Prefers cassette (or Beta or VHS videocassette) and lyric sheet. SASE. Reports in 2 months.
Music: Top 40/pop, rock and pop/country. Released *Touch of Fire*, by Touch of Fire (LP); *Gang Back*, by F. Cruz (LP); "Sana Christian," by Sana Christian (single), and "Helpless" (by R. Black), recorded by Les Staunton, all on AKO Records. Other artists include Rozzi and Cemas.

*ALCAZAR RECORDS, P.O. Box 429, Waterbury VT 05676. (802)244-7845. Manager: Lafe Dutton. Labels include Alcazar, Cole Harbor, Fogarty's Cove, Fretless, Alacazam!, Record Rak Records and TOAD. Estab. 1977. Releases 12 LPs and 12 CDs/year. Works with musicians/artists on record contract, songwriters on royalty contract and musicians on salary for in-house studio work. Pays 5-15% royalty to artists on contract. Pays statutory rate to publishers per song on records.
How to Contact: Write or call first and obtain permission to submit. Prefers cassette or VHS videocassette if available with 3 songs and lyric sheet. Does not return unsolicited materials. Reports in 4 weeks.
Music: Children's, folk and blues: also pop/soft rock and avant-garde. Released *Where . . . Fast Lane*, written and recorded by Fred Koller on Alcazar Records (folk LP); *Amy and Leslie*, written and recorded by *Amy and Leslie* on Alcazar Records (folk LP); and *Peter and the Wolf*, written and recorded by Dave Van Ronk on Alcazam! Records (children's LP). Other artists include Doc Watson, Odetta, George Gritzbach, Priscilla Herdman and Rory Block.
Tips: "Study our releases; are you/your songs appropriate for us? If someone knows everything we've put out and insists they're right for the label, that person/artist will get a serious listen."

ALEAR RECORDS, % McCoy, Route 2, Box 114, Berkeley Springs WV 25411. (304)258-2175. Labels include Master Records, Winchester Records and Real McCoy Records. Record company, music publisher (Jim McCoy Music, Clear Music, New Edition Music/BMI), record producer and recording studio. Releases 20 singles and 10 LPs/year. Works with artists and songwriters on contract; musicians on salary. Pays 2% minimum royalty to artists; statutory rate to publishers for each record sold.
How to Contact: Prefers 7½ ips reel-to-reel or cassette with 5-10 songs and lead sheet. SASE. Reports in 1 month.
Music: Bluegrass, church/religious, country, folk, gospel, progressive and rock. Released "Like Always," by Al Hogan (country single); and *Mr. Bluegrass Here's to You*, by Carroll County Ramblers (bluegrass LP). Other artists include Alvin Kesner, Jubilee Travelers, Jim McCoy, and Middleburg Harmonizers.

 The asterisk before a listing indicates that the listing is new in this edition. New markets are often the most receptive to unsolicited submissions.

ALHART MUSIC PUBLISHING, Box 1593, Lakeside CA 92040. (619)443-2170. President: Richard Phipps. Labels include Alhart Music. Record company and music publisher (Alhart Music Publishing/ BMI). Estab. 1981. Releases 4 singles/year. Works with songwriters on contract. Pays statutory rate.
How to Contact: Write or call first and obtain permission to submit. Prefers cassette with 2 songs and lyric or lead sheets. Does not return unsolicited material. Reports in 4 weeks.
Music: Mostly country; also R&B. Released "Party For One," "Don't Turn My Gold To Blue," and "Blue Lady" (by Dan Michaels), on Alhart Records (country). Other artists include Michael Hinton, Leo Boek, John Milazzo, Michel Sealy and Dan Michaels.

ALLAGASH COUNTRY RECORDS, 45 7th St., Auburn ME 04210. (207)784-7975. President/A&R Director: Richard E. Gowell. Labels include Allagash Country Records, Gowell Records and Allagash R&B Records. . Record company, music publisher (Richard E. Gowell Music, BMI) and record producer. Estab. 1986. Releases 3-5 singles and 1-3 LPs/year. Works with musicians/artists and song-writers on contract. Pays 3-50% royalty to artist on contract; statutory rate to publisher per song on record.
How to Contact: Prefers cassette with 2-10 songs and lyric or lead sheet. Returns unsolicited material, with SASE, 1-2 months.
Music: Mostly country, pop/country and country rock; also R&B/pop. Released "It'll be a Cold Day," (by L. Pritchett and R. Sanders), recorded by Ray Sanders on Allagash Country Records (country); "Savannah's Song" (by E. Seville), recorded by Eddie Seville on Allagash Country Records (progressive country/rock); "Long Way Home" (by E. Seville), recorded by Eddie Seville on Allagash Country Records (country/rock) and "Bump Goes Baby" (by Rick Johnson), recorded by Rick Johnson on Allagash Country Records (western swing c/w).
Tips: "Our label is currently seeking high quality finished masters with publishing open. Submit chrome cassette, copyrighted and ready for record pressing. Never send original master—copies only."

ALLEGIANCE RECORDS, 620 Hampshire Rd., Westlake Village CA 91362. (805)496-4960. Contact: A&R Department. Labels include Allegiance Records, Treasury of Recorded Classics and Takoma Records. Record company. Releases 12 singles and 12 LPs/year. Works with musicians/artists on contract.
How to Contact: Write first and obtain permission to submit. Prefers cassette "or finished product (master)." Does not return unsolicited material. Reports in 6 weeks.
Music: Dance, R&B, pop and jazz. Artists include John Fahey, Leo Kottke, and the Run Aways.

ALPHABEAT, Box 12 01, D-6980 Wertheim/Main, **West Germany**. Phone: (09342)841 55. Owner/ A&R Manager: Stephan Dehn. A&R National Manager: Marga Zimmermann. Press & Promotion: Alexander Burger. Disco Promotion: Matthias Marth. Music Service: Wolfgang Weinmann. Creative Services: Heiko Köferl.Labels include Alphabeat. Record company and record producer. Releases vary "depending on material available." Works with musicians/artists on contract; hires musicians for in-house studio work. Also works through "license contract with foreign labels." Payment to artists on contract "depends on product." Payment: conditional on German market.
How to Contact: Prefers cassette (or PAL videocassette) with maximum of 3 songs and lyric sheet. "When sending us your demo tapes, please advise us of your ideas and conditions." SAE and IRC. Reports in 1 month.
Music: Mostly dance/disco/pop, synth/pop and electronic; also R&B, hip hop/rap and ballads. Artists include Martin King, Red Sky, Fabian Harloff, Silent Degree, Mode Control, Mike M.C. & Master J., Skyline, Lost in the Dessert, Oriental Bazar, Voice In Your Head, Love Game, Alpha W. Synthoxx and Interface (ZYX Records). "We are a distributor of foreign labels. If foreign labels have interest in distribution of their productions in West Germany (also Swiss and Austria) they can contact us. We distribute all styles of music of foreign labels."

*ALTERNATIVE RECORD CO. LTD., 140 Prospect St., S.I. NY 10305. (718)447-3986. President/Chief Executive: Vinny DeGeorge. Record company and producer. Estab. 1976. Releases 5 singles/year, 2 12″ singles, 1 LP and 1 EP/year. Works with musicians/artists and songwriters on contract and hires musicians for in-house studio work and promotion for live acts. Royalty is negotiable; statutory rate to publishers per song on records.
How to Contact: Write first to arrange personal interview. Prefers cassette (or videocassette if available) with 3 songs. Does not return unsolicited material. Reports in 10 weeks.
Music: Interested in all types of music. Released *Rule of Thumb* (by Rule of Thumb), recorded by F.V. Sound on Alternative Records (pop LP); "Hot Strokes" (by Vinny DeGeorge), recorded by F.V. Sound on Alternative Records (reggae/rock song). Other artists include Social Numbers and Kenny and The Hearthrobs.

ALYSSA RECORDS, Box 181, Holbrook NY 11741-0181. President: Andy Marvel. Labels include Ricochet Records and Alyssa Records. Record company, music publisher (Andy Marvel Music/ASCAP, Bing Bing Bing Music/ASCAP, and Andysongs/BMI), and record producer (Marvel Productions). Estab. 1981. Releases 12-15 singles, 1 12" single and 4 LPs/year. Works with musicians/artists and songwriters on contract. Pays 50% royalty to artists on contract; statutory rate to publishers per song on record.
How to Contact: Prefers cassette (or VHS videocassette) with 3 songs and lyric sheet. Reports in 3 weeks only with SASE. No need for permission.
Music: Mostly pop, R&B, and Top 40; also country. Released "You Can't Hide Your Fantasies," by Andy Marvel, Steve Perri and Tom Siegel; "Express (10 Items Or Less)," by Andy Marvel; and "Meant To Be," by Andy Marvel and Don Levy, all recorded by Andy Marvel on Alyssa Records.

AMALGAMATED TULIP CORP., 117 W. Rockland Rd., Libertyville IL 60048. (708)362-4060. Director of Publishing and Administration: P. Johnson. Labels include Dharma Records. Record company and music publisher. Works with musicians on salary; artists and songwriters on contract. Pays royalty to artists and songwriters on contract.
How to Contact: Prefers cassette with 2-5 songs. SASE. Reports in 1-3 months.
Music: Rock (progressive and easy listening), dance/R&B and top 40/pop. Released *Songs by the Group Milwaukee*, by Milwaukee; "Sunday Meetin' In the Morning," by Ken Little and the Band; and "This Feels Like Love to Me," by Mirrors.

*AMAZING RECORDS, P.O. Box 2512, Austin TX 78768. (512)444-4666. Owner: Cass Hook. Record company, music publisher (Munificent Music/BMI) and record producer (Branch Productions). Estab. 1985. Releases 2-4 LPs and 2-4 CDs/year. Works with musicians/artists on record contract. Pays 7-10% royalty to artists on contract; statutory rate to publisher per song on record. Charges artists upfront for production.
How to Contact: Write or call first to arrange personal interview. Prefers cassette (or VHS videocassette) with 3 songs and lyric sheet. Does not return unsolicited material.
Music: Mostly rock & roll-all types, country rock and rhythm n' blues; also jazz, folk and reggae. Released *Texana Dames* (by Conni Hancock), recorded by Lloyd Maines (country rock LP); *Ty Gavin* (by Ty Gavin), recorded by Hunt Sales (hard rock LP); and *Juke Jumpers* (by Jim Colegrove), recorded by Jive (rock b LP), all on Amazing Records. Other artists include B.W. Stevenson, Freddie Steady's Wild Country, Teddy and the Tall Tops, Rosie Flores, Junior Brown and Eric Hokannen.
Tips: "Get in touch, submit materials, play Austin, keep in touch."

AMERICAN MUSIC COMPANY/CUCA RECORD AND CASSETTE MANUFACTURING COMPANY, Box 8604, Madison WI 53708. Vice-President: Daniel W. Miller. Labels include American, Cuca, Jolly Dutchman, Age of Aquarius, Top Gun, Sound Power and Night Owl Records. Record company and music publisher (American Legend Music/ASCAP and Apple-Glass Music/BMI). Works with artists and songwriters on contract. Pays 10% royalty to artists on contract; 50% royalty to songwriters on contract.
How to Contact: Prefers reel-to-reel tape (but will accept cassettes) with 2-20 songs; include photo and complete information. SASE. "No calls, please." Reports within 6 months.
Music: "Old time" (polkas, waltzes), bluegrass, folk and ethnic. Released "Hupsadyna," by Styczynski (ethnic single); *Polka 76*, by Meisner (ethnic LP); and "Muleskinner Blues," by the Fendermen.
Tips: "Cuca has an extensive catalog and is known as 'America's leading line of ethnic and old-time music.' Artists may have a superior chance of having their material released on Cuca, American or affiliated labels, if they present *studio-quality* tapes of *all original* material."

THE AMETHYST GROUP LTD. , 96 McGregor Downs, West Columbia SC 29169-2850. No phone calls please. Chairman: C.G. Butler. Labels include Amethyst Records and Antithesis Records. Record company, music publisher (Another Amethyst Song/BMI) and management firm. Estab. 1979. Releases 10 singles and 3 LPs/year. Works with musicians/artists on contract. Pays 5-15% royalty to artists on contract. Pays statutory rate to publishers per song on record. International distribution, management, marketing firm.
How to Contact: Prefers cassette (or VHS videocassette) with 3-7 songs and lyric sheet. SASE. Reports within 5 weeks only if interested.
Music: Mostly mainstream, pop and R&B; also rock, new music, jazz/rap and heavy metal. Released "Long Distance Lovers" recorded by Ted Neiland on Amethyst Records (pop); "Kommon Kourtesy" recorded by Kourtesy on Anthithesis Records (pop/rock) and "Age of Modern Man" recorded by Snythetic Meat on Antithesis Records (new music). Other artists include JR. Ellis, Unique Force, J. Blues, The Drysdales, Knightmare, Jeromeo, Carnage, True Identity, Ted Neiland, Synthetic Meat and Kourtesy.

Tips: "We develop and market recording artists, models, actresses and songwriters for international promotion. We promote to radio stations, promoters, distributors, and most major manufacturers of products. Also to booking agents, TV and movie production companies."

*AMIRON MUSIC/AZTEC PRODUCTIONS, 20531 Plummer St., Chatsworth CA 91311. (213)998-0443. General Manager: A. Sullivan. Labels include Dorn Records and Aztec Records. Record company, booking agency and music publisher (Amiron Music). Releases 2 singles/year. Works with artists and songwriters on contract. Pays 10% maximum royalty to artists on contract; standard royalty to songwriters on contract. Pays statutory rate to publishers.
How to Contact: Prefers 7½ ips reel-to-reel or cassette and lead sheet. SASE. Reports in 3 weeks.
Music: Dance, easy listening, folk, jazz, MOR, rock ("no heavy metal") and top 40/pop. Released "Look In Your Eyes," by Newstreet; and "Midnight Flight," recorded by Papillon.
Tips: "Be sure the material has a hook; it should make people want to make love or fight. Write something that will give a talented new artist that edge on current competition."

AMOK RECORDS, Box 159, Station G, Toronto, Ontario M4M 3G7 **Canada**. (416)854-0826. A&R: Lorenz Eppinger. Record company. Releases 2 singles, 3 12" singles, 14 LPs, 6 EPs and 2 CDs/year. Works with musicians/artists on contract and on lease agreement.
How to Contact: Call first and obtain permission to submit. Prefers cassette and lyric sheet. SAE and IRC. Reports in 3 weeks.
Music: Mostly pop, dance and ethnic; also rock, folk and New Age. Released *Dissidenten* (by Josch/Klein), recorded by Exil; *Whitenoise* (by Bill Grove); and *Whirleygigs* (by Alex Mortimer), all on AMOK Records (all LPs). Other artists include Tupac Amaru, Fluid Waffle, Two Men Laughing, FAT, Courage of Lassie, and Condition.

*ANTIQUE/CATFISH/BIG BRUTUS RECORDS, Box 192, Pittsburg KS 66762. (316)231-6443. Owner: Gene Strasser. Partner: John Poznich. Labels include Antique Records, Catfish Records and Big Brutus Records. Record company, music publisher and record producer (Big Brutus). Estab. 1975. Works with musicians/artists and songwriters on contract. Royalty negotiable; statutory rate to publisher per song on record.
How to Contact: Write or call first and obtain permission to submit. Prefers cassette with any number of songs and lyric sheets. "Must be unpublished and copyrighted material." Reports "immediately if we can use the material."
Music: Mostly country, rock and R&B; also gospel and novelty. Released "Ever Time I See a Pig I Think of You" recorded by Dave Talley; "The Chicken Hit Song" (by Witt), recorded by Weird Wilbur; and "Soap Operas on TV" (by Belk), recorded by Curly Belk all on Antique Records (novelty). Other artists include Genne Strasser, Big Johnny Allen, Jack Barlow and Tony Toeebo.
Tips: "Good demo's; copyrighted, unpublished hits."

ANTITHESIS RECORDS, Division of the Amethyst Group Ltd., 96 McGregor Downs, West Columbia SC 29169-2850. Contact: A&R Department. Record company. Estab. 1988. Releases 10 singles and 3 LPs/year. Works with songwriters on royalty contract. Pays statutory rate. International distribution, marketing with T.A.G. International.
How to Contact: Submit demo tape by mail. Unsolicited submissions are okay. Prefers cassette or VHS videocassettes with 3-7 songs and lyric sheet. SASE. Reports in 5 weeks on submissions, only if interested. "No phone calls, please."
Music: Mostly eclectic style, rock and heavy metal; also new wave, pop and R&B/rap/jazz. Released *Evil Dreams* (by Knightmare), recorded by Knightmare on Antithesis Records (heavy metal); "Over the Line" (by Bye-Bye), recorded by Bye-Bye on Antithesis Records (power pop); and "Love Talk" (by Gary Bowen), recorded by G.T. Bowen on Antithesis Records (pop). Other artists include Yo Yates and the Pain Killers, Kourtesy, and Nine Inch Drill, True Identity, Synthetic Meat, and Toy Bomb.
Tips: "Don't ever expect anyone to give you a perfect deal—it just doesn't happen. You will have to prove yourself or give in more to go anywhere in this biz. Be ready to sign. Development, management and representation are the main keys to success. It's *your* career. Be prepared to cooperate fully with anyone who desires to commit to you and your project(s). *Always* enclose return postage for *any* reply."

APON RECORD COMPANY, INC., Box 3082, 44-16 Broadway, Long Island City NY 11103. (718)721-5599. Contact: Don Zemann. Labels include Apon, Discapon and Amadeo. Record company, record producer and music publisher (Apon Publishing Company and Discapon Publishing Company). Estab. 1957. Releases 50 singles and 30 LPs/year. Works with artists and songwriters on contract. Pays according to agreements made with individual songwriters; statutory rate to publishers for each record sold.

How to Contact: Prefers cassette with 1-12 songs. SASE. Reports in 2 months.

Music: Church/religious, classical, dance-oriented, easy listening, folk and international. Released *Polka Fever*, by Slawko Kunst (polka); "Morning in Naples" (by K. Vagner), recorded by K. Vagner on Sv/Ap (instrumental); and "Pigi digi" (by Vejvoda), recorded by J. Vejvoda on Sv/Ap (instrumental). Specialists on background music for background music suppliers.

ARIANA RECORDS, 1312 S. Avenida Polae, #A8, Tucson, AZ 85710. (602)577-8669. President: James M. Gasper. Vice President: Thomas M. Dukes. Record company, record producer (Future 1 Productions) and music publisher (Myko Music). Estab. 1980. Releases 1 single and 2 LPs/year. Works with musicians/artists on contract; hires musicians for in-house studio work.

How to Contact: Prefers cassette with 3-5 songs and lyric sheet. Does not return unsolicited material. Reports in 1 month.

Music: Mostly top 40; also R&B, rock, dance rock, pop and AOR. Released "The Offering (by J. Gasper) recorded by Sketches on Ariana Records (pop ballad); "Cry to Me" (by T. Privett), recorded by Monkeyman on Ariana Records (funk pop) and "Rock N' Roll Surgery" (by J. Gasper/T. Privett), recorded by The Dead Doners on Ariana Records (trash rock). Other artists include The El Caminos, 4 Walls, Fellowship, The Presidents Club, Fat Ear, Sonny Moon, Happy Leggs, Ronnie G., The Kluter, Flavor of the Month and Biff Turbo.

Tips: "Be professional; first impressions are very important."

*ARWAY RECORDS & ENTERPRISES, INC., P.O. Box 584, Marion AR 72364. (501)732-6454. President: Mikii Hooper. Labels include Arway Records and RAJ Records. Record company and music publisher. Estab. 1989. Releases 3 singles, 1 12" single and 2 LPs/year. Works with musicians/artists and songwriters on contract. Pays 30-45% royalty to artists on contract; statutory rate to publishers per song on record.

How to Contact: Submit demo tape by mail. Unsolicited submissions are OK. Prefers cassette (or VHS videocassette) with 3 songs and lyric sheet. SASE. Reports in 2 months.

Music: Mostly R&B, pop and country; also gospel and blues. Released *Cole-Cashe* (R&B LP); Suicide (rock single); and "What About Us" (R&B single), all by C. Cashe/E & J Coleman, all recorded by Cole-Cashe on Arway Records. Other artists include F.L.O.C.

Tips: "Be straight. No substance abuse—controlled or otherwise. Have desire to work in growth-oriented independent environment. Send copyright protected work only. Submit proof of copyright ownership."

ARZEE RECORD COMPANY, 3010 N. Front St., Philadelphia PA 19133. (215)426-5682. President: Rex Zario. Labels include Arcade Records and Arzee Records. Record company, music publisher and record producer.

How to Contact: Prefers cassette with 4-5 songs and lead sheet. SASE. Reports in 5 weeks.

Music: MOR, rock and country.

ASSOCIATED ARTISTS RECORDS INTERNATIONAL, Maarschalklaan 47, 3417 SE Montfoort, **The Netherlands**. Phone: (0)3484-2860. FAX: 31-3484-2860. Release Manager: Joop Gerrits. Labels include Associated Artists, Disco-Dance Records and Italo. Record company, music publisher (Associated Artists International/BUMA-STEMRA, Hilversum Happy Music/BUMA-STEMRA, Intermedlodie/BUMA-STEMRA and Hollands Glorie Productions), record producer (Associated Artists Productions) and TV promotions. Estab. 1975. Releases 10 singles, 15 LPs and 15 CDs/year. Works with musicians/artists and songwriters on contract. Pays 10-16% royalty per record sold.

How to Contact: Prefers compact cassette or 19 cm/sec reel-to-reel (or VHS videocassette) with any number of songs and lyric or lead sheets. Records also accepted. SAE and IRC. Reports in 5 weeks.

Music: Mostly disco, Italian disco and pop; also ballads, gospel, jazz, Latin, MOR, etc. Released: "Hey Jack Ya Late" by The Hitsquad on Ramshorn records; "Touch Me" by the 49ers on Island Records-(top 10 in the U.K.-The Netherlands-Germany); "Let's All Chant" and "Traffic Jam" by the Michael Zagerband and "Esa Chicas Mia" by Sergio Dalma. We invite producers and independent record labels to send us their material for their entry on the European market. Mark all parcels as 'no commercial value—for demonstration only'. We license productions to record companies in all countries of Europe and South Africa.

ATLANTIC RECORDING CORP., 9229 Sunset Blvd., Los Angeles CA 90069. (213)205-7460. A&R Director: John Axelrod, Contact: Paul Cooper. Labels include Atco, Cotillion, East-West and Atlantic. "We distribute Island and Virgin." Record company, music publisher. Estab. 1948. Works with artists on contract, songwriters on royalty contract and musicians on salary for in-house studio work.

How to Contact: Prefers cassette with 3 songs (or VHS videocassette). SASE. Reports in 2 weeks. Does not return unsolicited material.
Music: Blues, disco, easy listening, folk, jazz, MOR, progressive, R&B, rock, soul and top 40/pop. Artists included Debbie Gibson, Mike & the Mechanics, INXS, Yes, AC/DC, Pete Townsend, Bette Midler, Ratt, Skid Row, Crosby, Stills, Nash & Young.

AUBURN RECORDS AND TAPES, 6621 N. 59th Ave., Glendale AZ 85301. (602)435-0314. Owner: Frank E. Koehl. Record company and music publisher (Speedster Music-BMI). Estab. 1962. Releases 1-4 singles, 9 12″ singles, 7 LPs, 7 EPs and 2 CDs/year. Works with musicians/artists and songwriters on contract. Pays statutory rate.
How to Contact: Submit a demo tape by mail. Unsolicited submissions are okay. SASE. Reports in 3 weeks.
Music: Mostly country, traditional and bluegrass. "Shacks Tree" (by Troy McCort), recorded by Troy McCort on Auburn Records (acoustic country); "Lottery Fever" (by Troy McCourt), recorded by Troy McCourt on Auburn (acoustic country); and "Burglar Man" (by D. Al Ferguson), on Auburn Records (acoustic folk comical).
Tips: "Keep it simple; I want to hear the words. We are recording traditional music and we want mostly songs featuring acoustic music."

*AUDEM RECORDS, Box 32A, Albany Post Road, Wallkill NY 12589. (914)895-8397. President: Tom Destry. Record company and record producer (Destry Music). Estab. 1986. Releases 2 singles, 2 LPs/year. Works with musicians/artists and songwriters on contract. Pays 4-9% royalty to artists on contract; statutory rate to publisher per song on record.
How to Contact: Submit demo tape by mail. Unsolicited submissions are okay. Prefers cassette, 7½ ips reel-to-reel (or VHS videocassette) with 3 songs and lyric sheet. SASE. Reports in 6 weeks.
Music: Mostly pop, rock and country; also contemporary gospel, R&B and dance. Released "I Hear You Knocking" (by Barthomomeu, King & Domino), recorded by Dave Kennedy and the U.S.A. Band (rock); "I'm Looking for a Miracle" and "Light of My Life" (by Tom Destry), recorded by Tom Destry (pop), all on Audem Records (all singles). Other artists include Susan Stanley (country), Helen Angelo (gospel) and Michele Lee (pop).
Tips: "The radio will give you your best key to creativity. Listen to the hits of today, then mold your talents around them. In turn, the combination makes you new."

AUTOGRAM & FOLK RECORDS ,Burgstr. 9, 4405 Nottula 1, **West Germany.** (02502) 6151. Contact: A&R Department. Labels include Autonom, Folk-Record, Autophon and Roots. Record company. Releases 10 CDs and 15 LPs/year. Works with musicians/artists and songwriters on contract. Pays "above average" royalty to artists on contract.
How to Contact: Prefers cassette with minimum 3 songs and lyric sheet. SAE and IRC. Reports in 1-10 weeks. "No stylistic imitations, (no cover versions)."
Music: Mostly ethnic folk music, blues and contemporary guitar music; also classical, contemporary, bluegrass and historical (reissues).

*AVANT-GARDE RECORDS CORP., Suite 306, 210 W. 100th Terr., Kansas City MO 64114. (816)942-8988. Director A&R/President: Scott Smith. Record company, music publisher and record producer. Estab. 1983. Releases 3 LPs and 3 CDs/year. Pays statutory rate.
How to Contact: Write or call first and obtain permission to submit. Prefers cassette (or VHS videocassette if available) with 4 songs. SASE. Reports in 2 weeks.
Music: Mostly themes, new standards and pop classical. Released *30th Anniversary on Stage, Dos Amigos* and *Favorites-On Stage* recorded by Ferrante & Teicher on Avant-Garde Records (LP).
Tips: "Dedicated solo/duo-pianist — no vocals. Variety of pianistic styles — no lightweights."

*AVM RECORDS/STAR MAKER INT'L, United Artist Tower, 50 Music Sq. W., #102, Nashville TN 37203. (615)327-9121. President: Troy Shondell. Record company, music publisher, record producer, artist management and development. Estab. 1989. Works with musicians/artists and songwriters on contract. Submit demo tape by mail. Unsolicited submissions are OK. Prefers cassette (or VHS videocassette if available) with 1 or more songs and lyric sheet. SASE.
Music: Mostly country.

AZRA INTERNATIONAL, Box 459, Maywood CA 90270. (213)560-4223. A&R: Jeff Simins. Labels include Azra, Iron Works, Not So Famous David's Records and Masque Records. Record company. Estab. 1978. Releases 20 LPs, 10 EPs and 10 CDs/year. Works with artists on contract. "Artists usually carry their own publishing." Pays 10% royalty to artists on contract; statutory rate to publishers for each record sold.

How to Contact: Prefers cassette (or VHS videocassette) with 3-5 songs and lyric sheet. Include bio and photo. SASE. Reports in 1 month.
Music: Mostly heavy metal, Christian and New Age; also novelty. Released "Riff Raff" by Riff Raff on Masque Records (12″EP); "Stepmother" by Stepmother on Iron Works Records (12″ EP) and "Quake Rap" by Scared Boy on NSFD Records.
Tips: "We prefer groups that have been together a minimum of 6 months and solo artists who can write for specific projects."

BAGATELLE RECORD COMPANY, 400 San Jacinto St., Houston TX 77002. (713)225-6654. President: Byron Benton. Record company, record producer and music publisher (Floyd Tillman Music Co.). Releases 20 singles and 10 LPs/year. Works with songwriters on contract; musicians on salary for in-house studio work. Pays negotiable royalty to artists on contract.
How to Contact: Prefers cassette and lyric sheet. SASE. Reports in 2 weeks.
Music: Mostly country; also gospel. Released "This is Real," by Floyd Tillman (country single); "Lucille," by Sherri Jerrico (country single); and "Everything You Touch," by Johnny Nelms (country single). Other artists include Jerry Irby, Bobby Beason, Bobby Burton, Donna Hazard, Danny Brown, Sonny Hall, Ben Gabus, Jimmy Copeland and Johnny B. Goode.

BILLY BAKER & ASSOCIATES – GO-RECORDS, 3345 Hollins Ferry Rd., Baltimore MD 21227. (301)247-7447. Contact: William E. Baker or John Anthony. Labels include Go-Records. Record company and record producer. Estab. 1988. Releases 10 singles and 5 LPs. Works with musicians/artists and songwriters on contract; demo sessions. Pays 5% royalty to artists on contract; statutory rate to publishers per song on record.
How to Contact: Submit a demo tape by mail. Unsolicited submissions are okay; or write first and obtain permission to submit. Prefers cassette or VHS videocassette with 3 songs and lyric sheets. Does not return unsolicited material. Reports in 1 week.
Music: Mostly country, gospel and top-40; also R&B and rock. Released "Carolina Blue" (by James Hession), recorded by Johnny Ray Anthony (country pop); "Sad Eyes" (by James Hession), recorded by Johnny Ray Anthony (country pop); "Coffee Jim," recorded by Ernie Cash (country); all on Go-Records.

BAL RECORDS, P.O. Box 369, La Canada CA 91012-0369. (818)548-1116. President: Adrian Bal. Record company, record producer and music publisher (Bal & Bal Music Publishing Co./ASCAP). Estab. 1965. Releases 2-4 12″ singles/year. Works with artists and songwriters on contract; musicians on salary for in-house studio work. Works with composers and lyricists; teams collaborators. Pays standard royalty to artists on contract; statutory rate to publishers for each record sold.
How to Contact: Prefers cassette (or videocassette) with 1-3 songs and lyric or lead sheet. SASE. Reports in 15-20 weeks.
Music: Mostly ballads, AC/rock, gospel and jazz; also blues, church/religious, R&B, soul and top 40/pop. Released "Fragile" (by James Jackson), recorded by Kathy Simmons on BAL West (med. rock); "Right to Know" (by James Jackson), recorded by Kathy Simmons on BAL West (med. rock); "Dance to the Beat of My Heart" (by Dan Gertz), recorded by Ace Baker on BAL Records (med. rock) and "You're A Part of Me," "Can't We Hame Some Time Together," "You and Me" and "Circles of Time" by Paul Richards on BAL Records (adult contemporary).

BARNETT PRODUCTIONS INC., 2305 Dickey Ave., No. Chicago IL 60064. (312)689-2726. Vice President: Walter T. Barnett. Labels include W.M.B. Records. Record company and music publisher (BMI, Thomas, Gordon, Barnett). Estab. 1980. Releases 2 singles and 3 12″ singles. Works with songwriters on contract and hires musicians for in-house studio work. Pays 6-12% royalty to artists on contract; pays statutory rate to publishers.
How to Contact: Submit demo tape by mail. Unsolicited submissions are okay. Prefers cassette with 4 songs and lyric sheets. SASE. Reports in 1 month.
Music: Mostly R&B, rock and rap; also reggae, house music, soul, country, dance music, and ballads. Released "Emotional Man" (by W. Barnett, M. Gordon), recorded by Shibeli on WMB Records, (R&B/ballad); "Get Next To You" (by W. Barnett, M. Gordon), recorded by Shibeli on WMB Records (R&B/dance) and "Do You Wanna Party" (by Fulldeck), WMB Records (rap/dance). Other artists included Candy and Fire & Ice
Tips: "Never say never, believe in your music and never stop trying to reach and expand, first impression could be the last, so make it good."

*BASSMENT RECORDS, 234 Columbus Drive, Jersey City NJ 07302. (201)963-1560. A&R Department: Craig Bevan or Barry Zeger. Record company. Estab. 1986. Releases 20 12″ singles and 3 LPs/year. Works with musicians/artists on contract and hires musicians on salary for in-house studio work. Royalties vary.

How To Contact: Submit demo tape by mail. Unsolicited submissions are OK. Prefers cassette (or VHS videocassette if available) with 1-3 songs and lyric sheet. SASE. Reports in 2 weeks.
Music: Released "Counting The Days" (by C. Bevan), recorded by Joey Kid (dance 12"), "Feelin' Moody" (by Loose Bruce), recorded by Loose Bruce (rap 12") and "Lose Control" (by C. Bevan, B. Zeger and C. Pridgen), recorded by Like This (rap 12") all on Bassment Records.
Tips: "We are interested in artist/songwriters with an awareness of the sounds/styles demanded by the marketplace, and a desire to work with a label whose production/songwriting expertise can guide and nurture their careers effectively and profitably."

*BEACHWOOD RECORDS, 6253 Hollywood Blvd #810, Los Angeles CA 90028. (213)461-1008. Manager: Stephen Chandler. Labels include Beachwood Records and Jolly Roger Records. Record company, music publisher (James Lee Stanley Music/BMI) and record producer (Beachwood Productions). Estab. 1985. Released 3 singles, 3 12" singles, 4 LPs and 4 CDs/year. Works with musicians/artists on contract. Pays negotiable percentage to artists on contract; .75% statutory rate to publisher per song on record.
How to Contact: Write or call first and obtain permission to submit. Prefers cassette (or VHS videocassette) with 3 songs and lyric sheet. Does not return unsolicited material. Reports in 1 month.
Music: Mostly pop/jazz, acoustic and new age; also dance. Released *Redux* (by Danny Okeefe), recorded by Danny Okeefe (singer/songwriter LP); "Rhiannon" (by Stevie Nicks), recorded by Pamala Stanley (dance 12"); and *Coming Out of Hiding The Sequel* (by various writers), recorded by Pamala Stanley (dance LP), all on Beachwood Records. Other artists include James Lee Stanley and Rick Ruskin.

BEAU-JIM RECORDS INC., Box 2401, Sarasota FL 34230-2401. President: Buddy Hooper. Record company, music publisher (Beau-Jim Music, Inc./ASCAP and Beau-Di Music, Inc./BMI), record producer and management firm. Estab. 1972. Member CMA, NSAI, NMA, AGAC. Releases 4 singles and 2 LPs/year. Works with artists and songwriters on contract.
How to Contact: Prefers cassette with lyrics (or videocassette) with 3-5 songs on demo. SASE. Reports in 3 weeks.
Music: Country. Artists include Debbie Kay and Joe Neddo.

BERANDOL RECORDS, 110A Sackville St., Toronto, Ontario M5A 3E7 **Canada.** (416)869-1872. A&R Director: Tony Procewiat. Labels include Plumtree. Record company, music publisher (Plum-tree Music/PRO CAN and Cee & Cee Music/CAPAC) and record producer. Estab. 1969. Releases 5-10 singles and 5-10 LPs/year. Works with musicians/artists on contract. Pays negotiable royalty to artists on contract; pays statutory rate to publisher per song on record.
How to Contact: Prefers cassette with 2-5 songs. SAE and IRC.
Music: Mostly top 40 and dance; also children's and serious. Released "Les Espirits," written and recorded by Cam Shearer on Berandol Records (instrumental); "From the Heart" (by M Bebis) recorded by Cyan on Berandol Records (Top 40) and "Comin Home" (by B. Zurtel), recorded by Bob Liddell on Berandol Records (MOR). Other artists include Suzanne Pinel and The Cosmic Orchestra.

*BEST WEST PRODUCTIONS, 1301 Morrison, Redlands CA 92374. (714)798-6449/370-1980. Contact: Deborah Harmon. Labels include Best West Records. Record company, music publisher (BMI) and record producer (Best West Records). Estab. 1988. Works with songwriters on royalty contract.
How to Contact: Submit demo tape by mail. Unsolicited submissions are OK. Prefers cassete (or any videocassette if available) with 3 songs and lyric sheet. SASE. Reports in 3 weeks.
Music: Mostly country and pop.
Tips: "Send your best material only. Simple guitar/vocal or piano/vocal demo preferred. Send bio."

BEVERLY HILLS MUSIC PUBLISHING, Record Division of Larrco Industries of Texas, P.O. Box 3842, Houston TX 77253-3842. Releases 1 single/year. Labels include Total Sound, Lawrence Herbst, Best-Way, Beverly Hills, D.T.I. and Larr Records. President: Dr. Lawrence Herbst. Record company, music publisher (Beverly Hills Music Publishing/BMI and Klarrco Music Publishing), record producer (Dr. Lawrence Herbst) and Klarrco Satellite Radio and TV. Estab. 1966. Works with artists and songwriters on contract; hires musicians for in-house studio work. Pays 35-50% royalty to artists on contract; statutory rate to publisher per song on record.
How to Contact: Prefers cassette, 7½ ips reel-to-reel (or videocassette) and lyric sheet. Does not return unsolicited material. Reports in 3 weeks.
Music: Mostly top 40/pop, country and rock; also bluegrass, blues, easy listening, folk, gospel, jazz, progressive, R&B, and soul.

BGM RECORDS, 10452 Sentinel, San Antonio TX 78217-3824. (512)654-8773. Contact: Bill Green. Labels include Zone 7, BGM and Rainforest Records. Record company, music publisher (Bill Green Music) and record producer. Estab. 1979. Releases 10 singles and 2-3 LPs/year. Works with songwriters on contract.
How to Contact: Prefers cassette. SASE. Reports in 2 months.
Music: Mostly contemporary country and traditional country. Released "Cajun Baby" (by H. Williams, H. Williams Jr.), recorded by Doug Kershaw (country cajun); "Photographic Memory" (by B. Boyd), recorded by Billy Mata (country); and "Boogie Queen" (by Jenkins, Green), recorded by Doug Karrhau (country cajun); all on BGM Records. Other artists include David Price.

BGS PRODUCTIONS LTD., Newtown St., Kilsyth, Glasgow G65 0JX, **Scotland.** Phone: 44-0236-821-81. Contact: Dougie Stevenson or Bill Garden. Labels include Scotdisc and Country House Records. Record company, record producer (Bill Garden) and music publisher (Garron Music). Estab. 1978. Member ARRS, PPL, MCPS. Releases 5 singles, 20 LPs and 10 CDs/year. Works with artists and songwriters on contract. Statutory rate paid to publishers for each record sold. Royalties paid to US songwriters and artists through US publishing or recording affiliate.
How to Contact: Prefers cassette (or videocassette) with 2-3 songs and lyric sheet. SAE and IRC. "Unable to report on submissions. When submitting please mention *Songwriters Market.*"
Music: Mostly country and folk; also easy listening and gospel. Released *If My World Should End Tomorrow,* (by S. Ross), recorded by Jim McLeod; *Play the Game,* (by Tommy Scott), recorded by Tommy Scott's Pipes and Dixie Banjo Band; and *The Ghostie* (by Garden), recorded by Stuart Anderson, Jr., all on Scotdisc Records.

BIG BEAR RECORDS, Box 944, Birmingham, B16 8UT, **England.** Phone: 44-021-454-7020. FAX: 44-021-454-9996. A&R Director: Jim Simpson. Labels include Big Bear, Truckers Delight and Grandstand Records. Record company, record producer and music publisher (Bearsongs). Releases 12 singles and 6 LPs/year. Works with artists and songwriters on contract. Teams collaborators. Pays 8-10% royalty to artists on contract; 6¼% to publishers for each record sold. Royalties paid directly to the songwriters and artists or through US publishing or recording affiliate.
How to Contact: Prefers 7½ or 15 ips reel-to-reel, DAT, or cassette (or videocassette) and lyric sheet. SAE and IRC. Reports in 2 weeks.
Music: Blues, jazz, R&B and soul. Artists include King Pleasure & the Biscuit Boys, Lady Sings the Blues, Bill Allred, Poorboys and jazz and blues artists. Released *This Is It* recorded by King Pleasure on Big Bear Records (R&B LP/CD/MC).

*BLACK DOG RECORDS, Rt. 2 Box 38, Summerland Key FL 33042. (305)745-3164. Executive Director: Marian Joy Ring. A&R Contact: Rusty Gordon, 1156 Park Lane, West Palm Beach, FL 33417. (407)686-1354. Record company. Estab. 1989. Releases 2-6 singles and 3 LPs/year. Pays standard royalty to artists on contract; statutory rate to publishers per song on record.
How to Contact: Submit demo tape by mail. Unsolicited submissions are OK. Write or call first and obtain permission to submit. Prefers cassette with 3-6 songs and lyric or lead sheet. SASE. Reports in 4-6 weeks.
Music: Mostly pop, R&B and folk-rock; also New Age and cabaret. Released *Rising Cost of Love* (written and recorded by Marian Joy Ring), on Black Day Records (cassette).

*BLACK MOON RECORDS, INC. % **Chris Owens,** 328 Flatbush Ave., #271, Brooklyn NY 01238. (718)297-4907. President: Spencer McAdams. Record company. Estab. 1989. Works with musicians/artists and producers on record contract. Pays 4-10% royalty to artists on contract for each record sold; statutory rate to publishers per song on record.
How to Contact: Call first and obtain permission to submit. Prefers cassette (or VHS videocassette) with 4 songs and lyric sheet. SASE.
Music: Mostly rap and R&B.
Tips: "Submit clean demos. Be original and to the point. We don't need 'bad attitudes'—just a willingness to work, patience and creativity!"

*BLIND PIG RECORDS, P.O. Box 2344, San Francisco CA 94126. (415)526-0373. Contact: Edward Chmelewski. Record company, record producer and music publisher (Viper Music/BMI). Member NAIRD. Estab. 1977. Releases 4-6 LPs and 4-6 CDs/year. Works with artists on contract. Pays negotiable royalty to artists on contract; negotiable rate to publishers for each record sold.
How to Contact: "Looking for finished master tapes of LP length by *performing artists only.* Send cassette with promo/press material. SASE a must." Reports in 3 months.
Music: Blues, R&B (40s, 50s) and rock (rockabilly). Released "Blues On The Range" by Roy Rogers on Blind Pig Records (blues instrumental); "Can't Let Go" by Big Daddy Kinsey on Blind Pig Records (contemporary blues) and "When You're Being Nice" by Joanna Connor on Blind Pig Records (contemporary blues).

*BLUE WAVE, 3221 Perryville Rd., Baldwinsville NY 13027. (315)638-4286. President/Producer: Greg Spencer. Labels include Blue Wave and Blue Wave/Horizon. Record company, music publisher (G.W. Spencer Music/ASCAP) and record producer (Blue Wave Productions). Estab. 1985. Releases 3 LPs and 3 CDs/year. Works with musicians/artists on contract. Royalty varies; statutory rate to publishers per song on records.
How to Contact: Submit demo tape by mail. Unsolicited submissions are OK. Prefers cassette (or VHS or Beta videocassette—live performance only) if available and as many songs as you like. Does not return unsolicited material. "We contact only if we are interested. Allow 6 weeks. Mostly blues, roots rock & roll and roots R&B; also cutting edge rock & roll, garage/60's rock & roll and roots country and rockabilly. Released *Trouble on the Run* written and recorded by Kingsnakes on Blue Wave (CD, LP, cass); *When Sanity Sleeps* (by Unholy Wives), recorded by Unholy Wives on Blue Wave/Horizon (CD, cass); and *Conviction* (by Hamell on Trial), recorded by Hamell On Trial on Blue Wave (LP, cass). Other artists include Jumpin' Joe Whiting and Backbone Slip.
Tips: "Don't send it unless it is great. I have enough good songs and I don't have the time or money to invest in good artists, only those who are great or unique. Please do not call; if it knocks me out I'll call you for sure!"

BOLIVIA RECORDS, 1219 Kerlin Ave., Brewton AL 36426. (205)867-2228. President: Roy Edwards. Labels include Known Artist Records. Record company, record producer and music publisher (Cheavoria Music Co.). Estab. 1972. Releases 10 singles and 3 LPs/year. Works with artists and songwriters on contract; musicians on salary for in-house studio work. Pays 4-5% royalty to artists on contract; statutory rate to publishers for each record sold.
How to Contact: Write first. Prefers cassette with 3 songs and lyric sheet. All tapes will be kept on file. Reports in 1 month.
Music: Mostly R&B , country and pop; also easy listening, MOR, and soul. Released "You Are My Sunshine" and "If You Only Knew" written and recorded by Roy Edwards on Bolivia Records (R&B). Other artists include Bobbie Roberson and Jim Portwood.

*BOLTS RECORDS, 619 Salisbury Prom, Green Lanes, Harringay, London N8 ORX **England**. (01)809-1460. Chairman: J.S. Batten. Labels include Bolts Records, Boy Records, Soultown Records, Hysteria Records. Record company. Estab. 1986. Releases 15 singles, 15 12″ singles and 2 LPs/year. Works with musicians/artists and songwriters on contract and hires musicians for in-house studio work. Pays 3-15% royalty to artists on contract; statutory rate to publisher per song.
How to Contact: Submit demo tape by mail. Unsolicited submissions are OK. Prefers cassette, 15 or 7 ips reel-to-reel, (or VHS PAL videocassette) with 3 songs and lyric or lead sheets. Does not return unsolicited material. Reports in 3 weeks.
Music: Mostly house/high NRG and dance music. Released "Don't Stop" (by Darral and Tim McKee), recorded by Dance Addiction (house 12″); "Trip On This," written and recorded by Asmo (techno 12″); and "Vindiloo Rap" (by Kelly and Chris Ferguson), recorded by Bagi Jon (comedy rap 7″); all on Bolts Records. Other artists include Gary Allen, Lise Lee, Mirror Image and Krukutz.

BOOGIE BAND RECORDS, Suite 206, 6245 Bristol Pkwy., Culver City CA 90230. Contact: Larry McGee. Labels include Dollar Bill Records and Mega Star Records. Record company, music publisher (Operation Pefection Publishing), record producer (Intrigue Productions) and management firm (LMP Management). Estab. 1976. Releases 6 singles, 3 12″ singles, 1 LP, 4 EPs and 2 CDs/year. Works with musicians/artists and songwriters on contract; musicians on salary for in-house studio work. Pays 10% royalty to artists on contract; statutory rate to publishers per song on record.
How to Contact: Prefers cassette with 1-4 songs and lyric sheet. Does not return unsolicited material. Reports in 2 months. "Please only send professional quality material."
Music: Rock, MOR/adult contemporary, pop, rap and R&B. Released "We're Number One" (by Liz Davis), recorded by The Saxon Sisters on Boogie Band Records (rock single); "Captain Freedom" (by Kenny Simms), recorded by Shena Kriss on Mega-Star Records (R&B single); and *I Feel Good With You*, written and recorded by Bill Sawyer on Dollar Bill Records (R&B LP). Other artists include the S-Quires, Jim Sapienza, The Allen Brothers, Terri Parondi, Roz Smith, Gary Walker, and Cindi Tulk.

BOUQUET RECORDS, Bouquet-Orchid Enterprises, Box 11686, Atlanta GA 30355. (404)355-7635. President: Bill Bohannon. Record company, music publisher (Orchid Publishing/BMI), record producer (Bouquet-Orchid Enterprises) and management firm. Releases 3-4 singles and 2 LPs/year. Works with artists and songwriters on contract. Pays 5% maximum royalty to artists on contract; pays statutory rate to publishers for each record sold.
How to Contact: Prefers cassette with 3-5 songs and lyric sheet. SASE. Reports in 1 month.
Music: Mostly religious (contemporary or country-gospel, Amy Grant, etc.), country ("the type suitable for Clint Black, George Strait, Patty Loveless, etc.") and top 100 ("the type suitable for Billy Joel, Whitney Houston, R.E.M., etc."); also rock and MOR. Released "Good Loving" by the Bandoleers,

"Starting All Over" by Adam Day and "Let Me Be Your Lover" by Susan Spencer.
Tips: "Submit material that relates to what is currently being charted. A strong story line will help."

BRIGHT & MORNINGSTAR RECORDS, Box 18A241, Los Angeles CA 90018. (213)969-4814. President: Stan Christopher. Record company. Estab. 1983. Releases 2 singles, 2 12" singles, 2 LPs, 1 EP and 3 CDs/year. Works with musicians/artists and songwriters on contract; musicians on salary for in-house studio work. Pays 3% royalty to artists on contract.
How to Contact: Prefers cassette or 15 ips reel-to-reel with 1-3 songs and lyric and lead sheet. SASE. Reports in 3 weeks.
Music: Mostly contemporary Christian, inspirational gospel and gospel rock; also "message music." Released "Agape Love," "Change Your Life," and "Which Way Are You Going," (all by Stan Christopher), all recorded by The Messenger on Bright & Morningstar Records (singles).
Tips: "Be honest in your writing and learn to be original."

*BRITISH RECORDS, 1015 Gayley Ave., Los Angeles CA 90024. A&R Representative: Geoff Gibbs. Labels include Songster Records. Record company. Estab. 1978. Works with musicians/artists and songwriters on contract.
How to Contact: Submit demo tape by mail. Unsolicited submissions are OK. Prefers cassette (or VHS videocassette) with 3-4 songs and lyric and/or lead sheet. SASE. Reports in 6 weeks.
Music: Mostly rock, heavy metal and pop; also blues, folk and R&B. Released "Save The World" (by Geoff Gibbs), by Janet Lee (pop/single); "Face of a Stranger," written and recorded by Janet Lee (pop/rock LP); and "Dress to Kill," written and recorded by Rick Montgomery (rock), all on British Records. Other artists include Montgomery/Silk, Chambermaid and Chris Ford/U.K.

BULL CITY RECORDS, Box 6, Rougemont NC 27572. (919)477-4077. Manager: Freddie Roberts. Record company, record producer and music publisher (Freddie Roberts Music). Releases 20 singles and 6 LPs/year. Works with songwriters on contract. Pays standard royalty to artists on contract; statutory rate to publishers for each record sold.
How to Contact: Write or call first about your interest or to arrange personal interview. Prefers 7½ ips reel-to-reel or cassette (or videocassette) with 1-5 songs and lyric sheet. "Submit a clear, up-to-date demo." SASE. Reports in 3 weeks.
Music: Mostly country, MOR, southern rock and top 40/pop; also bluegrass, church/religious, gospel and rock/country. Released "Redeemed" (by Jane Durham), recorded by Roberts Family on Bull City Records (southern gospel); "Almost" (by Rodney Hutchins), recorded by Billy McKellar on Bull City Records (country) and "Not This Time" (by D. Tyler), recorded by Sleepy Creek on Bull City Records (southern rock).

*C. P. I. RECORDS, division of Centaur®. %F.B. Swegal, 12220 Tiara St., N. Hollywood CA 91607. (818)762-7417. Contact: Franz B. Swegal, P.C.. Record company and record producer (F.B. Swegal, division of Centaur®). Estab. 1984. Royalties vary. Submit demo tape by mail. Unsolicited submissions are OK. "Simple release must absolve C. P. I. Records and/or affiliated Co's from infringement."
How to Contact: Prefers cassette (or ½" VHS videocassette if available) with best songs. SASE.
Music: Mostly AOR; also pop, country, R&B and rap.

CACTUS RECORDS, Breitenstrasse 82a/4, Vienna **Austria** 1140. (222)92-47-073. Contact: Hans Hartel. Labels include Cactus Records and Ha Ha Soundwave. Record company, music publisher and record producer (Hans Hartel). Estab. 1985. Releases 10 singles, 2 12" singles, 4 LPs and 2 CDs/year. Works with musicians/artists on contract, songwriters on contract and musicians on salary for in-house work.
How to Contact: Submit demo tape by mail. Prefers cassette with 3 songs and lyric sheet. SASE. Reports in 1 month.
Music: Mostly pop, German pop and instrumentals; also ethno and new age. Released "Ciao Amore," (by Jonny Blue), recorded by Hans Hartel on Cactus Records (German pop single); and "Open Hearts," (by Gunter Rath), recorded by Gunther Rath on Cactus Records (pop single). Other artists include Kids Can't Wait, Charly Hloch, Duncan Mlango, Christoph Hornstein, Chris White and Jonny Blue.
Tips: "You should have enough material for at least one LP."

THE CALVARY MUSIC GROUP, 142 8th Ave. N., Nashville TN 37203. (615)244-8800. Contact: Artist Development Department. Labels include Calvary, Lifestream, Frontline, Heart Song and Wedding Song. Record company, record producer, music publisher and distribution company. Member GMA. Releases 10 singles and 12 LPs/year. Works with artists and songwriters on contract. Pays statutory rate or negotiates rate to publishers for each record sold.

How to Contact: Not accepting unsolicited material at this time.
Music: Mostly gospel; also wedding music. Released *Soul Fillin' Station*, by the Hinsons (southern gospel single and LP); *Always*, by the Freemans (southern gospel single and LP); *Keep Your Eyes on Him*, by The Singing Echoes (old-time gospel single and LP); and "The Answer," by the Blackwood Brothers (gospel).

CAMBRIA RECORDS & PUBLISHING, Box 374, Lomita CA 90717. (213)831-1322. Director of Recording Operations: Lance Bowling. Labels include Charade Records. Record company and music publisher. Estab. 1979. Releases 5 cassettes and 6 CDs/year. Works with artists on contract; musicians on salary for in-house studio work. Pays 5-8% royalty to artists on contract; statutory rate to publisher for each record sold.
How to Contact: Write first. Prefers cassette. SASE. Reports in 1 month.
Music: Mostly classical; nostalgia and crossover. Released *Songs of Elinor Remick Warren* on Cambria Records (CD). Other artists include Marie Gibson (soprano), Mischa Leftkowitz (violin), Leigh Kaplan (piano), North Wind Quintet, Sierra Wind Quintet and many others.

CANYON CREEK RECORDS, Box 31351, Dallas TX 75231. (214)750-0720. Chief Executive Officer: Bart Barton. A&R: Mike Anthony. Record company, record producer. Estab. 1983. Works with musicians/artists and songwriters on contract. Pays 25% royalty to writers on contract. Releases 12 singles/year, 4 LP/year.
How to Contact: Write first and obtain permission to submit. Prefers cassette (or VHS videocassette) with 2 songs and lyric sheet. Reports in 10 weeks.
Music: Country and gospel. Artists include Audie Henry, Dana Presley, Billy Parker and Susie Calvin. Released "She's Sittin' Pretty" (by Bart Barton), recorded by Billy Parker on CCR/RCA Records (country); "I Didn't Know You" (by D. Kirkpatrick/M. McClain), recorded by Audie Henry on CCR/RCA Records (country) and "Alive and Lovin' It" (by D.Kirkpatrick/M. McClain) recorded by Geo Marie on Canyon Creek Records (country).

CAPITOL RECORDS, 1750 North Vine, Hollywood CA 90028. (213)462-6252. Associate Director of A&R: Simon Potts.
How to Contact: Does not accept unsolicited submissions.

*CAPRICORN LTD., Jungstrasse 15a, CH-8050 Zurich **Switzerland**. President: Freddy J. Angstmann. Record company, music publisher and record producer. Releases 12 LPs/year. Works with musicians/artists and songwriters on contract. Pays 3-6% royalty to artists on contract.
How to Contact: Prefers cassette (or VHS/PAL videocassette). SAE and IRC.
Music: Mostly gospel, blues and jazz; also classical. Released *Christmas Album*; and *Who Shall Abide* (by Johnny Thompson), and *Gospel at the Opera* (by Radio Zürich singers) both on Capricorn Records (all LPs). Other artists include Mickey Baker, Erich Lauer, Errol Dixon and Anne Morrëe.

CAPSTAN RECORD PRODUCTION, Box 211, East Prairie MO 63845. (314)649-2211. Nashville Branch: 38 Music Sq. E., Nashville TN 37203. (613)255-8005. Contact: Joe Silver or Tommy Loomas. Labels include Octagon and Capstan Records. Record company, music publisher (Lineage Publishing Co.) and record producer (Silver-Loomas Productions). Works with artists on contract. Pays 3-5% royalty to artists on contract.
How to Contact: Write first about your interest. Prefers cassette (or VHS videocassette) with 2-4 songs and lyric sheet. "Send photo and bio." SASE. Reports in 1 month.
Music: Country, easy listening, MOR, country rock and top 40/pop. Released "Dry Away the Pain," by Julia Brown (easy listening single); "Country Boy," by Alden Lambert (country single); "Yesterday's Teardrops," by The Burchetts (country single); and "Round & Round," by The Burchetts. Other artists include Bobby Lee Morgan, Skidrow Joe and Fleming.

CARITAS RECORDS, (formerly Helios Records), 28 Dalrymple Crescent, Edinburgh EH9 2NX **Great Britain**. Phone: (031)667-3633. A&R Manager: J. Douglas. Labels include Caritas and Electa. Record company, music publisher (Eschenbach Editions), record producer. Releases 50 singles and 20 LPs/year. Works with musicians/artists and songwriters on contract; hires musicians for in-house studio work. Pays 4½-6¼% royalty to artists on contract; statutory rate to publishers per song on records.
How to Contact: Write first to obtain permission to submit. Prefers cassette, 7½ ips reel-to-reel (or VHS videocassette) with 6 songs and lyric sheet or lead sheet. SAE and IRC. Reports in 6 weeks.
Music: "We want music which seeks an international market." Mostly rock, jazz and gospel; also folk/vocal, folk/instrumental and "serious music." Released *Summertime Song* (by A. Petersen) recorded by Catherine Nicholson on Caritas Records; and *Avalance* and *The Hills Are Lonely*, (by A. Petersen), recorded by Robert G. on Caritas Records (singles and LPs). Other artists include Glen Johnstone.
Tips: "We are particularly interested in adding to our instrumental sound library."

CARLYLE RECORDS, INC., 1217 16th Ave. South, Nashville TN 37212. (615)327-8129. President: Laura Fraser. Record company. Estab. 1986. Releases 3 12″ singles, 6 LPs/year, 4 EPs and 6 CDs. Works with musicians and artists on contract. Pays compulsory rate to publisher per song on record. **How to Contact:** Prefers cassette (or VHS videocassette). Does not return unsolicited material. Reports in 2 weeks. **Music:** Mostly rock. Released "Isolation" written and recorded by Dessau (dance/rock); "The Stand" written and recorded by The Stand on Aulyle Records (metal) and "Living in the Shadow of a Spirit" written and recorded by The Shakers (acoustic/rock); all on Carlyle Records. Other artists include Robb Houston, The Grinning Plowman, and F.U.C.T.

*CAROLINE RECORDS, INC., 114 W. 26th St., 11th Fl., New York NY 10001. (212)989-2929. Director Creative Operations: Yvonne Garrett. Labels include Caroline Records, exclusive manufacturing and distribution of Plan 9 Records, exclusive distribution in the U.S. of EG, Editions EG and Sub-Pop. Record company, music publisher (26th St. Songs, 26th St. Music) and independent record distributor (Caroline Records Inc.). Estab. 1985. Releases 3-4 12″ singles, 10 LPs, 1-2 EPs and 10 CDs/year. Works with musicians/artists on record contract. Pays varying royalty to artists on contract; statutory rate to publisher per song. **How to Contact:** Submit demo tape by mail. Unsolicited submissions are OK. Prefers cassette with lead sheets and press clippings. SASE. Reports in 3 weeks. **Music:** Mostly metal, "hardcore," and alternative/indie rock. Released *Quickness*, written and recorded by Bad Brains on Caroline Records (rock LP); *Bridge* (by Neil Young), recorded by V/A on NO.6 Records/Caroline Records (rock LP): and *God of Thunder* (by Kiss), recorded by White Zombie on Caroline Records (metal EP). Other artists include Naked Raygun, War Zone, Excel, Snake Nation, Unrest, Reverend, Mind Over 4, Pussy Galore, Primus. **Tips:** "When submitting a demo keep in mind that we have never signed an artist who does not have a strong underground buzz and live track record. We listen to all types of 'alternative' rock, metal, funk and rap but do not sign mainstream hard rock or dance. We send out rejection letters so do not call to find out what's happening with your demo."

CAROUSEL RECORDS, INC., 1273½ N. Crescent Hts. Blvd., Los Angeles CA 90046. (213)650-6500. A&R: Stuart Lanis. Record company, music publisher and record producer. Estab. 1963. Releases 3-6 12″ singles and 1-3 LPs/year. Works with musicians and songwriters on contract. Pays statutory rate. **How to Contact:** Prefers cassette with 3-6 songs and lyric sheet. SASE. Reports in 3-4 weeks. **Music:** Top 40, MOR, country, gospel and children's.

CBS RECORDS, 34 Music Square E., Nashville TN 37203. (615)742-4321. Labels include Columbia and Epic. Record Company. **How to Contact:** Write and ask for submission policy.

THE CCC GROUP, INC., Box 853, Ridgeland MS 39158. Professional Manager: King Corbett. Labels include Pleasure Records. Record company. Estab. 1987. Releases 6 singles and 6 LPs/year. Works with musicians/artists and songwriters on contract. Pays 10-20% royalty to artists on contract; statutory rate to publisher per song on record. **How to Contact:** Prefers cassette with 2 to 4 songs and lyric or lead sheet. SASE. Reports in 6 weeks. **Music:** Mostly R&B, blues and country; also spoken word, folk and jazz. **Tips:** "Send clean lyric sheets, labels on cassettes."

*CDE RECORDS AND TAPES, P.O. Box 310551, Atlanta GA 30331. (404)344-7621. President: Charles Edwards. Labels include TBS Records, Tapes Inc. and Nationwide Black Radio. Record Company. Estab. 1978. Releases 4-8 singles and 2-5 LPs/year. Works with musicians/artists on contract. Pays negotiable royalty to artists on contract. **How To Contact:** Submit demo tape by mail. Prefers cassette (or VHS videocassette) with "several" songs. Does not return unsolicited material. Reports ASAP. **Music:** Mostly interested in urban, R&B and rap; also gospel, jazz and pop. Released "Come Inside the Radio" (written and recorded by Chago) on CDE (urban single). **Tips:** "Be strong; keep the faith and don't give up. The music business needs new and creative people."

*CENTURY RECORDS, INC., 1429 Hawthorne St., Pittsburgh PA 15201. (412)781-4557. President: Edward J. Moschetti. Labels include Star Records. Record company. Works with songwriters on contract. **How to Contact:** Prefers cassette. SASE. **Music:** Country; all types of music.

CHARGE-COUPLED DEVICE RECORDS (CCD RECORDS), 7808 Green Lake Rd., Fayetteville NY 13066. (315)637-6656. Co-Owner: Matt Tucker. Or 940 NE 27th Ave., Hallandale FL 33009. (305)454-7044. Co-Owner: Chris Horvath. Labels include CCD. Record company. Estab. 1990. Releases 1-5 singles, 1-5 12″ singles, 1-2 LPs and 1-2 CDs/year. Works with musicians/artists and songwriters on contract. Pays 6-12% royalty to artists on contract; statutory rate to publisher per song on record.
How to Contact: Submit demo tape by mail. Unsolicited submissions are OK. Prefers cassette (or VHS videocassette) with up to 12 songs and lyric sheet. Reports in 6 weeks.
Music: Mostly top 40/rock, dance and rock; also rap and R&B. Released "Baha Your Body" recorded by Jodi Bilotti (single); "Without You" recorded by Blue Steel (single); and *Blue Steel* recorded by Blue Steel (LP), all written by Horvath/Tucker and recorded on CCD Records.
Tips: "We are currently expanding our roster. Send us your best work—singles or complete albums. Don't limit yourself to one type of music—we listen to everything. Be professional and be patient."

CHARTA RECORDS, 44 Music Sq. E., Nashville TN 37203. (615)255-2175. President: Charlie Fields. Labels include Delux Records. Record company, music publisher (Jason Dee Music, Inc./BMI and Mr. Mort Music/ASCAP), and record producer (Charlie Fields Productions). Estab. 1977. Releases 15 singles and 6-8 LPs/year. Works with musicians/artists on contract. Pays standard royalty to artists on contract; pays statutory rate to publisher per song on record.
How to Contact: Call first to arrange personal interview. Prefers cassette or reel-to-reel (or VHS videocassette) with 2-3 songs and lyric or lead sheets. Does not return unsolicited material. Reports in 3 weeks.
Music: Mostly uptempo MOR, blues and country; also light rock, pop and bluegrass. Released "Somewhere In Canada" (by D. Walsh, J Louiselle and P. Monet), recorded by David Walsh on Charta Records (country); "You Won the Battle" (by D. Erickson and J. Walker), recorded by Eddie Rivers on Charta Records (country); and "She's Layin' Down the Lovin'" (by C.W. Fields), recorded by Ronny C. Collins on Delux Records (country). Other artists include Donna Darlene and Nina Wyatt.
Tips: "Have good clean quality tape and production with typewritten lyrics."

CHATTAHOOCHEE RECORDS, 15230 Weddington St., Van Nuys CA 91411. (818)788-6863. Contact: Chris Yardum. Record company and music publisher (Etnoc/Conte). Member NARAS. Releases 4 singles/year. Works with artists and songwriters on contract.
How to Contact: Prefers cassette with 2-6 songs and lyric sheet. SASE. Reports in 6 weeks.
Music: Rock.

CHILTOWN RECORDS, Box 4164, Hartford CT 06147. (203)243-1396. A&R Director: James McGovern. Record company and music publisher (Modern Attack/BMI). Estab. 1987. Releases 8 singles, 8 12″ singles, and 3 LPs/year. Works with musicians/artists on contract. Pays 6-20% royalty to artists on contract.
How to Contact: Prefers cassette with 3 songs. SASE. Reports in 2 weeks.
Music: Mostly rap, pop and R&B. Released "Soft Like Margarine" recorded by Mc Kapr'e and "D-Doug From the Avenue" recorded by Mello-G-man (rap singles), both on Chiltown Records; and *Straight From the Heart*, recorded by Kings of Rapp on Ecal Records (rap LP). Other artists include Capital Punishment, Chris Walsh, MC T-Cool, Doctor Crew, and B-Easy/Seville.

*CHRYSALIS RECORDS, 645 Madison Ave., New York NY 10022. (212)758-3555. Senior Director of A&R: Paul Burton. Labels include Ensign, Cool Tempo. Record company. Works with musicians/artists and songwriters on contract and hires musicians for in-house studio work. Pays 12-14% royalty to artists on contract.
How to Contact: Call first and obtain permission to submit. Prefers cassette with 2-3 songs and lyric sheets. SASE. Reports in 2 months.
Music: Mostly pop, rock and rap; R&B, cross-over and modern/alternative. Recent releases include albums by Paul Carrack, Kevin Paige and The Angels. Other artists include Trouble Tribe, Ray Conteras, T.P.O.H., Child's Play, The Next School and Billy Idol.

THE CHU YEKO MUSICAL FOUNDATION, Box 10051, Beverly Hills CA 90213. (818)761-2646. Branch: Box 1314, Englewood Cliffs NJ 07632. Messages: (201)567-5524. Producer: Doris Chu. Labels include The Chu Yeko Musical Foundation, Take Home Tunes! Record Co., Original Cast Records and Broadway Baby Records. Record company and music publisher (Broadway/Hollywood International Music Publishers/ASCAP). Releases 5-10 LPs/year. Works with songwriters on contract. Teams collaborators. Pays 1-10% royalty to artists on contract; statutory rate or less to publishers for each record sold.

Close-up

Paul Burton
Senior Director of A&R, Chrysalis Records
New York, New York

Paul Burton says there is more to the job of an A&R representative than simply listening to tapes all day and hanging out in rock'n'roll clubs every night. He should know. After starting in the record business at MCA and working his way into its A&R department, he is now senior director of A&R at Chrysalis Records. Some of his recent signings include Trouble Tribe, Child's Play and Kevin Paige.

"There are a lot of misconceptions," says Paul, "but the truth is, it's a business. That took me a while to learn. An A&R rep is actually a band's manager within the record company. I've got to sell each department and make them believe in my bands as much as I do myself." To get some feel for the day-to-day operations of an A&R rep, I asked Paul to describe a typical week.

"This week I've spent a lot of time on new songs with a new artist. We're doing a lot with publishers and songwriters, trying to put this project together. We just mastered two records, for Trouble Tribe and Child's Play. I've been setting up showcases for both bands, so I've got to be a liaison between my department and the promotion, marketing and management departments of this company. I've also been working on a gig at the Cat Club which we're putting together with publicity here. And I usually spend a lot of time putting recording budgets together, working with the studios, trying to cut some good deals."

Of course, a big portion of Paul's time is spent dealing with performers who want to be recording artists and songwriters who would like to get songs to his current acts. For the "pure" (i.e. nonperforming) songwriter, Paul suggests calling the record company A&R department assistants once every other month or so to find out what kind of material they're looking for. "It's that easy," he says. "Like right now, I'm looking for material for an urban crossover/pop artist and people are sending me country songs. If they keep sending me things that are so off, I'm not likely to keep listening. It's easy enough to find out what we are looking for instead of just sending things in out of the blue."

One tough decision young bands from the middle of the country often face is whether to stay in their own region and hope to create enough of a fire so the smoke will attract A&R interest from the coasts or go ahead and move to New York or Los Angeles. Paul says stay at home. "A band can absolutely stay in their hometown. Bands will send me papers or invitations to where they're playing no matter where they're from. They'll call every once in a while, they'll send things in, just so I see their name around. I signed Child's Play out of Baltimore; they created a huge following there. Way before I saw the band I knew about them. Word does get out. But when these bands come to New York, it's very competitive. The club venue is very limited, and it changes—right now, in the hard rock market, it's a great place for a band to be. But in New York you're going to make no money. You can survive in your hometown and work, have a day job, whatever you need to do to keep your band together. I fly out to different areas all the time. Send me a tape. If it's great, I'll be out there."

—Mark Garvey

How to Contact: Prefers cassette (or VHS videocassette) with any number of songs and lyric sheet. "Final mix, top professional quality only." SASE. Reports in 1 month.
Music: Pop, rock, R&B and musicals in entirety.
Tips: "Need female singer or rock/pop/group touring L.A./CA area. Also need final mix songs for film scores. Only highly professional tapes are accepted. Include phone, address, SASE and cassette tape. We're seeking a "name" male rock, pop or R&B singer who can act for a major motion picture. Send tape, photo, resume, and VHS if available with SASE."

CIMIRRON/RAINBIRD RECORDS, 607 Piney Point Rd., Yorktown VA 23692. (804)898-8155. President: Lana Puckett. Vice President: Kim Person. Record company. Releases 2-3 singles, 3 LPs, 1 EP and 1 CD/year. Works with musicians/artists on contract. Pays variable royalty to artists on contract. Pays statutory rate.
How to Contact: Write. Prefers cassette with 1-3 songs and lyric sheet. SASE. Reports in 3 months.
Music: Mostly country-bluegrass, new age and pop. Released "Tangier Morning" (by Steve Bennett), recorded by Steve Bennett (bluegrass-new acoustic) and "I Don't Know If They Let Cowgirls In" (by Lana Puckett and Kim Person), recorded by Lana & Kim (country); all on Cimirron/Rainbow Records.

*CITA COMMUNICATIONS INC., 676 Pittsburgh Rd., Butler PA 16001. (412)586-6552. A&R/Producer: Mickii Taimuty. Labels include Phunn! Records and Tropē Records. Record company. Estab. 1989. Releases 6 singles, 3 12″ singles, 3 LPs, 2 EPs and 5 CDs/year. Works with musicians/artists on record contract. Pays artists 10% royalty on contract. Pays statutory rate to publishers per song on records.
How to Contact: Call first and obtain permission to submit. Prefers cassette (or VHS, Beta or ¾″ videocassette if available) with a maximum of 6 songs and lyric sheets. SASE. Reports in 8 weeks.
Music: Interested in rock/dance music and contemporary gospel; also rap, jazz and progressive country. Released "Forged by Fire", written and recorded by Sanxtion on Tropē Records; "I Cross My Heart" (by Taimuty/Nelson), recorded by Melissa Anne on Phunn! Records; and "Fight the Fight", written and recorded by M.J. Nelson on Tropē Records. Other artists include Most High, Sister Golden Hair and Countdown.

*CITY PIGEON RECORDS, P.O. Box 43135, Upper Montclair NJ 07043. (201)857-2935. President: Richard Reiter. Record company. Estab. 1983. Releases 3 LPs and 3 CDs/year. Works with musicians/artists on contract. Pays 10-13% royalty to artists on contract; statutory rate to publishers per song on record.
How to Contact: Write first and obtain permission to submit. Prefers cassette with 3 songs and lyric or lead sheet. SASE.
Music: Mostly jazz; also pop. Released *Listener Friendly* and *Point of No Return* recorded by Crossing Point (LP, jazz); and *Swing!* recorded by Tricia Slafta (LP, swing jazz), all on City Pigeon Records. Other artists include Richard Reiter and Lou Caimano.

CLOUDBURST RECORDS, Box 31, Edmonton KY 42129. (502)432-3183. President: Rev. Junior Lawson. Record company and music publisher (Holy Spirit Music). Releases 3 singles and 4 LPs/year. Works with songwriters on contract. Pays 4 royalty to artists on contract.
How to Contact: Call first. Prefers 7½ ips reel-to-reel or cassette and lyric sheet. SASE. Reports in 3 weeks.
Music: Mostly southern gospel; also country, gospel, MOR and progressive. Released *Introducing the Cornerstones* and *Extra! Extra!*, by The Cornerstones (southern gospel LPs); and *Old-Fashioned Ways*, by the Sounds of Joy (southern gospel LP). Other artists include The Southern-Aires.

*CODISCOS, P.O. Box 14-28, Medellin (Ant.) **Colombia**. (574)266-07-62. A&R Director: Fernando Lopez. Labels include La Discoteca, Musart, RMM and Coporacion Wilfrido Vargas. Record company. Estab. 1950. Releases 50 singles, 40 LPs and 15 CDs/year. Works with musicians/artists on record contract, songwriters on royalty contract and musicians on salary for in-house studio work. Pays artists 4-6% royalty for each record sold. Pays statutory rate to publisher per song on records.
How to Contact: Submit demo tape by mail. Unsolicited submissions are OK. Prefers cassette with 4 songs and lyric sheets. Does not return unsolicited material. Reports in 1 month.
Music: Interested in salsa, Caribbean music and merengue. Released "Mi Vecina" (by Diego Gale), recorded by Grupo Gale on Zeida Records; "Ayer La Vi" (by Cosmen A. Rico), recorded by Juan Carlos Coronel on Codiscos Records; and "Quiero Ser Feliz" (by Jose A. Cedeno), recorded by La Cheverisima on Zeida Records. Other artists include Binomio De Oro, Grupo Melao, The Rebels, Los Diablitos, Hermanos Piña and Los Cānoneros De Colombia.
Tips: "The songwriter must understand very well the feeling of Latin music; very important are rhythm and lyrics with themes about Latin people and their idiosyncrasies."

COLLECTOR RECORDS, Box 2296, Rotterdam 3000 CG **Holland**. Phone: (10)4224889. Research: Cees Klop. Labels include All Rock, Downsouth, Unknown, Pro Forma and White Label Records. Record company, music publisher (All Rock Music Pub.) and record producer (Cees Klop). Estab. 1967. Releases 10 singles and 30 LPs/year. Works with musicians/artists and songwriters on contract. Pays standard royalty to artist on contract.
How to Contact: Prefers cassette. SAE and IRC. Reports in 1 month.
Music: Mostly 50's rock, rockabilly, hillbilly boogie and country/rock; also piano boogie woogie. Released "Spring in April" (by Pepping/Jellema), recorded by Henk Pepping on Down South Records (50's rock); "Go Cat Go" (by Myers), recorded by Jimmy Myers on White Label Records (50's rock) and "Knocking On the Backside" (by T. Redell), recorded by T. Redell on White Label Records (50's rock).

COLT RECORDS, Box 431, Cornwall, Ontario K6H 5T2 **Canada**. (514)264-4473. President: Robbie Sexton. Record company, music publisher (Reid Publishing International/PROCAN) and record producer (Gilles Godard). Estab. 1987. Releases 3 singles/year. Works with musicians/artists and songwriters on contract; hires musicians for in-house studio work. Pays statutory rate to publisher per song on record.
How to Contact: Write or call first and obtain permission to submit. Prefers cassette (or VHS videocassette) with up to 4 songs and lyric sheet. SAE and IRC. Reports in 3 weeks.
Music: Mostly country, rock and pop; also R&B and new age. Released "Rage Rain" written and recorded by Boni Fon on Colt Records (rock); "After You Call" written and recorded by Eddy Rivette on Colt Records (country) and *Sub-Storms* written and recorded by Eclipse on Colt Records (pop).
Tips: "Your bio/package is your only selling tool when you can't be here in person. Make it as concise and professional as possible. If you want your material returned, pay for it. If you want a reply, enclose a stamped envelope. If you want us to read it, type it."

COMMA RECORDS & TAPES, Postbox 2148, 6078 Neu-Isenburg, **West Germany**. Phone: (6102)52696. General Manager: Roland Bauer. Labels include Big Sound, Comma International and Max-Banana-Tunes. Record company. Estab. 1969. Releases 50-70 singles and 20 LPs/year. Works with musicians/artists and songwriters on contract. Pays 7-10% royalty to artists on contract.
How to Contact: Prefers cassette and lyric sheet. Reports in 3 weeks. "Do not send advanced letter asking permission to submit, just send your material, SAE and minimum two IRCs."
Music: Mostly pop, disco, rock, R&B and country; also musicals.

COMPO RECORD AND PUBLISHING CO., Box 15222, Oklahoma City OK 73115. (405)677-6448. President: Yvonne De Vaney. General Manager: Sonny Lane. Record company and music publisher (Country Classics Music/BMI). Estab. 1972. Releases 4-6 singles and 1-2 LPs/year. Works with musicians/artists and songwriters on contract. Pays negotiable royalty to artists and songwriters on contract; statutory rate to publishers for each record sold.
How to Contact: Prefers cassette with 2-4 songs and lead sheet. SASE. Reports in 3 weeks.
Music: Mostly country/western, gospel and MOR. Released "Lovers Waltz"; "Yodel Love" and "Yodel Waltz" (all by Yvonne DeVaney), recorded by Wes Onley and Yvonne DeVaney on Compo Records (country duet).
Tips: "Songwriter: We like a simple song with a simple melody—a song you can whistle and hum. Artists: Develop a style."

COMSTOCK RECORDS LTD., 10603 N. Hayden Rd., Suite 114, Scottsdale AZ 85260. (602)951-3115. Canadian, United States and European distribution on Paylode & Comstock Records. Production Manager/Producer: Patty Parker. President: Frank Fara. Record company, music publisher (White Cat Music/ASCAP, Rocky Bell Music/BMI), Nashville Record Production, and International Record Promotions. Member CMA, GMA, CCMA, MACE, BCCMA, British & French C&W Associations, and CARAS. "Comstock Records, Ltd. has three primary divisions: Production, Promotion and Publishing. We distribute and promote both our self-produced recordings and outside master product." Releases 24-30 singles, 2 LPs and 2-4 CDs/year. Works with artists and songwriters on contract; musicians on salary. Pays 7% royalty to artists on contract; statutory rate to publishers for each record sold. "Artists pay distribution and promotion fee to press and release their masters."
How to Contact: Prefers cassette (or VHS videocassette) with 1-4 songs "plus word sheet. Enclose stamped return envelope if cassette is to be returned." Reports in 2 weeks.
Music: Adult contemporary and country. Released "Cherokee" recorded by Anne Lord; "Half A Fighting Chance" by Singer Steve Heske; "We Rise Again" by Priscilla Wright and "You're the Reason I Live" by Cheryl Maxim. Other artists include Ray Dean James, Doc & Dusty, Derek Carle and Gwen Bishop.

Tips: "We have an immediate need for country material for our European division. Our international division consists of master distribution and promotion to the following nations: England, France, Germany, Belgium, Ireland, Luxembourg, The Netherlands, Scotland, Switzerland, Norway and Canada. Also Denmark and Austria. We do video promotion with air play promotions to C&W networks across North America."

*CONTINENTAL RECORDS, Suite #C 435 Eastern Blvd., Baltimore MD 21221. (301)687-4100. President: Ernest W. Cash. Record company, music publisher, record producer (Vision Music Group, Inc.) and Ernie Cash Music, Inc. Estab. 1985. Releases 10 singles, 10 12″ singles, 10 LPs and 10 CDs/year. Works with musicians/artists and songwriters on contract. Pays statutory rate to publishers per song on record.
How to Contact: Write or call first and obtain permission to submit. Prefers cassette (or VHS videocassette) with 3-5 songs and lyric sheet. Does not return unsolicited material. Reports in 2 weeks.
Music: Mostly country, pop and gospel; also rock and R&B. Released "Coffee Jim" (by P. Parker), on Go-Records; "Show Me The Way" (by Art Daniels), on Compleat Records; and "Doctor of Love" (by Ernie Cash), on Continental Records, all recorded by Ernie Cash (singles with video). Other artists include Jimmy Peppers, Pam Bailey, Tall in the Saddle, Johnny Ray Anthony and Jo-Ann.
Tips: "Treat me the way you want to be treated, above all be honest with me."

COSMOPOLITAN COUNTRY RECORDS (CCR RECORDS), 2210 Raper Blvd., Arlington TX 76103. (817)461-8481. President: Jerry Abbott. Record company, music publisher (Valance Enterprises, BMI) and record producer (Pantego Sound Studio). Estab. 1973. Releases 4-6 singles and 2 LPs. Works with musicians/artists and songwriters on contract and hires musicians for in-house studio work. Pays 10-13% royalty to artists on contract; statutory rate to publisher per song on record.
How to Contact: Submit demo tape by mail. Unsolicited submissions are okay. Prefers cassette with 5 songs and lyric sheets. SASE. Reports in 6 weeks.
Music: Mostly country. Released "One More Night" (by Bolan/Katona), recorded by The Shoppe on CCR Records (country single); "Dreamer" (by Abbott/Jackson), recorded by Dow Jones on CCR Records (country single); and "Looking Out My Back Door" (by J. Fogerty), recorded by Marcy Carr on OL Records (country single). Other artists include Danny Wood, Johnny Park & Karol Bangs.

*COSMOTONE RECORDS, P.O. Box 71988. Los Angeles CA 90071-0988. President: Rafael Brom. Labels include Cosmotone Music and Center for the Queen of Peace. Record company and music publisher. Estab. 1984. Releases 1 single, 1 12″ single and 1 LP/year. Works with songwriters on contract and hires musicians on salary for in-house studio work. Pays statutory rate to publishers per song on record.
How to Contact: Write first and obtain permission to submit. Prefers cassette (or VHS videocassette). "Will contact only if interested."
Music: All types. Released "Padre Pio", "Love of The Father" and "O Let Me Be" (written and recorded by Lord Hamilton), on Cosmotone Records (Christian/pop/rock).

COUNTERPART CREATIVE STUDIOS, 3744 Applegate Ave., Cincinnati OH 45211. (513)661-8810. President: Shad O'Shea. Record company, music publisher (Hurdy Gurdy Music Co., Counterpart Music/BMI) and jingle company. Member RIAA. Releases 24 singles and 6 LPs/year. Works with musicians on salary.
How to Contact: Write first. Prefers 7½ ips reel-to-reel with 1-2 songs. Does not return unsolicited material. Reports in 1 week.
Music: Bluegrass, blues, children's, choral, church/religious, classical, country, dance, easy listening, folk, gospel, jazz, MOR, progressive, rock, funk, soul and top 40/pop. Released "McLove Story," by Shad O'Shea on Plantation Records; "Hot Fun in the Summertime," by Dayton on Capitol Records; "Freakazoid" and "Wet My Whistle," by Midnight Star on Warner Bros. Records.

COUNTRY BREEZE RECORDS, 1715 Marty, Kansas City KS 66103. (913)384-4454 or 384-1020. President: Ed Morgan. Labels include Country Breeze Records and Walkin' Hat Records. Record company, music publisher (Country Breeze Music/BMI and Walkin' Hat Music/ASCAP). Releases 10 singles, 8 12″ singles and 10 LPs/year. Works with musicians/artists and songwriters on contract. Pays 10-12% royalty to artists on contract; statutory rate to publisher per song on record.
How to Contact: Prefers cassette with 3 songs and lyric sheet. SASE. Reports in 2 weeks.
Music: Mostly southern/country gospel, country and pop; also duet material. Released "Angel is Her Name" (by Jamie Mitchell), recorded by Jamie Mitchell on C. Breeze Records (country); "Rainbow's End (by D. Ashton/J. Benjamin), recorded by Edging West on C. Breeze Records (country rock) ar.d "A Child From A Broken Home" (by Wilma Bell), recorded by Wilma Bell on C. Breeze Records (gospel). Other artists include Wendy Harrald and Dianne Schafer.

Tips: "When submitting as a writer make sure you have strong songs both in lyric and melody with voice out front. As an artist you must be willing to work hard to achieve your goal. One record release will not get you known as an artist; it takes several and promotion is a must."

COUNTRY SHOWCASE AMERICA, 14134 Brighton Dam Rd., Clarksville MD 21029-1327. (301)854-2917. President: Francis Gosman. Record company. Estab. 1971. Releases 2 singles/year. Works with musicians/artists and songwriters on contract. Pays 3% royalty to artists on contract; statutory rate to publishers for each record sold.
How to Contact: Prefers cassette and lyric sheet. SASE.
Music: Country. Released "Christmas Flower," (by Gosman/O'Leary), recorded by O'Leary; "Sweet Yesterdays," (by Marrino/Gellspie), recorded by Country Cavalier on CSA; and "Heavens Bed," and "The Iowa, Remember terrett #2" (by Gosman), recorded by J. Anthony on CSA Records (country).

COUNTRY STAR INTERNATIONAL, 439 Wiley Ave., Franklin PA 16323. (814)432-4633. President: Norman Kelly. Labels include CSI, Country Star, Process and Mersey Records. Record company, music publisher (Country Star/ASCAP, Process and Kelly/BMI) and record producer (Country Star Productions). Member AFM and AFTRA. Estab. 1970. Releases 5-10 singles and 5-6 LPs/year. Works with musician/artists and songwriters on contract. Works with lyricists and composers. Pays 18% royalty to artists on contract; statutory rate to publishers for each record sold. "Charges artists in advance only when they buy records to sell on personal appearances and show dates."
How to Contact: Prefers cassette with 2-4 songs and lyric or lead sheet. SASE. Reports in 2 weeks.
Music: Mostly country western, bluegrass, pop, easy listening; also rock, gospel, MOR and R&B. Released "A Part Of Me" (by Lisa Hadley Patton), on Country Star Records (country); "Your Place Or Mine" (by Tommy Davidson), on Country Star Records (country) and "Spinning In My Heart" (by Junie Lou) on Country Star Records (country). Other artists include Don Earl Mabury, Tara Bailey and Shelley Harris.
Tips: "Send only your best efforts."

COWBOY JUNCTION FLEA MARKET AND PUBLISHING CO., Highway 44 W., Lecanto FL 32661. (904)746-4754. Contact: Elizabeth Thompson. Record company, record producer (Cowboy Junction Publishing Co.)and music publisher (Cowboy Junction Flea Market and Publishing Co.). Estab. 1957. Releases 3 or more singles, 1-2 12" singles and 1-2 LPs/year. Works with musicians/artists and songwriters on contract. Pays 50% royalty.
How to Contact: Prefers cassette with 1-4 songs and lyric sheet. SASE. Reports ASAP.
Music: Country, gospel, bluegrass and country western. Released "Little Circle B," "Little Band of Gold," "With A Golden Screw and A Silver Nail" (by Boris Max Pastuch), recorded by Buddy Max on Cowboy Junction Records (country & western). Other artists include Izzy Miller, Wally Jones, Leo Vargason, Johnny Pastuck, Troy Holliday and Pappy Dunham.
Tips: "Come to one of our shows and present your song (Flea Market on Tuesdays and Fridays, country/bluegrass show every Saturday) or send a tape in."

COWGIRL RECORDS, Box 6085, Burbank CA 91510. Contact: Vice President. Record company and music publisher (Kingsport Creek). Estab. 1980. Works with musicians/artists and songwriters on contract. Pays statutory rate to publishers for each record sold.
How to Contact: Prefers cassette (or VHS videocassette) with any number of songs and lyric sheet or lead sheet. Does not return unsolicited material. "Include a photo and bio if possible."
Music: Mostly country, R&B, MOR and gospel. Released "I Do," (MOR) "Only Life I Know," (country) "1st Man" (country) written and recorded by Melvena Kaye on Cowgirl Records.

CRYSTAL RAM/APRIL RECORDS, 827 Brazil Pl., El Paso TX 79903. (915)772-7858. Owner: Harvey Marcus. Labels include Crystal Ram, April, T.S.B., and M.C.R. Records. Record company, music publisher and record producer (April Productions). Releases 1-3 singles, 1-3 12" singles, 1-5 LPs, 1-5 EPs, and 1-3 CDs/year. Works with musicians/artists and songwriters on contract; hires musicians for in-house studio work. Pays 25% royalty to artists on contract; statutory rate to publisher per song on record.
How to Contact: Prefers cassette or 7½ ips reel-to-reel (or VHS videocssette) with one song and lyric or lead sheet. SASE. Reports in 6 weeks.
Music: Mostly jazz/pop, top 40 (ballads) and tex-mex; also country, New Age and Christian/rock. Released *Are We In This for Love* (EP) and "Baby Blue Baby" (single), written and recorded by The Street Boys on T.S.B. Records; and *Endless Dreams*, written and recorded by Ruben Castillo on Crystal Ram Records (LP). Other artists include Ray Justin Vega.

*CUE MANAGEMENT PTY LTD., (formerly Umbrella Organization Pty. Ltd.), P.O. Box 35, Railway Square, Sydney 2000, **Australia**. Phone: (61)2-6984799. FAX: 61-2-2811778. Professional Manager: John Hopkins. Music publisher, record company and record producer. Estab. 1978. Works with songwriters on contract.
How to Contact: Prefers cassette (or VHS [PAL] videocassette). Does not return unsolicited material. Reports in 6 weeks.
Music: Mostly contemporary pop/rock, film soundtracks and country.

*CURRENT RECORDS, 366 Adelaide St. East, Toronto ON M5A 3X9 **Canada**. (416)361-1101. A&R, New Projects: Trevor G. Shelton. Labels include Rammit Records. Record company, music publisher (Brand New Sounds, Today's Tunes Music, Current Sounds) affiliated with SOCAN performing rights organization. Record producer (Trevor G. Shelton). Estab. 1983. Releases 5-10 singles, 5-10 12" singles, 5 LPs, 5 cassettes and 5 CDs/year. Works with musicians/artists on contract. Pays statutory rate to publisher per song.
How to Contact: Submit demo tape by mail. Unsolicited submissions are OK. Prefers cassette with 4 songs. SASE. Reports in 3-4 weeks.
Music: Mostly rock, pop and dance; also acid, hip hop and rap. Released *The Distance Between* (by Kromm/Arnott), recorded by Strange Advance (rock LP); *Alta Moda* (by Johnson/Orenstein), recorded by Alta Moda (dance/rock LP); and *Small Victories* (by Oates/Segato/Conger), recorded by The Parachute Club (dance LP); all on Current Records. Other artists include M&M, Machinations, Mystery Romance, Andy McLean.
Tips: "Realize you may be turned down, but work hard—don't be discouraged by "thank you—but no thanks" form letters. Keep writing and if A&R departments suggest ideas of improving your material—listen to them, if you think comments are valid, use them."

CURTISS RECORDS, Box 4740, Nashville TN 37216. (615)865-4740. President: Wade Curtiss. Record company and producer. Works with artists and songwriters on contract. Pays 8¢/record royalty to artists on contract; 2½¢/record royalty to songwriters on contract.
How to Contact: Prefers cassette with 2-8 songs and lead sheet. SASE. Reports in 3 weeks.
Music: Bluegrass, blues, country, disco, folk, gospel, jazz, rock, soul and top 40/pop. Released "Book of Matches," by Gary White; and "Rompin' " and "Punsky," by the Rhythm Rockers.

*DAGENE RECORDS, P.O. Box 410851, San Francisco CA 94141. (415)822-1530. President: David Alston. Labels include Dagene Records and Cabletown Corp. Record company, music publisher (Dagene Music) and record producer (David-Classic Disc Productions). Estab. 1987. Works with musicians/artists and songwriters on contract and hires musicians on salary for in-house studio work. Pays statutory rate to publishers per song on record.
How to Contact: Write or call first and obtain permission to submit. Prefers cassette (or VHS videocassette) with 2 songs and lyric sheet. Does not return unsolicited material.
Music: Mostly R&B/rap, dance and pop; also gospel. Released "Serving 'Em" (written and recorded by Frisco Kid) on Dagene Records; "Visions" (by Marcus Justice), recorded by 2-Dominatozs on Dagene Records; and "Started Life" (by David/M. Campbell), recorded by Primo on Cabletown Records, (all rap 12"). Other artists include "The D".

*DA-MON RECORDS, Orisa Productions Incorporated, 646 East Madison St., Lancaster PA 17602. (717)393-9115. President: Daoud A. Balewa. Labels include The Creative InterFace/TCI and Da-Mon Records/TCI. Record company and music publisher (DABA Music Publishers/BMI). Estab. 1979. Releases 3 LPs and 3 CDs/year. Works with songwriters on contract and musicians on salary for in-house studio work. Pays statutory rate to publishers per song on records. Charges prospective artists for promotion.
How To Contact: Submit demo tape by mail. Unsolicited submissions are OK. Prefers cassette (or BETA/VHS videocassette if available) with 3 songs, lyric sheet, artist bio, PR photos and contact information. SASE. Reports in 3-6 weeks.
Music: Mostly jazz/fusion, new age and black urban contemporary; also pop, crossover. Released "Raw Savage" (by Lady E), recorded by Lady E on DaMon Records (pop/rap single); "I'll Make It Up" (by E. Laws), recorded by E. Laws on DaMon Records (pop single); and *Colours In Spaces* (by Ambiance), recorded by Ambiance on DaMon/TCI (LP). Other artists include Matt Nathan, Jim Lum, Carol Merriwether and M.C. Penetrator.

DARK HORSE PRODUCTIONS, 1729 N. Third Ave., Upland CA 91786. (714)946-1398. A&R Director: Bill Huff. Record company, music publisher (see Lizard Licks Music, BMI), record producer (Dark Horse Productions). Estab. 1988. Releases 2 LPs and 2 CDs/year. Works with musicians/artists on contract. Pays 6-9% royalty on retail price; statutory rate to publishers per song on records.

How to Contact: Submit demo tape by mail. Prefers cassette with 3-5 songs. SASE. Reports in 4 weeks.
Music: Mostly contemporary jazz, New Age, and traditional jazz. Released *Iridescence* (by Brad Kaenel), recorded by Polyhedra on Dark Horse Records (contemporary jazz) and *Simply Simon* (by D.J. Alverson), recorded by Polyhedra on Dark Horse (contemporary jazz).

DEMI MONDE RECORDS AND PUBLISHING, LTD., Foel Studio, Llanfair Caereinion, Powys, Wales, United Kingdom. Phone: (0938)810758. Managing Director: Dave Anderson. Record company and music publisher (Demi Monde Records & Publishing, Lts.) and record producer (Dave Anderson). Estab. 1983. Releases 5 12" singles, 10 LPs and 6 CDs/year. Works with musicians/artists and songwriters on contract; hires musicians for in-house studio work. Pays 10-12% royalty to artists on contract; statutory rate to publisher per song on record.
How to Contact: Prefers cassette with 3-4 songs. SAE and IRC. Reports in 1 month.
Music: Rock, R&B and pop. Released *Hawkwind* and *Amon Doul II & Gong* (by Band), and *Groundhogs* (by T.S. McPhee), all on Demi Monde Records (LPs).

DHARMA RECORDS, 117 W. Rockland Rd., Box 615, Libertyville IL 60048. (708)362-4060. Vice President: Rick Johnson. Labels include Future and Homexercise. Record company, record producer and music publisher (Amalgamated Tulip Corp.). Releases 3 singles and 2 LPs/year. Works with artists and songwriters on contract. Pays negotiable royalty to artists on contract; negotiable rate to publishers for each record sold.
How to Contact: Prefers cassette with 3-5 songs and lyric sheet. Prefers studio produced demos. SASE. Reports in 1 month.
Music: Rock, top 40/pop, country, dance/R&B, MOR and progressive rock. Released *Active Music for Children*, by Bill Hooper (education LP); "Oh Boy," by Oh Boy (pop rock single); and *Not Marmosets Yet*, by Conrad Black (rock LP).

*DIGITAL MUSIC PRODUCTS, INC., 94-1301 Southfield Ave., Stamford CT 06902. (203)327-3800. Marketing: Paul Jung. Record company. Estab. 1983. Releases 6-8 CDs/year. Pays ¾ rate to publishers per song on record.
How to Contact: Write or call first and obtain permission to submit. Prefers cassette. SASE. Reports in 2 months.
Music: Mostly jazz. Released *Home Again* (written and recorded by Thom Rotella); *Magic Fingers* (by Chuck Loeb), recorded by Chuck Loeb/Andy Laverne; and *Bob's Diner* (by Bob Smith), recorded by Bob's Diner, all on DMP Records (jazz CD). Other artists include Bob Mintzer, The Dolphins, Joe Beck, Warden Bernhardt, Manfredo Fest and Bill Mays.
Tips: "Can you record direct to two-track? We are *not* a multi-track label."

*DIRECTIONS, 6 Rue Laurenain, Lyon France 69002. (33)7240-9212. Managing Director: Andre. Labels include Lucky French, Scycla and Elsa. Record company and music publisher (Directions, SACEM). Estab. 1988. Releases 150 singles, 50 12" singles, 90 LPs and 10 CDs/year. Works with musicians/artists on record contract, songwriters on royalty contract. Pays artists 8-12% royalty. Pays statutory rate to publishers per song on records.
How to Contact: Write first to arrange interview. Prefers cassette with 3 songs and lyric sheet. SASE. Reports in 2 weeks.
Music: Interested in rock and pop; also classical. Artists include The Suns, Lanterne Rouge, Deux and Philippe Richard.

DISQUES NOSFERATU RECORDS, C.P. 304 Succ. S, Montreal Quebec H4E 4J8 **Canada.** (514)769-9096. Promotion Director: Ginette Provost. Record company. Estab. 1986. Releases 1 single, 1 12" single, 1 cassette, and 1 EP/year. Works with musicians/artists on contract and hires musicians for in-house studio work. Pays statutory rate to publishers per song on records.
How to Contact: Write. Prefers cassette, VHS videocassette with 3 songs and lyric sheet. SASE. Reports in 1 month.
Music: Mostly rock, instrumental and heavy metal; also blues. Released "Suite Peer Gynt" (by E. Grieg), recorded by Tropfeeross on Nosferatu Records (classical rock); "Trop Fort" (by G. Provost), recorded by Tropfeeross on Nosferatu Records (hard rock) and "Brulé Par Leblues" (by Normand Gendron/Gisette Provost), recorded by Feeross on Nosferatu Records (blues/rock).
Tips: "Any artist who signs with us must be prepared to travel."

DOMINO RECORDS, LTD., Ridgewood Park Estates, 222 Tulane St., Garland TX 75043. Contact: Gene or Dea Summers. Public Relations/Artist and Fan Club Coordinator: Steve Summers. Labels include Front Row Records. Record company and music publisher (Silicon Music/BMI). Releases 5-

6 singles and 2-3 LPs/year. Works with artists and songwriters on contract. Pays negotiable royalties to artists on contract; standard royalty to songwriters on contract.

How to Contact: Prefers cassette (or VHS videocassette) with 1-3 songs. Does not return unsolicited material. SASE. Reports ASAP.

Music: Mostly 50's rock/rockabilly; also country, bluegrass, old-time blues and R&B. Released "The Music of Jerry Lee," by Joe Hardin Brown (country single); "Ready to Ride," (from the HBO Presentation *Backlot*), by Pat Minter (country single); and *Texas Rock and Roll* and *Gene Summers Live In Scandinavia*, by Gene Summers (50's LPs).

Tips: "If you own masters of 1950s rock and rock-a-billy, contact us first! We will work with you on a percentage basis for overseas release. We have active releases in Holland, Switzerland, Belgium, Australia, England, France, Sweden, Norway and the US at the present. We need original masters. You must be able to prove ownership of tapes before we can accept a deal. We're looking for little-known, obscure recordings. We have the market if you have the tapes!"

*DOWNTOWN RECORD COMPANY, Stenenmolenstraat 7, B-2580, St. Katelyne-Waver **Belgium**. (15) 41 13 31. Managing Director: Piroux Ghislain. Record company and record producer (Piroux G.C.J.). Releases 20-25 singles and 3-5 LPs/year. Works with musicians/artists and songwriters on contract. Pays negotiable royalty to artists on contract.

How to Contact: Prefers cassette or reel-to-reel (or videocassette) with 2-6 songs and lyric sheet. "Always addressed to Mr. Piroux Ghislain." SAE and IRC. Reports in 6 weeks.

Music: Mostly pop, mainstream rock, dance music, funk (disco/funk); also new wave, R&B, golden oldies. "No pop/rock or heavy metal." Released "Never In A Million Years," recorded by Linda Scott; "Jungle Drums," recorded by Clyde Otis; and "Happy Together," recorded by The Turtles, all on Downtown Records (all singles). Other artists include Guenaelle (new female singer), and Kokomo (female singer).

Tips: We are an independent company which is an enormous advantage in a small country like Belgium. We can easily distribute items ourselves. If it's a hit in Belgium, Europe is watching."

DUPUY RECORDS/PRODUCTIONS/PUBLISHING, INC., 10960 Ventura Blvd., Studio City CA 91604. (818)980-6412. President: Pedro Dupuy. Record company, record producer and music publisher (Dupuy Publishing, Inc./ASCAP). Releases 5 singles and 5 LPs/year. Works with artists and songwriters on contract; musicians on salary for in-house studio work. Pays negotiable rate to publishers for each record sold.

How to Contact: Write or call first or arrange personal interview. Prefers cassette with 2-4 songs and lyric sheet. SASE. Reports in 1 month.

Music: Easy listening, jazz, MOR, R&B, soul and top 40/pop. Artists include Gordon Gilman, David Daymon, Joe Trammel and James G. Sobo.

Tips: Needs "very definite lyrics with hook."

DYNAMIC RECORDING COMPANY, 2846 Dewey Ave., Rochester NY 14616. (716)621-6270. President: David R. Kaspersin. Record company, music publisher (Kaspersin Music Publishing Co./BMI) and record producer (David R. Kaspersin). Estab. 1976. Releases 10 singles, 10 LPs and 5 CDs/year. Works with musicians/artists on contract; musicians on salary for in-house studio work. Pays negotiable royalty to artists on contract; statutory rate to publishers for each record sold.

How to Contact: Write or call first and obtain permission to submit. Prefers cassette or reel-to-reel (or ¾ or ½" Beta or ½" VHS videocassette with digital sound) with 4 songs and lyric sheet. Reports in 6 weeks.

Music: Mostly country, R&B and gospel; also rock and straight country. Released "Too Much Fun too Early" written and recorded by J. Elliott; and "Your Fire Burns" written and recorded by Phyllis Bishop (pop), "Karrousel," written and recorded by David Kaspersin (rock); all on DRC Records. Other artists include Prospect Highway, The Coupes, Mary Maniak, Bonnie Abrams and Lou Sweigman.

Tips: "Submit clean simple demos, no fancy leads or introductions. Get right to the hook of the song."

DYNAMITE, 5 Aldom Circle, West Caldwell NJ 07006. Owner: Tar Heel Pete. Labels include Dynamite, Deadwood, Tar Heel and True Love. Record company, record producer and music publisher (Cactus Music and Gidget Publishing/ASCAP). Estab. 1974. Releases 3 singles, 2 cassettes and 1 EP/year. Works with musicians/artists and songwriters on contract.

How to Contact: Write first about your interest. Prefers cassette and lyric sheet. Does not return unsolicited material. Reports in 1 month.

Music: Jazz, R&B, country western, gospel and rock. Released "Give Me Roses" (by Hall-Morris-Wellman), recorded by Coleman O'Neal (country); "Bottom of the World" (by Bob Rose), recorded by Larry Baird (country); "My Home's the USA" (by Tony Ansems), on Dynamite Records (rock) and "Doorstep to Heaven" (by Don Collins), on Dynamite Records (gospel).

*ELEMENT RECORD(S), Box 30260, Bakersfield CA 93385-1260. President: Judge A. Robertson. Record company. Estab. 1978. Releases 5 singles and 5 EPs/year. Works with musicians/artists on contract. Pays standard royalty.
How to Contact: Write first to arrange personal interview. Prefers cassette with 1 or more songs and lyric sheet.
Music: All types. Released "You'll fighting for your life" written and recorded by Jar the Superstar (gospel single); "My child might not live as long as I have" (by Judge A. Robertson) (gospel single); and "You give me a smile," by Judge A. Robertson (pop single) all on Element Records.

EMI, 810 7th Ave., New York NY 10019. (212)603-8600. Contact: A&R Director. Record company and music publisher (Screen Gems). Releases several singles and LPs/month.
How to Contact: Prefers cassette and lyric sheet. "Mail in no more than 3 songs on a cassette at a time. Include an SASE that will support all the materials sent as we keep nothing on file." Reports in 3 weeks.
Music: Most types of music, except country or classical. Released "West End Girls," by Pet Shop Boys (pop single); "Do It to Me Good Tonight," by Michael Henderson (R&B single); and "The Knife Feels Like Justice," by Brian Setzer ("multi-format" single). Other artists include Peter Tosh, Corey Hart, Talk Talk, Sheena Easton, David Bowie, Kate Bush and Kim Carnes.

ESB RECORDS, Box 6429, Huntington Beach CA 92615-6429. (714)962-5618. Executive Producers: Eva and Stan Bonn. Record company, music publisher (Bonnfire Publishing/ASCAP, Gather' Round/BMI), record producer (ESB Records). Estab. 1987. Releases one single/year, 1 LP and 1 CD. Works with musicians/artists and songwriters on contract. Pays negotiable royalty to artists; pays statutory rate to publisher per song on record.
How to Contact: Call first. Does not return unsolicited material. Reports in one month.
Music: Mostly country, country/pop, MOR/country; also New Age, Spanish and gospel. Released "You're Workin on Leavin Me," by Marda Philpot, Nancy Cyril and Eva Bonn); "Lady By Day Lover By Night" and "There's A Memory In My Heart" (by Bobby Lee Caldwell) all recorded by Bobby Lee Caldwell on ESB Records (country single). Other artists include Marda Philpot, Robert Aviles and Tice Griffin.

ETIQUETTE/SUSPICIOUS RECORDS, 2442 N.W. Market #273, Seattle WA 98107. (206)524-1020; FAX: (206)524-1102. President: Buck Ormsby. Labels include Etiquette Records and Suspicious Records. Record company and music publisher (see Valet Publishing). Estab. 1962. Releases 2-3 LPs and 2-3 CDs/year. Works with musicians/artists and songwriters on contract. Pays varying royalty to artists on contract. Pays statutory or negotiated rate to publisher per song on record.
How to Contact: Prefers cassette (or VHS videocassette) with 3-4 songs and lyric sheets. SASE. Reports in 1 month.
Music: Mostly R&B, rock and pop; also country. Released *Crazy 'Bout You* (by Roger Rogers), recorded by Kinetics on Etiquette Records (rock cassette). Other artists include Kent Morrill and Jerry Roslie.
Tips: "Tapes submitted should be top quality—lyric sheets professional."

EXECUTIVE RECORDS, 11 Shady Oak Trail, Charlotte NC 28210-7409. (704)554-1162. Executive Producer: Butch Kelly Montgomery. Labels include KAM, Executive and Fresh Avenue Records. Record company, record producer (Butch Kelly Productions), music publisher (Butch Kelly Publishing/BMI and Music by Butch Kelly/BMI) and songwriter. Member AGAC. Estab. 1982. Releases 4 singles, 2 12" single, 2 CDs and 2 LPs/year. Works with musicians/artists songwriters on contract; hires musicians for in-house studio work. Pays 50% to artists on contract; statutory rate to publishers for each record sold.
How to Contact: Prefers cassette "on Maxell UDS-II tapes only" (or videocassette) with 3 songs and lyric sheet, pictures and bio. SASE. Submit pictures with demo. Reports in 2 months.
Music: Mostly R&B, pop dance, top 40, rap and country. Released "Waiting" (by Butch Kelly), recorded by Expansion on KAM Records (pop); "Stumping Blues (by Kelly), recorded by Factory Men on KAM Records (R&B) and "Think Aloud" (by Kelly), recorded by M. Jaron on KAM Records (pop).

*FACTORY BEAT RECORDS, INC., 521 5th Ave., New York NY 10175. (212)757-3638. A&R Director: Rena L. Romano. Labels include R&R, Ren Rom and Can Scor Productions, Inc. Record company, record producer and music publisher (Ren-Maur Music Corp.). Member NARAS, BMI and Songwriters Guild. Releases 4 12" singles and 2 LPs/year. Works with musicians/artists and songwriters on contract; hires musicians for in-house studio work. Pays 4-12% royalty to artists on contract; statutory rate to publishers for each record sold.

How to Contact: Submit cassette with 4 songs and lead sheet. SASE. Reports in 1 month. "Do not phone—we will return material."

Music: Mostly R&B, pop rock and country; also gospel. Released "That's Hot" (by B. Nichols) and "Rise Up" (by B. Nichols/R. Feeney), both recorded by Rena on Factory Beat Records (12" singles).

*FAME AND FORTUNE ENTERPRISES, P.O. Box 121679, Nashville TN 37212. (615)244-4898. Producer: Jim Cartwright or Scott Turner. Labels include National Foundation Records and Fame and Fortune Records. Record company, music publisher (Boff Board Music/BMI) and record producer. Estab. 1976. Releases 6 singles, 6 LPs and 6 CDs/year. Works with musicians/artists and songwriters on contract. Pays statutory rate to publishers per song on records. Charges for "production services on recordings sessions."

How to Contact: Submit demo tape by mail. Unsolicited submissions are okay. Prefers cassette (or VHS videocassette) with 4 songs and lyric sheet. SASE. Reports in 3 weeks.

Music: Mostly country, MOR and med. rock. Released "By Houston" (by S. Rose), recorded by Shane Darnell; "First That's on my Mind" (by J. Jamilton), recorded by Ted Deere; and "Phantom Cadillac" (by S. Rose), recorded by J. Cartwright all on Fame & Fortune Records (all country). Other artists include Angel Connell, Bill Berning and Teresa Dalton.

FAMOUS DOOR RECORDS, Box 92, Station A, Flushing NY 11358. (718)463-6281. Contact: Harry Lim. Record company. Member NARAS. Releases 6 LPs/year. Works with artists on contract. Pays 5% in royalty to artists on contract; statutory rate to publishers for each record sold.

How to Contact: Write first. Prefers cassette with minimum 3 songs. Prefers studio produced demos. SASE. Reports in 1 month.

Music: Jazz. Released *L.A. After Dark*, by Ross Tomkins Quartet; *More Miles and More Standards*, by the Butch Miles Sextet; and *Buenos Aires New York Swing Connections*, by George Anders Sextet.

Tips: Looking for "good instrumentals."

FINER ARTS RECORDS/TRANSWORLD RECORDS, 2170 S. Parker Rd., Denver CO 80231. President: R.J. Bernstein. Record company, music publisher (M. Bernstein Music Publishing Co.) and record producer. Estab. 1960. Releases 6 singles, 3 LPs and 2 CDs/year. Works with musicians/artists and songwriters on contract; musicians on salary for in-house studio work.

How to Contact: Write first and obtain permission to submit. Prefers cassette (or VHS videocassette) and lyric sheet or lead sheet. Reports in 3 weeks. "Please no telephone calls."

Music: R&B, pop and rap.

FIRST TIME RECORDS SOVEREIGN HOUSE, 12 Trewartha Rd., Praa Sands, Penzance, Cornwall TR20 9ST **England**. Phone (0736)762826. FAX: (0736)763328. Managing Director A&R: Roderick G. Jones. Labels include Fugore, Dance 808, Rainy Day Records, Mohock Records, Kernow and First Time Records. Record company and music publisher (First Time Music Publishing U.K. Ltd./MCPS/PRS), and record producer (First Time Management & Production Co.). Estab. 1986. Works with musicians/artists and songwriters on contract; hires musicians for in-house studio work and as commissioned. Royalty to artists on contract varies; pays statutory rate to publishers per song on record subject to deal.

How to Contact: Prefers cassette with unlimited number of songs and lyric or lead sheets, but not necessary. SAE and IRC. Reports in 1-3 months.

Music: Mostly country/folk, pop/soul/top 20, country with an Irish/Scottish crossover; also gospel/Christian and HI NRG/dance. Released "The Drums of Childhood Dreams," (by Pete Arnold), recorded by Pete Arnold on Mohock Records (folk) and *The Light and Shade of Eddie Blackstone* (by Eddie Blackstone), recorded by Eddie Blackstone on Digimix International Records (country).

Tips: "Writers should learn patience, tolerance and understanding of how the music industry works, and should present themselves and their product in a professional manner and always be polite. Listen always to constructive criticism and learn from the advice of people who have a track record in the music business. Your first impression may be the only chance you get, so it is advisable to get it right from the start."

JOHN FISHER & ASSOCIATES, Suite 201, 1300 Division St., Nashville TN 37203. (615)256-3616. President: John Fisher. Labels include Player International, Crusader, Gold Country and Pulsation. Record company, music publisher and record producer. Releases 2 singles and 1 LP/year. Works with musicians/artists on contract.

How to Contact: Prefers cassette with up to 6 songs and lyric or lead sheets. SASE. Reports in 2 weeks.

Music: Mostly country, 50s rock and blues; also rock-a-billy. Artists include Terry Stafford, Steve Ricks, Henson Cargill, Ray Peterson and Webb Pierce.

FLYING HEART RECORDS, 4026 NE 12th Ave., Portland OR 97212. (503)287-8045. Owner: Jan Celt. Labels include Flying Heart Records. Record company. Estab. 1982. Releases 2 LPs and 1 EP/year. Works with musicians/artists and songwriters on contract and hires musicians for in-house studio work. Pays 2-10% royalty to artists on contract; negotiable rate to publisher per song on record.
How to Contact: Submit a demo tape by mail. Unsolicited submissions are okay. Prefers cassette with 1-10 songs and lyric sheets. Does not return unsolicited material. Reports in 3 months.
Music; Mostly R&B, blues and jazz; also rock. Released "Get Movin" (by Chris Newman), recorded by Napalm Beach (rock); "Down Mexico Way" (by Chris Newman), recorded by Napalm Beach (rock); and "Which One Of You People" (by Jan Celt), recorded by The Esquires (R&B); all on Flying Heart Records. Other artists include Janice Scroggins, Tom McFarland and Obo Addy.
Tips: "Express your true feelings with creative originality and show some imagination."

FM-REVOLVER RECORDS LTD., 152 Goldthorn Hill, Wolverhampton WV23JA **England.** (902)345345. A&R Director: David Roberts. Labels include Heavy Metal Records, Heavy Metal America, Heavy Metal Worldwide, Revolver Records, Black, and FM Dance. Record company, music publisher (Rocksong Music Publishing Ltd./PRS). Estab. 1980. Releases 5 singles, 5 12″ singles, 20 LPs, 5 EPs and 20 CDs. Works with musicians/artists and songwriters on contract; also licenses masters. Pays 8-16% royalty to artists on contract; statutory rate to publisher per song on record.
How to Contact: Submit demo tape by mail. Prefers cassette with 4 songs. SASE. Reports in 4 weeks.
Music: Mostly AOR, alternative rock, hard rock, heavy metal, and rock. Released *Sally Cinamon* (by Squire/Brown), recorded by The Stone Roses on Black Records (indie pop); *Pure Sex* (by Bomb), recorded by Adam Bomb on FM Records (hard rock) and *Radar Love* (by Band), recorded by Golden Earring on FM Records (rock). Other artists include Vibrators, Torino, Lisa Dominique, MaccLads, Cloven Hoof and White Sister.

FOUNTAIN RECORDS, 1203 Biltmore Ave., High Point NC 27260. (919)882-9990. President: Doris W. Lindsay. Record company, music publisher (Better Times Publishing-BMI, Doris Lindsay Pub.-ASCAP) and record producer. Estab. 1979. Releases 4 singles and 1 LP/year. Works with musicians/artists and songwriters on contract. Pays 5% royalty to artists on contract; statutory rate to publishers per song on record.
How to Contact: Write first and obtain permission to submit. Prefers cassette with 2 songs and lyric sheets. SASE. Reports in 2 months.
Music: Mostly country, pop and gospel. Released "Right Smack Dab in the Middle of Love" (by P.A. Hanna), recorded by Pat Repose; "Sweet Baby" (by P.A. Hanna), recorded by Tim Sloan; and "Two Lane Life" (by D. Lindsay), recorded by Mitch Snow; all on Fountain Records (country). Other artists include Tom Powers, J.R. Bevers, George Pickard and Lisa De Lucca.
Tips: "Send a well recorded demo. Do not send more than 2 songs per submission. I prefer up tempo and positive, clean lyrics."

FOUR WINDS RECORD PRODUCTIONS INC., Box 4773, Fondren Station, Jackson MS 39216-0773. A&R Manager: J. Wooten. Labels include The Unusual Records. Record company. Works with musicians/artists on contract, songwriters on royalty contracts and hires musicians for in-house studio work. "We will work with composers, lyric writers and collaborators on unusual songs. Also new unusual talent is welcome." Pays 10-20% royalty to artists on contract; statutory rate to publishers for each record sold.
How to Contact: Write. Prefers cassette with 2-4 songs. SASE. Reports in 1 month.
Music: Mostly country; also R&B, bluegrass and "gut bucket blues." Released "As Long As God Is Witness," "Amazing Grace" and "Working On A Building" (by Thomas Patton), recorded by The Spiritual Kings on Four Winds Record (black gospel).

FRANNE RECORDS, Box 8135, Chicago IL 60680. (312)224-5612. A&R Director/Executive Producer: R.C. Hillsman. Labels include Superbe Records. Record company, music publisher and producer. Works with artists and songwriters on contract. Pays 3½% royalty to artists and songwriters on contract.
How to Contact: Write or call to arrange personal interview. Prefers 7½ or 15 ips ¼″ reel-to-reel or cassette with 4-6 songs (or videocassette) and lyric sheet. Send material "by registered mail only." SASE. Reports in 3 weeks.
Music: Church/religious, country, disco, gospel, jazz, MOR, rock and top 40/pop. Released "He's Love" and "You Better Get Right," by Allen Duo (gospel singles).

FRESH ENTERTAINMENT, 3542 Garfield Way SE, Atlanta GA 30354. (404)642-2645. Vice President, Marketing/A&R: Willie Hunter. Record company and music publisher (Hserf Music/ASCAP). Releases 5 singles and 2 LPs/year. Works with musicians/artists and songwriters on contract. Pays standard royalty to artists on contract.

How to Contact: Prefers cassette (or VHS videocassette) with at least 3 songs and lyric sheet. SASE. Reports in 2 weeks.

Music: Mostly R&B, rock and pop; also jazz, gospel and rap. Released "Girls with Me," written and recorded by Ede' (pop single); "Tell the Story" (by W. Gates), recorded by J. Gates (dance 12" single); and "Love to Live" (by F. McKinney/B. James), recorded by Heart to Heart (R&B 12" single), all on Fresh Records. Other artists include Sir Anthony with Rare Quality, and Larion.

Tips: "We're a new label looking for new ideas and acts."

FRONTLINE MUSIC GROUP, 2955 East Main Street, Irvine CA 92713. Brian K. Tong. Labels include Alarma Records, Frontline Kid's, Intense Records, Joyful Heart Music, Alarma Intl, Mercy, New Breed, Cantio and Graceland. Record company, music publisher (Broken Songs Publishing/ASCAP, Carlotta Music BMI). Estab. 1985. Releases 100 singles, 75 LPs, and 70 CDs/year. Works with musicians/artists and songwriters on contract; musicians on salary for in-house studio work. Pays 75-100% statutory rate to publishers per song on record.

How to Contact: Prefers cassette (or VHS videocassette) with any number of songs and lyric sheet. Does not return unsolicited material. Must include SASE for return of product. "We only reply on those of interest — but if you've not heard from us within 4 weeks we're not interested."

Music: Mostly gospel/contemporary/Christian, rock/pop and R&B; also worship and praise, children's product and instrumental/jazz. Released *Change of Heart*, written and recorded by Jon Gibson (R&B LP); *Just Another Injustice*, written and recorded by Mark Farner (rock LP); and *Perfect*, written and recorded by Benny Hester on Frontline Records.

Tips: "Put your best songs at the top of the tape. Listen to product on the label and try writing for a specific artist. Be professional; please don't hound the label with calls."

*FUTURA INTERNATIONAL RECORDS INC., 10188 NW 47th St., Sunrise FL 33351. (305)572-4573. President: Tolga Katas. Record company and record producer (Tolga Katas Productions Inc.). Estab. 1988. Releases 11 singles, 11 12" singles, 4 LPs and 4 CDs/year. Works with musicians/artists and songwriters on contract. Pays statutory rate to publisher per song.

How to Contact: Call first and obtain permission to submit. Prefers cassette with 1-3 songs and lyric sheets. SASE. Reports in 2 weeks.

Music: Mostly pop, R&B and rock; also dance, rap and gospel. Released "Sending All My Love" (by Linear); "Just Another Love" (by Ray Guell); and "Love You Feel" (by Tony Marino); all recorded by Tolga on Futura Records (dance 12"). Other artists include Dr. Lateness and the Anti-Clocks, Tears on Edge, Linear, Al Turner.

Tips: "Keep sending demos of your music and don't ever give up. We're very interested in lots of material."

FUTURE STEP SIRKLE, Box 2095, Philadelphia PA 19103. (215)848-7475. A&R Director: S. Deane Henderson. Labels include Molecules of Force Records. Record company, record producer, music publisher (Communication Concept) and management firm. Releases 6-10 singles and 3-6 LPs/year. Works with artists and songwriters on contract. Pays 4-10% royalty to artists on contract; statutory rate to publishers for each record sold.

How to Contact: Prefers cassette (or VHS videocassette) with 4-8 songs and lyric sheet. "Lyrics only are returned." Reports in 2 weeks.

Music: Mostly R&B, funk, rock and heavy metal; also dance-oriented, easy listening, gospel, MOR, soul and top 40/pop. Released *In God's Hands*, by Verdell; *Save Me Jesus*, by Offspring Gospel (gospel LP); and "Exercise," by M.D.F. (dance single). Other artists include Dean Morrow, and Shonee.

*GALLERY II RECORDS, INC., Box 630755, Miami FL 33163. (305)935-4880. President: Jack Gale. Labels include Playback, Ridgewood and Caramba Records. Record company, music publisher (Lovey Music/BMI, Cowabonga Music/ASCAP). and record producer. Estab. 1983. Releases 25 singles, 6 LPs and 5 CDs/year. Works with musicians/artists and songwriters on contract and hires musicians for in-house studio work. Pays statutory rate to publishers per song on record.

How to Contact: Submit demo tape by mail. Unsolicited submissions are OK. Prefers cassette (or VHS videocassette) with 2 songs and lyric sheet. Reports in 1 week "if interested."

Music: Mostly contemporary country and traditional country. Released "If You Want My Love" (by H. Davis), recorded by Joy Norris on Gallery II; "Louisiana Love" (by J. Henderson), recorded by Jinny C. Newman on Ridgewood Records; and "Shame on the Moon" (by Rodney Crowell), recorded by Bonnie Guitar on Playback Records. Other artists include Jim Newberry, Sammi Smith, Del Reeves, Eddie Carpenter, Margo Smith, Kitty Wells, Mickey Rooney, Lynn Thomas, Borderline, Dennis Yost and the Classics IV and Bobby Bare.

Tips: "Have determination, be realistic; have a clear demo."

GATEWAY, 4960 Timbercrest, Canfield OH 44406. (216)533-9024. President: A. Conti. Labels include Endive. Record company, music publisher (Ashleycon, BMI), and record producer. Estab. 1987. Releases 6 cassettes/year. Works with musicians/artists and songwriters on contract. Pays 1-7% royalty to artists on contract; statutory and negotiable rate to publisher per song on record.
How to Contact: Submit demo tape by mail. Prefers cassette with 3 songs and lyric sheets. Reports in 6 weeks.
Music: Mostly new algorithmic, computer generated, new age; also R&B and pop. Released "Communications I," (by A. Conti), on Endive Records (algorithmic); "Can Can Canfield" (by A. Conti), on Endive Records (Amerothrust) and "Busy Business" (by A. Conti) on Endive Records (Incan). Other artists include Art Boyz, Rhythm Machine and Compose, February's, Ada Vice, and Algorithmic.

GEIMSTEINN HF, Skolaveg 12, Keflavik 230 **Iceland**. Phone: (92)12717. President/Manager: Runar Juliusson. Labels include Hljomar. Record company, music publisher and record producer.Estab. 1976. Releases 3-4 LPs and 3-4 CDs/year. Works with musicians/artists and songwriters on contract; musicians on salary for in-house studio work.
How to Contact: Write first and obtain permission to submit or to arrange personal interview. Prefers cassette (or VHS videocassette) with 2-3 songs and lyric sheet. Does not return unsolicited material.
Music: Mostly pop, rock and country; also jazz, R&B and gospel. Released "Mandala" and "All I Wannado" (by RJ. MK. GP.), recorded by Qunar on Geimst Records (pop); and "I Have I Dream" written and recorded by R.J. Bullhead on Geimst Records (R&B). Other artists include Pandora, Bullhead, and Sing Sing.

*GENESEE RECORDS, INC., 7931 Genesee, Litchfield MI 49252. (517)542-3051. President: Junior A. Cole. Record company, music publisher (J.A. Cole Publishing) and record producer. Releases 3 singles/year. Works with musicians/artists on contract.
How to Contact: Prefers cassette. SASE. Reports in 6 weeks.
Music: Country. Released *In the Name Freedom*, by J. Cole (LP); and "Sleepless Blue," by D. Pack (single), both recorded by Country Express on Genesse Records.

GENLYD GRAMMOFON ApS, Haraldsgade 23, 8260 Viby J **Denmark**. Contact: A&R Director. Record company, music publisher (Genlyd Publishing, NCB/Denmark) and record producer (Genlyd Grammofon ApS.) Estab. 1975. Works with musicians/artists on contract and licenses foreign companies.
How to Contact: Submit demo tape by mail. Unsolicited submissions are okay. Prefers cassette with 1-3 songs and lyric sheets. SAE and IRC. Reports in 4 weeks.
Music: Mostly R&B, rock, pop and country. Artists include Gnags, Sos Fenger, Arvid, Thomas Helmig, and Henning Staerk. Released *Even Cowgirls*, by SOS Fenger (C&W); *Cheque Book*, by Henning Staerk (rock) and *I Don't Mind* by Henning Staerk.
Tips: "Being a Danish/Scandinavian label we are from time to time in need of experienced lyricists capable of working with highly successful local acts on English versions of local hits. That should, however, not prevent songwriters from getting in touch, since we are always interested in good songs for those of our acts who don't write their own material."

GET WIT IT PRODUCTION RECORDS, Mott Haven Station, Box 986, Bronx NY 10454. (212)292-8104. Executive Producer: Eddie Rivera. Labels include Get Wit It Production records. Record company (G.W.I.P Records/ASCAP) and record producer (G.W.I.P Records). Estab. 1988. Releases 3 12" singles, 2 LPs, 2 EPs/, and 2CDs/year. Works with musicians/artists on contract. Pays 7% royalty to artists on contract; statutory rate to publisher per song on record.
How to Contact: Submit demo tape by mail. Unsolicited submissions are okay. Prefers cassette, 30 ips reel-to-reel or VHS videocassette with song and lyric sheets. Does not return unsolicited material. Reports in 3 weeks.
Music: Mostly rap, R&B and pop; also non-commercial rap and R&B ballads. Released "Are You Ready?" (by Eddie/Dwayne), "Spanish Fly" (by Eddie Rivera) and "The Beat Goes On" (by Eddie/Dwayne); all recorded by K-Rock on G.W.I.P. Records (all rap singles).
Tips: "The quickest way to get our A&R directors attention is to prepare your demo the way you think the public would most accept your production. We focus and work on the artist's interest if we feel your style has potential."

GLOBAL PACIFIC RECORDS, 180 E. Napa St., Sonoma CA 95476. (707)996-2748. A&R Director: Howard Morris. Record company and music publisher (Global Pacific Publishing). Releases 12 LPs and 12 CDs/year. Works with musicians/artists and songwriters on contract; hires musicians for in-house studio work. Pays statutory rate to publishers per song on records.

How to Contact: Call first and obtain permission to submit. Prefers cassette with 3 songs. "Note style of music on envelope." Does not return unsolicited material. Reports in 3 months.
Music: Mostly new age, pop, jazz, "pop/quiet storm"; also rock, blues and classical. Released *Dolphin Smiles*, written and recorded by Steve Kindler and Teja Bell; *One Mind*, written and recorded by Joaquin Lievano; and *Global Village*, written and recorded by Tor Dietrichson, all on Global Pacific Records (all LPs). Other artists include Paul Horn, Bob Kindler, David Friesen, Georgia Kelly, Ben Tavera King and Paul Greaver.
Tips: "Write us a hit! Know your label and market you are targeting."

GLOBAL RECORD CO., P.O. Box 396, 133 Arbutus Ave., Manistique MI 49854-0396. President: Reg B. Christensen. Labels include Bakersfield Record Company. Record company and music publisher (Chris Music/BMI and Sara Lee Music/BMI). Estab. 1956. Releases 10-15 singles, 6-10 LPs, and 5 CDs/year. Works with artists and songwriters on contract. Pays 10-20% royalty to artists on contract; statutory rate to publishers for each record sold.
How to Contact: Prefers cassette with 3 songs and lyric sheet. SASE. Reports in 1 month.
Music: Mostly top 40, R&B, country, MOR, rock, and novelty types. Released "Stop, Don't Break My Heart (by P. Zoller), recorded by Dianna Greer on Global Records (MOR); "Cross the Line" (by Destiny), recorded by Destiny on Global Records (rock) and "Is It Really Christmas In L.A." (by P. Alter/S.Alter), recorded by Destiny on Global Records (Christmas rock). Other artists include The Motivators, The Agitators, and Intermissions.
Tips: "We hear from many lyric writers—we cannot use lyric only. We tell all of them to contact a musician through the musician's union, and if there is no union in your area, a musician who can work with you and come up with a melody. Songs should be 2½ to 3 minutes long. Be patient."

*GOLD CASTLE RECORDS, 3575 Cahuenga Blvd., West #435, Los Angeles CA 90068. (213)850-3321. President: Paula Jeffries. Record company. Estab. 1986. Releases 10 singles, 12 LPs and 12 CDs/year. Works with musicians/artists and songwriters on contract.
How to Contact: Write first and obtain permission to submit. Prefers cassette. SASE. Reports in 3 months.
Music: Mostly folk, new age/acoustic jazz. Released *Speaking of Dreams*, recorded by Joan Baez (folk LP); *Vanilla*, recorded by Cybill Shepherd (jazz vocal); and *Cardboard Confessional*, recorded by Darius (folk); all on Gold Castle Records. Other artists include Don McLean, Eliza Gilkyson, Eric Andersen, Peter, Paul and Mary, David Hayes, Bruce Cockburn and The Washington Squares.
Tips: "Don't just blindly send a tape. Find out our needs first. The best possible thing would be to submit through a manager, publisher or personal contact with the company. We return all unsolicited tapes!"

GOLD CITY RECORDS, INC., Box 24, Armonk NY 10504. (914)273-6457. President: Chris Jasper. Vice President: Margie Jasper. Labels include Gold City Label (with distribution through majors, including CBS). Record company. Estab. 1986. Releases 5-10 singles, 5-10 12" singles, 3-5 LPs and 3-5 CDs/year. Works with musicians/artists and songwriters on contract and hires musicians for in-house studio work. Pays negotiable rate to publisher per song on record.
How to Contact: Submit demo tape by mail. Unsolicited submissions are okay. Prefers cassette with 3 songs and lyric sheets. SASE. Reports in 6 weeks.
Music: Mostly R&B/rap, pop and rock. Released *Superbad* and "One Time Love," written and recorded by Chris Jasper; *Vicious & Fresh*, recorded by Liz Hogue; all on Gold City/CBS Records (all R&B/pop).

GOLDBAND RECORDS, Box 1485, Lake Charles LA 70602. (318)439-8839. President: Eddie Shuler. Labels include Folk-Star, Tek, Tic-Toc, Anla, Jador and Luffcin Records. Record company and record producer. Works with artists and songwriters on contract; musicians on salary for in-house studio work. Pays 3-5% royalty to artists on contract; standard royalty to songwriters on contract.
How to Contact: Prefers cassette with 2-6 songs and lyric sheet. SASE. Reports in 2 months.
Music: Blues, country, easy listening, folk, R&B, rock and top 40/pop. Released *Katie Webster Has the Blues* (blues LP), and "Things I Used to Do" (blues single), by Katie Webster; "Waiting For My Child," by Milford Scott (spiritual single); "Gabriel and Madaline," by Johnny Jano (cajun country single); and "Cajun Disco," by the La Salle Sisters (disco single). Other artists incude Jimmy House, John Henry III, Gary Paul Jackson, Junior Booth, Rockin Sidney, Ralph Young, Tedd Dupin, R. Sims, Mike Young and Everett Brady.

GOLDEN BOY RECORDS, 3929 Kentucky Dr., Los Angeles CA 90068. (818)980-7501. A&R Director: Billy Johnson. Labels include Golden Boy and Alva. Record company. Releases 6 singles and 2 LPs/year. Works with artists on contract.

How to Contact: Prefers cassette (or videocassette) with maximum 3 songs and lyric sheet. Reports in 3 weeks.
Music: Mostly R&B, urban, dance and soul; also jazz.

*GOLDEN TRIANGLE RECORDS, 1051 Saxonburg Blvd., Glenshaw PA 15116. Producer: Sunny James. Labels include Rocken Robin. Record company (Golden Triangle/BMI) and record producer (Sunny James). Estab. 1987. Releases 5 singles, 4 12" singles, 10 LPs and 1 CD/year. Works with musicians/artists and songwriters on contract and hires musicians for in-house studio work. Pays 7-8% royalty; statutory rate to publishers per song on record.
How to Contact: Submit demo tape by mail. Unsolicited submissions are okay. Prefers cassette, 15 IPS reel-to-reel (or ½" VHS videocassette) with 3 songs and lyric or lead sheets. Does not return unsolicited material.
Music: Mostly progressive R&B, rock and adult contemporary; also jazz and country. Released "Dreamboat" and San Antone" (by R. Craven), recorded by Sound Images; and "Blue Moon" (by Fred Johnson), recorded by Golden Triangle, all on Golden Triangle Records (singles). Other artists incvlude The original Mr. Bassman Fred Johnson of the Marcels (Blue Moon), Rick Holiday, Sonic Ted, Sil Rossini, Hotline, Arnel (Elvis) Pomp and Steve Grice (The Boxtops).
Tips: "Please contact us as we are always interested in the creativeness of new artists."

*GO-ROC-CO-POP RECORDS, 1611 Hickory Valley Rd., Chattanooga TN 37421. (615)899-9685. President: B.J. Keener. Labels include WAR Records. Record company. Estab. 1984. Releases 4-5 singles and 2-5 LPs/year. Works with musicians/artists and songwriters on contract and hires musicians for in-house studio work. Pays standard royalty to artists on contract.
How to Contact: Write first and obtain permission to submit. Prefers cassette with 1-2 songs and lyric and lead sheets. SASE. Reports in 3 months.
Music: Mostly country, gospel and MOR; also jazz, R&B and pop. Released *I Wonder* (by Stan Ramey), recorded by Tim Whalen (pop/cassette); *Tennessee Hills*, written and recorded by Tim Whalen (country/cassette); and *The Child* (by Dick Bell), recorded by Rapture (MOR/cassette); all on Go-Roc-Co-Pop Records. Other artists include LaWanda, Topaz, Joe Cleve, Johnny Sue, Scotty Duran and Billy Joe.
Tips: "Be sincere, hard working and flexible, with a desire to succeed."

GRASS ROOTS RECORD & TAPE/LMI RECORDS, Box 532, Malibu CA 90265. (213)463-5998. President: Lee Magid. Labels include Grass Roots and LMI Records. Record company, record producer, music publisher (Alexis/ASCAP, Marvelle/BMI, Lou-Lee/BMI) and management firm (Lee Magid Management Co.). Member AIMP, NARAC. Estab. 1967. Releases 4 LPs and 4 CDs/year. Works with musicians/artists and songwriters on contract. Pays 2-5% royalty to artists on contract; pays statutory rate to publishers per song record.
How to Contact: Prefers cassette with 3 songs and lyric sheet. "Please, no 45s." SASE. Reports in 1 month minimum.
Music: Mostly pop/rock, R&B, country, gospel, jazz/rock and blues; also bluegrass, children's and Latin. Released "What Shall I Do?" (by Quincy Fielding Jr.), "Whenever You Call" (by Calvin Rhone), and "I Got Joy" (by Quincy Fielding Jr.) all recorded by Tremaine Hawkins on Sparrow Records (gospel/R&B).Other artists include Gloria Lynne, L.A. Jazz Choir, Papa John Creach and Kim and Sam.

GROOVE AND MOVE RECORDS, Unit 11, Forest Business Park, South Access Rd., Walthamstow, London E17 8BA **England**. A&R Director: Glenn Payne. Labels include Jump Start Records. Record company, music publisher (Groove & Move Music, Leosong). Estab. 1987.
How to Contact: Submit demo tape by mail. Unsolicited submissions okay. Prefers cassette. SASE. Reports in 4 weeks.
Music: Mostly dance. Released "Rhythm Of The Night" (by Brailford/Thomas/Ell), recorded by Fatback (soul single); *Live* (by various), recorded by Betty Wright (soul LP); and "Instant Attitude" (by S. Sims), recorded by Nini (dance single); "Megamix" recorded by The Village People, all on Groove & Move Records. Other artists include Maria Chapelle, Zoo, and Michael Salaure.

 The asterisk before a listing indicates that the listing is new in this edition. New markets are often the most receptive to unsolicited submissions.

Tips: "Be professional in your approach. When appointments are made make sure you turn up. Use good quality cassettes so that your songs sound good when recorded. There is nothing worse than trying to listen to a completely muffled sound."

GULFSTREAM RECORDS, 4225 Palm St., Baton Rouge LA 70808. (504)383-7885. President: Barrie Edgar. Record company, music publisher (Silverfoot) and record producer (Hogar). Estab. 1980.Works with musicians/artists and songwriters on contract; musicians on salary for in-house studio work. Pays 3-6% royalty to artists on contract. Pays statutory rate to publishers per song on records.
How to Contact: Prefers cassette with 4 songs and lyric sheet. SASE. "Patience required on reports."
Music: Mostly rock and country. Released "Louisiana's Basin Child," by Top Secret on Gulfstream Records (rock single). Other artists include Joe Costa.

HACIENDA RECORDS, 1236 S. Staples, Corpus Christi TX 78404. (512)882-7066. Owner: Roland Garcia. Producer: Rick Garcia. Labels include Las Brisas. Record company, music publisher (Alpenglow Music, Dark Heart Music, El Palacio Music, Roland Garcia Music) and record producer. Releases 20-100 singles and 5-20 LPs/year. Works with artists and songwriters on contract; musicians on salary for in-house studio work. Pays royalties or per LP to artists on contract.
How to Contact: Prefers cassette. Does not return unsolicited material. Reporting time varies.
Music: Rock, Spanish and country, pop, MOR, international and gospel. Released "Ready as Hell," (by Jim D./Ricky R./Johnny C.), recorded by Jim Dandy's Black Oak Arkansas (rock single & LP), "It's Majic," (by Pio Trevino), recorded by Majic (English single from Spanish LP); and "Ran Kan Kan," (by Tito Puente), recorded by Steve Jordan (Spanish single), all on Hacienda Records. Other artists include Freddy Fender, Romance, Gary Hobbs, Fuego, Janie C., Steve Borth and Rowdy Friends.

H&S RECORDS, P.O. Box 515, Waterloo, Ontario N2J 4A9 **Canada**. (519)741-1252. President: William Seip. Record company and music publisher (William Seip Music, Inc.). Estab. 1978. Releases 1-2 LPs and 1-2 CDs/year. Works with musicians/artists on contract. Pays negotiable royalty to artists on contract.
How to Contact: Prefers cassette with 3 songs and lyric sheet. Does not return unsolicited material. Reports in 1 month.
Music: Mostly commercial rock, top 40 and hard rock. Released *Breaking Loose* and *White Lace and Black Leather*, written and recorded by Helix; and *Run For Cover*, written and recorded by Vigilants all on H&S Records (all hard rock LPs).

HAPPY BEAT RECORDS, Box 266775, Houston TX 77207. President: Roger L. Cummings. Labels include MSB Records. Record company, music publisher (Sirloin Music Publishing/BMI), promotion and distribution firm. Releases 5 singles and 3 LPs/year. Works with artists and songwriters on contract; and hires musicians for in-house studio work. Pays negotiable royalty to artists on contract; negotiable rate to publishers for each record sold.
How to Contact: Prefers cassette with 3-6 songs and lyric sheet. "Don't send your master. State speed on videocassette box. Artists should include photo." SASE. Reports in 1 month.
Music: Mostly rock, soul and dance; also blues, jazz, R&B and top 40/pop. Released "Let the Music in Your Mind," by Chance (dance single); and *Drum Licks*, by Friction (drum songs EP). Other artists include Carl Adams, Steve Cummings, Carl Stewart and Invasion.

HARD HAT RECORDS AND CASSETTES, 519 N. Halifax Ave., Daytona Beach FL 32118. (904)252-0381. President: Bobby Lee Cude. Labels include Hard Hat, Maricao, Blue Bandana and Indian Head. Record company, record producer and music publisher (Cude & Pickens Publishing/BMI). Estab. 1978. Releases 12 singles and 12 LPs/year.
How to Contact: Write first. Does not use outside material.
Music: Mostly country; also easy listening, gospel, MOR, top 40/pop and Broadway show. Released "V-A-C-A-T-I-O-N," (by Cude & Pickens) recorded by the Hard Hatters; "Just a Piece of Paper," and "Worried Worried Man," (both by Cude & Pickens) recorded by Blue Bandana Country Band; "Who's Lovin' You" and "Shot In the Dark" by Caz Allen (pop); "Tennessee's On My Mind" and "Texas Red, White and Blue Step" by Caz Allen (country); all are singles on Hard Hat Label. Other artists include "Pic" Pickens, Hula Kings, Caribbean Knights and Cityfolks Country Band.

Listings of companies in foreign countries have the name of the country in boldface type.

HARMONY STREET RECORDS, Box 4107, Kansas City, KS 66104. (913)299-2881. President: Charlie Beth. Record company, music publisher (Harmony Street Music/ASCAP and Harmony Lane Music/BMI), and record producer (Harmony Street Productions). Estab. 1985. Releases 10-20 singles and 4-6 LPs/year. Works with musicians/artists and songwriters on contract; musicians on salary for in-house studio work. Pays 10% royalty to artists on contract; pays statutory rate to publishers per song on record.

How to Contact: Prefers cassette (or VHS videocassette) with no more than 3 songs and lyric or lead sheet. SASE. Reports in 3 weeks.

Music: Mostly country (all types) and gospel (all types). Released "We Can't Live Together" written and recorded by Terry Allen (country); "Touch the Hem of His Garment" written and recorded by Darlene McCreary (gospel); and "Don't Put it Off" (by Judy Carroll) recorded by Jaycee Young (gospel), all on Harmony Street Records.Other artists include Perfect Harmony and 50/50.

Tips: "Songs submitted to us must be original, commercial and have a good strong hook. Submit only your best songs. Demos should be clear and clean with voice out front. We are interested in working with commercial artists with a commercial style and sound, professional attitude and career goals."

*HAZARDOUS RECORDS, 17 Water St., Dracut MA 01826. (508)957-5781. A&R: Henry Rowe. Labels include Moonview Records. Record company. Estab. 1986. Releases 2 singles and 2 LPs/year. Works with musicians/artists and songwriters on contract and hires musicians for in-house studio work. Pays statutory rate to publishers per song on records.

How to Contact: Submit demo tape by mail. Unsolicited submissions are okay. Prefers cassette, 15 IPS reel-to-reel (or VHS videocassette) with 4-6 songs and lyric sheet.

Music: Mostly metal, rock and pop; also fusion, jazz and New Age. Released "Half Life" and "Danger Zone," by Hazardous Waste (metal); and "Candle to the Magic," by Johann Smith (rock), all recorded by Makin Tracks on Hazardous Records.

HEART LAND RECORDS, P.O. Box 16572, Kansas City MO 64133. (816)358-2542. Executive Producer: Jimmy Lee. Record company, music publisher (Jellee Works Music/BMI, Jellee Music Works/ASCAP), record producer (Jimmy Lee/Heart Land Records) and Jellee Works Productions—doing songwriter demos mail order for 6 years. Estab. 1982. Releases 6-8 singles and 4-6 LPs/year. Works with musicians/artists and songwriters on contract and hires musicians for in-house studio work. Pays 8-10% royalty to artists on contract; statutory rate to publisher per song on record.

How to Contact: Write first and obtain permission to submit. Prefers cassette (or VHS videocassette) with no more than 2 songs and lyric sheets. SASE. Reports in 5 weeks.

Music: Mostly country, gospel and pop; also R&B and light rock. Released *You Just Never Know* by Joe Donovan; *Singing Mama's Songs* by Kevin Eason; and *Imagine* by Jimmy Lee, all on Heart Land Records. Other artists include Jimmy Lee, Kevin Eason and Max Berry.

Tips: "Be professional and be patient. Be willing to work hard. Success comes to those willing to work the hardest. Don't give up!"

HEATH & ASSOCIATES, #1058, E. Saint Catherine, Louisville KY 40204. (502)637-2877. General Partner: John V. Heath. Labels include Hillview Records and Estate Records. Record company, music publisher (Two John's Music/ASCAP), record producer (MTV Productions) and Just a Note/BMI. Estab. 1979. Releases 6 singles, 6-8 12″ singles, 4 LPs, 2 EPs and 4 CDs/year. Works with musicians/artists and songwriters on contract. Pays 5% royalty to artists on contract; statutory rate to publisher per song on record.

How to Contact: Submit demo tape by mail. Unsolicited submissions are okay. Prefers cassette, 7½ ips reel-to-reel or VHS videocassette with 3 songs and lead sheets. SASE. Reports in 2 weeks.

Music: Mostly pop, country, R&B and MOR; also gospel. Released "Country Music Memories" (by Cece Whittaker), recorded by Cece Whittaker on EOP Records (country); "Night Visions" (by Adonis), recorded by Adonis on Estate Records (R and R) and "Heartbreak Tears" (by Hebert Family), recorded by Hebert Family on Hillview Records (country) and *Album by Jimmy Lee* (by Jim Palko), recorded by Jimmy Lee on Estate Records (c&w). Other artists include Artis Steel.

*HEAVY METAL RECORDS, 152 Goldthorn Hill, Penn, Wolverhampton, WV2 3VA **England**. Phone: 44-(0902)-345345. A&R Director: David Roberts. Labels include Heavy Metal Records, Revolver Records, Heavy Metal America, Heavy Metal Worldwide and FM Records. Record company, record producer (FM-Revolver Records Ltd.) and music publisher (Rocksong Music Publishing Ltd./PRS). Releases 10 singles, 10 12″ singles, 20 LPs and 30 EPs/year. Works with musicians/artists and songwriters on contract. Pays negotiable royalty to artists on contract; statutory rate to publishers per song on record.

How to Contact: Prefers cassette with 1-3 songs. "Send photos and bios." Does not return unsolicited material. Reports in 1 month.

Music: Mostly heavy metal/hard rock, AOR/FM rock and "alternative" guitar-based rock; also dance and pop. Released *Waiting for a Miracle*, written and recorded by Bruce Cockburn on Revolver Records (LP); and *Mirador* (by Tony Clarkin), recorded by Magnum on FM Records (LP). Other artists include The Vibrators, Wrathchild, Lisa Dominique, White Sister, Tobruk and John Slaman.

Tips: "European record companies pay higher royalties than American record companies (though not necessarily higher advances)."

HELION RECORDS, 8306 Wilshire Blvd., Suite 216, Beverly Hills CA 90211. (818)845-2849. Vice President, Record Division: Nick Schepperle. Record company and record producer (Greg Knowles). Estab. 1984. Releases 4 LPs and 4 CDs/year. Works with musicians/artists on contract; hires musicians for in-house studio work. Pays 3-6% royalty to artists on contract; statutory rate to publisher for each record sold.

How to Contact: Prefers cassette with 3-4 songs and lyric or lead sheet. Does not return unsolicited material. Reports in 3 weeks.

Music: Mostly R&B and pop; also country and comedy. Released *Angel* and "Telephone Blues," by Diana Blair; *A Family of Friends* by Country West; a jazz album by Miriam Cutler and Swingstreet and *Groove With Me* by Jan Marie (R&B).

Tips: "Treat your work as a business first and an art form second. You need the business head to get you into the door – then we can see how good your music is."

HIGHLAND RECORDS, Box 554, Los Gatos CA 95031. (408)353-3952. Producer: Joe Weed. Record company, music publisher (Highland Records/BMI) and record producer (Joe Weed). Estab. 1987. Releases 2-3 LPs and 2-3 CDs/year. Works with songwriters on contract and hires musicians for in-house studio work. Pays current industry norm to publisher per song on record.

How to Contact: Write first and obtain permission to submit. Prefers cassette or 15 ips reel-to-reel. Does not return unsolicited material. Reports back in "a few weeks."

Music: Instrumental only and acoustic; also new age, folk, "new acoustic" and ethnic. Released "No Bow Tie," "Solomon's Dream" and "Dream of the Manatee" (by Joe Weed), recorded by Joe Weed on Gourd Records (folk). Other artists include Scott Freed and Chuck McCabe.

HIX STUDIOS, (formerly Perfect Pitch Recording and Production Co.), 2901 Hwy. 70 W., Hickory NC 28602. (704)328-2487. President: Marcus Kearns. Record company, music publisher (Melomuque Publishing) and record producer (Marcus Kearns). Releases 2 singles and 2 LPs/year. Works with musicians/artists and songwriters on contract. Pays variable royalty to artists on contract; pays statutory rate to publisher per song on record.

How to Contact: Prefers cassette or 15 ips reel-to-reel with 3-8 songs and lyric sheet. SASE. Reports in 3 months

Music: Mostly new age, soft A/C rock, jazz/classical fusion. Released *What the Wind Whispers*, by Marcus Kearns (cassette).

HOLLYROCK RECORDS, Suite C-300, 16776 Lakeshore Dr., Lake Elisnore CA 92330. A&R Director: Dave Paton. Record company, record producer and music publisher (Heaven Songs/BMI). Releases 4 singles and 6 LPs/year. Works with artists and songwriters on contract; musicians on salary for in-house studio work. Pays negotiable royalty to artists on contract; statutory rate to publishers for each record sold.

How to Contact: Prefers 7½ ips reel-to-reel or cassette with 3-6 songs and lyric sheet. SASE. Reports in 2 weeks.

Music: Progressive, top 40/pop, country, easy listening, folk, jazz, MOR and rock. Released *Everything* (movie soundtrack).

HOTTRAX RECORDS, 1957 Kilburn Dr., Atlanta GA 30324. (404)662-6661. Vice President, A&R: Oliver Cooper. Labels include: Dance-A-Thon, Hardkor. Record company and music publisher (Starfox Publishing). Releases 12 singles and 3-4 LPs/year. Works with musicians/artists and songwriters on contract. Pays 5-7% royalty to artists on contract.

How to Contact: Prefers cassette with 3 songs and lyric sheet. SASE. "We will not return tapes without adequate postage." Reports in 3 months.

Music: Mostly top 40/pop, rock and country; also hard core punk and jazz-fusion. Released *P Is For Pig*, written and recorded by The Pigs (top 40/pop LP); "The World May Not Like Me," (by Mike Fitzgerald), recorded by Mike Angelo (rock single); and *Introducing The Feel*, written and recorded by The Feel (new rock LP) all on Hottrax Records; and "The Condom Man," recorded by Big Al Jano. Other artists include Burl Compton (country), Michael Rozakis & Yorgos (pop), Starfoxx (rock), The Night Shadows (rock), The Bop (new wave), and Secret Lover.

ICE RECORDS INC., Suite 211A, Nypenn Trade Center, Johnson City NY 13790. (607)729-2291. President: Larry Lupole. Vice President/Marketing: Mike English. Music publisher (Larry Gene Music/BMI and J-Paul/ASCAP) and record company (Ice Records, Inc.). Releases 3-5 singles, 2-3 LPs, 1 EP and 2-3 CDs/year. Works with musicians/artists and songwriters on contract; hires musicians for in-house studio work. Pays negotiable royalty to artists on contract; statutory rate to publisher per song on record.

How to Contact: Query first. Prefers cassette or 7½ ips reel-to-reel with 2-6 songs and lyric or lead sheet. Does not return unsolicited material. Reports in 2 months.

Music: Mostly pop, country and rock; also R&B and gospel. Released *Ray Agnew*, self titled (country/folk CD and cassette); "Catskill Mountain Home" (country/folk single) written and recorded by Ray Agnew. Other artists include David Sweet (New Age) all on Ice Records.

Tips: "We can't stress enough to the beginner artist/songwriter that when creating compositions stick to one basic idea. Too many lyrics we recieve are too vague."

*IDAHO RECORDS AND CASSETTES, P.O. Box 474, Clayton ID 83227. (208)879-4677. Contact: Muzzie Braun. Record company and music publisher (Idaho Records and Cassettes and Muzzie Music/ASCAP). Estab. 1979. Releases 1-2 singles and 2 LPs/year. Pays statutory rate to publishers per song on records.

How to Contact: Write or call first and obtain permission to submit. Prefers cassette with 3 songs. Does not return unsolicited material. Reports in 2 months.

Music: Mostly Western, country-Western. Released *Braun Family Xmas*; *Muzzie Braun & Little Braun Bros*; and *Muzzie & The Boys* all (by M. Braun), recorded by Braun Family on Idaho Records (LP).

Tips: "We are looking for Western material to be sung in harmony by four sons and a father. No cry in yer beer stuff."

IGL AUDIO, Shore Acres, Box 100, Spirit Lake IA 51360. (712)336-2859. President: John Senn. Record company, record producer and music publisher (Okoboji Music). Releases 10 singles and 6 LPs/year. Works with artists and songwriters on contract; hires musicians for in-house studio work. Pays 8% maximum royalty to artists on contract; statutory rate to publishers for each record sold.

How to Contact: Prefers cassette with 1-5 songs and lyric sheet. SASE. Reports in 1 month.

Music: Mostly modern country (rock/pop) and church/religious; also gospel and top 40/pop. Released "Love Tender Love," by DJ & the Runaways (country single); and *American Heritage*, by American Heritage (religious LP). Other artists include Vegas and Becky Weber.

Tips: "We are looking for both up-tempo and slower-type country, pop and gospel songs with strong modern lyrics and melodies."

IMAGINARY RECORDS, 332 N. Dean Rd., Auburn AL 36830. (205)821-JASS. Proprietor: Lloyd Townsend, Jr. Record company, music publisher (Imaginary Music), record producer (Mood Swing Productions) and distribution firm (Imaginary Distribution). Estab. 1982. Releases 1-2 singles, 1-2 LPs, 1-2 EP and 2-3 CDs/year. Works with musicians/artists and songwriters on contract; "will manufacture custom cassettes for a set price." Pays sales royalty when song or artist is recorded, 10-12% royalty to artists on contract; statutory rate to publisher per song on record.

How to Contact: Prefers cassette or 7½ ips reel-to-reel with 4 songs and lyric or lead sheet. Submissions not returned unless accompanied by SASE. Tapes may be retained for future reference unless return is specifically requested." Reports in 3 months.

Music: Mostly jazz, blues and rock; also classical, folk and spoken word. Released *Electronic Syncopations* (by Scott Joplin), recorded by Patrick Mahoney on Imaginary Records (ragtime); *Hexaphony* (by Somtow Sucharitkul), recorded by Somtow Sucharitkul on Imaginary (avante-garde/world) and *Sonic Defense Initiative* on Imaginary (rock). Other artists include Slow Natives, Kidd Blue, The Moderns, Paul and The Quest, Bone Dali, Nothing Personal, Bob Richardson, Patrick Mahoney, Auburn Knights Orchestra and Yardbird Orchectra.

INTREPID RECORD, Box 2803, Grand Rapids MI 49501. (713)225-5775. Director of Operations: Rick Eyk. Record company and record producer (Rick Eyk). Releases 3 singles and 2 LPs/year. Works with musicians/artists and songwriters on contract. Pays "equitable" royalty to artists on contract; statutory rate to publisher per song on record.

How to Contact: Prefers cassette (or VHS videocassette) or 7½ ips reel-to-reel with maximum of 7 songs, lyric sheet and bio. SASE. Reports in 1 month.

Music: Mostly rock, new music, country and jazz; also classical and blues. Released *Somethin To Say* (by Rick Eyk), recorded by Litte Edward and The G Men on Intrepid Records (cassette).

Tips: "Along with your demo, it's nice to have a personal bio which includes some insight into the artist beyond the usual hype."

ISBA RECORDS, INC., 1327 Boul St. Joseph Est, Montréal (Québec) H2J 1M1 **Canada**. (514)522-4722. A&R: Maurice Velenosi. Record company and record producer. Estab. 1984. Releases 10 singles, 3 12″ singles, 6 LPs and 4 CDs/year. Works with musicians/artists on contract. Pays 5-7% royalty to artists on contract; statutory rate to publisher per song on record.
How to Contact: Write first and obtain permission to submit. Prefers cassette (or VHS videocassette) with 3 songs and lyric sheets. Does not return unsolicited material. Reports in 4 weeks.
Music: Mostly rock, pop and dance. Released *El Mundo* (by various writers), *Les B.B.*, by Les B.B. (pop rock); all on ISBA Records. Other artists include Diodati, Robert Sart, Nuance, Robert Stefan, Bogart, Robert Leroux, HDV, Paris and Black. musicians/artists on contract.

J.L.I. RECORDS, Box 74-R, Romeoville IL 60441. (815)886-3929. President: Julian Leal. Record company, music publisher (J.L.I. Music/BMI) and record producer (J.L.I. Productions). Estab. 1984. Releases 1-2 singles, 1 12″ single, 2 LPs, 1-2 EPs and 1-2 CDs/year. Works with musicians/artists and songwriters on contract. Pays "standard" royalty to artists on contract. Pays statutory rate to publisher per song on record.
How to Contact: Write first and obtain permission to submit. Prefers cassette (or VHS videocassette) with 3-6 songs. SASE. Reports in 6 weeks.
Music: Mostly rock and pop; also metal. Released "Just a Dream," written and recorded by Julian Leal (pop-rock single); "Little Darling" (by Julian Leal), recorded by The Villains (rock single); and *Forever*, written and recorded by The Villains (rock LP); all on J.L.I. Records. Other artists include The Villains, Fuller Forces, Comfort South, Beatwalker, and Duke Rocky.
Tips: "When writing for permission to submit, please enclose a press-sheet or bio information."

JALYN RECORDING CO., 351 Millwood Dr., Nashville TN 37217. (615)366-9999. President: Jack Lynch. Labels include Nashville Bluegrass and Nashville Country Recording Company. Record company, music publisher (Jaclyn Music/BMI), record producer, film company (Nashville Country Productions) and distributor (Nashville Music Sales). Estab. 1963. Releases 1-12 singles and 1-12 LPs/year. Works with musicians/artists and songwriters on contract; hires musicians for in-house studio work; also produces custom sessions. Pays 5-10% royalty to artists on contract; statutory rate to publisher per song on record.
How to Contact: Write or call first. Prefers cassette with 1 song and lyric sheet. SASE. Reports in 1 week.
Music: Country, bluegrass, gospel and MOR. Released "I Wonder Why" (by Ray Cline), recorded by Ralph Stanley on Nashville Country Records (bluegrass); "In My Mind" (by Richard Lynch), recorded by Richard Lynch on Nashville Country Records (country) and "Goldmine of Love" (by Lynch & Adkins), recorded by Jack Lynch on Nashville Country Records (bluegrass).Other artists include Ralph Stanley, Dave Evans, Country Gentlemen, Larry Sparks and Benny Williams.
Tips: "We prefer songs with good lyrics that tell a story with a certain amount of rhyming, a good melody sung by a good singer, and as good a production as is feasible. Our biggest need is good, commercial country songs."

JAMAKA RECORD CO., 3621 Heath Ln., Mesquite TX 75150. (214)279-5858. Contact: Jimmy Fields. Labels include Felco, and Kick Records. Record producer and music publisher (Cherie Music/BMI). Estab. 1955. Releases 2 singles/year. Works with artists and songwriters on contract; hires musicians for in-house studio work. Works with in-house studio musicians on salary. Pays .05% royalty to artists on contract; statutory rate to publishers for each record sold.
How to Contact: Prefers cassette with songs and lyric sheet. "A new singer should send a good tape with at least 4 strong songs, presumably recorded in a professional studio." Does not return without return postage and proper mailing package. "The post office has written me about returning cassettes in envelopes; they crush, and damage their equipment. I am holding over 5,000 tapes that came without return postage." Reports ASAP.
Music: Country and progressive country. Released "Stand Up For Your Country (And the Color of Your Flag)" (by J. Fields/D. Fields/Kern/Ray), recorded by Ronnie Ray; "Jessie James" and "Let's Save the Memories" (by Curk Ryles), recorded by Ronnie Ray; "Big Iron House" (by George McCoy), recorded by Cliff Price; all on Jamaka Records (modern country). Other artists include Bobby Belev, The Blue Lady, Jim Kern, George McCoy, Lucky LaRue, Bobby Crown, Billy Taylor and Susan Stutts.
Tips: "Songs should have strong lyrics with a good story, whether country or pop."

J&J MUSICAL ENTERPRISES LTD., Box 575, Kings Park NY 11754. (516)265-5584. Contact: Jeneane Claps. Labels include JAJ Records. Record company, music publisher (Jeneane & Jude Music/ASCAP) and record producer. Estab. 1983. Releases 2-3 singles, 1-2 12″ singles, 1-2 LPs, 1-2 EPs and 1-2 CDs/year. Works with musicians/artists on contract and hires musicians for in-house studio work. Pays variable royalty to artists on contract; varible rate to publisher per song on records.

How to Contact: Write first and obtain permission to submit. Prefers cassette with 4 songs and lyric sheet. Does not return unsolicited material. Reports in 1 month. "Typed letters preferred."
Music: Mostly progressive and jazz. Released *Textile*, recorded by Freeway Fusion on JAJ Records (progressive jazz).
Tips: "Be neat and clear as to what you're requesting from our company."

JEWISH FAMILY PRODUCTIONS, 8116 Aedan Ct., San Diego CA 92120. (619)582-5696. President: George Fogelman. Record company, music publisher (Jewish Music, BMI) and record producer (George Fogelman). Estab. 1982. Releases 6 singles, 6 12″ singles, 12 LPs and 12 CDs/year. Works with musicians/artists and songwriters on contract. Pays 6-15% royalty to artists on contract; ¼% to publisher per song on record.
How to Contact: Submit demo tape by mail. Unsolicited submissions are OK. Prefers cassette with 4 songs and lyric or lead sheets. Does not return unsolicited material. Reports in 6 weeks.
Music: Mostly Jewish ethnic, Jewish educational and Jewish contemporary. Released *Tzedaka* (by George Fogelman), *The Gelt Song* (by Cara Freedman) and *A Holy Place* (by Debbie Friedman) all on Jewish Family Productions.

*JIMCO RECORDS, a division of Jimco Japan, Jimco House, 4-7-7 Kachidoki, Chud-Ku, Tokyo 104 **Japan** Phone: (03)534-8771. A & R Manager: Eugene Otsuka. Labels include Motor-City, Nightmare, Jump-Street, Dr. York and Dr. Dream. Record company, music publisher (M.N.P./JASRAC) and record producer (Ian Levine/Nightmare). Estab. 1989. Releases 4 singles, 12 12″ singles and 150 CDs/year. Works with musicians/artists on contract.
How to Contact: Submit demo tape by mail. Unsolicited submissions are okay. Prefers cassette with 10 songs. SASE & IRC for outside the U.S. Reports in 1 month.
Music: Mostly dance, heavy metal and R&B; also rock and jazz. Released "Menace" (by Menace), recorded by Jump Street on Jump Street Records; "Rick Wakeman" (by Rick Wakeman), recorded by President on President Records; and "Frank Gambale" (by Frank Gambale), recorded by Legato on Legato Records (all CDs). Other artists include MacCoy Tyner and Stephen Grappelli.
Tips: "We wish to have finished masters. We can make record right away."

*J/L ENTERTAINMENT GROUP, 8730 Sunset Blvd., Los Angeles CA 90069. (213)657-1836. President: Jack Heller. Labels include Crown Records. Produces Japanese songs in English and vice-versa. Estab. 1985. Releases 100 CDs/year. Works with musicians/artists on record contract. Pays 25% royalty to artists on contract. Pays statutory rate to publishers per song on records. Charges for distribution.
How to Contact: Write or call first and obtain permission to submit. SASE. Reports in 1 month.
Music: Rock, R&B and pop.

JOEY BOY RECORDS INC., 3081 N.W. 24th St., Miami FL 33142. (305)635-5588. Contact: Lynse Young. Labels include J.R. Records, On Top Records. Record company. Estab. 1985. Releases 20 singles, 18 12″ singles, 4 LPs and 1 CD/year. Works with musicians/artists on contract. Pays 5-10% royalty to artists on contract; statutory rate to publisher per song on record.
How to Contact: Write or call first and obtain permission to submit. Prefers cassette with 3 songs and lyric sheets. SASE. Reports in 4 weeks.
Music: Mostly R&B, rap and pop; also gospel, jazz and comedy. Released *Let's Rock This Party*, written and recorded by Rock Force on Joey Boy Records; *Get Down* (by Rock Force), recorded by M4sers on J.R. Records; and *Do You Wanna Party* (by Brad Lester), recorded by Miami Boyz on On Top Records; all rap LPs. Other artists include Gwen Dickey, Vicious Bass, Rock Five and Timmy Thomas.
Tips: "Be creative in your writing and exercise patience in your business dealings."

JRM RECORDS, Box 993, Salem VA 24153. (703)387-0208. Contact: Ruby Mullins. Labels include Dominion. Record company and music publisher (Powhatan Music and Double Jack Publishing). Estab. 1957. Releases 3 singles and 3 LPs/year. Works with musicians/artists and songwriters on contract. Pays 30¢/LP; statutory rate to publishers for each record sold.
How to Contact: Prefers cassette (or videocassette) with 1-3 songs and lyric sheet. Does not return material. Reports if interested.
Music: Mostly specialty and novelty country rock, R&B and rock; also crossover country, bluegrass and country. Released "Snowfall," written and recorded by R. Slone (country rock); "Curly Buck The Raindeer" (by D. Counts), recorded by R. Slone (novelty country); and "Come Join the Party," written and recorded by D. Counts (novelty rock and roll); all on JRM Records. Other artists include "The Fabulous Flys", Rick Slone, JC Radford and Donna Dean.
Tips: "Submit a good quality demo of original song—should be of pro quality and have strong hooks."

*JTM RECORDS, Box 686 Best Ave., Knox PA 16232. (814)797-5883. President: Frank T. Battista. Labels include JTM. Record company, music publisher (BMI) and record producer. Estab. 1984. Releases 4 singles and 1 12″ singles/year. Works with musicians/artists on contract.
How to Contact: Write or call first and obtain permission to submit. Prefers cassette with 2 songs and lead sheet. SASE. Reports in 2 weeks.
Music: Mostly contemporary, country and rock; also heavy metal. Released "Love Will Survive" (by C. Wepple), recorded by C. Wepple (single); "Has My Love Been Good For You" (by C. Wepple), recorded by Point of View (single); and "Bet Your Heart on Me" (by Tom Battista), recorded by Longshot (single & album), all on JTM Records.
Tips: "Looking for exceptional talent—we pay all expenses relative to recording and housing. Have an excellent voice with good material."

JUMP RECORDS & MUSIC, Langemunt 71, Erpe-Mere 9460 **Belgium**. Phone: (053)62-73-77. General Manager: Eddy Van Mouffaert. Labels include Jump, Yeah Songs and Flower. Record company, music publisher (Jump Music) and record producer. Estab. 1976. Releases 40 singles, 3 LPs and 1 CD/year. Works with musicians/artists and songwriters on contract. Pays 5% royalty to artists on contract; statutory rate to publisher per song on record.
How to Contact: Prefers cassette. Does not return unsolicited material. Reports in 2 weeks.
Music: Mostly easy listening, disco and light pop; also instrumentals. Released "Laat Je Hart Toch Even Spreken," and "Summer Holiday," written and recorded by Eddy Govert; "First Day of Spring" (by Eddy Govert), recorded by Franky Francis, all on Scorpion Records (all singles). Other artists include Rocky, Le Grand Julot, Eigentijdse Jeugd, Marijn Van Duin, Connie-Linda, Guy Lovely, Tom Davys, Laurie, Cindy, Patrik, Allan David, Peggy Christy, Aswin, Little Cindy, Sandra More, Dolly, Danny Brendo, Christle Love, Sandra Tempsy, Dick Benson, Angie Halloway and Ricky Morgan.

*JUMP STREET RECORDS, INC., 200 W. 72 Street, New York NY 10023. (212)873-1248. A&R: Gregg Fore. Record company. Estab. 1985. Releases 10 12″ singles, 5 LPs and 5 CDs/year. Works with musicians/artists on record contract. Pays statutory rate to publishers per song on records.
How to Contact: Submit demo tape by mail. Unsolicited submissions are OK. Prefers cassette with 3 songs and lyric sheets. SASE. Reports in 3 weeks.
Music: Interested in dance, house and rap; also R&B. Released *Dog House* (by D. Weeden), recorded by Menace (LP); *Wanna Get to Know You Better* (by P. Herrera/B. Gooding), recorded by Romance (12″ single); and A.C. Kelly, recorded by *A.C. Kelly* (LP), all on Jump Street Records.

JUSTICE RECORDS INC., 80 Oriole Ave., Mississauga ON L5G IV2 **Canada**. (416)271-0951. President: Don Stanton. Record company, music publisher (Stanton Music/CAPAC) and record producer (Don Stanton). Estab. 1981. Releases 2 singles, 1 12″ single, 2 LPs and 1 EP/year. Works with musicians/artists on contract and hires musicians for in-house studio work.
How to Contact: Submit demo tape by mail. Unsolicited submissions are OK. Prefers cassette with 4 songs. SAE with IRC. Reports in 1 month.
Music: Mostly pop, R&B and rock. Released "Watch Out" (by Kumari/Stanton), "Shake" (by Kumari/Stanton) and "Rock Your Baby" (by C.W. Casey); all recorded by Kumari on Justice Records (singles).

KAM EXECUTIVE RECORDS, 11 Shady Oak Trail, Charlotte NC 28910. (704)554-1162. Director: Butch Kelly. Labels include Fresh Ave Records, KAM Records, Newtown. Record company (KAM/BMI) and record producer (Butch Kelly Production). Estab. 1981. Releases 3 singles, 3 12″ singles and 3 LPs/year. Works with musicians/artists on contract. Pays 6% royalty to artists on contract. Pays statutory rate.
How to Contact: Write or call first and obtain permission to submit. Prefers cassette (or VHS videocassette) with 3-6 songs and lyric and lead sheets. SASE. Reports in 2 months.
Music: Mostly R&B, pop and rock; also rap and gospel. Released "Waiting" (by Butch Kelly), recorded by A. Brown on KAM Records (R&B); "Miss You" (by Greg Johnston), recorded by Fresh Air on KAM Records (R&B) "Stumping Blues" (by Kelly Montgomery), on KAM Records (pop). Other artists include The Prep of Rap, Sharon Jordan (R&B), Richard Kirkpatrick (R&B) and Caro (R&B).

KANSA RECORDS CORP., Box 1014, Lebanon TN 37088. (615)444-3865. General Manager: Kit Johnson. Labels include Sunflower. Record company, music publisher (Great Leawood Music, Inc./ASCAP and Twinsong Music/BMI), record producer and promotion. Releases 5 singles and 2 LPs/year. Works with musicians/artists and songwriters on contract. Pays 6¢ per copy royalty to artists on contract.
How to Contact: Prefers cassette with 4 songs and lead sheet. SASE. Reports in 6 weeks "if we like it."
Music: Country, gospel, progressive country and country/rock. Released "I Remember Mama's Arms," recorded by Steffin Sisters; and "Memory Remover" (by Al Green), recorded by Geary Hanley. Other artists include Lea Ann Cox, Dan Davis and P.J. Allman.

*KATRON RECORD, 726 E. McLemore, Memphis TN 38106. (901)947-2553. President: Bob Karriem. Labels include Brian Manor Records and Boss Ugly Bob Records. Record company, music publisher. Estab. 1971. Releases 3 cassettes and 1 CD/year. Pays statutory rate to publisher per song on record. **How to Contact:** Write or call first and obtain permission to submit. Prefers cassette with 2 or more songs. Does not return unsolicited material.
Music: Mostly R&B, rap and gospel; also blues. Released "Leave My Do Do Alone" (by Robert Catron) (rap cassette) and "Death Ain't Nothin But a Trip" (rap) both recorded by Jimmy Ingle on Brian Manor Records and "Look at the Fool" written and recorded by Calvin Leary on Katron Records (blues cassette). Other artists include Sir Henry Ing and Alvin King Jr.

KICKING MULE RECORDS, INC., Box 158, Alderpoint CA 95411. (707)926-5312. Head of A&R: Ed Denson. Record company and music publisher (Kicking Mule Publishing/BMI and Desk Drawer Publishing/ASCAP). Member NAIRD. Releases 12 LPs/year. Works with artists on contract. Pays 10-16% royalty to artists on contract; standard royalty to songwriters on contract.
How to Contact: Prefers reel-to-reel or cassette with 3-5 songs. SASE. Reports in 1 month.
Music: Bluegrass, blues and folk. Released *Solo Guitar* by Tom Ball (folk), *Christmas Come Anew* by Maddie MacNeil (folk), and *Cats Like Angels* by Bob Griffin (piano folk). Other artists include Michael Rugg, Neal Hellman, Bert Jansch, John Renbourn, Stefan Grossman, John James, Happy Traum, Fred Sokolow, Bob Stanton, Bob Hadley, Leo Wijnkamp, Jr., Mark Nelson, Lea Nicholson and Hank Sapoznik.
Tips: "We are a label mostly for instrumentalists. The songs are brought to us by the artists but we contract the artists because of their playing, not their songs. First, listen to what we have released and don't send material that is outside our interests. Secondly, learn to play your instrument well. We have little interest in songs or songwriters, but we are quite interested in people who play guitar, banjo, or dulcimer well."

KILGORE RECORDS, INC., 706 West Mechanic St., Leesville LA 71446-3446. (318)238-0028. President: Mr. John E. Kilgore. Labels include Gotown Records and Kilgore Records. Record company, record producer and music publisher (Gotown Publishing Company/BMI). Releases 6 singles/year. Works with artists and songwriters on contract. Pays statutory rate to publishers for each record sold.
How to Contact: Prefers cassette with 4-6 songs and lead sheets. SASE. Reports in 3 months.
Music: Mostly gospel; also church/religious, contemporary gospel. Released "Rescue Me" (by The Golden Links) on Kilgore Records; and "The Uneducated Grandmother" (by Evangelists).
Tips: "I don't listen to poor quality demos that I can't understand. Submit good material with potential in today's market. Use good quality cassettes."

KIMBO EDUCATIONAL, 10 N. Third Ave., Long Branch NJ 07740. (201)229-4949. Production: James Kimble/Amy Laufer. Labels include Kimbo, KBH Productions Inc., S&R Records. Estab. 1962. Releases 8 LPs/year. Works with musicians/artists and songwriters on contract. Pays approximately 7% royalty to artists on contract; statutory rate to publisher per song on record.
How to Contact: Submit demo tape by mail. Unsolicited submissions are OK. Prefers cassette with 8-10 songs and lyric sheets. SASE. Reports in 2 months.
Music: Mostly children's music (ages 1-10) and simple rock or pop (easy for child to relate to). Released *Journey Into Space* (by Jane Murphy), recorded by Kimbo; *A Rainbow of Songs*, written and recorded by Bing Bingham; and *Me and My Bean Bag*, recorded by The Learning Station; all on Kimbo Records (all kids LPs). Other artists include Slim Goodbody, Carol Hammett, Dennis Buck, Georgiana Stewart, Priscilla Hegner and Laura Johnson.
Tips: "Kimbo seeks contemporary sounds with limited instrumentation so as not to appear too sophisticated or distracting for young children. Song lyrics should present topics that are of interest to today's children."

KING OF KINGS RECORD CO., 38603 Sage Tree St., Palmdale CA 93551-4311. (Branch office: P.O. Box 725, Daytona Beach FL 32015-0725. (904)252-4849.) President: Leroy Pritchett. A&R Director: Charles Vickers. Labels include King of Kings, L.A. International. Record company and music publisher (Pritchett Publications/BMI). Estab. 1978. Releases 1 single and 1 LP/year. Works with musicians/artists and songwriters on contract. Pays royalty to artists on contract; statutory rate to publishers per song on record.
How to Contact: Write first for permission to submit. Prefers cassette and lyric or lead sheet. SASE. Reports in 1 month.
Music: Mostly gospel; also country. Released "Walkin' on the Water," "Music in My Soul" and "Every Day is a Holy Day," all written and recorded by Charles Vickers on King of Kings Records (gospel).

*KINGSTON RECORDS, 15 Exeter Rd., Kingston NH 03848. (603)642-8493. Coordinator: Harry Mann. Labels include Kingston Records. Record company, music publisher (Strawberry Soda Pub. ASCAP). Estab. 1988. Releases 3-4 singles, 2-3 12" singles, 3 LPs and 2 CDs/year. Works with musicians/artists and songwriters on contract. Pays 3-5% royalty to artists on contract; statutory rate to publisher per song.

How to Contact: Submit demo tape by mail. Unsolicited submissions are OK. Prefers cassette, 15 ips reel-to-reel, VCR videocassette with 3 songs and lyric sheet. SASE. Reports in 6-8 weeks.

Music: Mostly rock, country and pop; "no heavy metal." Released *5¢ Strawberry Soda* (country rock LP) and "Message To You," written and recorded by Doug Mitchell; and *Songs Piped in from the Moon*, written and recorded by S. Pappas (avant-garde ballad LP); all on Kingston Records.

*KITTY RECORDS, INC., 1-8-4 Ohashi, Megro-Ku, Tokyo 153 **Japan**. Phone: (03)780-8646. Manager of International Division: Kazuo Munakata. Record company and music publisher (Kitty Music Corporation). Estab. 1982. Releases 30 singles, 5 12″ singles, 30 LPs, 30 EPs and 30 CDs/year. Works with musicians/artists and songwriters on contract. Pays 1% royalty to artists on contract.

How to Contact: Prefers cassette with 5 songs and lyric sheet. Does not return unsolicited material. Reports in 1 month.

Music: Mostly rock, pop and New Age (instrumental); also jazz (with classical music flavor) and soul (pop-soul). Released "I'm Dandy" (by Koji Tamaki), recorded by Koji, Tamaki on Kitty Records; "Juliette Game" (by Taichi, OHira), recorded by The Reds on Kitty Records and *Daisy Chain*, (by Isao Shigeto and Norico), recorded by Date of Birth on Mju Records.

SID KLEINER MUSIC ENTERPRISES INC., 10188 Winter View Dr., Naples Fl 33942. (813)566-7701 and (813)566-7702. Contact: Sid Kleiner. Labels include Musi-Poe, Top-Star, This Is It, Token, and Country-King Records. Record company and consulting firm to music industry. Releases 10 LPs/year. Works with musicians and songwriters on contract. Charges for some services: "We may, at our option, charge *actual* production expense. We are not get-rich-quickers or rip-off artists. But we are too small to pay all of these bills!"

How to Contact: Prefers cassette (or VHS videocassette) and lead sheet. SASE, "otherwise materials aren't returned." Reports in 3 weeks.

Music: Bluegrass, country, easy listening, folk, jazz, and "banjo and guitar soloists and features." Released *Burd Boys on Stage* and *Chartbusters and Other Hits* (country LPs), by the Burd Boys; and *Find a Simple Life*, by Dave Kleiner (folk/rock LP). Other artists include Sid Kleiner.

KOTTAGE RECORDS, Box 121626, Nashville TN 37212. (615)726-3556. President: Neal James. Record company, music publisher (Cottage Blue Music, BMI) and record producer (Neal James). Estab. 1979. Releases 4 singles and 2 LPs/year. Works with musicians/artists on contract. Pays 5% royalty to artists on contract; statutory rate to publisher per song on record.

How to Contact: Write or call first and obtain permission to submit. Prefers cassette with 2 songs and lyric sheet. SASE. Reports in 4 weeks.

Music: Mostly country, rock/pop and gospel; also R&B. Released "Shave This Night" (by Neal James), recorded by Jeremiah Hedge on Kottage Records (rock); "Maybe It Was Yesterday" (by Larry Lee and Dan Mitchell), recorded by Ted Yost on Kottage Records (country) and "Quite Like You" (by Neal James), recorded by Scott Randon on Kottage Records (country). Other artists include Roxie Dean and Terry Barbay.

KRYSDAHLARK MUSIC, P.O. Box 26160, Cincinnati OH 26160. President: Jeff Krys. Releases 2-3 LPs and 2 CDs/year. Works with musicians and artist on contract.Pays 4-8% royalty for each record sold. Production company and publisher. Estab 1986.

How to Contact: Not accepting unsolicited submissions at this time.

Music: Released "Elegant Earth" (by Billy Larkin), recorded by Blanche & Deux Boys; "Lonestar" (by Chris Dahlgren), recorded by Ekimi and "First Steps" (by Sylvain Acher) all on KDL Records (New Age). Other artists include Sleep Theatre (modern rock) and Chris Philpotts (oboe/composer).

L.S. RECORDS, 120 Hickory St., Madison TN 37115. (615)868-7171. Publisher: Kevin L. Stoller. Labels include L.S. Records. Record company, music publisher (ASCAP, BMI, SESAC) and record producer (Lee Stoller—L.S. Records). Estab. 1972. Releases 2 singles and 3-4 12″ singles/year. Works with songwriters on contract. Pays 50% royalty to artists on contract; statutory rate to publisher per song on record.

How to Contact: Call first and obtain permission to submit. Prefers cassette with 1 song and lyric or lead sheet. SASE. Reports in weeks.

Music: Mostly gospel, country ánd pop; also rock, rap and AC. Released *All in His Hands* and *He Sees My Heart* (both by Jimmie Young), and *How Great Thou Art*; all recorded by Cristy Lane on L.S. Records (LPs).

LA LOUISIANNE RECORDS, 711 Stevenson St., Lafayette LA 70501. (318)234-5577. Labels include Tamm and Belle. President: (Mr.) Carol J. Rachou, Sr. Record company, record producer, recording studio and music publisher (La Lou Music/BMI). Releases 10-20 singles and 4-6 LPs/year. Works with artists and songwriters on contract. "We also deal with promoters, managers, agents, etc." Pays statutory rate to publishers for each record sold.

How to Contact: Prefers 7½ ips reel-to-reel or cassette with 1-6 songs and lyric sheet. "If possible, submit different musical variations of songs (tempos, styles, keys, etc.)." SASE.

Music: Mostly Cajun/French; also blues, church/religious, classical, country, folk, gospel, jazz, MOR, progressive, R&B, rock, top 40/pop, comedy, French comedy and instrumental. Released *Lache Pas La Patate*, by Jimmy C. Newman (French Cajun LP — Gold record in Canada); *A Cajun Tradition Vol. 2*, by Nathan Abshire (French Cajun LP); *Cajun Fiddle*, by Rufus Thibodeaux (Cajun/country LP); *That Cajun Country Sound*, by Eddy Raven (French and English Cajun/country LP); and *Authentic French Music*, by Ambrose Thibodeaux (traditional Cajun LP). Other artists include Vin Bruce, Aldus Roger, Merlin Fontenot, L.J. Foret, Blackie Forestier, The Dusenbery Family, Alex Broussard and Bud Fletcher.

*LAMBDA RECORDS®, P.O. Box 14131, Denver CO 80214. Executive Producer: Sharon Soria. Record labels include SRSF Records®, SRSF Recordings/entertainments enterprises®, SRS Records®. Record Company, music publisher (Lambda Guild®/ASCAP) and record producer (Lambda Performing Arts Guild of America®. Estab. 1987. "We are a non-profit organization." Pays 50% royalty to artists on contract.

How to Contact: Submit demo tape by mail. Unsolicited submissions are okay. Prefers cassette (or VHS videocassette) with 1 song and lyric or lead sheets. SASE. Reports in 3 months.

Music: Mostly pop, country and MOR; also easy listening, bluegrass and folk. Released "Mother Earth" (by Barbara Labonne), recorded by Smith & LaBonne; "White Light" (by Sharon Soria), recorded by Sharon Soria; and "Hold On" (by Sharon Smith), recorded by Sharon Smith, all on Lamboa Records® (single cassettes).

Tips: "We currently only work with Lesbian artists. Our mission is to recognize and legitimize lesbian performers. As a Lesbian operated organization working with artists, managers, producers, etc., we have noticed a change in attitudes towards Lesbian artists. Society as a whole has become aware that this lifestyle is not based on myths and erroneous information. People have a right to live a life equal of all people. Including expression in music."

LANA RECORDS, Box 12444, Fresno CA 93777-2444. (209)266-8481. Executive Producer: Robby Roberson. Labels include Lana Records, Country Roots Records, GGT Records and El Country Records. Record company, music publisher (Happy Note Music), and record producer. Releases 3 singles and 2 LPs/year. Works with musicians/artists and songwriters on contract; musicians on salary for in-house studio work. Pays 7-10% royalty to artists on contract; statutory rate to publisher per song on record.

How to Contact: Prefers cassette with 3 songs and lyric sheet. SASE. Reports in 1 month.

Music: Mostly country, gospel, pop, Tex-Mex and soft rock. Released "The Master's Touch," "Mountain House Rendezvous," "Save the Train" and "The Western Iron Rail." Artists include Robby Roberson, Mikal Masters, Rosemarie Reedy and Jimmy Walker.

LANDMARK COMMUNICATIONS GROUP, Box 148296, Nashville TN 37214. Producers: Bill Anderson, Jr.. Labels include Jana, Livingsongs and Landmark Records. Record company, record producer and music publisher (Newcreature Music/BMI and Mary Megan Music/ASCAP) and management firm (Landmark Entertainment). Releases 10 singles, 8 LPs, and 3 CDs/year. Works with musicians/artists and songwriters on contract; hires musicians for in-house studio work. Teams collaborators. Pays 5-7% royalty to artists on contract; statutory rate to publishers for each record sold.

How to Contact: Prefers 7½ ips reel-to-reel or cassette with 4-10 songs and lyric sheet. SASE. Reports in 1 month.

Music: Country/crossover, gospel, jazz, R&B, rock and top 40/pop. Released *Joanne Cash Yates Live . . . w/Johnny Cash*, on Jana Records (gospel LP); *Play It Again Sam*, recorded by Michael L. Pickern on Landmark Records (country LP); *Millions of Miles*, recorded by Teddy Nelson/Skeeter Davis (Norway release) (country LP); *Always*, recorded by Debi Chasteen on Landmark Records (country LP); and *Someday Soon*, recorded by Pam Fenelon on Bil-Mar Records (country LP). Other artists include Anita Pearce and Dé Fox.

LANOR RECORDS, 329 N. Main St., Box 233, Church Point LA 70525. (318)684-2176. Contact: Lee Lavergne. Labels include Lanor and Joker Records. Record company and music publisher (Country Classics Music/BMI). Releases 12-18 singles and 1-3 LPs/year. Works with artists and songwriters on contract. Pays 3-5% royalty to artists on contract; statutory rate to writers for each record sold.

How to Contact: Prefers cassette with 2-6 songs. SASE. Reports in 2 weeks.

Music: Mostly country; also rock, and soul. Released "Good Hearted Man" and "Rockin' Zydeco," by Rockin' Sidney and Jim Olivier.

Tips: Submit "good material with potential in today's market. Use good quality cassettes — I don't listen to poor quality demos that I can't understand."

*LARI-JON RECORDS, 627 Countryview, Columbus NE 68601. (402)564-7034. Owner: Larry Good. Record company, music publisher (LariJon Pub. BMI) and record producer (Lari-Jon Prod.). Estab. 1967. Releases 10 singles and 5 LPs/year. Works with songwriters on royalty contract.
How to Contact: Submit demo tape by mail. Unsolicited submissions are okay. Prefers cassette with 5 songs and lyric sheet. SASE. Reports in 2 months.
Music: Mostly country, gospel-Southern and '50s rock. Released "Nebraskaland" recorded by Larry Good (country single); *Some Old Some New* recorded by Larry Good (country LP); *Oldies With New Swing* recorded by Kent Thompson (country LP) and "Her Favorite Song," recorded by Johnny Nace (country LP).

*LE MATT MUSIC LTD., % Stewart House, Hill Bottom Rd., Highwycombe, Buckinghamshire, HP12 4HJ**England**. Phone: 0494-436301/436401. FAX: 0494-461832. Telex: 837173. Contact: Ron or Cathrine Lee. Labels include Swoop, Zarg Records, Genouille, Pogo and Check Records. Record company, record producer and music publisher (Le Matt Music, Ltd., Lee Music, Ltd., R.T.F.M. and Pogo Records, Ltd.). Member MPA, PPL, PRS, MCPS. Estab. 1972. Releases more than 30 singles and 20 LPs/year. Pays negotiable royalty to artists on contract; statutory rate to publishers for each record sold. Royalties paid to US songwriters and artists through US publishing or recording affiliate.
How to Contact: Prefers 7½ or 15 ips reel-to-reel or cassette (or videocassette) with 1-3 songs and lyric sheet. Include bio and photo. SAE and IRC. Reports in 3 weeks.
Music: Mostly interested in pop/Top 40; also interested in bluegrass, blues, country, dance-oriented, easy listening, MOR, progressive, R&B, 50s rock, disco, new wave, rock and soul. Released *Mood Music* (by R.C. Bowman), recorded by R.C. Band on R.T.F.M. Records; *Rock 'n' Roll Revival* (by M. Shereden), recorded by Elmer Goodbody Jr. on Swoop Records; and *Swoop's Greatest Hits*, written and recorded by various artists on Swoop Records (all LPs). Other artists include Emmitt Till, Touche, Orphan, Jonny Moon, Ian "Sludge" Lees and Kyro Groucho.

LEMON RECORDS, Zollergasse 13, Vienna A-1070 **Austria**. Phone: (222)93 01 47. Record company. Estab. 1980. Releases 4 12″ singles, 2 LPs and 4 CDs/year. Works with musicians/artists and songwriters on contract and hires musicians for in-house studio work. Pays 8-14% royalty to artists on contract; pays statutory rate to publishers per song on record. Pays statutory rate to publisher per song on record.
How to Contact: Submit demo tape by mail. Unsolicited submissions are OK. Prefers cassette with lyric sheets. SASE. Reports in 8 weeks.
Music: Mostly pop/top 40 and dance.

JOHN LENNON RECORDS, Suite 300, Box 314, 131 Bloor St. W., Toronto M5S 1R8 **Canada**. (416)962-5000. Contact: Oliver Moore or P. Eastman. Labels include Music Live International Records. Record company, music publisher (PROCAN) and record producer (John Lennon Records). Estab. 1979. Releases 3 singles, 2 12″ singles, 1 LP and 2 CDs/year. Works with musicians/artists and songwriters on contract. Pays 12% royalty to artists on contract. Charges advance production fee.
How to Contact: Submit demo tape by mail. No unsolicited submissions. Prefers cassette (or VHS videocassette) with 4 songs and lyric sheets. SAE and IRC required. Reports in 1 month.
Music: Mostly top 40 pop, R&B dance and gospel/country. "You Are Changing" (by O. Hasful and R. Butler), recorded by Carl Ellison; "Summer Nights" (by R. Butler and C. Ellison), recorded by Carl Ellison; and "Get Rich Quick" (by R. Butler), recorded by Yvonne Moore; all on J.L.R.D. Records (all singles). Artists include Alex Jordan and Milton Price.
Tips: "Good quality demo and self addressed, stamped envelope are essential."

LEOPARD MUSIC, 23, Thrayle House, Stockwell Rd., London, SW9 0XU **England**. Phone: (01)274-9533 or (818)814-0293. Managing Director: Errol Jones. Labels include Jet Set Records International (USA). Record company (PRS, BMI) and record producer. Estab. 1978. Releases 15 singles and 2 LPs/year. Works with musicians/artists and songwriters on contract and hires musicians for in-house studio work. Pays 4-12% royalty to artists on contract; pays statutory rate to publishers per song on record.
How to Contact: Write first and obtain permission to submit. Prefers cassette (or VHS [PAL] video-cassette) with 3 songs. SASE. Reports in 2 weeks.
Music: Mostly dance music, soul and pop; also ballad, reggae and gospel. Released "Time After Time" (by Guy Spell), recorded by Rico J (single); "I Need You" (by E. Campbell and E. North Jr.), recorded by Big Africa (single); and *God is Beauty*, written and recorded by Evelyn Ladimeji (LP); all on Leopard Music Records. Other artists include Zoil Foundations, Terri Stevens and Samantha Simone.
Tips: "Create strong original song, and artists must have good image."

LOADSTONE RECORD CO., 163 Orizaba Ave., San Francisco CA 94132. (415)334-2247. President: W.C. Stone. Labels include Open—Lock and Loadstone Records. Record company and music publisher (Stonebess Music Co./BMI). Estab. 1963. Releases 2-4 singles and 2-4 12" singles/year. Works with musicians/artists and songwriters on contract; lease or rent (session or master tapes). Pays 80% royalty to artists on contract; pays statutory or contract to publishers per song on record.
How to Contact: Prefers cassette or 7½ ips reel-to-reel with 2 songs and lyric or lead sheet. SASE. Reports in 3 weeks.
Music: Mostly R&B, hard rock and pop. Released "Sinking Into Love" by Herman H. Harper II, "A Loving Mother" by Paula Lemont, "Love Is Good for You" by Peter Colly, and "Ocean Waves" by the Cats. Other artists include Retlaw Enots, and The Grape Wrath.
Tips: "Have all songs submitted set to words and music on lead sheet and a copy of copyright."

*LOVE DOVE PRODUCTIONS, 911 Crotona Park N., Bronx NY 10460. (212)294-6112. President A&R: Anthony De Veaux. Labels include New Vibe Records. Record company and music publisher (Love Dove Productions, Love Dove Music BMI). Estab. 1989. Works with musicians/artists and songwriters on contract and musicians on salary for in-house studio work. Pays statutory rate to publisher per song on records. Charges prospective artists for production and promotion.
How to Contact: Submit demo tape by mail. Prefers cassette (VHS and BETA videocassette if available) with a minimum of 4 songs. SASE. Reports in 5 weeks.
Music: Mostly R&B, house and gospel. Released "It's You" (by Lesia Dove), (house); "You Changes" (by Lesia Dove/A. DeVeaux) (R&B); and "In The Breeze" (by Gerald Trettman), (jazz) all recorded by New Vide Prod on New Vibe Records. Other artists include Lesia Dove and Gerald Trottman.

LRJ, Box 3, Belen NM 87002. (505)864-7441. Manager: Tony Palmer. Labels include LRJ, Little Richie, Chuckie. Record company. Estab. 1959. Releases 5 singles and 2 LPs/year. Works with musicians/artists on contract.
How to Contact: Submit demo tape by mail. Unsolicited submissions are okay. Prefers cassette. SASE. Reports in 1 month.
Music: Mostly country. Released "Step Aside" and "Yellow Bandana" written and recorded by Jerry Jaramillo on LRJ Records (singles).

LUCIFER RECORDS, INC., Box 263, Brigantine NJ 08203-0263. (609)266-2623. President: Ron Luciano. Labels include TVA Records. Record company, music publishers (Ciano Publishing and Legz Music), record producers (Pete Fragale and Tony Vallo) and management firm and booking agency (Ron Luciano Music Co. and TVA Productions). Works with artists and songwriters on salary and contract.
How to Contact: Arrange personal interview. Prefers cassette with 4-8 songs. SASE. Reports in 3 weeks.
Music: Dance, easy listening, MOR, rock, soul and top 40/pop. Released "I Who Have Nothing," by Spit-N-Image (rock single); "Lucky," and "Smoke Ya," by Legz (rock singles); and "Loves a Crazy Game," by Voyage (disco/ballad single).

*LUNAR RECORDS, 5-6 Lombard St. East, Dublin **Ireland**. Phone: (01)774229. Managing Director: Brian Molloy. Labels include Lunar, Unicorn, TTE, and J&B Records. Record company, music publisher (Squirrel Music) and record producer. Releases 25 singles and 10 LPs/year. Works with artists and songwriters.
How to Contact: Write first and obtain permission to submit. Prefers cassette (or VHS/PAL videocassette) with 3 songs and lyric sheet. SAE and IRC. Reports in 3 weeks.
Music: Mostly contemporary country, contemporary pop and MOR. Released "West Coast of Clare" (by Planxty), recorded by Barbara Dickson on Lunar Records (MOR/folk); "It Keeps Right On Hurtin' " (by Johnny Tillotson), recorded by Blazers on Unicorn Records (country/MOR); and "Distant Drum," recorded by Big Tom on Lunar Records (country/MOR). Other artists include "Irish MOR and contemporary artists with new country material, e.g. Nanci Griffith, Dwight Yoakam and Randy Travis."

M.R.C. RECORDS, Box 2072, Waynesboro VA 22980. (703)949-0106. Contact: John Major. Labels include MRC, Lark and Echo Records. Record company, music publisher and recording studio. Releases 10 singles and 20 LPs/year. Pays 5-7% royalty to artists on contract; statutory rate to publishers for each record sold.
How to Contact: Prefers cassette and lyric sheet. SASE. Reports in 2 weeks.
Music: Bluegrass, gospel, country, easy listening, dance, MOR, rock (country, hard), soul and top 40/pop. Released "Honky Tonk Angel," by Joey Davis (country single).
Tips: "Don't submit songs with tunes purchased from advertisements. Don't submit songs that have been rejected by other publishers."

LEE MACE'S OZARK OPRY RECORDS, INC., Box 242, Osage Beach MO 65065. (314)348-3383. President: Joyce Mace. Labels include Ozark Opry, Kajac, Ven Jence, Vision, KRC and Red Rock Records. Record company, music publisher and record producer (Ozark Opry Records, Inc.). Works with songwriters on contract; musicians on salary for in-house studio work. Pays standard royalty to songwriters on contract.
How to Contact: Arrange personal interview. Prefers 7½ ips reel-to-reel or cassette with 2-4 songs and lead sheet. SASE required for response of any kind. Reports in 2 weeks.
Music: Bluegrass, blues, church/religious, country, gospel and R&B. Released "Waylon Sing to Mama," by Darrell Thomas (country single); *Lee Mace 25 Years*, by the Ozark Opry (country LP); and *Songs Like We Sing*, by Lee Mace and the Ozark Opry (country LP).

MAD ROVER RECORDS, P.O. Box 22243, Sacramento CA 95822. (916)443-0373. President/A&R: John Baccígaluppí. Record company, music publisher (Next Wave Music/BMI), record producer (John Baccígaluppí) and recording studio (Enharmonik Studios). Estab. 1986. Releases 1 singles, 3 LPs and 3 CDs/year. Works with musicians/artists on contract. Pays 50% royalty to artists on contract; pays statutory rate to publishers per song on record.
How to Contact: Prefers cassette (or VHS videocassette) with 4 songs and lyric sheet. SASE. Reports in 6 weeks.
Music: Mostly new music (rock); also "anything but top 40." Released *The Song Retains the Name*, by various artists doing Led Zeppelin covers (compilation rock LP); *Man With the X-Ray Eyes*, (by Kellar/Clarke), recorded by Texas Midgets (rock LP/CD); *DIN* recorded by Helen Keller Plaid (rock/LP/CD); and *Out of State Plates* (by McGrath/Blair), recorded by Fool Killers (rock LP); all on Mad Rover Records.
Tips: "Don't listen to AOR/CHR Radio."

MADLYN RECORDS, 1096 Fulton #1, San Francisco CA 94117. (415)433-2267. Owner: Charles Unger. Record company. Estab. 1984. Releases 3 singles, 1 12" single, 2 LPs, 2 EPs and 1 CD/year. Works with musicians/artists and songwriters on contract; hires musicians for in-house studio work. Royalty paid to artists depends on contract; pays statutory rate to publishers per song on record.
How to Contact: Prefers cassette. SASE. Reports in 2 weeks.
Music: Mostly jazz, funk and pop. Released *Paris Calling* and *Love Angles*, both written and recorded by Valencia (jazz LPs); *Working for the C.I.A.*, written and recorded by Pizzazz (jazz EP); and "San Francisco After Dark," written and recorded by Charles Unger (jazz); all on Madlyn Records.

*MAIN TRIPP RECORDS INC., 2804 Beechtree Dr., Sanford NC 27330. (919)774-8926. President: Bill Tripp. Record company and music publisher (BMI). Estab. 1982. Releases 12 singles, and 12 LPs/year. Works with musicians/artsts and songwriters on contract. Pays statutory rate to publisher per song on record. Write first and obtain permission to submit or to arrange personal interview. Prefers cassette with 3 songs and lyric sheet. Does not return unsolicited material. Reports in 3 months.
Music: Mostly country, gospel and bluegrass. Released *Forever*, written and recorded by Raymond Barns (R&B); *Empty Places*, written and recorded by Don Keatley/Jim Watters (country gospel) both on MTR Records; and *Empty Places*, (by Jim Watters), recorded by The Helmsmen (gospel) on Morning Star Records. Other artists include Pioneers (gospel), Don Keatley, Shine On, Clyde Frazier, Raymond Barnes, Jim Watters.

*MAINROADS MUSIC INC., P.O. Box 999 Station "U", Toronto, Ontario M8Z 5P9 **Canada**. (416)984-6585. A&R Director: Stephen Nicolle. Music distributor. Estab. 1971. Releases 200 titles/year. Works with musicians/artists on contract. Pays 10-14% royalty to artists on contract; statutory rate to publisher per song on recording.
How to Contact: Prefers cassette with 3 songs and lyric sheet or lead sheet. Does not return unsolicited material. Reports in 6 weeks.
Music: All styles in gospel including pop, rock, jazz and country. Released *Classical Hymns Vol. 1* recorded by Phil Driscoll on Mighty Horn Records and *Petra Means Rock* recorded by Petra and *Big World* recorded by Lefevre and Broken Heart both on Starsong Records. Other artists distributed include Bill Gaither Trio, John Starnes, Degarmo and Key, Daniel Band, Joe English, Phil Keaggy, Whitecross, Mark Farner and the Imperials.

MAJEGA RECORDS, 240 E. Radcliffe Dr., Claremont CA 91711. (714)624-0677. President: Gary K. Buckley. Record company and record producer. Estab. 1976. Releases 1-5 singles and 1-5 LPs/year. Works with musicians/artists and songwriters on contract; hires musicians for in-house studio work. Pays negotiable royalty to artists on contract; standard royalty to songwriters on contract; statutory rate to publishers for each record sold.

How to Contact: Prefers cassette with 1-3 songs and lyric or lead sheet. SASE. Reports in 3 weeks.
Music: Country, country/pop crossover, easy listening, MOR, rock (country or pop) and top 40/pop. Released *Lyin' in Your Arms* (by George Wurzback/Jessee Goldberg) and *One Step Closer* (by Kevin McKelley), all recorded by Kevin McKelley on Majega Records (LPs); produced *Sky's The Limit* (by Michael Noll) on Gotta Be Hit Records (LP) and "Country Love" (by Jerry Roark) on JLR Records.
Tips: "Artists looking for a recording contract need to realize the competition that exists for a relative few production slots. A professional demo that clearly indicates their talent is required."

MARIAH RECORDS, P.O. Box 310, Carmichael CA 95609-310. President: Mari Minice. Record company (Mariah Records). Estab. 1986. Releases 1 single/year. Works with musicians/artists on contract. Pays varying royalty to artists on contract; statutory rate to pubilshers per song on records.
How to Contact: Submit demo tape by mail. Unsolicited submissions are okay. Prefers cassette with any number of songs and lyric sheets. Does not return unsolicited material. Reports in 2 months.
Music: Mostly country/contemporary, pop and rock. Released "Closer to Heaven" (by Jill Wood), recorded by Rachel Minke on Mariah Records (country single).
Tips: "Submit songs with wide vocal ranges, with a country feel."

THE MASTER'S COLLECTION LIMITED, Box 362, Station A, Rexdale, Toronto, Ontario M9W 5L3 **Canada.** (416)825-0464. President: Paul J. Young. Labels include Sharon, T.M.C., The Master's Collection, Pilgrim and Little Pilgrim. Record company and music publisher (T.M.C. Publishing/CAPAC and Master's Collection Publishing/PROCAN). Member CIRPA. Estab. 1977. Releases 6 LPs/year. Works with musicians/artists on contract. Pays 5-12% royalty to artists on contract; statutory rate to publishers for each record sold.
How to Contact: Write first. Prefers cassette with 3-6 songs. Does not return unsolicited material. Reports in 1 month.
Music: Mostly Christian gospel ("any style"); also church/religious. Released "Line of Vision," written and recorded by M. Barret (gospel contemporary); "Narnia," written and recorded by Aslan (rock); and "Traces of Light," written and recorded by G. Manus (country); all on TMC Records. Other artists include Ruth Fazel.

*MASTER-TRAK ENTERPRISES, 413 N. Parkerson, Crowley LA 70526. (318)788-0773. General Manager and Chief Engineer: Bobby Terry. Labels include Master-Trak, Showtime, Kajun, Blues Unlimited, Par T and MTE Records. Recording studio and record companies. Releases 20 singles and 6-8 LPs/year. Works with musicians/artists on contract. Pays 6% artist royalty. (No studio charges to contract artists.) Studio available on an hourly basis to the public. Charges for some services: "We charge for making audition tapes of any material that we do not publish."
How to Contact: Prefers cassette and lead sheet. SASE. Reports in 1 month.
Music: Mostly country, rock, R&B, cajun, blues and Zydeco. Released "Johnny Can't Dance" by Wayne Toups (Zydeco), "Tell Me What I Want to Hear Tonight" by Tammy Lynn, and "Only Passing Through" by Freddie Pate on MTE Records (country). Other artists include Al Ferrier, and Fernest & The Thunders.
Tips: "The song is the key. If we judge it to be a good song, we record it and it sells, we are happy. If we mis-judge the song and/or the artist and it does not sell, we must go back to the drawing board."

MAXIMA RECORDS, Suite 234, 24285 Sunnymead Blvd., Moreno Valley, CA 92388-9971. (714)653-1556. Professional Manager: LaDonna Kay. Record company, music publisher (KayDay Music) and record producer (Country Charts and OurWay Music). Releases 4-5 singles and 1-2 LPs/year. Works with musicians/artists and songwriters on contract. Pays standard royalty to artists on contract; compulsory rate to publisher per song on record.
How to Contact: Prefers cassette (or VHS videocassette) with 1-10 songs and lyric sheet. Reports in 1 month. "Please include a stamped and addressed postcard if you wish to know the date your material is received. We do not return material."
Music: Mostly contemporary country; also MOR and pop. Released "She Looks Like a Heartache" and "Small Town Dreams," recorded by Don Malena on Maxima Records (both singles).

MAXX RECORDS, Suite 207, 50 Music Square W., Nashville TN 37203. (615)329-2592. Publishing Manager: Karen Morris. Record company, music publisher (Maxx) and record producer (Fred Morris Music Group). Estab. 1987. Releases varying number of singles/year. Works with musicians/artists and songwriters on contract. Pays varying royalty to artists on contract; pays statutory rate to publisher per song on record.
How to Contact: Prefers cassette (or VHS videocassette if artists) with 3-5 songs and lyric sheet. SASE. Reports in 1 month.
Music: Mostly country, pop and rock; "no gospel." Released *Calendar Blues* (by Karren Pell/Dan E. James), recorded by Jill Jordan; and *We're Gonna Love Tonight* (by Eddy Rager/Vernis Pratt), recorded by Don Juan (both singles, LPs and CDs); *Panic* (by Fran Weber), recorded by Don Juan

(country rock LP); and "Ease My Mind" (by Sing Me Publishing), recorded by Jill Jordan (country LP); all on Maxx Records.

Tips: "Remember that the music business is that, a business. Talent is not enough anymore. You need an awareness of marketing and what is involved in making commercial decisions of where you are headed."

MCA RECORDS, 1755 Broadway, 8th Fl., New York NY 10019. (212)841-8000. East Coast A&R Director: Susan Dodes. East Coast Vice President: Bruce Dickinson. Labels include Costellation, Cranberry, Curb, IRS, Motown, London, Zebra and Philly World. Record company and music publisher (MCA Music). Works with musicians/artists on contract.
How to Contact: Call first and obtain permission to submit. Prefers cassete (or VHS videocassette) and lyric or lead sheet. SASE.

MEDA RECORDS INC., 19457 Shrewsbury, Detroit MI 45221. (313)862-5139. West Coast: 1621 Virginia Rd., Los Angeles CA 90019. (213)732-7009. A&R Director: Joe Hunter. Vice President/Marketing & Promotion: Mable John. Record company, record producer and music publisher (Mertis Music Company). Releases 4 singles and 4 LPs/year. Works with artists and songwriters on contract. Pays 4-12% royalty to artists on contract; statutory rate to publishers for each record sold.
How to Contact: Prefers cassette with 4-8 songs and lead sheet. SASE. Reports in 1 month or ASAP.
Music: Mostly R&B and pop; also gospel, jazz and top 40. Released "Christmas Comes Once a Year," by The Lamp Sisters (pop single); *A New Day*, by Mertis John (pop LP); *Heaven Bound*, by Mable John (gospel LP); *Where Can I Find Jesus?*, by Mable John (contemporary gospel) and *For Thee Lord I Sing*, by Lorine Thompson (gospel LP).

*MEGA RECORDS APS., Frederiksborggade 31, 1360 Copenhagen K **Denmark**. Phone: (4533)11 77 11. FAX: (4533)13 40 10. A&R Director: Martin Dodd. Labels include Mega Records, Mega Rock and Doctor Tilt. Record company and music publisher. Estab. 1982. Releases 150-200 singles, 75-100 12" singles, 50-75 LPs and 50-75 CDs/year. Works with musicians/artists and songwriters on contract; hires musicians for in-house studio work.
How to Contact: Write or call first and obtain permission to submit. Prefers cassette with 1 song and lyric sheet. Does not return unsolicited material. Reports in 3 weeks.
Music: Mostly crossover dance, pop/rock and hard rock; also strong ballads. Released "Mel & Kim," written and recorded by S.A.W. on Mega Records. Other artists include Disneyland After Dark, The Overlords, The Colours Turn Red, Laban, Seventy'Leven, Sky High, Technotronic, Jive Bunny, Sybil, Eric & The Good Good Feeling, De La Soul, Information Society, Digital Underground, Fancy, Camouflage and many more..

MEL VERN RECORDS, Box 412, Bronx NY 10462. (212)829-7033. President: Vernon Wilson. Record company and record producer (Wilson Productions). Releases 3 singles, 3 12" singles and 1 LP/year. Works with musicians/artists on contract; songwriters on royalty contract and in-house studio musicians on salary. Pays statutory rate to publisher per song on record.
How to Contact: Write or call first to arrange personal interview. Prefers cassette with 3 songs. Does not return unsolicited material. Reports in 1 month.
Music: Mostly top 40, love ballads and dance (commercial). Released "You Make Me Feel Like A Woman" (by Raymond Johnson/Vernon Wilson), Sandra Taylor on MelVern Records (ballad); "So In Love" (by Rick Robinson), recorded by Lisa Williamson on Lamar/Matala (R&B dance); and "Never Wanna Lose Your Love" (by Rick Robinson), recorded by Michael Foster on Lamar Records (R&B dance). Other artists include Lisa Williamson and Myleka Thompson.
Tips: "Work very hard and be determined. Most importantly, leave ego at home."

*METAL BLADE RECORDS, #311, 18653 Ventura, Tarzana CA 91356. (818)981-9050. A&R: Niels Schroeter. Labels include Death Records and No Wonder. Record company. Estab. 1982. Releases 4 singles, 2 12" singles, 30 LPs, 3 EPs and 33 CDs/year. Works with musicians/artists.
How to Contact: Write or call first and obtain permission to submit. Prefers cassette, (or ½" videocassette if available) with 3 songs and lyric and lead sheet. Does not return unsolicited submissions. Reports in 6 weeks.
Music: Mostly metal, rock and alternative; also rap and commercial. Released *Thrashzone* (by DRI), recorded by Bill Metoyes on Metal Blade Records (metal LP); *Perfect Symmetry* (by Fates Warning), recorded by Roger Probert on Metal Blade Records (progressive LP); and *Princess Pang*, (by Princes Pang) recorded Ron St. Germain on MB/Capitol Records (rock LP). Other artists include Artch, Bitter End, Goo Goo Dolls and Masi.
Tips: "Be organized, send complete promo pack, ba familiar with Metal Blade and all that is involved in acquiring a record deal. Have a representative for the band."

MICAH RECORDS, 43 Applemore Rd., Scarborough ON M1B 1R7 **Canada**. Phone: (416)298-3108. President: Oswald L. Burke. Record company and music publisher (CAPAC). Estab. 1985. Releases 4 LPs/year. Works with musicians/artists and songwriters on contract. Pays statutory rate to publisher per song on record.
How to Contact: No unsolicited material. Write first. Prefers cassette with 3 songs and lyric sheets. SASE. Reports in 2 months.
Music: Mostly gospel. Released *Introducing Brian Dungy*, written and recorded by Brian Dungy; and *One Day* (by various songwriters), recorded by Sweet Sound; all on Micah Records (gospel LPs). Other artists include the Toronto Mass Choir.

*MIGHTY RECORDS, Suite 6-D, 150 West End, New York NY 10023. (212)873-5968. Manager: Danny Darrow. Labels include Mighty Sounds & Filmworks. Record company, music publisher, record producer (Danny Darrow). Estab. 1958. Releases 1-2 singles, 1-2 12″ singles and 1-2 LPs/year. Works with songwriters on royalty contract and hires musicians for in-house studio work. Pays standard royalty to artists on contract; statutory rate to publishers per song on records.
How to Contact: Submit demo tape by mail. Unsolicited submittions are OK. "No phone calls." Prefers cassette with 3 songs and lyric sheet. SASE. Reports in 1 week.
Music: Mostly pop, country and dance; also jazz. Released *Carnival Nights* (by Vincent C. DeLucia and Raymond Squillacote), recorded by Danny Darrow (country LP); *Impulse* written and recorded by Danny Darrow (dance LP); and *Corporate Lady* (by Michael Greer), recorded by Danny Darrow (pop) all on Mighty Records. Other artists include Danny Darrow.
Tips: "Listen to the hits of Richie, Manilow, Houston and Rogers and write better songs."

MIRROR RECORDS, INC., 645 Titus Ave., Rochester NY 14617. (716)544-3500. Vice President: Armand Schaubroeck. Labels include Mirror and House of Guitars Records. Record company and music publisher. Works with artists and songwriters on contract and hires musicians for in-house studio work. Royalty paid to artists varies; negotiable royalty to songwriters on contract.
How to Contact: Prefers cassette or record (or videocassette). Include photo with submission. SASE. Reports in 2 months.
Music: Folk, progressive, rock, punk and heavy metal. Released "Don't Open Til Doomsday" by Chesterfield Kings; and "Through The Eyes of Youth" by Immaculate Mary.

MISSILE RECORDS, Box 5330, Moss Point MS 39563. (601)475-2098. "No collect calls."President (Owner): Joe F. Mitchell. Record company, music publisher (Bay Ridge Publishing/BMI), record producer (For Missile Records) and Myra Records, JB Records and RCI Records. Estab. 1974. Releases 16 singles and 3 LPs/year. Works with musicians/artists and songwriters on contract. Pays 8-10¢ royalty to artists on contract.
How to Contact: Write first and obtain permission to submit. SASE. Prefers cassette with 3 songs and lyric sheet. Does not return unsolicited material. Reports in 6 weeks.
Music: Mostly country, gospel and R&B; also rock, rap and pop. Released "No One Loves Me At Home" (by Terry Bullock), recorded by Jimmy Bullock; "The Mountains and the Eagles," written and recorded by Jimmy Bullock; and "He Will Not Come From Texas," written and recorded by Terry Bullock; all on Missile Records (C&W singles). Other artists include Gloria Nelson and The Harmoneers.
Tips: "If a songwriter recording artist has exceptional talent and has some backing, then Missile Records is open to sign a number of artists to contracts. A bio and cassette tape and pictures of the artists should be submitted along with songs the artists are singing and, most important, return postage (SASE)."

*MONOTONE RECORDS, 281 E. Kingsbridge Rd., Bronx NY 10458. (212)733-5342. President: Murray Fuller. Record company, record producer and music publisher (Sun Island Music Publishing Co.). Releases 1 single/year. Works with artists and songwriters on contract. Pays 3-5% royalty to artists on contract; statutory rate to publishers for each record sold.
How to Contact: Prefers cassette with 3-5 songs and lyric sheet. SASE. Reports in 6 weeks.
Music: Blues, dance-oriented, easy listening, jazz, R&B, soul and top 40/pop.

MONTICANA RECORDS, P.O. Box 702, Snowdon Station, Montreal, Quebec H3X 3X8 **Canada**. General Manager: David P. Leonard. Labels include Dynacom and Monticana Records. Record company, record producer, and music publisher (Montina Music/SOCAN). Estab. 1963. Works with artists and songwriters on contract. Pays negotiable royalty to artists on contract; statutory rate to publishers for each record sold.
How to Contact: Prefers phonograph record (or VHS videocassette) and lyric sheet. Does not return unsolicited material.
Music: Mostly top 40, blues, country, dance-oriented, easy listening, folk, gospel, jazz, MOR, progressive, R&B, rock and soul.

MOR RECORDS, 17596 Corbel Court, San Diego CA 92128. (619)485-1550. President: Stuart L. Glassman. Record company and record producer. Estab. 1980. Releases 3 singles/year. Works with musicians on salary for in-house studio work. Pays 4% royalty to artists on contract.
How to Contact: Prefers cassette (or VHS videocassette). Does not return unsolicited material. Reports in 2 months.
Music: Mostly pop instrumental/vocal MOR; also novelty songs. Released "Play On" (by Bob Cockneu/Cory Lerios), recorded by Dave Austin; "Colors of My Life" (by Bowy Sttow), recorded by Frank Sinatra, Jr; and "Shifting Whispering Sands" (by Gilbert/Gilbert), recorded by Wally Flaherty; "Happy Birthday/Happy Anniversary" and "Last Call," written and recorded by David Racan (pop); "First Fall of Snow/Happy Birthday Jesus," written and recorded by Al Rosa (pop); all on MOR Records (all singles).
Tips: "Send original work. Do not send 'copy' work."

MSM RECORDS, P.O. Box 105, Cooper TX 75432. Professional Manager: Jim Brewer. Labels include Hālo Records, Bronco Records. Record company and music publisher (Mount Scott Music/BMI), (Park The Hits Music/ASCAP). Estab. 1982. Releases 3-4 singles/year. Works with songwriters on contract and hires musicians for in-house studio work. Pays 5-10% royalty to artists on contract; statutory rate (or as negotiated) to publisher per song on record.
How to Contact: Write first and obtain permission to submit. Prefers cassette with 2 songs and lyric sheets. Does not return unsolicited material. Reports in 4 weeks.
Music: Mostly traditional country, contemporary country and pop-rock. Released "Lovers Mountain" and "I'm A Believer" (by J. Brewer), and "Angels Ain't Supposed to Cry" (by K. and J. Brewer); all recorded by J.L. Brewer on MSM Records (all country singles); "Soft Touch," (by M. Fox/J.Cross), "I Think It Might Be Love," (by J. Randall/R. Gillam/R.Randall) and "Your Love Keeps Bringing Me Back," (by Phil Sampson), all recorded by Gwen Newton on Halo Records (all country singles). Other artists include Robin Sorensen and Roger Young.
Tips: "Submit only those songs that a label is looking for."

*MUSCLE SHOALS SOUND GOSPEL, Box 915, Sheffield AL 35660. (205)381-2060. Executive Director: Butch McGhee. Record company and record producer (Butch McGhee). Estab. 1986. Releases 10 LPs and 10 CDs/year. Works with musicians/artists and songwriters on contract and hires musicians for in-house studio work. Pays statutory rate to publisher per song.
How to Contact: Write first and obtain permission to submit. Prefers cassette or VHS videocassette with 4 songs. Does not return unsolicited material. Reports in 8 weeks.
Music: Mostly gospel, inspirational. Released "Home Someday," (by Harvey Thompson, Jr./Shawn C. Lee, Sr.), recorded by Loretta Hinly on Ameka Records, "All To You," (by Derrick Lee), recorded by Keith Pringle and "In the Midst of it All," (by Butch McGhee), recorded by Charles Fold Singers, both on MSSG Records; (all gospel singles).

MUSIC CITY RECORDS, 4305 So. 70th St., Tampa FL 33619. (813)621-7055. Owner: Wayne Lacey. Record company, music publisher (Wayne and Lacey/BMI) and record producer (Wayne Lacey). Estab. 1982. Releases 4 singles and 20 LPs/year. Works with musicians/artists on contract and hires musicians for in-house studio work. Pays statutory rate to publisher per song on record.
How to Contact: Prefers cassette with 4 songs. Does not return unsolicited material. Reports in 1 month.
Music: Southern gospel only. Released *Expressions*, recorded by Apostals; "Wonderful Place," "Sing the Glory Down," and "Only the Blood" (by Wayne Lacey), recorded by The Laceys, all on Music City Records (all southern gospel). Other artists include Lighthouse Quartet and Messengers Quartet.

*MUSIC FOR LITTLE PEOPLE, P.O. Box 1460, Redway CA 95560. (707)723-3991. Director: Jim Deerhawk. Labels include Music For Little People and Earth Beat! Record company, music pubilsher (Music For Little People/BMI), record and video producer (Music For Little People). Estab. 1985. Releases 6-12 cassettes and 6-12 CDs/year. Works with musicians/artists on contract and hires musicians for in-house studio work. Pays 8-12% royalty to artists on contract; negotiable rate to publisher per song on record. Write or call first and obtain permission to submit.
How to Contact: Prefers cassette with 3 songs and lyric sheet. SASE. Reports in 3 months.
Music: Mostly children's music, world music and children's stories. Released *All For Freedom* (by various), recorded by Sweet Honey in the Rock; *Dirt Made My Lunch* (by S. Van Zandt), recorded by Banana Slug String Band; and *Percival The Froggy* (by D. Connolly), recorded by David Connolly all on MLP Records (kids cassette).
Tips: "We're interested in music that empowers children with creativity, self-respect, interactive choices and that promotes peace and environmental consciousness and celebrates cultural diversity."

MÚSICA ARROZ (ASCAP), (formerly Discos MM), 5626 Brock St., Houston TX 77023. (713)926-4436. Publications Manager: Barry Leavitt. Labels include Discos MM. Record company and publishing company. Estab. 1986. Releases 10 singles, 5 12″ singles, 10 LPs, 5 EPs and 10 CDs/year. Works with musicians/artists and songwriters on contract and hires musicians for in-house studio work. Pays 10-11% royalty to artists on contract; statutory rate to publisher per song on record.
How to Contact: Submit demo tape by mail. Unsolicited submissions are okay or write to arrange personal interview. Prefers cassette with less than 10 songs and lyric sheets. SASE. Reports in 6 months.
Music: Mostly Spanish pop, Spanish rock and Spanish regional and Tejano. Released "Todos Me Dicen" (by Albert Gonzales) recorded by Rick Gonzales & The Choice, on Mercury Latino Records (discos MM); "Otro Día" (by Gerardo Rodriguez) recorded by Jerry Rodriguez & Mercedez; and "Dime Si Tú Quieres" (by Maria G. Henson), recorded Laura Canales on Capitol/EMI (Latin Tejano).
Tips: "We're interested in anything with a Latin feel, of any type, English or Spanish. We translate if necessary."

MUSICA SCHALLPLATTEN VERTRIEB GES.M.B.H., Webgasse 43, Vienna A-1060 **Austria**. Phone: (1)597 56 46. A&R National: Manfred Blaschko. Labels include OK-Records. Record company, music publisher, record producer (OK-Musica) and publishing company (Ed. Musica). Estab. 1949. Works with musicians/artists and songwriters on contract. Pays varying royalty to artists on contract.
How to Contact: Submit demo tape by mail—unsolicited submissions are OK—or call first and obtain permission to submit. Prefers cassette with 4-6 songs. Does not return unsolicited material. Reports in 4 weeks.
Music: Mostly rock, pop and dance. Released "Live is Life," written and recorded by Opus on Polygram (USA) Records; "Touch by Touch," written and recorded by Joy on OK Records; and "I'm In It For Love" (by Goldmark-Henderson), recorded by Andy Baum on OK Records. Other artists include Chris Cramer, Freddy Jay (Ex-Singer JOY) and Fahrenheit.
Tips: "If we are interested in singer or song we will contact you. For overseas-artists we are more interested in songs."

*NARADA PRODUCTIONS, 1845 North Farwell Ave., Milwaukee WI 53202. (414)272-6700. Labels include Narada Equinox, Narada Lotus, Narada Mystique, Sona Gaia. Record company. Estab. 1979. Releases 25 LPs/year. Works with musicians/artists on contract.
How to Contact: Submit demo tape by mail. Unsolicited submissions are OK. Prefers cassette (or VHS videocassette if available). Does not return unsolicited material. Reports in 2 months.
Music: Mostly instrumental. Released *Mil Amones* written and recorded by Doug Cameron, on Euinox Records; *Dr. D* written and recorded by Spencer Brewer, on Equinox Records; and *Citizen of Time* written and recorded by David Arkenstone, on Mystique Records (instrumental).

NEON RECORDS, 88 Lenox Ave., Paterson NJ 07502. (201)790-7668. A&R Department: Scott Lea. Record company, music publisher (BMI, ASCAP), record producer (Scott Lea Productions) and Scott Lea Publishing. Estab. 1988. Releases 3-6 singles, 2-4 12″ singles, 1-2 LPs, 1-2 EPs and 1-2 CDs/year. Works with musicians/artists and songwriters on contract and hires musicians for in-house studio work. Pays varying royalty to artists on contract; negotiated rate to publisher per song on record.
How to Contact: Call first and obtain permission to submit. Prefers cassette with 3-5 songs and lyric sheet. SASE. Reports in 6 weeks.
Music: Mostly R&B, club, dance, adult contemporary and rock; also pop and jazz. Released "World Without Love" (by Claude S.), recorded by Anything Box on Neon Records (club/ballad); "Stop" (by R. Bonagura and D. Cintron), recorded by Myth on Neon Records (rock) and "How Does Your Heart Feel?" (by P. Castgilin and S. Lea), recorded by Paul Cast on Neon Records (adult contemporary/ rock ballad).

NEPHELIM RECORD (STUDIO WORKS), 404 ST-Henri, Montreal Quebec H3C 2P5 **Canada**. (514)871-8481. Producer: Mario Rubnikowich. Music publisher (SDE, CAPAC) and record producer. Estab. 1986. Releases 10 singles, 2 12″ singles, 6 LPs and 2 CDs/year. Works with musicians/artists and songwriters on contract and hires musicians for in-house studio work.
How to Contact: Submit demo tape by mail. Unsolicited submissions are OK. Prefers cassette with 3 songs and lyric or lead sheets. SASE. Reports in 5 weeks.
Music: Mostly new age, pop and R&B; also rock, metal and relaxation. Released "Young/Donato" (by Young/Donato), on Just In Times Records (jazz, LP/CD); "Paul Lauzon" (by Paul Lauzon) on Blue Wing Records (therapy, LP, cassettes); and "Just for Laughs" (by Serge Fiori), on Radio Quebec (radio comedy). Other artists include Michel Laverdiere, Robert LaFond, Oréalis, John Oakley, Marc Chapleau and John Bodine.

*NEPTUNE RECORDS, INC., Box 3011, Country Club IL 60478. (708)798-9408. A&R Department: Rick Stevens or Tony Shayne. Record company.
How to Contact: Prefers cassette (or VHS or Beta videocassette) with maximum of 5 songs; lyric sheet optional. SASE. Reports in 3 weeks.
Music: Mostly R&B, pop, dance. Works primarily with vocalists, dance bands, Christian rock and R&B acts. Current acts include Tony Shayne, Neew Breed and T.K. Drew.
Tips: "Submit a legible, thoughtful presentation. We prefer lyrics of a cleaner nature."

NERVOUS RECORDS, Unit 6, 7-11 Minerva Rd., London NW10 6HJ, **England**. Phone: 441-963-0352. Managing Director: R. Williams. Record company, record producer and music publisher (Nervous Publishing and Zorch Music). Member MCPS, PRS, PPL. Releases 20 LPs and 2 CDs/year. Works with songwriters on royalty contract. Pays 6-10% royalty to artists on contract; statutory rate to publishers per song on records. Royalties paid directly to US songwriters and artists or through US publishing or recording affiliate.
How to Contact: Submit demo tape with 4-15 songs and lyric sheet. SAE and IRC. Reports in 2 weeks.
Music: Mostly psychobilly and rockabilly. "NO HEAVY ROCK, AOR, STADIUM ROCK, DISCO, SOUL, POP—ONLY WILD ROCKABILLY AND PSYCHOBILLY." Released "She's the One," (by Corboy), recorded by The Rattlers (rockabilly), "Ghost Town," (by Harman), recorded by Restless (rockabilly) and "Gonna Slice You Baby," written and recorded by Harry Hepcat (psychobilly); all on Nervous Records. Other artists include The Griswalds, Rusti Steel and The Tintax Torment and The Nitros.
Tips: "Want wild and fast music—really demented rockabilly, not punk."

NETTWERK PRODUCTIONS, Box 330, 1755 Robson St., Vancouver, British Columbia V6G 1C9 **Canada**. A&R Directors: Mark Jowett and Rick Arboit. Record company, music publisher (Nettwerk Management/Nettoverboard Publishing/NTWK Publishing Ltd.) and management firm (Nettwerk Management). Estab. 1984. Releases 3 7" singles, 12 12" singles, 8 LPs and 1-2 EPs/year. Works with musicians/artists on contract. Pays 10-14% royalty to artists on contract; statutory rate to publisher per song on record.
How to Contact: Prefers cassette and lyric sheet. SAE and IRC. Reports in 1 month.
Music: Mostly progressive; also folk and modern classical. Released *Vox*, written and recorded by Sarah McLachlan; *Einstein*, written and recorded by Keith LeBlanc; *Yeah Whatever, Moev*, written and recorded by Ferris, Cook and Russell; all on Nettwerk Records. Other artists include SPK, Pretty Green, The Water Walk, After All, and Front 242.
Tips: "Be unique/experimentive—ignore radio formats and other role models for songs—be yourself and write what comes from the heart."

*NEW MUSIC ENTERPRISES, "Meredale," The Dell, Reach Lane, Near Leighton Buzzard Beds. **United Kingdom**. Phone: 052523-7700. Manager: Paul Davis. Labels/England: New Music, Herald, Pilot and Fig Tree. Labels/US: Herald. Record company and music publisher (New Music Enterprises). Member PRS, MCPS. Releases 20 LPs/year. Works with artists on contract; also licenses foreign LPs. Pays negotiable royalty to artists on contract; statutory rate to publishers for each record sold. Royalties paid to US songwriters and artists through US publishing or recording affiliate.
How to Contact: Write first. Prefers cassette with 2-4 songs. SAE and IRC.
Music: Mostly "Christian music of all styles if contemporary (i.e., non-classical);" also bluegrass, country, easy listening, MOR and rock. Released *Travelin' On* by Jerry Arhelger (country LP); and *Personally* by The Samuelsons (gospel LP). Other artists include Linda Hargrove Bartholomew, Erv Lewis, Judy Herring, Rosemary Wilhelm, Roland Friday and Eric Anders.

NEWSTAR INTERNATIONAL RECORDS, 29 S. Erie, Toledo OH 43602. President: J. Knorr. Labels include MDS, Northcoast, Heritage, Jamestune, Newstar, Toledo, 144 Records and Janisknorr. Record company, record producer and music publisher (Keeny-York, Park J. Tunes). Releases 12 singles and 8 LPs/year. Works with artists and songwriters on contract. Pays negotiable royalty to artists; statutory rate to publishers for each record sold.
How to Contact: Prefers cassette with 3 songs maximum and lyric sheet. SASE. Reports in 3 months or less.
Music: Mostly pop; also country, easy listening and MOR. "We're beginning to review jazz."

NICKEL RECORDS, 753 Capitol Ave., Hartford CT 06106. (203)524-5656. Producer: Jack Stang. Record company, record producer and music publisher (Stang Music Publishing). Estab. 1971. Releases 2 singles, 2 12" singles and 2 LPs/year. Works with musicians/artists and songwriters on contract. Pays statutory rate to publishers for each record sold.

How to Contact: Prefers cassette with 1-3 songs and lyric sheet. SASE. Reports in 3 weeks.
Music: Mostly dance and top 40/pop; also easy listening, MOR, R&B and rock. Released *Girls Like You*, written and recorded by Bill Chapin; *Smokin*, by Joe Frazier, all LPs on Nickel Records. Other artists include Kenny Hamber, Michael Kelly, Perfect Tommy, Alpha Sonas, Damon Sky and Dagmar.

*NICKLE PLATE RECORDS, 410 S. Michigan, Suite 470, Chicago IL 60605. (312)939-5581. President: Frederick S. Koger. Record company and music publisher ("L" Train Publishers—ASCAP). Estab. 1987. Releases 3 singles and 3 12″ singles/year. Works with musicians/artists and songwriters on contract. Pays 10% royalty to artist on contract.
How to Contact: Write or call first to arrange personal interview. Prefers cassette or 7½ ips reel-to-reel with 3-5 songs and lyric or lead sheets. Reports in 3 weeks.
Music: Mostly R&B, rap and pop; also rock and gospel. Released "Love Quarrel" (by Frederick S. Koger), recorded by Virgil/Rozlyn on Nickle Plate Records (single) and "Stop Watch" written and recorded by Jam 2000 and Derick on Nickel Plate Records (dance house). Other artists include Steven Lee and Orlando Sifney.

NISE PRODUCTIONS INC., 413 Cooper St., Camden NJ 08102. (609)963-6473. Contact: Dan McKeown. Labels include Power Up, Euro-American International. Record company (BMI) and record producer (Nise Productions, Inc.). Estab. 1981. Releases 1-5 singles and 1-5 LPs/year. Works with musicians/artists and songwriters on contract and hires musicians for in-house studio work. Pays statutory rate to publisher per song on record.
How to Contact: Submit demo tape by mail. Unsolicited submissions are okay. Prefers cassette with 3 songs and lyric sheets. SASE. Reports in 2 weeks.

NORTH STAR RECORDS, 116 Chestnut St., Providence RI 02903. (401)274-4119. Executive Vice President: Bruce R. Foulke. Record company and music publisher (Publishing Name: Blue Gate Music/ASCAP). Estab. 1985. Releases 4-5 LPs/year. Works with musicians/artists and songwriters on contract. Pays statutory royalty to artists on contract; statutory rate to publisher per song on record.
How to Contact: Write first and obtain permission to submit. Prefers cassette with 4-5 songs and lyric sheets. Does not return unsolicited material. Reports in 1 month.
Music: Mostly country, R&B and rock/folk; also acoustic traditional, classical and children's music. Released *Cheryl Wheeler* on North Star Records and *Half-A-Book* on Cypress Records, written and recorded by Cheryl Wheeler (rock/country LPs); and *Time Can Be So Magic*, written and recorded by Bill Thomas on North Star Records (children's LP). Other artists include Chili Brothers, Arturo Delmoni, New England Music Collection, Mair-Davis Duo and Hubbards.
Tips: "A professional, well thought-out presentation of your best material is necessary to attract the attention of record label personnel."

*NORTHEASTERN RECORDS, P.O. Box 3589, Saxonville MA 01701-0605. (508)820-4440. General Manager: L.E. Joiner. Record company. Estab. 1980. Releases 10 CDs/year. Pays statutory rate to publishers per song on records.
How to Contact: Submit demo tape by mail. Unsolicited submissions are OK. "Include SASE if you want anything back." Prefers cassette, "preferably a copy of final studio cut." Reports in 3 months.
Music: Interested in country/bluegrass, folk/international and jazz; also rock 'n roll. Released *That Old Mill*, written and recorded by John Lincoln Wright (country/folk CD/cassette); and *Maniz Traditions*, written and recorded by Les Miserables Brass Band (worldbeat/folk CD/cassette), both on Northeastern Records. Other artists include Didi Stewart (pop), The Fringe (jazz) and Barry and Holly Tashran (country).
Tips: "We are presently licensing finished masters for CD and cassette release, and are mainly interested in artists with a developed, original sound, who are also touring."

NUCLEUS RECORDS, Box 111, Sea Bright NJ 07760. President: Robert Bowden. Record company and music publisher (Roots Music/BMI). Member AFM (US and Canada). Estab. 1979. Releases 2 singles and 1 LP/year. Works with musicians/artists on contract and hires musicians for in-house studio work. Pays up to 10% royalty for each record sold; 50% rate to publisher per song on record. Charges artists/songwriters up-front for demo work.
How to Contact: Prefers cassette (or videocassette) with any number songs and lyric sheet. Prefers studio produced demos. SASE. Reports in 1 month.
Music: Mostly country and pop; also church/religious, classical, folk, MOR, progressive, rock (soft, mellow) and top 40. Released "Always," written and recorded by Marco Sison (pop singles); "Selfish Heart," written and recorded by Robert Bowden; and "Henrey C.," written and recorded by Robert Dowden (country); all on Nucleus Records.

*O.L. RECORDS, INC., 10051 Greenleaf, Santa Fe Springs CA 90670. (213)946-1524. President: Overton Lee. Record company, record producer, video production and music publisher (Boggy Depot, Overton Lee Music). Releases 6 singles and 2 LPs/year. Works with artists and songwriters on contract. Pays statutory rate to publishers for each record sold.
How to Contact: Prefers cassette with 1-3 songs and lyric sheet. Reports in 4 months.
Music: Mostly country and bluegrass; also blues and gospel.

*OPUS—RECORDS AND PUBLISHING HOUSE, Mlynské nivy 73, Bratislava 827 15 **Czechoslovakia**. Phone: 07/666 35 extn. 59 or 07/666 52. International Department: Eva Bauerová. Record company, studio rental, co-production recording, export/import of finished CDs, LPs, MCs. Releases 30 singles, 50 LPs and 60 CDs/year. Works with musicians/artists and songwriters on contract. Pays 8% royalty to artist on contract.
How to Contact: FAX No. 07/690 91 or the above stated phone.
Music: Mostly classical, also pop/rock, released *Schmidt - Symphonies 1-4*, all CDs, LPs and MCs on Opus Records.

*THE ORANGE RECORD COMPANY, Suite 119, 2166 W. Broadway, Anaheim CA 92804-2446. (714)525-5223. Vice President A&R: Harold Shmoduquet. Labels include Orange Records and Beet Records. Record company, music publisher (Tracy Sands Music/BMI) and record producer (Orange Productions). Estab. 1989. Releases 1-2 singles, 6-12 12″ singles, 4 LPs, 2 EPs and 4 CDs/year. Works with musicians/artists and songwriters on contract. Pays 1-9% royalty to artists on contract; statutory rate or negotiable rate to publishers per song on record. "Artists may, depending on negotiation, be responsible for a percentage of production costs in relation to the finished master tape. Songwriters are never charged for any reason."
How to Contact: Submit demo tape by mail. Unsolicited submissions are OK. Prefers cassette (or VHS videocassette) with 2-3 songs and lyric sheet. SASE. Reports in 2 months.
Music: Mostly melodic metal, progressive rock and sixties-sound; also ethnic, R&B and gospel. Released "Hot Summer Days" (by Daniel Dailey/Ted Greenberg), recorded by Wilson Dailey; "My Dreams Came True" (by Robert Wahlsteen/Brad Stanfield), recorded by Bob Chance; and "Look at Me" (by Chris Newman/Charles Hahn), recorded by Chris Newman, all on Orange Records (60's 12″ singles). Other artists include Mary Hart, Bastille, No Sweat and Manhunter.
Tips: "If you sound like the Beatles, we'll talk."

ORBIT RECORDS, Box 120675, Nashville TN 37212. (615)255-1068. Owner: Ray McGinnis. Record company, music publisher (Nautical Music Co.) and record producer (Ray Mack Productions). Estab. 1965. Releases 6 singles, 4 12″ singles and 4 LPs/year. Works with musicians/artists on contract. Pays 8-12% royalty to artists on contract; statutory rate to publisher per song on record.
How to Contact: Prefers cassette with 4 songs and lead sheet. Does not return unsolicited material. Reports in 6-8 weeks.
Music: Country, rock and R&B. Released "Burning Love," written and recorded by Alan Warren (hard rock); "I Need the Real Thing," written and recorded by Don Acuff (country); and "She's a Heartbreaker" (by L. Oldham), recorded by LeRoy Steele (country rock); all on Orbit Records. Other artists include LeRoy Steele, Dallas Taylor, Kim Tsoy and Alan Warren.
Tips: "We like artists with individual styles, not 'copy cats'; be original and unique."

ORINDA RECORDS, 111 Deerwood Place, San Ramon CA 94583. (415)831-4890. A&R Director: Harry Balk. Record company. Releases 30 LPs/year. Works with musicians/artists and songwriters on contract. Pays varying royalty to artists on contract; statutory rate to publishers.
How to Contact: Prefers cassette with lyric and lead sheet. SASE. Does not return unsolicited material. Reports in 2 months.
Music: Rock, pop, and jazz; also classical.

*PALMETTO PRODUCTIONS, P.O. Box 1376, Pickens SC 29671. (803)859-9614. FAX: (803)859-3814. President: Brian E. Raines. Labels include Palmetto Records (country) and Rosada Records (gospel). Record company, music publisher (Brian Raines Music Co./ASCAP and Brian Song Music Co./BMI) and record producer (Brian E. Raines/Palmetto Productions). Estab. 1985. Releases 1-3 singles and 2 LPs/year. Works with musicians/artists and songwriters on contract and hires musicians as independent contractors. Pays 20% royalty to artists on contract; statutory rate to publishers per song on record.
How to Contact: Submit demo tape by mail. Unsolicited submissions are okay. Prefers cassette (or VHS videocassette) with 2 songs and lyric sheet. SASE. Reports in 3 weeks.
Music: Mostly country, gospel and top 40; also contemporary Christian. Released "Since I Met You" (written and recorded by Brian Raines), on Palmetto Records (country, single); *Take It To Jesus* (by Dale Cassell), recorded by Trinity on Mark Five Records (gospel LP); and *From the Heart* (written and recorded by Jim Hubbard), on Hubbit Records (country LP).

PANDEM RECORDS INC., 1916 28th Ave. South, Birmingham AL 35209. (205)870-3239. President: Michael Panapento. Labels include Polymusic Records. Record company. Estab. 1985. Releases 3-4 singles, 2 12″ singles, 3-4 LPs, 3 EPs and 3-4 CDs/year. Works with musicians/artists on contract and hires musicians for in-house studio work; artist development. Pays varying percentage royalty to artists on contract.
How to Contact: Write first and obtain permission to submit. Prefers cassette with 3 song and lyric sheets. Reports in 6 weeks.
Music: Mostly pop/top 40, rock and R&B; also country and jazz. Released *Pass the Buck*, written and recorded by F. Fatts on Pandem Records (jazz LP); *Coming Out*, written and recorded by G. Motley on Jazz Harbor Records (jazz LP); and "This Time" (by J. Bradley), recorded by Dee Bradley on Smoke Stack Records (R&B 45). Other artists inlcude Randy Hunter, The Pedestrians and Tim Newton.

PARADE, 88 St. Francis St., Newark NJ 07105. (201)344-4214. Senior Vice President, Product Development/A&R Director: Joey Porello. Labels include Peter Pan, Power, Compose Records, Tronbound, Third Ear, Connection and Jammo. Record company. Estab. 1928. Releases 10-20 singles and 5-10 12″ singles, 10-20 LPs, and 10-20 CDs/year. Works with artists and songwriters on contract. Pays varying royalty to artists on contract; statutory rate to publishers for each record sold.
How to Contact: Prefers cassette with 1-3 songs and lyric sheet. SASE. Reports in 2 months.
Music: Mostly dance, children's and MOR; also country, R&B, New Age rock, novelty and classical. Released *Aerobics*, by Joanie Greggains (exercise LP). Other artists include Morton Downey, Jr. (country) and Gilead Limor (New Age).

PARAGOLD RECORDS & TAPES, Box 292101, Nashville TN 37216. (615)391-5955. Director: Teresa Bernard. Record company, music publisher (Rainbarrel Music Co./BMI) and record producer. Estab. 1972. Releases 5 singles, 5 LPs and 1 EP/year. Works with musicians/artists and songwriters on contract. Pays statutory rate to publishers.
How to Contact: Write first and obtain permission to submit. Prefers cassette (or VHS videocassette) with 2 songs and lyric or lead sheets. SASE. "Unpublished songs are welcome. Send only outstanding material." Reports in 6 weeks.
Music: Country and top 40. Released "Devil's Guitar" and "I Worked with O'l Lefty," both written and recorded by Johnny Bernard on Paragold Records (country). Other artists include Sunset Cowboys.

*PARC RECORDS INC., 3016 Dade Ave. 2ND Floor, Orlando FL 32804. (407)894-0021. Administrative Affairs: Gayle Boulware. Record company (Mister Sunshine Music/BMI). Estab. 1985. Releases 4+ singles, 2 12″ singles, 2 LPs and 2 CDs/year. Works with musicians/artists and songwriters on contract.
How to Contact: Prefers cassette (or VHS videocassette) with 3-5 songs and lyric sheet. SASE. Reports in 6-8 weeks.
Music: Mostly rock/metal, dance and jazz/new wave; also A/C and R&B. Released *Lighting Strikes* recorded by Molly Hatchet on Parc/Capitol Records (rock LP); *China Sky* recorded by China Sky on Parc/CBS Records (rock LP); and *Ana* recorded by Ana on Parc/CBS Records (dance LP) (all by various). Other artists include Glen Kelly and Deryle Hughes.
Tips: Quality songs with good hooks are more important than great production. If it's good, we can hear it."

PARHAM SOUND STUDIO, Rt. 3, Box 243-B, Stephenville TX 76401. (817)965-4132. Contact: Carroll Parham. Labels include Scotty Records of Texas and Cedar Valley Records. Record company, music publisher (Cedar Valley Publishing) and record producer. Releases 4 LPs/year. Works with musicians/artists and songwriters on contract. Pays standard royalty to artists on contract; pays statutory rate to publishers.
How to Contact: Prefers cassette. Does not return unsolicited material. "Please make sure demo is clean and presentable."
Music: Mostly country, gospel and swing. Released *Do You Ever Think of Me* (by Joan Hathcox), recorded by Joanie on Scotty Records; *What's Left of A Man*, (by J. Green), recorded by Curtis Lovejoy on Scotty Records; and *Texas Ranger Swing*, (by D. Rowell/J. Hathcox/ C. Parham), recorded by Country Express on GBC Records, (all LPs). Other artists include Tommy Horton, Derwood Rowell, and Ray Jones.

PARIS RECORDS, P.O. Box 2250, Canoga Park CA 91306. (818)883-8224. President: Jeff Gordon. Record company, music publisher (Gordon Music Co. Inc.) and management firm. Estab. 1975. Releases 2-4 singles and 3-5 LPs/year. Works with artists and songwriters on contract. Pays statutory rate to publishers for each record sold.

How to Contact: Call first and obtain permission to submit. Prefers cassette (or VHS videocassette) with 2-4 songs and lyric or lead sheet. Does not return unsolicited material. Reports in 1 month.
Music: Mostly children's, pop, rock and jazz. Released "Leave It To Beaver Theme" (by D Kahn, M. Lenard, M. Green), recorded by Pabo Frio on MCA Records (jazz); and "Mouse and Men" (by P. Bell), recorded by Chalk Talk on Paris Records (kids).

PARSIFAL PVBA, Gulden Vlieslaan, 67, Brugge 8000 **Belgium**. Phone: (050)339516. Contact: Nico Mertens. Labels include Parsifal, Sundown, Moonshine, Blue Sting and Discus. Record company, music publisher and record producer. Estab. 1977. Releases 2 singles and 10 LPs/year. Works with musicians/artists on contract; musicians on salary for in-house studio work.
How to Contact: Prefers cassette. Does not return unsolicited material. Reports in 1 month.
Music: R&B and blues. Other artists include Steve Samuels (USA), Paris Slim (USA), The Slime Hunters (BEL), The Moonlighters (BEL).

*PAULA RECORDS/JEWEL RECORDS/RONN RECORDS, P.O. Box 1125, Shreveport LA 71163-1125. (318)227-2228. Owner: Stanly J. Lewis. Labels include Jewell Records and Ronn Records. Record company and music publisher. Works with musicians/artists and songwriters on contract.
How to Contact: Submit demo tape by mail. Unsolicited submissions are OK. Prefers cassette with 3 songs and lyric sheet. SASE.
Music: Mostly R&B, gospel and country.

*PDS RECORDS, P.O. Box 412477, Kansas City MO 64141. (816)921-7621. Contact: A&R, Dept. 100. Labels include Universal Jazz, PDS Associated labels. Record company, music publisher (PDS Music Publishing/ASCAP/BMI) and record producer (PDS Productions). Estab. 1988. Releases 8-10 singles, 8-10 12″ singles, 3-5 LPs, 8-10 EPs and 3-5 CDs/year. Works with musicians/artists on contract.
How to Contact: Write first and obtain permission to submit. Prefers cassette (or VHS videocassette) with 4-5 songs and lyric sheet. Does not return unsolicited material. Reports in 2 months.

PEGASUS RECORDS, 1609 Congress, Eastover SC 29044. (803)776-8397. President: Howard A. Knight, Jr. Labels include Wago and Boss. Record company, music publisher (Tenallina Music) and record producer (Howard Knight Ent.). Releases 6 singles and 2 LPs/year. Works with musicians/artists and songwriters on contract; musicians on salary for in-house studio work. Pays statutory rate to publisher per song on record. Changes for "custom" sessions.
How to Contact: Submit demo tape by mail. Unsolicited submissions are OK. Prefers cassette with 3 songs and lyric sheet. Does not return any material. Reports only if interested.
Music: Mostly country, pop and rock. Released "Do You Wanna Fall in Love" (by K. Bell, R. Cox), recorded by Bandit Band; "Give In" (by J.P. McMeens), recorded by Randy Chapman; "A Woman's Way," written and recorded by Mundo Earwood; and "Knee Deep in Love" (by J. McMeens), recorded by The Bandit Band; all country singles on Pegasus Records.

*PENGUIN RECORDS, INC., P.O. Box 1274, Miami FL 33161. Product Manager: Michael J. McNamee; Operation Manager: Gregory J.Winters. Labels include Straitgate Records and Penguin Records. Record company, music publisher. Estab. 1990. Releases 6 singles, 6 12″ singles, 3 LPs and 3 CDs/year. Works with musicians/artists and songwriters/year. Pays varying royalty.
How to Contact: Submit demo tape by mail. Unsolicited submissions are OK. Prefers cassette (or VHS videocassette if available) with 3 songs and lyric sheet. Does not return unsolicited material. Reports in 2 months.
Music: Mostly dance, pop, rock R&B/rap and alternative/dance; also industrial and Christian. Released "What Time Is It?" (by R. Rodriguez), recorded by Don't Know Yet on Penguin Records distributed by Epic and "There's No Place" (by Rodriguez/Alonso/McNamee), recorded by Stereofonik on Penguin Records (singles).
Tips: "Be patient! There's a lot of music out there. Everyone will get their chance."

PENTHOUSE RECORDS, 6728 Eton Ave., Canoga Park CA 91303. (818)992-4777. Director: Toni Biggs-Andrews. Record company, music publisher (Tonina Music Publishing) and record producer.
How to Contact: Query by phone before submitting material.
Music: Mostly pop, New Age and rock; also R&B, dance, easy listening, progressive, soul, top 40/pop and "space wave/mod hot." Released "Bad to The Bone" (by George Thorogood) and "Summertime" (by George Gershwin), both recorded by Threshold on Penthouse Records (12″ singles). Currently producing music in-house for various video projects.

PHOENIX RECORDS, INC., Box 121076, Nashville TN 27212-1076. (615)244-5357 or 254-3436. President: Reggie M. Churchwell. Labels include Nashville International Records. Record company and music publisher (affiliated with both BMI and ASCAP). Estab. 1971. Releases 5-6 singles, 2-3 12″

singles, 2-3 LPs and 1-2 CDs/year. Works with musicians/artists and songwriters on contract. Pays standard royalty to artists on contract; statutory rate to publisher per song on record.
How to Contact: Write first and obtain permission to submit. Prefers cassette with lyric sheets. Does not return unsolicited material. Reports in 2-3 weeks.
Music: Mostly country, rock and pop; also gospel. Released "Left of Center Line" (by Howard Lips), recorded by Catfish on Phoenix Records (country/rock); and "Littlest Cowboy" written and recorded by Sonny Shroyer on Hazzard Records (children's). Other artists include Conrad Pierce and Clay Jerrolds.
Tips: "We are looking for songs with strong hooks and strong words. We are not simply looking for songs, we are looking for hits."

*PHOLK RECORDS, 609A Rosebank Ave., Nashville TN 37206. (615)226-8438. Co-Owner: Alice Rye. Record company. Estab. 1990. Releases 4 singles, 6 LPs and 6 CDs/year. Works with musicians/artists on contract. Pays 25% royalty to artists on contract; statutory rate to publisher per song.
How to Contact: Submit demo tape by mail. Unsolicited submissions are OK. Prefers cassette (or VHS videocassette) with 5 songs and lyric sheet. SASE. Reports in 1 month.
Music: Mostly contemporary folk, traditional folk and new age; also country. Released *What's Wrong With This Picture?* (folk LP), *Alice & Albert Sing No! to Drugs* (folk LP), and *One Night At a Time* (country LP); all written and recorded by Alice Rye and Albert Kennedy Williams on Pholk Records.
Tips: "Give us songs about world issues and about real people."

PILOT RECORDS AND TAPE COMPANY, 628 S. South St., Mount Airy NC 27030. (919)786-2865. President and Owner: Paul E. Johnson. Labels include Stork, Stark, Pilot, Hello, Kay, Sugarbear, Southcoast, Songcraft and Blue Jay. Record company, music publisher (Tompaul Music Company/ BMI) and record producer. Estab. 1960. Releases 6 singles and 4 LPs/year. Works with songwriters on contract; musicians on salary for in-house studio work. Pays 30% royalty to artists on contract; statutory rate to publishers per song on record.
How to Contact: Prefers cassette or 7 ½ ips reel-to-reel with 6 songs and lyric sheet. SASE. Reports in 1 month. "The songwriters should give their date of birth with submissions. This information will be used when copyrighting a songwriter's song."
Music: Mostly country, gospel and bluegrass; also rock, folk and blues. Released "I'm Ready To Go" and "Give Me Jesus," (by Leo Gravley), recorded by Ray Bryant and Leo Gravley (country gospel); and "God Is My Shepherd," (by Paul Edgar Johnson), recorded by Patsy L. Taylor; all on Pilot Records. Other artists include Bobby Atkins, Carl Tolbert, Sam Bray, Ralph Hill, Early Upchurch, Sanford Teague and Don Sawyers.

PLANKTON RECORDS, 236 Sebert Rd., Forest Gate, London E7 0NP **England**. Phone: (081)534-8500. Senior Partner: Simon Law. Labels include Plankton, Sea Dream, Embryo Arts (licensed, Belgium), Gutta (licensed, Sweden), and Radio (licensed, United Kingdom). Record company and music publisher (Sea Dream Music, Scarf Music Publishing, Light Factory Productions and Really Free Music). Estab. 1977. Releases 1 single, 4 LPs, and 1 EP/year. Works with musicians/artists and songwriters on contract. Pays 10% royalty to artists on contract; statutory rate to publishers per song on record.
How to Contact: Prefers cassette with 3 songs and lyric sheet. SAE and IRC. Reports in 6 weeks.
Music: Mostly funk/rock, R&B and gospel; also blues. Released *Gotta Keep Moving*, (by Paul Crick/ Greg Nash/Keith Dixon), recorded by Medals (jazz/rock); *Surrender*, (by Rue Randall), recorded by Solid Air (rock); and *Paris Airshow*, (by Simon Law), recorded by Fresh Claim (rock); (all LP/cassette) all on Plankton Records. Other artists include Pete Ward, Catch 22, Really Free, Ruth Turner and Cheryl Mead.
Tips: "We specialize in bands with a Christian bias, regardless of their musical style."

PLAY RECORDS, Box 6541, Cleveland OH 44101. (216)467-0300. President: John Latimer. Record company. Estab. 1985. Releases 3 LPs/year. Works with musicians/artists and songwriters on contract.
How to Contact: Submit demo tape by mail. Unsolicited submissions are OK. Prefers cassette (or VHS or ¾" videocassettes) with 5 songs and lyric or lead sheets. SASE. Reports in 6 weeks.
Music: Mostly rock, pop and alternative; also blues, jazz and R&B. Released "There Was a Time," written and recorded by The Bellows; "Bombs Away," written and recorded by Serious Nature; and "Mr. Sensible," written and recorded by Mr. Sensible; all on Play Records (rock). Other artists include The French Lenards, 15 60 75, The Adults, Cool Down Daddy, The Bomb, Earl Rays, Zero One, Holy Cows and Ronald Koal.
Tips: "Be patient but persistent. Please correspond by mail only."

PLAYBACK RECORDS, P.O. Box 630755, Miami FL 33163. (305)935-4880. President: Jack Gale. Labels include Playback Records, Gallery 11 Records, Inc., Caramba Records and Ridgewood Records. Record company. Estab. 1983. Releases 48 singles, 10 CDs and 10 LPs/year. Works with musicians/artists. Pays statutory rate to publisher per song on record.
How to Contact: Submit demo tape by mail. Unsolicited submissions are okay. Prefers cassette with 1-2 songs and lyric sheets. Does not return unsolicited material. Reports immediately "if we can use."
Music: Mostly country-crossover and country. Released "Southern Men" (by Horowitz, Spector, Curtiss), recorded by Cheryl K. Warner on Playback Records (country); "Southern Belle" (by Helms-Hall), recorded by Bobby Helms on Playback Records (country); "Gonna Lay Me Down Beside My Memories," (by Ray Griff), recorded by Sammi Smith; "Another One of My Near Mrs. (Misses)," (by Gillon/Hammond), recorded by Bobby Bare and Donne Bowser; and "Boudrouxs Candy," written and recorded by Jimmy C. Newman; (all country) all recorded on Playback Records. Other artists include David Heavener, Sammi Smith, Diane Lauren, Linda Borden and Terry Smith.
Tips: "Send demo of something that showcases your particular style. Don't sing Patsy Cline songs on your audition tape."

PLAYBONES RECORDS, Box 203312, D-2000 Hamburg 20, **West Germany**. Phone: (040) 4300339. FAX: (040)439.65.87. Producer: Arno v. Vught. Labels include Rondo Records. Record company, music publisher (Mento Music Group KG.) and record producer (Arteg Productions). Estab. 1975. Releases 12 singles and 15 CDs/year. Works with musicians/artists and songwriters on contract. Pays 8-16% royalty to artists on contract.
How to Contact: Write or call first to arrange personal interview. Prefers cassette (or VHS videocassette) and lyric or lead sheet. SASE. Reports in 2 weeks.
Music: Mostly instrumentals, country and jazz; also background music, rock and gospel. Released "Running Through," (by Pospichal), recorded by PPM Band on Playbones Records (12" single); *Feelsaitig*, recorded by Feelsatig on Playbones Records (LP/CD); and *One*, recorded by BBL on Playbones/BBL Records (LP/CD). Other artists include H.J. Knipphals, Gaby Knies, Jack Hals, H. Hausmann, Crabmeat and M. Frommhold.

PLEASURE RECORDS, Rt. 1, Box 187-A, Whitney TX 76692. (817)694-4047. President: Allen Newton. Labels include Cactus Flats, Pristine, MFN. Record company and music publisher (Four Newton Publishing-BMI). Estab. 1986. Releases 12 singles, 1 12" single and 1 LP/year. Works with musicians/artists and songwriters on contract. Pays statutory rate to publisher per song on record.
How to Contact: Submit demo tape by mail. Unsolicited submissions are OK. Prefers cassette with 3 songs and lyric or lead sheets. SASE. Reports in 4 weeks.
Music: Mostly country, gospel and rock; also rock-a-billy, R&B and Spanish. Released "I'll Hear Your Call" (by V. Smeaton), recorded by Victoria on Pristine Records (R&B single); "Dim Lit Bars," written and recorded by Charlie Locke on Pleasure Records (C&W single); "Carry Me Back,' written and recorded by Mickey Drum on Pleasure Records (C&W single); and "Starin-A-Haze," written and recorded by Thin Ice on Pristine Records (rock single). Other artists include Denny Glenn, Arch Brown, Sherry Fontaine, Blessed Carrion, Felix Van Slyke, Stylle and J. Sam.

PMA RECORDS, Rt. 4, Box 506, Alvarado TX 76009. (817)694-4047. President: Lee Dixon. Record company (BMI). Estab. 1986. Releases 3 singles and 1 LP/year. Works with musicians/artists and songwriters on contract. Pays statutory rate to publisher per song on record.
How to Contact: Submit demo tape by mail. Unsolicited submissions are OK. Prefers cassette with 3 songs and lyric or lead sheets. SASE. Reports in 4 weeks.
Music: Mostly country and rock-a-billy. Released "Don't Know What Steps," "Restless Kind of Man" and "I Was a Fool," all written and recorded by Lee Dixon on PMA Records (C&W singles). Other artists include the Dixon Brothers.

POLYGRAM RECORDS, 810 7th Ave., New York NY 10019. (212)333-8000. Contact: A&R Assistant. Record company. Works with artists on contract.
How to Contact: "We review songs submitted by established publishers. Not accepting unsolicited material, but welcome queries when accompanied by press and/or chart clippings and SASE. Do *not* send recordings or lyrics until requested." Recommends referral from a reputable industry source.
Music: Rock, top 40/pop, R&B and dance/urban. Current roster includes Bon Jovi, John Mellencamp, Cinderella, Robert Cray, The Rainmakers, Tom Kimmel, Billy Branigan, Kiss, The Everly Brothers, Kool and the Gang, Cameo, Commodores, Fat Boys, Gwenn Guthrie, Rush, Moody Blues, ELP and Scorpions.

Close-up

Bill Pettaway
Songwriter
Annapolis, Maryland

Photo by: Anthony Wayne Sterago

"I worked on the music for 'Girl You Know It's True' for about eight years," says hit songwriter Bill Pettaway. "I worked on it off and on trying to put together the 'magic.' I was doing my research by hanging out in the clubs, getting a lot of different musical influences and seeing what the people liked. I noticed that they really liked the stuff that was simple and easy to relate to. A lot of the songs in the clubs were just too busy and complicated—the words were too big for the average person to take the time to listen to and interpret. People like everything right on the spot and they like to feel the beat."

Bill produced "Girl You Know It's True" for a band called the New Marks, with lyrical input from the band members and others. "It got out and did pretty good in the States as far as local [Baltimore] radio and in some clubs throughout the U.S. Then it went over to Germany and started picking up, but the New Marks didn't have the promotion, the management or the marketing." A deal was then made with a publishing company to get the song to the group Milli Vanilli. "They released it and the rest is history," says Bill. "It won all kinds of awards and went further than anybody expected it to."

According to Bill, the success he has had with "Girl You Know It's True" is a direct result of the spirit of persistence he learned from one of his biggest influences—his mother. Bill had been involved with music from his childhood. He played in various bands while growing up, attended the Southwest Guitar Conservatory after high school and ended up in a band signed to a major record label. The band's first album didn't sell well, and eventually, due to changes at the label, Bill's band was dropped. Depressed, he returned home to Annapolis. "My mom kept saying, 'Get a job.' I kept telling her that I was a musician. She said, 'The only way you're ever going to make it in that business—or in whatever you want to do—is to work for it and do whatever you have to do to achieve success.' "

So Bill went to the gas station where he still works today. "My plan was to work and make enough money to build my own small recording studio so I could record and get songs published. And I stuck with that plan. After a couple months, I had steady money coming in and I was able to work and write the music I wanted to write, and I could shop it where I wanted to shop it. I still knew a lot of people in the music industry. I did work very hard on my music. I would get to work at seven in the morning and get off at maybe seven in the evening—then go to my music and stay up until four or five in the morning then go back to work. I read a lot of books about the state of the art, MIDI, computers and all that. I'm a musician of the nineties; you do what you have to do nowadays."

Why does Bill stay on at the gas station now that it is no longer a financial necessity? "It's hard to describe," he says, "It's like a feeling, something that you don't want to leave. Here I have peace of mind. On a rainy day, if it's not busy, sometimes I set up my drum machine and computer in the back room and I write songs here at work. I think it's good when you become a part of the community by working and staying where you came from."

—*Mark Garvey*

Tips: "Be patient—you will be contacted if there's interest. Keep in mind that most of the artists write their own material. We're most open to female-oriented and pop acts to balance out heavy-hitting hard rock and R&B roster."

POP RECORD RESEARCH, 17 Piping Rock Dr., Ossining NY 10502. (914)762-8499. Director: Gary Theroux. Labels include Surf City, GTP and Rock's Greatest Hits. Record company, music publisher (Surf City Music/ASCAP), record producer and archive of entertainment-related research materials (files on hits and hitmakers since 1877). Estab. 1962. Works with musicians/artists and songwriters on contract and writers/historians/biographers/radio, TV and film producers requiring research help or materials. Pays statutory rate to publisher per song on record.
How to Contact: Submit demo tape, press kits or review material by mail. Unsolicited submissions are OK. Prefers cassette (or VHS videocassette). Does not return unsolicited material.
Music: Mostly pop, country and R&B. Released "The Declaration" (by Theroux-Gilbert), recorded by An American on Bob Records; "Thoughts From a Summer Rain," written and recorded by Bob Gilbert on Bob Records; and "Tiger Paws," written and recorded by Bob Gilbert on BAL Records; all pop singles. Other artists include Gary and John, The Nightflight Singers and Ruth Zimmerman.
Tips: "Help us keep our biographical file on you and your career current by sending us updated bios/press kits, etc. They are most helpful to writers/researchers in search of accurate information on your success."

POST-AMBIENT MOTION, 5402 Camden Ave., Omaha NE 68104. (402)455-9575. Contact: Stephen Sheehan. Record company and record producer. Estab. 1983. Releases 1-2 LPs, 1-2 EPs and 1-2 CDs/year.
How to Contact: Submit demo tape by mail. Unsolicited submissions are OK. Prefers cassette (or videocassette) with 3 songs. Does not return unsolicited material. Reports in 3 weeks.
Music: Mostly rock, pop and instrumentals. Released "I Want to Tell You," written and recorded by Kazumichi Tatebayashi (electronic); "Fate" (by Jeff Runnings), recorded by For Against (modern pop); and "Idiosyncrasies" (by Tom Ware) (electro/funk); all on Post-Ambient Motion Records. Others artists include The Acorns, Shrödinger's Cats, Stephen Schneider, Stephen Sheehan, John Tingle, Jeff Clayman, Temporary Arts Ensemble and Atomic Breathing.
Tips: "Send me good ideas (at least), bio, what you're hoping to do with your music."

*PPI/PETER PAN INDUSTRIES, 88 St. Francis St., Newark NJ 07105. (201)344-4214. Product Manager: Marianne Eggleston. Labels include Compose Records, Current Records, Parade Video, Iron Bound Publishing/Guess Star Records. Record company, music publisher, record producer (Dunn Pearson, Jr.) and outside producers are used also. Estab. 1928. Releases over 100 singles, 50 12″ singles, over 100 LPs, over 100 EPs and over 100 CDs/year. Works with musicians/artist and songwriters on contract. Pays royalty per contract; statutory rater per contract to publisher per song on records. "All services are negotiable!"
How to Contact: Submit demo tape by mail. Unsolicited submissions are OK. Prefers cassette (or VHS videocassette if available) with 3-5 songs and lyric sheet. SASE. Reports in 1-2 months.
Music: Mostly children's—audio/video, R&B and jazz; also exercise—video, rock and classical—all forms of music. Released "Go For The Gusto" (R&B); "Programmed For Love" (jazz); and "Color Tapestry" (jazz) all written and recorded by Dunn Pearson, Jr. on Compose Records.

PRAIRIE MUSIC RECORDS LTD., Box 438, Walnut IA 51577. (712)366-1136. President: Robert Everhart. Record company (BMI) and record producer (Prairie Music Ltd.). Estab. 1964. Releases 2 singles and 2 LPs/year. Works with musicians/artists and songwriters on contract. Pays 5% royalty to artists on contract; statutory rate to publisher per song on record.
How to Contact: Submit demo tape by mail. Unsolicited submissions are OK. Prefers cassette. SASE. Reports in 4 months.
Music: Mostly traditional country, bluegrass and folk. Released "Time After Time," "Street Sleepers" and "Rock of Hollywood," all written and recorded by Bob Everhart on Folkways Records (traditional country). Other artists include Gospel Pilgrims.

 The asterisk before a listing indicates that the listing is new in this edition. New markets are often the most receptive to unsolicited submissions.

*PREMIÉRE RECORDS, P.O. Box 279, Hopkins MN 55343. (612)942-6119. President: Mitch Viegut. General Manager: Mark Alan. Record company. Estab. 1988. Releases 6 singles, 4-6 12″ singles, 3-5 LPs, 2-3 EPs and 3-5 CDs/year. Works with musicians/artists and songwriters on contract. Pays 10-12% royalty to artists on contract; statutory rate to publishers per song on record.
How to Contact: Submit demo tape by mail. Unsolicited submissions are okay. Prefers cassette (or VHS videocassette) with 3-4 songs. Does not return unsolicited material. Reports in 2 months.
Music: Mostly rock, pop and black contemporary. Released "Footsteps" (by Azhaar/Cavanagh), (pop single); "Midnight Confessions" (by Lou Josie), (pop single); and *Airkraft* (rock LP), all recorded by Airkraft on Premiére Records. Other artists include Airkraft and Zwarté.

*PRESIDENTIAL ENTERPRISES LTD., 127 Aldergate St., London **England** EC1A 6JQ. (44)71-2501910. Contact: Roland A. Radelli. Labels include Presidential; XXIst Century. Record company, music publisher (Risson Music (UR PRS) and record producer (The Club Studios). Estab. 1986. Releases 10-20 12″ singles and 2-4 LPs/year. Works with musicians/artists and songwriters on contract; also Disc-jockeys and remixers. Pays 8-12% royalty to artists on contract; statutory rate to publisher per song on record.
How to Contact: Write or call first. Prefers cassette with 2-5 songs and lyric sheet. Does not return unsolicited material. Reports in 2 weeks.
Music: Mostly house, hip-hop and soul; also pop, rock and reggae. Released "Bus Stop" (by Flippin'-Curtis), recorded by N93 on P.E.L. Records (12″-7″) and Garage Music (by various writers), recorded by various artists on P.E.L. Records (album).

*PRESTATION MUSIC, 24 Gachard Street, Brussels 1050 **Belgium**. Phone (02)649-2847. General Manager: Pierre Plentinckx. Labels include Selection Records, Multisound Music, B. Sharp. Record company and music publisher (Sabam). Releases 5 CDs/year. Works with musicians/artists and songwriters on contract; hires musicians for in-house studio work.
How to Contact: Submit demo tape by mail. Unsolicited submissions are OK. Prefers cassette. Does not return unsolicited material. Reports in 1 month.
Music: Mostly instrumental music, jazz and new age. *Artline* (by J. Pilotton); *Steve Houben Trio* (by S. Houben); and *Lemon Air* (by J. Coboy).

*PRESTO RECORDS, P.O. Box 1081, Lowell MA 01853. (617)893-2144. President: Christopher Porter. Record company. Affiliated with Chris Porter Productions Inc. (a booking and management company). Estab. 1989. Releases 3-4 LPs and 2-4 CDs/year. Work with musicians/artists on contract. Pays statutory rate to publisher per song on record.
How to Contact: Submit demo tape by mail. Unsolicited submissions OK. Prefers cassette with 3-4 songs. SASE or SAE and IRC. Reports in 1-2 months.
Music: Mostly guitar-oriented alternative rock. Released *Ruins Cafe* (by Frank Rowe), recorded by Classic Ruins; *Average* (by Adam Boc), recorded by Miranda Warning; and *Where Were You When the Lights When Out* (by Alan Grandy), recorded by The Terrible Parade all recorded on Presto Records (rock LP). Other artists include: Miles Dethmuffen and The Visigoths.
Tips: "We mainly deal with guitar-oriented rock—accessible but not overly commercial. If a songwriter has a band together and they are playing out live regularly, we would be happy to hear their material if it fits in our guidelines."

PRISTINE RECORDS, Route 1, Box 187-A, Whitney TX 76692. (817)694-4047. President: Allen Newton. Labels include Cactus Flats, MFN, Pleasure Records. Record company and mailing/distributor/promotion. Estab. 1981. Releases 10-12 singles; 1-2 12″ singles and 10-12 LPs/year. Works with musicians/artists on contract. Pays negotiable royalty to artists on contract.
How to Contact: Submit demo tape by mail. Unsolicited submissions are OK. Prefers cassette or 7½ ips reel-to-reel (or VHS videocassette) with 2 songs and lyric or lead sheets. SASE. Reports in 4 weeks.
Music: Mostly country, R&B and rock; also gospel. Released "Starin-A-Haze" and "All I Ever Wanted," (by J.Sylvis/F. Redder), recorded by Thin Ice on Pristine Records (rock); and "Styllin," (by Andre), recorded by Stylle on Pristine Records (R&B). Other artists include Linda Roper, Samuel Green, Mickey Drum, Thin Ice, Sherry Fontaine, Stylle.
Tips: "Read, study, listen, and prepare."

*PRODISC (PRODISC LIMITADA), Tomás Andrews 085, Santiago **Chile**. (562)34-1733. FAX: (562)34-40-64. A&R Director: Oscar Sayavedra. Labels include Cabal (Argentina), Leader Music (Argentina), American Recording (Argentina), Tico (USA), Fania (USA), Cotique (USA), Inca (USA), Barbaro (USA), Vaya (USA). Record company, Prodin Chile: Promoter & Production Company—same address. Estab. 1989 (Prodin was in 1969). Releases 40-50 singles, 120 LPs/year. Works with musicians/artists on contract. Pays 4-18% royalty to artists on contract; statutory rate to publisher per song.

How to Contact: Submit demo tape by mail. Unsolicited submissions are OK. Prefers cassette, 7½ or 15 ips reel-to-reel, or VHS videocassette with 2 or more songs. Reports in 4 weeks.
Music: Mostly rock/pop, Latin/salsa/tex mex and R&B; also folk/country, jazz/new age and classic. Released "Top Secret," written and recorded by Willie Colon on Fania/Wac Records (LP/Salsa); "Original Tango" (by various), recorded by Mellizas Del Tango on Prodisc Records (LP/tango); and "Don Quijote" (by G. Telemann), recorded by Camerata Bariloche on American Records (LP/Classic). Other artists include Luis Alberto Spinetta, Mariel Dupetit, Fontova Y Sus Sobrinos, Eduardo Falu, Facundo Cabral, Ruben Blades.
Tips: "We're working with a new record company but we're the biggest promotion and production agency in this country. We work to make records hits and big concerts,too."

PRODUCTIONS DIADEM, C.P. 33, Pointe-Gatineau J8T 4Y8 **Canada**. (819)561-4114. Director: Denyse Marleau. Labels include Jouvence. Record company (CAPAC) and record producer (Productions Diadem-Jouvence). Estab. 1982. Releases 2-4 singles, 2-4 LPs and 1-3 CDs/year. Works with musicians/artists on contract and hires musicians for in-house studio work. Pays 4% royalty to artists on contract; statutory rate to publisher per song on record.
How to Contact: Write first and obtain permission to submit. Prefers cassette (or VHS videocassette) with 3-5 songs and lyric sheet. SASE. Reports in 4 weeks.
Music: Mostly pop-middle of the road, ballads and children songs. Released *Fêtons et chantons* (by D.D.M.) (Marleau, childrens LP) and *Chansons de paix et d'amitié* (by various artists) (pop), both recorded by Diadem on Jouvence Records.
Tips: "French material is most welcome."

*PSP RECORDS, 6283-3410 Shelbourne St., Victoria, British Columbia V8P 5L5 **Canada**. (604)598-3651. Producer: Eduardo Pereira. Music publishers (Primavera Sound Productions. PROCAN/CAPAC). Releases 3-5 singles and 1-2 LPs/year. Works with musicians/artists on contract and hires musicians for in-house studio work. Pays 6-8% royalty to artists on contract; statutory rate to publishers per song on record.
How to Contact: Prefers cassette (or BETA videocassette) with 3 songs. Does not return material but we keep it on file. Reports in 6 weeks.
Music: Mostly pop, rock; also latin/jazz, salsa, merengue and cumbia. Released "Papa Nicolas" (merengue) written and recorded by Hugo Belran; "Let Me Know" (top 40/rock), (by DeGrassi/Walter), recorded by Julie Coy; "Pienso Tanto en Ti," (by Ruben Zunica), recorded by Yizeth.

*PSYCHOTRONIC RECORDS, P.O. Box 1384, Mobile AL 36633. (904)455-4585. A&R Director: Dave Carter. Labels include Psychotronic, Zyklon-B and Hitchcock-3 Records. Record company, music publisher (S.U.V.T Publishing/BMI and Lawsonsongs Music Ltd./BMI) and record producer. Estab. 1987. Releases 5 LPs, 7 EPs and 3 CDs/year. Works with musicians/artists and songwriters on contract. Royalty varies per contract; statutory rate to publishers per song on records.
How to Contact: Submit demo tape by mail. Unsolicited submissions are OK. Prefers cassette (or VHS videocassette if available) with 3-5 songs and lyric sheet. SASE. Reports in 6 weeks.
Music: Mostly alternative music, college rock and psychedelic, folk, progressive; also blues, R&B and rock-pop. Released *Underground* (by M. Lawson), recorded by Mike Lawson on Psychotronic Records (folk rock—EP); *The Last Legal Door to Perception* (by Dr. Dave Carter), recorded by Dr. Dave on Zykon-B (alternative—LP); and *A Collected Work of Sanity* (by Lawson/Carter), recorded by Lawson-Carter on Hitchcock 3 (psychedelic—CD).
Tips: "We're looking for college radio alternative music. Not mainstream top 40. Be willing to tour small clubs, colleges, etc. to promote product. We want acts who've already payed a lot of road dues and who know what it takes to make it. Work hard."

*PULSE MUSIC GROUP, Box 412, New York NY 10462. (914)668-3119. Associate Director: Darlene Barkley. Labels include Lamar, MelVern, Wilson, We-Us and Co. Pub. Record company, music publisher (BMI), and workshop organization. Estab. 1984. Releases 10-12 12″ singles and 2-4 LPs/year. Works with musicians/artists and songwriters on contract and hires musicians for in-house studio work. Pays standard royalty to artists on contract; statutory rate to publisher per song. "We change only if we are hired to do "work-for-hire" projects. Write first and obtain permission to submit. Prefers cassette with 2 songs. Does not return unsolicited material. Reports in 1 month.
Music: Mostly R&B, rap and pop. Released "So In Love" (by R. Robinson), recorded by L. Williams on Macola Records (R&B/dance); "Lose You Love" (by R. Robinson), recorded by M. Foster on Lamar Records (R&B/dance); and "Feel Like a Woman" (by Wilson/Johnson), recorded by S. Taylor on MelVern Records (R&B/ballad). Other artists include Barry Manderson and Co/Vern.
Tips: "Member of our company function as singers, songwriters, musicians, producers, executive producers. We basically have all graduated from college in areas related to music or music business. We either teach about music and the music business or we perform in the business. If you sincerely want

to be in this industry this is the type of work you will need to do in order to succeed. It is not as easy as you think."

PUZZLE RECORDS, P.O. Box 461892, Garland TX 75046. (214)271-8098. A&R Director: Don Ferguson. Record company, music publisher (Sultan Music Publishing/BMI and Illustrious Sultan/ASCAP), record producer and booking agency (Don Ferguson Agency). Estab. 1972. Releases 7-8 singles and 1-2 LPs/year. Works with artists and songwriters on contract.
How to Contact: Write first and obtain permission to submit.
Music: Mostly country; also MOR, jazz and light rock. Released "Leave Me Right Now," written and recorded by Bobby Teesdale (MOR); "Ain't No Way," (by Duke/Osborn/Fox), recorded by Flash Point (rock); and "I'm Hurtin," (by Roy Orbison/Joe Melson), recorded by Mary Craig (country); all on Puzzle Records.

R.E.F. RECORDS, 404 Bluegrass Ave., Madison TN 37115. (615)865-6380. Contact: Bob Frick. Record company, record producer and music publisher (Frick Music Publishing Co./BMI). Releases 10 LPs/year. Works with artists and songwriters on contract. Pays 3-5¢ royalty to artists on contract; statutory rate to publishers for each record sold.
How to Contact: Call first. Prefers 7½ ips reel-to-reel or cassette with 2-10 songs and lyric sheet. SASE. Reports in 1 month.
Music: Country, gospel, rock and top 40/pop. Released "I Love You In Jesus," "Warm Family Feeling," and "Our Favorites," all by Bob Scott Frick. Other artists include Larry Ahlborn, Francisco Morales, Candy Coleman, Peggy Beard, Bob Myers, The Backwoods Quartet, Jim Mattingly, David Barton, Jim Pommert, and The Vision Heirs.

RADIOACTIVE RECORDS, 1075 N.W. Murray Rd., Suite 250, Portland OR 97229. (503)642-4201. Contact: A&R Dept. Record company, music publisher (Mark Hannah Music Group/BMI), record producer (Mark Hannah Productions) and Mark Hannah Management/Personal Management. Estab. 1985. Releases 5-10 singles, 1-3 LPs, 1-3 EPs and 1-3 CDs/year. Works with musicians/artists and songwriters on record contract. Pays 5-10% royalty to artists on contract; statutory rate to publisher per song on record.
How to Contact: Write first and obtain permission to submit. Prefers cassette or 15 ips reel-to-reel with 1-3 songs and lyric or lead sheets. SASE. Reports in 1 month.
Music: Mostly rock, pop and country; also fusion, new age and jazz. "Forced to Have Sex With An Alien," written and recorded by M. Harrop (comedy single); "You Stole My Heart Away," written and recorded P. Witt (pop/rock single); and *Desert Moon*, written and recorded by M. Hannah (new age LP); all on Radioactive Records. Other artists include Rex E. Plew and Messenger (rock band).
Tips: "Learn as much as you can about the music business."

RAILROAD RECORDS, 300 Bedford St., Manchester NH 03101. (603)669-6353. President: Michael Skinner. Labels include Railroad Records. Record company and record producer (Skinner Productions) and talent manager. Estab. 1985. Releases 3 LPs and 3 EPs/year. Works with musicians/artists on contract. Pays negotiable royalty to artist on contract; statutory rate to publisher per song on record.
How to Contact: Submit demo tape by mail. Unsolicited submissions are OK. Prefers cassette with 3-4 songs and lyric sheets. SASE. Reports in 3 weeks.
Music: Mostly rock/hard rock and pop. Released "Blondes Have More Fun," recorded by T.T. Strip (hard rock EP); "Gypsy," written and recorded by First Strike (hard rock EP); and "Dreams," written and recorded by Marathon; all on Railroad Records. Other artists include Roxx, T.T. Strip, Marathon, Uncontrollable Urge and Photograph.

RAINBOW RIVER RECORDS, Box 1708, Auburn AL 36831-1708. (205)821-4876. Executive Vice President: Kittie Watson. Rainbow River Records. Record company, music publisher (Sound Spectra Music/BMI) and record producer (Spectra Productions). Estab. 1978. Releases 4-6 singles, 3-5 12" singles, 1-3 LPs and 2 CDs/year. Works with musicians/artists and songwriters on contract. Pays 5-15% royalty to artists on contract; statutory rate to publisher per song on record.
How to Contact: Write first and obtain permission to submit. Send SASE for reply. Prefers cassette with 3-4 songs and lyric sheets. Does not return unsolicited material. Reports in 6 weeks.
Music: Mostly rock, R&B and new age; also jazz, gospel and country. Released "It's Not Easy" (by Larry Barker), recorded by Lennie Hartzog; "It's Your Move" (by Wayman Hale and Deborah Barker), recorded by Wayman Hale; and "The Trash Bag's Been Ripped" (by Bruce Yandle), recorded by Mr. Resistor; all on Rainbow River Records (singles). Other artists include Second Wind, Ronald LaPread, Lynn Hammond, Circle, Mary Helen Brown and The McNair Family.
Tips: "Write first to determine current needs."

RANDOM RECORDS, 209 Madison Ave., Toronto, Ontario M5R 2S6 **Canada**. (416)929-2349. President: Peter Randall. Record company, music publisher (Random Image Music/PROCAN) and record producer (Random Image Productions). Estab. 1986. Releases 2 singles and 3 LPs/year. Works with musicians/artists and songwriters on contract; hires musicians for in-house studio work. Pays 12% royalty to artists on contract; statutory rate to publishers per song on record.
How to Contact: Prefers cassette (or VHS videocassette) with 2-3 songs and lyric or lead sheets. SAE and IRC. Reports in several weeks.
Music: Rock, pop and new age. Released "Lonely Eyes" (by Paul Simitkidis), recorded by Presh S; "What Do You Want," recorded by P. Randall; and "Without You" (by S. Firth), recorded by Timeline; all on Random Records (pop). Other artists include The Fact, Winter Heat, Shaun Firth, and Steven Long.

*RAZOR RECORDS, 2623 Bosworth, Chicago IL 60614. (312)549-3227. Owner: Mark Lefens. Record company. Estab. 1979. Releases 1 single and 1 LP/year. Works with musicians/artists on contract. Pays statutory rate to publisher per song on record.
How to Contact: Submit demo tape by mail. Unsolicited submissions are OK. Prefers cassette. SASE. "Will report only if interested."
Music: Mostly blues and R&B. Released *After Work* (by various writers), recorded by John Embry; *Set Me Free* (by various writers), recorded by Gloria Hardiman; and *Housefire* (written and recorded by Byther Smith), all on Razor Records (blues LPs).
Tips: "Come up with some good news blues."

*REALITY RECORDS PRODUCTIONS, 19 Roxborough Place, Willingboro NJ 08046. (609)877-7653. Producer: "Hank" Strasser. Record company and record producer (Reality Productions). Estab. 1972.
How to Contact: Prefers cassette; bios appreciated. Does not return unsolicited material. Reports "to selected artists only."
Music: Jazz and electronic music.
Tips: "We're looking for commercially viable jazz. Product choices probably won't stray too far from mainstream jazz. New age, fusion and electronic music welcome, but no vocals please."

*RECA MUSIC PRODUCTION, Nykobingvej 18, 4571 Grevinge DK 4571 **Denmark**. Phone: (45)345-9389. Director: Finn Reiner. Labels include Reca and Favorit. Record company and music publisher (Top Music). Releases 10 singles, 10 LPs and 5 CDs/year. Works with musicians/artists and songwriters on contract; hires musicians for in-house studio work. Pays 5% royalty to artists on contract; statutory rate to publishers per song on record.
How to Contact: Write or call first and obtain permission to submit. Prefers cassette (or VHS videocassette) with 2 songs. SAE and IRC. Reports in 2 weeks.
Music: Mostly pop, country and folk; also classical. Released *Skyrider with Tomboola Band*, by various writers (country LP); *Fast Train With Van Dang*, by Svend Petersen (shuffle LP); and *Classic*, by Peter Vesth (folk LP), all on RECA Records. Other artists include Bent Larsen, Peter Langberg, Jodle Johnny and The Kuhlau Quartet.

RED BUS RECORDS (INT.) LTD., Red Bus House, 48 Broadley Terrace, London NW1, **England**. (01) 258-0324. FAX: (01) 724-2163. Director: Ellis Elias. Record company and music publisher. Estab. 1969. Releases 7 singles, 3 CDs and 3 LPs/year. Works with musicians/artists on contract. Pays 6-10% royalty to artists on contract.
How to Contact: Prefers cassette. SAE and IRC. Reports in 6 weeks.
Music: Mostly dance. Artists include Room 101.

RED DOT/PUZZLE RECORDS, 1121 Market, Galveston TX 77550. (409)762-4590. President: A.W. Marullo Sr. Record company, record producer and music publisher (A.W. Marullo Music/BMI). Estab. 1952. "We also lease masters from artists." Releases 14 12" singles/year. Works with artists and songwriters on contract; musicians on salary for in-house studio work. Pays 8-10% royalty to artists on contract; statutory rate to publishers for each record sold.
How to Contact: Prefers cassette with 4-7 songs and lyric sheet. SASE. Reports in 2 months.
Music: Rock/top 40 dance songs. Released "Do You Feel Sexy," (by T. Pindrock), recorded by Flash Point (Top 40/rock); "You Put the Merry in My Christmas," (by E.Dunn), recorded by Mary Craig (rock/pop country) and "Love Machine," (by T. Pindrock), recorded by Susan Moninger; all on Puzzle/Red Dot Records.

RED-EYE RECORDS, Wern Fawr Farm, Pencoed, Mid-Glam CF35 6NB **United Kingdom**. Phone: (0656)86 00 41. Managing Director: M.R. Blanche. Record company, music publisher (Ever-Open-Eye Music/PRS). Estab. 1979. Releases 4 singles and 2-3 LPs/year. Works with musicians/artists on contract.

How to Contact: Prefers cassette (or VHS videocassette) or 7½ or 15 ips reel-to-reel with 4 songs. SAE and IRC.
Music: Mostly R&B, rock and gospel; also swing. Released "River River" (by D. John), recorded by The Boys; "Billy" (by G. Williams), recorded by The Cadillacs; and "Cadillac Walk" (by Moon Martin), recorded by the Cadillacs, all on Red-Eye Records. Other artists include Cartoon and Tiger Bay.

*RELATIVITY RECORDS INC., 18707 Henderson Ave., Hollis NY 11423. (718)740-5700. National Labels Director: Anne Adams. Labels include Relativity, Combat, Ineffect. Record company. Estab. 1979. Releases 35 LPs and 10 EPs/year. Works with musicians/artists on contract.
How to Contact: Submit demo tape by mail. Unsolicited submissions are OK. Prefers cassette or ½" videocassette. SASE. Reports in 8 weeks.
Music: Mostly metal and hard rock. Released "Flying In a Blue Dream," "Shotgun Messiah" and "Nuclear Assault."

REVONAH RECORDS, Box 217, Ferndale NY 12734. (914)292-5965. Contact: Paul Gerry. Record company and booking agency. Releases 2-4 LPs/year. Works with artists and songwriters on contract. Teams collaborators. Pays negotiable royalty to artists on contract; statutory rate to publishers for each record sold.
How to Contact: Arrange personal interview. Prefers reel-to-reel, cassette, 8-track cartridge (or videocassette) and lead sheet. SASE. Reports in 1 month.
Music: Bluegrass, country, folk and gospel. Released *The Fiddler & His Lady*, by Tater Tate (bluegrass LP); *Back Home in Madison County*, by Red Rector (bluegrass LP); *Saturday Night*, by Bristol Mountain Bluegrass (bluegrass LP); and *Before the Fire Comes Down*, by Northern Lights (bluegrass LP). Other artists include Mac Martin, the Shenandoah Cutups, Stacy Phillips, Simon St. Pierre, Gene Elders, Fred Pike, Roger Bellow, Del McCoury, The Stuart Family, Mountain Grass, Walter Hensley, Clinton King, Jerry Oland and The Gospelites.

RIC RAC RECORDS, % Ric Rac, Inc., Box 712, Nashville IN 47448. (812)837-9569. President: R.L. Hanson. Labels include Country Bump. Record company, music publisher (Ric Rac Music/ASCAP and Rick Hansen Music/BMI), record production and promotion firm, and management firm (Ric Rac, Inc.). Estab. 1985. Releases 4-6 singles/year. Works with musicians/artists and songwriters on contract. Pays 3-6% royalty to artists on contract; statutory rate to publishers for each record sold.
How to Contact: Write first and obtain permission to submit. Prefers cassette with 1-4 songs and lyric or lead sheet. SASE. Reports in 2 months. "Do not make phone inquiries as to status of material submitted. Material submitted to A&R must be represented by publisher. We are only interested in videos of live performances."
Music: Mostly country; also rock, gospel, folk and easy listening (MOR). Released "Same Old Barroom Melody," written and recorded by Rick Hanson; "Little Girl Blue" and "Down For More," recorded by Glori McFall; all on Ric Rac Records (country).
Tips: "Be as professional as possible and become active in songwriters workshops in your area."

RICOCHET RECORDS, P.O. Box 181, Holbrook NY 11741. President: Andy Marvel. Labels include Alyssa Records. Record company, music publisher (Andy Marvel Music), and record producer (Marvel Productions). Releases 9 singles, 18 CDs and 6 LPs/year. Works with musicians/artists and songwriters on contract.
How to Contact: Prefers cassette (or VHS videocassette) with 3 songs and lyric sheet. Reports in 3 weeks only with SASE. No need for permission.
Music: Mostly pop, R&B and top 40; also country.

*RIDGEWOOD RECORDS, Box 630755, Miami FL 33163. (305)935-4880. President: Jack Gale. Labels include Playback, Gallery II, Caramba! Record company, music publisher (Lovey Music/BMI, Cowabonga Music/ASCAP) and record producer (Jack Gale Productions). Estab. 1983. Releases 48 singles, 10 LPs and 10 CDs/year. Works with musicians/artists and songwriters on contract. Pays statutory rate to publisher per song on record.
How to Contact: Submit demo tape by mail. Unsolicited submissions are okay. Prefers cassette (or VHS videocassette) with 2 songs and lyric sheet. Reports in 2 weeks.
Music: Mostly country and contemporary country. Released "Cry Cry Darling" (written and recorded by J.C. Newman); "Have it Your Way" (by J. Fuller), recorded by Brittany; and "Tossin' & Turnin'", recorded by Stacy, all on Ridgewood Records (country). Other artists include Terry Smith, Mike O'Harra, Donnie Bowser, Kat Ballou, Carol Persell and Lynne Thomas.
Tips: "Don't be afraid to keep submitting. We listen to everything."

*RIGHTEOUS RECORDS, P.O. Box 289, B.U. Station, Boston MA 02215. (617)787-3615. A&R: Randy Frisch. Labels include Ox Cassettes. Record company, music publisher, BMI. Estab. 1985. Works with musicians/artists on record contract, songwriters on royalty contract.

How to Contact: Submit demo tape by mail. Unsolicited submissions are OK. Prefers cassette (or VHS videocassette if available) with 2-4 songs and lyric sheets. SASE. Reports in 2 weeks.

Music: Interested in rock/pop, rap and R&B. Released *Number One* (by Gunnion), recorded by Junglebook on Ox Records (rock LP) and *Winter, Spring, Summer* (by Thomas), recorded by Hammertung on Righteous Records (metal LP). Other artists include The McGuires and Randy X.

Tips: "Try us!"

RIPSAW RECORD CO., Suite 805, 4545 Connecticut Ave. NW, Washington DC 20008. (202)362-2286. President: Jonathan Strong. Record company, record producer, and music publisher (Southern Crescent Publishing/BMI and Sugar Mama Music/BMI). Estab. 1976. Releases 1-5 singles and 1-2 LPs/year. Works with musicians/artists and songwriters on contract. Payment negotiable with artists on contract. Pays standard royalty to songwriters on contract; statutory rate to publishers for each record sold.

How to Contact: Prefers cassette and lyric sheet. SASE. "Invite us to a club date to listen." Reports as soon as possible.

Music: Blues, rockabilly and "traditional" rock 'n' roll. Released *Oooh-Wow!*, by the Uptown Rhythm Kings (jump blues). Other artists include Bobby Smith, Billy Hancock, Kid Tater and Cheaters.

Tips: "Keep it true roots rock 'n' roll."

ROAD RECORDS, 252 Mennonite Rd., Collegeville PA 19426. (215)489-8810. President: Jim Femino. Labels include Road Records. Record company and music publisher (Fezsongs, ASCAP). Estab. 1980. Releases 2-5 singles, 1 LP and 1 CD/year. Works with musicians/artists and songwriters on contract. Pays varying royalty to artists on contract; statutory rate to publisher per song on record.

How to Contact: Write first and obtain permission to submit. Prefers cassette (or VHS videocassette) with 1-3 songs and lyric sheets. SASE. Reports in 8 weeks.

Music: Mostly rock, country and crossover. Released *All Night Party* (by Jim Femino), "Party Tonight" (by Jim Femino), *Just The Good Stuff* (album/CD) and "Nancy's Song" (by Jim Femino); all recorded by Jim Femino on Road Records (rock). Other artists include Kip Miller and Marionette.

ROBBINS RECORDS, INC., HC80, Box 5B, Leesville LA 71446. National Representative: Sherree Scott. Labels include Headliner Stars Records. Record company and music publisher (Headliner Stars Music and Universal Stars Music/BMI). Estab. 1973. Releases 12-14 singles and 1-3 LPs/year. Works with artists and songwriters on contract. Pays standard royalty to artists on contract; statutory rate to publishers for each record sold.

How to Contact: Prefers cassette with 1-6 songs and lyric sheet. Does not return unsolicited material. Reports only if interested.

Music: Mostly church/religious; also bluegrass, country, folk, gospel, and top 40/pop. Released "Jesus, You're Everywhere," "I Can Depend on You," and "I Just Came to Thank You Lord," by J.J. and Sherree Stephens (religious singles). Other artists include Renee Wills and Melodee McCanless.

ROCK CITY RECORDS, USA, P.O. Box 6553, Malibu CA 90264. (818)506-3789. President: Mike Danna. Record company (Rock City Records USA) and record producer (Mike Danna). Estab. 1984. Releases 3 singles, 3 cassette singles and 1 CD/year. Works with musicians/artists on contract. Pays negotiable royalty to artists on contract. Pays statutory rate to publishers per song on records.

How to Contact: Prefers cassette (or VHS videocassette) with 2-3 songs and lyric sheet. Does not return unsolicited material. Reports in 2 weeks. Send SASE for return of tapes.

Music: Mostly pop and rock; also soundtracks. Released "Words of Love" (by Mickey Dee), recorded by Mickey Dee/Bobbi Heart (pop single); and *Now Or Never* (pop/rock LP) and "Lovelights" (pop single), both written and recorded by M. Dee, all on Rock City Records.

Tips: "Sacrifice, patience, persistence, and knowing your abilities will ultimately get you where you're looking to go."

*ROCK IN RECORDS , Haven Commercial Bldg. 24/F, Room A Tsing Fung Street, **Hong Kong.** General Manager: Keith Yip. Record company. Estab. 1981. Releases 5 LPs and 5 CDs/year. Works with musicians/artists on contract and hires musicians for in-house studio work. Pays 5-7% royalty to artists on contract; statutory rate to publishers per song on record.

How to Contact: Submit demo tape by mail. Unsolicited submissions are OK. Prefers cassette (or VHS videocassette if available) with 2 or more songs. SASE.

Music: Mostly new age, rock and R&B.

*ROCKIT RECORDS, INC., Suite 306 35918 Union Lake Rd., Mt. Clemens MI 48043. (313)792-8452. Music Director: Joseph Trupiano. Record company and music publisher (Bad Grammar Music, Inc. BMI). Estab. 1985. Releases 5-10 singles, 5-10 cassette singles and 5-10 CDs/year. Works with musicians/artists and songwriters on contract. Pays statutory rate to publisher per song on records.

How to Contact: Submit demo by mail. Unsolicited submissions are OK. Prefers cassette (or VHS videocassette if available) with 3 songs and lyric sheet. SASE. Reports in 3 months.
Music: Mostly pop/dance, pop rock and rock; also alternative rock, new age and urban and R&B. Released "Runaround Sue" (by D. Dimucci), recorded by The Joey Harlow Project (CD and cassette single); "Back Beat of a Song" (by Laya Phelps), recorded by Laya Phelps (CD); and Busy" (by Kurt Dietz), by Kurt Deetz (CD) all on Rockit Records. Other artists include, The Mix, Bob's Night Off, David Hansen, Atlas, Micheal Duhnzigger and Sibilli.
Tips: "Competitiveness is the key. If you cannot sound at least as good with your recordings as the material you're hearing on radio, then your chances of getting a deal are quite slim. The industry operates on a drastically different level today. They no longer wish to take on a basement demo and proceed to developing the artist musically as well as visually. Instead, they are looking for the finished product that has been produced professionally."

*ROGUE RECORDS, 1614 N. Fairfax Ave., Los Angeles CA 90046. (213)874-0147. CEO: Ron Hitchcock. Record company and music publisher. Estab. 1975. Works with musicians/artists and songwriters on contract. Pays statutory rate to publishers per song on record.
How to Contact: Submit demo tape by mail. Unsolicited submissions are OK. Prefers cassette (or VHS videocassette if available) Does not return unsolicited material. Reports in 3 weeks.
Music: Mostly pop, rock and A/C; also jazz.

*ROHIT INTERNATIONAL RECORDS, 511 Commerce St., Franklin Lakes NJ 07417. (201)337-7325. Labels include Rohit International Records. Record company. Estab. 1979. Releases 30 CDs/year. Works with musicians/artists on contract. Pays statutory rate to publishers per song on record.
How to Contact: Submit demo tape by mail. Unsolicited submissions are OK. Prefers cassette with 3-5 songs. Does not return unsolicited material.
Music: Mostly reggae, soca and zouk. Released *Messenger From Yard*, recorded by Lee Perry; *Detrimental*, recorded by Frankie Paul; and *Transition*, recorded by Max Romeo/Upsetters, all on Rohit Records (CDs).
Tips: "Any great songwriter can be a great recording artist. Let's hear master qualtity recordings."

ROLL ON RECORDS®, 112 Widmar Pl., Clayton CA 94517. (415)672-8201. Owner: Edgar J. Brincat. Record company. Estab. 1985. Releases 2-4 singles/year. Works with musicians/artists and songwriters on contract and hires musicians for in-house studio work. Pays 10% royalty to artists on contract; statutory rate to publisher per song on record.
How to Contact: Submit demo tape by mail. Unsolicited submissions are OK. Prefers cassette with 3 songs and lyric sheet. SASE. Reports in 2-4 weeks.
Music: Mostly contemporary/country, MOR and R&B; also pop, light rock and modern gospel. Released "One Heart at a Time," (by Ann Leisten/John Covert); "I Only Put it On," (by Barbara Finnicum/Ed Davie); "Think Again," (by Barbara Finnicum); "Forever and Ever," (Patti Leidecker); "Thank God," (Ann Leisten/Jeff Powell/Walter Horban); "Still," (by Dick Wells); "Love Is" (by Michael Gooch); "Good Ol' Girl," (by Tim Horrigan); all recorded by Steve Jordan (contemporary country).

ROM RECORDS, Box 491212, Los Angeles CA 90049. (213)471-5000. Contact: A&R Department. Record company. Estab. 1987. Releases 8 LPs and 10 CDs/year. Works with musicians/artists on contract.
How to Contact: Write first and obtain permission to submit. Prefers cassette with 2-3 songs. Does not return unsolicited material. Reports in 4 weeks.
Music: Mostly eclectic, folk and singer-songwriters. Released *Violin Voyager*, written and recorded by Kim Angelis (CD/cassette); *Caminos* (by various artists), recorded by Huayucalitia (LP/CD); and *Play On* (by various artists), recorded by Rotondi (accordian jazz/LP/CD/cassette); all on ROM Records. Other artists include Sandy Bull and Ciro Hurtado.
Tips: "Write great material unique to your own vision. Don't attempt to emulate those on the charts."

ROSEWOOD RECORDS, P.O. Box 364, New Castle PA 16103. (412)654-3023. Owner: Wes Homner. Record company, music publisher (Mountain Therapy Music/BMI) and record producer (Rosewood Productions). Estab. 1975. Releases 2 singles, 5 cassettes, 2 LPs and 2 CDs/year. Works with musicians/artists and songwriters on contract. Pays according to contract signed with artist; statutory rate to publisher per song on record.
How to Contact: Submit demo tape by mail. Unsolicited submissions are okay. Prefers cassette with 3 songs and lyric sheets. Does not return unsolicited material. Reports in 3 weeks.
Music: Mostly southern gospel and bluegrass; also country. Released "Grave Digger," written and recorded by Ron Mesing (bluegrass); "Just Like You," (by Tim O'Brien), recorded by Full House; and "Sing A Song of Seasons," (by Judy Minouge), recorded by Millcreek Ramblers; all on Rosewood

Records. Other artists include Rainbow Valley Boys, Mac Martin, Bill Wright, Buzz Matheson, Wildwood Express and Judy Minouge.

Tips: "Please submit only, clean positive love songs and bluegrass/gospel."

ROTO-NOTO MUSIC, 148 Erin Ave., Hamilton Ontario L8K 4W3 **Canada**. (416)572-7474. President: R. Cousins. Labels include Roto-Noto, Marmot, Chandler. Record company, music publisher and record producer. Estab. 1979. Releases 20 singles, 2 12" singles, 5 LPs and 2 CDs/year. Works with musicians/artists and songwriters on contract and hires musicians for in-house studio work.

How to Contact: Write first and obtain permission to submit. Prefers cassette with 2 songs and lyric sheets. SASE. Reports in 4 weeks.

Music: Mostly country, pop and rock; also R&B and jazz. Released *Here Comes Trouble*, written and recorded by Mark La Forme (LP); "Hangin' By A Thread" (by S. Younger), recorded by Jenny Lee West (single); and *Rapid Transit* (by K. King), recorded by Rapid Transit (CD); all on Roto-Noto Records. Other artists include Bobby McGee, Jack Diamond Band, Eleven Degrees, Harrison Kennedy and Frequency.

*ROUND SOUND MUSIC, RR 2, Box 111-C, Cresco PA 18326. (717)595-3149. Owner: Tommy Lewis, Jr.. Labels include Round Sound Music, Geodesic Records; Positive Alternative. Record company and record producer. Estab. 1983. Releases 3-5 singles, 5 LPs and 5 CDs/year. Works with musicians/artists and songwriters on contract and hires musicians on salary for in-house studio work. Pays statutory rate to publishers per song on record.

How to Contact: Write or call first and obtain permission to submit. Prefers cassette, 15 ips reel-to-reel or VHS videocassette with 3 songs and lyric and lead sheet. SASE. Reports in 3 months.

Music: Mostly new age, pop and jazz; also country, R&B and gospel. Released "Listen" and "Dance All Night" all (by T. Lewis), recorded by Charade on Round Sound Records (pop/single). Other artists include J. Schick, Sacred Heart, Sandy Prior, Ransomed and Jim Hendershedt.

Tips: "Be honest with yourself, and professional with your presentation."

ROWENA RECORDS, 195 S. 26th St., San Jose CA 95116. (408)286-9840. A&R Director: G.J. O'Neal. Labels include Rowena Records, Chance Records and Jan-Ell Records. Record company. Releases 4 singles, 4 12" singles and 4 LPs/year. Works with musicians/artists and songwriters on contract; hires musicians for in-house studio work. Pays 10% royalty to artists on contract; pays statutory rate to publishers per song on record.

How to Contact: Prefers cassette with 4 or more songs and lyric sheet. SASE. Reports in 1 month.

Music: Mostly gospel, country and R&B; also pop, rock and new age. Released "Heartbeat" and "On The Road Again Without You," recorded by The Reed Sisters (country); "Before, After" and "Oh Why," recorded by Sister Suffragette (pop/rap); "Just A Kid," recorded by Jacque Lynn (country) and "According To You," recorded by Amy Clemens (modern country).

ROXTOWN RECORDS, 2124 Darby Dr., Massilon OH 44646. (216)833-2061. President: Nick Boldi. Labels include Roxtown Records and Bold One Records. Record company, music publisher (Bolnik Music/BMI) and record producer (NRB Productions). Estab. 1986. Releases 6 singles and 2 LPs/year. Works with musicians/artists and songwriters on contract. Pays 4-5% royalty to artists on contract; pays statutory rate to publishers per song on record.

How to Contact: Prefers cassette with 6 songs maximum and lyric sheet (1 per song). SASE. Reports in 6 weeks.

Music: Mostly country, rock and pop; also R&B. Released "Lover's Dreamland" (by N. Boldi/D. Glasser), recorded by Danny Pellegrine (country rock); "The Thief" (by Lewis Mischeff), recorded by Big Lou (contemporary rock); and "Stay" (by Werner/Mischeff), recorded by Big Lou (ballad); all on Roxtown Records.

*ROYAL RECORDS, 112 Hanapepe Lp., Honolulu HI 96825. (808)396-0221. President: Fred Jones. Record company and music publisher (Fred Jones ASCAP). Estab. 1984. Releases 6 singles, 6 12" singles and 6 LPs/year. Works with musicians/artists and songwriters on contract and hires musicians for in-house studio work. Pays 15% royalty to artists on contract.

How to Contact: Write and obtain permission to submit. Prefers cassette with 3 songs and lead sheet. SASE. Reports in 2 weeks.

Music: Mostly country, gospel and pop. Released "By My Side," written and recorded by Ed Riley; "Stay With Me," by Warren Johnson; and "Silver Seas" (by Fred Jones), recorded by Roland Atone; recorded on Royal Records (single). Other artists include Leroy Daves, Lou Canady, Al Romero, Taran Ericson, Jean Howard.

Tips: "Don't give up, keep writing and be dedicated to your work."

*RR&R RECORDS, Rt. 16, Box 560, Cain Cr., Gainsville, GA 30506. (404)889-8624. Contact: Ron Dennis. Labels include Rapture Records, Ready Records, Rapp Records, Y'Shua Records and RR&R Records. Record company, music publisher (Super Rapp Publishing/BMI and Do It Now Publishing/ASCAP), record producer (Ron Dennis Wheeler). Estab. 1966. Releases 5 singles, 5 12″ singles, 5 LPs, 5 EPs and 5 CDs/year. Works with musicians/artists and songwriters on contract; hires musicians for in-house studio work. Pays statutory rate to publishers per song on record.
How to Contact: Prefers cassette (or VHS videocassette) or 15 ips reel-to-reel with lyric or lead sheet. SASE. Reports in 3 months. "Send no demos. Masters only."
Music: Mostly gospel, rock, pop, country and R&B. Released "If Were Not In Love," recorded by Patty Weaver; "She Knows About Me" and "Your Music Make Me Cry," recorded by Jez Davidson; all performed on the Young and Restless Show. "K-Mart Christmas" and "Tribute to a King," by Chuck Carter. Other artists include Rita Van and Rob McInnis, Dan Carroll, Taylor Prichard and Peter Burwin.
Tips: "Send songs that are positive with good moral overtones in the message—melodic tunes with less electric synthesizer sound."

*RTP INTERNATIONAL, Box 311, 180 Pond St., Cohasset MA 02025. (617)383-9494. President: Rik Tinory. Artist Relations: Claire Babcock. Labels include Sequel and Old Boston. Record company, record producer and music publisher (Old Boston Publishing). Releases 10 singles and 8-12 LPs/year. Works with musicians/ artists and songwriters on contract; musicians on salary for in-house studio work.
How to Contact: Call first. Prefers cassette with 1-3 songs and lead sheet. Does not return unsolicited material. "All material submitted must be copyrighted."

*S.O.C., P.O. Box 897, Hartford CT 06101. (203)548-0212. A&R Head: Linda "Bottles" Polite. Labels include S.O.C., Light Source and Silsar Records. Record company, music publisher and record producer (Silver Sargent (Silsar). Estab. 1986. Releases 4-12 singles, 4-12 12″ singles 13 LPs, 13 EPs and 13 CDs/year. Works with musicians/artists and songwriters on contract. Pays 5-12% royalty to artists on contract; negotiable rate to publishers per song on record.
How to Contact: Submit demo tape by mail. Unsolicited submissions are okay. Prefers cassette (or VHS videocassette) with 4-5 songs and lyric sheet. SASE. Reports in 6 weeks.
Music: Mostly funk, R&B and soul and gospel; also rap. Released "Handwriting on the Wall," written and recorded by Silver Sargent (R&B single); *Meet Muffin* (by Herb Superb), recorded by Sarge "Muffin" (rap LP); and *Jesus is Real*, written and recorded by Silver Sargent (gospel LP), all on S.O.C. Records. Other artists include Drum Possie, Native American, The Uniques and Officer Muffin.
Tips: "Have a good hook, and a great look. A photo may help."

SABTECA RECORD CO., Box 10286, Oakland CA 94610. (415)465-2805. President: Duane Herring. Record company and music publisher (Sabteca Music Co./ASCAP, Toyiabe Music Co./BMI). Estab. 1980. Releases 3 singles and 1 12″ single/year. Works with songwriters on contract and hires musicians for in-house studio work. Pays statutory rate to publisher per song on record.
How to Contact: Write first and obtain permission to submit. Prefers cassette with lyric sheet. Reports in 3 weeks.
Music: Mostly R&B, pop and country. Released "Come Into My Arms" and "I Dare You," (by Duane Herring), recorded by Johnny B and The Rhythm Method; both on Sabteca Records.
Tips: "Improve your writing skills. Keep up with music trends."

*SAHARA RECORDS AND FILMWORKS ENTERTAINMENT, Suite 829, 4475 Allisonville Rd., Indianapolis IN 46205. (317)549-9006. President: Edward De Miles. Record company, music publisher (EDM Music/BMI) and record producer. Estab. 1981. Releases 15-20 12″ singles and 5-10 LPs/year. Works with musicians/artists and songwriters on contract and hires musicians for in-house studio work. "Pays varying royalty to artists on contract." Pays statutory rate to publishers per song on record.
How to Contact: Write or call first and obtain permission to submit. Prefers cassette with 3-5 songs and lyric sheet. Does not return unsolicited material. Reports in 1 month.
Music: Mostly R&B/dance, top 40 pop/rock and contemporary jazz; also TV-film themes, musical scores and jingles. Released "Need A Lover" (by S. Lynn), recorded by Steve Lynn (R&B single); "High Off Rhymes" (by D. Evans/A. Mitchell), recorded by Multiple Choice (rap single); and "Break Your Promise" recorded by Klas (R&B single), all on Sahara Records.
Other artists include "Lost in Wonder" and "Dvon Edwards".
Tips: "We're looking for strong mainstream material. Lyrics and melodies with good hooks that grab people's attention."

*SAM RECORDS INC., 76-05 51st Ave., Elmhurst NY 11373. Vice President: Michael Weiss. Record company. Estab. 1976. Releases 8 singles, 8 12″ singles, 3 LPs and 3 CDs/year. Works with musicians/artists on contract. Pays 10% royalty to artists on contract; statutory rate to publishers per song on record.

How to Contact: Sumit demo tape by mail. Unsolicited submissions are OK. Prefers cassette with 2 songs. Does not return unsolicited material.

Music: Mostly R&B, rap and dance. Released "(I'll Be Your) Dream Lover" (written by John Davis), and "Can't Stop Loving You" (written by Marshall Jefferson), recorded by Richard Rogers (urban single); and "Busted" (by N. Roman/D. Nabritt), recorded by Desire (rap single), all on Sam Records. Other artists include McRajah.

*SAN FRANCISCO SOUND, 29903 Harvester Rd., Malibu CA 90265. (213)457-4844. President: Matthew Kat. Labels include Malibu Record company, music publisher (After You Publishing/BMI) and Record producer (Matthew Katz Productions). Releases 6 singles, 6 12″ singles, 2 LPs and 2 CDs/year. Works with musicians/artists on record contract and hires musicians on salary for in-house studio work. Pays statutory rate to publishers per song on records.

How to Contact: Prefers cassette with 3 songs and lead sheet. Does not return unsolicited material.

Music: Mostly rock, pop and country. Interested in "message songs—about ecology, peace, the homeless, etc." Released *Moby Grape* (rock LP) and *Tim Hardin* (pop LP).

SAN-SUE RECORDING STUDIO, P.O. Box 773, Mt. Juliet TN 37122-3336. Labels include Basic Records. Owner: Buddy Powell. Record company, music publisher (Hoosier Hills/BMI) and recording studio. Estab. 1975. Works with artists and songwriters on contract. Releases 7 singles and 3 LPs/year. Pays 8% royalty to artists on contract; statutory rate to publishers for each record sold.

How to Contact: Prefers 7½ ips reel-to-reel or cassette with 2-4 songs. "Strong vocal with piano or guitar is suitable for demo, along with lyrics." SASE. Reports in 2 weeks.

Music: Church/religious, country, and MOR. Released "You'd Think I'd Learn," by Stacy Armstrong; "Slow Walk Out of Town," by Donny Abney; and "When I Woke Up You Were Gone," by Donny Abney; all country pop singles on Basic Records. Other artists include Camillo Phelps.

SCENE PRODUCTIONS, Box 1243, Beckley WV 25802. (304)252-4836. President/Producer: Richard L. Petry. Labels include Rising Sun and Country Road Records. Record company, record producer and music publisher (Purple Haze Music/BMI). Member of AFM. Releases 1-2 singles and 1-2 LPs/year. Works with musicians/artists and songwriters on contract. Pays 4-5% minimum royalty to artists on contract; standard royalty to songwriters on contract; statutory rate to publishers for each record sold. Charges "initial costs, which are conditionally paid back to artist."

How to Contact: Write first about your interest (recording only). Prefers cassette with 2-5 songs and lyric sheet. Prefers studio produced demos. SASE. Reports in 1 month.

Music: Mostly country, top 40, R&B/crossover and pop/rock; also MOR, light and commercial rock. Released "No Time for Play" and "I'm In Deep" (written and recorded by Chuck Paul) (pop). Other artists includes Dave Runion.

Tips: "Songs should be well thought-out and well constructed with good demo."

*SCORE PRODUCTIONS, (formerly Perfect Pitch Records), 3414 Peachtree Rd. NE 640, Atlanta GA 30326-1113. A&R Director: Amy Davis. Record company, music publisher and record producer (Score Productions, Inc.). Releases 10 singles, 1000 LPs and 5 CDs/year. Works with musicians/artists and songwriters on contract. Pays negotiable royalty to artists on contract.

How to Contact: Call first and obtain permission to submit. Prefers cassette with 1 song and lyric sheet. SASE. Reports in 1 month.

Music: Rock, country, MOR and pop. Released "Tone Up," "In Concert," and "Silver Anniversary Tribute to the Beatles," all on Perfect Pitch Records.

SCP RECORDS, Division of the Sound Column Companies, 160 Westgate Fine Arts Center, 342 W. 200 South, Salt Lake City UT 84101. (801)355-5327. A&R Professional Manager: Ron Simpson. Record company with affiliated record producer and music publisher (Ronarte Publications/ASCAP, Mountain Green Music/BMI and Macanudo Music/SESAC). Member CMA. Estab. 1970. Releases 3 singles and 4 LPs/year. Works with artists and songwriters on contract; hires musicians for in-house studio work. Pays negotiable royalty to artists on contract; statutory rate to publishers for each record sold.

How to Contact: Write first for specific instructions. SASE. "Demand varies—we favor our staff writers, and most artists have their own material. Query as to demand." Reports as soon as possible. "Once in awhile we get seriously behind—but you'll eventually be heard. We pay attention to the quality of the demo, including production values and overall feel."

Music: Pop (dance and AC), country and contemporary religious. Released *Three Again* (by various writers), recorded by The Jensens (country); *His Love*, (by various writers), recorded by Janine Lindsay (opening round Grammy contender) (contemporary religious); and "True Love," (by Romney/Simpson), recorded by Shawn.

*SEALED WITH A KISS, INC., Suite 119, 2166 W. Broadway, Anaheim CA 92804-2446. (714)992-2677. Vice President A&R: Tracy Sands. Labels include Swak Records and Cavern Records. Record company and music publisher (Lipstick Traces Music Publishing/BMI). Estab. 1989. Releases 6-12 singles, 4 LPs, 2 EPs and 4 CDs/year. Works with musicians/artists and songwriters on contract. Pays 1-9% royalty to artists on contract; statutory rate or negotiable rate to publisher per song.
How to Contact: Submit demo tape by mail. Unsolicited submissions are okay. Prefers cassette. SASE. Reports in 2 months.
Music: Mostly rock and psychedelic. Released "Dinah Wants Religion" (by Ellis/Clark/Cammack), recorded by The Fabs (rock 7' single); "One of These Days" (by Bruce Swift/Larry Gagnier), recorded by The Lords (rock 7" single); and *We're Not What We Are* (by Robert Wahlsteen), recorded by Jubal's Children (psychedelic 12" LP) all on SWAK Records. Other artists include The Yorkshires and Tracy Sands.
Tips: "If you own unsigned masters, demos, live recordings, garage rehearsal tapes of 1960's rock and psychedelic, contact us first! We're looking for obscure, little known groups from any region. Must prove ownership and authenticity. Then we talk."

SEASIDE RECORDS, 100 Labon St., Tabor City NC 28463. (919)653-2546. Owner: Elson H. Stevens. Labels include SeaSide and JCB. Record company, music publisher and record producer. Estab. 1978. Releases 10 singles and 15 LPs/year. Works with musicians/artists and songwriters on contract; musicians on salary for in-house studio work, and producers. Pays 3-10% royalty to artists on contract; statutory rate to publisher per song on record.
How to Contact: Write or call first to obtain permission to submit. Prefers cassette with 3 songs and lyric or lead sheet. SASE. Reports in 1 month.
Music: Mostly country, rock and gospel; also "beach music." Released "I'll Never Say Never Again" (by G. Todd), recorded by Sheila Dawn (country crossover); "I'm Ready" (by R. Dwand, P. King), recorded by Fred Rogers (50's rock); and "God's Blessing Me Now" (by Watson Family), recorded by E. Watson (gospel); all on Seaside Records. Other artists include (H-I-S Gospel) Gospel Entertainers, Macedonia Trio, Gospel Echoes, (Paul Stegall Country), and Robert Woodbury (beach rock).

SEEDS RECORDS, Box 20814, Oklahoma City OK 73156. (405)755-0315. Labels include Homa, Seeds and Okart Records. Record company, record producer, music publisher (Okisher Publishing/BMI), and Mickey Sherman Talent Management. Estab. 1973. Releases 6-12 12" singles, 3 LPs and 3 CDs/year. Works with songwriters on contract and hires in-house studio musicians. Pays 10% royalty to artists on contract; statutory rate to publishers for each record sold.
How to Contact: Prefers cassette (or videocassette) with 1-3 songs and lyric sheet. Does not return unsolicited material. Reports in 1 month.
Music: Mostly blues, country and ballads; also easy listening, jazz, MOR, R&B and soul. Released "Good Daddy" (by Mickey Sherman), recorded by Janjo (blues); "Scotch on a Fiddle," written and recorded by Benny Kubiak (country instrumental); and "Pickin and Winning," written and recorded by Tommy Langley (country LP); all on Seeds Records. Other artists include Charley Shaw, Ronnie McClendon, Jana Jarvis, The Langley Family.

SEPHORA DIFFUSION, B. P. 30, 51170 Fismes **France**. Phone: 26 48 83 48. FAX: 26.48.87.30. Director/Manager: Marc Brunet. Labels include MAYIM. Record company and record producer. Estab. 1984. Releases 10 LPs and 6 CDs/year. Works with musicians/artists on contract. Pays 7% royalty to artists on contract.
How to Contact: Submit demo tape by mail. Unsolicited submissions are OK. Prefers cassette with 3-4 songs and lyric sheets. SASE. Reports in 2 months.
Music: Mostly gospel, rock and MOR; all in French. Released *Corinne LaFitte* on Mayim Records (CD). Other artists include David Durham and Jude 25.

SHANACHIE RECORDS, 37 East Clinton St., Newton NJ 07860. (201)579-7763. A&R Director: Randall Grass. Labels include Greensleeves—USA, Message, Ogham and Meadow Lark. Releases 5 singles and 25 LPs/year. Works with musicians/artists on contract. Pays statutory rate to publisher per song on record.
How to Contact: Prefers cassette. SASE required for response. Reports in 1 month.
Music: Reggae, Irish and world beat; also folk, African and ethnic. Released *Music for Silences to Come* written and recorded by Dan Ar Bras on Shanachie (LP); *We've Come a Long Way*, written and recorded by Makem and Clancy on Shanachie Records (LP); and *Until* (by Willie Lindo), recorded

by Nadine Sutherland on Meadowlark Records (LP). Other artists incude Rita Marley, Judy Mowatt, Steeleye Span, Yellowan, Augusons Pablo and The Chieftains.

SHAOLIN FILM & RECORDS, P.O. Box 387, Hollywood CA 90078. (818)506-8660. President: Richard Del Connor. Record company, music publisher (Shaolin Music/ASCAP) and record producer (The Coyote). Estab. 1984. Releases 2 singles, 1 LP, 1CD and 1EP/year. Works with musicians/artists on record contract.
How to Contact: Prefers cassette with 3-4 songs and lyric sheet. Does not return unsolicited material. Reports in 3 months.
Music: Mostly rock, hard rock and pop; also soundtracks. Released "Show Girls," "Mother Mary" and "Bang Bang Boom Boom," written and recorded by Coyote on Shaolin Records (rock).

*SHEPERD RECORDS, 2307 N. Washington Ave., Scranton PA 18509. (717)347-7395; or P.O Box 20570, Columbus Circle Station, New York, NY 10023. (212)724-8404. A&R: Fran Grogan. Record company. Estab. 1981. Releases 1-3 singles/year and 1 LP year. Works with musicians/artists and songwriters on contract; musicians on salary for in-house studio work. Works with composers and lyricists; teams collaborators.
How to Contact: Prefers cassette with 1-2 songs. Does not return unsolicited material. Reports in 6 weeks.
Music: Mostly rock and pop. Released "Where's Danny," (by McGlynn/Spady), recorded by the Scranton Blues Band on Sheperd Records (R&B) and "Talkin' Bout Love," by Monroe (pop single); and *Encounter*, by McGlynn (pop LP).

SIGNATURE RECORDS, 500 Newbold St., London Ontario N6E 1K6 **Canada**. (519)686-5060. A&R Director: Geoff Keymer. Record company. Estab. 1982. Releases 5 LPs/year. Works with musicians/ artists on contract and hires musicians for in-house studio work. Pays statutory rate to publisher per song on record.
How to Contact: No unsolicited submissions. "Call or write and we will tell you when to submit."
Music: Mostly MOR/rock, rock and country ballads. Released "Statue," written and recorded by R. Piché; "Cassandra," written and recorded by Cassandra; and "Mike McKenna," written and recorded by Mike McKenna; all on Signature Records (all rock singles).

*SILENT RECORDS, Suite 315, 540 Alabama, San Francisco CA 94110. (415)864-7815. President: Kim Cascone. Record company and record producer (Kim Cascone). Estab. 1986. Releases 4 LPs/year. Works with musicians/artists on contract. Pays 10% royalty. Charges up front for buying tape, studio time deposit and pre-production labor.
How to Contact: Write first and obtain permission to submit. Prefers cassette (or VHS videocassette) with press kit (press clips, bio, etc.). Does not return unsolicited material. Reports in 6 months.
Music: Mostly experimental and industrial. Released "Euphoria," (by K. Cascone), recorded by PGR; "Dreamtime," (by G. Weisberg), recorded by Meterpool; and "Fire," (by G.X. Jupiter-Larsen), recorded by The Haters; all on Silent Records (experimental). Other artists include Organum, Keith Rowe and Arcane Device.

SIRR RODD RECORD & PUBLISHING CO., Box 58116, Philadelphia PA 19102-8116. President: Rodney J. Keitt. Record company, music publisher, record producer and management and booking firm. Releases 5 singles, 5 12″ singles and 2 LPs/year. Works with musicians/artists and songwriters on contract. Pays 5-10% royalty to artist on contract; statutory rate to publishers for each record sold.
How to Contact: Prefers cassette (or videocassette) with 3-5 songs and lyric sheet. SASE. Reports in 1 month.
Music: Top 40, pop, gospel, jazz, dance and rap. Released "Ghetto Jazz" and "Listen To Me" (by R.J. Keitt), "Fashion," "West Oak Lane Jam" and "I'm Serious" (by Klassy K/rap); "U-Crazy" and Strangelove" (by Ernie Kool); and *Monét The First Album* by Monét.

SLAK RECORDS, Suite 608, 214 St. George St., Toronto ON M5R 2N8 **Canada**. Phone: (416)964-0695. President: Al Kussin. Record company, music publisher (Clotille Publishing/PROCAN) and record producer (Slak Productions). Estab. 1986. Releases 2 singles, 2 12″ singles and 1 LP/year. Works with musicians/artists on contract. Pays statutory rate to publisher per song on record.
How to Contact: Submit demo tape by mail. Unsolicited submissions are OK. Prefers cassette with 3 songs and lyric sheets. SASE.
Music: Mostly pop, R&B and dance. Released "Hot For You" (dance 12″ single); "Crying for Love" (R&B/pop 7″ single); and "Never Be Lonely" (R&B/pop 7″ single); (all by A. Kussin), recorded by Lorraine Scott on Slak Records.
Tips: "Most of the material on Slak has been written by me. However, I wish to expand. A small label needs commercial, solid songwriting with good hooks and interesting lyrics."

SLAMDEK/SCRAMDOWN, Box 43551, Louisville KY 40253. Submissions Analyst: Kelly Kemper. Estab. 1986. Releases less than 5 singles, 10-15 cassettes, 3-5 CDs and 5-10 DATs/year. Works with musicians/artists on contract. Pays 10-25% royalty to artists on contract. Pays per individual set-up per record to publishers.
How to Contact: Prefers cassette with as many songs as possible, must include lyric sheet and photographs. Does not return unsolicited material. Reports in 1 month.
Music: Mostly progressive, creative and new rock and hardcore; also industrial, digital and static. Released "Dead" written and recorded by Hopscotch Army (college alternative); "Magenta Bent" written and recorded by Your Face (progressive rock); "Tools & Chrome," written and recorded by Jawbox (hardcore alternative); and "House" written and recorded by Cerebellum (progressive rock); all recorded on SLAMDEK/Scramdown Records. Other artists include Endpoint, Cold Mourning, Dez Kimberlin, John Burrows, Spot, Crawdad, Slambang Vanilla and Sunspring.
Tips: "We are interested in music that is creative, progressive and new, and would somehow make a significant contribution to the continuity and unity of the label. If you don't send lyrics and a photograph, don't expect to hear from us. We prefer music that is very loud."

*SOUND DEVELOPMENT RELEASING GROUP LTD., 1320 Sherman, Evanston IL 60201. (708)328-0400. Contact: A&R Department. Record company. Estab. 1988. Works with musicians/artists and songwriters on contract. Pays 6-10% royalty to artists on contract; ¾ rate to publishers per song on record.
How to Contact: Submit demo tape by mail. Unsolicited submissions are OK. Prefers cassette with 3 songs. SASE.
Music: Released *Toonz*, written and recorded by Mekoto Kuriya (jazz LP); *Pickit J.B.*, written and recorded by Jethro Burns (country LP); and *Whack!!* written and recorded by In Flight (rap LP), all on Sound Development Records.

SOUND IMAGE RECORDS, 6556 Wilkinson, North Hollywood CA 91606. (818)762-8881. President: Marty Eberhardt. Vice President Sales and Studio Manager: Chuck Kopp. Vice President and General Manager: David Chatfield. Vice President Business Affairs: John Bishop. Vice President A&R: Cathy Gibson. Labels include Sound Image and Harmony. Record company, record producer, music publisher (Sound Image Publishing), management firm (Sound Image Management), 24 track recording studio and video company. Member NARAS. Releases 8 singles and 4 LPs/year. Works with artists and songwriters on contract; hires musicians for in-house studio work. Pays 5-12% royalty to artists; statutory rate to publishers for each record sold.
How to Contact: Prefers cassette with 3 songs and lyric sheet. Include photo and bio. SASE. Prefers studio produced demos. Reports in 2 months.
Music: Mostly rock, AOR and R&B; also dance oriented. Currently working with "The Storm." Songs include "Walk The Line" and "I'll Be Loving You."

SOUND MASTERS, 9717 Jensen Dr., Houston TX 77093. (713)695-3648. Producer: A.V. Mittelstedt. Labels include Cherry Records and A.V. Records. Record company, music publisher (Publicare) and record producer. Estab. 1970. Releases 100 singles and 10 LPs/year. Works with musicians/artists and songwriters on contract; hires musicians for in-house studio work. Pays varying royalty to artists on contract; statutory rate to publisher per song on record.
How to Contact: Prefers cassette. SASE. Reports in 3 weeks.
Music: Mostly country, gospel and crossover; also MOR and rock. Released "Too Cold at Home" (by Bobby Hardin), recorded by Mark Chessnutt on Cherry Records (country); "You Got The Best of Me" (by J. Fuller/J Hobbs on Carolyn Stelle 'AV' Records (country); and "Let's Fall In Love Again" (by R. Shaw/S. Shaw), recorded by Ron Shaw on Cherry Records (country). Other artists include Geronimo Trevino, Jerry Calard, Roy Head and Randy Corner.

*SOUNDS OF WINCHESTER, Rt. 2, Box 116-H, Berkeley Springs, WV 25411. Contact: Jim or Bertha McCoy. Labels include Alear, Winchester and Real McCoy Records. Record company, music publisher (Jim McCoy Music, Alear Music and New Edition Music/BMI) and recording studio. Estab. 1973. Releases 20 singles and 20 LPs/year. Works with artists and songwriters on contract; musicians on salary for in-house studio work. Pays 2% royalty to artists and songwriters on contract; statutory rate to publishers for each record sold.
How to Contact: Arrange personal interview. Prefers 7½ ips reel-to-reel with 4-12 songs. Does not return unsolicited material. Reports in 1 month.
Music: Bluegrass, country, country rock, gospel and top 40/pop. Released "Jim McCoy Touches Your Heart," written and recorded by Jim McCoy; and "I've Got a Hold On You," written and recorded by Ronnie Flook; both on Winchester Records (country). Other artists include Carroll County Ramblers and Alvin Kesner.

SOUNDSHINE PRODUCTIONS, INC., 723 W. Sunrise, Ft. Lauderdale FL 33311. (305)463-9882. President: Tom Graefe. Labels include Soundshine Records. Record company, music publisher (Soundshine Publishing/BMI) and record producer (Soundshine Productions, Inc.). Estab. 1978. Releases 4 12″ singles, 2 LPs and 2-4 CDs/year. Works with musicians/artists and songwriters on contract and hires musicians for in-house studio work. Pays 20% royalty to artists on contract; statutory rate to publisher per song on record.
How to Contact: Submit demo tape by mail. Unsolicited submissions are okay. Prefers cassette. Does not return unsolicited material.
Music: Mostly R&B, pop and rock; also rap. Released "Party Line," written and recorded by Frankie Cee (single); "Mel Mac Rock" (by E. German), recorded by Soundshine (single); and *Tender Lover*, written and recorded by Frank Cornelius (LP); all on Soundshine Records. Other artists include Cornelius Bros. and Sister Rose.

*SOURCE RECORDS, INC., 39 S. LaSalle St. #825, Chicago IL. (312)287-2227. President: John Bellamy. Record company. Estab. 1974. Releases 2 singles, 3 12″ singles and 2 LPs/year. Works with musicians/artists and songwriters on contract. Pays statutory rate to publisher per song on record.
How to Contact: Submit demo tape by mail. Unsolicited submissions are OK. Prefers cassette (or VHS or ¾″ videocassette if available) with 2 songs and lyric sheet. Does not return unsolicited material. Reports in 3 weeks.
Music: Mostly R&B, pop and gospel. Released "You Got The Love" (by A. Stephens), recorded by Candi Staton; "Everybody Dance" (by D. Owens), recorded by Darnell Owens; and "Keepers of the Dream" (by N. Hughes), recorded by Clear Vision all on Source Records.

*SOURCE UNLIMITED RECORDS, 331 E. 9th St., New York NY 10003. (312)473-7833. Contact: Santo. Record company. Estab. 1982. Releases 3 LPS, 2 EPs and 3 CDs/year. Works with songwriters on contract. Psys 20% royalty to artists on contract; statutory rate to publisher per song on record.
How to Contact: Write first and obtain permission to submit. Prefers cassette and lyric sheet. SASE. Reports in 2 months.
Music: Mostly modern folk and gospel. Released *Self-Respect, A Night in the Life and Music From the Sea* all written and recorded by Santo (LP).
Tips: "Write about what you know! Be original."

SOUTHERN TRACKS RECORDS, 3051 Clairmont Rd. NE, Atlanta GA 30329. (404)325-0832. Contact: Mr. Carrier. Record company and record producer. Releases 15 singles and 2 LPs/year. Works with musicians/artists and songwriters on contract. Pays average of 5% royalty to artists on contract.
How to Contact: Prefers cassette with 3 unpublished songs and lyric sheet. Does not return unsolicited material.
Music: Interested in all types of music. Released "Burns Like a Rocket," recorded by Billy Joe Royal; "We Always Agree on Love," recorded by Atlanta; and "Sheet Music," recorded by Bill Anderson, all on Southern Tracks Records. Other artists include Bertie Higgins, Sammy Johns and Jimmy Ellis.

PHIL SPECTOR INTERNATIONAL AND WARNER/SPECTOR RECORDS INC., 686 S. Arroyo Pkwy. Penthouse, Pasadena CA 91105-3233. (818)846-9900. Labels include Philles Records Inc. Record company, music publisher (Mother Bertha Music Inc. and Back to Mono Music Inc.) and record producer (Phil Spector Productions). Releases varying number of singles/year. Pays varying royalty to artists on contract.
How to Contact: "Company is not accepting or reviewing any new material or artists. Any unsolicited material or correspondence will not be returned."

SPHEMUSATIONS, 12 Northfield Rd., Onehouse, Stowmarket Suffolk 1P14 3HF **England**. Contact: General Manager. Record company and music publisher. Estab. 1963. Releases 12 LPs/year. Works with musicians/artists and songwriters on contract and hires musicians for in-house studio work. Pays 10% royalty to artists on contract; statutory rate to publisher per song on record.
How to Contact: Write first and obtain permission to submit; write to arrange personal interview. Prefers cassette. SAE and IRC. Reports in 3 months.
Music: Mostly country, blues and jazz; also "serious modern." Released "The Weeper" (by J. Playford and J. Butt), recorded by K. Van Kampen; "The Lark" (by J. Playford and J. Butt), recorded by Simon Dresorgmer and "O Moon" (by J. Kears and J. Butt), recorded by Lorraine Anderson, all recorded on Sphemusations Records (light music).

*STARCREST PRODUCTIONS, INC., 209 Circle Hills Dr., Grand Forks ND 58201. (701)772-6831. President: George J. Hastings. Labels include Meadowlark and Minn-Dak Records. Record company, management firm and booking agency. Estab. 1970. Releases 2-6 singles and 1-2 LPs/year. Works with artists and songwriters on contract. Payment negotiable to artists on contract; statutory rate to publishers for each record sold.

How to Contact: Write first. Prefers cassette with 1-6 songs and lead sheet. SASE. Reports in 1 month.

Music: Country and top 40/pop. Released "Mr. Youcon Man" (by John Bass), recorded by Mary Joce on Meadowlark (country) and "The Long Nights of Winter" (by Bob Angle), recorded by Mary Joyce on Meadowlark (country).

STARDUST, Box 13, Estill Springs TN 37330. (615)649-2577. President: Buster Doss. Labels include Stardust, Wizard, Doss, Kimbolon, Flaming Star. Record company, music publisher (Buster Doss Music/BMI) and record producer (Colonel Buster Doss). Estab. 1959. Releases 50 singles and 25 LPs/year. Works with musicians/artists and songwriters on contract and hires musicians for in-house studio work. Pays 8% royalty to artists on contract; statutory rate to publisher per song on record.

How to Contact: Write or call first and obtain permission to submit. Prefers cassette with 2 songs and lyric sheets. SASE. Reports in 1 week.

Music: Mostly country; also rock. Released "Red Hot Fire," written and recorded by Benny Ray; "Where Were You" (by Buster Doss), recorded on Rooster Q.; and "Sad Memories," written and recorded by R.B. Stone; all on Stardust Records (all country singles). Other artists include Johnny Buck, Hobson Smith, Cliff Archer, Linda Wunder, Buck Cody and Tony Andrews.

STARGARD RECORDS, Box 138, Boston MA 02101. (617)296-3327. Artist Relations: Anthony Greenaway. Labels include Oak Groove Records. Record company, music publisher (Zatco Music/ASCAP and Stargard Publishing/BMI) and record producer. Estab. 1985. Releases 9 singles and 1 LP/year. Works with musicians/artists on contract; hires musicians for in-house studio work. Pays 6-8% royalty to artists on contract; statutory rate to publisher per song on record..

How to Contact: Write first to arrange personal interview. Prefers cassette (or VHS videocassette) and lyric and lead sheet. SASE. Reports in 2 months. "Sending bio along with picture or glossies is appreciated but not necessary."

Music: Mostly R&B, dance/hip hop. Released "Pipe Dreaming," (12" single), by Troy DeVoe, recorded by Tow Zone on Stargard Records; and "Run Me Down," (by Joseph Williams), recorded by Tiger Brown on Oak Groove Records (12" single). Other artists include Down Time and En-Control.

STARK RECORDS AND TAPE COMPANY, 628 S. South St., Mount Airy NC 27030. (919)786-2865. President and Owner: Paul E. Johnson. Labels include Stark, Pilot, Hello, Sugarbear, Kay and Red Bird. Record company, music publisher (Tompaul Music Company/BMI) and record producer (Stark Records and Tape Company). Estab. 1960. Releases 8 singles and 3 LPs/year. Works with songwriters on contract. Pays statutory rate to publisher per song on record.

How to Contact: Submit demo tape by mail. Unsolicited submissions are OK. Prefers cassette with 3-5 songs and lyric or lead sheets. SASE. Reports in 2 months.

Music: Mostly pop, country and country gospel; also bluegrass, bluegrass gospel and C&W country. Released "Blue Eyes Crying in the Rain" (by Paul E. Johnson), recorded by Bobby Atkins (country); "Love Valley," written and recorded by Bobby Atkins; all on Stark Records (C&W). Other artists include Carl Tolbert, Sam Bray, Ralph Hill, Early Upchurch, Sanford Teague and Don Sawyers.

*STARMAN RECORDS, P.O. Box 245604, Sacramento CA 95820. (916)441-1080. A&R: Virgal Covington. Labels include North Star Records, Diana Records and Starmaker Records. Record Company, music publisher (Ultime Thule Music, BMI), record producer (Starman Records) and in-house studios (8- and 16-track digital and analog). Estab. 1976. Releases 2-3 singles and 1-2 LPs/year. Works with musicians/artists on record contract, musicians on salary for in-house studio work. Pays 60% royalty to artists on contract; statutory rate publishers per song on records.

How To Contact: Write or call first and obtain permission to submit. Prefers cassette (½" videocassette if available) with 3 songs. SASE.

Music: Mostly pop, R&B and gospel; also spoken word, children's and country. Released "Goose Bumps" (by Mary Murphy), recorded by M. Boshears (country); "Those Spacemen Never Lie" (by V. Covington), recorded by G. Woltman (pop); and "Good Golly Miss Molly" (by J. Marascalco/R.A. Blackwell), recorded by G. Woltman (rock/R&B), all on Starman Records. Other artists include Roger Smith, Raymond Raymond, Friends, Kevin Archie and DeWayne Kennedy Singers.

STUDIO RECORDS INC., 5209 Indian Head Hwy., Oxon Hill MD 20745. (301)839-6567. President: Steven Franco. Record company (BMI). Estab. 1983. Releases 4-10 12" singles, 4CDs, 4EPs and 4 LPs/year. Works with musicians/artists and songwriters on contract and hires musicians for in-house studio work and commercial production. Pays 6-10% royalty to artists on contract; statutory rate to publisher per song on record.

How to Contact: Submit demo tape by mail. Unsolicited submissions are OK. Prefers cassette with 3 songs. Does not return unsolicited material. Reports in 2 weeks.
Music: Mostly pop, R&B and gospel. Released "Girl You Know Its True" (by Anedo, Lyles, Dehewy, Spencer, Hollang), recorded by Numarx on Studio Records (pop). Other artists include Tommi Gee, Foxfire, Barthalomew and Patrick Adams.

STUDIOEAST RECORDING, INC., 5457 Monroe Rd., Charlotte NC 28212. (704)536-0424. Owner: Tim Eaton. Labels include Pyramid Records, Metro Records, Sandblast Records, Sandman, East Coast Records and Peach. Record company, music publisher (Eastwood Publishing) and record producer. Releases 50 singles and 20 LPs/year. Works with musicians/artists and songwriters on contract; hires musicians for in-house studio work. Pays standard royalty to artists on contract.
How to Contact: Prefers cassette or 15 ips reel-to-reel (or VHS videocassette) with any number of songs. Does not return unsolicited material. Reports in 2 months. "If we feel material is unusable we will not contact artist. We will, however, keep material on file for possible future use."
Music: Mostly R&B, country and jazz; also rhythm and black gospel. Released "One More Step" by the Band of Oz on Metro Records; "Lovers' Holiday," by Dink Perry and the Breeze Band on Metro Records; "They Call Me Mr. Bassman"; "Whadja Do That Fo'" by the Catalinas on Metro Records (single). Presently recording: General Johnson & The Chairman Of The Board for Surfside Records, The Fantastic Shakers for Metro Records, The Catalinas for Metro Records and Part Time Party Time Band for Metro Records.

SUN DANCE RECORDS, 907 Baltimore St., Mobile AL 36605. Record company. Estab. 1987. Releases 12-15 singles, 8-10 12″ singles, 10 LPs and 10 CDs/year. Works with musicians/artists/songwriters on contract and in-house studio musicians on salary.
How to Contact: Submit demo tape by mail. Unsolicited submissions are OK. Prefers cassette (or VHS videocassette if available) with 2 songs and lyric sheets. SASE. Reports in 8 weeks.
Music: Mostly R&B, pop and rap; also rock, gospel and jazz. Released "In The Flesh," by Klye Bush (12″ single); *Emotion of Rock 'n Roll*, by Metal Communication (LP); and *Check Out My DJ*, by Jay Supreme (LP); all on Sun Dance Records. Other artists include La Shone Glover, Klye Bush and Magnetics.
Tips: "He that can have patience can have what he will."

*SUNDANCE MUSIC, Gammel Kongevej 47 B, Copenhagen 1610 **Denmark**. (45)31 22 6080. Managing Director: Dietmar Schmidt. Labels include Sundance Records and Stunt Records. Record company and music publisher. Estab. 1981. Releases 2 singles, 10 LPS, 2 12″ singles and 10 CDs/year. Works with musicians/artists and songwriters on contract and hires musicians for in-house studio work. Pays 5-14% royalty to artists on contract; statutory rate to publishers per song on record.
How to Contact: Submit demo tape by mail. Unsolicited submissions are okay. Prefers cassette with 3 songs. SASE.
Music: Mostly jazz, rock and pop. Released *Jukkis Uomla Live* (by Jukkis Uomla), recorded by Werner Studio on Stunt Records (jazz LP); "On the Loose," recorded by Sundance Studio on Sundance Records (rock); and "Reflections" (by Till Bar Meyer), recorded by Sundance Studio on Sundance Records (fusion). Other artists include Hamne Boel, Lars Moller, Gil Anderson, Thomas Franck, Page One and Jorgen Emborg.

*SUNDOWN RECORDS, P.O. Box 241, Newbury Park CA 91320. (805)499-9912. Owners: Gilbert Yslas and Richard Searles. Record company, distributor. Estab. 1985. Releases 2 CDs/year. Works with musicians/artists on contract.
How to Contact: Submit demo tape/CD by mail. Prefers cassette. SASE. Reports in weeks.
Music: Mostly New Age acoustic. Released "A Christmas Gift" written and recorded by Yslas/Searles on Sundown Records (New Age); "Dance of the Renaissance" (acoustic); and "Dream of the Troubadour" (acoustic).

SURESHOT RECORDS, Box 8734, Incline Village NV 89450. (702)831-9116. Contact: Alan Redstone. Record company and music publisher (Magic Message Music/ASCAP). Estab. 1979. Releases 1 single and 1 LP/year. Works with songwriters on contract.
How to Contact: Submit demo tape by mail. Unsolicited submissions are OK. Prefers cassette with 2 songs and lyric sheets. SASE. Reports in 1 week.
Music: Mostly country, A.C. and rock; also ballads. Released "This Time Around," written and recorded by Alan Redstone on Sureshot Records (country/rock).

SUSAN RECORDS, Box 4740, Nashville TN 37216. (615)865-4740. A&R Director: D. Daniels. Labels include Denco Records. Record company and music publisher. Releases 2-20 singles and 1-5 LPs/year. Works with artists and songwriters on contract. Pays 15¢/record to artists on contract. Buys some material outright; payment varies.

How to Contact: Prefers cassette with 1-6 songs and lead sheet. SASE. Reports in 2 weeks.
Music: Blues, country, dance, easy listening, folk, gospel, jazz, MOR, rock, soul and top 40/pop.

SWEET TALK RECORDS, P.O. Box 211, Westfield MA 01086. (413)783-8386. Operations Manager: Virginia L. Stewart. Labels include Sweet Talk Records. Record company and music publisher (Sariser Music/BMI). Estab. 1987. Releases 1-2 singles and 1-2 LPs. Works with musicians/artists and songwriters on contract. Pays statutory rate to publisher per song on record.
How to Contact: Write first and obtain permission to submit. No phone calls. Prefers cassette or 7½ ips reel-to-reel (or VHS #¼" videocassette) with 3-4 songs and lyric or lead sheet. SASE. Reports in 6 weeks.
Music: Mostly country/pop, country/rock and educational material; also soft rock and rockabilly. Released *She's A Riser,* written and recorded by Sparkie Allison (soft rock LP); and *Ride A Rainbow* by Sparkie Allison, recorded by Sparkie Allison and Ginny Cooper (contemporary Christian cassette and LP), both on Sweet Talk Records; "Highway to Heaven" written and recorded by Sparkie Allison on Sweet Talk Records (pop).
Tips: "Be unique. Try something different. Avoid the typical love songs. We look for material with a universal positive message. No cheatin' songs, no drinkin' songs."

*SWEN-DAUG RECORD INC., 322 T. St. N.W., Washington DC 20001. (202)232-8096. Record company, music publisher (Pressure Point Production) and record producer (David L. Sweeney—Swen-Daug and Sir Charles Dixon—Swen-Daug). Estab. 1988. Releases 2 singles/year. Works with musicians/artists on contract. "Pays varying royalty to artist on contract."
How to Contact: Submit demp tape by mail. Unsolicited submissions are OK. Prefers cassette (or VHS videocassette if available) with 3 songs and lyric sheet. Does not return unsolicited material.
Music: Mostly rap, R&B/dance and pop/dance; also jazz. Released "I Do Not Play" (by Donis Rice/Jeff Sease), recorded by Anthony Daughtry/David Sweeney on Swen-Daug Records; "Never Miss It, Til It's Gone" (by Jeff Sease/Donis Rice), recorded by Anthony Daughtry/David Sweeney on Swen-Daug; and "Original Posse" (by Shane Smith), recorded by Shane Smith on OP. Records, (all rap singles).
Tips: "When submitting a demo do not call to see if we are going to use it. If we are going to, you will be the first to know."

*SWOOP RECORDS, Stewart House, Hillbottom Rd., Highwycombe, Bucks, HP124HJ **England**. Phone: (0494)436301 or 436401. FAX: 0494-461832. Telex: 837173. A&R Director: Xavier Lee. Labels include Grenoullie, Zarg, Pogo and Check. Record company, music publisher (R.T.L. Music) and record producer (Ron Lee). Estab. 1976. Releases 60 singles, 20 12" singles and 90 LPs/year. Works with musicians/artists and songwriters on contract. Royalty paid to artists varies; statutory rate to publishers per song on record.
How to Contact: Prefers cassette, (or VHS or Beta videocassette) with 3 songs and lyric or lead sheet. SAE and IRC. Reports in 3 weeks.
Music: Interested in all types. Released "99" (by R.C. Bowman), recorded by The Chromatics on Swoop Records (hillbilly rock & roll); "Asylum" (by M.J. Lawson), recorded by Emmitt Till on Swoop Records (rock) and "Not Me" (by D. Boone) recorded by Daniel Boone on Swoop Records (rock). Other artists include Orphan, Groucho, Sight-n-Sound, Mike Sheridan, Daniel Boone, The Night Riders and Studs.
Tips: "Be original."

TABITHA RECORDS, Sandpiper Court, Harrington Lane, Exeter HX6 8N5 **England**. Phone: (0392)79914. Managing Director: Graham Sclater. Labels include Willow and Domino. Record company (PRS/MCPC/PPL) and record producer (Graham Sclater). Estab. 1975. Releases 6 singles, 2 12" singles, 4 LPs and 2 CDs/year. Works with musicians/artists on contract. Pays 4-8% royalty to artists on contract; statutory rate to publisher per song on record.
How to Contact: Submit demo tape by mail. Unsolicited submissions are okay. Prefers cassette (or VHS videocassette if available) with 4 songs. SASE. Reports in 1 month.
Music: Mostly pop, rock and country; also R&B and folk. Released "Aliens," written and recorded by Mark Fojo; "Fuzzin' The Tracks" (by Sting), recorded by Flic; "Not A Chance," written and recorded by Simon Galt; all on Tabitha Records (all pop singles). Other artists include Andy Ford, Deparate Measures and 'Ot Nuts.
Tips: "Send good quality demos."

TARGET RECORDS, Box 163, West Redding CT 06896. (203)438-5366. President: Paul Hotchkiss. Labels include Kastle Records. Record company, music publisher (Tutch Music/Blue Hill Music) and record producer (Red Kastle Prod.). Estab. 1975. Releases 6 singles and 2 LPs/year. Works with songwriters on contract. Pays statutory rate to publisher per song on record.

How to Contact: Write first and obtain permission to submit. Prefers cassette with 2 songs and lyric sheet. SASE. Reports in 3 weeks.
Music: Country and crossover. Released "Luv Radio" (by P. Hotchkiss/M. Terry), recorded by M. Terry (country pop); "Honky Tonk Darling" (by Paul Hotchkiss), recorded by Tony Worsley (country); and "Standing on Mountain" (by Cal Stewart), recorded by Lynn and Rebels (country rockabilly); all on Target/Roto Noto Records. Other artists include Fran Taylor, Malone & Hutch, Jimmy Hartley, Beverly's Hillbilly Band, Randy Burns, Susan Rose Manning and Donald Hotchkiss/Rodeo.

TAWAS RECORDS, 3515 Clovertree Lane, Flint MI 48532. (313)232-0083. President: Harry F. Chestler. Record company, music publisher (Chestler Publishing Co./BMI) and record producer (Harry F. Chestler). Releases varying number of singles/year. Pays statutory rate to publisher per song on record.
How to Contact: Write first and obtain permission to submit. Prefers cassette with 2 songs. Reports in 2 weeks.
Music: Mostly rock, country and gospel; also rap. Released "Lord I The Got Blues" and "Grizzly Bear" (by Harry F. Chestler), recorded by Hank Chess on Tawas Records (singles).

TEROCK RECORDS, Box 4740, Nashville TN 37216. (615)865-4740. Manager: S.D. Neal. Labels include Terock, Susan, Denco, Rock-A-Nash-A-Billy. Record company, record producer, and music publisher (Heavy Jamin' Music/ASCAP). Estab. 1959. "We also lease masters." Member ASCAP, BMI. Releases 8-12 singles and 3-6 12″ singles/year. Works with musicians/artists and songwriters on contract and hires musicians for in-house studio work. Pays artists on contract 15-25¢ per record sold; standard royalty to songwriters on contract.
How to Contact: Prefers cassette with 3-6 songs and lyric sheet. SASE. Reports in 3 weeks.
Music: Mostly rock'n'roll, country and rockabilly; also bluegrass, blues, easy listening, folk, gospel, jazz, MOR, progressive, Spanish, R&B, soul and top 40/pop. Released "That's Why I Love You," by Dixie Dee (country); "Born to Bum Around," by Curt Flemons (country); and "Big Heavy," by the Rhythm Rockers (rock).
Tips: "Send your best."

*3 G'S INDUSTRIES, 6015 Troost, Kansas City MO 64110. (816)361-8455. General Manager: Eugene Gold. Labels include NMI, Cory, 3 G's and Chris C's Records. Record company, record producer and music publisher (Eugene Gold Music and Gid-Gad Music). Releases 8 singles and 6 LPs/year. Works with musicians/artists and songwriters on contract; hires musicians for in-house studio work. Pays 4-6% royalty to artists on contract; statutory rate to publishers for each record sold.
How to Contact: Prefers cassette (or videocassette) with 4-8 songs and lyric sheet. SASE. Reports in 1 month.
Music: Mostly R&B and jazz; also church/religious, gospel and soul. Released "Solitude," written and recorded by Jeff Lucas; "Young Tender" (by M. Gilmore/J. Spradlin), recorded by Mark Gilmore; and "Remember" recorded by Wings of Graces, all on 3G's Records (singles). Other artists include Suspension, L. Washington, Thrust's, James "Fuzzy" West, Cal Green and L.S. Movement Band.

TIME CAPSULE RECORDS, 15533 Jacana Dr., La Mirada CA 90638. (714)521-1974. A&R Manager: Jacqueline Casey. Labels include Time Capsule Records. Record company, music publisher (Home Key Music/BMI) and record producer (Time Capsule Productions). Estab. 1983. Releases 1-2 singles, 1-2 LPs and 1-2 CDs/year. Works with musicians/artists and songwriters on contract. Pays statutory or negotiated rate to publisher per song on record.
How to Contact: Write first and obtain permission to submit. Prefers cassette or 15 ips reel-to-reel with 3-5 songs and lyric sheets. Does not return unsolicited material. Reports in 4 weeks.
Music: Mostly blues (electric); also delta blues. *Blues at the Bottom* (by Bruce King), recorded by "2120" (LP); *Downtown Shuffle* (by Mark Goldberg), recorded by Back Pocket Blues Band (LP); and "West Coast Thing" (by Brennan Totten), recorded by Dog-Tones (single); all on Time Capsule Records (all blues). Other artists include Luke and the Locomotives, Harry "The Harp" Harpoon and Magic Blues Band.
Tips: "Make sure material is strong and authentic blues; no 'Hybrids.' "

TIMELESS ENTERTAINMENT CORP., 10 Pebblewood, Irvine CA 92714-4530. (714)552-5231. Vice President: Fred Bailin. Labels include Perfect, Goldisc. Record company. Estab. 1978. Releases 3 singles, 3 12″ singles, 4 LPs and 4 CDs/year. Works with musicians/artists and songwriters on contract.

"How to Use Your Songwriter's Market" (at the front of this book) contains comments and suggestions to help you understand and use the information in these listings.

Pays 9% royalty to artists on contract; statutory or negotiated rate to publisher per song on record.
How to Contact: Submit demo tape by mail. Unsolicited submissions are OK. Prefers cassette with 3 songs and lead sheets. SASE. Reports in 2 weeks.
Music: Mostly R&B, pop and rock; also rap. Artists include Ecstacy, Passion and Pain.

*TITAN INTERNATIONAL PRODUCTIONS, LTD., 185A, Newmarket Rd., Norwich, Norfolk, NR4 6AP, **England**. Phone: 44-0603-51139. Director: Peter Newbrook. Labels include Esquire, Starlite and Titan. Record company and music publisher (Esquire Music Co.). Releases 12 LPs/year. Works with artists on contract. Pays negotiable royalty to artists on contract; 6¼% to publishers for each record sold. Royalties paid to US songwriters and artists through US publishing or recording affiliate.
How to Contact: "No more submissions can be accepted for the next year."
Music: Mostly jazz; also MOR. Artists include Cleo Laine, Teddy Wilson, John Dankworth, Mary Lou Williams, Stan Getz and Zoot Sims.

TOM THUMB MUSIC (Division of Rhythms Productions), Box 34485, Los Angeles CA 90034. President: R.S. White. Labels include Rhythms Productions and Tom Thumb. Record company. Estab. 1955. Works with songwriters on contract. Pays negotiable royalty to artists on contract. Requires completed tape masters.
How to Contact: Submit demo tape by mail. Unsolicited submissions are OK. Prefers cassette. SASE. Reports in 1 month.
Music: Mostly "children's concept albums with educational content. Can be songs or musical stories."
Tips: "Experience with children and educational content is desirable."

TOMARK RECORDS, 7560 Woodman Pl., #G3, Van Nuys CA 91405. (818)994-4862. Owners: Tom Willett and Mark Thornton. Labels include Tomark Records. Record company, music publisher (Schmerdley Music and Ocean Walk Music/BMI) and record producer. Estab. 1988. Releases 1 single and 1 LP/year. Works with musicians/artists and songwriters on contract.
How to Contact: Submit demo tape by mail. Unsolicited submissions are OK. Prefers cassette or 7½ ips reel-to-reel (or VHS videocassette) with songs. SASE. Reports in 4 weeks.
Music: Mostly country and novelty; also rock. Released "My Ex-Ex Wife" (by Tom Willett), recorded by Tomark (country novelty); "Christmas Will Be Blue in California," by Mark Thornton (Christmas country); and "Christopher Columbus," by Mark Thornton and Tom Willett (country).

TOMMY BOY MUSIC, INC., 1747 First Ave., New York NY 10128. (212)722-2211. A&R Director/ R&B, Dance: Tom Richardson. A&R Director/Rap: Kevin Maxwell. Record company, music publisher (T-Boy/T-Girl). Releases 15-20 singles and 5-10 LPs/year. Works with musicians/artists on contract; pays varying royalty to artists on contract.
How to Contact: Call first and obtain permission to submit. Prefers cassette with 1-3 songs and lyric sheet, clearly marked with submitter name and phone number. Materials not returnable. "When submitting a demo, please do not call to see if we are going to use it. If we are, you will be the first to know."
Music: Mostly rap, R&B and dance/pop. No rock or new age. 1989 releases included "Me Myself and I", "Say No Go" and "Buddy" by De La Soul; "Doowutchyalike" and "The Humpty Dance" by Digital Underground; "You Are the One" by TKA; "Dance for Me" and "Ladies First" by Queen Latifah.

TOP'S RECORDS, 9015 Owensmouth Ave., #106, Canoga Park CA 91304. (818)341-4766. Artist Development: Department Head. Record company. Estab. 1980. Releases 10 singles, 10 LPs and 10 CDs/ year. Works with musicians/artists on contract. Pays 20% to artists on contract; statutory rate to publisher per song on record.
How to Contact: Write first and obtain permission to submit. Does not return unsolicited material.
Music: Mostly rock, country and pop; also gospel and R&B. Released "Maria" (by G. Revel, A Meza, D. Tuttle), recorded by Dale Tuttle (country single); "I Know (We're Gonna Make It Love)" (by Gary Revel), recorded by Dale Tuttle (country single); and "Hollywood Star," written and recorded by Gary Revel (rock single); all on Top's Records.

TOUCHE RECORDS, Box 96, El Cerrito CA 94530. Executive Vice President: James Bronson, Jr. Record company, record producer (Mom and Pop Productions, Inc.) and music publisher (Toulouse Music Co./BMI). Member AIMP. Releases 2 LPs/year. Works with artists and songwriters on contract; musicians on salary for in-house studio work. Pays statutory rate to publishers per song on record.
How to Contact: Prefers cassette with 2-4 songs and lyric sheet. SASE. Reports in 1 month.
Music: Mostly jazz; also bluegrass, gospel, jazz, R&B and soul. Released *Bronson Blues* (by James Bronson), *Nigger Music* and *Touché Smiles* (by Smiley Winters), all recorded by Les Oublies du Jazz Ensemble on Touché Records (all LPs). Other artists include Hi Tide Harris.

TRAC RECORD CO., 170 N. Maple, Fresno CA 93702. (209)255-1717. Owner: Stan Anderson. Record company and music publisher (Sellwood Publishing/BMI). Estab. 1972. Releases 10-20 singles and 5 LPs and 2 CDs/year. Works with musicians/artists on contract, songwriters on royalty contract and in-house musicians on contract. Pays 13% royalty to artists on contract. Pays statutory rate to publisher per song on record.
How to Contact: Prefers cassette (or VHS videocassette) with 2-4 songs and lyric sheet. SASE. Reports in 2 months.
Music: Country, top 40 and rock. Released "Nevada State of Mind" written and recorded by Barry Best (country); "Don't Walk Away" written and recorded by B.G. White (country); and "Overnight Sensation" written and recorded by Ric Blake (top 40), all on Trac Records. Other artists include Gil Thomas, Ron Arlen and Robin Sharkey.

TRUE NORTH RECORDS, The Finkelstein Management Co. Ltd., Suite 302, 151 John St., Toronto, Ontario M5V 2T2 **Canada**. (416)596-8696. Contact: Jehanne Languedoc. Record company, management company, record producer, music publisher (Mummy Dust Music) and production company. Member CIRPA, CMPA, PROCAN, CAPAC. Releases approximately 18 singles and 6 LPs/year. Works with artists on contract. Pays negotiable royalty to artists on contract; negotiable rate to publishers for each record sold.
How to Contact: Call first and obtain permission to submit. Prefers cassette with 2-4 songs. Prefers studio produced demos. Include bio. Does not return unsolicited material. Reports in 1 month but tape will not be returned.
Music: Top 40/pop and CHR/AOR. Record and own all Bruce Cockburn material including "Stealing Fire" (If I Had a Rocket Launcher) and "Big Circumstance" (If a Tree Falls). Other artists include Barney Bentall and The Lengendary Hearts.

TRUSTY RECORDS, 8771 Rose Creek Rd., Nebo KY 42441. (502)249-3194. President: Elsie Childers. Record company and music publisher (Trusty Publications/BMI). Member NSAI, CMA. Estab. 1950. Releases 2 singles and 2 LPs/year. Works with musicians/artists and songwriters on contract. Pays 3% royalty to artists on contract; statutory rate to publishers for each record sold.
How to Contact: Prefers cassette with 2-4 songs and lead sheet. SASE. Reports in 1 month.
Music: Mostly country; also blues, church/religious, dance, easy listening, folk, gospel, MOR, soul and top 40/pop. Released "country album by Noah Williams with 10 songs from Trusty Publications Catalog on Trusty Records."
Tips: "Writer-artists and people with road tours are given top consideration."

TUG BOAT RECORDS, 1355 Peabody Dr., Hampton VA 23666. (804)838-9552. A&R: Judith Guthro. Record company, music publisher (Doc Publishing/BMI, Dream Machine/CAPAC) and record producer (Doc Holiday Productions). Estab. 1967. Releases 2 singles, 15 12" singles, 15 LPs, 5 EPs, and 2 CDs/year. Works with musicians/artists and songwriters on contract and hires musicians for in-house studio work. Pays varying royalty to artists on contract; statutory rate to publisher per song on record.
How to Contact: Submit demo tape by mail. Unsolicited submissions are OK. Prefers cassette with 1 song and lyric sheet. Reports in 3 weeks.
Music: Mostly country, top 40 and rock and roll. Released "If You Could Only See" written and recorded by Rickie Balin (top 40); "If Look Could Kill" written and recorded by Jon Washington (top 40); and "My Guy" written and recorded by Diane Darrah (country) all on Tug Boat Records. Other artists include Ronn Craddock, Tracy Wilson, Doc Holiday and Al Latta.

TURF HANDLER RECORDS, 807 NW 2nd Ave., #1, Ft. Lauderdale FL 33311. (305)764-2310. Manager: Gerry Wyche. Record company, music publisher (Wyche Publishing Co.) and record producer (Strawberry Jam Productions). Estab. 1987. Releases 1 12" singles and 2 LPs/year. Works with musicians/artists, songwriters and producers on contract. Pays 10-20% royalty to artists on contract; statutory rate to publishers per song on record.
How to Contact: Submit demo tape by mail. Unsolicited submissions are OK. Prefers cassette with 2 or more songs. Does not return unsolicited material. Reports in 1 week only if interested.
Music: Mostly R&B, rap and dance; also pop, reggae and rock. Released "We Can Make You Dance" (by R. Doresey), recorded by Classy Rock (rap 12"); "Finally" (by W. Jean), recorded by Cold Fly (rap 12"); "Feel So Good" (by M. Caldwell), recorded by Shattered Glass (R&B 12"); "Do it to the Drummers Beat" (by MC Kyle); and "Turf Handler: The Album," (rap compilation album); all on on Turf Handler Label. Other artists include Lady T Jazz, Gregory Bryant and Vikki Henderson.

UGLY DOG RECORDS, Box 1583, Brantford ON N3T 5V6 **Canada**. (519)753-2081. President: John Mars or A&R: Marilyn Guest. Labels include Ugly Dog Records. Record company, music publisher (Utter Nonsense Publishing/CAPAC) and record producer (John Mars). Estab. 1979. Releases 1 single and 1 LP/year. Works with musicians/artists and songwriters on contract. Pays 5-10% royalty to

artists on contract; negotiated or 50% rate to publisher per song on record.
How to Contact: Submit demo tape by mail. Unsolicited submissions are OK. Prefers cassette (or BETA videocassette if available) with 4 songs and lyric or lead sheets. SASE. Reports in 1 month.
Music: Mostly rock and roll, new jazz and R&B. Released "Oh Yeah" (by Mars; Templeton), recorded by Children and Daniel Lanois (single); *Annihilated Surprise* (by Broomer; Mars), recorded by J. Mars and Mark Wright (LP); and *Electric Playground* (by Mars/Lanzalone/Sinkowski/Tremblay), recorded by J. Mars and Bob Doidge (LP); all on Ugly Dog Records. Other artists include The Recognitions, The Martians and The Popp Tarts.
Tips: "Send high quality demo with lots of songs. Send pictures or video."

UNDERGROUND RELEASE RECORDS, #245, 1724 Sacramento St., San Francisco CA 94109. (415)474-0662. Contact: Robert Palacios. Record company. Estab. 1985. Releases 3-4 12″ singles, 3-4 LPs, 5 EPs and 1-2 CDs/year. Works with musicians/artists on contract. Pays 7-13% royalty to artists on contract.
How to Contact: Prefers cassette with 3 songs and lyric sheet. "Send as much relevant material (i.e., photos, press) as possible." Reports in 1 month.
Music: Mostly alternative rock, heavy metal and hard rock; also club/dance tracks. Released "Tsunami" (by Seiichi Tanaka), recorded by Taiko Dojo (ethnic); and "Hop on the Back," and "Somebody Else's Dream," (by Tina Blaine, Candice Pacheco, Patti Clements), recorded by d'Cückoo (college alternative); all on Underground Release Records.
Tips: "We listen to everything. All tapes are appreciated, but photos speed up response. If you have not received response, follow up mailing with a letter. We want to hear from you."

UNIVERSAL-ATHENA RECORDS, Box 1264, Peoria IL 61654-1264. (309)673-5755. A&R Director: Jerry Hanlon. Record company and music publisher (Jerjoy Music/BMI). Estab. 1978. Releases 1-2 singles and 1 LP/year. Works with musicians/artists on contract; hires musicians on salary for in-house studio work. Pays statutory rate to publishers for each record sold.
How to Contact: Prefers cassette with 4-8 songs and lyric sheet. SASE. Reports in 2 weeks.
Music: Country. Released "The Last Letter" (by Rex Griffin) and "T For Texas" (by Jimmie Rodgers); both recorded by Jerry Hanlon on Universal-Athena Records (country).

VELVET PRODUCTIONS, 517 W. 57th St., Los Angeles CA 90037. (213)753-7893. Manager: Aaron Johnson. Labels include Velvet, Kenya, Normar and Stoop Down Records. Record company, booking agency and promoter. BMI. Estab. 1965. Releases 5 singles, 2 12″ singles and 3 EPs/year. Works with artists and songwriters on contract. Pays 5% royalty to artists on contract.
How to Contact: Submit demo and/or lead sheet by mail. Arrange personal interview. Prefers cassette with 3-5 songs and lead sheet. SASE. Reports in 2 months.
Music: Blues, gospel, rock, soul and top 40/pop. Released "How I Wish You" (by Arlene Bell/Delais Ene), recorded by Arlene Bell on Velvet Records (single).

***VIBE RECORDS**, 2540 Woodburn Ave., Cincinnati OH 45206. (513)559-3999 or (513)681-5436. A&R Director: Smiley Hicks. Record company. Estab. 1985. Releases 2 singles and 3 12″ singles/year. Works with musicians/artists on contract. Pays varying royalty to artists on contract; statutory rate to publisher per song.
How to Contact: Write first and obtain permission to submit. Prefers cassette with 4 songs and lyric sheet. SASE. Reports in 4 weeks.
Music: Mostly R&B, gospel and pop; also rap and dance. Released "Heartbeat" (by Hicks) (R&B dance); "All About Town" (by Barber) (pop); and "Stingy" (by Waiver) (R&B dance); all on Vibe Records. Other artists include Kenny Hill, Greg Jackson, Trina Best, Sandy Childress, Tim Napier and Kim Seay.

***VICOR MUSIC CORP.**, 782 Aurora Blvd., Cubao, Quezon City, **Philippines**. Phone: 721-3331 to 39. President: Florendo Garcia, Jr. Labels include Blackgold Records, Sunshine Records and Vicor International. Record company, music publisher (Bayanihan Music Phils., Inc.), record producer (Vicor Music and Blackgold Records), and booking firm (Vicor Entertainment Corporation). Releases 60 singles, 10 CDs and 50 LPs/year. Works with musicians/artists and songwriters on contract; musicians on salary for in-house studio work. Pays 4-10% royalty to artists on contract.
How to Contact: Write or call first and obtain permission to submit. Prefers cassette or reel-to-reel with 2 songs and lyric or lead sheet. SAE and IRC. Reports in 3 weeks.
Music: Mostly ballads, country, rock and disco. Released "Hanggang Kailan" (by A.Dionisio), recorded by Martin Nievera (pop ballad); "Narito Ako" (by N. Pedero), recorded by Regine Velasquez (ballad); and " 'Pakita Mo" (by A. Dairocas), recorded by Archie D. (disco), all on Sunshine Records. Other artists include Randy Santiago, Basil Valdez, Louie Heredia, Joanne Lorenzana and Neocolours Band.

VOKES MUSIC PUBLISHING & RECORD CO., Box 12, New Kensington PA 15068. (412)335-2775. President: Howard Vokes. Labels include Vokes and Country Boy Records. Record company, booking agency and music publisher. Releases 8 singles and 5 LPs/year. Works with artists and songwriters on contract. Pays 2½-4½¢/song royalty to artists and songwriters on contract.
How to Contact: Submit cassette only and lead sheet. SASE. Reports in 2 weeks.
Music: Country, bluegrass, gospel-old time. Released "From Dusk Til Dawn" by Lenny Gee and "For The Sake of The Children" by Laura Lee Reddig, both on Vokes Records; and "Tribute To Riley Puckett" by Uncle Rufus Brewster on Country Boy Records.

*WALDEN RECORDS, 548 Broadway, Macon GA 31201. (912)471-6247. Vice President: Georgeanna Walden. Record company. Estab. 1989. Releases 3 singles, 1 LP and 1 EP/year. Works with musicians/ artist on record contract and songwriters on royalty contract. Royalty varies. Pays statutory rate to publishers per song on records.
How to Contact: Write first and obtain permission to submit. Prefers cassette (or VHS videocassette if available) with 2 songs and lyric sheets. SASE. Reports in 8 weeks.
Music: Interested in rock and pop; also R&B. Released Loose Change, written and recorded by *Loose Change* on Walden Records (rock LP).

WALK ON WATER RECORDS, Rt. 2 Box 566-H, New Braunfels TX 78130. (512)625-2768. Producer/ Manager: Kenneth D. Brazle. Record company, music publisher, record producer and recording studio. Estab. 1984. Releases 1-2 singles and 1 CD/year. Works with musicians/artists and songwriters on contract. Pays royalty to artists on contract. "Each deal is negotiated separately." Pays statutory rate to publisher per song on record.
How to Contact: Write first and obtain permission to submit. "Include SASE for reply." Prefers cassette, 7½ ips reel-to-reel (or VHS videocassette) with 2-3 songs and lyric sheet. Does not return unsolicited material. Reports in 6 weeks.
Music: Mostly AOR-pop/rock, blues, jazz, new music and country. Released "Blind Ambition" and "Fortune Tellers," written and recorded by Innerview on Walk on Water Records (cassette/rock). Other artists include Fax, Secrets.
Tips: "Give me something original with a good melody that people can sing to themselves."

WATCHESGRO MUSIC, Box 1794, Big Bear City CA 92314. (714)585-4645. Watch Us Climb Music President: Eddie Carr. Interstate 40 Records and videos by Watchesgro Productions. Estab. 1987. Releases 12 singles/year. Works with songwriters on contract. Pays 100% royalty to artists on contract; statutory rate to publisher per song on record.
How to Contact: Submit demo tape by mail. Unsolicited submissions are okay. Prefers cassette with minimum of 2 songs. Does not return unsolicited material. Reports in 1 week.
Music: Mostly country and country rock.

*WEBCO RECORDS, 414 Adahi Rd., Vienna VA 22180. (703)938-7846. President: Bill Emerson. General Manaer: John Emerson. Record company, music publisher (Old Home Place Music/BMI) and record producer (Webco Records). Estab. 1976. Releases 6-12 cassettes and 6-12 CDs/year. Works with musicians/artists and songwriters on contract. Pays 40% royalty to artists on contract; statutory rate to publishers per song on record.
How to Contact: Submit demo tape by mail. Unsolicited submissions are OK. Prefers cassette with at least 5 songs and lyric sheet. SASE. Reports in 1 month.
Music: Mostly bluegrass, country and gospel; also instrumental. Released *Larry and Wyatt Rice* (by Larry Rice), recorded by Larry and Wyatt Rice (traditional country duet); *Thinkin' 'Bout You* (by Gary Ferguson), recorded by Gary Ferguson (contemporary bluegrass); and *Timber* (by various writers), recorded by Larry Stephenson (bluegrass), all on Webco Records. Other artists include Chris Warner, Patent Pending, Jimmy Gaudreau, South Central Bluegrass, Bill Emerson & Pete Goble and James King.
Tips: "Artists should be willing and able to perform on a regular basis in order to sell product."

WEDGE RECORDS, P.O. Box 290186, Nashville TN 37229-0186. (615)754-2950. President: Ralph D. Johnson. Labels include Wedge Records, Dome Records and Fleet Records. Record company, music publisher (Big Wedge Music/BMI and Pro-Rite Music/ASCAP), record producer (Ralph D. Johnson) and Pro-Star Talent Agency. Estab. 1960. Releases 10 singles, 2 LPs and 2 CDs/year. Works with musicians/artists and songwriters on contract. Pays 10% royalty to artists on contract; statutory rate to publisher per song on record.
How to Contact: Write or call first to arrange personal interview. Prefers cassette and lyric or lead sheet. SASE.
Music: Mostly country and country crossover; also rock, gospel, pop and R&B. Released "They Final Got Around to You" (by L. Joe Christine); "Closest Thing to Love" (by Dean Mitchell); and "In the Middle of the Night Time" (by Joey Weltz), all on Wedge Records (all singles).

*WESTPARK MUSIC PRODUCTION, (formerly Plaene Records) Box 260227, Rathenauplatz 4D-5000 Cologne 1 **West Germany**. Phone: (49)221 247644. FAX: (49)221 231819. Contact: Ulli Hetscher. Labels distributed by BMG Ariola or German mail order chain *Zweitausendeins*. Estab. 1986. Releases 6-8 singles, no dance music and no 12″ singles, 8-10 LPs and 8-10 CDs/year. Works with musicians/ artists on contract; tape lease.
How to Contact: Submit demo tape by mail. Unsolicited submissions are OK. Prefers cassette with 5-6 songs and lyric sheets.
Music: Everything apart from mainstream-pop, jazz, classical. "The only other criterion is: we simply should love it; we're 49 percent businessmen and 51 percent music lovers."
Tips: "An overworked and underpaid company. So do not expect a quick response. If you have something to offer that should be released or produced *immediately*, contact any other company."

*WHITE CAR RECORDS, 10611 Cal Rd., Baton Rouge LA 70809. (504)295-1400. Owner: Nelson Blanchard. Labels include Techno Sound Records. Record company, music publisher (White Car Music/BMI, Charblanche/ASCAP) and independent record producer. Estab. 1980. Releases 6 singles and 1 LP/year. Works with musicians/artists and songwriters on contract. Pays up to 15% royalty to artists on contract; statutory rate to publisher per song.
How to Contact: Submit demo tape by mail. Unsolicited submissions are OK. Prefers cassette with 4 songs. Does not return unsolicited material. Reports in 2 weeks.
Music: Mostly country, rock and pop; also R&B. Released "The Back Burner" (by Waters, Garvin, Shapiro), recorded by Tareva on White Car Records; "Leading Man" (by Butch Reine), recorded by Atchafalaya on White Car Records; and "She's Still a Lady," written and recorded by Gale Lee Lamey; all country singles. Other artists include John Steve, Nelson Blanchard, B.J. Morgan and Bayon Country Band.

*THOMAS WIGGINS ASSOCIATES, (formerly No-Bull Records), Box 21118, Castro Valley CA 94546. (415)538-6195. President/A&R: Tom Wiggins. Labels include No-Bull Records, Nineveh Records, Persepolis Records, and Great Ethnic Records. Record company, music publisher (Udder Publishing/ ASCAP, Middleastern Music Organization, Great Ethnic Publishing Co., Big Jam Publishing, and Duxbury Publishing), record producer (Thomas Wiggins Associates), and management firm and booking agency (Thomas Wiggins Associates). Estab. 1980. Releases 4-10 LPs/year. Works with musicians/ artists and songwriters on contract; "We sometimes co-op deals with artists." Pays flat fee of 50¢ per album to artists on contract; statutory rate to publisher per song on record.
How to Contact: Prefers cassette (or VHS videocassette) with 3-6 songs and lyric sheet. SASE. "If we are interested in the material, we will contact them for further information and an interview within about 6 weeks."
Music: Mostly country, blues and ethnic; also cajun and bluegrass. Released *Times Gettin Tougher*, written and recorded by C. Musselwhite (blues LP); *Foolers Love* (by J. Miller), recorded by the Miller Brothers (country LP); and *Just for You* (by P. Houchin), recorded by Go For Broke (country LP), all on No-Bull Records. Other artists include Don Barnes (country) and Jon Jarvis (jazz pianist).
Tips: "Remember 'Time Is Money'—don't waste ours and we won't waste yours. Set realistic goals for your career and stick to them as much as possible. Watch out for the sharks, and be professional."

*WILD PITCH RECORDS LTD., 231 West 29th St., New York NY 10001. (212)594-5050. President: Stu Fine. Record company and music publisher (Frozen Soap Songs/ASCAP). Estab. 1989. Releases 1 single, 8-10 12″ singles and 5 LPs/year. Works with musicians/artists and songwriters on contract. Pays ¾ rate to publishers per song on records.
How to Contact: Submit demo tape by mail. Unsolicited submissions are OK. Prefers cassette (or ½″ videocassette if available) with 1-3 songs and lyric sheet. Does not return unsolicited material. Reports in 2 weeks.
Music: Mostly rap, dance and R&B. Released *Manifest* (by Elam Martin), recorded by Gary Starr and *Let Me Show You* (by R. Frazier), recorded by Chill Rob G all on Wild Pitch Records (LP; 12″). Other artists include Gary Starr, Lord Finesse and Chill Rob G.
Tips: "Work hard; write about something real!"

*WILSON'S MUSIC CO.; MAURIC/NE PRODUCTIONS, Suite 55-0 200 S. Glenn Dr., Camarille CA 93010. (805)987-3058. President: Morris Lee Wilson. Labels include Wilson Records, Time West Records and Imma Banks Records. Record company, music publisher (BMI) and record producer (Wilson Music Co.). Estab. 1978. Releases 10 singles, 5 LPs and 2 CDs/year. Works with musicians/ artists and songwriters on contract and hires musicians on salary for in-house studio work. Pays statutory rate.
How to Contact: Submit demo tape by mail. Unsolicited submissions are OK. Prefers cassette (VHS videocassette) with any number of songs and lyric and lead sheet. SASE for return "but we prefer to keep it on file." Reports in 2 weeks.

Music: Mostly easy listening, country and MOR; also R&B, jazz and children's. Released "Special Lady" (by Alex Zanetis and Morris Wilson), on Jack O'Diamonds Records (country; "Freedom Man" (by Morris Wilson and Bennie Lee Young), on Jack O-Diamonds (country); and "Burning Bridges" (by Morris Wilson and Maurine Moore), on Wilson's Records (MOR) all recorded by Morris Wilson. Other artists include Bonnie Lou Young, Linda Moore, Duane Crone, Bonnie Skinner, Greg Coleman and Wayne St. John.
Tips: "Songs must have a good hook line, have something to say, and be different from the norm."

WINCHESTER RECORDS, Rt. 2, Box 114H, Berkeley Springs WV 25411. Owners: Bertha or Jim McCoy. Labels include Master, Mountain Top and Winchester. Record company, music publisher and record producer (Jim McCoy Productions). Estab. 1973. Releases 12 singles, 6 CDs and 6 LPs/ year. Works with musicians/artists and songwriters on contract; musicians on salary for in-house studio work. Pays standard royalty to artists on contract.
How to Contact: Write or call first and obtain permission to submit. Prefers cassette, or 7½ or 15 ips reel-to-reel (or VHS or Beta videocassette) with 6 songs and lyric or lead sheet. SASE. Reports in 1 month.
Music: Mostly country, rock and gospel; also country/rock and bluegrass. Released "They Call the Wind Mariah" (by Mariah); "She Must Have Loved You Out of My Mind" (written and recorded by Don Campbell); and "She's Different" (written and recorded by E. Howard), all on Winchester Records (country).

WINDHAM HILL PRODUCTIONS, Box 9388, Palo Alto CA 94305. Contact: A&R Department. Labels include Windham Hill and Windham Hill Jazz. Record company. Estab. 1976. Works with musicians/ artists on contract.
How to Contact: Write first and obtain permission to submit. "We are not accepting unsolicited material. Detailed queries are welcome. Do not send recordings until requested. We prefer a referral from a reputable industry person." Prefers cassette with 3 songs. SASE. Reports in 2 months.
Music: Mostly pop, jazz and original instrumental. Released *Metropolis*, recorded by Turtle Island String Quartet (new acoustic jazz LP); *Sampler '89*, written and recorded by various artists on Windham Hill Records (instrumental LP); and *Switchback* (by S. Cossu, Van Manakas), recorded by Scott Cossu on Windham Hill Records (jazz, ensemble LP). Other artists include William Ackerman, George Winston, Philip Aaberg, Michael Hedges, The Nylons and Montreux.

WINGS RECORD COMPANY, Route 3, Box 172, Haynesville LA 71038. (318)927-5253. President: E. Dettenheim. Record company and music publisher (Darbonne Publishing Co./BMI). Estab. 1987. Releases 4 singles and 4-8 LPs/year. Works with musicians/artists on record contract. Pays 5-10% royalty to artists on contract; statutory rate to publishers per song on record.
How to Contact: Prefers cassette, 7½ ips reel-to-reel with at least 3 songs and lyric sheeet. Does not return unsolicited material. Reports in 3 months.
Music: Mostly country, rock and gospel; also pop and R&B. Released "Man in the Mirror" written and recorded by Leon Martin on Wings Records (country); "Still Haven't Let You Go" written and recorded by Kate Chandler on Wings Records (contemporary country); and "Turner Hotel" written by E. Dettenheim performed by Skidrow Joe on Wings Records (country).

WOODRICH RECORDS, P.O. Box 38, Lexington AL 35648. (205)247-3983. President: Woody Richardson. Record company and music publisher (Woodrich Publishing Co./BMI, Mernee Music/ASCAP and Tennessee Valley Music/SESAC) and record producer (Woody Richardson). Estab. 1959. Releases 6 singles and 6 LPs/year. Works with songwriters on contract. Pays 10% royalty to writers on contract; statutory rate to publisher per song on records.
How to Contact: Prefers cassette with 4 songs and lyric sheet. "Be sure to send a SASE (not a card) with sufficient return postage." Reports in 2 weeks. "We prefer a good studio demo."
Music: Mostly country; also gospel, comedy, bluegrass, rock and jazz. Released "The Wise Man" (by J. Meyers), recorded by Jody Morris (gospel); "Country Soul" (by S. Mitchell), recorded by Tom Hill (country); and "Our Love is Forever" (by Jim Evans), recorded by Tim King (country); all on Woodrich Records.

YELLOW JACKET RECORDS, 10303 Hickory Valley, Ft. Wayne IN 46835. President: Allan Straten. Record company. Estab. 1985. Releases 3-4 singles and 1 LP/year. Works with musicians/artists and songwriters on contract; hires musicians for in-house studio work. Pays 10-20% royalty to artists on contract; statutory rate to publisher per song on records.
How to Contact: Prefers cassette with 3-4 songs and lyric sheet. SASE. Reports in 1 month.
Music: Country and MOR. Released "Countin' Down to Love," "Call Me Each Evening" and "Love To See You Again" (by Grogg/Straten), recorded by April on YJR Records (single).

*Z-GWEET RECORDS, P.O. Box 2743, Joliet IL 60434. (815)722-8339. A&R Director: Ralph Williams Jr.. Record company. Estab. 1988. Releases 1-2 singles/year. Works with musicians on salary for in-house studio work. Pays statutory rate to publishers per song on records.
How to Contact: Write or call first and obtain permission to submit. Prefers cassette with 1-3 songs and lyric sheet. Does not return unsolicited material. Reports in 1 month.
Music: Mostly funk, jazz and reggae; also fusion, R&B and rap. Released 'Jah Gonna Bring Them Down" (by R. Williams, A Harris and E. Fortune), recorded by No Limitations on Z-Gweet Records (jazz/reggae). Other artists include Mike Collins, Alfredrick Harris, Mike Dennie and Eugene Fortune.
Tips: "Be persistent—don't give up hope."

ZONE RECORD CO., 2674 Steele, Memphis TN 38127. (901)357-0064. Owner: Marshall E. Ellis. Releases 4 singles/year. Record company, music publisher and record producer. Works with songwriters on contract; musicians paid by song. Pays 4¢/side royalty to artists on contract.
How to Contact: Prefers cassette with 4 songs. "Be sure the words are clear. Don't try to make a master—just a good clean tape." SASE. Reports in 2 weeks.
Music: Country and country/pop. Released "Mile High City" (by D. Wilson/B. Fletcher), recorded by B. Fletcher; "Deeper Shade of Blue"; and "Now I've Got a New Heart" recorded by J. Lea, all on Zone Records (c&w). Other artists include Lou Roberts and Lesa Stansford.

Geographic Index Record Companies

The U.S. Section of this handy geographic index will quickly give you the names of record companies located in the music centers of Los Angeles, New York and Nashville. Of course, there are many valuable contacts to be made in other cities, but you will probably want to plan a trip to one of these established music centers at some point in your career and try to visit as many of these companies as you think appropriate. The International section lists, geographically, markets for your songs in foreign countries.

Find the names of companies in this index, and then check listings within the Record Companies section for addresses, phone numbers and submission details.

United States

Los Angeles
Atlantic Recording Corp.
Beachwood Records
Bright & Morningstar Records
British Records
Carousel Records, Inc.
Cosmotone Records
Gold Castle Records
Golden Boy Records
J/L Entertainment Group
Rogue Records
Rom Records
Tom Thumb Music
Velvet Productions

Nashville
AVM Records/Star Maker Int'l
The Calvary Music Group
Carlyle Records, Inc.
CBS Records

Charta Records
Curtiss Records
Fame and Fortune Enterprises
John Fisher & Associates
Jalyn Recording Co.
Kottage Records
Landmark Communications
    Group
Maxx Records
Orbit Records
Paragold Records & Tapes
Phoenix Records, Inc.
Pholk Records
Susan Records
Terock Records
Wedge Records

New York
Caroline Records, Inc.
Chrysalis Records
EMI
Factory Beat Records, Inc.

Jump Street Records
MCA Records
Mighty Records
Polygram Records
Pulse Music Group
Source Unlimited Records
Tom Boy Music, Inc.
Wild Pitch Records Ltd.

International

Austria
Cactus Records
Lemon Records
Musica Schallplatten Vertrieb
    Gmbh

Belgium
Downtown Record Comany
Jump Records & Music
Parsifal PVBA
Prestation Music

Canada
Amok Records
Berandol Records
Colt Records
Current Records
Disques Nosferatu Records
H&S Records
ISBA Records, Inc.
Justice Records Inc.
John Lennon Records
Mainroads Music Inc.
The Master's Collection Limited
Micah Records
Monticana Records
Nephelim Record (Studio Works)
Productions Diadem
PSP Records
Random Records
Roto-Noto Music
Slak Records
True North Records
Ugly Dog Records

Chile
Prodisc (Prodisc Limitada)

Colombia
Codiscos

Czechoslovakia
Opus-Records and Publishing House

Denmark
Genlyd Grammofon ApS
Mega Records APS.
Reca Music Production
Sundance Music

England
Big Bear Records
Bolts Records
Caritas Records
Demi Monde Records and Publishing, Ltd.
First Time Records Sovereign House
FM-Revolver Records Ltd.
Groove and Move Records
Heavy Metal Records
Le Matt Music Ltd.
Leopard Music
Nervous Records
New Music Enterprises
Plankton Records
Presidential Enterprises Ltd.
Red Bus Records (Int.) Ltd.
Red-Eye Records
Sphemusations
Swoop Records
Tabitha Records
Titan International Productions, Ltd.

France
Directions
Sephora Diffusion

Germany
AIA Records
Alphabeat
Autogram & Folk Records
Comma Records & Tapes
Playbones Records
Westpark Music Production

Holland
Collector Records

Hong Kong
Rock in Records

Iceland
Geimsteinn HF

Ireland
Lunar Records

Japan
Jimco Records
Kitty Records, Inc.

The Netherlands
Associated Artists Records International

Philippines
Vicor Music Corp.

Scotland
BGS Productions Ltd.

Switzerland
Capricorn Ltd.

Record Companies/'90-'91 Changes

The following markets appeared in the 1990 edition of *Songwriter's Market* but do not appear in the 1991 edition. Those companies that did not respond to our request for an update of their listing may not have done so for a variety of reasons—they may be out of business, for example, or they may be overstocked with submissions.

A Street Records (asked to be deleted)
A&M Records of Canada (asked to be deleted)
ABR S.A. (did not respond)
All Star Productions (moved; no forwarding address)
American Artists (moved; no forwarding address)
Americatone Records (did not respond)
Amherst Records (asked to be deleted)
Anthem Records (asked to be deleted)
Arminia Musikproduktion Erich Storz (did not respond)
Ash Records Ltd. (did not respond)
Asteroid (moved; no forwarding address)
Atoll Music (did not respond)

Attack Records (asked to be deleted)
Avan-Guard Music Pty. Limited (asked to be deleted)
Bella Musica Tontraeger GMBH (did not respond)
Big L Productions Ltd., Inc. (asked to be deleted)
Kark V. Black Enterprises, Inc. (moved; no forwarding address)
Blue August Records (did not respond)
Blue Gem Records (did not respond)
Bouvier Records (asked to be deleted)
Bovine International Record Company (asked to be deleted)
Casa Grande Records (did not respond)

Century-American Records (moved; no forwarding address)
Cisum Records (moved; no forwarding address)
Da Car Recording (moved; no forwarding address)
DB Recs (asked to be deleted)
Deet Records (asked to be deleted)
Domain Record Co. (deleted)
Dragon Records, Inc. (asked to be deleted)
DVS Records (moved; no forwarding address)
Dynamic Artists Records (did not respond)
E.L.J. Record Co. (asked to be deleted)
Ears and Eyes Production Co. Ltd. (did not respond)
Earth Records Co. (did not

respond)
East Coast Records Inc. (did not respond)
Electric Records (asked to be deleted)
Encore Records, Inc. (deleted)
Eye Kill Records (asked to be deleted)
Fun City Records Co. (asked to be deleted)
GCS Records (did not respond)
GMT Records (did not respond)
Goldrose Records (did not respond)
Greentrax Records (did not respond)
Grove Music Ltd. (did not respond)
Gule Records Inc. (moved; no forwarding address)
Hectic House Records (did not respond)
Hi Tension Records (did not respond)
Higher Octave Music (asked to be deleted)
Hit-N-Run Records (asked to be deleted)
Holsam Records (asked to be deleted)
Hula Records Inc. (did not respond)
Hummingbird Recording Co. International Inc. (asked to be deleted)
IEA Records (deleted)
I'll Call You (I.C.Y.) Records (did not respond)
Joyful Sound Records (asked to be deleted)
K&K Records GmbH (did not respond)
Johann Kaplan Music Group (did not respond)
Kenning Records (moved; no forwarding address)
KLW International, Inc. (did not respond)
KRC Records (asked to be deleted)
Le Disque Holland B.V. (did not respond)
Legs Records (asked to be deleted)
Light Records (asked to be deleted)
Liphone Records (did not respond)
Little Feet Entertainment Corp. (asked to be deleted)
Longhorn Records (asked to be deleted)
Luna Records Corp. (asked to

be deleted)
Manhattan Country, Inc. (did not respond)
Brian Manor Records (did not respond)
MDS Entertainment (asked to be deleted)
Mendocino Record Co (asked to be deleted)
Midnight Sun/Fourth Floor Records (did not respond)
Move Records (did not respond)
Mr. Wonderful Productions, Inc. (asked to be deleted)
MSB Records, Ltd. (did not respond)
Mystic Oak Records (did not respond)
Neat Records (did not respond)
Ocean Records Inc. (did not respond)
One Eye Records, Inc. (asked to be deleted)
100 Grand Records (asked to be deleted)
Orleans Records (asked to be deleted)
Parallax Records (did not respond)
The Pasha Music House (asked to be deleted)
Phonogram Paris (did not respond)
Platinum Boulevard Records (did not respond)
Pointsound Records (did not respond)
Polygram Records Pty. Ltd. (did not respond)
Prime Cut Records (did not respond)
Rarefaction Records (asked to be deleted)
RCA Records (did not respond)
Rebel Records (asked to be deleted)
Red Bud Records (asked to be deleted)
Reed Records (asked to be deleted)
Reliance Records (asked to be deleted)
Rob-Lee Records (moved; no forwarding address)
RSO Records (asked to be deleted)
Ruby Records Inc. (moved; no forwarding address)
Shapes of Things (did not respond)
Sherwood Forest Records (did

not respond)
Sicamerican S.A.C.I.F.I. (did not respond)
Sometimes Y Music (did not respond)
Sonic Wave Records (deleted)
Sounds of Connecticut (did not respond)
Square One Records Limited (did not respond)
Star Record Co. (did not respond)
Stargem Records, Inc. (did not respond)
Statue Records (did not respond)
Strawberry Hill Productions (did not respond)
Stress Records (did not respond)
Sugarfoot Productions (asked to be deleted)
Sunset Records, Inc. (did not respond)
Suntana Records (moved; no forwarding address)
Survival Records (asked to be deleted)
T.C. Records (did not respond)
Tab Records (did not respond)
TBA (did not respond)
Tempe Records (deleted)
(TMR)Thunder Mountain Records (did not respond)
Rik Tinory Productions (did not respond)
Top Records (did not respond)
Torchlite Records (asked to be deleted)
Trend Records (did not respond)
Trilogy Records International (did not respond)
True Records, Inc. (did not respond)
Vandor Motion Pictures, Phonorecords, and Music Publishing Group (deleted)
Warner Bros. Records (did not respond)
WEA Music of Canada, Ltd. (did not respond)
Lori Lee Woods Music (did not respond)
World Artist (did not respond)
Wunschklang Music Publishing (did not respond)
Yellow Balloon Productions Ltd. (did not respond)
Yonge Street Records (did not respond)
Zanzibar Records (did not respond)

Record Producers

The record producer's job is analogous to that of a film director; he is usually the one person with the most creative control over the project and is responsible for the quality of the finished product. A producer is normally contracted by the record company or the artist or group to oversee a recording project. In fulfilling his obligations, a producer may perform any combination of the following tasks: choose the studio in which to work, negotiate the studio rate, rent any extra equipment needed for the session, hire the engineer and any necessary studio musicians, handle all financial transactions connected with the recording project, choose or write some or all of the music to be recorded, write the arrangements to be used, make judgments of quality about every take and even perform on the recording himself. For his trouble, he is paid either a flat fee or is given a royalty (percentage "points") based on record sales.

By virtue of the fact that the producer has a lot of say about what songs are recorded, he is a great contact for songwriters. A good song placed in the hands of the right producer at the right time stands a good chance of being cut. But it can be difficult to get your tape to that "right" producer. Many write their own songs, and even if they don't they're usually involved in their own publishing companies so they have instant access to all the songs in their catalogs.

It's important to understand the intricacies of the producer/publisher situation. If you pitch your song directly to a producer first, before another publishing company publishes the song, the producer may ask you for the publishing rights to your song. The problem is, he may not be an active publisher—one who is interested in getting the song recorded again and again; he may just want the publishing because he knows it means extra income for him from the current recording project. You have to decide the relative merit of refusing him use of the song and thus losing the cut versus getting the cut but giving the publishing to the producer. You may be able to work out a co-publishing deal, in which you and the producer split the publishing income from the song. That means that he will still receive his percentage of the publishing income, even if you secure a cover recording of the song by other artists in the future. If you co-write songs with a producer, those songs probably have an even better chance of being recorded.

Producers are likely to have contacts that you don't have. They work closely with artists whose records they produce. If they publish your song, they'll be able to pitch it to recording artists even if they don't use it on their own sessions. You can bet that if they co-write a song with you, that's exactly what they'll do. Independent producers sometimes record new acts with new material and try to sell the finished masters to various record companies. They may also go directly to record companies seeking contracts to produce specific acts already signed to that label (sometimes major recording artists). Either way, the producer needs material. Since independent producers are well-acquainted with record company executives and artists, they can often get your material through doors not open to you.

Extremely creative and artistic people, producers typically have a lot more freedom than people in executive positions, and they are often able to hear hit potential in a song or artist. Some producers work on the staff of a record company, and they often find new talent for executives who may be less creative. They are especially good contacts for songwriter/artists looking for a record deal with that specific label. Some producers even start up their own record label so they can produce and release whatever records they choose. If a producer is working for a record company, the company should finance the recording session. If the producer is independent, he may pay for the project upfront himself, hoping to recoup his investment from sales royalties once the record is released. Or he may find it necessary to charge a production fee, paid by the recording artist. Usually, a songwriter is not expected to pay anything unless he is also the artist.

The listings that follow outline which aspects of the music industry each producer is involved in, what type of music he is looking for, what records and artists he's recently produced and what other artists he produces on a regular basis. Study the listings carefully, noting the names of artists each is working with, and consider if any of your songs might fit a particular artist's style. For a weekly update on who's producing what and whom, refer to the charts in *Billboard* and *Cash Box*.

A STREET MUSIC, Suite 9W, 701 7th Ave., New York NY 10036. (212)764-3872. A&R Director: K. Hall. Record producer, music publisher (A Street Music/ASCAP) and record company (A Street Records). Estab. 1986. Produces 6 LPs, 1 EP and 5 CDs/year. Deals with artists and songwriters. Fee derived from sales royalty or outright fee from recording artist or record company.
How to Contact: Prefers cassette with 3 songs. No lyric sheets. Artists send pictures. *SASE only* will receive reply; include adequate postage for tape return if desired.
Music: Mostly rock, heavy metal and pop/rock; will listen to R&B, R&B/pop and dance. Produced *Master of the Metal* recorded by Messiah Prophet on Pure Metal/Refuge Records; *What Goes Around* recorded by Bad Lee White on A Street Records; *No Rules* recorded by Hybrid Ice on Pilot Records (all LPs). Other artists include Private Life, Inside Out, Wild Rose, Without Warning, Zeudus, Ripper Jack and Dark 30.
Tips: "Don't over-produce your demo; we want to hear the song. A good vocalist will help. Enclose an SASE."

JERRY ABBOTT, 2210 Raper Blvd., Arlington TX 76013. (817)461-8481. President: Jerry Abbott. Record producer, music publisher (Valance Enterprises/BMI) and record company (CCR Records). Estab. 1973. Deals with artists and songwriters. Produces 25 singles and 4-5 LPs/year. Fee derived from outright fee from recording artist or record company.
How to Contact: Submit demo tape by mail. Unsolicited submissions are okay. Prefers cassette with lyric sheets. SASE. Reports in 6 weeks.
Music: Mostly country. Produced "Dreamer" (by Abbott/Jackson), recorded by Karol Ann Backstreet on CCR Records; "TLCPDQ" (by Abbott/Ryle), recorded by Shoppe on CCR Records; and "Country Time" (by Abbott/Jackson) recorded by Liz Calendar on CCR Records. Other artists include Danny Wood, Shiloh Wood, Johnny Park and Karol Bangs.
Tips: "Work on your own material. The more you work on songwriting, the better you will become and the better feel you will have for whether songs presented to you as an artist are right for you or not. As an artist, search for something unique in what you do—your presentation, your look, etc. The talent that is at the top of the charts certainly isn't the best that's out there. Work on your style as an artist and work on your business contacts. It takes money to get there."

ABERDEEN PRODUCTIONS, (A.K.A. Scott Turner Productions), 524 Doral Country Dr., Nashville TN 37221. (615)646-9750. President: Scott Turner. Record producer and music publisher (Buried Treasure/ASCAP, Captain Kidd/BMI). Estab. 1971. Deals with artists and songwriters. Works with 30 new songwriters/year. Produces 10 singles, 15-20 12" singles, 8 LPs and 8 CDs/year. Fee derived from sales royalty and production fee.
How to Contact: Prefers cassette with maximum 4 songs and lead sheet. SASE. Reports in 3 weeks.
Music: Mostly country, MOR and rock; also top 40/pop. Produced "Classic Cowboy," (by Fisher/Turner) recorded by Roy Clark (country); and "What If I Didn't Have You," (Murphy/Turner/D. Baumgartner) recorded by Roy Clark (country). Other artists include Slim Whitman, Jonathan Edwards, Hal Goodson, Jimmy Clanton, Bobby Lewis, and Del Reeves.
Tips: "Be unique. A great song doesn't care who sings it."

ACCENT RECORDS, 71906 Highway 111, Rancho Mirage CA 92270. (619)346-0075. CEO: Scott Seely. Record producer and music publisher (S&R Music). Deals with artists. Produces 10 singles and 5 LPs/year. Fee derived from sales royalty.
How to Contact: Prefers cassette with any number of songs and lyric sheet. SASE.
Music: Mostly A/C, country and MOR; also all other types. Produced *Armendares*, by J. Armendares (contemporary gospel, JRA Records); *Along the Line*, by Richard Christopher (pop, Accent Records); and *Classics in Rythmn*, by Buddy Merrill. Other artists include Chante, Kirby Hamilton, Eddie Rose, Don Malena, The Last Live Band, Jeri Sullivan and Jeffer.

*MICHAEL AHARON MUSIC, 1439 S. 2nd St., Philadelphia PA 19147. (215)336-6339. Owner: Michael Aharon. Record producer. Estab. 1984. Deals with artists and songwriters. Produces 3 LPs, 4 EPs and 3 CDs/year. Fee derived from outright fee from recording artist or record company. "Advance fee includes all studio time, musician fees and tape costs."
How to Contact: Submit demo tape by mail. Unsolicited submissions are OK. Prefers cassette with 3-6 songs. SASE. Reports in 3 weeks.
Music: Mostly folk-rock, singer-songwriters and pop/urban contemporary; also New Age, world-beat and experimental. Produced *I Will Stand Fast* written and recorded by Fred Small on Flying Fish Records (folk/rock LP); *Threads of Justice* written and recorded by Tom Juravitch on Flying Fish Records (folk-rock LP) and *Odyssey* written and recorded by Julia Haines on A. Howl Records (New Age/Acoustic LP).
Tips: "Send material which exhibits your personal style and creativity, even if it is not 'commercial' material. Individuality is starting to matter again. Lyrics are starting to matter again. Singer-songwriters are on the radio again."

AKO PRODUCTION, 20531 Plummer, Chatsworth CA 91311. (818)998-0443. President: A. Sullivan. Record producer and music publisher (Amiron). Deals with artists and songwriters. Produces 2-6 singles and 2-3 LPs/year. Fee derived from sales royalty.
How to Contact: Write first and obtain permission to submit. Prefers cassette (or Beta or VHS videocassette) and lyric sheet. SASE.
Music: Pop/rock and modern country. Produced *Lies in Disguise*, by Gang Back (pop LP); and *Touch of Fire* (LP) and "Try Me," (pop single) by Sana Christian; all on AKO Records.

ALL STAR SOUND STUDIOS, Box 1605, Bloomfield NJ 07003. President: S. Becker. Recording studio (pre and post production). Estab. 1980. Deals with artists and songwriters. Produces 5 singles, 5 12″ singles and 3 LPs/year. Fee derived from outright fee from record company.
How to Contact: Submit demo tape by mail. Unsolicited submissions are okay. Prefers cassette with lyric sheets. Does not return unsolicited material.
Music: Mostly pop, rock and R&B. Produced "Slow Dance," written and recorded by Southside Johnny on Cypress Records; "Did I Dream You," written and recorded by Tawatha on CBS Records; and "Theatre of the Mind," written and recorded by Mtume on Epic Records; all R&B singles.

*JIM ALLISON/ALLISONGS INC., 1603 Horton Avenue, Nashville TN 37212. (615)292-9899. A&R: Anne Reeves. Record producer, music publisher (Jim's AlliSongs/BMI; Annie Green Eyes Music/ BMI) and record company (ARIA Records). Estab. 1985. Deals with artists and songwriters. Fee derived from sales royalty.
How To Contact: Submit demo tape by mail. Unsolicited submissions are okay. Prefers cassette with 3 songs and lyric sheet. "Prefer chrome tape; clear and clean sound." Does not return unsolicited material. Reports in 6 weeks.
Music: Mostly country and pop. Produced "Hard Headed Heart" (by Allison/Chauvin), recorded by Bruce VanDyke (single); "It's All in the Touch" (by Bourke/Bogart/Giles), recorded by Bruce VanDyke (single/LP); and *Down in Paradise* (by Allison/Burns), recorded by Brent Burns (LP), all recorded on Aria Records.
Tips: "Submit top-of-the-line material; be organized; be willing to work hard."

STUART J. ALLYN, Skylight Run, Irvington NY 10533. (212)486-0856. Associate: Jack Walker. Record producer. Estab. 1972. Deals with artists and songwriters. Produces 6 singles, 3-6 LPs and 3-6 CDs/ year. Fee derived from sales royalty and outright fee from recording artist and record company.
How to Contact: Write first and obtain permission to submit. Prefers cassette or 15 ips reel-to-reel (VHS videocassette) with 3 songs and lyric or lead sheets. Does not return unsolicited material. Reports in 12 months.
Music: Mostly pop, rock, jazz and theatrical; also R&B and country. Produced *Mel Lewis & Jazz Orchestra*, on Atlantic Records (jazz LP); *Me & Him*, on Columbia Records (film score LP); and "Set Sail & Sea Fans," on Passage Home Records (video release); all by various artists, recorded by S. Allyn. Other artists include Carole Demas, Harry Stone, Bob Stewart, The Dixie Peppers, Nora York, Buddy Barnes and various video and film scores.

*AMERICAN COMMUNICATION ENTERPRISES, Box 444, Taylor MI 48180-0444. (313)942-0634. Producer: John D. Lollio. Record producer and music publisher (Lo Pine Music). Fee derived from sales royalty when song or artist is recorded. Deals with artists and songwriters. Produces 5 singles and 1 LP/year.

How to Contact: Prefers cassette and lyric sheet or lead sheet. SASE. Reports in 2 weeks.
Music: Mostly country and gospel. Produced "Truth of the Matter" (by Lollio/Parnell) recorded by Johni Dee on ACE Records; "Let's Make Love" (by Lollio/Parnell) recorded by Dee & Sullivan on ACE Records; and "It Takes Two" (by Carnes) recorded by A.C. Jones on Timestar Records. Other artists include David Atkins and Marty Parker.

*AMETHYST RECORDS, INC., P.O. Box 82158, Oklahoma City OK 73148. (405)632-2000. General Manager: Russell Canaday. Record company (Amethyst Records, Inc.). Estab. 1988. Deals with artists and songwriters. Produces 10 singles, 25 LPs, 3 EPs and 3 CDs/year. Recording cost derived from recording artist or Amethyst record company. "If artist is unknown, we sometimes charge an outright fee. It depends on exposure and work."
How to Contact: Submit demo tape by mail. Unsolicited submissions are OK. Prefers cassette with 3 songs and lyric or lead sheets. SASE. Reports in 2 months.
Music: Mostly country, gospel, easy listening; also R&B. Produced *Jehovah God* (by Danny Chambers), recorded by Sherman Andrus (gospel LP); *Blues Man* (by Hank Williams, Jr.), recorded by Henson Cargi (country); and *Just Us Two* (by Mark Bryant), recorded by Sherman Andrus (R&B); all on Amethyst Records. Other artists include Cissie Lynn, Jody Miller, David B. Hooten, Wanda Jackson, Branson Brothers and Willie Lewis.
Tips: "Don't get on the record company's bad side by encouraging us to use your material. Don't call us, we will contact you if you have the right stuff. Don't send your only copy of the songs you want us to consider."

BILL ANDERSON JR., Box 148296, Nashville TN 37214. (615)868-0425. Record producer. Estab. 1976. Deals with artists only. Produces 4 singles and 5 LPs/year. Fee derived from outright fee from recording artist and record company.
How to Contact: Submit demo tape by mail. Unsolicited submissions are OK. Prefers cassette with 4 songs and lyric sheets. SASE.
Music: Mostly country, gospel and pop/crossover. Produced "Jesus Is Lord'" (by Randy Weiss), recorded by Joanne Cash Yates with Johnny Cash on Crosstalkin' Records (gospel); and *Debi Chasteen*, recorded by Debi Chasteen on Lan Records (country). Other artists include Dottie L. Snow, Vernon Oxford and Meredith.

*ANGELA PRODUCTIONS, Rt. 2, 47 Colonial Estates, Belden MS 38826. (601)840-2006. President: Ronnie Hughes. Record producer, music publisher, record company (Angela Records) and Next To Impossible Music—BMI. Estab. 1986. Deals with artists and songwriters. Produces 2 singles and 2 LPs/year. Fee derived from sales royalty or outright fee from recording artist.
How to Contact: Submit demo tape by mail. Unsolicited submissions are OK. Prefers cassette with 3-5 songs and lyric sheet. SASE. Reports in 4 weeks.
Music: Mostly country, gospel; also rock, pop & R&B. Produced "Lying Here In Love" and "The Other Woman," written and recorded by Glenda Malone on Evergreen Records (country singles); and "Because He Cares," written and recorded by Sid Davis on Angela Records (gospel single). Other artists include Ronnie Hughes and Ron Lee.
Tips: "Send me a great song and I'll work hard to get you a cut."

APON RECORD COMPANY, INC., Box 3082, Steinway Station, Long Island City NY 11103. (718)721-5599. Manager: Don Zemann. Record producer and music publisher (Apon Publishing). Estab. 1957. Deals with artists and songwriters. Produces 100 singles, 50 LPs and 50 CDs/year. Fee derived from sales royalty and outright fee from recording artist or record company.
How to Contact: Prefers cassette with 2-6 songs and lyric sheet. SASE. Reports in 1 month.
Music: Classical, folk, Spanish, Slavic, polkas and Hungarian gypsy (international folk music). Produced *Czech Polkas* (by Slavko Kunst), recorded by Prague Singers on Apon Records; *Hungarian Gypsy* (by Deki Lakatos), recorded by Budapest on Apon Records; and *Polka - Dance With Me* (by Slavko Kunst), recorded by Prague on Apon Records.

APRIL RECORDING STUDIOS/PRODUCTIONS, 827 Brazil Pl., El Paso TX 79903. (915)772-7858. Owner: Harvey Marcus. Record producer, music publisher (Crystal Ram Records Publishing/BMI), record company (April and Crystal Ram Records) and recording studio. Deals with artists and songwriters. Produces 1-3 singles/year 1-3 12″ singles, 1-5 LPs, 1-5 EPs and 1-3 CDS/year. Fee derived from sales royalty and/or outright fee from record company.
How to Contact: Prefers cassette or 7½ ips reel-to-reel (or VHS videocassette) with 1-3 songs and lyric or lead sheets. "Include current up-dated listing of all available past recordings, publishing, and performances of your material." SASE. Reports in 2 months.

Music: Mostly jazz, R&B and new wave/rock; also "all ballads, and material with crossover possibilities such as Mex/Tex, country and instrumental." Produced *Are We in This for Love* (EP) and "Baby Blue Baby" (single), written and recorded by The Street Boys on T.S.B. Records; and *Endless Dreams* (LP), written and recorded by Ruben Castillo on Crystal Ram Records. Other artists include Cecilia Noel, Mark David, Ruben Cruz and Robert Cast.

Tips: "Please be patient! We answer and listen to all material. Also, leave out all the flashy solos unless the song is an instrumental."

ART OF MUSIC PRODUCTIONS, 6531 S. Owensboro, West Jordan UT 84084. Record producer, band coach, CEO: R. Mark Hansen. Estab. 1989 (as AMP). Deals with artists and songwriters. Produces 1 LP and 1 EP/year. Fee derived from sales royalty, outright fee from songwriter/artist and/or outright fee from record company.

How to Contact: Prefers cassette with 3-4 songs and lyric sheet. SASE.

Music: Any, especially metal, new music, rap, music in Spanish. Produced *The Unveiling* recorded by Sadistic Intent (speed metal EP) and *Blood for Real Estate* recorded by BioHazard (hardcore EP), both as independent releases.

Tips: "Believe what you are saying in your music. Have a professional attitude, and deal on a professional level."

ARZEE, ARCADE AND CLYMAX RECORDS, 3010 N. Front St., Philadelphia PA 19133. (215)426-5682. Production Manager: Lucky Taylor. Record producer and music publisher (Rex Zario Music/BMI, Seabreeze Music/BMI, Jack Howard Publishing/BMI, Arcade Music Co./ASCAP, Valley Brook Publishing/ASCAP). Deals with artists and songwriters. Produces 8-12 singles and 1-3 LPs/year. Fee derived from sales royalty.

How to Contact: Prefers 7½ ips reel-to-reel or cassette with 4-6 songs and lyric sheet. SASE. Reports in 1 month.

Music: Mostly country; also bluegrass, MOR and rock. Produced "Ten Gallon Stetson," by Bill Haley (country, Arzee Records); "This World of Mine," by Shorty Long (country, Arzee Records); and "Blues on the Block," by Charlie Stone (MOR, Arzee Records). Other artists include Dick Thomas, Rusty Wellington, Al Taber, Ben Taber, Willis Meyers, James E. Myers, Al Rex, Frank Marshall, Ray Coleman, Ray Hatcher, Bob Saver, Tex Carson, Eddie Thompson, Dallas Turner, Tommy Carr, Bob Dean, Jimmy Collett and Rex Zario.

*ASSOCIATED MUSIC PRODUCERS, 50 Music Sq. W. #207, Nashville TN 37203. (615)329-2591. President: Fred Morris. Record producer and record company (Rite Turns). Estab. 1983. Deals with artists and songwriters. Produces 5 singles, 2 LPs and 2 CDs/year. Fee derived from outright fee from recording artist or record company. "We charge an advance fee for recording studios, musicians and production fee."

How to Contact: Submit demo tape by mail. Unsolicited submissions are OK. Prefers cassette with 3 songs and lyric sheet. SASE. Reports in 2 weeks.

Music: Mostly country, pop and R&B; also rock.

Tips: "Associated Music Producers is a production company only. Produces acts for various labels or artists seeking a label. Artist needs professional press kit and recordings to compete in today's market."

*aUDIOFILE TAPES, 209-25 18 Ave., Bayside NY 11360. Sherriff, aT County: Carl Howard. Cassette-only label of alternative music. Estab. 1984. Deals with artists and songwriters. Produces about 25 cassettes/year. "Money is solely from sales. Some artists ask $1 per tape sold."

How to Contact: Submit demo tape by mail. Unsolicited submissions are OK. Prefers cassette. "Relevant artist information is nice. Master copies accepted on metal cassette. We trade submissions for cassettes on the label." Reports in 1-2 weeks.

Music: Mostly psych/electronic rock, non-rock electronic music, progressive rock; also free jazz and world music. Produced "The Greenhouse Effect," written and recorded by Alien Planetscapes (electronic improvisation cassette); "(self-titled)," written and recorded by Every New Dead Ghost (psych rock cassette); and "Ssaxophones," written and recorded by Jack Wright (free sax improvisation cassette); all on audiofile Tapes. Other artists include Nomuzic, David Prescott, Sponge, Cephalic Index, Big City Orchestra and The Venus Fly Trap.

Tips: "Please, no industrial music, no deliberately shocking images of racism and sexual brutality. And no New Age sleeping pills. Outside of that, go go go."

SUZAN BADER/D.S.M. PRODUCERS, 161 W. 54th St., New York NY 10019. (212)245-0006. Director of Publishing: Trina R. James. Contact: Associate Producer. Record producer, music publisher (ASCAP) and music library music. Estab. 1979. Deals with artists and songwriters. Produces 3-5 12" singles, 3 LPs and 20 CDs/year. Fee derived from sales royalty (publishing) or outright fee from recording artist (production) or record company (production and studio costs).

How to Contact: Write or call first and obtain permission to submit. Prefers cassette (or VHS videocassette) with 2 songs and lyric or lead sheets. SASE. Reports in 6-8 weeks.
Music: Mostly dance, rock and pop; also country, jazz and instrumental. Produced "I'm Over You," written and recorded by Shpresa (dance); "You're All I Need" (by Tracy Smith), recorded by Spoiled Brat (rock); and "I'm A Victim of Romance" (by Mauge), recorded by Celeste (R&B dance); labels to be announced. Other artists include Maugé and Frank Lakewood.
Tips: "Have your manager or lawyer contact us to produce you. If you are a new artist, follow the above procedure. It's getting more difficult for an artist who cannot present a master demo to a label. You're going to need financing in the future. Prepare."

BAL RECORDS, P.O. Box 369, LaCanada CA 91012-0369. (818)548-1116. President: Adrian Bal. Record producer and music publisher (Bal & Bal Music). Estab. 1965. Bal West estab. 1988. Deals with artists and songwriters. Produces 3-6 singles/year. Fee derived from sales royalty.
How to Contact: Prefers cassette with 3 songs and lyric sheet. SASE.
Music: Mostly MOR, country, jazz, R&B, rock and top 40/pop; also blues, church/religious, easy listening and soul. Produced "Right To Know" and "Fragile" (by James Jackson), recorded by Kathy Simmons on BAL Records (rock); To The Beat of My Heart" (by Dan Gertz), recorded by Ace Baker on BAL Records (rock); and "You're A Part of Me," "Can't We Hve Some Time Together," "You and Me," and "Circles of Time," written and recorded by Paul Richards on BAL Records (adult contemporary).
Tips: "Write and compose what you believe to be commercial."

BARNETT PRODUCTIONS INC., 2305 Dickey Ave., No. Chicago IL 60064. (312)689-2726. Vice President: Walter T. Barnett. Record producer, music publisher (BMI) and record company (WMB Records). Estab. 1980. Deals with artists and songwriters. Produces 2 LPs and 10 singles/year. Fee derived from sales royalty or outright fee from record company.
How to Contact: Submit demo tape by mail. Unsolicited submissions are OK. Prefers cassette with 4 songs and lyric sheets. SASE. Reports in 1 month.
Music: Mostly R&B, rock, ballad, blues, pop and rap; also reggae, house and soul. Produced "Takin' Applications," written and recorded by Jackie "B" (dance/R&B); *Shibeli*, (by W. Barnett/M.Gordon/ W. Thomas/Shibeli) recorded by Shibeli (dance/R&B); and *Full Deck*, (by M. SAnders/T. Pierson/R. Coleman/G. Cunningham) recorded by Full Deck; all on WMB Records. Other artists include Full Deck, Clint, Too Fresh, Wild Style and Andrea.
Tips: "Be persistent and patient; send only your best material."

JOHN BAUERS MUSIC PRODUCTIONS, 1200 Park Ave., Hoboken NJ 07030. Creative Department: John Bauers and Tim Dobel. Record producer and music publisher. Estab. 1981. Deals with artists and songwriters. Produces 3-7 singles and 1-2 LPs/year. Fee derived from sales royalty.
How to Contact: Prefers cassette with 1-3 songs and lyric sheet. SASE. Reports in 1 month.
Music: Mostly R&B, dance and top 40/pop. New releases include "Sexual Voodoo," on Dice Records (dance/funk); and "Harder to Be a Friend" (by Bauers), recorded by Moore Soule on Heavyweight Records (MOR).

HAL BERNARD ENTERPRISES, INC., Box 20244, Cincinnati OH 45220-0244. (513)861-1500. President: Stan Hertzmann. Record producer and music publisher (Sunnyslope Music Inc. and Bumpershoot Music Inc.). Deals with artists and songwriters. Produces 5 singles and 3-4 LPs/year. Fee derived from sales royalty.
How to Contact: Prefers cassette with 1-3 songs and lyric sheet. SASE. Reports in 1 month.
Music: Produced *Lone Rhino* and *Desire Caught By The Tail*, by Adrian Belew on Island Records (rock LPs); *The Bears* and *Rise and Shine*, by The Bears on PMRC/MCA records (rock LPs); and *Mr. Music Head* and "Young Lions," by Adrian Belew on Atlantic Records.

RICHARD BERNSTEIN, 2170 S. Parker Rd., Denver CO 80231. (303)755-2613. Contact: Richard Bernstein. Estab. 1960. Record producer, music publisher (M. Bernstein Music Publishing Co.) and record label. Deals with artists and songwriters. Produces 6 singles/year, 2 CDs and 2-3 LPs/year. Fee derived from sales royalty, outright fee from songwriter/artist and/or outright fee from record company.
How to Contact: Prefers cassette and lyric or lead sheets. Does not return unsolicited material. Reports in 6-8 weeks.
Music: Rock, jazz and country.
Tips: "No telephone calls *please*."

*BEST BUDDIES PRODUCTIONS, Box 121738, Nashville TN 37212-1738. (615)320-7664. President: Phil Efron. Record producer, music publisher (Best Buddies Music—BMI, Swing Set Music—AS-CAP) and record company (X-cuse Me Records). Estab. 1981. Deals with artists and songwriters.

Produces 5-8 singles and 2-3 LPs/year. Fee derived from outright fee from recording artist or record company.

How to Contact: Write first and obtain permission to submit. Prefers cassette or VHS videocassette with 4-6 songs and lyric sheets. "Include bio and promo package, details on management, etc." SASE. Reports in 3 months.

Music: Mostly country, rock, R&B; also gospel. Produced *Tie Me Up* (by Jamie O'Hara), recorded by David Speegle on Bitter Creek Records; "I Want to Be the Cowgirl in the Drifting Cowboy Band" (by Efron), recorded by Misty on Universal Records (Holland); and "If I Were You," written and recorded by Sandy Garwood on Bitter Creek Records; all country.

Tips: "Send professional package. Be well organized and businesslike."

BIG BEAR, Box 944, Birmingham, B16 8UT, **England.** 44-21-454-7020. Managing Director: Jim Simpson. Record producer, music publisher (Bearsongs) and record company (Big Bear Records). Works with lyricists and composers and teams collaborators. Produces 15 singles and 10 LPs/year. Fee derived from sales royalty.

How to Contact: Write first about your interest, then submit demo tape and lyric sheet. Reports in 2 weeks.

Music: Blues, jazz, R&B and soul.

*BLACK DIAMOND MUSIC PUBLISHING & PRODUCTION GROUP, Box 467, Yeadon PA 19050-3505. (215)476-2071. President: Allen Gabriel. Record producer and publisher. Deals with artists, songwriters, producers, record companies and musicians. Fee derived from product sales. Administrative service charge to contractor.

How to Contact: Prefers cassette (or VHS or Beta videocassette) with 2 songs and lyric sheet. "All demos must be of good quality and all lyric sheets must be clearly printed." Does not return unsolicited material, but include SASE for written reply. Reports within 6 weeks.

Music: Contemporary Christian, Gospel, jazz, R&B, commercial jingles ("various, product orientation") and top 40/pop.

BLACK OLIVE, 1745 Hickory St., Sand City CA 93955. (408)394-7176. Owner/Manager: Nick Olivo. A&R Director: Dale Kurokawa. Record producer and music publisher (Black Olive Productions). Deals with artists and songwriters. Produces 12 singles, 3 12″ singles, 2 LPs and 4 EPs/year. Fee is derived from sales royalty when song or artist is recorded (negotiable).

How to Contact: Prefers cassette (or VHS videocassette) with 3-5 songs and lyric sheet. SASE. Reports in 6 weeks.

Music: Mostly pop, rock and R&B; also Latin, gospel and country. Produced *August & the Spirits* (by Daryle Smith), recorded by August/Spirits on Macola Records (R&B/Rap EP); and *Slaughter II* (R&B EP) and "Summer Nights" (R&B single) (both by John Johnson), both recorded by Slaughter II. Other artists include Medflys, Jeff Conrad, The Swatters, The Young Presidents, Bob Waldrup and Born Again.

Tips: "Be punctual, disciplined and dedicated to work in the music field. Be professional."

*BLADE TO THE RHYTHM PRODUCTIONS, 114-22 116 St., Ozone Park NY 11420. (718)672-8755 or 845-4417. President: Juan-Kato Lemus. Record producer, music publisher (see Blade to the Rhythm/ASCAP), production company. Estab. 1987. Deals with artists and songwriters. Fee derived from sales royalty or outright fee from record company. "May charge in advance for services, depending on deal made with artist or songwriter."

How to Contact: Submit demo tape by mail. Unsolicited submissions are OK. Prefers cassette with 2-4 songs and lyric sheet. "Send photograph and brief bio and tell us what type of music you do." Does not return unsolicited material. Reports in 1 month.

Music: Mostly dance/pop, house and R&B; also rap, freestyle and ballads. Produced "Touch Me with Your Heart" (by Nelson Cruz), recorded by Eileen Flores on Mic Macrec Records (12″); "Don't Make Me Promises" (by Sara Ramos), recorded by Maribel on Cruzin Nelson Records (12″); *No Para* (by Bladerunner's), recorded by Sound Factor on Warlock Records (LP cut). Other artists include Exotic Touch, FFWD, Aviance, Mari, Max Tiana Raskin, Tiny T, Hugo Fernandez, Magic Juan and Davidson.

Tips: "Be patient and the time and effort will pay off. The good songs sell because of the proper steps taken at the appropriate time."

*NELSON BLANCHARD, 11724 Industriplex, Baton Rouge LA 70809. (504)295-1400. Contact: Nelson Blanchard. Record producer, music publisher (White Car Music/BMI) and record company (White Car Records). Estab. 1980. Deals with artists and songwriters. Produces 12 singles, 2 12″ singles, 6 LPs, 6 EPs and 2 CDs/year. Fee derived from sales royalty or outright fee from recording artist.

How to Contact: Submit demo tape by mail. Unsolicited submissions are OK. Prefers cassette with 4 songs and lyric or lead sheets. Does not return unsolicited material. Reports in 2 weeks.
Music: Mostly country, rock, pop; also R&B. Produced "Leading Man" (by Butch Reine), recorded by Atchafalaya on White Car Records; "The Black Burner" (by Waters, Garvin, Shapiro), recorded by Tareva on White Car Records; and "She's Still a Lady," written and recorded by Gale Lee Lamey on Techno Sound Records; all country singles. Other artists include John Steve, Bayou Country Band, B.J. Morgan, Red Vines.

*BLUE SUN PRODUCTIONS, P.O. Box 67, Covina CA 91723. (714)592-3098. President: Steve Mortensen. Record producer, music publisher (Single Phase Music/BMI) and record company (Blue Sun Records). Estab. 1986. Deals with artists and songwriters. Produces 15-20 singles, 1-2 LPs and 4-5 EPs/year. Fee derived from sales royalty or outright fee from recording artist or record company.
How to Contact: Submit demo tape by mail. Unsolicited submissions are OK. Prefers cassette with 2-3 songs and lyric sheet. Submit demo tape by mail. Unsolicited submissions are OK. Prefers cassette with 2-3 songs and lyric sheet. Does not return unsolicited material. Reports in 1-2 months.
Music: Mostly pop-European, rock and R&B. Produced "Off And On" and "Private Masquerade" (by Basque), recorded by Single Phase; and "She's a Beauty" (by Mortensen/Amato), recorded by Emotion; all on Blue Sun Records (pop singles). Other artists include Mike Finley and Mike Stewart.
Tips: "Indicate several major recording artists who you feel the song could best be done by."

JACK P. BLUESTEIN, P.O. Box 630175, Miami FL 33163. (305)472-7757. President: Jack Bluestein. Record producer and music publisher (Twister Music, Lantana Music and Pine Island Music). Estab. 1973. Deals with artists and songwriters. Produces 1-6 singles and 1-2 LPs/year. Works with 10-15 new songwriters/year. Fee derived from sales royalty.
How to Contact: Prefers reel-to-reel or cassette with 2-6 songs and lyric sheet. SASE. Reports in 1 month.
Music: Blues, country, gospel, MOR, R&B, rock and top 40/pop. Produced "It's Over" and "Dreaming For Two," by Beth Thliveris (pop) on Twister Records.

BOLDEN PRODUCTIONS, (formerly Beau Winters Productions), 1138 E. Price St., Philadelphia PA 19138. Producer: Bolden Abrams, Jr.. Record producer, music publisher (Coffee and Cream Publishing Company/ASCAP) and record company (Torch Records). Produces 12 singles, 12 12″ singles and 6 LPs/year. Fee derived from sales royalty or outright fee from recording artist or record company.
How to Contact: Prefers cassette with 1-4 songs and lyric sheet. Does not return unsolicited material. Reports in 2 weeks.
Music: Mostly R&B, pop and country; also gospel, funk and punk/funk. Produced "No Time for Tears," (by Beau Winters and Keith Batts), recorded by Gabrielle on Saphire Records; and "Starting All Over Again," (by Oscar Patterson and Jim Avery) and 'Ooh I Can't Get Over You," (by Oscar Patterson, Ross Barnes and Jim Avery), both recorded by Wayne Hunter on Spiketown Records. Other artists include Novella "Sweet" Briar, Michael Anderson, Sheree Sano, Jose Gomez, Tony Gilmore, Bran Stratton, Deborah McNeil, Gabrielle, and Michael Holloman.

*PETER L. BONTA, 1518 Pr. Anne St., Fredericksburg VA 22401. (703)373-6511. Studio Manager: Chris Ippolito. Record producer. Estab. 1980. Deals with artists and songwriters. Produces 8-12 singles, 5-8 LPs and 3-5 CDs/year. Fee derived from sales royalty, outright fee from recording artist or record company.
How to Contact: Write or call first and obtain permission to submit. Prefers cassette with 3-4 songs and lyric sheet. SASE. Reports in 6 weeks.
Music: Mostly roots rock, country rock and blues; also country and Bluegrass. Produced *Ooh-Wow* (by Uptown Rhythm Kings), recorded by Uptown Rhythm Kings on Ripsaw Records (R&B LP); *Running in the Night* (Rob Carroll), recorded by ESCAPE on ERC Records (rock CD); and *Southern Soul* by Jerry Arnold), recorded by Jimmy Arnold on Rebel records (bluegrass LP). Other artists include Gary Herrewig (Artful Dodger).

ROBERT BOWDEN, P.O. Box 111, Sea Bright NJ 07760. President: Robert Bowden. Record producer, music publisher (Roots Music/BMI) and record company (Nucleus Records). Estab. 1979. Deals with artists and songwriters. Produces 2 singles and 1 LP/year. Fees derived from sales royalty.
How to Contact: Submit demo tape or write to arrange personal interview. Prefers cassette (or VHS videocassette) with 3 songs and lyric sheet. SASE. Reports in 1 month.
Music: Mostly country; also pop. Produced "Pressure Cooker" written and recorded by Sweitzer; "Always," written and recorded by Marco Sission; "Selfish Heart," written and recorded by Bowden, all on Nucleus Records (all singles). Produces "only freelance artists."

*RAFAEL BROM, P.O. Box 71988, Los Angeles CA 90071-0988. Producer: Rafael Brom. Record producer, music publisher (ASCAP), record company (Cosmotone Records). Estab. 1984. Deals with artists and songwriters. Produces 1 single, 1 12″ single and 1 LP/year.
How to Contact: Write first to obtain permission to submit. Prefers cassette (or VHS videocassette if available) with all songs and lyric sheet. Does not return unsolicited material. "Will contact only if interested."
Music: All types. Produced "Padre Pio"; Sonnet XVIII"; and "O Let Me Be . . ." all written and recorded by Lord Hamilton on Cosmotone Records (Christian/rock pop). Other artists include Adrian Romero and Thomas Emmett Dufficy.

*BROOKE PRODUCTIONS, INC., 1721 Ferrari Dr., Beverly Hills CA 90210. President: Skip Drinkwater. Record producer. Estab. 1971. Deals with artists and songwriters. Produces 10 singles, 5 12″ singles and 5 LPs/year. Fee derived from sales royalty or outright fee from recording artist or record company.
How to Contact: Submit demo tape by mail. Unsolicited submissions are OK. Prefers cassette or ½″ VHS videocassette with 1-3 songs. SASE. Mostly R&B, pop and dance. Produced "Occupy My Love" (by Armor/Haynes), recorded by Bert Robinson on Capitol Records (R&B/pop); "El Watusi" (by R. Baretto and Grp.), recorded by Latin Fresh on Island Records (latin-rap); and "You Don't Know" (by Grp.), recorded by Scarlet and Black on Virgin Records (pop).

L. MARION BROWN, Box 15117, Kansas City MO 64106. Executive Producer: L. Marion Brown. Record producer (QP, Paradise Rock). Estab. 1980. Deals with artists and songwriters. Produces 10 singles and 5 LPs/year. Fee derived from sales royalty or outright fee from record company or lease of master. Ultima Sound Studio Facility available.
How to Contact: Write first and obtain permission to submit. Prefers cassette (or VHS videocassette) with 4 songs and lyric or lead sheets. Enclose any bio/resume information available. SASE. Reports in 8 weeks.
Music: Mostly R&B, dance and country/pop; also contemporary gospel. Produced "Paradise," "Shake Me Up," "Love You Girl," "You're So Cold," "Move Your Body," "It's Too Late," "I Need Your Lovin' " and "Struck Out," all recorded by Demetrius; "In The Corp" and "I Rock It Hard," written and recorded by Eddie Austen (Easy Eddie) on Paradise Rock Record (rap singles). Other artists include Elise Pointer, Awl Dawg, Mike Tyss and Samuel Cole.

*BURNING TYGER MUSIC, 684 Indiana, San Francisco CA 94107. (415)821-2321. President/Producer: Michael Molenda. Record producer and music publisher (Burning Tyger Music/BMI). Deals with artists and songwriters. Produces 4 12″ singles, 2 CDs and 2 LPs/year. Fee derived from sales royalty (songwriters), or outright fee from recording artist or record company (artists). "Contract production services for demos or records are on a fee basis. Percentage contracts or conventional songwriter-royalty contracts are, of course, offered at no advance fee."
How to Contact: Write first and obtain permission to submit. Prefers cassette with 3-5 songs and lyric sheet. "A few concise lines detailing your artistic concepts or goals are helpful." SASE. Reports in 2 weeks.
Music: Mostly modern rock, dance-oriented and pop; also gospel, R&B and rap. Produced *Wobblies*, by Wobblies (modern rock CD) for Marimba Records, West Germany; *Exotic*, by Key of Magic (New Age rock) and *One Thing*, by Friends of Sarah Connor (hard rock), both on Sound & Vision Records; *Misery*, by Boom Box Orchestra (rock film soundtrack) for Castlerock Films; and *Too Little, Too Late*, by Eslaves d Orphee (modern rock) for Infantes Records, France.
Tips: "We develop 'visionary' artists who approach the 'song' like a film director stages a movie scene. Lyrics should be meaningful and alive with images – the music should evoke a mood consistent with the message inherent in the work."

*CALLIOPE PRODUCTIONS, 265 W. 37th St., New York NY 10018. (212)704-9626. Attn: Andy Lasseter. Record producer, music publisher (Gizzard/ASCAP) and record company (Calliope). Estab. 1985. Deals with artists and songwriters. Produces 2 singles, 2 12″ singles, 2 LPs, 2 EPs and 2 CDs/year. Fee derived from combination of sales royalty when song or artist is recorded, outright fee from recording artist, outright fee from record company and percentage of publishing.
How to Contact: Write first and obtain permission to submit. Prefers cassette (or ½″ or ¾″ videocassette if available) with 3 songs and lyric sheet. Does not return unsolicited material. Reports in 1 month.
Music: Mostly R&B, pop and rock; also rap, gospel and jazz. Produced "Baby Baby" (by Christian Julian), on RKO Records (pop); "Why" (by Roland Clark), recorded by Roland Clark on Atlantic Records (dance single); and "Yo Spring Break" (by Julian/Kennedy) recorded by Justin Time on

Calliope Records (rap single). Other artists include Kinky Pink and Arthur Mason.

PETER CARDINALI, 12 Ecclesfield Dr., Scarborough ON M1W 3J6 **Canada**. (416)494-2000. Record producer/Arranger (Peter Cardinali Productions Inc./CAPAC) and Cardstar Music (publishing), CAPAC and BMI (PROCAN). Estab. 1975. Deals with artists and songwriters. Produces 6-8 singles, 4-5 12″ singles, 8-10 LPs and 8-10 CDs/year.
How to Contact: Write or call first and obtain permission to submit. Prefers cassette with 4-6 songs and lyric sheets. SASE. Reports within weeks.
Music: Mostly pop, R&B, dance and funk/jazz. Produced *Big Fat Soul*, written and recorded by John James on Attic/A&M Records (dance LP); "The Bear Walks" (by P. Cardinali/H. Marsh), recorded by Hugh Marsh on Duke St./WEA Records (R&B/jazz LP); and "Moments" (by J. Nessle), recorded by See on A&M Records (pop single). Other artists include Rick James and Teena Marie.

CAROLINA PRIDE PRODUCTIONS, Box 6, Rougemont NC 27572. (919)477-4077. Manager: Freddie Roberts. Record producer, music publisher (Freddie Roberts Music/BMI), record company, and management firm and booking agency. Estab. 1967. Deals with artists, songwriters and session musicians. Produces 12 singles, 7 LPs, 2 EPs and 3 CDs/year. Fee derived from sales royalty.
How to Contact: Call or write first. Prefers 7½ ips reel-to-reel or cassette with 1-5 songs and lyric sheet. SASE. Reports in 3 weeks.
Music: Mostly country, MOR and top 40/pop; also bluegrass, church/religious, gospel and country rock. Produced "Restless Feeling," written and recorded by Rodney Hutchins (country/rock) on Catalina Records; "Empty," (by David Laws) recorded by Jerry Harrison (country) on Celebrity Circle Records; and "Redeemed," (by Jane Durham) recorded by the Roberts Family (Southern gospel) on Bull City Records. Other artists include Sleepy Creek, Lady Luck, Billy McKellar and C.J. Jackson.

EDDIE CARR, Box 1794, Big Bear City CA 92314. (714)585-4645. President: Eddie Carr. Record producer, music publisher (Watchesgro Music) and record company (Interstate 40 Records). Estab. 1987. Deals with artists and songwriters. Produces 12 singles/year. Fee derived from sales royalty or outright fee from recording artist.
How to Contact: Submit demo tape by mail. Unsolicited submissions are okay. Prefers cassette with 2 songs and lyric sheets. Does not return unsolicited submissions. Reports in 1 week.
Music: Mostly country. Produced "Bottom of a Mountain" (Soundwaves Records), "Fairy Tales" (Master Records), and "Cripple Cowboy" (Tracker #1 Records); all written and recorded by Don McKinnon (all singles). Other artists include B.B. Brad, Joyce Campbell, Scott Ellison, Rita Aileen and Jesse James Project.
Tips: "I want publishing on songs. Will try to place artist. It's costing more to break in new artists, so songs must be strong."

STEVE CARR, % Hit & Run Studios, 18704 Muncaster Rd., Rockville MD 20855. (301)948-6715. Owner/Producer: Steve Carr. Record producer (Hit & Run Studios). Estab. 1979. Deals with artists and songwriters. Produces 7 singles, 4 12″ singles, 15 LPs, 3 EPs and 4 CDs/year. Fee derived from outright fee from recording artist.
How to Contact: Write or call first and obtain permission to submit. Prefers cassette with 3 songs. "Do NOT send unsolicited material! Write name and phone number on cassette shell. Will call back if I can do anything with your material."
Music: Mostly pop, rock and R&B; also country. Produced/recorded *Billy Kemp* (by Billy Kemp), on Essential Records (LP); *Classic Rock*, written and recorded by various artists (oldies digital remaster) on Warner Bros. Records; "Frontier Theory," (by R. Kelley) recorded by Frontier Theory (CD/rock) on TOP Records; *The Wolves* (by Band), on Top Records (LP); and "Bomb Squad" (by Lorenzo) on Their Own Records (single); all recorded by Hit & Run. Other artists include Beyond Words, Steve Nally/Deep End, Oho, Voodoo, Love Gods, Necrosis, Debra Brown and Universe. Produces and digitally remasters Time-Life Music's Rock n' Roll, and Country Classics.

*CARRIE/TRIBAL RECORDS CO., P.O. Box 90639, Nashville TN 37209. (615)321-3319. A & R Director: James Hendrix. Record producer, music publisher (Jimerlean Music/BMI) record company (Carrie/Tribal Records) and distributor (Theoda Records; Abbey Records). Carrie estab. 1940, Tribal estab. 1989. Deals with artists and songwriters. Produces 6 singles, 4 12″ singles, 4 LPs and 2 EPs/year. Fee derived from sales royalty.
How to Contact: Submit demo tape by mail. Unsolicited submissions are okay. Prefers cassette with 2 songs and lyric sheet. SASE.
Music: Mostly easy listening, traditional gospel and hymns & anthems; also seasonal songs. Produced "The Sound of Saints" (by Betty Barksdale), recorded by B. Barksdale on Carrie 1700 (gospel 45 rpm); and "Lord Coming Back Soon" (by Jerry Aiken), recorded by J. Aiken on Carrie (strong gospel). Other artists include Michael Hunter, Steve Lester, Ms. Gail Glenn and Jeff (Jay Dog) Scott.

Close-up

Frankie Previte
Singer/Songwriter
New Brunswick, New Jersey

"In 1985, a friend of mine, a musical director for Vestron Films, called me up and said, 'Listen, I've got this little movie called "Dirty Dancing," and I want you to write a song for it.' I told him, 'Jim, I'm in the studio. I'm doing some producing now and I don't really have any time.' And he said, 'Make some time; this is gonna change your life.' I laughed at him and said, 'Right, Jim.' "

Frankie Previte had worked for many years in the music business before that phone call. He is a singer, lyricist, composer and former front man of his own successful band, Franke and the Knockouts. Despite his full schedule, he did take his friend's advice and made time to work on the song.

"I called a friend of mine and said, 'I need a track; it needs to start slow and I want it to be a fast song with a mambo beat.' So he sent me a track, I listened to it, then we reworked it and arranged it a little differently. I played the track for Jim over the phone and he said, 'Oh, I like the music a lot. Make a song out of that.' So one day I'm in the car on the way to this recording session, the tape is in the cassette deck and I'm singing 'Nuh nuh nuh nuh . . . of my life.' I scribbled 'time of my life' on an envelope. Right there at exit 140 on the parkway, 'I've Had the Time of My Life' got created."

The story of the creation of that very successful song gives some clues as to how Frankie likes to work. "The first thing that has to happen is a musical track has to be created, either by me or a co-writer. Then I will scat a melody on top of that musical track. From that melody, or usually as I'm jamming to find the melody, phonetic sounds come out of my mouth—I do this with a tape recorder on." Frankie then tries to establish a phonetic or rhyming pattern that will dictate how the lyrics are to be laid out. "If I have one gift," says Frankie, "it's finding melodies. If I have to work at something, it's my lyrics."

Frankie strives to keep a high level of excellence in his work and credits much of his success to the fact that he is not afraid to rewrite. "I've rewritten some things five times. I think many writers fail because once they write the initial lyric, they think, 'Ah, there it is. It's done.' I work with a lot of writers, and that's a common problem."

Frankie's career has left him with a clear perspective on the music business and what it takes to make it as a songwriter. "It only takes one right song and one right person who's in a power position to do it for you. It doesn't take 20 of them, it takes one to push the button. That doesn't mean it's gonna get done, but without that one person pushing the button, you'll have a hard time. It takes a lot of fortitude to get knocked down and get back up, especially after years and years of people saying, 'No, not quite good enough; no, go back and rewrite; no, I don't think so.' If I had a dollar for every time that happened, I would be over the top. You have to be able to accept that and then find out how to make it better or move away from it and write another song."

—Mark Garvey

DON CASALE MUSIC, INC., 377 Plainfield St., Westbury NY 11590. (516)333-7898. President: Don Casale. Record production, music publishing, artist management; affiliated recording studio. Estab. 1979. Deals with artists, songwriters, managers and agents. Fee derived from sales royalty.
Affiliates: ELASAC MUSIC (ASCAP), Don Casale Music (BMI).
How to Contact: "I will accept unsolicited cassettes (except during August and September) with one or two songs and legible, typed lyric sheets (no registered mail). No "lyrics-only" submissions. Please include address and phone number and letter stating exact purpose (publishing deal?; record deal?; etc.); anything else you'd like to say is welcome, too (I frown on 'form' letters). Press kit, bio and photo(s) or VHS videocassette are helpful, if available. For return of your material, always include SASE (envelope *must* be large enough to handle contents). If you don't need your material returned, include a *signed* note saying so and only include SASE for my response letter. Sorry, but I will not listen or correspond without SASE. A call first is very welcome (between 12 noon and 12 midnight EST), but not necessary, or you may inquire first by mail (with SASE). I'll listen to every note of your music and respond to you as soon as possible, usually between two weeks and two months, depending on volume of submissions."
Music: Everything but jazz and classical.
Tips: "Submitted songs should have a 'special' nature about them; a different quality and lyric. Melodies should be paritularly 'catchy' and memorable. Songs should be in tune with the current radio market. I want only 'career-starting', top 10 singles; not B sides or album fillers. Please try to be SELECTIVE and send me that ONE SONG you think is a KILLER; that ONE SONG that JUMPS OFF THE TAPE! Don't include a second song just because there's room on the cassette. Songwriters seeking a publishing contract need only a simple, in-tune, clear version of the song(s); a big production and recording, although welcome, is not necessary. Artists seeking a recording contract should submit a 'quality' performance (musically & vocally), incorporating their very best effort and their own, preferably unique, style. Your recording needn't be master quality, but your performance should be. I give extra points for following my instructions to the letter."

JAN CELT, 4026 NE 12th Ave., Portland OR 97212. (503)287-8045. Owner: Jan Celt. Record producer, music publisher (Wiosna Nasza Music/BMI) and record company (Flying Heart Records). Estab. 1982. Deals with artists and songwriters. Produces 2 LPs, 1 EP and 2 CDs/year.
How to Contact: Submit demo tape by mail. Unsolicited submissions are okay. Prefers cassette with 1-10 songs and lyric sheets. Does not return unsolicited material. Reports in 3 months.
Music: Mostly R&B, rock and blues; also jazz. Produced *Liquid Love* (by Chris Newman), recorded by Napalm Beach; *Maple Leaf Rag* (by Scott Joplin), recorded by Janice Scroggins; and *Unemployment Blues* (by Mary Reynolds), recorded by The Esquires; all on Flying Heart Records (all LPs). Other artists include Tom McFarland and Obo Addy.
Tips: "Be sure your lyrics are heartfelt; they are what makes a song your own. Abandon rigid stylistic conceptions and go for total honesty of expression."

CHROME DREAMS PRODUCTIONS, 5852 Sentinel St., San Jose CA 95120. (408)268-6066. Owner: Leonard Giacinto. Record producer. Estab. 1982. Deals with artists and songwriters. Produces 15 singles and 8 12" singles/year. Fee derived from outright fee from recording artist.
How to Contact: Submit demo tape by mail. Unsolicited submissions are okay. Write or call first to arrange personal interview. Prefers cassette (or ½" VHS videocassette). SASE. Reports in 1 month.
Music: Mostly rock, New Age, avant garde and college radio. Produced "Your Place or Mine?" (by Monette Paparotti), recorded by Spinach Head on Indie Records (crunch rock); "Lennie Has a Checker" (by D. MacArther), recorded by The Binge on Indie Records (college radio). Other artists included are Waxed Dolphin (cover band) and Love Stooges (European electronic).
Tips: "Try to get emotion across in your work."

LOU CICCHETTI, 836 Darwin St., Charleston SC 29412. (803)795-5612. Contact: Lou Cicchetti. Record producer and music publisher (Cousins Music). Estab. 1948. Deals with artists and songwriters. Produces 2-3 singles/year. Fee derived from sales royalty.
How to Contact: Prefers 7½ or 15 ips reel-to-reel or cassette with 3 songs and lyric sheet. SASE. Reports in 3 weeks.
Music: 50s and 60s country and rock. Produced "The Dancer" (by S. Corrente/J.O'Daniel), recorded by The Dials (rock single); and "One More Heartache" (by T. Percoco), recorded by Coco and Squirt Band (country single), both on Cousins Records.
Tips: "Please come back to melody or strong riffs and let's get some sanity back into the music scene. Let's return to writers instead of sound-effects people."

*THE CLUB STUDIOS, 127 Aldersgate St., London England EC1A ULQ. (66)71-2501910. Contact: Roland A. Radaelli. Record producer, music publisher (Risson Music UK-PRS) and record company (Presidential Enterprises, Ltd.). Estab. 1986. Deals with artists and songwriters. Produces 20-30 sin-

gles, 20-30 12″ singles and 2-4 LPs/year. Fee derived from sales royalty or outright fee from recording artist or record company. Charges for services in advance "only when productions are for other labels or publishers."
How to Contact: Prefers cassette with 2-5 songs and lyric sheet. Does not return unsolicited material. Reports in 2 weeks.
Music: Mostly house and hip-hop. Produced "Loud And Clear" (by J. Gray), recorded by Fly Girls on Bite (single); "London Rhyme Synd." (by Various), recorded by LRS on Rhyme and Reason Records (single); and "Hit the Bit" (by F. Bellini), recorded by French Connection on P.E.L. Records (single/album). Other artists include Tube Generation and Alberto.

COLLECTOR RECORDS, Box 2296, Rotterdam Holland 3000 CG **The Netherlands**. Phone: (10)4224889. Research: Cees Klop. Record producer and music publisher (All Rock Music). Deals with artists and songwriters. Produces 8-10 singles and up to 30 LPs/year. Fee derived from sales royalty.
How to Contact: Prefers cassette. SAE and IRC. Reports in 1 month.
Music: Mostly 50s rock, rockabilly and country rock; also piano boogie woogie. Produced *Eddie Bond* (by Bond), recorded by Bond/Klop on White Label Records (rock LP); *Louis Gittens*, written and recorded by Gittens on White Label Records (rock LP); and *Rob Hoeke* (by Hoeke), recorded by Cees Klop on Downsouth Records (boogie LP). Other artists include Teddy Redell, Gene Summers and Benny Joy.

MICHAEL COLLINS/REFINED RECORDS, 2105 Maryland Ave., Baltimore MD 21218. (301)685-8500. Deals with artists only. Produces 3 LPs/year. Fee derived from outright fee from recording artist.
How to Contact: Prefers cassette with at least 4 songs. Does not return unsolicited material. Reports in 1 month.
Music: Mostly rock. Produced *Two Thirds*, by Bazooka Joe and *Funk Wagon McGuillicuddy*, by Krack, both on Merkin Records.

*****COLOSSAL RECORDS**, 14-16 Wilson Ave., Melbourne Victoria 3044 **Australia**. (3)387-0555. A&R Director: Jimmy Jiménez. Record producer, music publisher (Colossal Music Publisher-APRA) and record company (Colossal Records). Estab. 1974. Produces 5 singles, 5 12″ singles, 5 LPs and 3 CDs/year. Fee derived from sales royalty or from sales of imported records.
How to Contact: Write or call first and obtain permission to submit. Prefers cassette or VHS video-cassette and lyric sheet. Does not return unsolicited material.
Music: Mostly commercial pop, dance music, disco music; also commercial rock. Produced "Zah-House," written and recorded by Zah-Zah-Zam (hi-energy); "My House" (by Evan Kelly), recorded by Vika (dance music); and "Everybody," written and recorded by Jamie O'Neil (dance music).
Tips: "In Australia the radio won't play commercial dance music unless it's 'rock'—influenced by the late 60's or early 70's music."

COPPELIA, 21 rue de Pondichery, Paris 75015 **France**. Phone: (1)45673066. FAX: (1)43063026. Manager: Jean-Philippe Olivi. Record producer, music publisher (Coppelia/SACEM), record company (Olivi Records) and music print publisher. Deals with artists and songwriters. Produces 8 singles and 4 LPs/year. Fee derived from sales royalty or outright fee from recording artist or record company.
How to Contact: Prefers cassette. SAE and IRC. Reports in 1 month.
Music: Mostly pop, rock and New Age; also background music and film/series music. Produced "No'mad" written and recorded by Alain Mion (jazz); "Fille Facile," written and recorded by Henry Stoltz (pop); and "Carte Postale" (by Remy-Ferchit), recorded by Dominique Bodin (French folk), all on Olivi Records. Other artists include Pino Lattuca and Patrick Martini.

RON CORNELIUS, 803 18th Ave. South, Nashville TN 37203. (615)321-5333. Owner/Manager: Ron Cornelius. Record producer and music publisher (The Cornelius Companies). Estab. 1987. Deals with artists and songwriters. Produces 3-4 singles and 1-2 LPs/year. Fee derived from sales royalty or outright fee from record company.
How to Contact: Call first and obtain permission to submit. Prefers cassette with 2-3 songs. SASE. Reports in 2 months.
Music: Mostly country and pop. Published "Time Off for Bad Behavior" recorded by David Allen Coe on CBS Records (single); and "You're Slowly Going Out of My Mind" (by Larry Latimer) recorded by Gordon Dee on Southern Tracks Records (single).

DAN O. CORWIN, (formerly Danny Johnson), 5839 Silver Creek, Azle Rd., Azle TX 76020. (817)281-7988. Manager: Dan O. Corwin. Record producer, music video and sound production company. Estab. 1986. Works with artists and songwriters. Produces 10 singles, 4 12″ singles, 3 LPs, 7 EPs and 2 CDs/year. Fee usually derived from sales royalty, but negotiated on case-by-case basis.

How to Contact: Prefers cassette (or VHS videocassette) with 3 songs and lyric sheet. "Keep songs under 4 minutes. Only copyrighted material will be reviewed. Please do not send material without copyright notices." SASE, "but prefers to keep material on file." Reports in 6 weeks.
Music: Mostly rock; also pop, New Age and dance. Produced "Time Won't Let Me," (by Craig Cole/Keny McKlurg) recorded by Demur Cull (rock/single) on MLM Records; *Beggars Ride*, (by Craig Cole/Keny McKlurg) by Demur Cull (rock/EP/CD) on MLM Records; and "Z-Time," (by M. Howard) recorded by W-4's (rock/single) on BIG M Records. Other artists include The Kindreds, Toni Mc and The Score and The Instamatics.
Tips: "Keep songs simple and melodic."

COUNTRY STAR PRODUCTIONS, P.O. Box 569, Franklin PA 16323. (814)432-4633. President: Norman Kelly. Record producer, music publisher (Country Star Music/ASCAP, Kelly Music/BMI and Process Music/BMI) and record company (Country Star, Process, Mersey and CSI Records). Estab. 1970. Deals with artists and songwriters. Produces 5-10 singles and 4-6 LPs/year. Works with 3-4 new songwriters/year. Works with composers and lyricists; teams collaborators. Fee derived from sales royalty or outright fee from recording artist or record company.
How to Contact: Prefers cassette with 2-4 songs and lyric or lead sheet. SASE. Reports in 2 weeks.
Music: Mostly country (80%); also rock (5%), MOR (5%), gospel (5%) and R&B (5%). Produced "Every Bird's Gotta Fly," by Ron Lauer and "Burning Leaves," by Gary Cochran, both on Country Star Records (country); and "This World We Live In," by Virge Brown on CSI Records (gospel). Other artists include Bob Stamper, Elmer Blanchard, John York, Vince Smith, Virge Brown, Bonnie Baldwin, Junie Lou, Lisa Hadley Patton, Debbie Sue, Tommy Davidson, Ron Lauer, George Conrad, J.C. Young and Silver Dollar Country Band.
Tips: "Submit only your best efforts."

COWBOY JUNCTION FLEA MARKET AND PUBLISHING CO., Hwy. 44 and Jct. 490, Lecanto FL 32661. (904)746-4754. Contact: Elizabeth Thompson. Record producer and music publisher (Cowboy Junction/BMI). Deals with artists and songwriters. Produces 2-3 singles and 2 12″ singles/year. Works with 6 new songwriters/year. Works with lyricists and composers and teams collaborators. Fee derived from sales royalty.
How to Contact: Prefers 7½ ips reel-to-reel or cassette with 3 songs and lyric sheet. SASE. Reports ASAP.
Music: Mostly C&W, country gospel and bluegrass. Produced "Tell Me How You've Been" (by Boris Max Pastuch), recorded by Buddy Max on Cowboy Junction Records (country/western); "Where The Maple Syrup Flows" (by Boris Max Pastuch), recorded by Buddy Max on Cowboy Junction Records (country/bluegrass); and "Thank You Lord" written and recorded by Wally Jones on Cowboy Junction Records (inspirational/country). Other artists include Leo Vargason, Johnny Pastuck, Ruth Hanson, Elie Jenkins, Wayne Lairson, Charlie Floyd, Lloyd Stevens, Troy Holliday, Cowboy Bill Lockrey, Bill Gray and Hillard Bergman.
Tips: "Come to our Flea Market on Tuesday or Friday and show to the public, and who knows? Also, if possible, come to our Music Show at Country Junction on Saturday at 2 p.m. and ask to be placed on stage to present your material to the public. (We are closed and on tour July and August of each year.)"

THE COYOTE, P.O. Box 387, Hollywood CA 90078. (818)506-8660. Producer: The Coyote. Record producer, music publisher (Shaolin Music/ASCAP) and record company (Shaolin Film & Records). Estab. 1984. Deals with artists and songwriters. Produces 3 singles and 2 LPs/year. Fee derived from sales royalty or outright fee from record company.
How to Contact: Write first and obtain permission to submit. Does not return unsolicited material.
Music: Mostly rock, hard rock and pop; also sound tracks. Produced "Coyote Graveyard" and "Sid's Place," written and recorded by Coyote (rock) on Shaolin Records.

*CREATIVE PRODUCTIONS, P.O. Box 3091, Charlotte NC 28210. (704)333-6362. Owner: Robert Tavaglione. Record producer. Estab. 1989. Deals with artists only. Fee derived from outright fee from recording artist.
How to Contact: Write or call first and obtain permission to submit. Prefers cassette with maximum of 3 songs. Does not return unsolicited material. Reports in 1 month.
Music: Mostly alternative rock, rock and heavy metal; also thrash, hardcore and psychedelic. Produced *House of Mirth* (by House of Mirth), recorded by House of Mirth on Creative Productions Records (EP).
Tips: "Please include artist bid and describe overall goals of project in question."

CUMMINGS PRODUCTIONS, Box 266775, Houston TX 77207. (713)641-0793. A&R Director: Robert Jackson. Record producer, music publisher (Sirloin Music Publishing), and record company (Happy Beat and MSB Records). Deals with artists and songwriters. Produces 20 singles and 6 LPs/year.

Works with 25 new songwriters/year. Works with lyricists and composers; teams collaborators. Fee derived from sales royalty or outright fee from songwriter/artist or record company.
How to Contact: Write first. Prefers cassette (or videocassette) with 3-6 songs and lyric sheet. "Don't send the master copy of your video. Indicate speed of video sent." SASE. Reports in 1 month.
Music: Mostly rock, soul and dance; also blues, country, gospel, jazz, R&B and top 40/pop. Produced "Drag Lady," by Max (dance/top 40 single); "Gimme The Chance," by Chance on Happy Beat Records (pop single); "I Would Like To Know You," by Carl Stewart on Happy Beat Records (soul single); and "Expectation," by Martha Bryant (pop single). Other artists include Invasion and Friction.

*WADE CURTISS, P.O. Box 4740, Nashville, TN 37216. A&R Director: Wade Curtiss. Record producer and record company (Terock Records). Estab. 1959. Deals with artists and songwriters. Produces 12-20 singles, 6 12" singles, 12-20 LPs, 4 EPs and 6 CDs/year. Fee derived from outright fee from recording artist. Charges "artists for sessions."
How to Contact: Submit demo tape by mail. Unsolicited submissions are OK. Prefers IPS reel-to-reel or "all kinds" of videocassettes (if available) with 4-10 songs and lyric sheets. SASE.
Music: Interested in "all kinds." Produced "Changes", written and recorded by R. Derwald and Rock, written and recorded by Mickey Finn (rock LP), both on Terock Records. Other artists include Dixie Dee, Greg Paul and Rhythm Rockers.

*S. KWAKU DADDY, P.O. Box 4794, San Francisco CA 94101. (415)239-3640. President: S. Kwaku Daddy. Record producer and record company (African Heritage Records Co.). Deals with artists and songwriters. Produces 6 LPs/year.
How to Contact: Prefers cassette. Sometimes returns unsolicited material. Reports in 3 weeks.
Music: Mostly pop, R&B and gospel. Produced *Heritage I*, *Heritage II* and *Heritage III*, all by S. Kwaku Daddy, all on African Heritage Records (all LPs).

*ARNEANDO CURTIS DARBY, 3933 5th Ave. South, Minneapolis MN 55409. (612)832-6485. Producer: Arneando Curtis Darby. Record producer and record company (Key Idea International Record Co.). Estab. 1988. Deals with artists and songwriters. Produces 6 singles, 8 12" singles and 3 LPs/year. Fee derived from sales royalty.
How to Contact: Write first to arrange personal interview. Prefers cassette with 3 songs and lyric sheet. Reports in 3 weeks.
Music: Mostly pop, R&B and rock; also country. Produced "April Eyes," (by A.C. Darby) recorded by La Day Singers (R&B) on Van Records; "Man on the Radio," (by A.C. Darby) recorded by C.D. Band (R&B) on Key Idea Records International; and "Amstradone," (by Jil Enyke) recorded by La Day Singers (R&B) on Key Idea Records International. Other artists include Funky Stuff, Candy Dulfer, Stane Sisters and Kane.

DARK HORSE PRODUCTIONS, 1729 N. Third Ave., Upland CA 91786. (714)946-1398. A&R Director: Bill Huff. Record producer, music publisher (Lizard Licks Music/BMI) and record company (Dark Horse Productions). Estab. 1988. Deals with artists and songwriters. Produces 2 LPs and 2 CDs/year. Fee derived from sales royalty.
How to Contact: Submit demo tape by mail. Unsolicited submissions are OK. Prefers cassette with 3-5 songs. SASE. Reports in 4 weeks.
Music: Mostly contemporary jazz, New Age and traditional jazz. Produced *Iridescence* (by Brad Kaenel, LP); and "Simply Simon" (by DJ Alversen, single); both recorded by Polyhedra on Dark Horse Records (contemporary jazz).
Tips: "The growth in progressive AC programming over the last 2-3 years will continue into the 90s, creating strong market niches for jazz and New Age products."

*DANNY DARROW, Suite 6-D, 150 West End Ave., New York NY 10023. (212)873-5968. Manager: Danny Darrow. Record producer, music publisher (BMI, ASCAP), record company (Mighty Records) and Colley Phonographics – Europe. Estab. 1958. Deals with songwriters only. Produces 1-2 singles, 1-2 12" singles and 1-2 LPs/year. Fee derived from royalty.
How to Contact: Submit demo tape by mail. Unsolicited submissions are OK. "No phone calls." Prefers cassette with 3 songs and lyric sheet. SASE. Reports in 1 week.
Music: Mostly pop, country and dance; also jazz. Produced *Carnival Nights* (by Vincent C. Delucia and Raymond Squillacote), (country LP); *Impulse* (by Danny Darrow), (dance LP); and *Corporate Lady* (by Michael Greer), (pop) all recorded by Danny Darrow on Mighty Records.
Tips: "Listen to the hits of Richie, Manilow, Houston and Rogers and write better songs."

*EDWARD DE MILES, 4475 Allisonville Rd., 8th Floor, Indianapolis IN 46205. (317)549-9006. President: Edward De Miles. Record producer, music publisher (Edward De Miles Music Co./BMI), record company (Sahara Records). Estab. 1981. Deals with artists and songwriters. Produces 15-20 12" singles and 5-10 LPs/year. Fee derived from sales royalty.

How to Contact: Write or call first and obtain permission to submit. Prefers cassette (or VHS or Beta ½" videocassette if available) with 1-3 songs and lyric sheet. Does not return unsolicited material. Reports in 1 week.
Music: Mostly R&B/dance, top 40 pop/rock and contemporary jazz; also country, TV and film themes—songs and jingles. Produced "High Off Rhymes" (by D. Evans and A. Mitchell), recorded by Multiple Choice (rap single); "Need a Lover" and "Don't Want Control" both written and recorded by Steve Lynn (R&B single); all on Sahara Records. Other artists include Lost in Wonder and D'von Edwards.
Tips: "Copywright all material before submitting. Equipment and showmanship a must."

*DEMI MONDE RECORDS & PUBLISHING LTD., Foel Studio, Llanfair Caereinion, Powys, **Wales** 5421 ORZ. 0938-810758. Managing Director: Dave Anderson. Record producer, music publisher (P.R.S & M.C.P.S.) and record company (Demi Monde Records). Estab. 1982. Deals with artists and songwriters. Produces 5 singles, 15 12" singles, 15 LPs and 10 CDs/year. Fee derived from combination of sales royalty, outright fee from recording artist, outright fee from record company and studio production time.
How to Contact: Submit demo tape by mail. Unsolicited submissions are okay. Prefers cassette with 3 or 4 songs and lyric sheet. SASE. Reports in 2 months.
Music: Mostly rock, pop and blues. Produces *Hawkwind* (by D. Brock); *Atomic Rooster* (by J. Ducann); and *Ozril Tentacles* (by E. Wynn), all recorded by Demi Monde on Demi Ronde Records (LP).

*ED DETTENHEIM, Rt. 3, Box 172, Haynesville LA 71038. (318)927-5253. Contact: Ed Dettenheim. Record producer, music publisher (Darbonne Publishing Co., BMI) and record company (Wings Record Co.). Produces 12 singles and 1 LP/year. Fee derived from sales royalty when song or artist is recorded, outright fee from recording artist, outright fee from record company.
How to Contact: Submit demo tape by mail. Unsolicited submissions are OK. Prefers cassette with up to 4 songs and lyric sheets. Include photo and musical resume. Reports in 1 week.
Music: Country. Produced "Shooters Place" and "Man in the Mirror", written and recorded by Leon Martin; and "It Ain't Over" (by E. Dettenheim), recorded by the Old Man, all on Wings Records (all country singles).
Tips: "Your demo should prove you've got what it takes to sell records."

CARLO DITTA, 828 Royal St., #536, New Orleans LA 70116. Contact: Carlo Ditta. Record producer, music publisher (Attid Music Co/ASCAP) and record company (Orleans Records). Estab. 1986. Deals with artists and songwriters. Produces 3 LPs and 2 CDs/year. Fee derived from sales royalty when song or artists is recorded or outright fee from record company. Charges artists in advance for production services.
How to Contact: Submit demo tape by mail. Unsolicited submissions are okay. Prefers cassette (or VHS videocassette) with 5 songs and lyric sheets. SASE.
Music: Mostly folk and country; also pop, gospel and R&B. Produced *Why* (by Carlo Ditta), recorded by Mighty Sam; *Miss Bea* (by Sam Melain), recorded by Mighty Sam; and *The Story of My Life* (by Eddie Jones), recorded by Guitar Slim Jr.; all on Orleans Records (all LPs). Other artists include The New Indians.

DKP PRODUCTIONS, INC., 731 N Harvard, Villa Park IL 60181. (708)941-0232. President: Diana Cummings. Production/management company. Estab. 1986. Deals with artists and songwriters. Produces 1 12" single, 1 EP and 1 CD/year. Fee derived from sales royalty.
How to Contact: Submit demo tape by mail. Unsolicited submissions are okay. Prefers cassette (or VHS videocassette) wth 3 songs and lyric sheets. SASE.
Music: Mostly rock and pop. Produced *Renaissance Junkyard*, recorded by The Ultraviolet (LP); and *Unleashed*, recorded by Unleashed (EP); both on ION Records. Other artists include Defcon and Jim Bartz.

DODGY PRODUCTIONS, 1 Prince of Wales Passage, London NW1 3EE **England**. (01)388-8635. FAX: (01)387-0233. Managing Director: Safta Jaffery. Record producer and manager. Estab. 1985. Deals with artists and songwriters. Produces 20 singles, 15 12" singles, 5 LPs, 2 EPs and 10 CDs/year. Fee derived from sales royalty and/or outright fee from record company.
How to Contact: Prefers cassette (or VHS videocassette) with 3 songs and lyric sheet. Include bio and photo. SAE and IRC. Reports in 6 weeks.
Music: Mostly rock; also pop and heavy metal. Producers have produced *The Stone Roses*, (by Ian Brown/John Squire) recorded by The Stone Roses on Silvertone Records (LP/cassette/CD); *Anthrax*, written and recorded by Anthrax on Megaforce/Island Records (LP/cassette/CD); and *Bizarro*, (by David Gedge), recorded by The Wedding Present on BMG Records (LP/cassette/CD). Other artists

include Accept, XTC, Roger Waters, Wa Wa Nee, The Wooden Tops, Anthrax, The Stone Roses and Najma.
Tips: "Send demos of only what you regard as your best songs."

COL. BUSTER DOSS PRESENTS, Box 13, Estill Springs TN 37330. (615)649-2577. Producer: Col. Buster Doss. Record producer, record company (Stardust, Wizard) and music publisher (Buster Doss Music/BMI). Estab. 1959. Deals with artists and songwriters. Produces 100 singles, 10 12" singles, 20 LPs and 10 CDs/year.
How to Contact: Submit demo tape by mail. Prefers cassette with 2 songs and lyric sheet. SASE. Reports in 2 weeks.
Music: Pop, country and gospel. Produced "Hard Times" (by Bennie Ray), "Where Were You" (by B. Doss) and "Shoebox of Memories" (by Hobson Smith), all on Stardust Records. Other artists include Johnny Buck, Tony Andrews, Cliff Archer, R.B. Stone, Linda Wunder and Sonny Carson.

*DOWNTOWN RECORD PRODUCTIONS, Steenmolenstraat, 7, St. Katelijne Waver B-2580 **Belgium**. (15)553809. Managing Director: Piroux Ghislain. Record producer and record company. Deals with artists and songwriters. Produces 20-25 singles and 3-5 LPs/year. Fee derived from sales royalty.
How to Contact: Prefers cassette or reel-to-reel (or videocassette) with 2-6 songs and lyric sheet. SAE and IRC. Reports in 6 weeks.
Music: Mostly pop, mainstream rock, funk (and disco/funk); also new wave, R&B and "golden oldies" (no heavy metal). Produced "Never In A Million Years," recorded by Linda Scott; "Jungle Drums," recorded by Johnny Otis; and "Happy Together," recorded by The Turtles; all on Downtown Records (all singles). Other artists include Kokomo and Guenaelle.
Tips: "We are an independent company which is an enormous advantage in a small country like Belgium. We can easily distribute the product ourselves. If it's a hit in Belgium—the other countries of Europe are all watching. In our country a product stands much more chance of becoming a hit if it is danceable. As Europe's prime date (1/1/93) approaches, new release horizons are in view."

DRAGON RECORDS, INC., 872 Morris Park Ave., Bronx NY 10462. (212)792-2198. Vice President: Mr. "G". Record producer and music publisher (Vin-Joy Publishing). Estab. 1954. Deals with artists and songwriters. Produces 12 singles, 5 12" singles and 3 LPs/year. Fee derived from sales royalty.
How to Contact: "We accept material by recommendation only."
Music: Easy listening, country, MOR and top 40/pop. Produced "Promise Me," (by J. Heath), recorded by Smokey Heath; "A Letter to D.J.," (by V. Gagliano), and "One Prayer," (by Gagliano and Heath), both recorded by Joyce Heath(both singles). Other artists include Dickie Do and The Don'ts, The Go-Go's and Prometheus.

*LEO J. EIFFERT, P.O. Box 5412, Buena Park CA 90620. (213)721-7260. Owner: Leo J. Eiffert, Jr.. Record producer, music publisher (Eb-Tide Music/BMI), record company (Plain Country) and Young Country Music/BMI. Estab. 1967. Deals with artists and songwriters. Produces 15-20 singles and 5 LPs/year. Fee derived from sales royalty.
How to Contact: Submit demo tape by mail. Unsolicited submissions are OK. Prefers cassette with 2-3 songs, lyric and lead sheet. SASE. Reports in 3 weeks.
Music: Mostly country and gospel. Produced "Summer School" (by Mario Burnes and Leo J. Eiffert), recorded by Leo J. Eiffert, Jr.; "Tears Will Never Fall" written and recorded by Joe Eiffert; and "Single Life" (by Leo J. Eiffert, Jr.), recorded by Donna Jean all on Plain Country Records (single). Other artists include Duane Austin, Crawfish Band, Wayne Meadows, Teeci Clarke, Debbie Collins and David Busson.
Tips: "Just keep it real country."

*8TH STREET MUSIC, 204 E. 8th St., Dixon IL 61021. Manager: "Rob". Record producer. Estab. 1988. Deals with artists and songwriters. Fee derived from sales royalty when song or artist is recorded.
How to Contact: Submit demo tape by mail. Unsolicited submissions are OK. Prefers cassette with 1-3 songs and lyric sheet. "No phone calls please. Just submit material and we will contact if interested." SASE. Reports is 1 month.
Music: Mostly interested in top 40/pop, dance and new rock; also R&B, country and teen pop. Produced "Traffic Wars" (by Van/McInnis), recorded by Bob's Night Off on Rockit Records (alternative rock CD single) and "Bob's Night Off" on Sonic Wave Records (top 40 LP). Other artists include Rita Van (top 40), Jason Kermeen (country), Jay Pauley (top 40/rock), J&J (teen pop) and J.J. Brooks (R&B).

*ELEMENT & SUPERSTAR PRODUCTION, Box 30260, Bakersfield CA 93385-1260. Producer: Jar the Superstar. Record producer, music publisher (BMI), record company (Element Records and International Motion Pictures) L.T.D. Estab. 1987. Deals with artists and songwriters. Produces 40 singles and 5 LPs/year. Fee derived from standard record sales.

How to Contact: Write first to arrange personal interview. Prefers cassette (or VHS videocassette if available) with 1 or more songs, lyric and lead sheet. Does not return unsolicited material.
Music: Mostly Christian/gospel, C/W and R&B; also pop, rap and rock. Produced "Where Ever You Are" (by Judge A. Robertson), recorded by Jar the Superstar (pop); "No One Wants to be Sad" written and recorded by JAR (R&B) both on Element Records and "Brite & Morning Lite" (by JAR) recorded by Jar the Superstar on E/R (Christian).

GEOFFREY ENGLAND, 2810 McBain, Redondo Beach CA 90278. (213)371-5793. Contact: Geoffrey England. Record producer. Deals with artists and songwriters. Produces 10 singles/year. Fee derived from sales royalty and/or outright fee from record company.
How to Contact: Prefers cassette and lyric sheet. SASE. Reports in 2 weeks.
Music: Mainstream melodic rock. Produced "Steppenwolf Live," on Dunhill Records; and "If Licks Could Kill," by Virgin on Statue Records.

*ESQUIRE INTERNATIONAL, Box 6032, Station B, Miami FL 33123. (305)547-1424. President: Jeb Stuart. Record producer, music publisher and management firm. Deals with artists and songwriters. Produces 6 singles and 2 LPs/year. Fee derived from sales royalty or independent leasing of masters and placing songs.
How to Contact: Write or call first. Prefers cassette or disc with 2-4 songs and lead sheet. SASE. Reports in 1 month.
Music: Blues, church/religious, country, dance, gospel, jazz, rock, soul and top 40/pop. Produced "Can't Count the Days," (R&B single, Kent Records); "Sitba," (R&B single, King Records); and "You're So Right For Me," (disco single, Esquire Records), all by Jeb Stuart. Other artists include Valerie and Stone Foxx.
Tips: "When sending out material make sure it is well organized, put together as neatly as possible and it is of good sound quality."

JESSE EVATTE, P.O. Box 1913, Easley SC 29641. (803)295-3177. Owner/Producer: Jesse Evatte. Record producer and music publisher (Sivatt Music Publisher). Estab. 1972. Produces 6 singles and 10 LPs/year. Deals with artists and songwriters. Fee derived from outright fee from artist and/or record company.
How to Contact: Prefers cassette with 3-4 songs and lyric sheet. SASE. Reports in 6 weeks.
Music: Gospel and inspirational. Produced "City Heart," written and recorded by Candace Bryan (country); "My Shepherd," (by L. Tripp) recorded by Mel Corey (country gospel); and "It's Raining Miracles," written and recorded by Martha Miranda (gospel), all on Sivatt Records. Other artists include Jimmy Orr, Cathy Gulden, Joyce Owens and Jesse Evatte.

FACTORY BEAT RECORDS, INC., 521 5th Ave., New York NY 10175. (212)757-3638. Producer/President: Rena L. Feeney. Record producer, music publisher (Ren-Maur Music/BMI) and record company (R&R and Rer-Rom Records). Produces 4-6 singles, 4 12" singles and 2 LPs/year. Fee derived from sales royalty.
How to Contact: Prefers cassette with 2-4 songs and lyric sheet only. SASE. Reports in 3 weeks.
Music: R&B, rock, soul and top 40/pop. Produced *That's Hot* and *Same Language* (by B. Nichols), and *Rise Up* (by R. Feeney/B. Nichols), all recorded by "Rena" on F.B.R. Inc. Records (all LPs).
Tips: "Have a finished product, ready to master and press for commercial use."

*DOUG FAIELLA PRODUCTIONS, 16591 County Home Rd., Marysville OH 43040. (513)644-8295. President: Doug Faiella. Record producer, music publisher (Doug Faiella Pubishing—BMI), record company (Studio 7 Records) and recording studio. Estab. 1984. Deals with artists and songwriters. Produces 10 singles and 5 LPs/year. Fee derived from outright fee from recording artist. "Charges a flat rate per song."
How to Contact: Write first and obtain permission to submit. Prefers cassette with 3 songs and lyric sheets. Does not return unsolicited material. Reports in 4 weeks.
Music: Mostly country, gospel and rock. Produced *Yesterday Country*, recorded by Dago Red on Studio 7 Records (country LP).
How to Contact: Submit demo tape by mail; call first and obtain permission to submit. Prefers cassette with 3-4 songs and lyric sheets. SASE. Reports in 4 weeks.

*FARALLONE PRODUCTIONS, INC., P.O. Box 156, Saratoga CA 95071. Producer: B.H. Yoshida. Record producer, music publisher (Farallones/BMI) and record company (Farallones Productions). Estab. 1982. Deals with artists and songwriters. Produces 50 LPs and 50 CDs/year. Fee derived from sales royalty, outright fee from songwriter/artist and/or outright fee from record company.

How to Contact: Write first and obtain permission to submit. Prefers cassette. Does not return unsolicited material. Reports ASAP if interested.
Music: Mostly light rock, jazz fusion, New Age and country; also radio/TV commercials.

*VITO FERA PRODUCTIONS, 119 Peachwood Dr., Swedesboro NJ 08085. (609)467-1682. Producer: Vito Fera. Record producer, music publisher (Network Sound Music Publishing/ASCAP and Fera Music Publishing/BMI). Estab. 1980. Produces 5 singles, 1 12″ single, 2 LPs, 4 EPs and 1 CD/year. Fee derived from outright fee from artist or record company.
How to Contact: Write first and obtain permission to submit. Prefers cassette (or VHS videocassette if available) with 3 songs, lyric sheet, lead sheet (optional). "Carefully label cassette and cassette insert with name, address and phone number, typed lyric sheets. Photo and bio helpful." SASE. Reports in 1 month.
Music: Mostly pop/dance, pop/R&B and medium rock; also ad/jingles and adult contemporary. Produced "Come Back" (by Steve Clarke), recorded by Chill on S.P.I.N. Records (pop/R&B single); "Can't Wait" (by Vito Fera), recorded by Vincent James on Di'Pop Records (dance/pop single); and "Steve" written and recorded by Marcia Dickerson on M.A.D. Records (R&B adult single). Other artists include The Session, Kathy Lamborn, Carmen Tomassetti, P.J. Clement and Joe Molinaro.
Tips: "Submit a clean vocal demo with a commercial tempo. A good hook and strong chorus is a must. Write in a major key for contemporary songs. Always send your best songs and don't be afraid to accept constructive criticism."

*DON FERGUSON PRODUCTIONS, P.O. Box 461892, Garland TX 75046. (214)271-8098. Producer: Don Ferguson. Record producer (Sultan Music/BMI and Illustrious Sultan/ASCAP), record company (Puzzle Records). Estab. 1972. Deals with artists and songwriters. Produces 10-15 singles, 4-5 cassettes and 2 CDs/year. "Fees are negotiated."
How to Contact: Submit demo tape by mail. Unsolicited submissions are OK. Prefers cassette with 3 songs and lyric sheet. "Send bio." SASE. Reports in 2 weeks.
Music: C&W, pop and MOR. Produced "Shatter Me" (by L. Thomas), recorded by Diane Elliott (C&W single); "Leave Me Right Now" written and recorded by B. Teesdale (MOR); and "Apple Jack" (by P. Rodgers), recorded by Phil Rodgers (pop) all on Puzzle Records. Other artists include Mary Craig, Rita Anderson, Flashpoint (band), Charlie Shearer, Wallace Mitchell and Derek Hartis.

*CHARLIE FIELDS, 44 Music Sq. E., Nashville TN 37203. (615)255-2175. President: Charlie Fields. Record producer, music publisher (Jason Dee Music/BMI and Mr. Mort Music/ASCAP) and records company (Charta Records and Delux Records). Deals with artists and songwriters. Produces 10 singles/year and 8 LPs/year. Fee derived from sales.
How to Contact: Prefers cassette or reel-to-reel with 3-4 songs and lyric sheet. SASE. Reports in 3 weeks.
Music: Mostly rock, pop and country; also bluegrass. Produced "You Won the Battle," (by D. Erickson/J. Walker) recorded by Eddie Rivers; "Standing on the Edge," (by C. Fields) recorded by David Walsh; and "Blue Collar Man," (by J. Foster) recorded by Ronnie Klein, all recorded on Charta Records (country). Other artists include David Walsh, The Marshall and The Lady, Fran Nickens, Nina Wyatt and Lisa Rogers.

FIRST TIME MANAGEMENT & PRODUCTION CO., Sovereign House, 12 Trewartha Rd., Praa Sands, Penzance, Cornwall TR20 9ST **England**. Phone (0736)762826. FAX: (0736)763328. Managing Director: Roderick G. Jones. Record producer, music publisher (First Time Music Publishing U.K. Ltd. MCPS/PRS), record company (First Time, Kernow, Fugore, Mohock Records, Rainy Day Records and Dance 808 Records), licensed and subsidiary labels and management firm (First Time Management & Production Co.). Estab. 1986. Deals with artists and songwriters. Produces 5-10 singles and 5 LPs/year. EPs and CDs subject to requirements. Fee derived from sales royalty.
How to Contact: Prefers cassette with unlimited number of songs and lyric or lead sheets. SAE and IRC. Reports in 10 weeks.
Music: Mostly country/folk, pop/soul/top 20, country with an Irish/Scottish crossover, rock, jazz funk, fusion, dance and reggae. Produced "Jazz," (by Lockwood/Pusey) recorded by Fadermaster and the Beat (dance) on Digimix International Records; "Here I Stand," (by Jones/Cook) recorded by Colin Eade (instrumental library music) on First Time Records; and "When Tomorrow Never Comes," (by C. Eade/Q. Hafeez) recorded by Kenny McKie (pop ballad) on Rainy Day Records. Other artists include Willow (pop-folk), Nick White (country) and compilation of artists on LPs (pop-soul).

FOLSOM PRODUCTIONS, 43 McKee Dr., Mahwah NJ 07430. (201)529-3550. President: Edward Feldsott. Vice President: Robert Feldsott. Record producer and artist management company. Estab. 1988. Deals with artists and songwriters. Fee derived from sales royalty.

How to Contact: Submit demo tape by mail. Unsolicited submissions are OK. Prefers cassette with 1-3 songs. SASE. Reports in 1 month.
Music: Mostly rock, pop and blues. Artists include Mick Taylor, Rag Doll and Riff Raff.
Tips: "Dedicate yourself to your convictions. Keep in mind the artist you are writing for and his/her limits."

FOX FARM RECORDING, 2731 Saundersville Ferry Rd., Mt. Juliet TN 37122. (615)754-2444. President: Kent Fox. Record producer (Mercantile Productions) and music publisher (Mercantile Music/ BMI and Blueford Music/ASCAP). Estab. 1970. Deals with artists and songwriters. Produces 20 singles/year. Fee derived from outright fee from recording atists. Charges in advance for studio time.
How to Contact: Submit demo tape by mail. Unsolicited submissions are OK. Prefers cassette (or VHS videocassette). SASE. Reports in 3 months.
Music: Country, bluegrass and gospel.

FOXWORTHY PRODUCTIONS, 4002 Liggett Dr., San Diego CA 92106. (619)226-4152. Vice President A&R: Dottye. Music publisher (Foxworthy Music/BMI) and record company (Foxworthy Records). Estab. 1978. Deals with artists and songwriters. Produces 4 singles, 1 12″ single, 4 LPs and 4 CDs/year. Fee derived from sales royalty.
How to Contact: Submit demo tape by mail. Unsolicited submissions are OK. Prefers cassette with 3 songs and lyric or lead sheets. Does not return unsolicited material. Reports in 4 weeks.
Music: Mostly pop, rock/rap and R&B; also New Age. Produced *Black & White* (by Michael Redmond), recorded by D. Foxworthy on Foxworthy Records (rap LP/single); *Street Poet Ray* (by Tim Armstrong), recorded by D. Foxworthy on Foxworthy Records (R&B LP); and *I'm In Love* (by Garth Beale), recorded by S. McClintoch on 37 Records (rock LP). Other artists include Gary Hyde.

BOB SCOTT FRICK, 404 Bluegrass Ave., Madison TN 37115. (615)865-6380. Contact: Bob Scott Frick. Record producer and music publisher (R.E.F.); different labels. Estab. 1958. Deals with artists and songwriters only. Produces 12 singles, 30 12″ singles and 30 LPs.
How to Contact: Submit demo tape by mail. Unsolicited submissions are OK. Write first and obtain permission to submit.
Music: Produced "I Found Jesus in Nashville," recorded by Bob Scott Frick; "Love Divine," recorded by Backwoods; and "A Tribute," recorded by Visionheirs on R.E.F. (gospel). Other artists include Larry Ahlborn, Bob Myers Family, David Barton, The Mattingleys and Jim Pommert.

*FUN CITY RECORD CO., (formerly Rawls Brothers Productions Co., 5664A Hiberna Pl., Columbus OH 43232. Executive Producer: L.A. Rawls. A&R Director: M. "Tub" Sharp. Record producer and record company (Fun City Records). Deals with artists. Produces 3-6 LPs/year. Fee derived from sales royalty.
How to Contact: Write first and obtain permission to submit. Prefers cassette with 3-4 songs and lyric sheet. Does not return unsolicited material. Reports in 6 weeks.
Music: R&B, gospel and top 40/pop. Produced "Victims," written and recorded by Jeff Jones on Fun City Records (single).

FYDAQ PRODUCTIONS, 240 E. Radcliffe Dr., Claremont CA 91711. (714)624-0677. President: Gary K. Buckley. Record producer, music publisher (Fydac Music/BMI and Jubilation Music/BMI) and record company (Majega Records). Estab. 1976. Deals with artists, songwriters and record companies. Produces 4-10 singles and 2-8 LPs/year. Fee derived from sales royalty, outright fee from record company or outright fee from songwriter/artist.
How to Contact: Write first. Prefers cassette with 1-3 songs and lyric or lead sheet. SASE. Reports in 3 weeks.
Music: Country, country/pop crossover, MOR, rock and top 40/pop. Produced *Sending A Copy Home* (by multiple songwriters), recorded by Jody Barry (gospel LP) and *Used To Be's* (by Stephen Brinton) recorded by Kevin McKelley (LP), both on Mejega Records; and *Country Love* (by multiple songwriters), recorded by Jerry Roark (country LP) on JLR Records; *Sky's The Limit* (by multiple songwriters), recorded by Michael Noll on GB Records (LP); and Buché (by multiple songwriters), recorded by Rick Buché (Top 40/pop LP) on Paradise Records. Other artists include Gold, Kevin McKelley and Castaways.
Tips: "Submit product which reflects ability. We receive hundreds of packages each month. We only pursue the best."

JACK GALE, P.O. Box 630755, Miami FL 33163. (305)935-4880. Contact: Jack Gale. Record producer. Estab. 1983. Deals with artists and songwriters. Produces 48 singles, 10 LPs and 10 CDs/year. Fee derived from sales royalty.

How to Contact: Submit demo tape by mail. Unsolicited submissions are okay. Prefers cassette (or VHS videocassette) with 2 songs and lyric sheets. Does not return unsolicited material. "We report back immediately if we are interested."

Music: Mostly contemporary country and country crossover. Produced "Shame on the Moon," (by Rodney Crowell) recorded by Bonnie Guitar; "Another One of My Near Mrs. (Misses)," (by Gillon/Hammond) recorded by Bobby Bare and Donnie Bowser; and "Blue Christmas," by David Frizzell; all on Playback Records (country). Other artists include PJ Allman, Del Reeves, Dennis Yost & Classics Four, Juanita Rose, Sammi Smith, Darnell Miller, Sylvie & Her Silver Dollar Band, Mac Bailey and David Heavener.

Tips: "Our doors are always open to new artists and writers, just keep at it. If you have talent and are persistent, it will happen. Just learn to overcome the magic word in the music business . . . rejection."

*GEIMSTEINN, THOR BALDURSSON, RUNAR JULIUSSON, Skolaveg 12, Keflavik 230 **Iceland**. Phone: (92)12717. Manager: Runar Juliusson. Record producer, music publisher and record company (Artists Arrangers Records). Deals with artists and songwriters. Produces 5-10 LPs/year. Fee derived from sales royalty or outright fee from recording artist or record company.

How to Contact: Write first and obtain permission to submit or to arrange personal interview. Prefers cassette (or VHS videocassette) with 2-3 songs and lyric sheet. Does not return unsolicited material. Reports in 6 weeks.

Music: Mostly pop, rock and country; also jazz, R&B and gospel. Produced *All I Wanna Do*, written and recorded by Runar Juliusson; *Hvar*, written and recorded by Thor; and *Gammar*, (by Thor), recorded by Gammar, all on Geimsteinn Records (all LPs).

*THE GLAND PUPPIES, INC., 203 Westmoreland, Naperville IL 60540. (708)357-3353. President: John Klopp. Record producer. Estab. 1989. Deals with artists and songwriters. Produces 7-10 singles, 5 LPs and 3 EPs/year. Fee derived from sales royalty.

How to Contact: Submit demo tape by mail. Unsolicited submissions are OK. Prefers cassette with 4-8 songs and lyric sheet. "Send *your* favorite songs, not the songs your friends like, just because they sound like what's being played on the radio." SASE. Reports in 3 weeks.

Music: Mostly New Age, pop/dance and folk songs; also comedy, gypsy/dance and thrash metal. Produced *Soccer-Ear-Fob* written and recorded by The Gland Puppies on Sick Dog Records (rock LP); *Toaster Head* (by Captain Stain), recorded by That Stain on Bland Yuppy Records (New Age LP); and "Hyena-Q" (by Ron Sutton), recorded by My Taco on Sick Dog Records (children's single). Other artists include Exotic Food (Edy Heady).

Tips: "Don't try to be a Bon Jovi sound alike. Do your own music without holding anything back."

*GO JO PRODUCTION, 195 S. 26th St., San Jose CA 95116. (408)286-9840. Owner: G.J. O'Neal. Estab. 1980. Deals with artists and songwriters. Fee derived from outright fee from recording artist or record company. Charges for arranging.

How to Contact: Submit demo tape by mail. Prefers cassette. SASE. Reports in 1 week.

Music: Mostly country, gospel, Mexican; also rock and pop. Other artists include Amy Clements, Pat Larocca, Jaque Lynn, Jeannine O'Neal, Johnny Gitar and Petrella.

GOLDEN GOOSE PRODUCTIONS, 2074 Pomona Ave., Costa Mesa CA 92627. (714)548-3694. Owner: Dennis Peter Rose. Record producer, music publisher and record company (DANTZ Records). Estab. 1965. Deals with artists and songwriters. Produces up to 4 singles, 2-4 LPs and up to 2 CDs/year. Fee derived from sales royalty, outright fee from recording artist or record company. Works on speculation and for hire.

How to Contact: Write or call first and obtain permission to submit or to arrange personal interview. Prefers cassette (or VHS videocassette) with 3 or more songs and lyric or lead sheets. SASE. Reports in 8 weeks.

Music: Mostly rock/R&B, R&B fusion and New Age; also classical, folk and blues. Produced *Charles*, written and recorded by Charles Qualiq on Brofeel Records; *John Belezijikian*, recorded by John B. on Dantz Records; and *Ahmose Sara-Blue Alchemy*, written and recorded by Ahmose Sara on Khepera Records (all LPs). Other artists include Michale B. Holdene, Rick Delong, Harry Smith Trio, Perris Alexander, Harvey Sulivan and Head Hunter.

GO-RECORDS, 3345, Hollins Ferry Road, Baltimore MD 21227. (301)247-7447. Producer: William E. Baker. Record producer, music publisher (Billy Baker Music/BMI) and record company (Go-Records). Estab. 1988. Deals with artists and songwriters. Produces 6-10 12" singles. Fee derived from sales royalty.

How to Contact: Submit demo tape by mail. Unsolicited submissions are okay. Prefers cassette (or VHS videocassette) with 3 songs and lyric or lead sheets. Does not return unsolicited material. Reports in 2 weeks.

Music: Mostly country, pop and R&B; also gospel and rock. Produced "Carolina Blue," by Johnny Ray Anthony; "We Can't Go On Leaving Like This," by Doug Lester; and "Behind a Numbered Door," by Douglas Wayne; all on Go Records (all country). Other artists include Michael Major and Douglas Wayne.
Tips: "Call me. Believe in what you do; send a quality tape and never give up."

BILL GREEN, 10450 Sentinel, San Antonio TX 78217-3824. (512)654-8773. Contact: Bill Green. Record producer and music publisher. Estab. 1979. Deals with artists and songwriters. Produces 20 singles, 2 LPs and 1 CD/year. Fee derived from outright fee from songwriter/artists or record company.
How to Contact: Prefers cassette with 1-4 songs and lyric sheet. SASE. Reports in 2 months.
Music: Mostly contemporary country, traditional country and cajun. Produced "Boogie Queen" (by R. Jenkins/D. Green) recorded by Doug Kershaw on BGM Records (country/cajun); "Photographic Memory" (by B.Boyd) recorded by Billy Mata on BGM Records (country); and *Hot Diggidy Doug*, recorded by Doug Kershaw on BGM Records (country/cajun LP).

*TOMMY GREENE, 3608 Harrogate Rd., Cola SC 29218. (803)798-7298. Producer/Pubisher: Tommy Greene. Record producer, music publisher (Tomy Don/ASCAP). Estab. 1986. Deals with artists and songwriters. Produces 50-60 singles and 5-10 LPs/year. Fee derived from sales royalty or outright fee from recording artist or record company.
How to Contact: Write or call first and obtain permission to submit. Prefers cassette, 7½ or 15 ips reel-to-reel, (or VHS videocassette if available) with 1-3 songs and lyric or lead sheet. "Send short bio of experience." SASE. Reports in 1 month.
Music: Mostly country and country gospel. Produced "Take It Slow with Me," "Don't Leave Me Alone" and "Cry in My Sleep," all recorded by Donna G on Pegasus Records. Other artists include Whyte Christmas and Lolita Jackson.

*CHARLES HALL, 400 56th St., Fairfield AL 35064. (205)786-6924. Owner/Operator: Charles Hall. Record producer, music publisher (Chasann Music/BMI) and record company (Radioactive Records). Record company estab. 1989. Publishing company estab. 1975. Deals with artists and songwriters. Produces 3 singles and 1 LP/year. Fee derived from sales royalty. "Charges in advance for services if not under contract."
How to Contact: Submit demo tape by mail. Prefers cassette (or VHS videocassette if available) with 2 songs and lyric sheet. SASE. Reports in 3 weeks-1 month.
Music: Mostly pop, R&B and gospel; also jazz and country. Produced "Wait She's Coming" (by Parnell), recorded by A. William on A&W Records (R&B single); *Working Undercover* (by L. Battle), recorded by C. Hall on Radio Active Records (pop LP); and "Love Me Tonight" (by K. Ruff), recorded by Hall/Ruff on Radioactive Records (gospel single).
Tips: "We are looking for good songs and artists with material that can be played before the public."

MARK HANNAH PRODUCTIONS, Suite 250, 1075 N.W. Murray Rd., Portland OR 97229. (503)642-4201. Owner: Mark Hannah. Record producer, music publisher (Mark Hannah Music Group/BMI), record company (Radioactive Records) and Mark Hannah Management/personal manager. Estab. 1985. Deals with artists and songwriters. Produces 5-10 singles, 1-3 LPs and 1-3 EPs/year. Fee derived from sales royalty.
How to Contact: Write first and obtain permission to submit. Prefers cassette or 15 ips reel-to-reel with 1-3 songs and lyric or lead sheets. SASE. Reports in 1 month.
Music: Mostly rock, pop and country; also fusion, New Age and jazz. "You Stole My Heart Away," written and recorded by P. Witt (pop-rock single); "Forced to Have Sex with an Alien," written and recorded by M. Harrop (comedy single); and *Desert Moon*, written and recorded by M. Hannah (New Age LP); all on Radioactive Records. Other artists include Rex E. Plew and Messenger (rock band).

RICK HANSON PRODUCTIONS, %Ric Rac Inc., Box 712, Nashville IN 47448. (812)837-9569. Executive Producer: Rick Hanson. Record producer, music publisher (Ric Rac Music/ASCAP and Rick Hanson Music/BMI), record company (Ric Rac Records and Country Bump Records) and management firm (Ric Rac Inc.). Estab. 1985. Deals with artists and songwriters. Produces 4-6 12″ singles and 2-4 LPs/year. Works with 2 new songwriters/year. Fee derived from sales royalty.
How to Contact: Write first and obtain permission to submit. Prefers cassette with 3 songs and lyric sheet. "Do not make phone inquiries as to status of material submitted." SASE. Reports in 2 months.
Music: Mostly country, pop and rock; also gospel, R&B and classical. Produced "Little Girl Blue," recorded by Glori McFall (country); "Same Old Barroom Melody," written and recorded by Rick Hanson on Ric Rac Records (country); and "My Love Is Safe With You," written and recorded by Rick Hanson on Ric Rac Records (country).Other artists include Jack Lawles.
Tips: "Have a good understanding of the music business overall. Be as professional as possible. Get involved with songwriters' workshops in your area. Don't give up."

HAPPY DAYS MUSIC/JEREMY MCCLAIN, Box 852, Beverly Hills CA 90213. (818)769-2842. President: Jeremy McClain. Record producer and music publisher (Happy Days Music). Deals with artists and songwriters. Produces 12 singles, 1-2 12″ singles and 3 LPs/year. Fee derived from sales royalty or outright fee from record company.
How to Contact: Write first to arrange personal interview or submit demo tape. Prefers cassette (or VHS videocassette) and lyric or lead sheet. SASE. Reports in 6 weeks.
Music: Mostly rock, top 40, and country; also contemporary gospel. Produced "Devil With The Blue Dress," by Pratt & McClain/Warner Brothers Records (rock single); and "The Way Things Used To Be," by Tom Gillan/Brother Love Records (country single). "Worked with Michael Bolton. In addition, we have direct publishing access to Christopher Cross, Donna Summer and Debbie Boone."

HARD HAT PRODUCTIONS, 519 N. Halifax Ave., Daytona Beach FL 32018. (904)252-0381. President/Producer: Bobby Lee Cude. Record producer, music publisher (Cude & Pickens Publishing) and record company (Hard Hat). Estab. 1978. Works with artists only. Fee derived from contract. Produces 12 singles and 4 LPs/year.
How to Contact: Produces "only in-house material." Write first and obtain permission to submit. Prefers cassette with 4 songs and lyric sheet "from performing artists only."
Music: Mostly pop, country and easy listening; also MOR, top 40/pop and Broadway show. Produced "V-A-C-A-T-I-O-N" (by Cude/Pickens), recorded by The Hard Hatters (pop single); "Just a Piece of Paper" and "Worried Worried Men" (by Cude/Pickens), recorded by the Blue Bandana Country Band (country singles); all on Hard Hat Records. Also, "Tennessee's On My Mind" (country), "Texas Red White & Blue Step" (country) and "Who's Loving You," (pop/rock) all by Caz Allen on Hard Hat Records.

*STEPHEN A. HART/HART PRODUCTIONS, 1690 Creekview Cir., Petaluma CA 94954. (707)762-2521. Executive Producer: Stephen A. Hart. Record producer. Estab. 1975. Deals with artists and songwriters. Produces 8 LPs and 8 CDs/year. Fee derived from outright fee from recording artist or record company.
How to Contact: Submit demo by mail. Prefers cassette with 3 songs and lyric sheet. Does not return unsolicited material. Reports in 6 weeks.
Music: Mostly pop, rock and instrumental. Produced *Liberi-Liberi* (by Vasco Rossi), on EMI Records; *Stien/Walder* (by Stien/Walder) on Narada/MCA Records; and *Uzeb Club* (by Carron/Brouchu/Cusson) on Select Records, all recorded by Stephen Hart (CD/LP).

*HATCHERY PRODUCTIONS/STUDIOS, 2175 Michael, Warren MI 48091. (313)754-8200. President: Dave Sell. Record producer. Estab. 1986. Deals with artists and songwriters. Produces 5-6 singles, 5-6 LPs and 5-6 CDs/year. Fee derived from sales royalty. Charges in advance for studio time.
How to Contact: Submit demo tape by mail. Unsolicited submissions are okay. Prefers cassette with 3 songs and lyric sheet. Does not return unsolicited material. Reports in 1 month.
Music: Mostly jazz/fusion/New Age, rock/pop and Christian/gospel. Produced *Teen Angels* (by J. Oliver), on Rat Records (LP); *Metro Music Masters* (by J. Oliver), on Sterling Diversion (LP); and "Mike Novak" (by M. Novak), on Handsome Bros. Records (single), all engineered and produced by Dave Sell.
Tips: "Have your act together. Be drug-free. Approach your music seriously by giving it your best effort always. We look for serious, hard working artists."

*ERNIE HATTON/BILL WINBORNE/SANDY CONTELLA, P.O. Box 4157, Winter Park FL 32793. (407)657-6016. Contact: Producer. Record producer, music publisher (BMI), record company (Earth & Sky Records). Estab. 1977. Deals with artists and songwriters. "Just starting up again after a 3 year layoff." Fee derived from royalty.
How to Contact: Submit demo tape by mail. Unsolicited submissions are OK. Prefers cassette (or VHS videocassette if available) with 3 songs and lyric sheet. SASE. Reports in 2 months.
Music: Mostly up-tempo pop, pop ballad and soft rock; also country. Produced "Catch a Snowflake" (by Hatton-Scott), recorded by Janet O. Neale (pop Christmas); "Plant a Tree" (by Hatton-Baumer), recorded by Beach Girls (pop); and "Seasons" (by Hatton-Hurley), recorded by Sandy Contella (pop ballad) all on E&S Records.
Tips: "Send good demo — strong lyrics and very good hook; up-tempo material (pop) needed now for young teenage female (Gibson — Tiffany type material). Also ballads for strong Englebert type and pop jazz for female."

HAWORTH PRODUCTIONS, 6219 Lathrop, Kansas City KS 66104. (913)299-8107. President/Producer: Dann E. Haworth. Record producer and music publisher (Southern Most Publishing/BMI). Estab. 1985. Deals with artists and songwriters. Produces 5 singles, 3 12″ singles, 10 LPs, 5 EPs and 10 CDs/year. Fee derived from sales royalty or outright fee from recording artist or record company.

How to Contact: Submit demo tape by mail. Unsolicited submissions are OK. Prefers cassette or 7½ ips reel-to-reel with 3 songs and lyric or lead sheets. SASE. Reports in 3 weeks.
Music: Mostly rock, country and gospel; also jazz, R&B and New Age. Produced *In The Heart, Wonder Where You're Wandering* and *Praise Him*, all written and recorded by Tracy Creech (gospel LPs). Other artists include The Hollowmen, Jordan Border, Jim Wilson, Esther Kreek and Tony Glise.

JAY HENRY/VISUAL MUSIC, Zeckendorf Towers Suite 355, 111 East 14th St.New York NY 10003. (212)505-9281. Record producer/engineer (MCA, Warner Bros., CBS, Epic,Columbia, Arista, Island, DEF Jam, New Antilles, Jive, Select, Profile & Emergency labels); record company and music publisher (VMEG associated labels); recording and production services, demo production, artist development, packaging. Contracts with artists, songwriters, major and indie labels. Video production and post-production services available. Fees derived from record sales, writer's royalties, record companies, outright artist/songwriter production fee.
How to Contact: Cassette, DAT (or VHS videocassette), 3-4 songs (copywritten) with lyric sheets, bio and picture. Include SASE for return. Allow 4 weeks for response or follow-up call.
Music: R&B, hip hop, dance, rock jazz and Latin. Produced "Poison," by BB&D (R&B) on MCA Records; "Broken Hearts," by Living Colour (rock) on Epic Records; and "Rock the Bass," by Heavy D (rap) on MCA Records.
Tips: "Never give up!!!"

LAWRENCE HERBST, P.O. Box 3842, Houston TX 77253. President: Lawrence Herbst. Record producer, music publisher (Beverly Hills Music Publishing/BMI, Klarr Music Publishing) and record company (Beverly Hills, Lawrence Herbst, Best-Way, Total Sound, D.T.I. and Larr Records) and Klarrco Satellite Radio and TV. Estab. 1966. Deals with songwriters and artists. Produces 1 12″ single and 1 LP/year. Fee derived from sales royalty or outright fee from record company.
How to Contact: Prefers 7½ ips reel-to-reel (or VHS videocassette) with 1 song and lead sheet. "Do a professional recording tape in a studio if you want to work with us." SASE. Reports in 6 weeks.
Music: Mostly rock, country and gospel; also interested in all types of music.

*GORDON HICKLAND, 2540 Woodburn Ave., Cincinnati OH 45206. (513)559-3999 or 681-5436. Producer: Gordon Hickland. Record producer (BMI). Estab. 1985. Deals with artists only. Produces 6 singles, 5 12″ singles, 1 LP and 5 EPs/year. Fee derived from sales royalty or outright fee from record company. Charges per diem, travel and hotel costs in advance.
How to Contact: Write first and obtain permission to submit. Prefers cassette with 4 songs and lyric sheet. "No porno, dirt or filth." Does not return unsolicited material. Reports in 4 weeks.
Music: Mostly R&B, gospel and pop; also dance and rap. Produced "Stingy" (by Wavier/Hicks) (R&B dance); "All About Town" (by Hickland, Barber) (pop); and "Heartbeat" (by Hickland) (R&B dance); all recorded on Vibe Records. Other artists include Trina Best, Angelic Choir, Eddie Barber and Kenny Johnson.

*HIGHLAND RECORDS, P.O. Box 554, Los Gatos CA 95031. (408)353-3952. Producer: Joe Weed. Record producer, music publisher (Highland Records/BMI), record company (Highland Records). Estab. 1986. Deals with artists and songwriters. Produces 3-4 LPs and 3-4 CDs/year. Fee derived from sales royalty or outright fee from recording artist.
How to Contact: Write to obtain permission to submit. Prefers cassette with 3 songs; no vocals. Instrumental music only. Does not return unsolicited material. Reports in 4-6 weeks.
Music: Mostly acoustic New Age, new acoustic, folk; also country. Produced *Dream of the Manatee* written and recorded by Weed/Hellman on Gouro Music (New Age/folk CD); *Indiana Moon* written and recorded by Scott Freed on LKA Records (country LP cassette); *Waltz of the Whippoorwill* written and recorded by Joe Weed on Highland Records (new acoustic, all album formats). Other artists include Steve Kritzer.
Tips: "Submit only well-composed, all-instrumental music in new acoustic, New Age or folk styles."

HIT AND RUN STUDIOS INC., 18704 Muncaster Rd., Rockville MD 20855. (301)948-6715. Owner/Producer: Steve Carr. Record producer and recording studio. Deals with artists and songwriters. Produces 12 singles, 2 12″ singles, 7 LPs and 6 EPs/year. Fee derived from outright fee from songwriter/artist and/or record company.
How to Contact: Call or write first and obtain permission to submit. Prefers cassette. Does not return unsolicited material. "Write your name and phone number on the cassette shell. I'll call you back if I can do anything with your material."
Music: Mostly rock, rockabilly and funk; also reggae, country and blues. Produced *Indestroy* on New Renasance Records (LP); "Slickee Boys" on New Rose France Records (single); and *Carnival Season* on What Goes On Records (EP); all by Band, recorded by Steve Carr. Other artists include Crippled

Pilgrims, Hyaai, Bomb Squad, May Day, Billy Kemp and The Paradise Rocker, Greg Royal, Bobby Kinzer, Benjamin Sands and D.V.S.

*HOBAR PRODUCTION, 27 Newton Pl., Irvinston NJ 07111. (201)375-6633. President: Randall Burney. Record producer, record company (Independent). Estab. 1987. Deals with artists and songwriters. Produces 4 singles, 6 12″ singles and 2 LPs/year. Fee derived from outright fee from record company.
How to Contact: Submit demo tape by mail. Unsolicited submissions are okay. Prefers cassette (or VHS videocassette if available) with 4 songs and 2 lyric or lead sheets. SASE. Reports in 3 weeks.
Music: Mostly R&B, pop and gospel; also country and rap.

HOGAR MUSICAL PRODUCTIONS, 4225 Palm St., Baton Rouge LA 70808. (504)383-7885. President: Barrie Edgar. Record producer and music publisher (Silverfoot). Deals with artists and songwriters. Produces 0-5 singles and 0-2 LPs/year. Fee derived from outright fee from record company.
How to Contact: Prefers cassette with maximum 4 songs and lyric sheet. SASE.
Music: Mostly rock, blues ("not soul"), country and pop. Produced "Louisiana's Basin Child," by Top Secret (rock single, Gulfstream Records).
Tips: "Send me a happy, story song (light hearted beat)."

HOMEBOY/RAGTIME PRODUCTIONS, (AUSTIN HALL PRODUCER) 68 Old Canton Rd. N.E., Cartersville GA 30120. (404)382-1442. Contact: Jack Hill. Record producer. Estab. 1988. Deals with artists and songwriters. Produces 3 singles, 1 12″ single and 1 LP/year. Fee derived from sales royalty.
How to Contact: Submit demo tape by mail. Unsolicited submissions are okay. prefers cassette with 3 songs and lyric sheet. SASE. Reports in 1 month.
Music: Mostly R&B, dance, rap, house and pop. Produced "Giving Good Loving," (by Austin Hall) recorded by Timonthy Gaye (R&B); "I Need You Tonight" and "Oh Father," (by Maurice Carroll) recorded by Simply Suave (house); all recorded on Westview Records.

HORIZON PRODUCTIONS, 435 Main St., Johnson City NY 13790. (607)770-0191. FAX: (607)797-6007. Estab. 1988. General Managers: Larry Lupole and Michael English. Producer/Engineer:Robert Damiano (owner recording studio Neo-Sync Labs). Specializes in cassette duplication, studio production, graphic design & printing, laser sheet music printing, audio wall displays, blank tapes and all manufacturing needs.
How to Contact: Write or call for free brochure of our services.

*HORRIGAN PRODUCTIONS, P.O. Box 41243, Los Angeles CA 90041. (213)256-0215. President/Owner: Tim Horrigan. Record producer and music publisher (Buck Young Music—BMI). Estab. 1982. Deals with artists and songwriters. Produces 5-10 singles, 5-10 12″ singles, 3-5 LPs and 3-5 CDs/year. Fee derived from sales royalty or outright fee from recording artist or record company. "We do some work on spec but the majority of the time we work on a work-for-hire basis."
How to Contact: Submit demo tape by mail. Unsolicited submissions are OK. Prefers cassette or VHS videocassette with 1-5 songs and lyric sheets. "Please do not call first; just let your music do the talking." SASE. Reports in 2 weeks.
Music: Mostly R&B, pop and rock; also country. Produced *Perfect World*, recorded by The Amazing Platters on Activ Records (pop LP—Switzerland); "Just For Awhile," recorded by Jimmy Roland on SGP Records (R&B single); and "If You Don't Think," recorded by Mike Quick on SGP Records (R&B single). Other artists include Johnny Legend and Keo.
Tips: "Get to know me."

*JOHN R. HUDSON, 11A Sharpleshall St., London, UK NW1 8YN **England.** (071)586-7746. Contact: John Hudson. Record producer, recording studio. Estab. 1964. Deals with artists and songwriters. Produces 10 singles, 10 12″ singles, 3 LPs and 3 CDs/year. Fee derived from sales royalty or outright fee from record company.
How to Contact: Call first and obtain permission to submit. Prefers cassette with 20 songs. Does not return unsolicited material. Reports in 2 months.
Music: Mostly pop and rock.
Tips: "Submit at least 20 songs and at least half should have a great hook and proper melody. Record companies require better quality produced demos now—voice and piano is no good; a full production is required."

*HUMANITY PRODUCTIONS, P.O. Box 885, Jamaica Plain MA 02130. (617)522-4589. President: Peter Brach. Record producer, demo tape producer and marketing service. Estab. 1987. Deals with artists and songwriters. Fee derived from outright fee from recording artist. "A deposit is required for engineering, marketing and production services."

How to Contact: Write or call first to arrange personal interview. Prefers cassette with 1-100 songs and lyric sheet. SASE. Reports in 1 month.

Music: All types of music. Other artists include Emerson Harrington, Luis Clemente, John Orr, Nicholas, Martin, April DeFord.

*INDEPENDENT AUDIO SERVICES, 235 West 76th St., New York NY 10023. (212)580-9825. Producer-Engineer: Stephen Fitzstephens. Record producer and production and engineering service. Produces 10 singles, 2 LPs and 2 CDs/year. Estab. 1977. Deals with artists and songwriters. Fee derived from hourly rate.

How to Contact: Write or call first to arrange personal interview. Prefers cassette, 15 or 7.5 ips reel-to-reel, or VHS or U-matic videocassette with 3 songs and lyric sheets. "Save your money and write or call first. I don't need much material to start off project." Does not return unsolicited material. Reports in 2 weeks.

Music: Produced *In the Key of Z* (by Lance Tait), on Tait Records (LP demo folk/rock); "Traditional Tunes" (by Bill Mulligan), on Prime Records (folk rock single); and "Untitled" (by Mark Newstetter) on Unreleased Records (blues rock single demo); all recorded by Fitz. Other artists include Steven Sacher and Steven Farzan.

Tips: "Write or call to book a presentation (performance or listening interview) at a studio of mutual choice. No synths, drum synths or sequencers."

*INDEPENDENT RECORDING STUDIO, P.O. Box 6487, Kokomo IN 46904-6487. (317)455-0308. President: David B. Bentzler. Record producer. Estab. 1984. Deals with artists and songwriters. Produces 3-5 singles, and 2-4 LPs/year. Fee derived from sales royalty or outright fee from recording artist or record company.

How to Contact: Write or call first and obtain permission to submit. Prefers cassette (or VHS videocassette if available) with 3-7 songs and lyric sheet. "Please include music background and career goals, SASE." Reports in 6 weeks.

Music: Mostly hard rock, rock fusion and pop; also jazz, country and MOR. Produced *It's Time* (by Gary Rhum) (rock/cassette/CD); "Everyday's a Holiday" (by Von Hiatt) (pop/single); and *The Veteran* (by Ron Jones) (MOR/cassette) all recorded by David Bentzler. Other artists include Hank Merrill, Brad Williams and Craig Neff.

Tips: "This is a business, learn everything you can to understand it before jumping in to it."

INDIE MUSIC PRODUCTIONS, INC., P.O. Box 326, Wanaque NJ 07465. (201)835-2991. A&R Director: Scott Patterson. Record producer. Estab. 1985. Deals with artists and songwriters. Each project is reviewed on payment.

How to Contact: Write or call first and obtain permission to submit. Prefers cassette and lyric or lead sheets. SASE. Reports in 3 weeks.

Music: Mostly rock, New Age and pop; also jazz.

INTRIGUE PRODUCTION, Suite 206, 6245 Bristol Parkway, Culver CA 90230. (213)417-3084 ext. 206. Producer: Larry McGee. Record producer and record company (Intrigue Productions). Estab. 1986. Deals with artists and songwriters. Produces 6 singles, 3 12″ singles, 1 LP, 4 EPs and 2 CDs/year. Fee derived from sales royalty.

How to Contact: Submit demo tape by mail. Unsolicited submissions are OK. Prefers cassette or normal ips reel-to-reel (or VHS videocassette) with 1-4 songs and lyric sheets. "Please put your strongest performance upfront. Select material based on other person's opinions." Does not return unsolicited material. Reports in 8 weeks.

Music: Mostly R&B, pop, rap and rock; also dance and adult contemporary. Produced "We're No. 1" (by Liz Davis), recorded by Saxon Sisters on Boogie Band Records (pop 12″); "Captain Freedom" (by Kenny Simms), recorded by Shena Kriss on Mega Star Records (R&B single and EP); and *I Feel Good With You*, written and recorded by Bill Sawyer on Dollar Bill Records (R&B LP). Other artists include S-Quires, Jim Sapienza, Terri Parondi, Roz Smith, Allen Brothers and Gary Walker.

Tips: "Decide which marketplace you would be more competitive in. Then create a commercial concept for you or your group."

*IRONWOOD PRODUCTIONS, 601 NW 80th St., Seattle WA 98117. (206)789-7569. Producer: Paul Scoles. Record producer, music publisher (see Wooden Iron music/BMI), record company (Ironwood Records) and recording studio. Estab. 1976. Deals with artists and songwriters. Produces 6-8 LPs and 4 CDs/year. Fee derived from sales royalty or outright fee from recording artist or record company.

How to Contact: Write or call first and obtain permission to submit. Prefers cassette (or VHS videocassette if available) with 3 songs and lyric sheet. "Clean, good quality demos are a must." Does not return unsolicited material. Reports in 1 month.

Music: Mostly rock, pop and country; also New Age and jazz. Produced *Dream Maker* written and recorded by Royce Taylor on RTO Records (LP); *Emerald City Jazz* (by Mike Corda), recorded by Great Goehle on Ironwood Records (LP/CD); *Over the Rainbow* (by various writers) recorded by The Jazz Police on Camelot records (LP/CD).

DAVID IVORY PRODUCTIONS, 237 Main St., Royersford PA 19468. (215)948-3448. Manager: Darrah Ribble. Record producer. Estab. 1986. Deals with artists only. Produces 3 singles, 2 12″ singles, 5 LPs and 4 CDs/year. Fee derived from "varying proportions of outright fee and royalties."
How to Contact: Call first to arrange personal interview. Prefers cassette with 3 songs. Does not return unsolicited material. Reports in 1 month.
Music: Mostly rock, pop and R&B; jazz and metal. Produced "So This is Life," written and recorded by The Daves (rock/single); and *The Spelvins*, written and recorded by The Spelvins (rock/LP) on SIRE Records. Other artists include Zooboys, The Bensons, Aftershokk, Beat Clinic, April Fool.

*SUNNY JAMES, 1051 Saxonburg Blvd., Glenshaw PA 15116. Producer: Sunny James. Record producer, music publisher, record company (Golden Triangle). Estab. 1987. Deals with artists only. Produces 6 singles, 2 12″ singles, 14 LPs and 1 CD/year. Fee derived from sales royalty or outright fee from record company.
How to Contact: Submit demo tape by mail. Unsolicited submissions are OK. Prefers cassette, 15 ips reel-to-reel (or ½″ VHS videocassette if available) with 3 songs and lyric or lead sheet. SASE. Reports in 1 month.
Music: Mostly R&B, country, rock; also adult contemporary and jazz. Produced "Dreamboat" and "San Antone" (by R. Craven), recorded by Sound Images and "Blue Moon" (by F. Johnson), recorded by Golden Triangle, all on Golden Triangle Records (all singles). Other artists include Jimmy Sapienza, Loney Smith, Joe DeSimone Arnel (Elvis) Pomp., Steve Grice (The Boxtops) and The Miracles.

ALEXANDER JANOULIS PRODUCTIONS, 1957 Kilburn Dr., Atlanta GA 30324. (404)662-6661. President: Alex Janoulis. Record producer. Deals with artists and songwriters. Produces 6 singles and 2 LPs/year. Fee derived from sales royalty or outright fee from recording artist or record company.
How to Contact: Write first and obtain permission to submit. "Letters should be short, requesting submission permission." Prefers cassette with 1-3 songs. "Tapes will not be returned without SASE." Reports in 2 months.
Music: Mostly top 40, rock, pop; also black and disco. Produced "He's A Rebel," (by Gene Pitney), recorded by Secret Lover on HotTrax Records (pop single); *Stop!*, written and recorded by the Chesterfield Kings on Mirror Records (rock LP); and *P is For Pig*, written and recorded by The Pigs on HotTrax Records (pop LP). Other artists include Night Shadows, Starfoxx, Splatter and Big Al Jano. "Album produced for Chesterfield Kings was reviewed in *Rolling Stone*."

PIERRE JAUBERT, 105 Rue De Normandie, Courbevoie 92 400 **France**. Phone: (1)4333-6515. Contact: President. Casting agent for singers to perform songs in movie soundtracks. Estab. 1959. Deals with singers and songwriters. Produces 3 singles, 2 12″ singles and 5 LPs/year. Fee derived from sales royalty.
How to Contact: Submit demo tape by mail. Prefers cassette with one song only.
Music: Dance and pop/top 40. Produced "You Call It Love" (by Karoline Kruger), by Virugen on Carrere Records (pop); "Si Je Te Mens" (by Xenia), recorded by Cariaire on Carreng Records (disco/pop); and "Mirabelle" (by E. Dooh), recorded by Farid Feajer on Marshall Records (ballad). Other artists include Richard Sanderson, Cook da Books and Katla Blas.

JAZZ & PRODUCTIONS, 12 Micieli Pl., Brooklyn NY 11218. (718)972-1220. President: Rick Stone. Record producer, music publisher (BMI) and record company (Jazzanne Records). Estab. 1984. Deals with artists only. Produces 1 LP/year. Fee derived from outright fee from recording artist or record company.
How to Contact: Write or call first and obtain permission to submit. Prefers cassette. Does not return unsolicited material. Reports in 2 weeks.
Music: Mostly jazz (straight ahead), bebop and hard bop. Produced *Blues for Nobody* and *Far East* (CD), both written and recorded by Rick Stone on Jazzanne Records (jazz).
Tips: "We are a small artist-owned label. We may in the future consider doing collaborative projects with other artists and labels. Our main concern is good music; we don't expect to get rich doing this."

*JAZZMARK SOUND, 47-51 43rd St., Queens NY 11377. (718)706-7071. Owner, Engineer/Producer: Mark J. Romero. Estab. 1984. Deals with artists only. Fee derived from any combination of sales royalty when song or artist is recorded, outright fee from recording artist and outright fee from record company. Charges depending upon contract status of the artist.

How to Contact: Submit demo tape by mail. Unsolicited submissions are okay. Prefers cassette with 4 songs. "If artist wants the material returned, he/she should provide mailing materials and postage." SASE. Reports in 3-4 weeks.
Music: Mostly jazz, R&B and funk; also New Age and pop. Artist include Jorge Nila and the Jazz Ninjas and The Scott Napoli Band.
Tips: "I'm glad to see musicians playing with each other in the studio again. I'm all for live tracking sessions with everyone playing together, sometimes even directly to 2-track."

*JOHNNY JET RECORDS, 304-68 Water St., Vancouver B.C. V6B 1A4 **Canada.** (604)685-2002. A&R: Dave Penner or John Livingston. Record producer, music publisher (Johnny Jet Music/BMI/PRO-CAN) and record company (Johnny Jet Records). Estab. 1990. Deals with artists and songwriters. Produces 12 singles and 6 LPs/year. Fee derived from sales royalty.
How to Contact: Submit demo tape by mail. Unsolicited submissions are okey. Prefers cassette with a maximum of 3 songs and lyric sheet. "Artists should include photo." SASE. Reports in 2 months.
Music: Mostly pop, rock and R&B. Produced *Dream A Little Dream* and *Tima B!* (by John Dexter & others), recorded by various artists on A&M Records (pop LP).

*JK'S UNDERGROUND RECORDING SERVICE, 800 Surrey Dr., E. Meadow NY 11554. (516)483-9747. Owner: John Kutkowski. Record producer, record company (Catchem Records, Unlaced Records) and producer of subliminal tapes (Alphasonics International). Estab. 1985. Deals with artists and songwriters. Produces 10 singles, 10 LPs and 10 CDs/year. Fee derived from sales royalty and outright fee from recording artist. Charges in advance for studio time.
How to Contact: Write first and obtain permission to submit. Prefers cassette with 2 songs. Does not return unsolicited material.
Music: Mostly hard rock, metal and pop-rock. Produced *Partners in Crime* (by Secrecy) on Catchem Records (rock); *The Night* (by Lace), on Unlaced Records (Glam-rock); and *Citi-Tricks Vol. 3* (by various artists), on Catchem Records (rock 2-record set), all recorded by JK.

*RALPH D. JOHNSON, 114 Catalpa Dr., Mt. Juliet TN 37122. (615)754-2950. President: Ralph D. Johnson. Record producer, music publisher (Big Wedge Music) and record company. Estab. 1960. Deals with artists and songwriters. Produces 10 singles/year. Fee derived from sales royalty and outright fee from record company.
How to Contact: Write or call first to arrange personal interview. Prefers cassette with maximum of 4 songs.
Music: Mostly country and novelty. Recorded "Little Green Worm" (by Cal Veale), recorded by Dave Martiv (novelty); "In the Middle of the Nighttime" (by Ralph O. Johnson), recorded by Joey Weltz (country); and "They Finally Got Around to You" (by T. Joe Christian), recorded by T. Joe Christian (country), all on Wedge Records.

JUMP PRODUCTIONS, 71 Langemunt, Erpe-Mere 9460 **Belgium.** (053)62-73-77. General Manager: Eddy Van Mouffaert. Record producer and music publisher (Jump Music). Estab. 1976. Deals with artists and songwriters. Produces 40 singles, 3 LPs and 1 CD/year. Fee derived from sales royalty.
How to Contact: Prefers cassette. Does not return unsolicited material. Reports in 2 weeks.
Music: Mostly ballads, up-tempo, easy listening, disco and light pop; also instrumentals. Produced "In Jouw Armen," recorded by Eddy Govert (Flemish); "Serenade for a Young Heart," recorded by Didier (ballad); and "Muziek," recorded by Sandra More (Flemish pop); all written by Eddy Govert on Scorpion Records. Other artists include Angie Halloway, Debby Jackson, Ricky Morgan and Sandra Tempsy.
Tips: Submit "easy, catching melodies (very commercial songs)."

JUNE PRODUCTIONS LTD., "Toftrees," Church Rd., Woldingham, Surrey CR3 7JH **England.** Managing Director: David Mackay. Record producer, music producer (Sabre Music) and record company (Tamarin, PRT Records). Estab. 1970. Produces 6 singles, 3 LPs and 3 CDs/year. Deals with artists and songwriters. Fee derived from sales royalty.
How to Contact: Prefers cassette with 1-2 songs and lyric sheet. SAE and IRC. Reports in 2 weeks.
Music: MOR, rock and top 40/pop. Produced "The Way Love Is" (by Marvin Gaye), recorded by Jimmy Nail on Virgin Records; "Younger Days," recorded by Jon English on Mushroom Records; and "Then There Was You," recorded by Ornella Mutti on WEA Records (all singles). Other artists include Joe Fagin, Max Boyce, Upwith People and No Hat Moon.

*TOLGA KATAS PRODUCTIONS, 10188 NW 47th St., Sunrise FL 33351. President: Tolga Katas. Record producer (BMI) and record company (LMR Records). Estab. 1986. Deals with artists and songwriters. Produces 43 singles, 43 12″ singles, 6 LPs and 6 CDs/year. Fee derived from outright fee from recording artist and record company. "If we charge the artist we give them a complete 12″ single masters."

How to Contact: Prefers cassette with 1-3 songs and lyric sheet. SASE. Reports in 2 weeks.

Music: Mostly pop, R&B and rock; also dance, rap and gospel. Produced *Party Your Body* (by Stevie B.), on LMR Records (LP); *In My Eyes* (by Stevie B.), on LMR Records (LP); and *I Need You* (by G.T.) on Atlantic Records (12″ single); all recorded by Tolga (pop).

Tips: "Be consistent and don't give up."

MATTHEW KATZ PRODUCTIONS, 29903 Harvester Rd., Malibu CA 90265. (213)457-4844. President: Matthew Katz. Record producer, music publisher (After You Publishing/BMI) and record company (San Francisco Sound, Malibu Records). Deals with artists and songwriters. Produces 6 singles, 6 12″ singles, 2 LPs and 2 CDs/year. Fee derived from sales royalty.

How to Contact: Prefers cassette (or 8mm videocassette) and lead sheet. Does not return unsolicited material.

Music: Mostly rock, pop and country. Produced *Moby Grape* (rock LP), and *Tim Hardin* (pop LP). Other artists include It's A Beautiful Day and Siberian Express.

BUTCH KELLY PRODUCTION, 11 Shady Oak Trail, Charlotte NC 28210. (704)554-1162. Executive Director: Butch Kelly. Record producer, music publisher (Butch Kelly Publishing/ASCAP and Music by Butch Kelly/BMI) and record company (KAM Executive and Fresh Avenue Records). Estab. 1985. Deals with artists and songwriters. Produces 4 singles, 4 12″ singles, 4 CDs and 4 LPs/year. Fee derived from sales royalty or outright fee from recording artist or record company.

How to Contact: Write first and obtain permission to submit. Prefers cassette (or videocassette) with 1-6 songs and lyric or lead sheet. "Send your best song on Maxell UDS II along with picture and bio." SASE. Reports in 4 months.

Music: Mostly pop and R&B; also rock and jazz. Produced "Where Have You Been," (by Butch Kelly) recorded by A. Brown (R&B); "Stumping Blues," (by Butch Kelly) recorded by Caro (R&B); and "Waiting," written and recorded by Butch Kelly (R&B/pop); all on KAM Records. Other artists include Melissa Kelly.

Tips: "Send your best songs."

GENE KENNEDY ENTERPRISES, INC., 315 Mt. Juliet Rd., Mt. Juliet TN 37122. (615)754-0417. President: Gene Kennedy. Vice President: Karen Jeglum Kennedy. Record producer, independent distribution and promotion firm and music publisher (Chip 'N' Dale Music Publishers, Inc./ASCAP, Door Knob Music Publishing, Inc./BMI and Lodestar Music/SESAC). Estab. 1975. Deals with artists and songwriters. Produces 40-50 singles and 3-5 LPs/year. Fee derived from sales royalty or outright fee from recording artist or record company.

How to Contact: Prefers 7½ ips reel-to-reel or cassette with up to 3 songs and lyric sheet. "Do not send in a way that has to be signed for." SASE. Reports in 3 weeks.

Music: Country and gospel. Produced "Labor of Love" (by Karen Mills and Marcia Sanford), recorded by Andi & the Brown Sisters (country); "I've Had Enough of You" (by Johnette Burton), recorded by Debbie Rich (country); and "Praise Ye the Lord" (by Linda Almond), recorded by Dave Jeglum (gospel); all on Door Knob Records. Other artists include Bobby G. Rice and Marilyn Mundy.

KINGSPORT CREEK MUSIC, Box 6085, Burbank CA 91510. Contact: Vice President. Record producer and music publisher. Deals with artists and songwriters.

How to Contact: Prefers cassette (or VHS videocassette). Does not return unsolicited material. "Include photo and bio if possible."

Music: Mostly country, MOR, R&B, pop and gospel. Produced "Tennessee Cowgirl" (country); "Pour Me a Stiff One" (R&B); and "My Daddy" written and recorded by Melvena Kaye on Cowgirl Records.

*KINGSTON RECORDS AND TALENT, 15 Exeter Rd., Kingston NH 03848. (603)642-8493. Coordinator: Harry Mann. Record producer, music publisher (Strawberry Soda Publishing—ASCAP) and record company (Kingston Records). Estab. 1988. Deals with artists and songwriters. Produces 3-4 singles, 2-3 12″ singles; 2-3 LPs and 1-2 CDs/year. Fee derived from sales royalty.

The asterisk before a listing indicates that the listing is new in this edition. New markets are often the most receptive to unsolicited submissions.

How to Contact: Submit demo tape by mail. Unsolicited submissions are OK. Prefers cassette with 1-2 songs and lyric sheet. SASE. Reports in 6-8 weeks.

Music: Mostly rock, country and pop; "no heavy metal." Produced *5¢ Strawberry Soda* (country rock LP) and "Message To You" (ballad rock single), written and recorded by Doug Mitchell; and *Songs Piped from the Moon*, written and recorded by S. Pappas (rock ballads, avante guard LP); all on Kingston Records. Other artists include Bob Moore, Candy Striper Death Orgy, Pocket Band, Jeff Walker, J. Evans, NTM and Miss Bliss.

Tips: "I believe electronic music is going a bit too far and there is an opportunity for a comeback of real as opposed to sequenced music."

HOWARD KNIGHT ENTERPRISES, 1609 Congress Rd., Eastover SC 29044. (803)776-8397. President: Howard A. Knight, Jr. Record producer, music publisher (Tenalina Music/ASCAP), record company (Pegasus Records), management firm and booking agency (Howard Knight Entertainment). Parent company estab. 1969. Deals with artists and songwriters. Produces 20 singles and 4 LPs/year. Fee derived from sales royalty or outright fee from recording artist or record company.

How to Contact: Prefers cassette with 3 songs and lyric sheet. Does not return unsolicited material. Reports in 2-6 weeks only if interested. "We do listen to all material. We do reply. We do not return any material."

Music: Mostly country, pop and rock; also gospel. Produced "A Woman's Way," written and recorded by Mundo Earwood; "Knee Deep In Love," (by John McMeens) recorded by Bandit Band; and "Airwaves of Love," (by John Joslin) recorded by Bandit Band; all on Pegasus Records (all country singles). Other artists include Almost Nuts Band, Jesse Blevins, Felix Rust and Brewer Brothers.

GREG KNOWLES, Suite 216, 8306 Wilshire Blvd., Beverly Hills CA 91502. (818)845-2849. Vice President/Record Division: Nick Schepperle. Record producer and record company (Helion Records). Estab. 1984. Deals with artists and songwriters. Produces 4 LPs/CDs/cassettes per year. Fee derived from outright fee from recording artist or record company. Charges for "production services for artists not signed to our company."

How to Contact: Write or call first and obtain permission to submit. Prefers cassette with 3-4 songs and lyric or lead sheet. "Mention in your cover letter if your demo is a production submission rather than for label consideration." Does not return unsolicited material. Reports in 3 weeks.

Music: Produced *Angel*, written and recorded by Diana Blair (country LP); *Swingstreet* (by Miriam Cutler), recorded by Swingstreet (jazz LP); and *Country West* (by Bob Duncan), recorded by Country West (country LP); all on Helion Records. Other artists include Dave Wagner, Jan Marie Cheatum and Johnny Rey.

Tips: "The quality of demos has risen dramatically over the last couple years. Send in a high quality tape with a nice (promo) package. This way we hear and see you at your best."

KNOWN ARTIST PRODUCTIONS, 1219 Kerlin Ave., Brewton AL 36426. (205)867-2228. President: Roy Edwards. Record producer, music publisher (Cheavoria Music Co./BMI and Baitstring Music/ASCAP) and record company (Bolivia Records and Known Artist Records). Estab. 1972. Deals with artists and songwriters. Produces 10 singles and 3 LPs/year. Fee derived from sales royalty.

How to Contact: "Write first about your interest." Prefers cassette with 3 songs and lyric sheet. Reports in 1 month. "All tapes will be kept on file."

Music: Mostly country, R&B and pop; also easy listening, MOR and soul. Produced "Got To Let You Know," "You Are My Sunshine" and "You Make My Life So Wonderful," all written and recorded by Roy Edwards on Bolivia Records (R&B). Other artists include Jim Portwood, Bobbie Roberson and Brad Smiley.

Tips: "Write a good song that tells a good story."

FRANK E. KOEHL, 6621 N. 59th Ave., Glendale AZ 95301. (602)435-0314. Owner: Frank E. Koehl. Record producer and music publisher (Auburn Records & Tapes, estab. 1962. Speedstar Music/BMI, estab. 1989.). Deals with artists and songwriters. Produces 9 singles and 3 12″ singles. Fee derived from sales royalty.

How to Contact: Submit demo tape by mail. Unsolicited submissions are okay. Prefers cassette with 2-4 songs and lyric sheet. SASE. Reports in 3 weeks.

Music: Mostly country, bluegrass and traditional music. Produced "Shade Tree" and "Lottery Fever" recorded by Troy McCourt on Auburn Records (acoustic country); also "The Buglarman," recorded by Al Ferguson, on Auburn PD Records (acoustic country). Other artists include Cherry River Boys and Ken Willson.

Tips: "Keep it country. No rock. Looking for traditional country and bluegrass, mostly acoustic. Country is going back to the older traditional songs."

ROBERT R. KOVACH, P.O. Box 7018, Warner Robins GA 31095-7018. (912)953-2800. Producer: Robert R. Kovach. Record producer. Estab. 1976. Deals with artists and songwriters. Produces 6 singles, 2 cassettes and 1 CD/year. Works with composers. Fee derived from sales royalty.
How to Contact: Prefers cassette with 4 songs and lyric sheet. SASE. Reports in 3 months.
Music: Mostly country and pop; also easy listening, R&B, rock and gospel..
Tips: "Be simple and sincere in what you write."

*LAMBDA PERFORMING ARTS GUILD OF AMERICA, P.O. Box 14131, Denver CO 80214. Executive Producer: Sharon Soria. Record producer, music publisher (Lambda Guild®/ASCAP), record company (Lambda Records®) and music referral service. Estab. 1987. Deals with artists and songwriters. "We are a nonprofit organization."
How to Contact: Submit demo tape by mail. Unsolicited submissions are OK. Prefers cassette (or VHS videocassette if available) with 1 song and lyric or lead sheet. "Include the following: the song title, lyric sheet and/or lead sheet, along with magnetic tape enclosed. No others follow." SASE. Reports in 3 months.
Music: Mostly pop, country, MOR; also easy listening, bluegrass and folk. Produced "Mother Earth," (by Barbara LaBonne), recorded by Smith & LaBonne (folk); "White Light," written and recorded by Sharon Soria (instrumental); and "Hold On," written and recorded by Sharon Smith (MOR/folk) all on Lambda Records®.
Tips: "We currently only work with lesbian artists. Our mission is to recognize and legitimize lesbian performers."

LAMON RECORDS/PANHANDEL RECORDS, P.O. Box 25371, Charlotte NC 28229. (704)537-0133. President: Dwight Moody. A&R: Carlton Moody. Record producer and music publisher (Laymond Publishing Co. and CDT Productions). Estab. 1962. Deals with artists, songwriters and publishers. Produces 33 singles, 4 12″ singles, 20 LPs and 5 CDs/year. Fee derived from outright fee from recording artist.
How to Contact: Write first and obtain permission to submit. Prefers cassette (or VHS videocassette) with minimum 2 songs. Does not return unsolicited material. Reports in 1 month.
Music: Mostly country, beach, gospel, rock & roll and R&B. Produced "Great Song Medley" recorded by Moody Bros. (country, Grammy nominated); "Give Me Love" (written by Tillman), recorded by Gady Ray (country, top 100 Cashbox); and "If It Ain't Love," recorded by Vanessa Parker (country, top 100 Cashbox), all on Lamon Records. Other artists include Allen Ray, Hutchins Brothers, Routabouts, Nelson Young, George Hamilton, IV and Dale Upton.

*LARI-JON PRODUCTIONS, 627 Countryview, Columbus NE 68601. (402)564-7034. Owner: Larry Good. Record producer, music publisher (Lari-Jon Publishing/BMI) and record company (Lari-Jon Records). Estab. 1967. Deals with artists and songwriters. Produces 10 singles and 5 LPs/year. "Producer's fees are added into session costs."
How to Contact: Submit demo tape by mail. Unsolicited submissions are okay. "Must be a professional demo." SASE. Reports in 2 months.
Music: Country, gospel-Southern and 50's rock. Produced "Rock & Rollin' Memories" (by Larry Good), recorded by Larry Good on Hornet Records (country single); "Nebraskaland" (by Larry Good), recorded by Larry Good on Lari-Jon Records (country single); and *Oldies With New Swing* recorded by Kent Thompson on Lari-Jon Records (country LP). Other artists include Tommy Campbell and Johnny Nace.
Tips: "Be professional in all aspects of the music business."

*LAUREL CANYON PRODUCTIONS, 8001 Jovenita Canyon Rd., Los Angeles CA 90046. (213)650-5408. Artist Acquisitions/Manager: Lena Michals. ASCAP and BMI. Estab. 1980. Deals with artists and songwriters. Fee derived from sales royalties or outright fee from record company. Charges for studio time and materials.
How to Contact: Submit demo tape by mail. Unsolicited submissions are OK. Prefers cassette with 3-4 songs and lyric sheet. Reports in 3-4 weeks.
Music: Mostly R&B, dance/pop, rock; also instrumental and country. Produced all 6 *Fame* albums (by Barry Fasman), recorded by Fame cast on RCA Records (pop LPs); *Champaign* (by Dana Walden), recorded by Champaign on CBS Records (R&B LP); and *Pauli Carman* (by Barry Fasman), recorded by Pauli Carman on CBS Records (R&B LP). Other artists include Debbie Allen, Johnny Mathis and Michelle Forrester.
Tips: "Be persistant and believe in yourself."

*LEE SOUND PRODUCTIONS, RON LEE, VALUE FOR MONEY, HOPPY PRODUCTIONS, Stewart House, Hill Bottom Road, Sands-Ind. Est., Highwycombe, Buckinghamshire HP12-4HJ **England.** 0494-36301-36401. Contact: Catherine Lee. Record producer. Estab. 1971. Deals with artists and

songwriters. Fee derived from sales royalty or outright fee from recording artist and record company.
How to Contact: Submit demo tape by mail. Unsolicited submissions are OK. Prefers cassette or Beta-VHS (PAL) videocassette with 3 songs and lyric sheet or lead sheets. SASE. Reports in 6 weeks.
Music: All types. Produced *Orphan In The Storm* (by Lansom), recorded by Emmit Till on Swoop Records (single and LP); *Ambition* (by Dunn), recorded by Orphan on Puk Records (LP and single); and *Street Fighters* (by Boone), recorded by Daniel Boone on Puk Records (LP and single). Other artists include Nightmare, The Chromatics, Sight-N-Sound, Suburban Studs and Groucho.

LEMON SQUARE PRODUCTIONS, P.O. Box 31819, Dallas TX 75231. (214)750-0720. A&R: Mike Anthony. Producer: Bart Barton. Record producer, music publisher and record label. Deals with artists and songwriters. Produces 2 singles and 3 LPs/year. Fee derived from sales royalty.
How to Contact: Write first and obtain permission to submit. Prefers cassette and lyric sheet or lead sheet. Does not return unsolicited material. Reports in 2 months.
Music: Mostly country and gospel. Produced "Like Goin' Home," (by Allison Gilliam) recorded by Susie Calvin (country) on Canyon Creek Records; "Still Fallin'," (by Dave Garner) recorded by Audie Henry (country) on RCA/Canada Records; and "Lord If I Make It To Heaven," (by Dale Vest/T. Overstreet) recorded by Billy Parker (country) on RCA/Canada Records. Other artists include Glen Baily, Susie Calvin, Larry Denny, Carol Garr and Bev Marie.

*TOMMY LEWIS, JR., RR 2, Box 111-C, Cresco PA 18326. (717)595-3149. Owner/Producer: Tommy Lewis, Jr. Record producer and record company (Round Sound Music). Estab. 1983. Deals with artists and songwriters. Produces 3-5 singles, 5 LPs and 5 CDs/year. Sales royalty. "Generally doesn't charge up-front, but if co-production is desired, advance payment is negotiated."
How to Contact: Write or call first and obtain permission to submit. Prefers cassette (or VHS videocassette if available) with 3 songs and lyric and lead sheet. "Be professional in your presentation." SASE. Reports in 6-8 weeks.
Music: Mostly New Age, pop and jazz; also country, R&B and gospel. Produced "After Your Heart" (by J. Schick), recorded by J. Schick (pop/single); *He Died For You* (by various artists), recorded by Ransomed on W.C. Productions Records (Christian rock/album); and "No Easy Way" (by T. Lewis, Jr), recorded by Gloria Kay (country/single).
Tips: "Be honest with yourself, do what you believe in, and always give your absolute very best!"

LINEAR CYCLE PRODUCTIONS, P.O. Box 2827, Carbondale IL 62902. (618)687-3515. Producer: R. Borowy. Record producer. Estab. 1980. Deals with artists and songwriters. Produces 15-25 singles, 6-10 12″ singles, 15-20 LPs and 10 CDs/year. Fee derived from sales royalty or outright fee from recording artist.
How to Contact: Prefers cassette or 7⅞ ips reel-to-reel (or ½″ VHS or ¾″ videocassette) . Does not return unsolicited material. Reports in 1 month.
Music: Mostly rock/pop, R&B/blues and country; also gospel and comedy. Produced "Smoothin' Smooth," (by E. Link) recorded by Eugene Cornblatt (A/C) on H. Hour Records; "Mom & Beer," (by T. Hické) recorded by Twangy Thumper & Gee-Tar (country) on Workin' Records; and "Froot," (by N.P.L.D.) recorded by M.C. Jail with P.D.R.-36A. Other artists include Smash, The Hip-Hop Brothers, Eugene Cornblatt, Rotary Engine, M.C. Melvin, Forgotten Men, Can't Find A Job and Saddle-Sore.

*LISTEN PRODUCTIONS, P.O. Box 1155, Hollywood CA 90078. (213)374-2468. President: Daniel Keller. Record producer. Estab. 1986. Deals with artists and songwriters. Fee derived from sales royalty or outright fee from recording artist or record company.
How to Contact: Submit demo tape by mail. Unsolicited submissions are OK. Prefers cassette or VHS videocassette with 4 songs and lyric sheet. "If artist, submit photos if available." SASE. Reports in 6 weeks.
Music: Mostly R&B (uptempo and ballads), pop and rock/alternative; also New Age and acoustic.

LITTLE RICHIE JOHNSON, Box 3, Belen NM 87002. (505)864-7441. Contact: Tony Palmer. Record producer, music publisher (BMI) and record company (LRJ). Estab. 1959. Deals with artists only. Produces 6 singles, 3 12″ singles, 6 CDs and 6 LPs/year. Fee derived from outright fee from recording artist.
How to Contact: Submit demo tape by mail. Unsolicited submissions are okay. Prefers cassette with 4 songs. SASE. Reports in 1 month.
Music: Mostly country. Produced "Step Aside," (by Ray Griff); "Big Big Love," (by Wynn Steward); and "I Don't Want to See You Cry," (by Johnny Herrea); all recorded by Jerry Jaramills on LRJ Records (all country). Other artists include Sam West IV, Elmer Fudpucker, Tommy Thompson, Rowe Bros., Bonnie Lou Bishop and Lacy Salazas.

LOCONTO PRODUCTIONS, P.O. Box 16540, Plantation FL 33318. (305)741-7766. President: Frank X. Loconto. Record producer and music publisher. Estab. 1978. Deals with artists and songwriters. Produces 20 singles and 20 LPs/year. Fee derived from sales royalty, outright fee from songwriter/artist and/or outright fee from record company.
How to Contact: Write first and obtain permission to submit. Prefers cassette. SASE.
Music: Produced "Back in Bimini," (by various writers) recorded by The Calypsonians (island); "Come Follow Me," written and recorded by Frank X. Loconto (gospel); and "Minnie Song," (by Frank X. Loconto) recorded by the Sunrise Pops Orchestra; all on FXL Records. Other artists include Bruce Mullin, Obediah Colebrook, Bill Dillon and James Billie (folk music).

*LOMAN CRAIG PRODUCTIONS, 1300 Division St. #104, Nashville TN 37203. (615)244-3505. President: Loman Craig. Record producer, music publisher (Loman Craig Music—ASCAP, Outlaw Music of Memphis—BMI, Doulikit Music—SESAC) and record company (Bandit Records). Estab. 1979. Deals with artists and songwriters. Produces 3 singles and 2 LPs/year. Fee derived from sales royalty or outright fee from recording artist.
How to Contact: Submit demo tape by mail. Unsolicited submissions are OK. Prefers cassette with 2-3 songs and lyric sheets. SASE. Reports in 3 weeks.
Music: Mostly country, country rock and bluegrass; also pop and gospel. Produced "One Woman To Love" (by Craig-Craig), recorded by Wally Jemmings on USA Records (country rock); "Security" (by Gray-Harper), recorded by Allen Gray on Bandit Records (country); and "Newborn Daddy," written and recorded by Steve Thomas on Bandit Records (MOR). Other artists include Pat Riley, Mark Wayne and Sherri Hollars.

*LOVE DOVE PRODUCTIONS, 811 Crotona Pk. N #B1, Bronx NY 10460. (212)294-6112. President A&R: Anthony De Veaux. Record producer, music publisher (Love Dove Music Pub./BMI) and record company (New Vibe Records). Estab. 1989. Deals with artists and songwriters. Produces 2 singles, 2 12″ singles, 1 LP and 1 EP/year. Fee derived from sales royalty or outright fee from record company.
How to Contact: Submit demo tape by mail. Unsolicited submissions are okay. Prefers cassette (or VHS or Beta videocassette if available) with minimum of 3 songs and lyric sheet and 1 lead sheet. "Good quality submissions only." SASE. Reports in 5 weeks.
Music: Mostly R&B, pop and gospel (contemporary); also rap. Produced "It's You," by Lesia Dove, (house single); "You Changed Me," by Lesia Dove/A. DeVeaux, (R&B duet); and "In The Breeze," by Gerald Trottmen (R&B 12″), all on New Vibe Records.
Tips: "Be dedicated, work hard and keep trying. Trends include house music being the next revolution in the business."

HAROLD LUICK & ASSOCIATES, Box B, 110 Garfield St., Carlisle IA 50047. (515)989-3679. Record producer, music industry consultant and music publisher. Deals with artists and songwriters. Produces 20 singles and 6 LPs/year. Fee derived from sales royalty, outright fee from artist/songwriter or record company, and from consulting fees for information or services.
How to Contact: Call or write first. Prefers cassette with 3-5 songs and lyric sheet. SASE. Reports in 3 weeks.
Music: Traditional country, gospel, contemporary country and MOR. Produced "It Must Be Love," (by Roger Davis/Sandy Davis), recorded by Lee Mace on Foot Stomper Records (country single); "For A Little While/Before I Go," (by T. Neil Smith); and "She Is America" (by Tony E. Palmer), recorded by Trade Mark. "Over a 12-year period, Harold Luick has produced and recorded 412 singles and 478 albums, seven of which charted and some of which have enjoyed independent sales in excess of 30,000 units."
Tips: "We are interested in helping the new artist/songwriter make it 'the independent way.' This is the wave of the future. As music industry consultants, our company sells ideas, information and results. Songwriters can increase their chances by understanding that recording and songwriting is a business. 80% of the people who travel to large recording/publishing areas of our nation arrive there totally unprepared as to what the industry wants or needs from them. Do yourself a favor. Prepare, investigate and only listen to people who are qualified to give you advice. Do not implement anything until you understand the rules and pitfalls."

M.R. PRODUCTIONS, 404 St-Henri, Montreal Quebec H3C 2P5 Canada. (514)871-8481. Producer: Mario Rubnikowich. Record producer, record company (Nephelim Records, MGR). Estab. 1987. Deals with artists and songwriters. Produces 3 singles, 3 LPs and 4 CDs/year. Fee derived from outright fee from record company and sales.
How to Contact: Submit demo tape by mail. Prefers cassette, 15 ips reel-to-reel with 3 songs and lyric or lead sheets. SASE. Reports in 5 weeks.
Music: Mostly New Age, pop and rock.

*MAC-ATTACK PRODUCTIONS, INC., 14699 N.E. 18th Ave., #6J, N. Miami FL 33181. (305)947-8315. President: Michael J. McNamee. Record producer and music pubilsher (see Mac-Attack Pub./ASCAP). Estab. 1987. Deals with artists and songwriters. Produces 15-30 singles, 15-30 12″ singles, 3-10 LPs, 3-10 EPs and 3-10 CDs/year. Fee derived from sales royalty or outright fee from recording artist or record company. "Depending upon the contract, a percentage to cover expenses that *will* be made."

How to Contact: Submit demo tape by mail. Unsolicited submissions are OK. Prefers cassette (or VHS videocassette if available) with a maximum of 3 songs and lyric sheet. "I can't stand formalities. Be yourself when writing your letter. Communication is the key to a great relationship." SASE. Reports in 1-2 months.

Music: Mostly pop, progressive rock and alternative; also progressive dance, R&B and New Age. Produced *Burn This Record* written and recorded by The Lead on R.E.X. Records (LP); "What Time Is It?" (by R. Rodriguez) on Dial Records re-released on Epic (single) and *Blowfly for President* (by various) recorded by Blowfly on Oops! Records (LP).

Tips: "There's no need to rush anything. Let it come naturally—don't try to force it. Remember, you and I will be gone one day, but our songs will never die."

RANDY B. MCCOY, P.O. Box 678, Baird TX 79504. (915)893-2616. Producer: Randy B. McCoy. Record producer. Estab. 1985. Deals with artists and songwriters. Produces 10 singles and 4 LPs/year. Fee derived from outright fee from artist. Charges artist up front for "all phases of project from start to finish, including production, arrangements, presentation, etc."

How to Contact: Prefers cassette with 3-4 songs and lyric sheet. "Make sure vocals can be clearly heard, and keep the arrangments simple and basic." SASE. Reports in 3 weeks.

Music: Mostly contemporary Christian; also easy listening, New Age, rock, country and R&B. Produced "Back to the Basics," written and recorded by Jeff Roach (easy listening) on Pit Productions Records; "Yahweh: Name Above All Names," written and recorded by House of Yahweh (religious) on House of Yahweh Records; and "Relaxation," written and recorded by Sarah Mulkey (easy listening) on Hendrick Medical Center Records. We are doing commercial (jingle) production and demo production for *many* individuals/agencies in Central Texas. The key role of the producer is to get the ultimate expression of feeling in the material he produces. I endeavor to get every ounce of creativity and emotion from the artist however possible."

Tips: "Get to the basics of what makes a unique, commercial song or act. No amount of 'overdubs' or 'costuming' can hide mediocrity. Originality usually presents itself in simple form."

*BUTCH MCGHEE, TYRA MANAGEMENT GROUP, P.O. Box 915, Sheffield AL 35660. (205)381-2060. President: Butch McGhee. Record producer and record company (Muscle Shoals Sound Gospel Records, Ameika Records). Estab. 1985. Deals with artists and songwriters. Produces 4 12″ singles, 10 LPs and 10 CDs/year. Fee derived from sales royalty. "Before project a production fee is charged."

How to Contact: Write first and obtain permission to submit. Prefers cassette or VHS videocassette with 3 songs and lyric sheets. "Send biography and photo is possible." Does not return unsolicited material. Reports in 8 weeks.

Music: Mostly gospel, R&B and country. Produced *2nd Chance*, recorded by Loretta Handy on Ameika Records (LP); *Anybody Can, God Can*, recorded by Voices of Cosmo on MSSG Records (LP); and *Pamela Davies and True Spirit*, recorded on MSSG Records (LP). Other artists include Keith Pringle, Stefania Stone Fierson, Vanessa Bell Armstrong, Charles Fold and Fold Singers.

Tips: "Supply gospel and inspirational material with a strong message. Clean demos and lyric sheets."

DAVID MACKAY, "Toftrees," Church Rd., Woldingham, Surrey CR3 7JH **England**. Managing Director: David Mackay. Record producer (June Productions) and music publisher. Works with artists and songwriters. Produces 10 singles, 10 12″ singles, 4 LPs and varying number of CDs/year. Fee derived from sales royalty.

How to Contact: Prefers cassette with 2 songs. SAE and IRC. Reports in 1 month.

Music: Mostly contemporary and rock. Produced "It Should've Been Me," recorded by David Ride on Phonorac Records; and "Younger Days,'" recorded by John English on Mushroom Records (both rock singles). Other artists include Joe Fagin, Ornella Mutti, Marica Hines, Upwith People and Barry Humphries.

LEE MAGID PRODUCTIONS, Box 532, Malibu CA 90265. (213)463-5998. President: Lee Magid. Record producer and music publisher (Alexis Music, Inc./ASCAP, Marvelle Music Co./BMI), record company (Grass Roots Records and LMI Records) and management firm (Lee Magid Management). Estab. 1950. Deals with artists, songwriters and producers. Produces 4 singles, 4 12″ singles, 8 LPs and 8 CDs/year. Publishes 10-15 new songwriters/year. Works with artists and songwriters; teams collaborators. Fee derived from sales royalty and outright fee from recording artist.

How to Contact: "Send cassette giving address and phone number; include SASE." Prefers cassette (or VHS videocassette) with 3-6 songs and lyric sheet. "Please only one cassette, and photos if you are an artist/writer." Does not return unsolicited material. Reports only if interested, "as soon as we can after listening."
Music: Mostly R&B, rock, jazz and gospel; also pop, bluegrass, church/religious, easy listening, folk, blues, MOR, progressive, soul, instrumental and top 40. Produced "What Shall I Do?" (by Quincy Fielding, Jr.); "I Got Joy" (by Quincy Fielding, Jr.), "Whenever You Call" (by Calvin Rhone); all recorded by Tramaine Hawkins on Sparrow Records (gospel rock). Other artists include Perry "The Prince" Wacker.
Tips: "The visual effect is just as important as the audio. An act should have theatrical as well as musical ability."

*COOKIE MARENCO, P.O. Box 874, Belmont CA 94002. Manager: Willa Rabinovitch. Record producer. Estab. 1981. Deals with artists and songwriters. Produces 10 LPs and 10 CDs/year. Fee derived form sales royalty or outright fee from recording artist or record company. "Charges 50% of projected cost in advance."
How to Contact: Write first and obtain permission to submit. Prefers cassette with 8 songs and lyric sheet. Does not return unsolicited material. Reports in 3 months.
Music: Mostly R&B dance, alternative modern rock, instrumental, ethnic and avante-garde; also classical, pop and jazz. Producer on *Winter Solstice II* written and recorded by various artists; *Heresay* (Paul McCandless); and *Turtle Island String Quartet* (by Turtle Island), all on Windham Hill Records (instrumental LP/CD). Other artists include Modern Mandolin Quartet, Blue Rubies, Alex DeGrassi and Art Lande.

JOHN MARS, P.O. Box 1583, Brantford ON N3T 5V6 **Canada**. Phone: (519)753-2081. Contact: John Mars. Record producer, music publisher (Utter Nonsense Publishing/CAPAC) and record company (Ugly Dog Records). Estab. 1979. Deals with artists and songwriters. Produces 1 single and 1 LP/year. Fee derived from sales royalty or outright fee from recording artist.
How to Contact: Submit demo tape by mail. Unsolicited submissions are OK. Prefers cassette (or BETA videocassette if available) with 4 songs and lyric or lead sheets. "Submit black and white photo of artist or group." SASE. Reports in 1 month.
Music: Mostly rock and roll, new jazz and R&B. Produced "Oh Yeah" (by Mars/Templeton), recorded Children and Daniel Lanois; *Annihilated Surprise* (by Broomer/Mars), recorded by J. Mars and Mark Wright; and *Electric Playground* (by Mars/Lanzalone/Sinkowski/Tremblay), recorded by J. Mars and Bob Doidge; all on Ugly Dog Records. Other artists include The Recognitions, The Martians and The Pop Tarts.

PETE MARTIN/VAAM MUSIC PRODUCTIONS, P.O. Box 29688, Hollywood CA 90029-0688. (213)664-7765. President: Pete Martin. Record producer, music publisher (Vaam Music/BMI, Pete Martin Music/ASCAP) and record company (Blue Gem Records). Estab. 1982. Deals with artists and songwriters. Produces 12 singles and 5 LPs/year. Fee derived from sales royalty. (Send small packages only.)
How to Contact: Prefers cassette with 2 songs and lyric sheet. SASE. Reports in 1 month.
Music: Mostly top 40/pop, country and R&B. Producer of country acts; Sherry Weston, Frank Loren, Brian Smith & The Renedages. Pop acts; Victoria Limon, Cory Canyon.
Tips: "Study the market in the style that you write. Songs must be capable of reaching top five on charts."

MARVEL PRODUCTIONS, P.O. Box 181, Holbrook NY 11741. Producer: Andy Marvel. Record producer, music publisher (Andy Marvel Music and Ricochet Records). Estab. 1981. Deals with artists and songwriters. Produces 12 singles and 3 LPs/year. Fee derived from sales royalty.
How to Contact: Prefers cassette (or VHS videocassette) with 3 songs and lyric sheet. SASE. Reports in 2 weeks. "No need to write for permission."
Music: Mostly pop, R&B and rock; also country. Produced *You Can't Hide Your Fantasies* (by Andy Marvel/Steve Perri/Tom Siegel); *Express (10 Items or Less)*, and *Meant to Be* (by Andy Marvel); all recorded by Andy Marvel on Alyssa Records (all LPs).

*DAVID MATHES PRODUCTIONS, P.O. Box 22653, Nashville TN 37202. President: David W. Mathes. Record producer. Estab. 1962. Deals with artists and songwriters. Produces 6-10 singles, 4-16 12" singles and 4-6 LPs/year. Fee derived from sales royalty.
How to Contact: Prefers 7½ or 15 ips reel-to-reel or cassette (or videocassette) with 2-4 songs and lyric sheet. "Enclose correctly stamped envelope for demo return." Reports as soon as possible.
Music: Mostly country and gospel; also bluegrass, R&B and top 40/pop. Produced "Simple Love Song" (by Bass/Mathes/Pelleteri), recorded by DeAnna (MOR/country, Rising Star/Sapphire Records); "Changes" written and recorded by Don Frost on NRS Records (MOR); "Moon Over Naples,"

(by John Rich), recorded by Silver Eagle Band (country pop, Sapphire Records) and "I Found Jesus In Nashville" (by Lin Butler), recorded by DeAnna (country/gospel, Nashville Gold Records). Other artists include George Westling, Johnny Newman, Nashville Sidemen and Singers and Silver Eagle Band.
Tips: "We look for professional material and presentations. Don't expect miracles on the first song released. Try to be different in style."

MEDA RECORDS INC., P.O. Box 21748, Detroit MI 48221. (313)862-5880. A&R Department: Joseph Hunter or Mertis John. Record producer, music publisher (Mertis Music Co., Inc./BMI) and record company (Meda Records Inc.). Music company estab. 1961; record company estab. 1981. Works with artists and songwriters. Produces 20 singles, 4-6 CDs and 4-6 LPs/year. Fee derived from sales royalty.
How to Contact: Prefers cassette with 4 songs and lyric and lead sheet. SASE. Reports in 1 month.
Music: Mostly pop, R&B and blues; also gospel. Produced "Christmas Comes Once a Year" (by Mertis John), recorded by Lamp Sisters (pop single); *Jesus Is Mine,* written and recorded by L. Williams (gospel LP); and "Why Did You Leave Me" (by Mertis John), recorded by Chicago Pete (blues single), all on Meda Records. Other artists include Buddy Lamp, Kevin & Keith John, Chicago Pete, Lorine Thompson, Joel Webster, Mable John and James Helms.

MICAH PRODUCTION, 43 Applemore Rd., Scarborough ON M1B 1R7 **Canada.** President: Oswald L. Burke. Record producer. Estab. 1987. Deals with artists and songwriters. Produces 3 LPs/year. Fee derived from sales royalty or outright fee from recording artist and record company.
How to Contact: No unsolicited material. Prefers cassette with lyric sheets. SASE. Reports in 8 weeks.
Music: Gospel. Produced *Introducing Brian Dungy,* written and recorded by Brian Dungy; *One Day,* written and recorded by Sweet Sound; and "Great Is Thy Glory" (by various artists), recorded by Toronto Mass Choir; all on Micah Records (gospel LPs).

*MIDI CITY, 701 Seventh Ave., New York NY 10036. (212)921-1711. Vice President: Joanne Georgio-Nathan. Record producer and record company (Midi City Records). Estab. 1988. Deals with artists and songwriters. Produces 5 singles and 10 12" singles/year. Fee derived from sales royalty and outright fee from recording artist.
How to Contact: Submit demo tape by mail. Unsolicited submissions are okay. Prefers cassette (or VHS videocassette if available) with 3 songs and lyric sheet and lead sheet (if possible). "Do not call—just send material." SASE. Reports in 1 month.
Music: Mostly pop/dance/rap with pop dance groove only. Produced "Walk on the Wild Side" (by Lou Reed), recorded by Bobby Nathan on Midi City Records (dance/single); *Black is Black* (by Rod Argent), recorded by Paul Pesw on Sire/Warner Records (dance/reggae/album); and *Easter Girl* (by Doug Gee), recorded by Doug Gee on Midi City Records. Other artists include Lady Unique, Mercedes Hall, Warren Doris and Deano Georgio.
Tips: "Send great songs only with great hooks! Rap dance is getting bigger!"

MIGHTY SOUNDS AND FILMWORKS, Suite 6-D, 150 West End Ave., New York NY 10023. (212)873-5968. Manager: Danny Darrow. Record producer, music publisher (Rockford Music Co./BMI) and record company (Mighty Sounds and Filmworks). Works with artists and songwriters. Produces 1-2 singles, 1-2 12" singles and 1-2 LPs/year. Fee derived from sales royalty.
How to Contact: Prefers cassette with 2-3 songs. SASE. No phone calls. Reports in 1 week.
Music: Mostly adult contemporary, country and adult rock. Produced *Dooms Day* (by various writers) on Colley Records (LP); *Great Folk Songs* (by various writers) on Mighty Records (LP); and "Carnival Nights," (by Vincent Delugia/Raymond Squillacote) (country/western), "I Sing You," (by Michael Greer) (pop), "Impulse," (by Danny Darrow) (jazz disco), all recorded by Danny Darrow on Mighty Records.

JAY MILLER PRODUCTIONS, 413 N. Parkerson Ave., Crowley LA 70526. (318)783-1601 or 788-0773. Contact: Jay Miller. Record producer and music publisher. Deals with artists and songwriters. Produces 50 singles and 15 LPs/year. Fee derived from sales royalty.
How to Contact: Arrange personal interview. Inquiries are invited. Prefers cassette for audition.
Music: Mostly country; also blues, Cajun, disco, folk, gospel, MOR, rock, top 40/pop and comedy. Working on video productions. Produced *Zydecajun,* by Wayne Toups on Mercury Records (LP); "I Wish I Had A Job," by Paul Marx (single); and "The Likes Of Texas," by Sammy Kershaw (single). Other artists include Wayne Toups, Tammy Lynn and Camey Doucet.

MR. MORT ENTERPRISES, 44 Music Sq. E, Nashville TN 37203. (615)255-2175. Vice President: Bernice Fields. Music publisher (BMI-ASCAP) and record company (Charta Records/Deluxe Records). Estab. 1977. Deals with artists and songwriters. Produces 20 singles and 8 LPs/year. Fee derived from sales royalty.

How to Contact: Submit demo tape by mail. Unsolicited submissions are OK. Prefers cassette (VHS videocassette) with 3-4 songs and lyric sheets. SASE. Reports in 4 weeks.
Music: Mostly country and MOR. Produced "Home Is Where The Love Is," (by C. Fields), recorded by Eddie Rivers; "Jealous Hearts and Suspicious Minds" (by C. Fields), recorded by Ronnie Klein; and "All The Things We are Not" (by M. Taylor), recorded by David Walsh; all on Charta Records (all country singles). Other artists include Fran Nickens, Donna Darlene and Nina Wyatt.
Tips: "Call or write for an appointment. Have a good quality cassette of three to four songs and a video cassette or pictures with bio. A super talented artist or group has a chance to make it in the business today.

***MR. WONDERFUL PRODUCTIONS, INC.**, 1730 Kennedy Rd., Lousiville KY 40216. (502)774-4118. President: Ronald C. Lewis. Record producer, music publisher (Ron "MisterWonderful" Music/BMI and 1730 Music/ASCAP) and record company (Wonderful Records and Ham Sem Records). Estab. 1984. Deals with artists and songwriters. Produces 2 singles and 3 12" singles/year. Fee is derived from outright fee from recording artist or record company.
How to Contact: Prefers cassette with 4 songs and lyric sheet. SASE. Reports in 3 weeks.
Music: Mostly R&B, black gospel and rap. Produced "Wanted" (by Ricky Henderson), recorded by Foul Play on Wonderful Records (rap); "Connect" (by Harold Johnson), recorded by Jerry Green on BroFeel Records; "First on the Dance Floor" written and recorded by Jerry Green on Wonderful Records; and "I'm the One for You" (by Jerry Green) on HamSem Records (all singles). Other artists include Tabitha Brown, Margaret Beaumont, Maxx Franklin, Nocomo and Golden Crowns (gospel).

MJD PRODUCTIONS, INC., P.O. Box 153, Sea Isle City NJ 08243. (609)263-1777. President: Marc J. Dicciani. Record producer, music publisher (Allora Music Publishing/BMI) and producer of audio for video, film, commercial. Estab. 1980. Deals with artists and songwriters. Produces 10 singles, 2-3 LPs and 1 CD/year. Fee derived from sales royalty or outright fee from recording artist or record company.
How to Contact: Prefers cassette (or VHS videocassette) with 2-3 songs and lyric sheet. SASE. Reports in 3 weeks.
Music: Mostly rock, pop and R&B; also jazz. Produced *Bodywaves* (by Tony Ventura), recorded by Ben Vereen on Manhattan Records (LP); *Every Light on Broadway* (by Doug Frank), recorded by Bobby Rydell on Applause Records (album cut); "Someone," written and recorded by Mary Welch on Atlantic Records (single); and "Dream By Dream" (by Jim Evans), recorded by Trish Bowman on Sunshine Records (pop). Other artists include Ant and Bobby Rydell.
Tips: "Keep song and artist demos uncluttered, with the vocals out front. Material must have strong melody and lyrics. Artist must have a unique but marketable sound."

MOM AND POP PRODUCTIONS, INC., P.O. Box 96, El Cerrito CA 94530. Executive Vice President: James Bronson, Jr. Record producer, record company and music publisher (Toulouse Music/BMI). Deals with artists, songwriters and music publishers. Fee derived from sales royalty.
How to Contact: Prefers cassette with 2-4 songs and lyric sheet. SASE. Reports in 1 month.
Music: Bluegrass, gospel, jazz, R&B and soul. Artists include Les Oublies du Jazz Ensemble.

MONTICANA PRODUCTIONS, P.O. Box 702, Snowdon Station, Montreal, Quebec H3X 3X8 **Canada**. Executive Producer: David Leonard. Record producer. Estab. 1963. Deals with artists, songwriters and artists' managers. Fee derived from sales royalty.
How to Contact: Prefers cassette, phonograph record (or VHS videocassette) with maximum 10 songs and lyric sheet. "Demos should be as tightly produced as a master." Does not return unsolicited material.
Music: Mostly top 40; also bluegrass, blues, country, dance-oriented, easy listening, folk, gospel, jazz, MOR, progressive, R&B, rock and soul.

MOOD SWING PRODUCTIONS, 332 N. Dean Rd., Auburn AL 36830. (205)821-JASS. Contact: Lloyd Townsend, Jr. Record producer, music publisher (Imaginary Music), record company (Imaginary Records) and distribution (Imaginary Distribution). Estab. 1982. Deals with artists. Produces 1-2 singles, 1-2 LPs, 1-2 EPs and 1-2 CDs/year. Fee derived from sales royalty.
How to Contact: Prefers cassette or 7½ ips reel-to-reel with 4 songs and lyric sheet or lead sheet. "Submissions not returned unless accompanied by SASE; may be retained for future reference unless return specifically requested." Reports in 3 months.
Music: Mostly jazz; also classical, blues and rock. Produced "Hexaphony," written and recorded by Somtow Sucharitkul (avant garde); "Sonic Defense Initiative," by various artists (rock), both on Imaginary Records. Other artists include Patrick Mahoney, and the Auburn Knights Orchestra.

*MORE COFFEE PRODUCTIONS/WESLEY BULLA, Suite B, 2113 Elliott Ave., Nashville TN 37204. (615)297-6939. A&R Director: Wesley Bulla. Record producer, music publisher (Sadhana Music Publishing/ASCAP). Estab. 1981. "We mostly work with major labels: EMI, Curb, Warner Chappel, RCA." Fee derived from sales royalty or outright fee from recording artist or record company.
How to Contact: Submit demo tape by mail. Unsolicited submissions are OK. Prefers cassette (or VHS videocassette if available) with 3 songs and lyric sheet. SASE.
Music: Mostly pop/rock, country, R&B; also gospel and New Age/jazz.
Tips: "Know your market, find a producer with music industry contacts. Produce quality demos. Publishers and record companies are expecting record quality demos."

*MARK J. MORETTE/MARK MANTON, 10815 Bodine Rd., Clarence NY 14031. (716)759-2600. Owner: Mark J. Morette. Record producer and record company (MarkJazz/Epigram). Estab. 1962. Deals with artists and songwriters. Produces 5-10 singles and 3-5 CDs/year. Fee derived from sales, pre-arranged agreements. "Changes for studio time, production time and personal time."
How to Contact: Write or call first and obtain permission to submit. Prefers cassette with 5-10 songs and lyric or lead sheets. Does not return unsolicited material. Reports in 6 months.
Music: Mostly New Age/jazz, heavy metal, heavy pop. Produced *When It Rains* (by Jeff Jarris), on Mark Records (New Age CD); *Slow But Sure* (by Kafi Wilmot), on Mark/Alhorst Records (New Age CD); and *Rockabye* (by Rockabye), on Epigram Records (heavy metal CD); all recorded by Mak Studias.

*ERIC MORGESON, 5619 N. Beech Daly, Dearborn Heights MI 48127. President: Eric Morgeson. Record producer. Estab. 1980. Deals with artists and songwriters. Produces more than 15 singles and 5 albums/year. Fee derived from sales royalty or outright fee from recording artist or record company.
How to Contact: Submit demo tape by mail. Unsolicited submissions are OK. Prefers cassette with 3 songs and lyric sheet. Include a SASE. Reports in 6 weeks.
Music: Mostly R&B, pop and rock. Produced "Don't Call My House," recorded by Ada Dyer on Motown Records (R&B); "Something 'Bout Your Touch," recorded by Sharon Bryant on Wing Records (R&B) and "Stay With Me," recorded by Gerry Woo on Polygram Records (R&B). Other artists include Tamika Patton, Billy Always, Fred Hammond, Krystol and Chris Bender.
Tips: "Be willing to rewrite. We just need A-sides."

FRED MORRIS MUSIC GROUP, 50 Music Sq. W., Nashville TN 37203. (615)329-2591. Record producer, music publisher (Maxx) and record company (Maxx Records). Works with artists and songwriters. Produces various number of singles/year. Fee varies.
How to Contact: Prefers cassette with 3-5 songs. If artist, send videocassette or picture and bio. SASE. Reports in 6 weeks.
Music: Mostly country, crossover and pop. Produced *Calendar Blues* (by Karen Pell/Dan E. James), recorded by Jill Jordan; and *We're Gonna' Love Tonight* (by Eddy Rager/Vernis Pratt), recorded by Don Juan, both on Maxx Records (both country crossover singles, LPs and CDs).
Tips: "If you want success in this business, treat it as a *profession*. Persistence and professionalism count as much as talent."

*MOTHER'S PRODUCTIONS, 37 Kosciusko Ave., Cohoes NY 12047. Owner: Michael Popowsky. Record producer and record company (Faraway Land). Estab. 1985. Deals with artists and songwriters. Produces about 30 singles, 10 LPs, 15 EPs and 5 CDs/year. Fee derived from outright fee from recording artist.
How To Contact: Submit demo tape by mail. Unsolicited submissions are OK. Prefers cassette (or VHS videocassette) with 4-5 songs and lyric sheets. "Please send cover letter describing background and musical interests (goals) and photograph." Reports in 2 months.
Music: Mostly interested in alternative, psychedelic/quirky pop and non-commercial rock; also R&B and jazz. Produced *Never No* (by Mick Sky); *One Good People the Peaces* (by Nathan Eldrin); and *Cosmic Accident* (by Sir Charles), all recorded by Mothers on Faraway Land Records (pop LPs). Other artists include Purple Light Bulb, the Spot, Vertigo, The Bapshees, Good and Colours.
Tips: "Be creative with your product! As people learn to use more effectively the new technologies emphasis will shift from overindulgent production skills to stronger songwriting/performance skills."

MOUNTAIN THERAPY MUSIC, (formerly Rosewood Productions), P.O. Box 364, New Castle PA 16103. (412)654-3023. Contact: Jay Moore. Record producer and record company (Rosewood Records). Deals with artists and songwriters. Produces 5 singles, 2 12" singles, 2 CDs and 6 LPs/year. Fee derived from outright fee from recording artist.

How to Contact: Prefers cassette and lyric sheet. Does not return unsolicited material. Reports in 3 weeks.

Music: Bluegrass/gospel and country. Produced "Grave's Digger," by Ron Mesing (bluegrass); "Remembrance," by Wes Homner (gospel); and "Mike Lilly," by Mike Lilly (country); all on Rosewood Records. Other artists include Full House, Wildwood Express and Mac Martin.

Tips: "Please send only the type of music requested. No more than 3 songs per demo. Strong lyrics and melody."

GARY JOHN MRAZ, 1324 Cambridge Dr., Glendale CA 91205. (818)246-PLAY. Producer: Gary Mraz. Record producer. Estab. 1984. Deals with artists and songwriters. Produces 6-12 12″ singles and 2-6 LPs/year. Fee derived from sales royalty or outright fee from record company.

How to Contact: Submit demo tape by mail. Unsolicited submissions are OK. Prefers cassette (VHS videocassette) with 3 songs and lyric sheets. "Does not return unsolicited material." Reports in 6 weeks.

Music: Mostly dance, pop and R&B. Produced "Flip" (by Ray/Sooen), recorded by Mraz/Ray on Draw Records (dance) and "Fontana/Game of Love" (by Jinni Fontana), recorded by Mraz on Banana Records (dance). Other artists include Jon Holland, Stacy O, Bunji Jumpers and The Moosters.

Tips: "Give me grooves that make you move. Just do what you do best."

*****MULTIMEDIA PRODUCTIONS**, Suite J, 1201 W. Pratt St., Baltimore MD 21223. (800)229-0355. President: Erik Steensen. Estab. 1986. Deals with artists and songwriters. Produces 2 singles, 1 12″ single and 1 LP/year. Fee derived from sales royalty or outright fee from recording artist or record company. "We charge for studio time in advance (not for production)."

How to Contact: Write first to arrange personal interview. Prefers cassette with 4 songs and lyric sheet. SASE. Reports in 2-4 weeks.

Music: Mostly progressive pop, R&B, rap, dance, New Age, jazz. Produced *Original Sound Track*, written and recorded by Gary Blanchard on Phlamingo Records (new wave LP); "Steven L. Miles," written and recorded by Bob Pyle on PB Records (novelty 12″); and "Submensas," written and recorded by Demon Norko on Urban Profane Records (alternative 45). Other artists include Mike Cochran, Craig Thomas, Kyo, Ashita and Charles Johnson.

*****MUNICH PRODUCTIONS/RECORDS B.V. EDESEWEG 33**, 9 Albert Schweitzerlaan, Bennekom 6721 **JN Holland.** (31)8389-16777 and 19377. FAX: (31)16588. Producer/President: Job Zomer. Record producer, music publisher (Munich Music) and record company (Munich Records B.V.). Deals with artists and songwriters. 24-track studio. Produces 10 CD singles, 20 12″ singles and 20 CDs/year. Fee derived from "percentage of net income."

How to Contact: Prefers cassette (or Beta or VHS PAL videocassette). Does not return unsolicited material.

Music: Mostly jazz, reggae and blues; also folk, ethnic and new classical. Produced *Turning Point*, written and recorded by Rory Block; *Jack of Hearts*, written and recorded by Jack of Hearts; *16 Titles* (by Mr. & Mrs. Bergman), recorded by Greed & Kauffeld; all on Munich Records (all LP/CD/cassette).

Tips: "Better chance with co-production and income of moneypower."

*****MUSIC FOR LITTLE PEOPLE**, P.O. Box 1460, Redway CA 85560. (707)923-3991. Director: Jim Deerhawk. Record producer, music publisher (Music for Little People/BMI), record company (Music for Little People, EarthBeat!). Estab. 1985. Deals with artists only. Produces 6-12 LPs and 6-12 CDs/year. Fee derived from royalty sales.

How to Contact: Write or call first and obtain permission to submit. Prefers cassette (or VHS videocassette if available) with 3 songs and lyric sheet. SASE. Reports in 3 months.

Music: Mostly chilcren's music, world music and children's stories.

*****MUSIDEO (JIM DEAN)**, Box 117008, Burlingame CA 94010. (415)344-4434. President: Jim Dean. Record producer. Estab. 1984. Deals with artists and songwriters. Produces 3 LPs and 4 CDs/year. Fee derived from sales royalty, outright fee from recording artist or record company, or "percentage of advance due artist or writer from record company." "If I am producing demo materials for hire when I am not aiding in getting a deal, I charge in advance for services."

Listings of companies in foreign countries have the name of the country in boldface type.

How to Contact: Submit demo tape by mail. Unsolicited submissions are OK. Prefers cassette with 4 songs and lyric sheet. SASE. Reports in 6 weeks.

Music: Mostly rock, pop, acoustic; also jazz, dance and R&B. Produced *The UpTones* (by the Up-tones), recorded by Jim Dean on Beserkeley Records (LP); *Jonnie Lipps* (by various artists), recorded by Jim Dean on Boardhead Records (LP); and "Penny in the Sky" (by Pat Winningham), recorded by Jim Dean on Compilation Records (single). Other artists include Hobo, The Queen Bees, World Zap Art, Anne Willingham, BSSB and Masters SME.

Tips: "Concentrate on lyrics and simple productions of good quality. As the industry separates the 'sound writing' approach into separate markets such as 'dance', there is more room for good songs."

TOMMY MUSTO/NORTHCOTT PRODUCTIONS, LTD., 972 Lexington Ave., New York NY 10021. (212)472-7972. FAX: (212)904-1737. V.P./Head A&R: Tommy Musto. Record producer, music publisher (Northcott Music/BMI, Tancott Music/ASCAP), record company (Midnight Sun, Fourth Floor Records). Management and remix services. Estab. 1980. Deals with artists, producers and songwriters. Produces 25-30 singles/year. Fee derived from sales royalty, outright fee from record company and advance/and or points on production.

How to Contact: Submit demo tape by mail to Tom Musto, 419 Elverton Ave., Staten Island NY 10308-1552. Prefers cassette with 3 songs. SASE. Reports in 4 weeks.

Music: Mostly dance/pop, R&B, house; also sample records, ballads and freestyle. Produced "Who Will It Be" (by T. Musto, J. Torres), recorded by Arlene on Midnight Sun Records (dance 12″); "Come On Lover" (by Mike and Wendi Rogers), recorded by Wendi Rogers on Midnight Records (dance 12″); and "Betrayel," written and recorded by Spiritmatter on Tropical Heat Records (Latin freestyle 12″). Other artists include Stacey Parris, Nadia, Barbara Tucker, Pink Noise, Fallout, Wired, Break Boys and Royal Orchestra.

NASHVILLE COUNTRY PRODUCTIONS, 351 Millwood Dr., Nashville TN 37217. (615)366-9999. President/Producer: Colonel Jack Lynch. Record producer, music publisher (Jaclyn Music/BMI), record company (Jaclyn and Nashville Country Records) and distributor (Nashville Music Sales). Estab. 1987. Works with artists and songwriters. Produces 1-12 singles and 1-12 LPs/year. Fee derived from sales royalty or outright fee from artist or record company; "We do both contract and custom producing."

How to Contact: Submit demo tape, or write or call first and obtain permission to submit or arrange personal interview. Prefers cassette with 1-4 songs and lyric or lead sheet. SASE. Reports in 10 days.

Music: Mostly country, bluegrass, MOR and gospel; also comedy. Produced *Making My Way Back To You* (country LP); "Bluegrass & Black Diamonds," recorded by Jack Lynch & The Nashville Travelers on Nashville Country Records (bluegrass); and "The Deputy" (by Ray Cline), recorded by Ralph Stanley on Nashville Country Records (bluegrass). Other artists include Larry Sparks, Country Gentlemen and Dave Evans. "We produced Keith Whitley and Ricky Skaggs' first album."

NASHVILLE INTERNATIONAL ENTERTAINMENT GROUP, Box 121076, Nashville TN 37212-1076. (615)244-5357. President: Reggie M. Churchwell. Vice President: Mark Churchwell. General Manager, Music Group: Ben Haynes. Record producer, music publisher (Sir Winston Music/BMI and Four Seasons Music/ASCAP) and Reggie M. Churchwell Artist Management, Nashville International Talent and Nashville International Concerts. Labels include Phoenix Records and Nashville International Records. Deals with songwriters only. Produces 6 singles, 2 LPs and 2 CDs/year. Fee derived from sales royalty.

How to Contact: Write first about your interest. Prefers cassette with 1-4 songs and lyric sheet. Does not return unsolicited material "unless prior contact has been made and SASE included."

Music: Country, MOR, pop and gospel (contemporary); also R&B (crossover), rock (country, pop, power pop), soul (crossover) and top 40/pop. Produced "Letter in Red," written and recorded by Kenny Durham (pop/gospel single); and *A Little Left of Center Line*, written and recorded by Howard Lips (LP), both on Phoenix Records; "Unluckiest Songwriter in Nashville," written and recorded by Sonny Shroger on Hazzard Records (single); and "Please," recorded by Howard Lips Christian Blues on Phoenix Records (single).

*NEBO RECORD COMPANY, P.O. Box 194 or 457, New Hope AL 35760. Manager: Jim Lewis. Record producer, music publisher (Nebo Ridge Publishing/ASCAP) and record company (Nebo Record Company). Estab. 1985. Deals with artists and songwriters. Fee negotiable.

How to Contact: Submit demo cassette tape by mail. Unsolicited submissions are OK. Prefers cassette tape or VHS videocassette with 1 song and lyric sheet. "It is OK to send a videocassette, but not a must. Send 1 song only. Songwriters should be sure to send a SASE. Send a neat professional package. Send only 1 song." Does not return unsolicited material. Reports "as soon as possible."

Music: Mostly modern country, traditional country and gospel; also rock, R&B and pop. Produced "Mama's Candyman," written and recorded by Osie Whitaker (traditional country single); "My Everlastin' Savior," recorded by Charles W. Cooper (gospel single); and "Nothin' Without You" (by

Walker Ikard), recorded by Walker Ikard and Anita Biss (modern country single); all on Nebo Records. Other artists include James W. Hilliard, James Pence and Jim Lewis.
Tips: "Because of the cost factor in the music industry today, music professionals are looking for hit songs only, so send only your best songs for a review."

*NEON JUKEBOX PRODUCTION, P.O. Box 16, Hampton VA 23669. (804)838-6930. Producer: Doc Holiday; Producer & Engineer: Tom Breeden. Record producer and music publisher (Live Note Publishing/BMI, Doc Publishing/BMI). Estab. 1985. Deals with artists and songwriters. Produces 15-20 singles, 3-5 LPs and 5-10 EPs/year. Fee derived from sales royalty or outright fee from recording artist or record company.
How to Contact: Submit demo tape by mail. Unsolicited submissions are OK. Prefers cassette with 2-3 songs and lyric sheets. "Artist: bios and photos helpful but not a must." SASE. Reports in 4 weeks.
Music: All types. Produced "If You Could Only See" (by Judith Guthro/Richie Balin), recorded by Richie Balin (country/single); "Seven Wonders of the World," written and recorded by Richie Balin (country/single); and "Canadian State of Mind" (by Tom Breeden/Judith Guthro), recorded by Dock Holiday (country folk EP); all recorded on Tugboat Records. Other artists include Kevin Irwin and Jon Washington. Produced 16 records charting in the top 100's on Cashbox and Billboard charts in the last 20 months. "If You Could Only See" went #1 on Cashbox Country Indies Charts and to #44 on Cashbox 100's Country Singles Chart. "Seven Wonder's of the World" is presently at #49 on Cashbox Top 100's Country Charts and at #5 on Cashbox Country Indies Charts and still climbing! "Although to date a majority of product has been focused on a country market, we are expanding to also include A&R departments for rock and top-40 projects."
Tips: "Send good quality demos with lyric sheets and be sure to include SASE and phone number for reply."

*NERVOUS MUSIC, 4/36 Dabbs Hill Lane, Northolt, Middlesex, London **England**. Phone: 44-01-422-3462. Managing Director: Roy Williams. Record producer, music publisher (Nervous Publishing) and record company (Nervous Records). Produces 2 12" singles, 4 CDs and 10 LPs/year. Deals with artists and songwriters. Fee derived from sales royalty.
How to Contact: Prefers cassette with 3-10 songs and lyric sheet. "Include photo and a letter giving your age and career goals." SAE and IRC. Reports in 2 weeks.
Music: Mostly rock 'n' roll, psychobilly and rockabilly. Produced "Never Say Die" (by Peck), recorded by Rattlers on Nervous Records (rockabilly); "Slide" (by Lovett), recorded by Niteshift Trio on Fury Records (rockabilly); and "Kick Down Low" (by Brawd), recorded by Torment on Nervous Records (psychobilly). Produces Lost Souls, Catmen and Pharoahs regularly.
Tips: "Send wild, fast music. No AOR, disco, heavy rock, stadium rock, pop, reggae or soul."

NEW HORIZON RECORDS, 3398 Nahatan Way, Las Vegas NV 89109. (702)732-2576. President: Mike Corda. Record producer. Deals with singers preferably. Fee derived by sales royalty.
How to Contact: Prefers cassette with 1-3 songs and lyric sheet. SASE.
Music: Blues, easy listening, jazz and MOR. Artists include Mickey Rooney, Bob Anderson, Jan Rooney, Joe Williams and Robert Goulet.

NICK NACK PADDYWACK RECORDS, P.O. Box 3248 Yale Station, New Haven CT 06520. (212)348-8288. Vice President/A&R Department: Casper Krantz. Record producer, music publisher (Nicholas Astor-Grouf Enterprises), record company (Nick Nack Paddywack Records) and advertising agency/jingle commercial music production house (Nicholas Astor-Grouf Enterprises). Works with artists and songwriters. Produces 25 singles, 10 12" singles, 5 LPs, 1 EP and 2 CDs/year. Pays negotiable royalty to artists; statutory rate to publishers for each record sold.
How to Contact: Prefers cassette (or VHS videocassette) with 3-5 songs and lyric sheet. SASE. Reports in 6 weeks.
Music: Mostly new rock, top 40/pop, jazz; also folk, ethereal New Age and classical. Produced "Alone" (by Astor), recorded by Nicky Groove (new rock/top 40); "Do We Have to Talk About It" (by Liftin/Bennahum), recorded by Burn that Groove (post modernist extract); and "Big Ass Jewel" (by Cooper), recorded by Sprawl (Tex/Mex/funk/punk); all on Nick Nack Paddywack Records. Other artists include Withering Torso, Life of Sport, Bolo, Lullabye Commandos, Cattle Collision and Squirm.
Tips: "Songs should be both witty and literate with a careful attention paid to subject matter and motif; author should have an understanding of his role in a consumer post-modernist generation and a vision of his position in the 1990s. We, as an unaffiliated Yale organization, press a number of albums and one double compilation effort which achieves international distribution. We consider all contributions and encourage communication."

NIGHTWORK RECORDS, 355 W. Potter Dr., Anchorage AK 99502. (907)562-3754. Contact: Kurt Riemann. Record producer and music licensor (electronic). Deals with artists and songwriters. Produces 2 singles, 8 LPs and 2 CDs/year. Fees derived from sales royalty or outright fee from recording artist.
How to Contact: Prefers cassette or 15 ips reel-to-reel with 2-3 songs "produced as fully as possible. Send jingles and songs on separate reels." Does not return unsolicited material. Reports in 1 month.
Music: Mostly electronic and electronic jingles. Produced *Gaia*, by K. Riemann; *Aurora*, by Eelshake; and *Denali*, by Boxer, all LPs on Nightworks Records. Other artists include "most Alaskan artists and independent producers."

*NOT-2-PERFECT PRODUCTIONS, 615 Valley Rd., Upper Montclair NJ 07043. (201)741-2359. Owner: George Louvis. Record producer. Estab. 1989. Deals with artists and songwriters. Produces 10-15 12″ singles and 3-5 LPs/year. "We pay all recording costs then recoup from record companies advance and royalties."
How to Contact: Write or call first and obtain permission to submit. Prefers cassette with 1-2 songs and lyric sheet. "If you are submitting as an artist include a picture and bio if available." Does not return unsolicited material. Reports in 5 weeks.
Music: Mostly R&B, club dance and rap; also pop rock, pop dance and pop metal. Produced "To the Maximum" (by Steven McGhee, G. Louvis, Sly Stone), recorded by Steve D the Destroyer on Q-Rap (rap 12″ single); "Gotta Have It" (G. Louvis), recorded by Liberation on Republic Records (club 12″ single); "Love Me True" (by G. Louvis), recorded by Kimiesha Holmes on Quark Records (Club 12″ single). Other artists include Tammy Francica, Blaze (co-produce), One & One.
Tips: "Be patient. In the first six months of 1989 we signed 3 artists, produced them, shopped deals for them and got deals for all three. Submit your best material and learn to be objective. Don't believe that just because you wrote it, it's great. If you wouldn't buy it don't send it."

NUCLEUS RECORDS, P.O. Box 111, Sea Bright NJ 07760. President: Robert Bowden. Record producer, music publisher (Roots Music/BMI) and record company (Nucleus Records). Estab. 1979. Deals with artists and songwriters. Produces 2 singles and 1 LP/year. Fee derived from sales royalty.
How to Contact: Submit demo tape by mail. Unsolicited submissions are OK. Prefers cassette with 3 songs and lyric sheets. SASE. Reports in 4 weeks.
Music: Mostly country and gospel; also pop. Produced "Pressure Cooker," written and recorded by Jean Schweitzer (country); "Always," written and recorded by Marco Sision (pop); and "Selfish Heart," written and recorded by Robert Bowden (country); all on Nucleus.

JEANNINE O'NEAL PRODUCTIONS, 195 S. 26th St., San Jose CA 95116. (408)286-9840. Producer: Jeannine O'Neal. Record producer and arranger. Deals with artists and songwriters. Produces 10 singles, 5 12″ singles, 6 LPs and 2 CDs/year. Fee derived from sales royalty, outright fee from songwriter/artist and/or outright fee from record company.
How to Contact: Submit demo tape or write or call first to arrange personal interview. Prefers cassette with 3 songs and lyric or lead sheets. SASE.
Music: Mostly rock/pop, country and gospel; also jazz and international. Produced "Before, After" and "Oh Why," recorded by Sister Suffragette (pop/rap); "Heartbeat" and "On the Road Again Without You," recorded by The Reed Sisters (country); *Blanca Carrasco Family LP* (Mexican contemporary Christian); and "According to You" and "Rockin' By You Baby," by Amy Clemens (modern country).

*ORANGE PRODUCTIONS, Suite 119, 2166 W. Broadway, Anaheim CA 92804-2446. (714)992-2677. CEO: Maxwell Edison. Record producer, music publisher (Tracy Sands Music/BMI), record company (Orange, Beet, Swak, Cavern). Estab. 1989. Deals with artists and songwriters. Produces 12 singles, 12 12″ singles, 8 LPs, 2-3 EPs and 8 CDs/year. Fee derived from sales royalty or outright fee from recording artist or record company.
How to Contact: Submit demo tape by mail. Unsolicited submissions are OK. Prefers cassette with 2-3 songs and lyric sheet. SASE. Reports in 2 months.
Music: All types. Produced "Black Will Be the Color" (by Tom Harris), recorded by Manhunter (country 7″); "Ain't No Big Thing" (by Robert Wahlsteen), recorded by Bob Chance (rock 7″), both on Orange Records; and "I'm Down" (by John Lennon and Paul McCartney), recorded by Tracy Sands on Swak Records (rock 7″). Other artists include Mary Hart and Jonah.
Tips: "Looking for high skill level; craftsmen – artisans."

*ORDER PRODUCTIONS, 6503 York Rd., Baltimore MD 21212. (301)377-2270. President: Jeff Order. Record producer and music publisher (Order Publishing/ASCAP). Estab. 1986. Deals with artists and songwriters. Produces 6 singles, 3 12″ singles, 12 LPs, 4 EPs and 2 CDs/year. Fee derived from sales royalty and outright fee from recording artist and record company.

How to Contact: Submit demo tape by mail. Unsolicited submissions are okay. Prefers cassette with 4 songs and lyric or lead sheet. "Send photo and resume." Does not return unsolicited material. Reports in 1 month.

Music: Works with all types of music. Produced "Won't You Dance With Me" (by Jeff Order), recorded by Tiny Tim on (dance/single); "Sea of Tranquility" (by Jeff Order), recorded by Jeff Order (New Age LP); and "Joy!" (by Fernando Allen), recorded by The Fernando Allen Singers (gospel LP). Other artists include Gabrielle Goodman, Rob Fahey, Oral 69, Firestorm and Tracy Hamlin.

Tips: "We only work with songwriters and artists who are seriously committed to a career in music. Submissions should be professionally recorded."

JOHN "BUCK" ORMSBY/ETIQUETTE PRODUCTIONS, Suite 273, 2442 N.W. Market, Seattle WA 98107. (206)524-1020. FAX: (206)524-1102. Publishing Director: John Ormsby. Record producer (Etiquette/Suspicious Records) and music publisher (Valet Publishing). Estab. 1980. Deals with artists and songwriters. Produces 1-2 singles, 3-5 LPs, and 3-5 CDs/year. Fee derived from sales royalty.

How to Contact: Prefers cassette (or VHS videocassette) with lyric or lead sheet. SASE.

Music: R&B, rock, pop and country. Produced *Snake Dance* (by Rogers), recorded by Kinetics on Etiquette Records (LP); and *Hard to Rock Alone*, written and recorded by K. Morrill on Suspicious Records (LP); and *Crazy 'Bout You*, (by R. Rogers), recorded by Kinetics on Etiquette Records. Other artists include Jerry Roslie.

Tips: "Tape production must be top quality; lead or lyric sheet professional."

*OUTLOOK PRODUCTIONS, Box 180, Star Route, Bethel ME 04217. (207)824-3246. Record producer. Deals with artists and songwriters. Produces 12 singles and 6 LPs/year. Fee derived from sales royalty and/or outright fee from record company.

How to Contact: Prefers cassette or 15 ips reel-to-reel (or VHS videocassette) with 1 song and lyric sheet. "Please include your name and phone number on the tape." Does not return unsolicited material.

Music: Mostly rock, pop and country; also new wave, heavy metal and avant-garde. Produced *Private WA I&II*, by Willie Alexander (rock/avant garde EPs, Tourmaline Records); "Orgone Box", by The Twitch on Tourmaline Records (rock cassette album); *Sky Frontier* and *Innocent Condemned* by Sky Frontier on Tourmaline Records (rock albums); "Facets", by Jewel Clark on Tourmaline Records (country EP).

MICHAEL PANEPENTO, #811, 225 Oxmoor Circle, Birmingham AL 35209. (205)942-3222. President: Michael Panepento. Record producer, music publisher (Weedhopper Music/BMI and Panepentunes/ASCAP), record company (Pandem Records Inc.) and recording studio. Estab. 1983. Deals with artists and songwriters. Produces 3-5 singles, 1-3 LPs and 3-5 EPs/year. Fee derived from sales royalty or outright fee from recording artist.

How to Contact: Write first and obtain permission to submit or arrange personal interview. Prefers cassette or 15 ips reel-to-reel with 3 songs and lyric sheet. SASE. Reports in 3 weeks.

Music: Mostly rock, top 40 and R&B; also MOR, pop, AOR, jazz/R&B, country, jazz/straight and classical. Produced *Elvis'Grave* (movie soundtrack); *Listen To Me* (by Randy Hunter), recorded by Hunter/Panepento (LP); *Elvis' Grave* (by various writers), recorded by various artists on Pandem Records (movie soundtrack); "The Diptones" (by various writers), recorded by various artists on Pendem Records (MOR vocal). Other artists include Tim Newton (country) and Foxxy's Company/The Pedestrians, Paradox.

PANIO BROTHERS LABEL, Box 99, Montmartre, Saskatchewan S0G 3M0 **Canada**. Executive Director: John Panio, Jr. Record producer. Estab. 1977. Deals with artists and songwriters. Produces 1 single and 1 LP/year. Works with lyricists and composers and teams collaborators. Fee derived from sales royalty or outright fee from artist/songwriter or record company.

How to Contact: Prefers cassette with any number of songs and lyric sheet. Does not return unsolicited material. Reports in 1 month.

Music: Country, dance, easy listening and Ukrainian. Produced "Christmas Is Near," by the Panio Brothers Band (Christmas single); "Celebrate Saskatchewan," by the Panio Brothers (Ukrainian); and *Best of the Panio Brothers*, by the Panio Brothers on PB Records (cassette).

*PARADISE RECORDS, Box 15511, Kansas City MO 64106. Manager/Producer: Marion Sheyke. Music publisher (Louie B. Publishing BMI), Releases varied number of singles/year. Labels include QP, Kaytown, Paradise, Soulsearch. Works with artists and songwriters on contract. "May consider producing artists with exceptional talent."

How to Contact: Prefers cassette (or VHS videocassette) with 3 songs and lyric or lead sheet. Include 8x10 photo if available. SASE, bio.
Music: Top 40 (dance), R&B crossover, R&B, blues and gospel; also country. Produced "Sing The Love Song" (top 40 ballad) and "I'll Always Be there," (top 40 dance), both by Cotton Candy; "Paradise" (dance), "Shake Me Up" (ballad) and "I Need Your Lovin" (dance).
Tips: "We are looking for hit single material with strong hook. Songs relating to everyday life are great. Send the best quality tape you can afford."

MICK PARKER, Gateway Studio, Kingston Hill Centre, Surrey KT2 7LB **England**. Managing Director: Mick Parker. Record producer. Also produces and writes TV commercials and film soundtracks. Estab. 1985. Works with artists and songwriters. Produces 6-10 singles, 2-3 LPs and 2-3 CDs/year. Fee derived from sales royalty or outright fee from record company.
How to Contact: Prefers cassette with up to 5 songs and lyric or lead sheet. SAE and IRC. Reports in 3 weeks.
Music: Mostly rock, jazz/rock, dance; also pop, soul and funk. Produced "So Macho" (by G. Hargreaves), recorded by Sinitta on Fanfare Records; "I'll Reach Out" (by M. Parker/D. Williams), recorded by Chantal on Frontier Records; and "Set Me On Fire" (by John Read), recorded by Vivian Wray on A.J.S. Records. Other artists include Rosie Patterson, Bob Kerr's Whoopee Band, Lee Prentiss and Lewis Sisters.
Tips: "Don't worry about the production too much and I want to hear good songs, well sung and with the minimum of fussy arrangement."

***PATTY PARKER**, Suite 114, 10603 N. Hayden Rd., Scottsdale AZ 85260. (602)951-3115. Producer: Patty Parker. Record producer, record company (Comstock, Paylode), miscellaneous independent releases. Estab. 1978. Deals with artists and songwriters. Produces 24 singles, 3 LPs and 1 CD/year. Fee derived from outright fee from recording artist or recording company. "We *never* charge to songwriters!! Artist's fee for studio production/session costs."
How to Contact: Submit demo tape by mail. Unsolicited submissions are OK. Prefers cassette, (or VHS videocassette if available) with 4 songs and lyric sheet. Voice up front on demos. SASE. Reports in 1 week.
Music: Mostly country, adult contemporary and top 40.

DAVE PATON, The Idea Bank, 16776 Lakeshore Dr., C-300, Lake Elsinore CA 92330. Contact: Dave Paton. Record producer and music publisher (Heaven Songs/BMI). Deals with artists and songwriters. Produces 20 singles and 3-5 LPs/year. Fee negotiable.
How to Contact: Write first. Prefers 7½ ips reel-to-reel or cassette with 3-6 songs and lyric sheet. SASE. Reports in 2 weeks.
Music: Country, dance, easy listening, jazz, MOR, progressive, R&B, rock, top 40/pop and comedy.

***SANDY PEARLMAN, INC.**, 245 Hyde St., San Francisco CA 94102. (415)885-4999. A&R Director: Natasha V. Record producer, record company (Popular Metaphysics, formerly 415), recording studio (Alpha & Omega Recording, Hyde Street Studios). Estab. 1972. Deals with artists and songwriters. Produces 1 LP/year. Fee is negotiable; depends upon the circumstances. "Producer's fee is advanced before beginning project."
How to Contact: Submit demo tape by mail. Unsolicited submissions are OK. Prefers cassette, record or CD with 3 or more songs. "If you want a written response to your submissions, please include an SASE. Do not call the office. Include photograph(s) and bio, contact phone numbers and addresses. Write on tape: band name, names of songs on tape in order plus phone number." Reporting time "variable due to number of submissions. If an SASE is included, response will follow within one month after listening. However, sometimes because of the number of submissions, listening to the tape is delayed from the time of submission."
Music: Cutting-edge intelligent rock or heavy metal, over the top funk and R&B; also all forms of experimental music and sound, country beyond the fringe. Released *And You*, written and recorded by Manitoba's Wild Kingdom on Popular Metaphysics Records (rock LP, CD, cassette); *Lime Twigs and Treachery*, written and recorded by Love Club on Popular Metaphysics Records (rock LP, CD, cassette). Both are distributed by MCA Records. Produced *Imaginos* (by S. Pearlman), recorded by Blue Oyster Cult on CBS Records (rock LP); *Club Ninja*, written and recorded by Blue Oyster Cult on CBS Records (rock LP); and *Medicine Show*, written and recorded by Dream Syndicate on A&M Records (rock LP). Other artists include The Clash, The Dictators and Pavlov's Dog.
Tips: "Punt! Go ahead, blow my mind.

JOHN PENNY, 484 Lexington St., Waltham MA 02154. (617)891-7800. President: John Penny. Record producer, music publisher (Penny Thoughts Music/BMI) and record company (Belmont Records, Waverly Records). Produces 15 singles and 6 LPs/year. Deals with songwriters and artists. Fee derived from fee from recording artist.

How to Contact: Write first and obtain permission to submit. Prefers cassette with 3-4 songs. SASE. Reports in 2 weeks.
Music: Mostly c&w, rock. Produced *Hands of a Dreamer*, written and recorded by Larry Flint (LP and single); "Good Timer" written and recorded by Stan Jr. Anderson (single); and "Nights Out at the Days Inn" (by J. Fox/L. Wilson/R. Ball), recorded by Jimmy Allen; all country/western on Belmont Records. Other artists include Jackie Lee Williams, Tim Barrett, John Hicks, Paul Metcalf, Rick Robinson and The Bayou Boys, and Mike Cummings.

*PERSIA STUDIOS, 378 Bement Ave., Staten Island NY 10310. (718)816-6384. Studio Owner: Chris Vollor, producer/engineer. Estab. 1982. Deals with artists and songwriters. Produces 5-10 singles, 2 LPs and 3 CDs/year. Fee derived from recording artist or record company. Charges for studio time—session players.
How to Contact: Prefers cassette (or VHS videocassette if available) with 3-4 songs. Does not return unsolicited material. Reports in 2 months.
Music: Mostly rock, pop and R&B; also alternative, dance and industrial and jazz/New Age. Recently produced *House of Strangeness* (by Nebraska), on Quite Unusual Records (LP); "New Rose" (by Phil Portuesi), on New Rose Records (single); and *XXY* (by XXY), on Dead Issue Records (compilation LP), all recorded by Persia Studios.

PAUL PETERSON CREATIVE MANAGEMENT, 9005 Cynthia, #309, Los Angeles CA 90069. (213)273-7255. Contact: Paul Peterson. Record producer, music publisher and personal management firm. Estab. 1983. Deals with artists and songwriters. Produces 2 LPs and 2 CDs/year. Fee derived from sales royalty or outright fee from songwriter/artist or record company.
How to Contact: Prefers cassette and lyric sheet. SASE. Reports in 1 month.
Music: Mostly rock, pop and jazz; also country. Produced *Spring Fever* written and recorded by Brian Savage on USA Records (jazz/pop); *Lost Cabin Sessions*, recorded by Ozark Mountain Daredevils on Legend Records (country/rock LP); "Love At First Sight," (by Conrad Stolze), recorded by Dogs? on Dogs? Records (rock EP); and *Everything's Alright*, written and recorded by Priscilla Bowman on Legend Records (blues/rock LP). Other artists include Second Language (modern rock) and Man About Town (modern rock).

MICHAEL ROBERT PHILLIPS, % Orinda Records, Suite 200, 111 Deerwood Place, San Ramon CA 94583. (415)831-4890. Producer: Michael Robert Phillips. Record and video producer and record company (Orinda Records). Estab. 1982. Deals with artists and songwriters. Produces 10-20 LPs and 10-20 CDs/year. Fee derived from sales royalty or outright fee from record company and advance.
How to Contact: Prefers cassette (or ½" videocassette) and lyric sheet or lead sheet. Does not return unsolicited material. Reports in 2 months.
Music: Mostly rock, pop rock, pop; also jazz.

*JIM PIERCE, 101 Hurts Ln., Hendersonville TN 37075. (615)824-5900. FAX: (615)824-8800. President: Jim Pierce. Record producer, music publisher (see Strawboss Music/BMI) and record company (Round Robin Records). Estab. 1974. Deals with artists and songwriters. Produces 50 singles, 5-6 EPs and 2-3 CDs/year. Fee derived from sales royalty or outright fee from recording artist. "Some artists pay me in advance for my services."
How to Contact: Write or call first to arrange personal interview. Prefers cassette with any number of songs and lyric sheet. Does not return unsolicited material. Reports in 2 months.
Music: Mostly country, contemporary, country/pop and traditional country. Produced "Don't Call Us, We'll Call You," written and recorded by Harlen Helgeson; "You Can't Keep a Good Love Down" (by Jerry Fuller), recorded by Lenny Valenson and "If I Live To Be A Hundred" (by Mae Borden Axton), recorded by Arne Benoni all on Round Robin Records (country singles). Other artists include Bonnie Guitar, Jimmy C. Newman, Margo Smith, Bobby Helms, Sammi Smith and Blaine Dakota.
Tips: "Don't let a 'no' stop you from trying."

PLANET DALLAS, (formerly Patrick Keel), P.O. Box 191447, Dallas TX 75219. (214)521-2216. Record producer, music publisher (Planet Dallas/BMI, Stoli Music/ASCAP) and recording studio (Planet Dallas). Estab. 1985. Deals with artists and songwriters. Produces 4-6 singles, 10 12" singles, 5 LPs, 3 EPs and 2 CDs/year. Fee derived from sales royalty or outright fee from recording artist or record company.
How to Contact: Submit demo tape by mail or write first and obtain permission to submit. Prefers cassette with 1-3 songs and lyric sheet. Reports in 4-6 weeks. Send SASE for reply.
Music: Mostly modern rock and top 40. Produced *Princess Tex*, (by Hal West) recorded by Princess Tex (pop/LP) on Horsehead Records; *King*, written and recorded by The Daylights (punk/funk/EP) on 109 Records; and *To Hell and Back*, written and recorded by Nemesis (rap/LP) on Profile Records. Other artists include Shock Tu, The Trees and The Mystics.

POPS NEON ENTERPRISES, P.O. Box 4125, West Hills CA 91308. Director: Steve Hobson. Record producer and music publisher (Auntie Argon Music/BMI). Estab. 1988. Deals with artists and songwriters. Produces 2-4 singles/year. Fee derived from sales royalty or outright fee from recording artist. Retainer required for production services.
How to Contact: Write first and obtain permission to submit. Prefers cassette with 1-3 songs and lyric sheets. "Type lyric sheets. Don't overproduce demos. Piano/vocal or guitar/vocal are OK." Does not return unsolicited material. Reports in 2 weeks.
Music: Mostly mainstream pop/top 40, country and novelty. Produced "City Boy Gone Country" and "Go Mountaineers" (both by S. Hobson), recorded by Daddy Hoedown on Pops Neon Records (country singles) and "The Hand" (by Steve Hobson/Jill Baker), recorded by Jill Baker on Pops Neon Records (pop).
Tips: "Submit songs that best represent your direction and best showcases your talents as an artist. No one can predict a hit . . . so anything has a chance."

PRAIRIE MUSIC LTD., P.O. Box 438, Walnut IA 51577. (712)366-1136. President: Robert Everhart. Record producer, music publisher (BMI) and record company (Prairie Music). Estab. 1964. Deals with artists and songwriters. Produces 2 singles and 2 LPs/year. Fee derived from outright fee from recording artist or record company.
How to Contact: Submit demo tape by mail. Unsolicited submissions are OK. Prefers cassette. SASE. Reports in 4 months.
Music: Mostly traditional country, bluegrass and folk. Produced "Time After Time," "Street Sleepers" and "Rock of Hollywood"; all written and recorded by Bob Everhart on Folkways Records (traditional country). Other artists include Bonnie Sanford and Fiddlin' Grandad Kephart.

THE PRESCRIPTION CO., 70 Murray Ave., Port Washington NY 10050. (516)767-1929. President: David F. Gasman. Vice President A&R: Kirk Nordstrom. Tour Coordinator/Shipping: Bill Fearn. Secretary: Debbie Fearn. Record producer and music publisher (Prescription Co./BMI). Deals with artists and songwriters. Fee derived from sales royalty or outright fee from record company.
How to Contact: Write or call first about your interest then submit demo. Prefers cassette with any number of songs and lyric sheet. Does not return unsolicited material. Reports in 1 month. "Send all submissions with SASE or no returns."
Music: Bluegrass, blues, children's, country, dance, easy listening, jazz, MOR, progressive, R&B, rock, soul and top 40/pop. Produced "You Came In" and "Rock 'n' Roll Blues," by Medicine Mike (pop singles, Prescription Records); and *Just What the Doctor Ordered*, by Medicine Mike (LP).
Tips: "We want quality—fads mean nothing to us. Familiarity with the artist's material helps too."

*****NICKY PRICE**, 619 Salisbury from Green Lanes, Harringay N8 ORX **England**. Contact: Nicky Price. Record producer and record company (Bolts Records). Estab. 1989. Deals with artists and songwriters. Produces 3-4 singles, 1 EP and 1 CD/year. Fee derived from sales royalty when song or artist is recorded, outright fee from artist or record company, depending on deal. Charges a small advance or recording fee where applicable.
How to Contact: Submit demo tape by mail. Unsolicited submissions are okay. Prefers 7½ or 15 IPS reel-to-reel (or VHS PAL videocassette) with 1 song and lyric sheet. SASE. Reports in 3 weeks.
Music: All types of dance house/high NGR, etc. Produced "Jack it Up" (by Nicky Price), recorded by Mirrior Image (12" house); "Winner Takes it All," recorded by Sandra Edwards (high NRG 12"); and "Eurobeat" (by Mikki Zone), recorded by Man to Man (high NRG 12"), all on Bolts Records. Other artists include Krukuts.

*****PRIMAL PRODUCTIONS, INC.**, 3701 Inglewood Ave., Suite 133, Redondo Beach CA 90278. (213)214-0370. Vice President/Producer: Jeffrey Howard. Record producer, music publisher (Primal Visions Music/BMI) and record company (Primal Records). Estab. 1985. Deals with artists and songwriters. Produces 6 singles and 3 LPs/year. Production charges vary from project to project.
How to Contact: Write or call first and obtain permission to submit or to arrange personal interview. Prefers cassette, DAT, or VHS videocassette with 1-5 songs and lyric sheet. "Send only your best and strongest material. Demos are OK but use of high quality cassettes and packaging does reflect on your level of professionalism." SASE. Reports in 6 weeks.
Music: Mostly rock and hard rock, pop and R&B/dance/rap; also country, New Age and heavy metal. Produced "Desperate Angel" and "Kid Rocker," recorded by Desperate Angel (rock singles); and *The Passion*, recorded by Jeffrey Howard (rock LP), all written by J. Howard and recorded on Primal Records. Other artists include Christopher Fedrov and Jeffrey Laine.
Tips: "Always believe in yourself and your material. Don't write what you think *we* want to hear. We're interested in strong material performed by people with a passion for what they do. I have recently seen a trend toward rap music on the West Coast, and there seems to be no end in sight to

that. Commercial hard rock has literally turned radio into the 'Rock 40' and that also will continue to be a strong contender in the commercial music market."

PRODUCTIONS DIADEM, C.P. 33, Pointe-Gatineau, Quebec J8T 4Y8 **Canada**. (819)561-4114. Record producer (CAPAC) and record company (Jouvence). Estab. 1982. Deals with artists and songwriters. Produces 2 singles, 1-3 LPs and 1-3 CDs/year. Fee derived from outright fee to record company.
How to Contact: Write first and obtain permission to submit. Prefers cassette (or VHS videocassette) with 3-5 songs and lyric sheet. SASE. Reports in 4 weeks.
Music: Mostly pop, ballads and children's songs. Produced *Fêtons et chantons* (by D.D.M. Marleau) (children's CD/LP); and *Chansons de paix* (by various artists) (pop LP); both recorded by Diadem on Jouvence.
Tips: "Knowledge of French or French material is most welcome."

QUADRAPHONIC TALENT, INC., P.O. Box 630175, Miami FL 33163. (305)472-7757. President: Jack P. Bluestein. Record producer and music publisher. Estab. 1973. Deals with artists and songwriters. Produces 5-10 singles/year. Fee derived from sales royalty.
How to Contact: Query, submit demo tape (artist), submit demo tape and lead sheet (songwriter). Prefers cassette or 7½ ips reel-to-reel with 1-4 songs. SASE. Reports in 1 month.
Music: Blues, country, easy listening, folk, gospel, jazz, MOR, rock, soul and top 40/pop. Produced "Three Things" and "A Miracle in You," by Ray Marquis on Twister Records (country singles); "Red Velvet Clown" and "Love Day," by Dottie Leonard on AMG Records (pop singles); and "Terrorism" and "Ginger," by Winn Thumpkins.

R.E.F. RECORDS, 404 Bluegrass Ave., Madison TN 37115. (615)865-6380. President: Bob Frick. Manager: Shawn Frick. A&R Director: Scott Frick. Record producer and music publisher (Frick Music Publishing Co./BMI). Deals with artists, songwriters and producers. Produces 2 singles and 10 LPs/year. Fee derived from sales royalty.
How to Contact: Write or call first and obtain permission to submit, then submit 7½ ips reel-to-reel or cassette with 2-10 songs and lyric sheet. SASE. Reports in 1 month.
Music: Mostly gospel; also country, rock and top 40/pop. Produced "Unworthy," recorded by Bob Myers; and "One Day Closer to Jesus" and "Heading for Heaven," recorded by Bob Scott Frick (all gospel singles, R.E.F. Records). Other artists include Larry Ahlborn.

*RADIO MAGIC/BSO RECORDS, Via Carmine Modestino, 64, Paternopoli AV 83052 **Italy**. (0827)71073 or 71033. FAX: 0827-71033. President: Sal Barbieri. Record producer and music publisher (Conypol Music/BMI). Produces 10 singles and 4 LPs/year. Deals with artists and songwriters. Works with 4 new songwriters/year. Fee derived from outright fee from artist/songwriter.
How to Contact: Prefers cassette and lyric sheet. Prefers studio produced demos. SAE and IRC. Reports in 1 month.
Music: Mostly dance and top 40/pop; also country, easy listening, MOR, progressive, R&B, rock and soul. Produced "In the Name of Love," by S. Barbieri (dance single, BSO Europe Records); "Coming Up," by Sigfrida (top 40 single, BSO Europe Records); and "Heavy Stuff," by S. Barbieri (top 40 single, BSO Records).

RANDOM IMAGE PRODUCTIONS, 209 Madison Ave., Toronto, Ontario M5R-2S6 **Canada**. (416)929-2349. President: Peter Randall. Record producer, music publisher (Random Image Music/PROCAN) and record company (Random Records). Works with artists and songwriters. Produces 3 singles and 3 LPs/year. Fee derived from sales royalty or outright fee from artist or record company. Sometimes charges 50% up front.
How to Contact: Prefers cassette (or VHS videocassette) with 2-3 songs and lyrics (must) and lead sheets (optional). SASE. Reports in several weeks.
Music: Rock, pop and New Age. Produced "What Do You Want," written and recorded by P. Randall (pop); "Without You," written and recorded by S. Firth (pop); and "Shelley" (by A. Mangus), recorded by Quadras (pop). All on Random Records.

RAPP PRODUCTIONS, INC., Rt. 16, Box 560 Caine Cir., Gainesville GA 30506. (404)889-8624. Owner/President: Ron Dennis. Record producer, music publisher (Super Rapp Publishing/BMI) and record company (Rapp Records, Rapture, Ready Records and Yshua Records). Estab. 1964. Works with artists and songwriters. Produces 10-20 singles, 10-20 LPs, 10-20 EPs and 10-20 CDs/year. Fee derived from sales royalty and outright fee from artist or record company.
How to Contact: Write or call first and obtain permission to submit or to arrange personal interview. Prefers cassette or 15 or 30 ips reel-to-reel (or VHS videocassette) with lyric chords and lead sheet. "Demo should have lead vocal and music and also a recording of music tracks without vocals." SASE. Reports in 3 months.

Music: Mostly gospel and pop rock. Produced "She Knows About Me," written and recorded by Jez Davidson (country single); "If We're Not In Love" (by Jez Davidson), recorded by Patty Weaver (ballad single) of the Young and the Restless; and "Baby Have a Memory On Me" (by Lewis Brown/ Sandi Rules), recorded by Linda Marr (country single), all on Rapp Records. Other artists include Lisa Westmoreland and Mike Bell, Dan Carroll, Sydney Australia's Stephen Concon, Chuck Carter, Peter Bunwen, Taylor Prichard, Wesley Furumoto, Jan Nielson and Otis Reding; also Patty Weaver on Warner Brothers and approximately 50 others in the past to reach the charts.

*RAVENSHEAD PRODUCTIONS, P.O. Box 354 Cuyahoga Falls OH 44222. Chairman: Steve Hammond. Estab. 1987. Deals with artists and songwriters. Produces 5 singles and 1 EP/year. Fee derived from outright fee from recording artist.
How to Contact: Write first and obtain permission to submit. Prefers cassette (or VHS video cassette) with 4 songs and lyric sheets. SASE. Reports in 2 weeks.
Music: Mostly hard rock, metal and progressive rock. Produced "Come On" (by Jeff Bechter), recorded by Typhoid Mary on Inspector Records (single); "Loose & Free" (by J. Bechter, S. Hammond, G. Smith), recorded by The Attix on Attix Records (single); and "Akron Stolen Car Blues" (by S. Hammond), recorded by Typhoid Mary on Daylight Disc (single).
Tips: "Be honest. I'm not interested in hype, make-up, big hair or lies."

*RED KASTLE PRODUCTIONS, P.O. Box 163, West Redding CT 06896. (203)438-5366. President: Paul Hotchkiss. Record producer and music publisher. Deals with artists and songwriters. Produces 10 singles, 2 EPs and 2 LPs/year. Fee derived from sales royalty.
How to Contact: Prefers cassette with 2 songs and lyric sheet. Include bio. SASE. Reports in 3 qweeks.
Music: Mostly country and country/pop. Produced "Luv Radio" (by P.Hotchkiss), recorded by Michael Berry on Ol Records (contemporary country); "Heart of Luv" (by Hotchkiss/Terry), recorded by Michael Berry on Roto Noto Noto Records (country); and "Love Me Back Together" (by K. Bracey/P. Hotchkiss), recorded by Jack Diamond Band on Roto Noto Records (country). Other artists include Big John Hartman, Beverly's Hill Billy Band and Leigh Henry.

GARY REVEL, 9015 Owensmouth Ave., #106, Canoga Park CA 91304. (818)341-7825. Record producer and record company (produces for Top's Records). Estab. 1973. Deals with artists and songwriters. Produces 4 singles, 2 LPs and 6 CDs/year. Fee derived from sales royalty.
How to Contact: Write first and obtain permission to submit. "Referrals from agent, manager or lawyer are preferred." Does not return unsolicited material.
Music: Mostly rock, pop and country; also gospel and R&B. Produced "Maria" (by G. Revel, D. Tuttle, A. Meza), recorded by Dale Tuttle (country single); "I Know (We're Gonna Make It Love)" (by Gary Revel), recorded by Dale Tuttle (country); and "Hollywood Star," written and recorded by Gary Revel (rock); all on Top's Records. Other artists include Czar Tuck.

*FRITZ RIHA, 1150, Palmgasse 10, Vienna 1150 **Austria**. Phone: 0222-834474. FAX: 0222-838569/2. Contact: Mrs. Jeanny Siegel. Record producer, music publisher and record company (RIHA Record Company). Estab. 1976. Deals with artists and songwriters. Produces 10-12 singles, 3-4 12″ singles, 3-4 LPs and 2-3 CDs/year. Fee derived from royalty or outright fee from recording artist or record company.
How to Contact: Submit demo tape by mail. Unsolicited submissions are okay. Prefers cassette (or VHS or Beta videocassette) with several songs and lyric sheets. SASE.
Music: Mostly rock, pop, R&B and Austria country music.

RIPSAW PRODUCTIONS, #805, 4545 Connecticut Ave. NW, Washington DC 20008. (202)362-2286. President: Jonathan Strong. Record producer, music publisher (Sugar Mama Music/BMI) and record company (Ripsaw Records). Deals with artists and songwriters. Produces 0-4 singles and 0-3 LPs/year.
How to Contact: Prefers cassette and lyric sheet. SASE.
Music: Blues, rockabilly and roots rock. Helped produce "Oooh-Wow!" recorded by Uptown Rhythm Kings (LP); produced *Two Sides*, written and recorded by Bobby Smith (EP); and *Wanted: True R&R*, written and recorded by Billy Hancock (EP); all recorded on Ripsaw Records.

ROBBY ROBERSON PRODUCTIONS, Box 12444, Fresno CA 93777. (209)266-8481.Owner: Robby Roberson, Executive Producer for Lana Records, Top Secret Records, Lair Music and GGT Music Group, Inc. Record producer, music publisher (Three Kings Music/BMI) and television and record production. Estab. 1964. Produces 10 singles, 4 12″ singles and 4 LPs/year. Fee derived from sales royalty or outright fee from record company.

How to Contact: Prefers cassette with 3 songs and lyric sheet. SASE.

Music: Country-western, gospel, soft rock, and crossover. Produced *Iron Butterfly* written and recorded by Mikal Masters on Top Secret Records (rock LP); *Secret Place* written and recorded by Robert Hooks on GGT Records (Christian LP); and "By Family Request" written and recorded by Robby Roberson on Lana Records (country). Other artists include Hud Rose, The Jacksons (Christian), Cottonmouth (country rock), and Alexandria (Spanish country).

Tips: "Get educated as to what is really happening in the business, before you make application."

*ROCKIT RECORDS, INC., (formerly Bad Grammar Enterprises), Suite 107, 35918 Union Lake Rd., Mt. Clemens MI 48043. Production Director:Joe Trupiano. Record Producer: J. D. Dudick. Record producer, music publisher, in house studio (Ruffcut Recording Studio, Bad Grammar Music/BMI and Broadcast Music, Inc./BMI), record company (Bad Grammar Records) and management company. Estab. 1982. Deals with artists and songwriters. Produces 10-20 singles and 4 CDs/year. Fee derived from outright fee from recording artist.

How to Contact: Prefers cassette (or videocassette) with 3-4 songs and lyric sheet. SASE. Reports in 6 weeks.

Music: Mostly pop/rock, R&B/pop, mainstream rock, New Age and heavy metal; also jingles, easy listening, ballads, dance oriented and MOR. Produced "Nightmares (by Dave Hentosh), recorded by The Joey Harlow Project (pop/rock); "Red Tape" (by Frank Abass), recorded by Messenger; and "Car Crazy" (by Joey Harlow), recorded by The Joey Harlow Project (rock), all on Rockit Records. Other artists include Tuff Kids, Thionne Carpenter, Bamboo Blonde, David Hensen and Jami Bauer.

Tips: "We are presently open for producing outside projects *with self-supporting budget*. This allows our clients the opportunity to shop their own master or sign it to Bad Grammar Records *if* our A&R approves and also considering whether we have an open door policy at the time."

ROCKLAND MUSIC, INC., 117 W. Rockland Rd., Libertyville IL 60048. (312)362-4060. President: Perry Johnson. Record producer (Destiny Productions, Inc. and Mo Fo Music) and music publisher (Rockland Music and Amalgamated Tulip Corp.). Deals with artists and songwriters. Produces 4-12 singles and 2 LPs/year. Fee derived from sales royalty.

How to Contact: Prefers cassette with 1-5 songs and lyric sheet. SASE. Reports in 2 months.

Music: Mostly dance/R&B, top 40/pop, rock and country; also pop, MOR and blues. Produced *Animation*, by Animation (pop/rock LP); *Taxi*, by Taxi (hard rock LP); and *Nightbeat*, by Oh Boy (pop LP on Rockland Records). Other artists include Madelyn Brown, McCormick Sinclair, Linda Quick, and Slim Huston.

Tips: "Send single commercial songs, not album cuts."

ROCKSTAR PRODUCTIONS, P.O. Box 131, Southeastern PA 19399. (215)964-7833. Executive Vice President: Jeffrey Sacks. Director of Marketing: Roni Sacks. Record producer and record company (Rockstar Records). Estab. 1988. Deals with artists and songwriters. Produces 5 singles/year. Fee derived from sales royalty.

How to Contact: Submit demo tape by mail. Unsolicited submissions are okay. Prefers cassette (or ½" videocassette) with 2 songs and lyric sheets. Does not return unsolicited material. Reports in 2 weeks.

Music: Mostly rock and pop. Produced "If I Catch You Laughing," "If Love Was Fair" and "Jenny On T.V.," all written and recorded by Scot Sax on Rockstar Records (all pop singles).

ROCKY MOUNTAIN HEARTLAND PRODUCTIONS, Box 6904, Denver CO 80206. (303)424-3216. Executive Producer: Steve Dyer. Record and video producer and advertising firm. Deals with artists and songwriters. Fee derived from sales royalty or outright fee from songwriter/artist or record company.

How to Contact: Submit demos. Prefers cassette (or videocassette) with 3-5 songs and lyric sheet or lead sheet. Does not return unsolicited material.

Music: Mostly gospel, top 40 and rock; also jazz and country. "Music open and not limited to these types." Produced *The Best Is Yet to Come*, by Kent Parry (big band and orchestra gospel LP); *From Here to Kingdom Come*, by Heart Song (mild gospel/top 40 LP); and *Going, Going, Gone*, by Heart Song (gospel rock LP); all on Record Harvest Records; and *From My Heart*, by Beth Chase.

Tips: "We are interested in new, up and coming artists."

MARK J. ROMERO/JAZZMARK SOUND, 47-51 43rd St., Woodside NY 11377. (718)706-7071. Producer/Engineer: Mark J. Romero. Record producer and engineer. Estab. 1986. Deals with artists only (or personal management). Fee derived from outright fee from recording artist or record company with points negotiable.

How to Contact: Submit demo tape by mail. Unsolicited submissions are okay. Prefers cassette with songs. "Include a phone number and address where the artist can be reached. I deal with performers and songwriters." Does not return unsolicited material. Reports in 1 month.

Music: Mostly jazz.
Tips: "Know exactly what you want. Be able to communicate. Be flexible and open to suggestions."

ROSE HILL GROUP, 1326 Midland Ave., Syracuse NY 13205. (315)475-2936. A&R Director: Vincent Taft. Record producer and music publisher (Katch Nazar Music/ASCAP, Bleecker Street Music/BMI). Produces 5 singles and 2 LPs/year. Fee derived from sales royalty or outright fee from artist/songwriter or record company.
How to Contact: Prefers cassette with 3 songs maximum. SASE. Reports in 2 weeks.
Music: Mostly top 40/pop, rock, dance; also jazz and MOR. Produced "Hot Button," by Prowlers (dance/R&B single); "Free World," by Z Team (dance/pop single); and "So What," by IO (dance/rock single).

MIKE ROSENMAN, 45-14 215 Pl., Bayside NY 11361. (718)224-7424. Producer: Mike Rosenman. Record producer and arranger. Estab. 1984. Deals with artists and songwriters. Produces 4-6 singles, 1-2 LPs and 1 EP/year. Fee derived from sales royalty or outright fee from recording artist.
How to Contact: Write before submitting. Prefers cassette (or VHS videocassette), with 2-4 songs and lyric sheet. Include address and phone number. Put phone number on cassette. Does not return unsolicited material. Will not return tapes without SASE. Reports in 8 weeks.
Music: Mostly pop, R&B, dance/disco and rock; also hard rock, rap and foreign languages. Produced "Jamie Morad," written and recorded by Jamie Morad (foreign language dance cassette); "Lawn Chair Hero," written and recorded by The Upstartz on Tab Records (rock 7" single); and "Here She Comes," written and recorded by The Upstartz on Tab Records (rock 7" single). "We also produce jingles and 'sound-alike' song parodies."
Tips: "Send simple demos of good songs. Please write, don't phone to ask about sending tapes. Include SASE if you want your tape back."

*HENRY ROWE, 17 Water St., Dracut MA 01826. (508)957-5781. Producer: Henry Rowe. Record producer, music publisher and record company (Hazardous Records). Estab. 1986. Deals with artists and songwriters. Produces 50 singles and 5 LPs/year. Fee derived from sales royalty or outright fee from recording artist or record company.
How to Contact: Write or call first to arrange personal interview. Prefers cassette (or VHS videocassette) with 4 songs and lyric sheet. Does not return unsolicited material. Reports in 6-8 weeks.
Music: Mostly metal, rock and pop; also fusion, jazz and New Age. Produced "Half Life" and "Danger Zone" (by Hazardous Waste) (metal); "Candle to the Magic" (by Johann Smith), (rock), all recorded by Making Tracks on Hazardous Records.

RUF-MIX PRODUCTIONS INCORPORATED, P.O. Box 55878, Sherman Oaks CA 91413. (818)760-0269. President: Taavi Mote. Record producer/Engineer. Deals with artists labels and songwriters. Produces and mixes"many" singles and LPs/year. Fee derived from sales royalty, outright fee from recording artist and/or outright fee from record company.
How to Contact: Prefers cassette with maximum of 4 songs and lyric sheet. For return reply, SASE *must be included.* Reports in 1½ months.
Music: Mostly rock, R&B and pop; also gospel and dance. "Looking for songs that are in direct competition with Billboards' top singles. Demos need to be as finished as possible." Produced remix of "Looking For a New Love," by Jody Watley on MCA, the Hollywood remix of U2's "Desire," Stacy Lattisaw's "Call Me" and Jeff Lorber's *Private Passion.* Other artists include Judson Spence, Ready For the World, El DeBarge, Nu Shooz, Pebbles, Cool'R, Native, Jody Watley, Madonna, Natalie Cole, Gladys Knight, Jeffrey Osbourne and Patty LaBelle. Also produced the soundtracks for *Beverly Hills Cop I* and *II.*

RUSHWIN PRODUCTIONS, P.O. Box 1150-SM91, Buna TX 77612. (409)423-2521. Owner/Manager: James L. Gibson. Record producer, music publisher (Rushwin Publishing and Gibson Davidsong Publishing), record company (Fountain Records). Estab. 1985. Deals with artists and songwriters. Produces 2-3 singles and 3-4 LPs/year. Fee derived from sales royalty, outright fee from songwriter/artist and/or outright fee from record company, depending on the project.
How to Contact: Prefers cassette with 1-4 songs and "typed lyric sheet. Clearly label each item sent. Include photo and bio if available. SASE (6x9 or larger)." Reports ASAP.
Music: Southern/country only. Produced "Reachin' Thru The Thorns" (by James Gibson), recorded by the Gibsons (gospel single); *You're a Saint or You Ain't* (by Randy Lawrence and Bill Fisher), recorded by The Harbringers (gospel LP); and *Jesus I Love You* (by Paul A. Hammock), recorded by The Gibsons (gospel LP); all on Gold Street Records.
Tips: "We consider sincere, hard working artists who are willing to grow with us. We are a small independent operation on the grow. It would be most helpful if the artists would include a press package with their submissions. This would familiarize us with their ministry/music (past, present and future plans). We have an open door policy for songwriters."

Close-up

Taavi Mote
Ruf-Mix Productions
Sherman Oaks, California

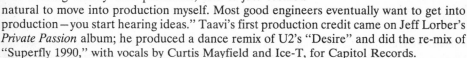

"One of the most important things a producer does is to try to bring out the best in an artist—to let the style and strengths of the artist come through," says Taavi Mote, of Ruf-Mix Productions.

Taavi entered the world of recording engineering in the mid-seventies. "I got into mixing and recording records. I was working closely with producers, and it just seemed natural to move into production myself. Most good engineers eventually want to get into production—you start hearing ideas." Taavi's first production credit came on Jeff Lorber's *Private Passion* album; he produced a dance remix of U2's "Desire" and did the re-mix of "Superfly 1990," with vocals by Curtis Mayfield and Ice-T, for Capitol Records.

Ruf-Mix Productions has been listed in every edition of *Songwriter's Market* since 1988. In that time, Taavi has received hundreds of submissions from our readers. Like many of our listed companies, Taavi has changed his listing a little each year in an effort to more clearly define his needs and submission policies. Despite the clarity of his listing, Taavi says he receives many inappropriate submissions every year. When we interviewed him, he shared some practical advice with *Songwriter's Market* about how our readers might improve their chances and give their demos an edge over the competition.

"The most important thing to do, if you have a particular artist in mind, is to really listen closely to what they've done before and make sure your song fits into their style lyrically and melodically," says Taavi. "I've gotten songs before that people have said would be perfect for such-and-such an artist, but they're not even close. I also get a lot of songs expressing deep, heartfelt ideas, but the lyrics are so personal—so much an extension or expression of the writer's feelings—that nobody else would want to cut them."

Taavi suggests a writer can be more successful by sticking to the proven themes of pop music—love gained and love lost—but by approaching them from a fresh angle. "A hit song is a song that says something that's been said before but in a more creative way, a way that people never heard it before. It's a real tough thing, but it needs to be unique, with a clear lyric that gets the message across," says Taavi.

When a producer puts your tape in his cassette player, you may have less than a minute for the music to capture his imagination and make him want to hear more. I asked Taavi what sorts of things make him reach for the "off" button. "I don't like lyrics that are not going anywhere or saying anything—that aren't well centered. Also, I find that someone singing out of tune is a fast turnoff. Another thing is over-production; people sometimes try so hard to make the demo sound like a finished record that they overdo it. You can't rely on production to carry the song. A strong song will show through even on a simple piano/vocal demo."

The elements that keep Taavi listening are simply a good melody, meaningful lyrics, and a catchy, well-crafted hook. "A hit song just has something about it that makes you want to come back for more."

—Mark Garvey

*RUSTRON MUSIC PRODUCTIONS, 1156 Park Lane, West Palm Beach FL 33417. (407)686-1354. A&R Directors: Ron Caruso and Rusty Gordon. Record producer, manager and music publisher (Rustron Music Publishers/BMI). Estab. 1970. Works with artists and songwriters. Produces 2-4 singles and 4-6 LPs/cassette albums/year. Fee derived from sales royalty or outright fee from record company.
How to Contact: Prefers cassette with 1-3 songs and lyric or lead sheet. "Songs should be 3½ minutes long or less and must be commercially viable for today's market. Singer/songwriters and collaborators are preferred." SASE. Reports in 1 month.
Music: Mostly progressive country, pop (ballads, blues, theatrical, cabaret), folk/rock; also R&B and New Age. Produced "The Rising Cost of Love", written and recorded by Marian Joy Ring on Black Dog Records (folk/jazz fusion); "The Shores of Mexico", written and recorded by Janet Bratter on Rustron Records (contemporary/folk); and "Appalachian Wind" (by Sue Massek), recorded by The Reel World String Band on Flying Fish Records (country/folk). Other artists include Robin Plitt, Marie Nofsinger, Circle and Star and Elaine Silver.
Tips: "Avoid redundant lyrics. Follow a theme, tell a story. Create innovative phrase hooks. Seek original ideas for songs."

SACCO PRODUCTIONS, Box 371, Bogota NJ 07603. (201)489-4206. General Manager: Sam Sacco. Record producer. Estab. 1987. Deals with artists and songwriters. Produces 2 LPs and 1 EP/year. Fee derived outright from recording artist.
How to Contact: Submit demo by mail. Unsolicited submissions are OK. Prefers cassette with 8 songs, lyric sheets and lead sheets. Does not return unsolicited material. Reports in 3 weeks.
Music: Mostly gospel, rock and pop; also R&B. Produced "Child of the 80's" (by Greg Suriano), recorded by Sam Sacco on Behold Records (EP).
Tips: "You must be dedicated and willing to spend a lot of time pushing your product."

SAGITTAR RECORDS, 1311 Candlelight Ave., Dallas TX 75116. (214)298-9576. President: Paul Ketter. Record producer, record company and music publisher. Deals with artists and songwriters. Produces 12 singles and 3 LPs/year. Works with 3 new songwriters/year. Works with composers and lyricists; teams collaborators.
How to Contact: Query. "Send a business-length SASE for our current needs."
Music: Mostly country; also folk, MOR (country) and progressive (country). Produced "Stay Till I Don't Love You Anymore," "I Wanna Say 'I Do'" and "Lovin' Bound," by P.J. Kamel (country singles); "Theodore Csanta's Right-Hand-Man," by Dave Gregory (country single); *Only A Woman* by Bunnie Mills (country LP); and *Joe Johnson* by Joe Johnson (pop LP), all on Sagittar Records. Other artists include Jay Douglas, Jackie Rosser, Buddy Howard and Jodi Witt.

JOJO ST. MITCHELL, 96 McGregor Downs, West Columbia SC 29169-2850. Executive Producer: Jojo St. Mitchell. Record producer. Deals with artists and songwriters. Produces 12 singles and 4 LPs/year. Fee derived from sales royalty, booking and licensing.
How to Contact: Prefers cassette (or VHS videocassette) with 3-7 songs; include any photos, biography. SASE. Reports in 3-6 weeks, if interested. Enclose return postage.
Music: Mostly mainstream, pop and R&B; also rock, new music and jazz/rap. Produced *Wheels of Steel* (by R. Clavon/J. Aiken), recorded by Unique Force (rap LP); *Can't Stop Thinking of You* (by L.S. Skinkle), recorded by Jr. Ellis (pop ballad, LP); "Complicated Love" recorded by True Identity; "Cassandra" recorded by Kourtesy; and *Miracle* (by K. Lyon/T. Lyon), recorded by Kat Lyon (pop LP); all on Amethyst Records. Other artists include J. Blues, Jeromeo, Commandment, Carnage and Fresh Fruit and Synthetic Meat.

*SCEPTRE PRODUCTIONS, 7308 S. Congress, Austin TX 78745. (512)462-2209. Record Producer: Mark Hallman. Estab. 1980. Produces 10 LPs, 10 EPs and 3 CDs/year. Fee derived from sales royalty, or outright fee from recording artist or record company. "½ up front and ½ when project is complete."
How to Contact: Submit demo tape by mail. Unsolicited submissions are OK. Prefers cassette with 3 songs and lyric sheet. Does not return material. Reports in 1 month.
Music: Mostly rock, contemporary folk and alternative pop. Produced *Legends of Rainmaker*, written and recorded by Eliza Gilkyson on Gold Castle Records (folk LP); *Walking a Changing Line* (by Jules Shear), recorded by Ian Matthews on Windham Hill Records (folk LP); and *Splashes on the Surface*, written and recorded by Water the Dog on Broken Records (rock LP). Other artists include Tish Hinojosa, Anneke and Duke Jupiter.

SCI PRODUCTIONS, P.O. Box 941, N.D.G., Montreal Quebec H4A 3S3 **Canada**. (514)487-4551. President: Bill Szawlowski and Gary Moffet. Record producer. Estab. 1984. Deals with artists and songwriters. Produces 10 singles, 5 LPs and 5 CDs/year. Fee derived from sales royalty.

How to Contact: Write or call first and obtain permission to submit. Prefers cassette with 3-10 songs and lyric sheets. SASE. Reports in 1 month.

Music: Mostly rock, pop and metal. Produced *Mindstorm* (by Mindstorm) on Capitol Records; *Marjo* (by Marjo) on Quebec Disc Records; and *Dans La Peau* (by Marie Carmen) on Double Disc Records; all recorded by SCI (LPs). Other artists include Gilt, Korea and Sneaky James.

SEGAL'S PRODUCTIONS, Box 507, Newton MA 02159. (617)969-6196. Contact: Charles Segal. Record producer, music publisher (Segal's Publications/BMI, Samro South Africa) and record company (Spin Records). Works with artists and songwriters. Produces 6 singles and 6 LPs/year. Fee derived from sales royalty.

How to Contact: Write or call first and obtain permission to submit or to arrange personal interview. Prefers cassette (or VCR videocassette) with 3 songs and lyric sheet or lead sheet of melody, words, chords. "Please record keyboard/voice or guitar/voice if you can't get a group." Does not return unsolicited material. Reports in 6 weeks.

Music: Mostly rock, pop and country; also R&B and comedy. Produced "Glenda" (by Clark/Segal), recorded by Roy Clark on CBS Records; "It's Too Late" (by Biluska/Segal), recorded by Biluska on Epic Records; and "Tom Boy" (by Stanton/Segal), recorded by Ronnie Dove on Mercury Records; all singles. Other artists include Gus Wyburd.

Tips: "I find that lots of artists are not ready for the big time when they've had their first hit record. So do your studying before that and listen to lots of artists/styles."

SGB PRODUCTION, Box 714, Guelph ON N1H 6L3 **Canada**. Phone: (519)767-0142. Contact: Sue Richards. Record producer (CAPAC), record company (SGB Production) and Freedom Records. Deals with artists only. Produces 1 single, 2 LPs and 1 CD/year. Fee derived from sales royalty.

How to Contact: Submit demo tape by mail. Unsolicited submissions are OK. Prefers cassette with 3 songs and lyric sheets. SASE. Reports in 2 months.

Music: Mostly folk, new music and children's. Produced "Looking for Livingstone," written and recorded by James Gordon on Freedom Records (new music); "Shave the Bear" (by Tamarack) on SGB Records (folk/traditional); and "A Pleasant Gale" (by Tamarack) on SGB Records (folk/traditional).

Tips: "We are not able to help with distribution in any way."

*MARK S. SHEARER, P.O. Box 540, Dearborn Heights MI 48127. (313)278-6068 or (313)561-2134. President: Mark S. Shearer. Record producer. Deals with artists and songwriters. Produces 1 12" single, 3 LPs, 2 EPs and 3 CDs/year. Fee derived from outright fee from recording artist.

How to Contact: Call first and obtain permission to submit. Prefers cassette (or VHS videocassette if available) with 3 songs and lyric sheet. "Please send promo packages with complete information." Does not return unsolicited material. Reports in 3 weeks.

Music: Mostly hard rock/heavy metal, alternative and pop. Produced "Dangerous Love" (by L. Crystal), recorded by Crystal Rose (single); "On The Edge" written and recorded by Glastteter (single); *Viscious Demo* (by Brian Thomas), recorded by Halloween on M.C.M. Records (hard rock); *Street Kid* (by Glen Harr), recorded by Street Kid on Hardway Records (hard rock); *Roxx* (by Joey St. John), recorded by Roxx on Hardway Records (hard rock); and *Shut Up and Sit Down* (by R. Miller), recorded by Mao Hatter (LP) all on Hardway Records. Other artists include Roxx and Jimmy Reich.

Tips: "Strong songs with a good image. A strong song is the most important aspect, but in today's market an image is almost as important."

*SILSAR PRODUCTIONS, P.O. Box 897, Hartford CT 06101. (203)548-0212. A&R: Linda "Bottles" Polite. Music publisher (BMI) and record company (S.O.C. Records and Silsar Music). Estab. 1986. Deals with artists and songwriters. Produces 4-12 singles, 4-12 12" singles, 13 LPs, 13 EPs and 13 CDs/year. Fee derives from sales royalty.

How to Contact: Submit demo tape by mail. Unsolicited submissions are OK. Prefers cassette (or VHS videocassette if available) with 4-5 songs and lyric sheet. SASE. Returns in 6 weeks.

Music: Mostly funk, R&B/soul and gospel; also rap. Produced "Keepers of the Dream" (by Silsar), recorded by Silver Sargent (R&B single); "Co-Co" written and recorded by Muffin (rap single); and *Dreamin* (by The Uniques), recorded by Silsar (R&B LP), all on S.O.C. Records. Other artists include Drum and Red Rappin Hood.

*SILVER BLUE PRODUCTIONS, Penthouse, 220 Central Park S, New York NY 10019. (212)586-3535. Contact: Joel Diamond. Record producer and music publisher. Deals with artists and songwriters. Fee derived from sales royalty.

How to Contact: Prefers cassette with 1-3 songs and lyric sheet. SASE.

Music: Dance, easy listening, country, R&B, rock, soul and top 40/pop. Produced "Love is the Reason" by Engelbert Humperdinck on BMG Records; "Do You Love Me" by David Hasselhoff on BMG Records; "Heaven In The Afternoon" by Lew Kyrton on Timeless; "I Am What I Am," by

Gloria Gaynor (single); "Where the Boys Are," by Lorna; and "One Night In Bangkok," by Robey.

*SILVER-LOOMAS PRODUCTIONS, 38 Music Square E., Nashville TN 37203. (615)255-8005. Production Managers: Tommy Loomas and Alan Carter. Executive Director: Joe Silver. Record producer, music publisher (Lineage Publishing Co.) and record company (Capstan Records and Octagon Records). Deals with artists and songwriters. Produces 10 singles and 4 LPs/year. Fee derived from sales royalty, outright fee from songwriter/artist and/or outright fee from record company.
How to Contact: Write or call first and obtain permission to submit to arrange personal interview. Prefers cassette (or VHS videocassette) with 4 songs and lyric or lead sheets. "Submissions must be professional." Reports in 6 weeks.
Music: Mostly country, easy listening and bluegrass; also rock. Produced "Angel," by Rock Candy (rock single, Capstan Records). Other artists include Fleming McWilliams and Skidrow Joe.

SIR GARRETT PRODUCTIONS, 10346 NE Chowning, Kansas MO 64155. (816)734-2159. Contact: Auska Garrett. Record producer (Sir Garrett Productions) and record company. Estab. 1987. Deals with artists and songwriters. Produces 2 singles, 3 12″ singles and 2 LPs. Fee derived from sales royalty.
How to Contact: Submit demo tape by mail. Unsolicited submissions are okay. Prefers cassette (or VHS videocassette) with 3 songs and lyric sheets. "Include a short resume of music background along with cassette and picture." SASE. Reports in 1 month.
Music: Mostly R&B, rock, pop and gospel; also jazz, soul and blues. Produced "Let Me Have The Stranger" (R&B single) and "Nita Chyree" (slow single), written and recorded by Auska Garrett; and "Percent of Profit" (by Rap Inc.), recorded by Auska Garrett (rap single); all on SGP Records. Other artists include Rap Inc., Ralf Dixon, Gavin Johnson, Cal Green, Unidos Band and Mac Lace Band.
Tips: "Keep your songs short and simple. Always have a good beat."

*DONOVAN "SOUND" SMITH AUDIO ACHIEVEMENTS,INC., 1327 Cabrillo, Torrance CA 90501. (213)320-8100. President: Donovan Smith. Estab. 1978. Record producer/engineer. Deals with artists and songwriters. Produces 12 singles and 6 LPs/year. Fee is derived from outright fee from songwriter/artist and/or outright fee from record company.
How to Contact: Prefers cassette or 15 ips reel-to-reel (or VHS videocassette) with 4 songs and lyric sheet or lead sheets. SASE. Reports in 6 weeks.
Music: Mostly AOR/pop, R&B/pop; and rap. Recently recorded albums by Michel'le and J.J. Fad (Ruthless/Atco); N.W.A. and Eazy-E (Ruthless/Priority); The D.O.C. (Ruthless/Atlantic); Above the Law (Ruthless/Epic); Tairrie B. (Camtaur/MCA). Other clients include Toyota Motor Sales, Mattel Toys and Pioneer Electronics.
Tips: "A good demo never hurts—not a master production, just a good representation of the song."

SOMETIMES Y MUSIC, 1962 Beachwood, Los Angeles CA 90068. (213)461-4043. Partner: Jim Witcher or Jeff Glass. Producer: Kevin Taylor. Record producer, music publisher (BMI) and record company (Sometimes Y Music). Estab. 1988. Deals with artists and songwriters. Produces 10 singles, 1-2 LPs and 1 CD/year. Fee derived from sales royalty.
How to Contact: Submit demo tape by mail. Unsolicited submissions are okay. Prefers cassette with songs and lyric or lead sheets. Reports in 6-8 weeks.
Music: Post modern, reggae, African and Latin American Sounds. Produced *Ice Monkey in Amsterdam*, by Kevin Taylor (modern CD); and *Catch-22*, by Catch-22 (modern LP); all recorded by Sometimes Y on Sometimes Y Records.
Tips: "Let the music speak for itself."

SONGWRITERS' NETWORK, P.O. Box 190446, Dallas TX 75219. (214)823-1113. President: Phil Ayliffe. Record producer, music publisher (Songwriters' Network Music Publishing/ASCAP), and record company (Meridian Records, Songwriters' Network Records). Estab. 1983. Deals with artists and songwriters. Produces 1 LP/year. Fee derived from sales royalty.
How to Contact: Prefers cassette (or videocassette) with 5 songs and lyric sheet. "Five songs should include an uptempo opener; an uptempo, positive song; a ballad; a hand-clapping rouser; and a dramatic, personal philosophy song as a closer. Vocal must be mixed up-front. Any straining to hear the lyric and the tape is immediately rejected. Material is returned only if accompanied by an SASE." Reports in 6 weeks.
Music: Mostly adult contemporary, pop and MOR. Produced "Flying Free," written and recorded by Phil Ayliffe on Songwriters Network Records (New Age/pop).
Tips: "We are most interested in working with the singer/songwriter/producer entrepreneur, so we would like the best produced material possible, though vocal and instrument demo is OK. "Be patient with me and the process. With patience and perseverance, we shall have it."

SOUND ARTS RECORDING STUDIO, 2036 Pasket, Houston TX 77092. (713)688-8067. President: Jeff Wells. Record producer and music publisher (Earthscream Music). Deals with artists and songwriters. Estab. 1974. Produces 12 singles and 3 LPs/year. Fee derived from outright fee from recording artist.
How to Contact: Prefers cassette with 2-5 songs and lyric sheet. SASE. Reports in 1 month.
Music: Mostly pop/rock and dance. Produced "Always Happens," written and recorded by Barbara Pennington; "Show Me Reaction" (by Wells), recorded by Rick Bardon; and "New Guy" (by Wells), recorded by Valerie Starr, all on Earth Records.

SOUND COLUMN PRODUCTIONS, Division of Sound Column Companies, 160 Westgate Fine Arts Center, 342 W. Second South, Salt Lake City UT 84101. (801)355-5327. President/General Manager: Ron Simpson. Record producer, music publisher (Ronarte Publications/ASCAP, Mountain Green Music/BMI and Macanudo Music/SESAC) and record company (SCP Records). Estab. 1970. Deals with artists. Produces 4 singles and 8 LPs/year. Fee derived from sales royalty.
How to Contact: Write first for specific submission guidelines. SASE. "We work mainly with staff writers at our affiliated publishing companies and other established publishers. Our demand fluctuates according to projects we're doing." Reports as soon as possible — "honestly we do get backed up, but you'll eventually be heard."
Music: Pop (dance and A/C), country, contemporary religious. Produced country album *Three Again* (various writers), for artist The Jensens on SCP Records; contempoary religious album *His Love* (various writers) recorded by Janine Lindsay on SCP Records (opening round Grammy contender); single "True Love" (writers Romney/Simpson) recorded by Shawn for SCP Records; contemporary religious album *The Measure of a Man* (writer Clive Romney) for Embryo Records.
Tips: "Send clear, precise demos and always include lyric sheets. The artists usually have their own album cuts — we're looking for singles. Would like to hear from more SESAC writers. No correspondence or return materials without SASE."

SOUND IMAGE PRODUCTIONS, 6556 Wilkinson, North Hollywood CA 91606. (818)762-8881. President: Marty Eberhardt. Vice President and General Manager: David Chatfield. Vice President Sales/Studio Manager: Chuck Kopp. Record producer, music publisher (Sound Image Publishing), record company and 24-track recording studio. Manages artists, songwriters and producers. Produces 8 singles and 4 LPs/year. Fee derived from sales royalty, outright fee from artist/songwriter and/or record company.
How to Contact: Submit finished masters. Prefers cassette (or VHS stereo hi-fi) with 2-6 songs and lyric sheet. Does not return unsolicited material. Reports in 2 months.
Music: Mostly rock; also dance and R&B. Currently working with The Storm. Songs include "Walk The Line" and "I'll Be Loving You."

SOUNDS OF WINCHESTER, Rt. 2 Box 116 H, Berkley Springs WV 25411. Contact: Jim McCoy. Record producer, music publisher (New Edition Music, Jim McCoy Music and Sleepy Creek Music) and record company (Winchester, Faith and Master Records). Deals with artists and songwriters. Produces 20 singles and 10 LPs/year. Fee derived from sales royalty.
How to Contact: Prefers 7½ ips reel-to-reel or cassette with 4-10 songs and lead sheet. SASE. Reports in 1 month.
Music: Bluegrass, country, gospel and country/rock. Produced "Always," written and recorded by Alvin Kesner (single); "Run-away-Girl," written and recorded by Earl Howard (single); and *Tryin to Quit*, written and recorded by Jim McCoy (LP), all on Winchester Records. Other artists include Dave Elliott, Alvin Kesner, Carroll County Ramblers and Troubadour Band.

SOUTHERN SOUND PRODUCTIONS, 100 Labon St., Tabor City NC 28463. (919)653-2546. President: Elson H. Stevens. Record producer, music publisher (Creekside Publishing, SeaSide Records/BMI) and record company. Estab. 1978. Deals with artists, songwriters and radio stations. Produces 12 singles, 12 12″ singles and 18 LPs/year. Fee derived from sales royalty or outright fee from recording artist.
How to Contact: Write first about your interest. Prefers cassette or 8-track tape with 1-3 songs and lyric or lead sheets. SASE. Reports in 1 month.
Music: Mostly country; also bluegrass, gospel, rock (country and hard) and beach music. Produced "Being in Love" (by J. Knight), recorded by Angela (country); "Child of the King" (by W. Ormond), recorded by Twilights (black gospel); "Here I Go Again" (by E. Stevens), recorded by Angela (country); and "On the Downside" (by J. Gibson), recorded by T.J. Gibson all recorded on Seaside Records (country). Other artists include Mitch Todd, T.J. Gibson, Crossroads, Coppper Creek, Gospel Entertainers, Glin Todd, Sheila Gore, Gayle Mathies, Gospel Echoes, Don Casper, Mary Jane Cooper and Buck Johnson.
Tips: "Please make sure that all songs submitted have a very strong hook. Limit of 3 songs per submission."

*SOVEREIGN PRODUCTIONS, Suite 1203, 161 West 54 St., New York NY 10019. President: Eric Colodne. Record producer and music publisher. Estab. 1985. Deals with artists and songwriters. Produces 40 singles, 10 12″ singles, 6 LPs, 6 EPs and 10 CDs/year. Fee derived from sales royalty.
How to Contact: Submit demo tape by mail. Unsolicited submissions are OK. Prefers cassette (or VHS videocassette) with 3-5 songs and lyric or lead sheet. "Send 3 best songs of self-contained artist, preferably. I want *new* unpublished unreleased materials and best quality recording." SASE. Reports in 1 month.
Music: Mostly R&B/soul, rap and rock; also pop, Brazilian/Afro and reggae.

SPECTRA PRODUCTIONS, P.O. Box 2474, Auburn AL 36831-0474. (205)821-4876. President: Larry Barker. Record producer, music publisher (Sound Spectra Music) and record company (Rainbow River Records). Estab. 1978. Deals with artists and songwriters. Produces 8-10 singles, 3-5 12″ singles, 3-5 LPs and 2 CDs/year. Fee derived from sales royalty.
How to Contact: Write first and obtain permission to submit. Send SASE for reply. Prefers cassette with 3-4 songs and lyric sheets. Does not return unsolicited material. Reports in 6 weeks.
Music: Mostly rock, R&B and new age; also jazz, gospel and country. Produced "Let's Keep the Music Playin' " (by L. Barker, K. Smith, R. Orr, D. Barker, R. La Pread), recorded by Ronald La Pread on Little Records (12″ single); "The Trash Bag's Been Ripped" (by Bruce Yandle), recorded by Mr. Resistor on Rainbow River Records (single); and "The Enquirer" (by M. Brown, L. Barker, R. Orr), recorded by Lennie Hartzog on Rainbow River Records (single). Other artists include Horace Whitaker, "The Gallileans," "Second Wind," Waymon Hale, "The McNair Family" and "Mary Helen Brown."

SPHERE PRODUCTIONS, 1 Teal Lane, Bedminster NJ 07921. (201)781-1650. President: Tony Zarrella. Record producer, artist development, management and placement of artists with major/independent labels. Film soundtracks. Estab. 1988. Deals with artists and songwriters. Fee derived from percentage royalty of deal, outright fee from record company.
How to Contact: Submit demo tape by mail. Unsolicited submissions are okay. Prefers cassette (or VHS videocassette) with 3-5 songs and lyric sheets."Include as much information as possible: photos, press, resume, goals and specifics on character of project submitted, etc." SASE. Reports in 6 weeks.
Music: Specialize in pop (mainstream), progressive/rock, New Age and cross-over country/pop. Produce/represent Machine, 4 of Hearts, Oona Falcon, The Snowmen and Traveller.
Tips: "Develop a personal style and stick with it. Have faith in the individuals you are working with, especially if the chemistry is right and move ahead until you reach your goal. Mainstream music is now comprised of various kinds/types of music; incorporating existing and past styles."

JACK STANG, 753 Capitol Ave., Hartford CT 06106. (203)524-5656. Producer: Jack Stang. Record producer, music publisher (Stang Music/BMI) and record company (Nickel Records). Estab. 1970. Deals with artists and songwriters. Produces 5 singles and 5 12″ singles/year. Fee derived from sales royalty.
How to Contact: Submit demo tape by mail. Unsolicited submissions are okay. Prefers cassette with 3 songs and lyric sheets. SASE. Reports in 3 weeks.
Music: Mostly pop, rock and dance; also country. Produced "Can't Believe My Eyes," written and recorded by Billy Chapin; "Crazy Old Soldier" (by Mosher), recorded by Deserts Sky; and "Goodnight Song" (by Alpha-Soxas), recorded by Greylock; all on Nickel Records (all singles).

STARK RECORDS AND TAPE CO., 628 S. South St., Mount Airy NC 27030. (919)786-2865. Contact: Paul E. Johnson. Record producer and music publisher (TomPaul Music Company/BMI). Estab. 1960. Deals with artists, songwriters, publishers and recording companies. Produces 8 singles and 3 LPs/year. Works with 80 new songwriters/year. Fee derived from sales royalty.
How to Contact: Prefers 7½ ips reel-to-reel or cassette with 4-6 songs and lyric sheet. SASE. "My return address should be on the SASE." Reports in 1 month.
Music: Country, bluegrass, pop and gospel. Produced "Blue Eyes Crying in the Rain" (by Paul Edgar Johnson), recorded by Bobby Atkins (country); "Love Valley" written and recorded by Bobby Atkins (country); and "Paul's Ministry" written and recorded by Early Upchurch (country gospel), all on Stark Records. Other artists include Carl Tolbert, Sam Bray, Ralph Hill, Early Upchurch, Sanford Teague and Don Sawyers.

*STARMAKER INT'L INC., United Artist Tower, 50 Music Sq. W#102, Nashville TN 37203. (615)327-9121. Contact: Troy Shondell. Record producer, music publisher (see Starmaker Int'l/AVM Records/BMI) and artist development and management. Estab. 1989. Deals with artists and songwriters.
How to Contact: Submit demo tape by mail. Unsolicited submissions are OK. Prefers cassette (or VHS videocassette if available) with 1 or more songs and lyric sheet. SASE. Reports in 2 or more weeks.

Music: Mostly country.
Tips: "First impressions on a demo are lasting. Try to make sure it is as good as possible, something you feel proud of. Photos and bio's are also helpful if you are a recording artist."

STEPHEN STEWART-SHORT, % Magic Music, 155 Oxford St., London WI **United Kingdom**. Phone: (01)4372642. Contact: J.P. Iliesco. Record producer. Estab. 1986. Works with artists only. Produces 4 singles and 4 LPs/year. Fee derived from sales royalty and advance from record company. Charges upfront for "pre-production and production."
How to Contact: Prefers cassette. SAE and IRC. Reports in 3 weeks.
Music: Mostly rock and pop. Produced *B-Movie* (LP); *Modern English (LP)* (both on Sire Records); *Space Opera*, written and recorded by Marovani on EMI Records (new age LP) and *I'm Alone*, recorded by Skagarak on MCA Records (rock LP). ASOLP on EMI Records A.O.R. on Enigma for U.S. and Canada.

LEE STOLLER, 120 Hickory St., Madison TN 37115. (615)868-7171. Publisher: Kevin L. Stoller. Music publisher (ASCAP, SESAC, BMI) and record company (L.S. Records). Estab. 1972. Deals with artists and songwriters. Produces 2 singles and 3 12″ singles. Fee derived from sales royalty.
How to Contact: Write first and obtain permission to submit. Prefers cassette with 1 song and lyric or lead sheets. SASE. Reports in 1 week.
Music: Mostly gospel, country and rock; also pop and rap. Produced *All In His Hands, He Sees My Heart* (both by Jimmie Young) and *How Great Thou Art*, all recorded by Cristy Lane on L.S. Records (LPs).

STRAIGHT ARROW RECORDINGS, 5 School Ave., Montpelier VT 05602. (802)223-2551. Producer: Mike Billingsley. Record producer, record company (Straight Arrow Recordings), Straight Arrow Productions and recording studio (Backtracks). Estab. 1984. "We are not a music publisher. Do not send songs for consideration." Produces 12 cassettes, 4 EPs and 6 CDs/year. Deals with artists only. Fee derived from sales royalty or outright fee from recording artist or record company.
How to Contact: Write or call first and obtain permission to submit. Prefers cassette or 7½ or 15 ips reel-to-reel (or Beta videocassette – digital or hi-fi) with 1-4 songs. "We assist with demos and produce live performance recordings. We release recordings on our own label." SASE. Reports in 3 weeks.
Music: Mostly acoustic "folk"/ethnic/blues/contemporary experimental/jazz; also classically-derived, ethnically-derived and native Third World compositions. Produced Susan Halligan by Goldberg variations on Bell Bird Records (classical) cassette/CD; and Classical Jazz (by various groups), recorded Michael Arrowitt on Musical Heritage Records cassette/CD. Other artists include Catherine Orr, Michael Arnowitt, Banjo Dan & The Midnight Plowboys, World Music Ensemble, Champlain Valley Music Fest.
Tips: "All new projects are recorded direct-to-digital. We appreciate artists who are prepared to reap the rewards of tight musical productions, without overdubs, in natural acoustic spaces. Musical style is not a primary consideration. Rather, we are looking for interesting, tight, heartfelt music that can exploit the dynamic range and airiness of digital. For us, it's helpful if you live in New England or nearby Canada, if you're already established as a performer, and have concise demos that demonstrate your spirit and ability. Think professionally right from the start – be practiced and use preparation time to work out arrangements; study the business end and understand costs and contracts."

SUNSET PRODUCTIONS, 117 W. 8th, Hays KS 67601. (913)625-9634. President: Mark Meckel. Record producer, music publisher (Street Singer Music, BMI) and record company. Estab. 1980. Deals with artists and songwriters. Produces 6 singles, 6 LPs and 2 CDs/year. Fee derived from sales royalty.
How to Contact: Prefers cassette with 3 songs and lyric or lead sheet. SASE.
Music: Mostly pop, country rock, gospel and 50s rock. Produced "I'm Gona Win You Over" written and recorded by M. Selby (slow rock); "20", written and recorded by C. Connelly (rock); and "Getting Nothen Done At All" written and recorded by M. Benish (country), all on M.D.M. Records; *The Heat* (various songwriters), recorded by The Heat (rock); and *The Jimmy Dee Band 50's Rock 'n Roll*; all recorded on M.D.M. Records. Other artists include Mark Selby, Mike Benish and C. Connelly.

 The asterisk before a listing indicates that the listing is new in this edition. New markets are often the most receptive to unsolicited submissions.

SURPRIZE RECORDS, INC., P.O. Box 42707, Philadelphia PA 19101-2707. (215)276-8861. President: W. Lloyd Lucas. Record producer, music publisher (Delev Music Co./BMI, Sign of the Ram Music/ASCAP) and management firm. Estab. 1981. Deals with artists, songwriters and publishers. Produces 3-6 singles and 1-3 LPs/year. Fee derived from sales royalty.

How to Contact: Write or call first and obtain permission to submit. Prefers cassette with 1-3 songs and lyric or lead sheet. SASE. Reports in 1 month.

Music: R&B, soul, top 40/pop, dance-oriented and MOR. Co-produced "What Can I Do" by Vincent Knight. Company currently seeking artists in the Philadelphia area. Artists are needed for "R&B" material. One female vocalist, one male vocalist and one male vocal group who are able to both sing and dance well. Also one gospel group for religious music recording.

Tips: "We are impressed with very positive lyrics and great hooklines and near finished demo 'masters'. It does not matter if the artist has or has not had extensive experience working in front of an audience, but it does matter if his or her attitude is in a positive posture. Determination and the ability to take constructive criticism most important. We have no time for ego trippers."

SWEET INSPIRATION MUSIC, 112 Widmar Pl., Clayton CA 94517. (415)672-8201. Owner: Edgar J. Brincat. Record producer, music publisher (California Country Music/BMI, Sweet Inspirations Music/ASCAP) and record company (Roll On Records). Estab. 1986. Deals with artists and songwriters. Produces 2-4 singles/year. Pays standard royalty.

How to Contact: Submit demo tape by mail. Unsolicited submissions are OK. Prefers cassette with 3 songs and lyric sheets. SASE. Reports in 6 weeks.

Music: Mostly middle of the road, contemporary country or pop; also R&B, gospel and light rock. Published "I'll Take Country Music Anytime" (by John Covert, Ann Leisten, Phil Monton), recorded by John Covert on Roll On Records.

*F.B. SWEGAL, division of Centaur®, 12220 Tiara St., N. Hollywood CA 91607. (818)762-7417. Contact: Franz B. Swegal, P.C. Record producer and record company (C.P.I. Records). Estab. 1979. Deals with artists only. Fee derived from sales royalty.

How to Contact: Submit demo tape by mail. Unsolicited submissions are okay. Prefers cassette (or ½" videocassette if available) with best songs. "Unsolicited submissions should be released to simply 'absolve F.B. Swegal, division of Centaur® and affiliated and/or associated companies from infringement per each titled submission.'" SASE. Reports in 3 weeks.

Music: Mostly rock & roll, pop, country and R&B; also rap.

Tips: "Only submit radio hits!"

*SYNDICATE SOUND, 311 Poland Ave., Struthers OH 44471. (216)755-1331. Owner: Jeff Wormley. Record producer and recording studio. Estab. 1987. Deals with artists and songwriters. Produces 4-5 singles, 1-2 12" singles, 15-20 LPs, 10-15 EPs and 1-2 CDs/year. Fee derived from combination of sales royalty when song or artist is recorded, outright fee from recording artist or record company and third party financing.

How to Contact: Submit demo tape by mail. Unsolicited submissions are okay. "Please send a promo package or biography (with pictures) of band stating past and present concerts and records." SASE. Reports in 1 month.

Music: Mostly rock, pop and Christian rock; also country, R&B and hardcore. Produces "Whom Shall I Fear" (by Wayne Mackie), on Good Records (single); *Rule of Time* (by David James), on DJS Records (LP-CD); and *Terry Barrett* (by Terry Barret), on TNT Productions Records (LP) all recorded by Syndicate Sound.

SYSTEM, P.O. Box 11301, Kansas City KS 66111. (913)287-3495. Executive Producer: Steve Vail. Record producer, management firm, booking agency and film company. Estab. 1978. Deals with artists and songwriters. Produces 1-3 LPs/year. Fee derived from outright fee from songwriter/artist or record company.

How to Contact: Prefers cassette or 7½ ips reel-to-reel (or ½" or ¾" VHS or ½" Beta videocassette) with 1-10 songs and lyric sheet. Does not return unsolicited material. Reports in 6 weeks.

Music: "Classical rock, New Age, jazz fusion and art rock." Produced *Time Tales*, recorded by Realm (art rock LP); *Outlines*, recorded by Navigator (dance rock LP); and *Rituals*, written and recorded by Vail, all on System Records.

TABITHA PRODUCTIONS, Sandpiper Court, Harrington Lane, Exeter EX4 8N5 **England**. Phone: 44-0392-79914. Producer: Graham Sclater. Record producer, music publisher (Tabitha Music, Ltd.) and record company (Tabitha/Willow Records). Works with artists and songwriters. Produces 6 singles and 2 LPs/year. Works with 6 new songwriters/year and works with composers. Fee derived from sales royalty.

How to Contact: Prefers cassette with 2-6 songs and lyric sheet. SAE and IRC. Reports in 3 weeks.
Music: Mostly AOR, MOR and pop; also country, dance, soul and rock. Produced "I'm Your Man," written and recorded by Tony Carey on Tabitha Records (pop); "Groovy Kind of Love" (by Bayer-Sager), recorded by Andy Ford (pop/reggae); and "Summer Love Affair" (by Bradbury/Artes), recorded by Beat the Heat (pop). Other artists include Shoot to Kill, Colin Wilson, FLIC, Simon Galt and Mark Fojo.

TCR PRODUCTIONS LTD., P.O. Box 590, Charlotte Hall MD 20622. Director: R.T. Crabb. Record producer. Deals with artists and songwriters. Estab. 1985. Produces 22 singles, 14 LPs, 7 EPs and 2 CDs/year. Fee derived from sales royalty or outright fee from recording artist or record company.
How to Contact: Prefers cassette with 2-3 songs and lyric sheet. Does not return unsolicited material. Reports in 6 weeks.
Music: Mostly rock, country, metal and Tex-Mex. Produced "Original Bluegrass" (by D. Norris), recorded by Dixie Ramblers on db Records (bluegrass); and "Overload" (by M. Dyer), recorded by Mol Dyer on db Records (metal). Other artists include Romeo Bang, Sam Neely, Buster Cherry, Catch-22, TC Roberts, Man O'War, Patricia Lyan.

TEROCK RECORDS, Box 4740, Nashville TN 37216. President: Wade Curtiss. Record producer and music publisher. Deals with artists and songwriters. Fee derived from sales royalty.
How to Contact: Prefers cassette tape with 2-6 songs and lyric sheet. SASE. Reports in 3 weeks.
Music: Bluegrass, blues, country, dance, easy listening, folk, gospel, progressive, R&B, hard rock, soul and top 40/pop.

***MIKE THEODORE PRODUCTIONS**, P.O. Box 841, Montclair NJ 07042. Contact: Mike Theodore. Record producer (BMI/ASCAP). Estab. 1968. Deals with artists and songwriters. Produces 5 singles, 5 12" singles and 5 LPs/year. Fee derived from sales royalty and outright fee from record company.
How to Contact: Submit demo tape by mail. Unsolicited submissions are okay. Prefers cassette. SASE. Reports in 2 weeks.
Music: Mostly R&B, pop and rock.

***THE THOMAS GROUP**, (formerly Target Communications), 3649 Norwood Rd., Shaker Heights OH 44122. (216)991-9217. CEO: Tony Thomas. Record producer and advertising music production company. Deals with artists and songwriters. Produces varying number of singles and LPs/year. Fee depends on project.
How to Contact: Submit demo tape by mail. Write or call first to arrange personal interview. Prefers cassette or 7½ ips reel-to-reel (or videocassette) and lyric sheet. "Please label submissions." Does not return unsolicited material. Reports in 6 weeks.
Music: Mostly pop, jazz/fusion instrumentals and R&B; also jingles, "stingers/music beds and bumpers."
Tips: "Develop your own style and make sure that style shines through on your demo."

***TIMELESS RECORDS BV**, Box 201, Wageningen 6700 AE **Holland**. Phone: (8370)13440. Record producer, music publisher (WW Music) and record company (Timeless, Timeless Traditional/Timeless Historical Records). Works with artists and songwriters. Produces 20 LPs and 50 CDs/year. Fee derived from sales royalty or outright fee from artist or record company.
How to Contact: Write first and obtain permission to submit. Does not return unsolicited material.
Music: Mostly jazz, salsa and blues.

***TMC PRODUCTIONS**, P.O. Box 12353, San Antonio TX 78212. (512)829-1909. Producer: Joe Scates. Record producer, music publisher (Axbar Productions/BMI, Scates & Blanton/BMI and Axe Handle Music/ASCAP), record company (Axbar, Trophy, Jato, Prince and Charro Records) and record distribution and promotion. Deals with artists and songwriters. Produces 12-15 singles, 3-4 LPs and 1-2 CDs/year. Fee derived from sales royalty or outright fee from recording artist or record company.
How to Contact: Prefers cassette with 1-5 songs and lyric sheet. SASE. Reports "as soon as possible, but don't rush us."
Music: Mostly traditional country; also blues, comedy and rock (soft). Produced *Versatility* written and recorded by Kenny Dale on EMI/Axbar Records (country LP); and "Old Five & Dimer" (by Billy J. Shaver), recorded by Billy D. Hunter, and "Country Girl Going to Town," written and recorded by Terrah Sloane, both on Axbar Records (country singles). Other artists include Mark Chesnutt, Juni Moon, Rusty Button, George Chambers and Bubba Littrell.
Tips: "Competition is very keen, so the average 'good' songs just don't make it anymore. Submit only your best efforts that have strong commercial possibilities. If we produce an artist, we prefer to use our own professional contract musicians but will consider recording a band intact if they are a quality group."

*TnT PRODUCTIONS, North: 7808 Green Lake Rd., Fayetteville NY 13066. (315)637-6656. Producer: Matt Tucker. South: 940 NE 27th Ave., Hallandale FL 33009. (305)454-7044. Producer: Chris Horvath. Record producer. Estab. 1988. Deals with artists and songwriters. Produces 1-5 singles, 1-5 12" singles 1-2 LPs and 1-2 CDs. Fee derived from sales royalty or outright fee from recording artist or record company. Negotiable.
How to Contact: Submit demo tape by mail. Unsolicited submissions are OK. Prefers cassette (or VHS videocassette if available) with 1-5 songs and lyric sheet. "Send photo, press kit or bio if available. No calls." SASE. Reports in 4-6 weeks.
Music: Mostly top 40/pop, dance and rock; also rap and R&B. Produced "Baha Your Body" recorded by Jodi Bilotti (single); "Without You" recorded by Blue Steel (single); and *Blue Steel* recorded by Blue Steel (LP) all by Horvath/Tucker and all on CCD Records.
Tips: "Send what you feel is your best work. Don't restrict yourself to one type of music. We listen to everything. Be professional and be patient."

*TOMSICK BROTHERS PRODUCTIONS, 21271 Chardon Rd.,Euclid OH 44117. (216)481-8380. President: Ken Tomsick. Record producer and record company (Recording Studio). Estab. 1982. Deals with artists and songwriters. Produces 2-5 LPs/year. Fee derived from outright fee from recording artist. Charges in advance for studio time.
How to Contact: Write first and obtain permission to submit. Prefers cassette. "We have arrangers to help produce your sound." Does not return unsolicited material. Reports in 1 month.
Music: Mostly ethnic, polka and New Age/experimental. Produced *Joey T & Lynn Marie* (by Joey Tomsick), (ethnic LP); *Proud of Cleveland* (by Joey Tomsick Orchestra), (polka LP); and *Tag YR It* (by Dale Stevens (electronic LP) all recorded by Tomsick Brothers on TBP Records.

TONY'S PRODUCTION, 907 Baltimore St., Mobile AL 36605. (205)433-1023. Record producer and record company (Sun Dance Records). Estab. 1984. Deals with artists and songwriters. Produces 10 singles, 8-10 12" singles and 6-8 LPs/year. Fee derived from sales royalty.
How to Contact: Submit demo tape by mail. Unsolicited submissions are OK. Prefers cassette (or VHS videocassette) with 2-3 songs and lyric sheets. SASE. Reports in 5 weeks.
Music: Mostly R&B, pop and rap; also rock, gospel and country. Produced "Jaye In The House" (by Jeffrey Reese), recorded by Jaye Supreme (12" single); "Midnight Love" (by Antonio Pritchett), recorded by Erica (single); and *Erica*, recorded by Erica (LP); all on Sun Dance Records. Other artists include Pumpkin P, Magnetics and LaShone Glover.
Tips: "Be patient and success will await."

TORO'NA INT'L., (formerly Inga McDaniel) P.O. Box 88022, Indianapolis IN 46208. Contact: Inga McDaniel. Professional record producer and musical arranger. A&R Director: Anthony Wiggins. Estab. 1987. Produces 3 singles and 1 12" single/year. Fee derived from sales royalty.
How to Contact: Write first and obtain permission to submit. Prefers cassette with 3 songs. Does not return unsolicited material. Reports in 8 weeks.
Music: Mostly top 40, R&B and gospel; also rap. Produced *Second Chance* (ballad LP) and *Freestyle* (jazz LP), written and recorded by I. McDaniel on Toro'na Records; and *Don't Say No* (by I. McDaniel), recorded by Payage (ballad LP). Other artists include Kevin Allen, M. Ware, Anthony Wiggins and Henry Fuse.
Tips: "Write first about your interests. No phone calls."

TRAC RECORD CO., 170 N. Maple, Fresno CA 93702. (209)255-1717. Owner: Stan Anderson. Record producer, music publisher (Sellwood Publishing/BMI) and record company (Trace Record Company). Estab. 1972. Works with artists and songwriters. Produces 10-20 12" singles, 5 LPs and 1 CD/year. Fee derived from sales royalty or outright fee from artist.
How to Contact: Prefers cassette with 2 songs and lyric sheet. SASE. Reports in 2 weeks.
Music: Mostly country, gospel, pop and rock. Produced "Nevada State of Mind", written and recorded by Barry Best and "Don't Walk Away" written and recorded by B.G. White (country); and "Overnight Sensation", written and recorded by Rick Blake (top 40), all on Tract Records. Other artists include Jessica James, Robin Sharkey, Ron Arlen and The Deacon.

*TURNER PRODUCTIONS, P.O. Box 64895, Baton Rouge LA 70896. (504)925-0988. Indie Producer: Henry Turner. Record producer (BMI), record companies (Hit City Records and Genesis Gospel Records). Estab. 1984. Deals with artists and songwriters. Produces 2-5 singles and 2-5 LPs/year. Fee derived from sales royalty or outright fee from recording artist or record company. "We charge a production fee."

How to Contact: Write or call first and obtain permissions to submit. Prefers cassette with 3 songs and lyric sheet. "Stay basic in your ideas." Does not return unsolicited material. Reports in 1 month.
Music: All types. Produced "What A Wonderful God We Serve", written and recorded by Marvin Griffin, formerly of the Five Blind Boys, on Genesis Records (gospel single); "Little Heart", written and recorded by Valaree Brock on Hit City Records (country single); and "The Fall of Englatine", written and recorded by Tim Grabus & Once Upon A Time, on Hit City Records (rock single). Other artists include Tracy Star, Stanley Winston, Wanda Rivera and Billy Averett.
Tips: "Think reality and be prepared to work for the things you want."

CHARLES VICKERS MUSIC ASSOCIATION, Box 725, Daytona Beach FL 32015-0725. (904)252-4849. President/Producer: Dr. Charles H. Vickers D.M. Record producer, music publisher (Pritchett Publication/BMI, Alison Music/ASCAP) and record company (King of Kings Records and L.A. International Records). Deals with artists and songwriters. Produces 3 singles and 6 LPs/year. Works with 1 new songwriter/year. Teams collaborators. Fee derived from sales royalty.
How to Contact: Write first. Prefers 7½ ips reel-to-reel or cassette with 1-6 songs. SASE. Reports in 1 week.
Music: Mostly church/religious, gospel and hymns; also bluegrass, blues, classical, country, easy listening, jazz, MOR, progressive, reggae (pop), R&B, rock, soul and top 40/pop. Produced "Walking on the Water," "Let Us Pray," "Always Depend on Jesus," "The Lord is My Proctor," and "Everyday is a Holy Day," all written and recorded by C. Vickers on King of King Records (L.A. Int'l).

*THE VICTORY LABEL, 1054 Conifer Lane, Petaluma CA 94954. (707)762-4858. Director of A&R: Shelly Trumbo. Record company, music publisher. ASCAP affiliate. Estab. 1985. Deals with artists and songwriters. Produces 5 singles, 2 12″ singles, 7 LPs, 10 EPs and 10 CDs/year. Fee is derived from sales royalty.
How to Contact: Write first and obtain permission to submit. Prefers cassette (or VHS videocassette if available) with 3 songs and lyric sheet. Does not return unsolicited material. Reports in 3 months.
Music: Mostly rock, pop and Christian rock; also dance. Produced "Out of Control" and "Shelly T", both recorded by Shelly T. on Victory Records (rock). Other artists regularly produced include Jeff Brockman.

WILLIAM F. WAGNER, Suite 218, 14343 Addison St., Sherman Oaks CA 91423. (818)905-1033. Contact: Bill Wagner. Record producer. Estab. 1957. Deals with artists and songwriters. Produces 4-6 singles, 2-4 LPs and 2-4 CDs/year and 4-8 CDs/year. Works with 25 new songwriters/year. Fee derived from sales royalty or outright fee from recording artist record company.
How to Contact: Prefers cassette with 1-5 songs and lead sheets; "no lyric sheets. Material should be copyrighted." SASE. Reports in 1 month.
Music: Mostly top 40, pop, country and jazz; also blues, choral, gospel, easy listening, MOR, progressive, rock, soul and pop. Produced "Sings Mercer" recorded by Dewey Erney on Legend Records (MOR-jazz); "Digital Page" recorded by Page Cavanaugh on Legend Records (jazz). Other artists include Dewey Erney, Frank Sinatra, Jr., Candace Bennett, Mike Randall, Page Cavanaugh and Sandy Graham.
Tips: "Tune up the band and/or piano. Let's hear the singer. Quit using 'friends'; use pro players and singers instead."

*CORNELL WARD, P.O. Box 57, LaGrange IL 60525. (708)759-4271. President: Cornell Ward. Record producer, music publisher (Gilcon Music/BMI) and arranger. Estab. 1983. Deals with artists and songwriters. Produces 8-16 singles, 3-4 12″ singles, 2-3 LPs and 2-3 CDs/year. Fee derived from sales royalty and outright fee from record company. "Charge if services are on a for-hire basis. Does not charge if artist or songwriter or song is assigned/signed to my production company or publishing company."
How to Contact: Submit demo tape by mail. Unsolicited submissions accepted. Prefers cassette (or VHS videocassette if available) with 3-5 songs and lyric and lead sheet if available. "Absolutely no metal! or hard rock!! Absolutely no phone calls. If interested will call!" SASE. Reports in 3-4 weeks.
Music: Mostly pop, top 40, R&B, easy listening, country/soft rock; also gospel, rap and New Age vocals & instrumentals. Produced *The Second Time*, recorded by The Dells on King-Japan Veterans-USA Records (pop/R&B LP) and *Will Clayton* recorded by Will Clayton on Timeless Records (R&B LP) both written by C. Ward, A. Miller and various other writers. Other artists include Pop Staples of Staple Singers, Will Clayton, Tracee and Roy Hytower.
Tips: "Submit your best. Be yourself. Be creative. Don't expect overnight success. Be patient. Music is returning to a more musical style, rather than the 1-2 chord changes of the dance craze."

WE-B RECORDS AND PROMOTIONS, (formerly T.C. Records and Promotions), 121 Meadowbrook Dr., Somerville NJ 08876. (201)359-5110. Producer: Tony Camillo. Record producer, music publisher and production company. Deals with artists and songwriters. Produces 21-25 singles and 5-8 LPs/year. Fee derived from sales royalty or outright fee from record company.
How to Contact: Query. Prefers cassette with 2-5 songs and lead sheet. "Send as complete a package as possible." SASE. Reports in "1 month or longer depending on schedule."
Music: Dance, soul, MOR, rock and top 40/pop; "excellent material only." Produced "Midnight Train to Georgia" (by Jim Weatherly), recorded by Gladys Knight and the Pips on Buddah Records.

THE WEISMAN PRODUCTION GROUP, 449 N. Vista St., Los Angeles CA 90036. (213)653-0693. Contact: Ben Weisman. Record producer and music publisher (Audio Music Publishers). Estab. 1965. Deals with artists and songwriters. Produces 15 singles/year. Fee derived from sales royalty.
How to Contact: Prefers cassette with 3-10 songs and lyric sheet. SASE. "Mention *Songwriter's Market*. Please make return envelope the same size as the envelopes you send material in, otherwise we cannot send everything back. Don't query first; just send tape." Reports in 1 month.
Music: Mostly R&B, soul, dance, rap and top 40/pop; also all types of rock.
Tips: "Do not write for permission to submit, just send tapes of new songs."

THOMAS WIGGINS ASSOCIATES, P.O. Box 21118, Castro Valley CA 94546. (415)538-6195. President: Tom Wiggins. Record producer, music publisher (Udder Publishing/ASCAP, Middleastern Music Organization, Great Ethnic Publishing Co., Big Jam Publishing and Duxbury Publishing), record company (No-Bull, Nineveh, Persepolis, Elite Records and Great Ethnic Records), and management firm and booking agency (Thomas Wiggins and Associates). Estab. 1969. Deals with artists and songwriters. Produces 4-10 singles and 4-10 LPs/year. Fee derived from sales royalty, outright fee from recording artist or record company. "All deals are negotiable for responsible artists."
How to Contact: Prefers cassette (or VHS videocassette) with 3-6 songs and lyric sheet. SASE. Reports in 6 weeks. "Be patient, and please try and send listenable quality representations of your work."
Music: Mostly country, blues and cajun/ethnic; also R&B. Produced *Times Getting Tougher*, written and recorded by C. Musselwhite (blues LP); *Foolers Love* (by J. Miller), recorded by Miller Brothers (country LP); and *Just for You* (by P. Houchin), recorded by Go For Broke (country LP), all on No-Bull Records. Other artists include Taj Mahal, Cal Tjader, Merl Saunders, The Dillards, Laurindo Almeida, Carlos Montoya, and John Lee Hooker.

SHANE WILDER PRODUCTIONS, Box 3503, Hollywood CA 90078. President: Shane Wilder. Record producer and music publisher. Deals with artists and songwriters. Produces 25-30 singles and 10-15 LPs/year. Fee derived from sales royalty plus production fee.
How to Contact: Prefers cassette with 6-8 songs and lyric sheet. SASE. Reports in 4 weeks.
Music: Country. Produced "Are There Any Angels in Nashville,""I'm Not Cookin' Your Eggs No More" and "I Just Love a Good Story," by Jane Tyler; "We Graduate This Summer," by Teresa O'Dell (country single); "Part Time Love," by Crystal Blue (disco single); and "Old Liars, Umpires and a Woman Who Knows," by Mike Franklin (country single, N.S.D. Records). Other artists include Priscilla Emerson, Laurie Loman (MCA recording artist) and Terry Brooks (rock artist, Jet Records).
Tips: "Looking for top country acts for record contract and management — acts must be highly commercial."

*TOM WILLETT, TOMARK RECORDS, 7560 Woodman Pl.,#G3, Van Nuys CA 91405. (818)994-4862. Owners: Tom Willett and Mark Thornton. Record producer, music publisher (Schmerdley Music/BMI) and record company (Tomark Records). Estab. 1988. Deals with artists and songwriters. Produces 1-4 singles and 1-4 LPs/year.
How to Contact: Submit demo tape by mail. Unsolicited submissions are okay. Prefers cassette (or VHS videocassette if available) with any number of songs and lyric sheets. SASE. Reports in 4 weeks.
Music: Mostly country and novelty; also folk. Produced "Come on Home" (by Ray Corbin), recorded by Herman Schmerdley (country single); and "Walk Right In" recorded by Mark Thornton (country single). Both on Tomark Records.
Tips: "Submit bio, resume, cassette. Send a good quality recording. Music is becoming even more lucrative than before. A good song can generate a good albumor even a TV program or movie."

*ALBERT KENNEDY WILLIAMS, 609A Rosebank Ave., Nashville TN 37206. (615)226-8438. Studio Manager: Alice Rye. Record producer. Estab. 1990. Deals with artists and songwriters. Produces 5 LPs and 1 CD/year. Fees derived from sales royalty. "Charges for demos and projects not associated with our custom labels."

How to Contact: Submit demo tape by mail. Unsolicited submissions are okay. Prefers cassette with 3 songs and lyric sheets. "We are interested in lyrical content. Song must say something, or have strong emotional power." SASE. Reports in 1 month.

Music: Mostly folk, country and New Age (vocal); also New Age (instrumental) and gospel/christian. Produced *Miracle Record Sampler*, written and recorded by Johnny Bellar and Alice & Albert on Miracle (folk LP); *Alice & Albert Sing No to Drugs*, written and recorded by Alice & Albert on Pholk (folk LP); and *Wayne from Maine*, written and recorded by Wayne Osnoe on Wildwood (folk LP). Other artists include David Wilson.

Tips: "Know the market you're writing for. Write from the heart, but work at marrying art and craft. We are not interested in trivial subjects. Folk music, particulary issue-oriented folk, is making its cyclical appearance, and will thrive in the 90s."

FRANK WILLSON, 308-46 Bypass, Sequin TX 78151. (512)372-1600. Producer: Frank Willson. Record producer (BMI) and record company (BSW Records). Deals with artists and songwriters. Estab. 1987. Produces 3 singles, 12 12″ singles and 5 EPs/year. Fee derived from sales royalty.

How to Contact: Submit demo tape by mail. Unsolicited submissions are okay. Prefers cassette with 3-4 songs and lyric sheets. SASE. Reports in 4 weeks.

Music: Mostly country and rock. Produced "Memory of a Memory" (by J. Paycheck), recorded by Bobby Lloyd; "Last Song" (by Roy Orbison), recorded by Mike Lord; and "I Will Be Home When I Get There" (by Barry Roberts), recorded by Lost Prairie, all on BSW Records (country). Other artists include Larry Noland, Candeeland.

WINBERN COUP PRODUCTIONS, 98-15 Horace Harding Exp. #8G, Rego Park NY 11368. (212)459-4141. Contact: Wingate. Record producer, music publisher (WinBern Coup Publishing/BMI). Estab. 1987. Deals with artists and songwriters. Produces 30 singles and 20 12″ singles/year. Fee derived from sales royalty.

How to Contact: Write or call first and obtain permission to submit. Prefers cassette with 3 songs and lyric sheets. SASE. Reports in 1 month.

Music: Mostly R&B and pop; also ballads. Produced *On The Rocks!* (by M. Wingate), recorded by Alyson Williams on Def Jam/Columbia Records (R&B LP), "Sexy Minded" (by M. Wingate/T. McConnell), recorded by Skyy on Atlantic Records; and remix of "Take It Over", recorded by Grason Hugh on RCA Records. Other artists include Def Jam/Columbia artists.

Tips: "Be persistent."

*GEOFF WORKMAN/ORIGINAL PROJECTS UNLIMITED, 36 West 3rd Ave., Denver CO 80223. (303)722-9653. President: Lauri Day-Workman. Record producer. Estab. 1986. Deals with artists and songwriters. Produces 3 LPs, 3 EPs and 3 CDs/year. Fee derived from sales royalty or outright fee from recording artist or record company. "Requires deposit for time block of a project."

How to Contact: Submit demo tape by mail. Unsolicited submissions are okay. Prefers cassette with 3-4 songs and lyric sheet. Include promotional kit and picture. SASE. Reports in 6 weeks.

Music: Mostly rock, heavy metal and pop; also alternative. Engineered *Every Dog Has It's Day* (by Salty Dog), recorded by Salty Dog and *Last Decade, Dead Century* (by Warrior Soul), recorded by Warrior Soul, both on Geffen Records (rock LP). Other artists include Strange Parade.

*LONNIE WRIGHT, Rt. 14 Box 1039, Hwy 64 E., Tyler TX 75707. (214)566-5653. Vice President: Lonnie Wright. Record producer. Estab. 1987. Deals with artists and songwriters. Produces 175 singles and 10-12 LPs/year. Fee derived from outright fee from recording artist.

How to Contact: Submit demo tape by mail. Unsolicited submissions are okay. Prefers cassette with 3 songs and lyric sheet. Does not return unsolicited material.

Music: Mostly country, gospel and rock & roll. Produced "Every Heart" (by Mae Axton), recorded by Pat Murphy on OL Records (country single); and "Bright Light" (by Jeff Wright), recorded by Beau Dean on OL (country single). Other artist include The Bonner, Ronnie Redd and Ken Shepard.

*CHRISTOFF WYBOUW, 21A Oude Dorpsweg, Varsenare 8202 **Belgium**. (050)387910. FAX: 050/382835. Producer: Christoff Wybouw. Record producer, music publisher (Onadisc) and recording studio. Estab. 1980. Deals with artists and songwriters. Produces 10 singles, 5 12″ singles, 2 LPs and 5 CDs/year. Fee derived from sales royalty.

How to Contact: Prefers cassette. SAE and IRC. Reports in 1 month.

Music: Mostly disco, rock and new wave; also "crooners." Produced "No Police," by Ziggy (disco single, Holy Hole/Carrere); "5 Jaar," by Lode der torck (chanson single, Holy Hole); and "I Need Your Love," by Chris Clark (disco single, Holy Hole).

*STEVE WYTAS PRODUCTIONS, 165 Linden St., New Britain CT 06051. (203)224-1811. Contact: Steven J. Wytas. Record producer. Estab. 1984. Deals with artists only. Produces 4-8 singles, 6 12″ singles, 3 LPs, 3 EPs and 2 CDs/year. Fee derived from outright fee from recording artist or record company. "Expenses, sub-contractor fees, etc."
How to Contact: Submit demo tape by mail. Unsolicited submissions are OK. Prefers cassette or VHS-¾″ videocassette) with several songs and lyric or lead sheet. "Include live material if possible." Does not return unsolicited material. Reports in 2 months.
Music: Mostly rock, metal, pop, top 40, country/acoustic; also R&B, soul and comedy. Produced "Mental Gymnastics" on MGA records, (single) and *Free World* on TOTC Records (album disc) and "Indy Records" (single), both written and recorded by Leigh Gregory. Other artists include Flying Nuns, Sons of Bob, MG's, Mud Solo, Stupe, Wayne and Garth.

*JOHN YOUNG, Suite 101, 50 Music Square W., Nashville TN 37203. (615)320-5707. Record producer, music pubilsher, record company (Bear Records) and Young Graham Music. Estab. 1989. Deals with artists and songwriters. Produces 10 singles/year. Fee derived from sales royalty and outright fee from recording artist. Charges artists in advance for services.
How to Contact: Write or call first and obtain permission to submit. Prefers cassette with 3 songs and lyric sheet. SASE.
Music: Mostly country and gospel. Produced "Girls Like Her" (by Gant), recorded by J. Wright; "Red Neck Blue Monday" (by Shafer) recorded by J. Wright; and "Down Home" (by Shephard), recorded by T. Roberson, all on Bear Records (all country). Other artists include Patton Ray and Brice Long.

*ZAR MUSIK, (formerly Masters Production), Dreilindenstr. 42, Saint Gall, CH 9011 **Switzerland**. Phone: (071)255-666. A&R Director: Victor Waldburger. Record producer, music publisher and record company (Masters Records). Deals with artists and songwriters. Estab. 1980. Produces 5 singles, 5 LPs and 5 CDs/year. Fee derived from sales royalty, outright fee from recording artist or record company.
How to Contact: Send cassette (or VHS videocassette) and lyric or lead sheet. Reports only if interested.
Music: Mostly commercial pop, dance and rock/heavy metal. Produced "Miracles" (by Tony Sachary) on CBS Records (pop); "Gold for Lion" (by Carlos Perou) on WEA Records (techno); and "Check and Mate" (by Sultan) on Zar Records (HM).
Tips: "Have a strong, original song with a strong vocal!"

*ZEKE PRODUCTIONS, INC., 345 E. 80th St., 15H, New York NY 10021. (212)744-2312. President: Chuck Dembrak. Record producer and music publisher (Cool One Music/ASCAP). Estab. 1978. Deals with artists and songwriters. Produces 3-6 12″ singles and 1-2 LPs/year. Fees derived from sales royalty and outright fee from record company. "Charges for consultation."
How to Contact: Submit demo tape by mail. Unsolicited submissions are okay. Call first to arrange personal interview. Prefers cassetts (or VHS videocassette if available) with 3-4 songs and lyric sheets. SASE. Reports in 4 weeks.
Music: Mostly R&B, pop and rock. Produced "Use Me" (by B. Withers), recorded by B. Frazier on Sutra (R&B single); "Drive Me" (by A. Forbes), recorded by P. Day on Starway (pop single); and "This Time" written and recorded by C. Leak on Warlock (R&B single). Other artists include Michele Johnson and Rob Hegel.

Record Producers/'90-'91 changes

The following markets appeared in the 1990 edition of *Songwriter's Market* but do not appear in the 1991 edition. Those companies that did not respond to our request for an update of their listing may not have done so for a variety of reasons—they may be out of business, for example, or they may be overstocked with submissions.

Ala Bianca Publishing Group (did not respond)
All Star Productions (did not respond)
Alphabeat (asked to be deleted)
Junior Alphonso (did not respond)
Bill Anderson Jr. (did not respond)
Audioloft Recording Studios (asked to be deleted)

Dough Productions and Management (did not respond)
Duane Music, Inc. (did not respond)
Jamie Dyce/Radio Active Records (did not respond)
Jack Eubanks Productions (did not respond)
Rick Eyk (did not respond)
Bobby Farrell Phonorecord Productions (deleted)
John Fisher & Associates (did

(did not respond)
David R. Kaspersin (did not respond)
Kenning Productions (did not respond)
Barbara King (moved; no forwarding address)
Paul Kitchen/The Insync Asylum (did not respond)
KLW International, Inc. (did not respond)
Kren Music Productions (did

John Baccigaluppi (asked to deleted)

Jim Barg/Electric Ear Productions (did not respond)

The Beau-Jim Agency, Inc. (did not respond)

Mark S. Berry (did not respond)

The Best of All Musical Worlds (did not respond)

Blaze Productions (did not respond)

David Bluefield (did not respond)

Bouquet-Orchid Enterprises (did not respond)

Brasil Musical Record Producers Ltda. (did not respond)

Breakfast Communications (moved; no forwarding address)

Broadway Productions, Inc. (moved; no forwarding address)

Bill Byron Productions (did not respond)

The Calvary Music Group (did not respond)

Cantus Productions Limited (did not respond)

Don Casale Music, Inc. (did not respond)

Harry F. Chestler (moved; no forwarding address)

Cloudburst Records (did not respond)

Continental Communications Corp. (did not respond)

Country Charts (did not respond)

Crusader Records and Tapes (did not respond)

Mal Davis (did not respond)

Chris Dawkins (asked to be deleted)

Al Delory and Music Makers (did not respond)

DMI Productions (asked to be deleted)

Doc Holiday Productions (did not respond)

New Dawn Productions/South Bound Productions (did not respond)

Keith Nichol (did not respond)

Nise Productions, Inc. (did not respond)

Northcott Productions, Inc. (did not respond)

Of-Oz Productions (did not respond)

100 Grand Records (asked to be deleted)

Original Projects Unlimited (asked to be deleted)

Pad Records and Demo Studio (moved; no forwarding address)

Sue K. Patton/SKP Productions, Inc. (did not respond)

Pisces Productions Limited (did not respond)

not respond)

FM-Revolver Records Ltd. (did not respond)

Foojoonjoy Productions (asked to be deleted)

GCS Productions (did not respond)

Jay Gold-Turbo Records (did not respond)

Greentrax Records (did not respond)

Eric "Griffy" Grief/Edge Entertainment Inc. (asked to be deleted)

James A. Griffin (asked to be deleted)

Grove Music Ltd. (did not respond)

Chris Gussa (did not respond)

R L Hammel Associates, Inc. (did not respond)

Geoffrey Hansen Ents. Ltd. (did not respond)

Ken Harnden (did not respond)

John Harvey Enterprises (did not respond)

Hippogriff Productions, Inc. (asked to be deleted)

Homestead Productions (deleted)

Humdinger (asked to be deleted)

Hup Hup Sdn. Bhd. (did not respond)

IGL Audio (did not respond)

Igloo (did not respond)

International Songbank (did not respond)

ISBA Records, Inc. (did not respond)

Ivory Tower Studios (did not respond)

J.L.I. Productions (did not respond)

Jellee Works Productions (asked to be deleted)

Jewish Family Productions (asked to be deleted)

Danny Jones Productions (did not respond)

Johann Kaplan Music Group

RMS Triad Productions (did not respond)

Rob Roberts/Oceanhills Music Group (did not respond)

Rooster Productions (did not respond)

RSD Productions (did not respond)

Silver J. Sargent (did not respond)

Charles Scott (did not respond)

Jim Scott (did not respond)

Hal Shaper Ltd. (HSL) London (did not respond)

Stephen Sheehan/Post-Ambient Productions (did not respond)

Silver Bullet Productions/Truly Fine Records (did not respond)

Soundshine Productions, Inc.

not respond)

Jury Krytiuk Productions (did not respond)

L & A Productions (did not respond)

Landmark Audio of Nashville (did not respond)

Landmark Communications Group (moved; no forwarding address)

John Latimer (did not respond)

Roosevelt Lee International Records (did not respond)

Leopard Music (did not respond)

Reggie Lucas Productions (did not respond)

Harold Luick & Associates (did not respond)

Lust Enterprises (did not respond)

Jim McCoy Productions, Inc. (did not respond)

MacDonald-Daller Productions (did not respond)

Ray Mack Productions (did not respond)

Madison Station Productions (did not respond)

Manhattan Country, Inc. (did not respond)

Harvey Marcus (did not respond)

Masloh (did not respond)

Melody Dawn Productions (asked to be deleted)

Midwest Records (did not respond)

A.V. Mittelstedt (did not respond)

Modern Music Ventures, Inc. (did not respond)

Modern World Music (did not respond)

Les Monahan Productions (did not respond)

Ross Munro/Random Entertainment Inc. (did not respond)

My Production (did not respond)

(did not respond)

Sunset Records, Inc. (did not respond)

Lanny Swaim (did not respond)

Tempe/Borgata Productions (deleted)

Third Ear (did not respond)

Third Floor Productions/Steve R. Pinkston (did not respond)

Rik Tinory Productions (did not respond)

Trend Productions (did not respond)

Twelve Oaks Productions (did not respond)

Nik Venet/Summerwind Productions (did not respond)

Walk on Water Productions (did not respond)

Scott Warner (did not respond)

Pottemus Productions (did not respond)
Praise Sound Productions Ltd. (did not respond)
Quinto Productions/Records (did not respond)
R.C. Enterprises, Inc. (did not respond)
Redbud Records (asked to be deleted)
Redwood Productions (did not respond)
Bobby D. Reed (did not respond)

(did not respond)
Don Stanton (did not respond)
Fabio Steels (moved; no forwarding address)
A. Stewart Productions (did not respond)
Stonedog Productions (did not respond)
Strawberry Hill Productions (did not respond)
Strawberry Jam Productions (did not respond)
Studioeast (did not respond)
Preston Sullivan Enterprises

Welchy Grape Records and Publishing Company (did not respond)
Wildlife Productions Ltd. (did not respond)
Win Bern Coup Productions (did not respond)
WIR (World International Records) (did not respond)
Zaleski and Associates (did not respond)
Zenith/DB Studios (asked to be deleted)

Managers and Booking Agents

Managers are responsible for steering and developing artists' careers. Good ones are knowledgeable about promotion, publishing, recording, contracts and almost anything else that concerns a recording artist's professional life. An effective manager is an expert who is hired to stand between the artist and the thousand-and-one mundane details of a career in the music business. For his services, the manager usually takes between 10 and 25% of the artist's earnings.

The booking agent is the person responsible for setting up the artist's performance schedule and securing bookings. Agents tend to represent many more clients than do managers. They may review material for the artists they work with, but probably don't get to know each one as well as the manager. A booking agent's fee is typically between 10 and 20% of the gross earnings from the jobs he books. Each listing in this section specifies whether the company is a booking agency, management firm or both.

Both managers and booking agents have a great interest in the songs their clients record. A successful song increases earnings all around: the manager reaps the rewards of greater record sales, and the booking agent profits from a busier, more lucrative performance schedule. For that reason, both managers and booking agents are viable contacts for songwriters hoping to place songs with particular artists.

If you wish to submit songs to managers for their artists, notice the names of the acts they represent and the types of music they need. Managers of nationally-known artists and groups are located mostly in Los Angeles, New York or Nashville. But you can probably find performers in or near your home town who need songs. Managers of smaller, regional acts will usually have more to say in the choice of material than those located in music centers (where the producer often makes the final decision about which songs an artist should record). Local acts work hard to make a reputation for themselves in hope of going on to stardom. It certainly doesn't hurt to become a favorite songwriter of a talented local group. If the act goes on to bigger things, they'll take your songs with them. If a manager or booking agent works only with local or regional acts, it will be indicated in the listing. Otherwise, you can assume that the firm works with acts from anywhere.

Managers and booking agents are particularly good contacts for performing writers/artists. The more acts they can successfully represent, the more their potential earnings. If you want to perform your songs regularly in a concert situation—and possibly tour regionally, nationally or even internationally—then you may want to contact a manager or booking agent about considering you as an artist/client.

You may want to send a query letter asking a firm what their current needs are. When contacting them, always be specific as to your intentions: whether you are a nonperforming songwriter wishing to have your material reviewed for other artists, or a writer/artist wishing to hire a manager or agent to handle your own career. If you are a songwriter/artist looking for a manager, you should include in your submission a glossy photo, a list of songs you perform (both originals and covers), a current itinerary, and any relevant press clippings. You may want to submit a live demo recording or a videocassette to show off your performing abilities. If you are an entertainer or if a local group is performing your songs, make arrangements for managers and/or agents to see your work live.

ACADEMY AWARD ENTERTAINMENT, 11 Shady Oak Trail, Charlotte NC 28210. (704)554-1162. Agent: Butch Kelly. Management firm, music publisher (Butch Kelly Productions, Music By Butch Kelly/BMI), record company (KAM Executive and Fresh Avenue Records), record producer and Sunshine Record Promotions. Estab. 1987. Represents national acts and comedians. Currently handles 10 acts. Receives 20% commission. Reviews material for acts.
How to Contact: Prefers cassette or records (or VHS videocassette) with 5-10 songs. "Send bio information, 8x10 photo, press kit or news clips if possible." SASE. Reports in 2 months.
Music: Rock, pop, R&B, rap, beach, soul, gospel, country and comedy. Works primarily with show and dance groups, vocalists, bar bands and concerts. Current acts include Fresh Air (R&B), Lady Crush (rapper), Dean Mancuso (country), Melisa Kelly (R&B/pop), L.A. Star (R&B), Caro (R&B), and Platters (show).
Tips: "Be professional and want to work."

*THE ACT AGENCY, P.O. Box 157652, Irving TX 75015. (214)259-1890. Manager and Agent: Sharon Rone. Management firm and booking agency. Estab. 1989. Represents local and regional artists and groups, (South and Southwest, but all tour nationally); currently handles 6 acts. Receives 10-15% commission. Reviews material for acts.
How to Contact: Write and obtain permission to submit. Prefers cassette with maximum of 3 songs and lyric sheet. "Finished demos only. No roughs." Does not return unsolicited material. Reports in 2-3 months.
Music: Mostly country, adult contemporary and pop-rock. Works primarily with self-contained groups—concert and dance oriented. Current acts include The Shoppe (country pop nostalgia), Ricky Lynn (singer/songwriter of country/rock), White Brothers (country) and Texas The Band (country).
Tips: "Write first. List all previous credits of recorded material. Submit professional finished demo."

*ACT "1" ENTERTAINMENT, Box 1079, New Haven CT 06504. (203)785-8338. President: Johnny Parris. Management firm and booking agency. Represents individual artists and groups; currently handles 40 acts. Reviews material for acts. Receives 10-20% commission.
How to Contact: Query by mail, arrange personal interview or submit demo and lead sheet. Prefers cassette (or VHS videocassette) with 5-10 songs. "Also include bio, photo, repertoire and a list of personnel and equipment if you're looking to be booked. Material will not be returned without sufficient SASE". Reports in 1 month.
Music: Mostly top 40, pop, soul, R&B and dance; also, easy listening, jazz, MOR and rock. Current acts include Tara (top 40), David Quick (pop/folk), Dirtybird (rhythm & blues/soul), Chaser (top 40), Bob Mel (top 40/pop), Splash (rock/top 40), Thin Ice (rock/top 40), The Carl Martin Show (R&B/soul), Nite Co. (top 40), Just Us (top 40), Secrets (top 40/R&B) and Marci 8 Michael (top 40/R&B).
Tips: "I'm looking for people with a professional attitude and drive and determination—people who are ethical and not into drugs. If you are ethical and stay completely away from drugs, you will make a lot of friends who will help you in your career, whether it's song writing, performing or managing. Looking for that one artist that we can take to the top of the music world in 1991."

AFTERSCHOOL PUBLISHING COMPANY, P.O. Box 14157, Detroit MI 48214. (313)873-5449. President: Herman Kelly. Management firm, booking agency, record company (Afterschool Co.) and music publisher (Afterschool Pub. Co.). Estab. 1978. Represents individual artists, songwriters, producer, arrangers and musicians. Currently handles 5 acts. Receives 20% commission. Reviews material for acts.
How to Contact: Prefers cassette with 3 songs and lyric or lead sheet. SASE. Reports in 1 month.
Music: Mostly pop, jazz, rap, country and folk. "What we are seeking now is comedy on the subjects of food, clothes, sports, cars and love." Works primarily with show or dance bands and folk groups. Current acts include Herman Kelly, Raymond Ellis (pop/jazz/folk), James Garland (pop/jazz,folk) and T. Stevenson.

AGF ENTERTAINMENT LTD., Suite 1703, 1500 Broadway, New York NY 10036. Management and production firm and music publisher (AGF Music LTD/ASCAP). Estab. 1982. Represents individual artists, groups and songwriters. Receives 20% commission. Reviews material for acts.
How to Contact: Prefers cassette (or VHS videocassette) with 4-6 songs maximum and lyric sheet. Does not return unsolicited material.
Music: Mostly rock and pop; also folk. Works with singer/songwriters and groups with original material. Current acts include Suzanne Vega, Eric Andersen, Pierce Turner and Shawn Colvin.

AIM HIGH PRODUCTIONS/IMA, 2022 Powers Ferry Rd., #210, Atlanta GA 30339. (404)956-8742. Contact: Jim Stephens. Management firm, booking agency and record company (JDS Records). Estab. 1982. Represents local, Southeast and national individual artists and groups. Currently handles 12-15 acts. Receives 15-20% commission. Reviews material for acts.
How to Contact: Submit demo tape by mail. Unsolicited submissions are okay; or call first to arrange personal interview. Prefers cassette (or VHS videocassette) with 4 songs. SASE. Reports in 2 weeks.
Music: Mostly pop, metal, top 40 and R&B. Works primarily with top 40 dance bands, soloists, duos and vocalists. Current acts include Desaint (rock/writers), Party Boys (top 40) and Ouija (heavy rock/writers).
Tips: "Have a complete kit on yourself pointing out your best talents and the type of material that you are best suited for. Your presentation should be brief but to the point. Your tapes should be labeled clearly and always have a phone number of them. As long as your tape is clear it doesn't have to be 24-track master quality. Send in material that is current and not dated. Watch the charts in the trades to see what is up and coming."

*AKO PRODUCTIONS, 20531 Plummer, Chatsworth CA 91311. (818)998-0443. President: A.E. Sullivan. Management firm, booking agency, music publisher and record company (AKO Records, Dorn Records, Aztec Records). Estab. 1980. Represents local and international artists, groups and songwriters; currently handles 3 acts. Receives 10-25% commission. Reviews material for acts.
How to Contact: Write first and obtain permission to submit. Prefers cassette with maximum of 5 songs and lyric sheet. Does not return unsolicited material. Reports in 1 month.
Music: Mostly pop, rock and top-40. Works primarily with vocalist, dance bands and original groups. No heavy metal. Current acts include Les Staunton's, Touch of Fire and The Stereo Band.

MARK ALAN AGENCY, P.O. Box 279, Hopkins MN 55343. (612)942-6119. President: Mark Alan. Management and booking firm. Represents individual artists, groups and songwriters; currently handles 10 acts. Receives 15% commission. Reviews material for acts.
How to Contact: Prefers cassette (or VHS videocassette). Does not return unsolicited material. Reports in 90 days.
Music: Rock, pop, R&B (black) and new wave. Works primarily with groups and solo artists. "We work with rock bands that tour nationally and regionally and record their original songs and release them on major labels or independent labels. We book clubs, colleges and concerts." Current acts include Airkraft, Mercedez, Sly Dog, Zwarté, Raggedy Ann, Montage, Constable Jones, Audra Shay, L.A. Babe's and Empyre.

*DAVID ALEKSANDER PRODUCTIONS, Suite 125, 4712 Avenue N, Brooklyn NY 11234. Managing Director-Artist Relations: David Aleksander. Management firm. Estab. 1986. Represents individual artists, groups and songwriters from anywhere; currently handles 3 acts. Receives 10-25% (depends) commission. Reviews material for acts.
How to Contact: Submit demo tape by mail. Unsolicited submissions are okay, accompanied by release form and SASE. "Do not call to submit tapes. Mail in for review. No calls will be returned, unsolicited or accepted, under any conditions." Prefers cassette (or VHS and/or ¾" videocassette) with 3-6 songs and lyric sheet. "We do not return unsolicited material if international." Reports in 2 months.
Music: Mostly commercial rock (all kinds), pop/dance/rap, post modern rock/folk rock; also novelty/comedy songs. Works primarily with commercial, original, solo artists and groups, songwriters in the rock, pop, dance areas (no country, no thrash, no punk). Current acts include Aleks Decarvalho (rock) and Bella (pop/dance artist).
Tips: "Submit a package of completed songs along with lyrics, photo of artist/group, or songwriter credits if any. A video on VHS accepted if available. If no package available send a cassette of what you as an artist consider best represents your style. Strong meaningful songs are preferred as well as light pop rock for top 40 release. Will submit quality songwriter's material to name artists. All materials must be accompanied by a release form and all songs must be copyrighted."

ALL STAR TALENT AGENCY, P.O. Box 82, Greenbrier TN 37073. (615)643-4208. Agent: Joyce Brown. Booking agency. Estab. 1966. Represents professional individuals, groups and songwriters; currently handles 6 acts. Receives 15% commission. Reviews material for acts.
How to Contact: Prefers reel-to-reel or cassette with 1-4 songs and lead sheet (VHS videocassette if available). SASE. Reports ASAP.
Music: Mostly country; also bluegrass, gospel, MOR, rock (country) and top 40/pop. Works primarily with dance, show and bar bands, vocalists, club acts and concerts. Current acts include Bill Carlisle and the Carlisles (country group), Ronnie Dove (MOR/country artist), Randy Parton (pop artist), Charlie McCoy (instrumentalist), Tommy Overstreet (country artist) and Alex Houston (MOR-country).

ALLEGIANCE ENTERTAINMENT CORP., INC., Box 370386, Atlanta GA 30037. (404)373-7000. Contact: Creative Department. Management firm, record company (Major Label Records) and music publisher (Bohdisattva). Represents individual artists, groups and songwriters; currently handles 3 acts. Receives 20% commission. Reviews material for acts.
How to Contact: Prefers cassette (or videocassette) with lyric or lead sheet. Does not return unsolicited material. Reports in 1 month.
Music: Mostly R&B, pop and jazz fusion; also experimental acoustic. Works primarily with "any self-contained artist or act that is commercially marketable." Current acts include Dale Sanders, Earl Johnson and First Reaction.
Tips: "We prefer to work with those who are actively involved in the music industry on a professional level."

MICHAEL ALLEN ENTERTAINMENT DEVELOPMENT, Box 111510, Nashville TN 37222. (615)754-0059. Contact: Michael Allen. Management firm. Represents individual artists, groups and songwriters; currently handles 5 acts. Receives 15-25% commission. Reviews material for acts.
How to Contact: Prefers cassette (or VHS videocassette) with 3 songs and lyric or lead sheets. SASE. Reports in 2 months.
Music: Mostly country, pop, R&B; also rock and gospel. Works primarily with vocalists and bands. Currently doing public relations for David Frizzell and Shotgun Red.

AMERICAN ARTIST, INC., 604 Glover Dr., Runnemede NJ 08078-1225. (609)931-8389. President: Anthony Messina. Management firm. Represent local, regional or international individual artists, groups and songwriters; currently handles 4 acts. Receives 15% commission. Reviews material for acts.
How to Contact: Submit demo tape by mail. Unsolicited submissions are OK. Prefers cassette or 7½ ips reel-to-reel (or VHS videocassette) with 3 songs and lyric sheets. Does not return unsolicited material. Reports in 6 weeks.
Music: Mostly MOR, rock and R&B. Works primarily with vocalists and dance bands. Current acts include Harold Melvin, Delfonics, Electric City and The Bluenotes.
Tips: "Hard work excels."

*AMERICAN CONCERT, P.O. Box 24599, Nashville TN 37202. (615)244-2290. Contact: Receptionist. Booking agency. Estab. 1987. Represents individual artists, groups and songwriters and established recording stars; currently handles 7 acts.
How to Contact: Call first and obtain permission to submit. SASE.
Music: Mostly country, adult contemporary and nostalgic rock. Works primarily with self-contained groups and solo artists who are songwriters. Current acts include Dan Seals (country), Charly McClain (country), Wayne Massey (light rock), Rhonda Gunn (country), Cheryl Wheeler (folk) and Johnny Rivers (nostalgic rock).

AMERICOM, 5150 Wilshire Blvd., Los Angeles CA 90036. (213)937-1101. President: Keith Vezensky. Management firm. Represents individual artists, groups and songwriters; currently handles 6 acts. Receives 10-20% commission. Reviews material for acts.
How to Contact: Write first and obtain permission to submit. Prefers cassette (or VHS videocassette). SASE. Reports in 1 month.
Music: Mostly rock, pop, dance, AOR and R&B. Works primarily with rock-pop artists and bands looking for tours and record deals. Current acts include Roger Williams and Roger Rose.

THE AMETHYST GROUP LTD., (formerly Mr. Agent), 96 McGregor Downs, W Columbia SC 29169-2850. Management firm. Represents individual artists, groups and songwriters; currently handles 11 acts. Receives 25% commission. Reviews material for acts.
How to Contact: Prefers cassette (or VHS videocassette) with 3-7 songs and lyric sheet. "Be creative, simple and to the point." Reports in 5 weeks. "No phone calls, please."
Music: Mostly mainstream, rock, metal and pop; also R&B and new music. Current acts include Jeromeo, Knightmare, Jr. Ellis, Carnage, Bye-Bye, Commandment, True Identity and Ted Neiland.
Tips: "Be prepared to sign, if we're interested. We won't spend a lot of time convincing anyone what we can do for them. We are way too busy with current recording artists. We help organize radio, retail, promotion for three record labels in the U.S. We develop recording artists and market them for further distribution, promotion. Our resources cover booking agencies, major and independent record companies, distributors, TV and radio stations, newspapers and trade publications, independent talent, record promoters and producers—all on national level. Most artists we represent are not in S.C."

AMUSE AMERICA, INC., 407 Park Ave. S., New York NY 10016. (212)213-9595. Management firm and music publisher (Brainstorm/ASCAP). Represents individual artists and groups; currently handles 4 acts. Reviews material for acts.
How to Contact: Write first and obtain permission to submit. Prefers cassette with 3 songs and lyric sheet. Does not return unsolicited material. Reports in 6 weeks.
Music: Mostly rock and pop. Works primarily with hard rock bands. Current acts include EZO (hard rock), Kataro (new age), and Dead End (hard rock).

*ANCIENT SPRINGS MUSIC, P.O. Box 590, Charlotte Hall MD 20622. (301)884-8484. Publishers Assistant: Kathy Kelly. Management firm, music publisher (Ancient Springs Music, BMI), record company (db Records) and recording studio. Estab. 1985. Represents individual artists, groups and songwriters. Deals with artists from anywhere. Currently handles 15 acts. Receives 10-20% commission. Reviews material for acts.
How to Contact: Submit demo tape by mail. Unsolicited submissions are OK. Prefers cassette with 3 songs and lyric sheets. Does not return unsolicited material. Reports in 6-8 weeks.
Music: Mostly interested in rock, country and pop; also Latin and folk. Works primarily with singer/songwriters. Current acts include Sam Neely (singer/songwriter), Quade and Catch-22 (both groups/songwriters).
Tips: "We look for writers who have something to say. We believe you can change the world with a song!"

*ANGELWOOD INC., #158 22968 Victory Blvd., Woodland Hills CA 91367. (818)348-8819. Manager: Dennis Rodriguez. Management firm. Estab. 1981. Represents international individual artists, groups (self-contained) and songwriters; currently handles 1 recording artist/3 songwriters.
How to Contact: Call first and obtain permission to submit. Prefers cassette with 3 songs. Does not return unsolicited material. Reports in 3 weeks.
Music: Mostly rock and pop; R&B and inspirational. Current acts include The Fuzztones (rock group), Rick Elias and The Confessions (singer/songwriter group) and Randy Hunter (singer/songwriter).

*ANIMAL CRACKERS ENTERTAINMENT, 5142 Warner Ave., Huntington Beach CA 92649. (714)846-4726. Owner: Susan Gilbert. Booking agency. Estab. 1978. Represents local, regional or international individual artists or groups; currently handles 300 acts. Reviews material for acts.
How to Contact: Submit demo tape by mail. Unsolicited submissions are OK. Prefers cassette or videocassette. Does not return unsolicited material. Reports in 1 week.
Music: All types of music.
Tips: "Send a good professional video."

ANJOLI PRODUCTIONS, 24 Center Square Rd., Leola PA 17540. (717)656-8215. President: Terry Gehman. Management firm, booking agency and music publisher (Younger Bros. Music). Estab. 1984. Represents individual artists, groups and songwriters; currently handles 20 acts. Receives 15% commission. Reviews material for acts.
How to Contact: Prefers cassette or VHS videocassette (Preferably a live show video, good quality. Segments of a variety of material. 15 minute maximum length.) with 5 songs and lyric sheet. Does not return unsolicited material.
Music: Country, pop and R&B. Works primarily with vocalists and show groups. Current acts include Shucks (country show), Crossover (country shows), Marsha Miller (country show) and Anita Stapleton (country vocalist).

*DAVID ANTHONY PROMOTIONS, 649 Knutsford Rd., Latchford, Warrington Cheshire WA4 1JJ **England**. Phone: (0925)32496. Projects Manager: Allan J. Crookes. Management firm and booking agency. Represents local individual artists, groups and songwriters; currently represents 6 acts; standard commission of 20%. Reviews material for acts.
How to Contact: Prefers cassette with 3 songs and lyric sheet. SAE and IRC. Reports in 3 weeks.
Music: Mostly country, rock; also pop. Current acts include Rick Astley (vocalist/songwriter), Poacher (country rock band/songwriters) and Steve Millinsten (songwriter).

APRIL PRODUCTIONS, 827 Brazil Pl., El Paso TX 79903. (915)772-7858. Owner: Harvey Marcus. Management firm, music publisher and record company (Crystal Ram, April/BMI). Represents local individual artists, groups, songwriters and national artists already signed; currently handles 5 acts. Receives 15-25% commission. Reviews material for acts.

How to Contact: Prefers cassete or 7½ ips reel-to-reel (or VHS videocassette) with 1 song and lyric sheet. SASE. Reports in 6 weeks.
Music: Mostly jazz/pop, top 40 ballads and Tex-Mex; also country, new age and Christian/rock. Works primarily with self-contained acts and/or songwriters that perform their own material. Current acts include Ruben Castillo (jazz-rock/songwriter), Mark David (rock/songwriter) and Ray Justin Vega (country/songwriter).
Tips: "Be patient, follow directions, and don't give up. Be as business-like and as professional as possible at all times. Don't send material or a bio on yourself until the majority of people that have seen you or heard of you say you're good (and the majority being total strangers not friends or family)."

ARISTO MUSIC GROUP, Box 22765, Nashville TN 37202. (615)269-7074. President: Jeff Walker. Publishing Manager: Terri Walker. Publicity/media management firm. Represents artists, groups and songwriters. "We deal with artists on a national and international level." Currently handles 8 clients. Receives negotiable commission for public relations services "based on estimated time and services involved." Reviews material for acts.
How to Contact: Query by mail. "At present we are only interested in artists with national distribution." Prefers cassette with 1-2 songs or videocassette if available. Prefers a "low-key, patient approach." SASE. Reports in 1 month.
Music: Country, easy listening, MOR and top 40/pop. Works primarily with country groups and artists. Current acts include the Nashville roster of Atlantic Records including Billy Joe Royal, Girls Next Door, Robin Lee and Jeff Stevens and the Bullets; and the Nashville roster of the Entertainment Artists Agency.
Tips: Songwriters "need to be professional in their approach to the music business. Have established affiliated publishing companies. See the Marco Music Group Inc."

*VIC ARKILIC, P.O. Box 261, Mt. Vernon VA 22121. (703)780-4726. Manager: Vic Arkilic. Management firm. Estab. 1986. Represents local individual artists and groups; currently handles 1 act. Receives 15% commission. Reviews material for acts.
How to Contact: Submit demo tape by mail. Unsolicited submissions are okay. Prefers cassette (or VHS videocassette) with 4 songs and lyric sheet. SASE. Reports in 3 weeks.
Music: Mostly rock, pop and folk. "We work with self-contained groups who are also songwriters." Current acts include The Tools (rock group).
Tips: "Please submit finished demos only!"

*THE ARTIST GROUP, 13176 Royal Pines Dr., St. Louis MO 63146. (314)576-7625. Manager: Keith Davis. Management firm and booking agency. Estab. 1987. Represents individual artists and groups from anywhere; currently handles 3 acts. Receives 15-25% commission. Reviews material for acts.
How to Contact: Submit demo tape by mail. Unsolicited submission are okay. Prefers cassette (or VHS videocassette) with 4 songs and lyric sheet. Does not return unsolicited material. Reports in 1 month.
Music: Mostly rock, alternative (new music) and funk. Works primarily with rock bands—dance funk bands. Current acts include Aynthem (objectivist rock), The Pods (progressive alternative) and Weaponz (rock show group).
Tips: "Submit quality demos, lyric sheets. Wait for a response. We will respond within 4 weeks of receipt."

ARTISTS'/HELLER AGENCY, #N, 21430 Strathern, Canoga Park CA 91304-4153. (818)702-9276. President: Jerry Heller. Management firm. Represents artists, groups and songwriters; currently handles 15 acts. Reviews material for acts. Receives 15-25% commission.
How to Contact: Query by mail. Prefers cassette with 4-7 songs. SASE. Reports in 1 month.
Music: Mostly R&B, rap and jazz; also rock, soul and progressive. Works primarily with concert groups. Current acts include Rose Royce (R&B), Rodney Franklin (jazz/R&B), Bobby Jimmy & The Critters, Russ Parr, World Class Wreckin' Cru, C.I.A., Eazy E, N.W.A., J.J. Fad, The D.O.C., and Michélle.

*ATTRACTIONS, LTD., P.O. Box 10013, Dallas TX 75207. (214)941-6971. President: R. Edward Cobb. Management firm. Estab. 1977. Represents individual artists and groups from anywhere; currently handles 2 acts. Reviews material for acts.
How to Contact: Submit demo tape by mail. Unsolicited submissions are okay. Prefers cassette (or VHS videocassette). Does not return unsolicited material.
Music: Mostly pop, country and rock; also variety. Current acts include Chisholm and Vince Vance.
Tips: "Send your best and simplest."

BABY SUE, Box 1111, Decatur GA 30031-1111. (404)288-2073. President: Don W. Seven. Management firm, booking agency, record company (Baby Sue); we also publish a magazine which reviews music. Estab. 1983. Represents local, regional or international individual artists, groups and songwriters; currently handles 3 acts. Receives 10% commission. Reviews material for acts.
How to Contact: Submit demo tape by mail. Unsolicited submissions are OK. Prefers cassette (or VHS videocassette) with 4 songs and lyric sheets. Does not return unsolicited material. Reports in 2 weeks.
Music: Mostly rock, pop and alternative; also country and religious. Works primarily with multi-talented artists (those who play more than 1 instrument). Current acts include LMNOP (rock), Stephen Fievet (pop) and Bringbring (poetic music).

BACKSTAGE PRODUCTIONS INTERNATIONAL, 1-3015 Kennedy Rd., Scarborough, Ontario M1V 1E7 **Canada.** (416)291-4913. President: Steve Thomson. Management firm, booking agency (Steve Thomson Agency), record company (Trilogy Records International), music publisher (Melmar Publishing/Procan and Star-Sattelite/CAPAC), and record producer. Represents individual artists, groups and songwriters. Currently handles 3 acts. Reviews material for acts.
How to Contact: Write or call first and obtain permission to submit. Prefers cassette (or VHS videocassette). SAE and IRC. Reports in 6 weeks.
Music: Mostly rock, pop and country/crossover. Works primarily with pop vocalists and rock bands; rock and country vocals. Current acts include Ronnie Hawkins and The Hawks (rockabilly), Patti Jannetta (pop), Wiz Bryant (folk) and JK Gulley (country).

GARY BAILEY ENTERTAINMENT AGENCY, 207 Queen St., Port Stanley, Ontario, **Canada.** (519)782-3570. President: Gary Bailey. Booking agency. Represents artists and groups in Ontario; currently handles 15 acts. Receives 15-20% commission. Reviews material for acts.
How to Contact: Query by mail. Prefers cassette or videocassette with 3-5 songs. Does not return unsolicited material. Reports in 2 weeks.
Music: Mostly MOR, 50s-60s and top 40; also dance, easy listening and rock. Works primarily with dance bands and bar bands. Current acts include Rudy Davis (MOR), Player (MOR), Bustin Loose (60s), Wildcats, and Dolly Hartt (country recording artist).
Tips: "Be honest, hard working and have a clean appearance."

BANDSTAND (INTERNATIONAL) ENTERTAINMENT AGENCY, Box 1010, Simcoe, Ontario N3Y 5B3 **Canada.** (519)426-0000. FAX: (519)426-3799. Florida Address: Unit 392, 1475 Flamingo Drive, Englewood FL 34224. President: Wayne Elliot. Management firm. Represents artists and groups. Estab. 1960. Receives 10% commission. Reviews material for acts.
How to Contact: Send promo kit. Prefers video—8mm or VHS. Good lighting and video precessing important. Does not return unsolicited material. Reports in 2 weeks.
Music: Mostly top 40 and comedy; also rock and pop. Works primarily with female vocalists, models, actresses and comedians. Current acts include Count Desmond (daredevil) and Sohia Lynn (country artist) and various local artists.

BARNARD MANAGEMENT SERVICES (BMS), 2219 Main St., Santa Monica CA 90405. (213)396-1440. Agent: Russell Barnard. Management firm. Estab. 1979. Represents artists, groups and songwriters; currently handles 3 acts. Receives 10-20% commission. Reviews material for acts.
How to Contact: Write first and obtain permission to submit cassette with 3-10 songs and lead sheet. Artists may submit VHS videocassette (15-30 minutes by permission only). SASE. Reports in 1 month.
Music: Mostly country crossover; also blues, country, R&B, rock and soul. Works primarily with country crossover singers/songwriters and show bands. Current acts include Helen Hudson (singer/songwriter), Mark Shipper (songwriter/author), Mel Trotter (singer/songwriter) and Sally Spurs (singer).
Tips: "Semi-produced demos are of little value. Either save the time and money by submitting material 'in the raw', or do a finished production version."

BILL BATZKALL PRODUCTIONS, INC., 1100 Cheltenham Rd, Elk Grove IL 60007. (312)981-0198. President: Bill Batzkall. Management firm, record company (Lake Effect Records, Inc.) and music publisher (Lake Effect Publishing, Inc.). Estab. 1983. Represents local individual artists, groups and songwriters. Receives 15-20% commission. Reviews material for acts.
How to Contact: Prefers cassette or 7½ ips reel-to-reel (or VHS videocassette) with 4 songs and lead sheet. SASE. Reports in 2 weeks.
Music: Jazz. Works primarily with artists of original "hit oriented" material. Current acts include Michael Mason (jazz flutist) and Joe Sonnefeldt (jazz Vibraphonist).

BDO SEIDMAN, 1200 Statler Towers, Buffalo NY 14202. (716)853-9333. Partner: Richard A. Romer. Management firm. Estab. 1972. Represents individual artists and groups; currently handles 5 acts. Commission is "based on hourly rate of $175/hour." Reviews material for acts.
How to Contact: Prefers cassette. Does not return unsolicited material. Reports in 2 weeks.
Music: Mostly R&B and pop. Works primarily with R&B acts and vocalists. Current acts include Rick James and other R&B groups.
Tips: "Have original material that has a different sound."

*BELKIN PERSONAL MANAGEMENT, 44 N. Main St., Chagrin Falls OH 44022. (216)247-2722. Assistant: Susan Haffey. Management firm. Represents local, regional or international individual artists, groups and songwriters; currently handles 4 acts. Receives 10-20% commission.
How to Contact: Submit demo tape by mail. Unsolicited submissions are OK. Prefers cassette with 3 songs. SASE. Reports in 3 weeks.
Music: Mostly rock, pop and R&B; also female vocalists. Works primarily with rock performance bands and female vocalists. Current acts include Mason Ruffner (blues rock singer/songwriter), Donnie Iris and The Cruisers (rock) and Cellarful of Noise (pop).

BARRY BERGMAN MANAGEMENT, 2555 East 12 St., Brooklyn NY 11235. (718)332-8500. Owner: Barry Bergman. Management firm and music publisher (Wood Monkey Music/ASCAP and Ellymax Music Co./BMI). Estab. 1982. Represents local, regional or international individual artists, groups, songwriters and producers; currently handles 5 acts. Receives 20% commission. "Acts are self-contained."
How to Contact: Call first and obtain permission to submit or to arrange personal interview. Prefers cassette (or VHS videocassette if available) with 3 songs and lyric sheets. Does not return unsolicited material. Reports in 1 month.
Music: Mostly rock and pop. Primarily works with self-contained acts, rock bands who also write and singer/songwriters. Current acts include Worlds Away (pop rock band), Rob Friedman (singer/songwriter) and Bob Halligan Jr. (singer/songwriter).
Tips: "The essence of your work must come from the heart and be real."

BEST BUDDIES, INC., Box 121738, Nashville TN 37212-1738. (615)383-7664. Professional Manager: Paul Sanders. Management firm and music publisher (Swing Set Music/ASCAP and Best Buddies Music/BMI). Estab. 1981. Represents individual artists, groups and songwriters from anywhere. Prefers "self-contained songwriter/artists." Currently handles 5 acts. Receives 10-20% commission. Reviews material for acts.
How to Contact: Write first and obtain permission to submit a demo. Prefers cassette (or VHS videocassette) with 4-5 songs and lyric sheet. Does not return unsolicited material. Reports in 6 weeks.
Music: Mostly country, rock and pop; also gospel and R&B. Works primarily with vocalists/musicians. Current acts include Ray Lynch (singer/writer); Sandy Garwood (singer/writer); and Jamie Bowles (singer/writer).
Tips: "Shoot your very best shot. This is a business and has to be treated as such."

*BIG HOUSE MANAGEMENT PTY LTD., P.O. Box 10, Broadway, Sydney NSW **Australia** 2007. (02)360 2550. Directors: Jon Ashcroft and Michael Dibbs. Management firm and booking agency. Estab. 1987. Represents local and international individual artists, groups and songwriters; currently handles 12 acts. Receives 20% commission. Reviews material for acts.
How to Contact: Submit demo tape by mail. Unsolicited submissions are okay. Prefers cassette (or VHS/PAL videocassette) with 4 songs and lyric sheet. Does not return unsolicited material. Reports in 1 month.
Music: Mostly rock, pop and soul/R&B; also country rock, country pop and contemporary jazz. Works primarily with vocalists, original contemporary bands and dance bands. Current acts include Jim Chaney (rock singer/songwriter), Jeff St. John (rock singer/songwriter) and Baby Loves to Cha Cha Dance Band (songwriters).
Tips: "Present submissions with all pertinent details."

BIG J PRODUCTIONS, Box 24455, New Orleans LA 70184. (504)488-8821. Agent: Frankie Jay. Booking agency. Estab. 1968. Represents individual artists, groups and songwriters; currently handles over 50 acts. Receives 15-25% commission. Reviews material for acts.
How to Contact: Write or call first and obtain permission to submit. Prefers cassette (or VHS videocassette) with 3-6 songs and lyric or lead sheet. "It would be best for an artist to lip-sync to a prerecorded track. The object is for someone to see how an artist would perform more than simply assessing song content." Does not return unsolicited material. Reports in 2 weeks.

Music: Mostly rock, pop and R&B. Works primarily with groups with self-contained songwriters. Current acts include Zebra (original rock group), Lillian Axe (original rock group), Kyper, (original dance) Razor White (original rock group) and Top Cats (original pop group).

Tips: "Have determination. Be ready to make a serious commitment to your craft because becoming successful in the music industry is generally not an "overnight" process."

J. BIRD BOOKING – THE ENTERTAINMENT AGENCY, 250 N. Kepler Rd., Deland FL 32724. (904)734-9446. Contact: John R. Bird II. Management firm and booking agency. Estab. 1963. Represents artists, groups and songwriters; currently handles 55 acts. Receives 15-25% commission. Reviews material for acts.

How to Contact: Prefers cassette (or VHS videocassette, short, 3-10 min., segments of performance. Preview a varity of material. Original songwriters should submit complete version of song) with 3-4 songs. "Initial interview is usually by phone; after demo material is received we usually ask person to contact us again in 1 week-10 days." Does not return unsolicited material.

Music: Mostly folk, rock, dance and top 40/pop. Works primarily with dance bands, vocalists and recording acts. Current acts include The Drifters, Greg Allman, Molly Hatchet, Doobie Brothers, Tams, Swinging Medallions, and Nantucket (original concert rock/RCA label).

Tips: "We solicit established professional acts interested in touring full time. The groups should have or be willing to prepare a promotional package containing audio and/or videotape, photos; and personnel, and equipment lists."

BLANK & BLANK, 1530 Chestnut St., Philadelphia PA 19102. (215)568-4310. Treasurer, Manager: E. Robert Blank. Management firm. Represents individual artists and groups. Reviews material for acts.

How to Contact: Write or call first to obtain permission to submit (prefers videocassette).

*BLUE OX TALENT AGENCY, 7458 E. Vista Dr., Scottsdale AZ 85250. (602)423-8669. Principal: Claudia Stewart. Booking agency and record company (Blue Ox Records). Estab. 1982. Represents international individual artists and groups; currently handles 50 acts. Receives 15% commission. Reviews material for acts.

How to Contact: Submit demo tape by mail. Unsolicited submissions are okay. Prefers cassette (or VHS videocassette if available). SASE. Reports in 1 month.

Music: Mostly pop, country and R&B; also children's music. Works primarily with vocalists and dance bands. Current acts include David Sebastian Bach (vocalist/songwriter), Standing Room Only (top 40 dance band) and Tom Porras (The Singing Quarterback).

Tips: "Be professional, go through the 'channels' and be patient!"

*BLUE RIDGE BOOKING, 10506 Timberlake Rd., Lynchburg VA 24502. (804)239-0724. President: Jim Robinson. Management firm, booking agency and record company (Blue Ridge Records). Estab. 1982. Represents international individual artists; currently handles 4 acts. Receives 10% commission. Reviews material for acts.

How to Contact: Submit demo tape by mail. Unsolicited submissions are okay. Prefers cassette. SASE. Reports in 3 weeks.

Music: Mostly country, gospel and pop. Works primarily with vocalists. Current acts include Robin Robinson (country), Kevin Garber (gospel) and Chris Robinson (actor).

WILLIS BLUME AGENCY, Box 509, Orangeburg SC 29116. (803)536-2951. President: Willis Blume. Management firm and booking agency. Estab. 1972. Represents artists and groups in the southeast; currently handles 30 acts. Receives minimum 15% commission. Reviews material for acts.

How to Contact: Query by mail. Prefers cassette with maximum of 4 songs. Artists may submit videocassette. SASE.

Music: "Only interested in adult contemporary songs and artists." Motown type, R&B, dance and Top 40. Works primarily with show and dance bands with horns. Current acts include Shagtime, The Swingin' Medalions, and The Catalinas (all show and dance bands/recording acts), the Tams (beach/top 40/pop artists), Archie Bell, The Kicks, The Impressions, Bank of Oz, The Drifters, The Clovers and The Entertainers.

BODÖ MUSIC, 186 Ashley Rd., Hale, Altrincham Cheshire WA15 9SF **England**. Phone: 061-928-8136. Director: Francois L. Marshall. Management firm. Estab. 1985. Represents local, regional and international individual artists and groups. Currently handles 2 acts. Receives 20% commission. Reviews material for acts.

How to Contact: Submit demo cassette/record/CD. Unsolicited submissions are okay. SASE if wish returned. Reports in 6 weeks.
Music: Mostly soul/funk/dance and rock/pop. Works primarily with bands/groups/vocalists if they write their own material. Current acts include Green 2000 (rock/pop band) and Paris (funk, dance band).
Tips: "Make sure songs have a good hook, strong melody and good vocals. Keep each song to 3 minutes or as near as possible. Maximum 3 songs and your best. I'm tough, I'm blunt and I'm honest. The music business is tough. Are you tough enough? Wanting fame and money is not enough."

*BOGGY DEPOT MUSIC, 10051 Greenleaf Ave., Santa Fe Springs CA 90670. (213)946-3193. President: Overton Lee. Management firm, booking agency, music publisher (BMI) and record company (O.L. Records). Estab. 1980. Represents international individual artists and groups; currently handles 5 acts. Receives 20% commission. Reviews material for acts.
How to Contact: Submit demo tape by mail. Unsolicited submissions are okay. Prefers cassette with 3 songs with lyric sheet. SASE. Reports in 6 weeks.
Music: Mostly country, R&B, pop and gospel; also rap, Spanish and rock & roll. Works primarily with vocalists and groups. Current acts include Touch of Country (group), Marcy Carr (vocalist) and Beau Dean (singer/songwriter).
Tips: "Write great songs and demo them right."

BOJO PRODUCTIONS INC., 3935 Cliftondale Pl., College Park GA 30349. (404)969-1913. Management firm and record company (Bojo Records). Estab. 1982. Represents local, regional or international individual artists, groups and songwriters; currently handles 5 acts. Receives 15% commission. Reviews material for acts.
How to Contact: Submit demo tape by mail. Unsolicited submissions are OK. Prefers cassette (or videocassette) with 3 songs and lyric or lead sheets. SASE. Reports in 2 weeks.
Music: Mostly R&B, gospel and country; also MOR. Works primarily with vocalists and dance bands. Current acts include Francell Burton (R&B), Flavor (R&B and MOR) and George Smith (country and jazz and MOR).

BONNIE LOU ENTERPRISES, RD 3, Box 322-B, Seaford DE 19973. (302)629-0401. Manager: Bonnie L. Carver. Management firm, booking agency (April One Inc.). Estab. 1988. Represents individual artists and groups. Currently handles 2 acts. Receives 10-20% commission. Reviews material for acts.
How to Contact: Prefers cassette (or videocassette) with 3 songs and lyric sheet. SASE. Reports in 3 weeks.
Music: Country. Works primarily with dance and show bands.
Tips: "Make sure your songs have good hooks and are original and commercial. We are looking for hardworking and disciplined people who are honest and not into drugs. You must have the perseverance to hang in there over the long haul. Be professional at all times."

T.J. BOOKER LTD., Box 969, Rossland, B.C. V0G 1YO **Canada**. (604)362-7795. Contact: Tom Jones. Management firm, booking agency and music publisher. Estab. 1976. Represents local, regional or international individual artists, groups and songwriters; currently handles 25 acts. Receives 10-15% commission. Reviews material for acts.
How to Contact: Submit demo tape by mail. Unsolicited submissions are OK. Prefers cassette (or videocassette) with 3 songs. Does not return unsolicited material.
Music: Mostly MOR, crossover, rock, pop and country. Works primarily with vocalists, show bands, dance bands and bar bands. Current acts include Kirk Orr, Tommy and T Birds and Second Nature.
Tips: "There is always a market for excellence."

*BOOMTOWN MUSIC, 129 E. Fulton Ave., Roosevelt NY 11575. (212)713-5229. President: Barry Yearwood. Estab. 1987. Represents local individual artists, groups, songwriters and producers. Reviews material for acts.
How to Contact: Submit demo tape by mail. Unsolicited submissions are OK. Prefers cassette with 4 songs. Does not return unsolicited material. Reports in 2 months.
Music: Mostly R&B, dance and pop. Works primarily vocalists. Current acts include Richard Bush (R&B), Group Work (dance music) and Valez (dance music).
Tips: "Have a positive attitude but not a huge ego."

BOUQUET-ORCHID ENTERPRISES, Box 11686, Atlanta GA 30355. (404)355-7635. President: Bill Bohannon. Management firm, booking agency, music publisher (Orchid Publishing/BMI) and record company (Bouquet Records). Represents individuals and groups; currently handles 4 acts. Receives 10-15% commission. Reviews material for acts.

How to Contact: Prefers cassette (or videocassette if available) with 3-5 songs, song list and lyric sheet. Include brief resume. SASE. Reports in 1 month.

Music: Mostly country, rock , and top 40/pop; also gospel and R&B. Works primarily with vocalists and groups. Current acts include Teresa Gilbert, Adam Day and the Bandoleers (top 40/pop group).

*BILL BOYD PRODUCTIONS, Suite 245, 4219 W. Olive, Burbank CA 91505. (818)955-7570. Contact: Bill Boyd. Management firm and music publishers. Estab. 1984. Represents international individual artists, groups and songwriters; currently handles 2 acts. Receives 20% commission. Reviews material for acts.

How to Contact: Call first and obtain permission to submit. Prefers cassette with 3 songs and lyric sheet. Does not return unsolicited material. Reports in 2 weeks.

Music: Mostly country; also blues. Current acts include Maripat (country singer) and Doc Wah Rivers (country/rock band).

*TIM BRACK MANAGEMENT, 677 Passaic Ave., 1st Floor, Nutley NJ 07110. (201)667-3010. Vice President A&R: Tony Kee. Management firm. Estab. 1988. Represents international individual artists, groups, songwriters, producers and engineers. Receives 10-20% commission. Reviews material for acts.

How to Contact: Call first and obtain permission to submit. Prefers cassette (or VHS videocassette if available) with 3 songs and lyric or lead sheet. Does not return unsolicited material. Reports in 1 month.

Music: Mostly rock (new), pop and hard rock; also adult contemporary. Works primarily with writers and performers. Current acts include Immaculate Fools (folk based acoustic rock band), Schoolly D (street credible rap artist) and Andy Ross (pop singer/writer producer and performer).

Tips: "Always wait to submit material until it is in the best 'form' you feel is representative *fully* of either songs or a band. We need to see and hear potential, not finished masters!"

BROCK & ASSOCIATES, Suite 200, 7106 Moores Ln., Brentwood TN 37027. (615)327-1880. President: Dan R. Brock. Management firm, music publisher (The Forefront Communications Group/ASCAP) and record company (Forefront Records). Estab. 1987. Represents individual artists, groups and songwriters; currently handles 3 acts. Reviews material for acts.

How to Contact: Prefers cassette with maximum of 3 songs and lyric sheet. SASE.

Music: Mostly rock, pop and inspirational. Works primarily with singer/songwriters. Current acts include DeGarmo & Key (gospel/rock), Jeoff Benward (inspirational) and Steve Geyer (comedian).

*DAVID BRODY PRODUCTIONS, 4086 Royal Crest, Memphis TN 38115. (901)362-1719. President: David or Gina Brody. Management firm and music publisher (Brody-Segerson Publishing/BMI). Estab. 1986. Represents international individual artists, groups and songwriters; currently handles 5 acts. Receives 15-25% commission. Reviews material for acts.

How to Contact: Call first and obtain permission to submit. Prefers cassette (or VHS videocassette if available) with 3 songs and lyric sheet.

Music: Interested in all music. Works primarily with comedians, announcers, singer and actors. Current acts include Cousin Bubba (comedian), Jonathan Michaels (actor) Billy Davis, Jr. (singer) and Frazer Smith (radio personality).

BROTHERS MANAGEMENT ASSOCIATES, 141 Dunbar Ave., Fords NJ 08863. (201)738-0880 or 738-0883. President: Allen A. Faucera. Management firm and booking agency. Estab. 1972. Represents artists, groups and songwriters; currently handles over 100 acts. Receives 15-20% commission. Reviews material for acts.

How to Contact: Query by mail. Prefers cassette (or VHS videocassette) with 3-6 songs and lyric sheet. Include photographs and resume. SASE. Reports in 2 months.

Music: Mostly pop, rock, MOR and R&B. Works primarily with vocalists and established groups. Current acts include Ben E. King, Makana (rock), Waterfront (top 40/show), Chelsea (top 40/rock), Benny Troy and Company (top 40/show), and James Brown, and other track artists.

Tips: "We need very commercial, chart-oriented material."

*BSC PRODUCTIONS, INC., P.O. Box 2250, Culver City CA 90231. (213)419-8142. President/General Manager: Kenn E. Kingsbury, Jr. Management firm and music publisher (Black Stallion Country Publishing, BMI). Estab. 1979. Represents individual artists and songwriters. Deals with local, national and international artists. Currently handles 2 acts. Reviews material for acts.

How to Contact: Submit demo tape by mail. Unsolicited submissions are OK. Prefers cassette (or 7½ IPS reel-to-reel with 3 songs and lyric sheets. SASE. Reports back in 6 weeks.

Music: Country, blues and adult contemporary. Works primiarily with vocalists, comedians, magicians and film/TV actors and actresses. Current acts include Billy Barty (actor/performer), Jenny James (singer/songwriter) and Suze Lanier (songwriter/singer/actress).

*AL BUNETTA MANAGEMENT, INC., Suite 204, 4121 Wilshire Blvd., Los Angeles CA 90010. (213)385-0882. President: Al Bunetta. Management firm. Represents producers, artists and songwriters. Reviews material for acts.
How to Contact: Prefers cassette with 1-3 songs and lead sheet. SASE. Reports in 1 month.
Music: R&B, rock, new music, top 40/pop and adult contemporary. Works primarily with national recording artists. Current acts include John Prine (singer/songwriter/recording artist).

*C & M PRODUCTIONS INC., 6312 Landmark, Waco TX 76710. (817)772-6357. Manager: Ronald W. Cotton. Management firm, booking agency, music publisher (Triangle Songworks ASCAP) and C.M.R. Music Group (BMI). Estab. 1980. Represents international individual artists; currently handles 2 acts on Polygram Records. Receives 10% commission.
How to Contact: Call first and obtain permission to submit. Prefers cassette. SASE. Reports in 2 weeks.
Music: Mostly country, rock and pop. Current acts include Rowne Reeves and B.B. Watson.

*C & S TALENT INC., P.O. Box 1104, Harvey LA 70059. (504)340-4068. Contact: Sandy Terry. Management firm, booking agency and music publisher (Cowboy Boot's/BMI). Estab. 1980. Represents international individual artists and songwriters; currently handles 2 acts. Reviews material for acts.
How to Contact: Write or call first and obtain permission to submit. Prefers cassette (or VHS videocassette if available) with 3 songs and lyric or lead sheet. SASE. Reports in 2 weeks.
Music: Mostly country. Current acts include Don Malena and Sonny Anglin.

*CACTUS INDUSTRIES MUSIC INC., P.O. Box 322, Ingomar PA 15127. (412)364-5095. President: Chuck Surman. Management firm, publisher and record producer. Represents artists, musical groups and songwriters from anywhere; currently handles 10 acts. Receives publishing administration fee plus 20% of artist's earnings. Reviews material for acts.
How to Contact: Prefers cassette with 3-15 songs. Writers should include a short bio. SASE. Reports ASAP if interested. Send video cassette if available.
Music: Mostly metal, pop, rock, R&B and dance; also country, MOR and top 40/pop. Works primarily with bar bands, rock/top 40/pop bands and black dance and R&B groups.

CAHN-MAN, 5332 College Ave., Oakland CA 94618. (415)652-1615. Contact: Elliot Cahn/Jeff Saltzman. Management and law firm. Estab. 1986. Represents local, regional and international individual artists, groups and songwriters. Receives 20% commission; $125/hour as attorneys. Reviews material for acts.
How to Contact: Submit demo tape by mail. Unsolicited submissions are okay. Prefers cassette (or videocassette). We do not return unsolicited material. Reports in 2 weeks.
Music: Mostly rock, metal and pop; also R&B. Current acts include Testament (metal), Exodus (metal) and Phil Aaberg (pianist).
Tips: "Send a tape!"

*CAM MUSIC, LTD., 1423 Lee Blvd., Berkeley IL 60163. (708)544-4771. President: Chip Messineo. Management firm, booking agent and producer. Estab. 1983. Represents local and regional individual artists, groups and songwriters; currently handles 6 acts. Receives 15-25% commission. Reviews material for acts.
How to Contact: Write first and obtain permission to submit. Prefers cassette with 3 songs, lyric sheets and SASE. Does not return unsolicited material. Reports in 2 months.
Music: Mostly country, bluegrass and folk; also MOR, jazz and children's. Works primarily with solo vocalists, bands and writers. Current acts include Wendy Como, Strait Southern (country) and Special Concensus (bluegrass).
Tips: "A career in music does not happen overnight. If it did you wouldn't know what to do with your overnight success. You have to work for it. Be professional. Don't send out sloppy promotional kits. Your demo is the first impression that we hear. Impress me. One of the things that will make me turn off the tape machine is a demo that does not have the vocal UP front and solos. I want to hear the song. And whatever you do, don't give up!"

CARMAN PRODUCTIONS, INC., 15456 Cabrito Rd., Van Nuys CA 91406. (213)873-7370. A&R: Joey Vieira. Management firm, music publisher (Namrac/BMI, Souci/ASCAP) and record production company. Estab. 1969. Represents local, regional and international individual artists, groups, songwriters, producers and actors. Currently handles 6 acts. Receives 15% commission. Reviews material for acts.

How to Contact: Write first and obtain permission to submit. Prefers cassette with 5 songs and lyric sheets. Does not return unsolicited material. Reports in 2 months.
Music: Mostly rock, dance, R&B, pop and country; also dance and R&B. Current acts include Richard Carpenter, Tom Harriman, Michael Botts, Kuh Ledesma and the Dressler Sisters.

ERNIE CASH MANAGEMENT/VISION MUSIC GROUP INC., Suite C, 435 Eastern Blvd., Baltimore MD 21221. (301)687-4100. Owner: Ernie Cash. Management firm, music publisher (BMI) and record company (Continental Records). Estab. 1988. Represents individual artists; currently handles 12 acts. Receives 20% commission. Reviews material for acts.
How to Contact: Write or call first to arrange a personal interview. Prefers cassette (or VHS videocassette) with maximum of 10 songs and lyric or lead sheets. Does not return unsolicited material. Reports in 2 weeks.
Music: Mostly country, pop, R&B; also gospel. Works primarily with vocalists/bands. Current acts include Ernie Cash (country/western singer), Johnny Anthony (top 40) and David Wayne (country).

*CAT PRODUCTION AB, Rörstrandsgatan 21, Stockholm 11340 **Sweden**. Phone: (08)317277. Managing Director: Christina Nilsson. Management firm and booking agency. Estab. 1972. Represents individual artists, groups and songwriters; currently handles 3 acts. Receives 15% commission. Reviews material for acts.
How to Contact: Prefers cassette (or VHS videocassette) with 4-6 songs and lyric or lead sheet. SAE and IRC. Reports in 2 months.
Music: Mostly R&B, rock and gospel; also "texts for stand-up comedian." Works primarily with "concert bands like Janne Schaffers' Earmeal. Rock-blues-imitation shows." Current acts include Jan Schaffer (lead guitar, songwriter), Tod Ashton (singer, blues/rock guitar and harmonica player, stand up comedian), and Malou Berg (gospel singer).

*CEDAR HILL STUDIO A Division of Chisholm Entertainment, Rt. 14 Box 1039, Tyler TX 75707. (214)566-5653. Vice President: Lonnie Wright. Management firm, music publisher (Boggy Depot/BMI) and record company (OL, New Act, Juke Box, Quazar). Estab. 1967. Represents international individual artists, groups and songwriters; currently handles 5 acts. Receives 20% commission. Reviews material for acts.
How to Contact: Submit demo tape by mail. Prefers cassette with 3 songs. SASE.
Music: Mostly country, gospel and blues. Works primarily with vocalists, writers and dance bands. Current acts include Touch of Country (band), Pat Murphy (singer), Marcy Carr (singer) and Beau Dean (writer/singer).
Tips: "Be professional with demos!"

*CFB PRODUCTIONS, 101 River Rd., Collinsville CT 06022. (203)693-1637. Vice President: Wanda J. Rodgers. Management firm. Estab. 1970. Represents international individual artists, groups and songwriters; currently handles 4 acts. Receives negotiable commission. Reviews material for acts.
How to Contact: Write and obtain permission to submit. Prefers cassette with 3 songs and lyric sheet. SASE. Reports in 1 month.
Music: Mostly pop, country and film and TV scores. Interested in composers and touring vocalists.
Tips: "Submit only finished demos—no rough cassettes."

*CHARDON BOOKING AND MANAGEMENT, 3198 Royal Lane, #204, Dallas TX 75229. (214)350-4650. Vice President: Dan Hexter. Management firm and booking agency. Estab. 1975. Represents local, regional or international individual artists and groups. Currently handles six acts. Receives 10-15% commission. Reviews material for acts.
How to Contact: Write first and obtain permission to submit. Prefers cassette (or VHS videocassette if available) with 3 songs and lyric sheets. Does not return unsolicited material. Reports in 2 months.
Music: Mostly country.

CHARTA RECORDS, 44 Music Sq. E., Nashville TN 37203. (615)255-2175. President: Charlie Fields. Record company (Charta Records/Delux Records) and public relations firm (Debbie Dean & Associates). Estab. 1972. Represents local, regional and international individual artists and groups. Currently handles 4-5 acts. Reviews material for acts.
How to Contact: Submit demo tape by mail. Unsolicited submissions are okay. Prefers cassette (or VHS videocassette) with 3 songs and lyric sheets. SASE. Reports in 1 week.
Music: Mostly country, pop and R&B. "So far we have worked with single vocalists, though we have had a duo." Current acts include David Walsh (country singer/songwriter), Nina Wyatt (country singer/songwriter) and Ronnie Klein (country).

CIRCUIT RIDER TALENT & MANAGEMENT CO., 123 Walton Ferry Rd., 2nd Floor, Hendersonville TN 37075. (615)824-1947. FAX: (615)264-0462. President: Linda S. Dotson. Management firm, booking agency and music publisher (Channel Music, Cordial Music). Represents individual artists, songwriters and actors; currently handles 5 acts. Receives 15% commission. Reviews material for acts.
How to Contact: Write or call first and obtain permission to submit. Prefers cassette (or videocassette) with 3 songs and lyric sheet. Videocassettes required of artists only. SASE. Reports in 6 weeks.
Music: Mostly pop, country and gospel; also R&B and comedy. Works primarily with vocalists, special concerts, movies and TV. Current acts include Sheb Wooley, Buck Trent, Russ Roberts, Ben Colder and Benji Wilhoite.
Tips: "Artists have your act together. Have a full press kit, videos, and be professional. Attitudes are a big factor in my agreeing to work with you (no egotistics). This is a business and your career we will be building."

*CITI MUZIK, P.O. Box 434, Hopkins MN 50343. (612)472-9892. Contact: Jodi/Deb. Management firm and Promotion/Publicity. Represents international individual artists and groups; currently handles 8 acts. Receives 7½% commission. Reviews material for acts.
How to Contact: Submit demo tape by mail. Unsolicited submissions are okay. Prefers cassette with 2-4 songs and lyric or lead sheet. Does not return unsolicited material. Reports in 1 month.
Music: Mostly rock (heavy) and rock-pop; also dance. Current acts include 7th Heaven (rock), White Widow (rock) and Boys Next Door (dance).

*CITY LIGHTS MANAGEMENT, INC., 2037 Pine St., Philadelphia PA 19103. (215)732-1223. President: Bill Eib. Management firm and music publisher (Heroic Music/ASCAP). Estab. 1978. Represents international individual artists, groups, songwriters and producers; currently handles 6 acts. Reviews material for acts.
How to Contact: Write first and obtain permission to submit. Prefers cassette with 3 songs and lyric sheet. Does not return unsolicited material. Reports in 1-2 months.
Music: Mostly pop, rock and R&B; also "anything incredible." Current acts include Pretty Poison (pop), Robert Hazard (folk rock) and Martial Law (rock).

*CLASS ACT TALENT % **Indie Bullet Magazine**, Rt. 14, Box 272, Hwy. 64E, Tyler TX 75707. (214)566-4202. Booking agency. Estab. 1990. Represents individual artists and groups; currently handles 10 acts. Receives 15% commission. Reviews material for acts.
How to Contact: Write first and obtain permission to submit.
Music: Country only. Works primarily with vocalists and groups. Current acts include David Houston, Don Nutt, Touch of Country, Bruce Gosse and Don Malena.
Tips: "Have exposure through independent record releases to country radio to create public demand. Most have had a Top 20 Indie Bullet charted single or 'pick' record review to be considered."

*CLAYTON PRODUCTIONS, Box 2745, Harrisburg PA 17105. (717)657-1111. President: Michael Lee Clayton. Management firm and booking agency. Estab. 1979. Represents international individual artists, groups, songwriters and variety acts; currently handles 23 acts. Commission received varies. Reviews material for acts.
How to Contact: Submit demo tape by mail. Unsolicited submissions are okay. Prefers cassette (VHS videocassette if available) with lyric or lead sheet.
Music: Mostly country, gospel and R&B; also 50's style pop. Works primarily with dance bands, vocalists and recording artists.
Tips: "Keep writing, keep performing, keep learning and *don't give up.*"

CLOCKWORK ENTERTAINMENT MANAGEMENT AGENCY, Box 1600, Haverhill MA 01831. (508)373-6010. President: Bill Macek. Management firm and booking agency. Represents groups and songwriters throughout New England; currently handles 6 acts. Receives 15% commission. Reviews material for acts.
How to Contact: Query or submit demo tape. Prefers cassette with 3-12 songs. "Also submit promotion and cover letter with interesting facts about yourself." Does not return unsolicited material unless accompanied by SASE. Reports in 1 month.
Music: Rock (all types) and top 40/pop. Works primarily with bar bands and original acts. Current acts include Tizzy (4-piece original rocker), The Gail Savage Band (original rock), and The Broadcast (5-piece high energy top 40/dance/rock).

C.M. MANAGEMENT, 7957 Nita Ave., Canoga Park CA 91304-4706. (818)704-7800. President: Craig Miller. Management firm and music publisher. Estab. 1975. Represents individual artists; currently handles 4 acts. Receives 15-20% commission—"occasional flat fee."

How to Contact: Write or call first and obtain permission to submit. Prefers cassette with 3 songs and lyric sheet. Submit material "with the best package, (i.e., representation) possible." Does not return unsolicited material. SASE. Reports in 1 month.
Music: Mostly instrumental and session artists; also jazz, new acoustic and fusion. Works primarily with highest caliber recording artists. Current acts include David Grisman (MCA Records recording act), Mark O'Connor (WB Recording act) and Strength In Numbers (MCA Records recording act).
Tips: "Unless you feel that you are really *exceptional*, don't bother to contact us."

*COCOS ISLAND RECORDS, INC., P.O. Box 773 Bondi Junction, NSW **Australia** 2022. (02)5171451. A&R Manager: Sam Nun. Management firm and record company (Cocos Island Records). Estab. 1980. Represents international individual artists, groups and songwriters; currently handles 10 acts. Receives 20% commission. Reviews material for acts.
How to Contact: "Suggest one video featuring marketable song on first album. Aim: Worldwide release through major labels." Does not return unsolicited material. Reports in 1 month.
Music: Interested in any music. Current acts include No Screaming Kids (pop), Noel Wilson (folk) and Peter Liberty (Christian).
Tips: "Aim for the top. We'll take you over the top."

*COLE CLASSIC MANAGEMENT, Suite 207, 4150 Riverside Dr., Burbank CA 91505. (818)841-6365. A&R Manager: Stephanie McCravey. Management firm. Represents local, regional, international individual artists, groups and producers. Currently handles 7 acts. Receives 10-15% commission. Reviews material for acts.
How to Contact: Submit demo tape by mail. Unsolicited submissions are okay. Prefers cassette with 2-3 songs and lyric sheets. Does not return solicited material. Reports in 3-4 weeks.
Music: Mostly R&B, pop and jazz; also gospel. Works primarily with vocalists and dance bands. Current acts include Atlantic Starr (R&B band/songwriter), Mac Band (R&B) and Surface (R&B group/songwriters producers).

*COMMUNITY MUSIC CENTER OF HOUSTON, 5613 Almeda, Houston TX 77004. (712)523-9710. Managing Director: Ron Scales. Management firm and booking agency. Estab. 1979. International individual artists and groups; currently handles 6 acts. Receives 10-20% commission. Reviews material for acts.
How to Contact: Submit demo tape by mail. Unsolicited submissions are okay. Prefers cassette (VHS videocassette if available) with 4 songs and lyric or lead sheet. SASE. Reports in 2 months.
Music: Jazz, R&B and blues; also gospel and folk. Works primarily with solo vocalists, vocal groups and jazz bands. Current acts include Rhapsody (jazz vocal ensemble), Scott Joplin Chamber Orchestra (classical music by African-American composers) and Diedre Curnell (folk singer/songwriter).

*BURT COMPTON AGENCY, Box 160373, Miami FL 33116. (305)271-6880. Contact: Burt Compton. Booking agency. Estab. 1978. Represents groups; currently handles 47 acts. Receives 10-20% commission. Reviews material for acts.
How to Contact: Query by mail, then submit demo tape. Prefers cassette (or videocassette) with 3-6 songs. "Include complete repertoire, 8x10 photo and resume." Does not return unsolicited material.
Music: Mostly top 40/nostalgia. Works primarily with dance bands. Current acts include Heroes (dance band), Fantasy (recording/concert group), and Wildlife (recording/concert group).
Tips: "Have your promotional materials professionally packaged. We don't like having to decipher handwritten resumes with misspelled words and incomplete sentences."

*CONCEPT 2000 INC., 2447 W. Mound St., Columbus OH 43204. President: Brian Wallace. Management firm and booking agency (Concept 2000 Music/ASCAP). Estab. 1981. Represents international individual artists, groups and songwriters; currently handles 5 acts. Receives 10-20% commission. Reviews material for acts.
How to Contact: Submit demo tape by mail. Unsolicited submissions are okay. Prefers cassette with 4 songs. Does not return unsolicited material. Reports in 2 weeks.
Music: Mostly country, gospel and pop; also jazz, R&B and soul. Current acts include McGuffey Lane (country group), Oasis (gospel group) and Dave McCall (singer/songwriter).

*CORVALAN-CONDLIFFE MANAGEMENT, Suite 5, 1010 Fourth St., Santa Monica CA 90403. (213)393-6507. Manager: Brian Condliffe. Management firm. Estab. 1982. Represents local and international individual artists, groups and songwriters; currently handles 4 acts. Receives 15% commission. Reviews material for acts.

How to Contact: Call first and obtain permission to submit. Prefers cassette with 4-6 songs. Does not return unsolicited material. Reports in 1 month.
Music: Mostly R&B, pop and rock; also Latin and dance. Works primarily with self-contained band with vocals and solo singer. Current acts include The Wild Cards (R&B-Latin-pop), Victor Bailey (jazz), T-Square (jazz, NAC) and Dolette McDonald ("Blue-eyed"-soul).
Tips: "Submit as professional a package or presentation as possible."

COUNTRY MUSIC SHOWCASE INTERNATIONAL, INC., Box 368, Carlisle IA 50047. (515)989-3676. President: Harold L. Luick. Vice President: Barbara A. Lancaster. Management firm and booking agency for acts and entertainers that are members of our organization. Represents individual artists, groups and songwriters; currently handles 18-20 acts. Receives 5-20% commission.
How to Contact: Prefers cassette with 3 songs and lyric sheet (or VHS videocassette-video should show artist on the job, 3 different venues). SASE. Reports in 3 weeks.
Music: Mostly contemporary, hard core country and traditional country; also bluegrass, western swing and comedy. Works primarily with "single acts and group acts that are self contained and uniformed." Current acts include Mr. Elmer Bird (banjo virtuoso), Country Classics USA (12-piece stage show), The Dena Kaye Show, and Britt Small and Festival (12 piece show band).
Tips: "We want artists who are willing to work hard to achieve success and songwriters that are skilled in their craft. Through educational and informative seminars and showcases we have helped many artists and songwriter members achieve a degree of success in a very tough business. For information on how to become a member of our organization, send SASE to the above address. Memberships cost $20.00 per year for artist or songwriter memberships."

COUNTRY STAR ATTRACTIONS, 439 Wiley Ave., Franklin PA 16323. (814)432-4633. Contact: Norman Kelly. Management firm and booking agency, music publisher (Country Star Music/ASCAP), and record company (Country Star, Process, Mersey and CSI Records). Estab. 1970. Represents artists and musical groups; currently handles 8-10 acts. Receives 10-15% commission. Reviews material for acts.
How to Contact: Prefers cassette with 2-4 songs and lyric or lead sheet; include photo. SASE. Reports in 2 weeks.
Music: Mostly country (80%); rock (5%) and gospel (5%). Works primarily with vocalists. Current acts include Remember When (country/MOR) and Junie Lou (country).
Tips: "Send only your very best efforts."

COUNTRYWIDE PRODUCERS, (formerly Bob Englar Theatrical Agency), 2466 Wildon Dr., York PA 17403. (717)741-2658. President: Bob Englar. Booking agency. Represents individuals and groups; currently handles 2 acts. Receives 15% commission. Reviews material for acts.
How to Contact: Query or submit demo. Include photo. SASE. Reports in 3 weeks.
Music: Bluegrass, blues, children's, choral, church/religious, classical, country, disco, folk, gospel, jazz, polka, rock (light), soul and top 40/pop. Works primarily with show bands and dance bands. Current acts include Carroll County Ramblers (bluegrass) and Ken Lightner (country).

COVER AGENCY, 300 North 240 West #103, Salt Lake City UT 84103. (801)364-9706. Booking Agent: William Larned. Mangement firm and booking agency. Estab. 1984. Represents local, regional and international individual artists and groups. Currently handles 90 acts. Receives 15% commission. Reviews material for acts.
How to Contact: Submit demo tape by mail. Unsolicited submissions are okay. Prefers cassette (or VHS videocassette) with 4 songs and lead sheets. Does not return unsolicited material.
Music: Mostly rock, R&B and country; also pop/top 40, modern and jazz. Works primarily with dance bands, rock bands, duos and trios. Current acts include Irie Heights (reggae), Tempo Timers (R&B/blues) and The Gamma Rays (modern).
Tips: "Be open to suggestions and developmental ideas. Be willing to listen."

CRASH PRODUCTIONS, P.O. Box 40, Bangor ME 04401-0040. (207)794-6686. Manager: Jim Moreau. Booking agency. Estab. 1967. Represents individuals and groups; currently handles 9 acts. Receives 10-25% commission.
How to Contact: Query. Prefers cassette (or VHS videocassette) with 4-8 songs. "To all artists who submit a video: We will keep it on file for presentation to prospective buyers of talent in our area— no longer than 15 minutes please." Include resume and photos. "We prefer to hear groups at an actual performance." SASE. Reports in 3 weeks.
Music: Mostly 50s-60s and country rock, top 40; also rock and polish. Works primarily with groups who perform at night clubs (with an average of 150-200 patrons) and outdoor events (festivals and fairs). Current acts include Coyote (country rock), Bushwhack (50s and 60s), Air Fare (top 40), Boot Leg (country/rock), and Kaktus (country).

Tips: "We are a small company with no big promises that we cannot fulfill."

*CRAWFISH PRODUCTIONS, P.O. Box 5412, Buena Park CA 90620. (213)721-7260. Producer: Leo J. Eiffert, Jr. Music publisher (Young Country/BMI) and record company (Plain Country Records). Estab. 1968. Represents local and international individual artists and songwriters; currently handles 4 acts. Commission received is open. Reviews material for acts.
How to Contact: Submit a demo tape by mail. Unsolicited submissions are okay. Prefers cassette with 2-3 songs and lyric sheet. SASE. Reports in 3 weeks.
Music: Mostly country and gospel. Works primarily with vocalists. Current acts include Duane Austin (country), Joe Eiffert (country/gospel) and Crawfish Band (country).

CREATIVE TALENT, INC., Suite 301, 214 Lincoln St., Allston MA 02134. (617)789-4747. Vice President: Lauren Codish. Management firm and booking agency. Represents individual artists and groups; currently handles 17 acts. Reviews material for acts. Receives 20% commission.
How to Contact: Prefers cassette (or videocassette) with 4 songs. SASE. Reports in 1 month. "Accurate, *not* dubbed tape important for submission."
Music: Works primarily with dance bands, novelty performers and a cappella. Current acts include Murph (physical comedian), Where's The Band? (a cappella), Calypso Hurricane (calypso - dance), and Flashback (50s and 60s).
Tips: "Send materials that are a good representation of the artists."

*BOBBY LEE CUDE'S GOOD AMERICAN MUSIC/TALENT/CASTING AGENCY, 519 N. Halifax Ave., Daytona Beach FL 32118. FAX: (904)252-0381. CEO: Bobby Lee Cude. Music publisher (BMI) and record company (Hard Hat). Estab. 1978. Represents international individual artists. Receives 15% commission. Reviews material for acts.
How to Contact: Write first and obtain permission to submit. Prefers cassette (or videocassette) with 2 songs, lyrics and lead sheets. "No unsolicited material reviewed."
Music: Mostly pop and country. Current acts include Caz Allen and "Pic" Pickens.
Tips: "Read music books for the trade."

THE CURRENT ENTERTAINMENT CORPORATION, 47 Jefferson Ave., Toronto, Ontario, **Canada** M6K 1Y3. (416)361-1101. President: Jerry Young. Office Manager: Judy Tottorti. A&R Special Projects: Trevor G. Shelton. Project Manager: Shelly Buybus. Management firm (Current Management), music publisher (Current Sounds/CAPAC and Brand New Sounds Music/PROCAN) and record company (Rammit Records). Represents individual artists, groups and songwriters; currently handles 6 acts. Reviews material for acts.
How to Contact: Prefers cassette (or ½" VHS videocassette) with 3-4 songs and lyric sheet. SAE and IRC. Reports in 1 month.
Music: Mostly intelligent dance/pop; also rock and new music. Works primarily with groups, vocalists. Current acts include Strange Advance (band), Alta Moda (pop band), M&M (pop band), The Parachute Club (pop band), Mystery Romance (pop), Andy McLean (rock), Betty Moon, S.E. Jam and Uncertain Edge.

*CURRENT RECORDS/MANAGEMENT, Suite 437, 366 Adelaide St. E., Toronto, Ontario, M5A 3X9 **Canada**. (416)361-1101. A&R - New Projects: Trevor G. Shelton. Management firm, music publisher (Current Sounds - CAPAC/PROCAN) and record company (Current Records). Estab. 1983. Represents local, regional or international individual artists, groups and songwriters; currently handles 10 acts. Reviews material for acts.
How to Contact: Submit demo tape by mail. Unsolicited submissions are okay. Prefers cassettes (or VHS videocassette if available) with 4-5 songs and lyric sheets. SASE. Reports in 3-4 weeks.
Music: Mostly dance, pop and rock; also R&B, alternative, rap/hip, house etc. Works primarily with dance, pop and rock bands. Current acts include Mystery Romance, Machinations and The Black Earth (artists-songwriters).
Tips: "If you have a videocassette of your performance, please send it, but it's not a necessity. Performances can be simple. No need for big-budget videos."

D.A.G. PROMOTIONS LTD., 28 Bolton St., London WI **England**. Phone: (01)876-4433. Director: D. Gordon. Management firm. Estab. 1983. Represents individual artists and groups. Receives 20% commission. Reviews material for acts.
How to Contact: Write or call first and obtain permission to submit. Prefers cassette (videocassette) with 4 songs and lyric sheet. Does not return unsolicited material.
Music: Mostly pop and rock. Works primarily with singer/songwriter, solo artists and rock bands. Current acts include Julian Lennon (singer/songwriter), Paul Jackson (singer/songwriter), Shannon Sweeney (singer/songwriter), Hold The Frame (rock) and Eddie Kidd (rock).

*D & M ENTERTAINMENT AGENCY, 15 Vincent Dr., Johnston RI 02919. (401)944-6823. President and Manager: Ray DiMillio. Management firm and booking agency. Estab. 1968. Represents local groups; currently handles 30 acts. Receives 15% commission. Reviews material for acts.
How to Contact: Call first to arrange personal interview. Prefers cassette (or VHS videocassette) with 3 songs and lyric or lead sheet. SASE. Reports in 2 weeks.
Music: Mostly R&B and pop; also rock.

*D & R ENTERTAINMENT, 1541 Crescent, Duncanville TX 75137. (214)298-5779. President: Don Walton. Management firm. Estab. 1987. Represents international individual artists and groups; currently handles 4 acts. Receives 15-20% commission. Reviews material for acts.
How to Contact: Submit demo tape by mail. Unsolicited submissions are okay. Prefers cassette with any number of songs and lyric or lead sheet. SASE. Reports in 1 month.
Music: Mostly country, country metal rock or hard rock; also pop country. Current acts include Roze (metal), Nanette Garner (country), Rick Thompson (country) and Mid Knights (hard rock).
Tips: "Make sure everything submitted is copyrighted! If it isn't I won't consider it."

D MANAGEMENT COMPANY, Box 121682, Nashville TN 37212. President: Douglas Casmus. Management firm and music publisher: N2D (ASCAP) and Breezeway (BMI). Estab. 1987. Represents individual artists and songwriters; currently handles 2 acts. Receives 15-25% commission. Reviews material for acts.
How to Contact: Write first and obtain permission to submit (include SASE for response). Prefers cassette with 2 songs and lyric sheets. Does not return unsolicited material. "Will contact only if interested."
Music: Mostly rock, pop and country. Current acts include Dobie Gray and David Murphy.

D.S.M. PRODUCERS ENT. PUBLISHING COMPANY, 161 West 54th St., Suite 1204, New York NY 10019. (212)245-0006. Directors of Publishing: Trina R. James and Marcus Angelett. Production firm and music publisher (ASCAP) and producers. Estab. 1979. Represents local, regional and international individual artists, groups and songwriters. Currently handles 6 acts. Commission is negotiated. Reviews material for acts.
How to Contact: Write or call first and obtain permission to submit. Prefers cassette (or VHS videocassette - "Be sure you and your vocals are up front in sound. Be sure to eye the camera so we can get to know you.") with 2 songs and lyric or lead sheets. SASE. Reports in 2 months.
Music: Mostly pop, dance, top 40, Latin and rock; also country, R&B and new age jazz/instrumental. Works primarily with vocalists, instrumentalists—we produce 10 albums a year of instrumental music, and vocal groups. Current acts include Chena (pop), Spoiled Brat (rock) and Mauge (R&B).
Tips: "Be sure the vocal is up in the mix so we can hear the words as well as the music."

*D&D TALENT ASSOCIATES, P.O. Box 308, Burkeville VA 23922. (804)767-4150. Owner: J.W. Dooley, Jr. Booking agency. Estab. 1976. Represents international individual artists and groups; currently handles 2 acts. Receives 15% commission.
How to Contact: Write first and obtain permission to submit. Prefers cassette with 1-6 songs and lead sheet. SASE. Reports in 1-2 weeks.
Music: Mostly jazz, 40's-50's music, and country. Works primarily with vocalists, comics. Current acts include Johnny Pursley (humorist) and David Allyn (vocalist).
Tips: "Just send the best songs possible—although I am doing no booking now, for practical reasons, I will try to give free advice if possible. Since I am not in a metro area, possible contacts are probably out at this time. Don't contact me to produce miracles, I can be a sounding board for the music only—someone to at least listen and hopefully, make suggestion."

*DARKHORSE ENTERTAINMENT, 3903 S.W. Kelly, Portland OR 97201. (503)221-0288. Contact: Michael Mavrolas or Marlow McClain. Management firm. Estab. 1986. Represents international individual artists, groups and songwriters; currently handles 6 acts. Receives 15% commission.
How to Contact: Submit demo tape by mail. Unsolicited submissions are okay. Prefers cassette and lyric sheet. SASE. Reports in 1-3 weeks.
Music: Mostly R&B dance and rap. Current acts include The U-Krew (R&B rap Enigma Records), Nyssa Dickson (R&B dance female vocals black) and Kurt Green (R&B male vocalist black).
Tips: "Keep sending quality demos!"

THE EDWARD DE MILES COMPANY, Vantage Point Towers, 4475 N. Allisonville Rd., 8th Floor, Indianapolis, IN 46205. (317)549-9006. FAX: (317)549-9007. President & CEO: Edward De Miles. Management firm, booking agency, entertainment/sports promoter, and TV/radio broadcast producer. Estab. 1984. Represents film, television, radio and musical artists; currently handles 15 acts. Receives 10-20% commission. Reviews material for acts. Regional operations in Chicago, Dallas, Houston, and

Nashville through marketing representatives. Licensed A.F. of M. booking agent.

How to Contact: Write first about your interest. Prefers cassette with 3-5 songs, 8x10 black and white photo and lyric sheet. "Copyright all material before submitting." SASE. Reports in 1 month.

Music: Mostly country, dance, R&B/soul, rock, top 40/pop, and urban contemporary; also looking for material for television, radio, and film productions. Works primarily with show bands and dance bands. Current acts include Lost in Wonder (progressive rock/dance band), Steve Lynn (R&B/dance), and Multiple Choice (rap).

Tips: "Performers need to be well prepared with their presentations (equipment, showmanship a must)."

*PETER DEAN MANAGEMENT, 9 McDonald St. W., Osborne Park, Perth WA 6017 **Australia.** (09)242-2577. Manager: Peter Dean. Management firm. Estab. 1988. Represents individual artists and groups from anywhere. Currently handles 1 act. Receives 10% commission. Reviews material for acts.

How to Contact: Submit demo tape by mail. Unsolicited submissions are OK. Prefers reel-to-reel with lyric and lead sheets. SAE and IRC. Reports in 4 weeks.

Music: Hard rock, rock ballads and R&B. Works with rock groups and vocalists. Current acts include Jets (rock) and Zep Boys (rock).

DMR AGENCY, P.O. Box 401, Fayetteville NY 13066-0401. (315)637-4471. Contact: David M. Rezak. Booking agency. Represents individuals and groups; currently handles 25 acts. Receives 15% commission.

How to Contact: Submit cassette (or videocassette) with 1-4 songs and press kit. SASE.

Music: Mostly rock (all styles); also jazz, R&B and progressive. Works primarily with dance, bar and concert bands; all kinds of rock for schools, clubs, concerts, etc. Current acts include Kingsnakes (blues), Screentest (pop), Zoid (rock), Neverly Brothers (oldies/pop), and Jumpin' Joe and His Rockin' Rhythm Revue (R&B).

Tips: "We strictly do booking and have no involvement in artists repetoire. We prefer regionally-based bands with a high percentage of cover material."

COL. BUSTER DOSS PRESENTS, Drawer 40, Estill Springs TN 37330. (615)649-2577. Producer: Col. Buster Doss. Management firm, booking agency, record company (Stardust) and music publisher (Buster Doss Music/BMI). Estab. 1959. Represents individual artists, groups, songwriters and shows; currently handles 15 acts. Receives 15% commission. Reviews material for acts.

How to Contact: Prefers cassette with 2-4 songs and lyric sheet. SASE. Reports in 2 weeks.

Music: Country, gospel and progressive. Works primarily with show and dance bands, single acts and package shows. Current acts include Rooster Quantrell, Sonny Carson, R. B. Stone, Hobson Smith, Tony Caldarona, Buck Cody, Cliff Archer, Linda Wunder, Benny Ray, Clayton Michaels, Honey James, Gilbert Gann, The Border Raiders, Tony Andrews, and Jess Demaine.

Tips: "Tell the truth! No hype."

*PHYLLIS DUMONT AGENCY, P.O. Box 701248, San Antonio TX 78270-1248. (512)366-0096. Owner/ Agent/Manager: Phyllis Dumont. Management firm and booking agency. Estab. 1986. Represents international individual artists and groups; currently handles 15 acts. Receives 20% commission. Reviews material for acts.

How to Contact: Prefers cassette (VHS ½" videocassette) with 3 songs and lyric sheet. SASE. Reports in 2 weeks.

Music: Mostly Spanish & Tejano, country and pop. Works primarily with vocalists, dance bands, vocalist/pianist or vocalist/guitarists, mariachis. Current acts include Olives (trio/songwriters), Patsy Torres (Tejano-country) and Maria Elena (contemporary & Hispanic vocalist).

Tips: "Send first class promotional material (i.e., pictures, videotapes, cassettes, songlists, specialty are a MUST). If you don't have this promo material, we have no way to sell you to a prospective client."

*DUNCAN MANAGEMENT INC., 366 Fifth Ave., New York NY 10001. (212)564-2100. President: Ellis Duncan. Management firm. Estab. 1988. Represents local and regional (Central-East Coast) individual artists and groups; currently handles 2 acts. Receives 20% commission. Reviews material for acts.

How to Contact: Submit demo tape by mail. Unsolicited submissions are okay. Prefers cassette (VHS videocassette) with 3-5 songs. Does not return unsolicited material. Reports in 2 months.

Music: Mostly R&B, rock and country; also gospel, pop and bluegrass. "All types are considered, but usually individual artist and groups." Current acts include Danny Gatton (guitarist), David Quick (rock & roll singer/guitarist) and Greystone (hard rock band).

*JIM DUNLOP PRODUCTIONS, 1272 Pinehurst Place, London, Ontario **Canada** N5X 2K9. (519)663-9039. President: Jim Dunlop. Management firm and record company (Auto). Estab. 1985. Represents international individual artists, groups and songwriters; currently handles 5 acts. Receives 10-20% commission. Reviews material for acts.
How to Contact: Submit demo tape by mail. Unsolicited submissions are okay. Prefers cassette (or VHS videocassette) with 3-5 songs and lyric sheet. SASE. Reports in 3-4 weeks.
Music: Mostly country, pop and rock; also children's and classical. Works primarily with individuals and groups. Current acts include Michael Dee (country), Monkey See (rock) and Glenn Bennett (children's music).
Tips: "Send only your very best songs. You need to be totally committed if you want to make it in this business. If you're not, then save yourself the headaches and heartaches."

*E.Z. MONEY PRODUCTIONS, P.O. Box 50063, Austin TX 78763. (512)474-5545. Owner: Louis Meyers. Management firm. Estab. 1983. Represents local artists, groups and songwriters; currently handles 4 acts. Receives 15% commission. Reviews material for acts.
How to Contact: Submit demo tape by mail. Unsolicited submissions are okay. Prefers cassette with 3-5 songs and lyric sheets. Live video of performance. Does not return unsolicited material. Reports in 2 months.
Music: Mostly reggae, rap/hip-hop and folk-rock; also hard rock, calypso and college rock. Works primarily with club and recording groups. Current acts include Michael E. Johnson & Killer Bees (reggae), Grains of Faith (folk-rock) and Hand of Glory (hard rock).
Tips: "Don't bore us—get to the chorus."

*STEVE ECK ENTERTAINMENT, 721 Boundary Ave., Hanover PA 17331. (717)632-4075. Owner: Steve Eck. Management firm, booking agency and record company (Aria Records). Represents regional (Mid-Atlantic states) individual artists, groups and songwriters; currently handles 3 acts. Receives 10-15% commission. Reviews material for acts.
How to Contact: Submit demo tape by mail. Unsolicited submissions are okay. Prefers cassette with minimum of 2 songs and lyric sheet. Does not return unsolicited material. Material is reviewed with artist and then sent on to Nashville to our record label.
Music: Mostly country, pop and rock. Works primarily with country and country rock recording artists and groups. Current acts include Bruce Van Dyke, Longshot Band and Freedom Express.
Tips: "Send a top quality demo with lyric sheet keeping in mind that we will send this to our record company in Nashville for consideration."

*EDGE ENTERTAINMENT, INC./PRODUCER ERIC "GRIFFY" GREIF, 152 W. Wisconsin Ave., 9th floor, Milwaukee WI 53203. (414)223-3343. FAX: (414)276-8283. Artistic Director: John Kujawa. Management firm and music publisher (Griffy Guy Music/BMI) and record producer with digital recording facility. Estab. 1987. Represents local, regional (Midwest) and international individual artists and groups. "Will work with management as recording producer and creative direction. We manage five acts and are perhaps the busiest demo producers in Midwest." Commission negotiable.
How to Contact: Submit demo tape by mail. Unsolicited submissions are okay. Prefers cassette (or VHS videocassette) with 3-5 songs and lyric sheet. Does not return unsolicited material. Reports in 2 months.
Music: Mostly heavy metal, commercial rock and alternative new music; also thrash metal, death metal and speed metal. "We mostly work with groups,but will produce demos of individual performers." Current acts include Death, (Relativity death metal band/songwriters), Acrophet, (Triple X thrash metal band/songwriters) and the Lazarus Effect (alternative new music band/songwriters).
Tips: "We will consider working with talented acts with great material, either as representation, or if they are seeking a producer to channel their energy and abilities. We specialize in competitive, cutting edge demo production as well as representation of the finished product to independent and major labels if requested. Remember that it is the songs that perk the interest—if they aren't happening, you're not happening as an artist!"

ELLIPSE PERSONAL MANAGMENT, Box 665, Manhattan Beach CA 90266. (213)546-2224. Contact: L. Elsman. Management firm. Represents local individual artists, vocalists and vocalist/songwriters. Receives 15% commission and up (P.M. contract). Reviews material for acts.
How to Contact: Write or call first and obtain permission to submit. Prefers cassette with 3 songs and lyric sheet. Does not return unsolicited material. Reports in 5 weeks.
Music: Mostly pop rock, mellow rock and soft rock; also MOR, easy listening and ballads. Works primarily with vocalists and vocalist/songwriters.
Tips: "We usually will listen to unsolicited material, however we do not return audio tapes and we may not even reply. Songwriters, do not neglect to put the copyright notice (©, Your Name, year) on all your original material. As of this writing we are considering one (more) vocalist. (We have a self-

imposed limitation of just 3 Acts. See "Choosing A Manager" in the August 1990 issue of *Gig Magazine*.) Vocalists, if you are past your voice change, send your name, age, address, a snapshot and a brief outline of your ambitions."

*EMARCO MANAGEMENT, P.O. Box 867, Woodland Hills CA 91365. President: Mark Robert. (818)712-9069. Management firm and record company (Burbank Records). Estab 1982. Represents local, regional or individual artists, groups and songwriters. Receives 15% commission. Reviews material for acts.
How to Contact: Write first and obtain permission to submit. Prefers cassette with 3 songs or less and lyric sheets. Returns with SASE. Reports in 3 weeks.
Music: Mostly pop and rock. Current acts include Paul Pope, Gabriele Rozzi, and Robbie Rist (pop-rock).

*ENCORE TALENT, INC., 2137 Zercher Rd., San Antonio TX 78209. (512)822-2655. President: Ronnie Spillman. Management firm and booking agency. Estab. 1979. Represents local individual artists; currently handles 5 acts. Receives 10-15% commission. Reviews material for acts.
How to Contact: Write first and obtain permission to submit. Prefers cassette. SASE.
Music: Mostly country and western.

*ENTERTAINING VENTURES MANAGEMENT INC., 25 Convoy Ave., Halifax NS **Canada** B3N 2P5. (902)443-7324. Artist Representative: Robert McLellan. Management firm. Estab. 1988. Represents international individual artists; currently handles 1 act. Receives 15% commission. Reviews material for acts.
How to Contact: Call first and obtain permission to submit. Prefers cassette (VHS videocassette) with 3-4 songs and lyric sheet. SASE. Reports in 1-2 months.
Music: Mostly contemporary country, pop and traditional. Works primarily with vocalists/groups with strong visuals, variety entertainment potential. Current acts include Jimmy Flynn — "Canada's top musical comedy act."
Tips: "Call first, but our doors are always open."

ENTERTAINMENT INTERNATIONAL USA, P.O. Box 20736, Canton OH 44701-0736. (216)454-4843. National President: Don Bennafield. Management firm, booking agency (Trident Enterprises, Venus Concert Division and Cobra Productions), music publisher (TA Grace Music & Trident Enterprises) and owners of Global Trade Association of Entertainment Industry. Represents individual artists, groups and songwriters; currently handles 4 acts. Receives 10-20% commission. Reviews material for acts.
How to Contact: Write first and obtain permission to submit. Prefers cassette (or VHS videocassette) with 4-5 songs and lyric or lead sheet "Prepare a good portfolio. If submitting a videocassette, be sure more than one song is on it." SASE. Reports in 3 weeks.
Music: R&B, country and rock. Works primarily with show bands, dance bands and bar bands. Current acts include Unique, Sirene and Chico. Works produced include "Car Wash," "Which Way Is Up," "Cooley High," "Looking For Mr. Goodbar," "I Don't Know Why," "I Gotta Have A Song," "Thunderthumbs & Lightning Licks," and "What Becomes Of The Broken Hearted." Artists produced include Bill Withers, Les McCann, Ashford and Simpson, and Luther Vandross.
Tips: "All materials are scrutinized carefully by Paul Riser, well-renowned songwriter and composer for such stars as Aretha Franklin, Stevie Wonder, Diana Ross, Teena Marie, Irene Cara, Temptations and Rose Royce."

ENTERTAINMENT MANAGEMENT ENTERPRISES, 454 Alps Rd., Wayne NJ 07470. (201)694-3333. President: Richard Zielinski. Management firm. Estab. 1982. Represents artists and musical groups; currently handles 2 acts. Receives minimum of 20% commission. Reviews material for acts.
How to Contact: Prefers cassette (or VHS videocassette) with 4-6 songs and lyric sheet. Include 8×10 glossy and bio. "Let us know, by mail or phone, about any New York area performances so we can attend." SASE. Reports in 2 weeks.
Music: Mostly rock. Works primarily with rock groups with vocals, synthesized rock, contemporary singers and club bands. Current acts include Voyager (progressive rock) and Mirrors' Image (metal).
Tips: "A good press kit is important."

ENTERTAINMENT USA, P.O. Box 28247, Tempe AZ 85285. (602)839-9635. President: Keith Miller. Management firm and booking agency. Estab. 1987. Represents individual artists and groups; currently handles 15 acts. Receives 10-20% commission. Reviews material for acts.

How to Contact: Prefers cassette (or VHS videocassette-"short, one camera shoots ok") with 5 songs and lyric or lead sheets. SASE. Reports in 3 weeks.
Music: Mostly pop, rock, country, top 40; also R&B. Works primarily with dance bands, show bands and bar bands. Current acts include Dolan Ellis, Back to Eden, Edy Gainer and Dezire, Byron McHale and Impact and Plan B.

ESCHENBACH EDITIONS, 28 Dalrymple Crescent, Edinburh EH9 2NX **Great Britain**. Phone: (031)667-3033. A&R Director: J. Douglas. Music publisher (Eschenbach Editions), record company (Helios Records, Caritas Records) and record producer (Helios Records). Estab. 1986. Represents individual artists, groups and songwriters. Receives 15% commission. Reviews material for acts.
How to Contact: Write or call and obtain permission to submit. Prefers cassette or 7½ ips reel-to-reel (or VHS videocassette) with 6 songs. Does not return unsolicited material. Reports in 6 weeks.
Music: Mostly classical, pop and jazz; also serious. Current acts include Andreas Petersen (keyboards), Philip Shevchuk (electronic keyboards) and Catherine Nicholson (singer).
Tips: "We are particularly interested in ethnic music. We're also adding to our sound library."

EVENTS UNLIMITED, P.O. 6541, Cleveland OH 44101. (216)467-0300. President: John Latimer. Management firm, booking agency, record company (Play Records) and TV show ("Alternate Beat"). Estab. 1985. Represents local, regional and international individual artists, groups and songwriters. Currently handles 18 acts. Receives 25% commission. Reviews material for acts.
How to Contact: Submit demo tape by mail. Unsolicited submissions are okay. Prefers cassette with 5 songs. SASE. Reports in 6 weeks.
Music: Mostly rock and alternative. Current acts include I-Tal (reggae club band), The Bellows (rock concert acts) and Serious Nature (rock concert act).
Tips: "Be professional, persistent, and patient. Correspond by mail only."

FALK & MORROW TALENT/EARZA MUSIC, 143 S. Cedros, Solana Beach CA 92075. (619)481-3030. Agent/Manager: Kevin Morrow. Mangement firm, booking agency and music publisher. Represents groups and songwriters; currently handles 10 acts. Receives 10% commission. Reviews material for acts.
How to Contact: Prefers cassette with 3 songs and lyric sheet. Does not return unsolicited material. Reports in 1 month.
Music: Mostly R&B/rock and country works primarily with dance bands. Current acts include Paladins (R&B/rock act), Little Charlie & The Nightscats (R&B, swing), Charlie Musselwhite (blues), the Bonedaddys (world beat) and Clarence Fountain and The 5 Blind Boys (gospel).
Tips: "Send demos, bio, picture; follow up with calls, be ready to work."

*FAR WEST ENTERTAINMENT, INC., 123 Boylston Avenue East, Seattle WA 98102. (206)324-6750. Booking agency. Estab. 1971. Represents local and regional (Northwest) artists and groups; currently handles 20 acts. Receives 10-15% commission.
How to Contact: Submit demo tape by mail. Unsolicited submissions are okay. Prefers cassette (VHS videocassette) with 3-4 songs. SASE. Reports in 2-3 weeks.
Music: Mostly pop-dance, rock and R&B. Works primarily with pop-dance-top 40 club bands. Current acts include Boy Toy (top 40 rock) Zerod' Zero (top 40/dance) and New London (rock/dance).
Tips: "Please send in professional looking and sounding promo and tape! The better you present yourself the better chance you have of getting bookings!"

*FAT CITY ARTISTS, Suite #2, 1226 17th Ave. South, Nashville TN 37212. (615)320-7678. President: Rusty Michael. Management firm, booking agency and lecture bureau. Estab. 1972. Represents international individual artists, groups, songwriters and authors; currently handles 50 acts. Receives 20% commission. Reviews material for acts.
How to Contact: Submit demo tape by mail. Unsolicited submissions are okay. Prefers cassette (videocassette) with 4-6 songs. Does not return unsolicited material. Reports in 2 weeks.
Music: Mostly rock, pop and R&B; also jazz, country/western and new wave heavy metal. "We represent all types of artists." Current acts include Archie Bell and the Drells (top 40), Doug Clark and the Hot Nuts (top 40), Little Milton (blues), Clockhammer (rock), John Kodi and the Greg Henson Band (reggae).
Tips: "Send all available information including audio, video, photo and print. If you do not have a professional package available, inquire. We also have adv/promo department to develop effective promo kits."

FRED T. FENCHEL ENTERTAINMENT AGENCY, 2104 S. Jefferson Avenue, Mason City IA 50401. (515)423-4177. General Manager: Fred T. Fenchel. Booking agency. Estab. 1964. Represents local and international individual artists and groups. Receives 15% commission. Reviews material for acts.

How to Contact: Submit demo tape by mail. Unsolicited submissions are OK. Does not return unsolicited material.

Music: Mostly country, pop and some gospel. Works primarily with dance bands, show groups; "artists we can use on club dates, fairs, etc." Current acts include The Memories, D. C. Drifters, Show groups. "We deal primarily with established name acts with recording contracts, or those with a label and starting into popularity."

Tips: "Submit good material with universal appeal (hopefully) and be informative on artists background, etc."

FESTIVAL FAMILY ENTERPRISES, LTD., Box 87, Skidmore MO 64487. (816)928-3631. Personal Manager: Jonnie Kay. Management firm (Max Stout Publishing/BMI) and record company (Max Stout Records). Estab. 1973. Currently handles 1 act. Receives 10-15% commission. Reviews material for acts.

How to Contact: Submit demo tape by mail. Unsolicited submissions are OK. Prefers cassette with 2 songs with lyric and lead sheets. Reports in 1 year.

Music: Mostly ballads, pop and country; also patriotic. Works primarily with variety showbands. Current acts include Britt Small and Festival (brass band/variety).

Tips: "We're looking for ballads written for a bass voice, mass vocals and brass; also looking for comedy tunes and patriotic songs."

FINKELSTEIN MANAGEMENT COMPANY LTD., 151 John St., Suite 301, Toronto, Ontario M5C 2T2 **Canada.** (416)596-8696. A&R Director: Jehanne Languedoc. Management firm, music publisher (Golden Mountain Music Corp./PRO, Middle Kingdom Music/CAPAC) and record company (True North Records). Estab. 1969. Represents regional (Canada) individual artists and songwriters. Currently handles 3 acts. Reviews material for acts.

How to Contact: Call first and obtain permission to submit. Prefers cassette (or VHS videocassette) with 3 songs. Does not return unsolicited material. Reports in 2 months.

Music: Mostly folk/rock, rock/pop and acoustic rock. Works primarily with singer/songwriters. Current acts include Bruce Cockburn, Barney Bentall and The Legendary Hearts.

Tips: "When you call, get to the point quickly and tell us exactly what you would like from us."

FIREBALL MANAGEMENT, Box 588, Freeport NY 11520. (516)223-1244. President: Joel Peskin. Management firm. Estab. 1979. "We advance nationwide tours and coordinate promotion with record companies." Currently handles 2 acts. Receives 20% commission. Reviews material for acts.

How to Contact: Query by mail. Prefers cassette with 2-5 songs. "Send press clippings."

Music: Rock (hard). Works primarily with hard rock concert groups. Current acts include Kashmir and Passion Kills (concert acts).

Tips: "Be dedicated and hardworking."

FIRST TIME MANAGEMENT, Sovereign House, 12 Trewartha Rd., Praa Sands-Penzance, Cornwall TR20 9ST **England.** Phone: (0736)762826. FAX: (0736)763328. Managing Director: Roderick G. Jones. Management firm. Estab. 1986. Represents local, regional and international individual aritsts, groups and songwriters. Receives 20% commission. Reviews material for acts.

How to Contact: Submit demo tape by mail. Unsolicited submissions are okay. Prefers cassette or 15 ips reel-to-reel or VHS videocassette with 3 songs and lyric sheets. SASE. Reports in 4-8 weeks.

Music: Mostly country, gospel and pop; also all styles. Works primarily with songwriters, composers, vocalists, groups and choirs. Current acts include Pete Arnold (folk), and Willow.

Tips: "Become a member of the Society of International Songwriters and Composers. Keep everything as professional as possible. Be patient and dedicated to your aims and objectives."

FIVE STAR ENTERTAINMENT, 10188 Winter View Dr., Naples FL 33942. (813)566-7701 and (813)566-7702. Assistant Manager: Sid Kleiner. Management firm and booking agency (Kleiner Entertainment Services), record company and audiovisual firm (Sid Kleiner Music Enterprises, Inc.) and record producer. Represents individual artists and groups; currently handles over 15 acts. Receives 15-25% commission. Reviews material for acts.

The asterisk before a listing indicates that the listing is new in this edition. New markets are often the most receptive to unsolicited submissions.

How to Contact: Prefers VHS (or super VHS) videocassette only with maximum of 6 songs. SASE. Reports in 1 month.
Music: Mostly swing, MOR and country; also ethnic, pop and rock. Works primarily with organized dance bands and self-contained singles. Current acts include Sid Kleiner (guitar/one-man band), Ron Hart (vocal/instrumental single), Ray King (vocal/piano/band) and Johnny Dee ("All Stars").
Tips: "Furnish as much information as possible: glossies, VHS video demo tapes (1½ choruses), song lists, equipment lists, availability, price per single engagement, price per on-going weekly engagement, costuming, etc."

*FOURSQUARE MANAGEMENT CO., 6911 Picnic Woods, Middletown MD 21769. (301)694-8618. A&R Director: Rodger Ekenberg. Management agency and record company (Reflex Records). Estab. 1982. Represents individual artists and groups; currently handles 3 acts. Receives varying commission. Reviews material for acts.
How to Contact: Prefers cassette (or VHS or BETA videocassette). SASE. Reports in 1 month.
Music: Gospel, country and blues. Works primarily with vocalists and groups. Current acts include Mark DeNoel, Ron Reeley and Frank Shockley.

FOXWORTHY MUSIC INC., 4002 Liggett Dr., San Diego CA 92106. (619)226-4152. President: Douglas Foxworthy. Management firm, music publisher (Foxworthy Music/BMI), record company (Foxworthy Entertainment) and EXU Records. Estab. 1976. Represents local, regional and international individual artists, groups and songwriters. Currently handles 3 acts. Receives 20% commission. Reviews material for acts.
How to Contact: Write or call first and obtain permission to submit. Prefers cassette (or VHS videocassette of performance-no longer than 10 minutes) with 3 songs and lyric sheets. SASE. Reports in 3 weeks.
Music: Mostly rock, pop and R&B; also country. Works primarily with vocalists, singers and songwriters. Current acts include Street Poet Ray (rap/songwriter), Gary Hyde (pop/rock), and The Expanding Universe Orchestra (big band/rock).
Tips: "Have very good songs, include both audio and video demo, bio and photos."

THE FRANKLYN AGENCY, #312, 1010 Hammond St., West Hollywood CA 90069. (213)272-6080. President: Audrey P. Franklyn. Management firm and public relations firm and cable production company plus part owner of A&E Productions. "Producing weekend singer showcases at Ramada hotel, Beverly Hills, CA." Represents artists, musical groups and businesses; currently handles 5 acts. Receives 5-15% commission. Reviews material for acts.
How to Contact: Query by mail, arrange personal interview, or submit demo. Prefers cassette or videocassette with 4 songs and lead sheet. SASE. Reports in 1 month.
Music: Mosly rock, country and pop; also blues, easy listening, gospel, jazz, MOR, progressive and R&B. Works primarily with rock bands and single soloist singers. Current acts include Merrell Fankhauser (writer of "Wipe Out"), Exetta Murphy (singer), and Gay Goodenough (comic).
Tips: "No amateurs—be funded for promotional efforts."

FREADE SOUNDS ENTERTAINMENT & RECORDING STUDIO, North 37311 Valley Rd., Chattaroy WA 99003. (509)292-2201. FAX: (509)292-2205. Agent/Engineer: Tom Lapsansky. Booking agency and recording studio. Represents groups; currently handles 13 acts. Receives 10-15% commission. Reviews material for acts.
How to Contact: Query by mail or submit demo. Prefers cassette (or videocassette, "please pick best vocal song, best instrumental and best song performer likes to perform") with 4-6 songs and pictures/song list. SASE. Reports in 2 weeks.
Music: Mostly top 40/pop; also R&B, rock 'n' roll and production rock. Works primarily with dance/concert groups and bar bands. Current acts include Top Secret, Nasty Habit, Showboat, Justin Sayne, Lynx, and Defiant (all top 40/production rock acts).

BOB SCOTT FRICK ENTERPRISES, 404 Bluegrass Ave., Madison TN 37115. (615)865-6380. President: Bob Frick. Booking agency, music publisher (Frick Music Publishing Co./BMI and Sugarbaker Music Publishing/ASCAP) and record company (R.E.F. Recording Co). Represents individual artists and songwriters; currently handles 5 acts. Reviews material for acts.
How to Contact: Submit demo tape by mail, or write or call first to arrange personal interview. Prefers cassette with 3 songs and lyric sheet. SASE. Reports in 1 month.
Music: Mostly gospel, country and R&B. Works primarily with vocalists. Current acts include Bob Scott Frick (guitarist, singer), Larry Ahlborn (singer) and Bob Myers (singer).

FROST & FROST ENTERTAINMENT, 3985 W. Taft Dr., Spokane WA 99208. (509)325-1777. Agent: Dick Frost. Booking agency. Represents individuals and groups; currently handles 12-15 acts. Receives 10-15% commission.

How to Contact: Query. Prefers cassette (or videocassette "a sample performance of what artist/band does") with 5 songs and lyric sheet. Include information on past appearances, as well as list of references. SASE. Reports in 2 weeks.
Music: Mostly MOR (50's and 60's); also Country, dance-oriented, easy listening, modern country, rock (country and 50s) and top 40/pop (no heavy metal). Works primarily with dance bands, show bands and individual artists. Current acts include Justus (dance band), Stagecoach West (show band) and Sweetwater (dance band).
Tips: "Send promo package, glossy and performing locations. Be commercial and appeal to wide variety of tastes in music."

*GAIRA PRODUCTIONS, 2058 Cacique St., Ocean Park, Santurce, 00911 **Puerto Rico** Phone: (809)728-2441 or 727-6973. or Aptdo. 250564, Bogota, Chico **Colombia**, S.A. Phone: 2577995. Manager: Liesa Dileo. Management firm, booking agency and public relations. Estab. 1983. Represents individual artists, groups, songwriters; currently handles CBS recording artist "Carlos Vives" and 2 other acts. Receives 20-25% commission. Reviews material for acts.
How to Contact: Prefers cassette (or VHS videocassette) with 3-4 songs and lyric or lead sheets. SASE. Reports in 1 month.
Music: Pop, ballad, and rock.

BOB GALLION PRODUCTIONS, Box 78, Fairview OH 43736. (614)758-5812. President: R.H. Gallion. Management firm, booking agency, music publisher (Bo-Gal Music and Green-Up Music) and record company (Arby Records). Estab. 1969. Represents individuals, groups and songwriters; currently handles 44 acts. Receives 15% commission. Reviews material for acts.
How to Contact: Write first or submit demo tape. Prefers cassette. Does not return unsolicited material. Reports in 2 months.
Music: Mostly country; also bluegrass, folk, gospel, MOR and top 40/pop. Works primarily with show bands, big name acts and country songwriters. Current acts include Lew DeWitt, Beaver Creek and Vicksburgs (all country acts).

GANGLAND ARTISTS, 707-810 W. Broadway, Vancouver, British Columbia V5Z 1J8 **Canada**. (604)872-0052. Contact: Allen Moy. Management firm, production house and music publisher. Estab. 1985. Represents artists and songwriters; currently handles 3 acts. Reviews material for acts.
How to Contact: Prefers cassette (or VHS videocassette) and lyric sheet. "Videos are not entirely necessary for our company! It is certainly a nice touch. If you feel your audio cassette is strong—send the video upon later request. Something wildly creative and individual will grab our attention!" SAE and IRC. Reports in 1 month.
Music: Rock, pop and R&B. Works primarily with "original rock/left of center" show bands. Current acts include 54-40 (rock/pop), Sons of Freedom (hard/rock), and Bolero Lava (pop/rock).

*JO-ANN GEFFEN & ASSOCIATES, 4570 Encino Ave., Encino CA 91316. (818)905-5511. Contact: Jo-Ann Geffen. Management firm and public relations company. Estab. 1971. Represents local, regional or international individual artists, groups and songwriters; currently handles 5 acts. Reviews material for acts.
How to Contact: Call first and obtain permission to submit. Prefers cassette. SASE.
Music: Pop and R&B. Current acts include Commodores, Tuesday Knight and Audrey Landers.
Tips: "Send material geared specifically for the artists listed."

GODWIN MUSIC GROUP, Suite 3, 1226 17th Ave. S., Nashville TN 37212. (615)327-1632. Vice President: Maurice Godwin. Management firm, booking agency, music publisher (Old Empress Music/BMI, Un-Der 16 Songs/SESAC). Represents international individual artists, groups and songwriters; currently handles 20 acts. Receives 20% commission. Reviews material for acts.
How to Contact: Submit demo tape by mail. Unsolicited submissions are okay. Prefers cassette with 4 songs and lyric sheet. SASE. Reports in 1 month.
Music: Mostly rock, pop and R&B; also country, black blues, reggae and dance. Works primarily with rock bands playing the clubs and artists that have 24 track master completed. Current acts include Eric McClure (pop/rock).

*LINDY GOETZ MANAGEMENT, 11116 Aqua Vista #39, Studio City CA 91602. (818)508-1875. Managers: Lindy Goetz and Krissi Lannin. Management firm. Estab. 1984. Represents local and international individual artists, groups and songwriters; currently handles 3 acts. Receives 15% commission.
How to Contact: Write first and obtain permission to submit. Prefers cassette with 3 songs and lyric sheet. SASE. Reports in 1 month.
Music: Mostly rock, rap and funk; also pop, punk and R&B. Works primarily with rock/metal, rock/funk/punk, A/C/MOR. Current acts include Red Hot Chili Peppers (rock/funk/punk), Guy Mann Dude (rock/metal) and Dennis Sarokin (A/C, MOR).

Tips: "Don't bug our office with a million phone calls after you make your submission."

*GOLDEN BULL PRODUCTIONS, 9954 S. Peoria, Chicago IL 60643. (312)238-1373. Manager: Jesse Dearing. Management firm. Estab. 1984. Represents local and regional (Midwest) individual artists, groups and songwriters; currently handles 4 acts. Receives 12-20% commission. Reviews material for acts.
How to Contact: Submit demo tape by mail. Unsolicited submissions are okay. Prefers cassette (VHS videocassette) with 4-5 songs and lyric or lead sheet. SASE.
Music: Mostly R&B, pop and rock; also gospel, jazz and blues. Works primarily with vocalists, bands. Current acts include Lost and Found (band), Keith Steward (songwriter) and Lock (singer).

*GOLDEN CITY INTERNATIONAL, P.O. Box 410851, San Francisco CA 94141. (415)822-1530. Manager: Mr. Alston. Management firm, booking agency and record company (Dagene Records/Cabletown). Estab. 1987. Represents regional (Bay area) individual artists, groups and songwriters; currently handles 3 acts. Receives 25% commission. Reviews material for acts.
How to Contact: Write or call first and obtain permission to submit. Prefers cassette with 2 songs and lyric sheet. Does not return unsolicited material. Reports in 3 weeks.
Music: Mostly R&B/dance, rap and pop; also gospel. Current clients include Marcus Justice (songwriter), Primo (artist) and David Alston (producer).

*GRAVITY PIRATES MANAGEMENT, G.P.O. Box 697, Sydney NSW **Australia** 2001. (2)332-2929. Manager: Steven Hindes. Management firm. Estab. 1983. Represents local artists and groups; currently handles 1 act. Receives 10% commission. Reviews material for acts.
How to Contact: Submit demo tape by mail. Unsolicited submissions are okay. Prefers cassette with 2 songs and lyric or lead sheet. Does not return unsolicited material. Reports in 1 month.
Music: Mostly rock, pop and R&B. Works primarily with rock bands. Current acts include Gravity Pirates (rock band).
Tips: "We prefer songs that lend themselves to different arrangements and styles."

GREIF-GARRIS MANAGEMENT, Suite 309, 1484 South Beverly Dr., Beverly Hills CA 90035-3042. (213)552-9443. Vice President: Sid Garris. Management firm. Represents artists, groups and songwriters; currently handles 3 acts. Receives minimum 10% commission. Reviews material for acts.
How to Contact: Write first and obtain permission to submit. Prefers cassette with 3-5 songs. SASE. Reports ASAP.
Music: All types of "good music" (no heavy rock, metal or rap). Current acts include The New Christy Minstrels (folk), The Crusaders (jazz fusion) and Nelson Riddle Orchestra (MOR).
Tips: "Artists and writers should be critical enough to ensure that what is being sent is the *best* of their ability."

*JOSEPH GUNCHES MANAGEMENT, 12827 Sylvan St., N. Hollywood CA 91606. (818)761-5683. Management firm and music publisher (Brunson Brothers/ASCAP). Represents individual artists, groups and songwriters; currently handles 6 acts. Receives 20-25% commission. Reviews material for acts.
How to Contact: Write first and obtain permission to submit. Prefers cassette (or VHS videocassette) with 3 songs. SASE. Reports in 2 months.
Music: Open to all types. Current acts inlcude Brunson Brothers, Raspyni Brothers and Johnny Fox.

HALE ENTERPRISES, Rt. 1, Box 49, Worthington IN 47471. (812)875-3664. Contact: Rodger Hale. Management firm, booking agency and record company (Projection Unlimited). Estab. 1976. Represents artists, groups, songwriters and studio musicians; currently handles 15 acts. Receives 10-15% commission. Reviews material for acts.
How to Contact: Query by mail or call to arrange personal interview. Prefers cassette (or videocassette) with 2-10 songs and lyric sheet. "Include personal and business bio, photo and references." Does not return unsolicited material. Reports in 2 weeks.
Music: Mostly country and top 40; also MOR, progressive, rock and pop. Works primarily with show bands, dance bands and bar bands. Current acts include Indiana (country show band); Seventh Heaven (top 40 show) and Cotton (show band).

"How to Use Your Songwriter's Market" (at the front of this book) contains comments and suggestions to help you understand and use the information in these listings.

*BILL HALL ENTERTAINMENT & EVENTS, 138 Frog Hollow Rd., Churchville PA 18966. (215)357-5189. Contact: William B. Hall III. Booking agency and production company. Represents individuals and groups; currently handles 30 acts. Receives 15% commission. Reviews material for acts, depending on engagement and type of attraction.

How to Contact: "Letter of inquiry preferred as initial contact." Prefers cassette with 2-3 songs "and photos, promo material, and record or tape". Does not return unsolicited material. Reports in 1 month.

Music: Marching band, circus and novelty ethnic. Works primarily with "unusual or novelty attractions in musical line, preferably those that appeal to family groups." Current acts include Fralinger and Polish-American Philadelphia Championship Mummers String Bands (marching and concert group); Erwin Chandler Orchestra (show band); "Mr. Polynesian" Show Band and Hawaiian Revue (ethnic group); the "New Phillies Band" of Philadelphia Phillies Baseball team; Phillies organist-entertainer Paul Richardson; and numerous solo pianists and vocalists.

LYN HARKINS & ASSOCIATES, P.O. Box 24032, Nashville TN 37203-4032. (615)868-8926. President: Lyn Harkins. Management firm. Estab. 1988. Represents local, regional or international individual artists, groups and songwriters. Receives 10-15% commission. Currently handles 4 acts. Reviews material for acts.

How to Contact: Submit demo tape by mail. Unsolicited submissions are OK. Prefers cassette (or VHS videocassette) with 1 or more songs. SASE. Reports "ASAP."

Music: Country, rock and R&B; also gospel, new age or any type. Works primarily with groups/country, country rock, original and rock vocalists. Current acts include Russ Harkins (country/R&B singer/songwriter), Terry Pollock and Thunderhead North (Southwestern original).

Tips: "Don't sit on it! Send it in."

GEORGE HARNESS ASSOCIATES, 1 Timberline Dr., Springfield IL 62707. (217)529-8550. President: George Harness. Management firm and booking agency. Estab. 1978. Represents artists and groups. Receives 15-20% commission. Reviews material for acts.

How to Contact: Query by mail. Prefers cassette (or videocassette) with 6-8 songs and lyric sheet. SASE. Reports in 2 weeks.

Music: Mostly MOR and top 40/pop; also dance. Current acts include 7th Heaven, Earl Turner & Earl Turner Group, Todd Bradley and Next Level, Phlash, Alcazar, Crush and Moses & Highbrows (all show & dance acts).

KEN HATLEY & ASSOCIATES, INC., 520 Georgetown, Casselberry FL 32707. (407)834-0920. Contact: Ken Hatley. Management firm, music publisher (Greater Orlando Music/BMI) and record company (represents Sounds of America). Estab. 1987. Represents major individual artists and songwriters; currently handles 5 acts. Receives 10-15% commission. Reviews material for acts.

How to Contact: Write first and obtain permission to submit. Prefers cassette with 1-4 songs and lyric sheets. Does not return unsolicited material.

Music: Mostly country, pop and R&B; also gospel and contemporary Christian. Current acts include Razzy Bailey (country artist).

Tips: "Make sure all demos are clear and lyrics definitely distinct; send a SASE postcard for any return comments, status or advice."

HAWKEYE ATTRACTIONS, 102 Geiger St., Huntingburg IN 47542. (812)683-3657. President: David Mounts. Booking agency. Estab. 1982. Represents individual artists and groups. Currently handles 1 act. Receives 10% commission. Reviews material for acts.

How to Contact: Prefers cassette with 4 songs and lyric sheet. SASE. Reports in 6 weeks.

Music: Mostly country and western swing. Works primarily with show bands, Grand Ole Opry style form of artist and music. Current acts include Bill Mounts (singer/songwriter) and His Midwest Cowboys (country/western swing).

Tips: "Don't copy anybody, just be yourself. If you have talent it will show through."

HEAD OFFICE MANAGEMENT, Suite #305, 296 Richmond St., W., Toronto, Ontario M5V 1X2 **Canada**. (416)979-8455. FAX: (416)979-8766. Los Angeles Office: Head Office Management, 523 23rd St., Manhattan Beach, CA 90266. Phone: (213)546-6670. FAX: (213)546-3454. President: Stephen Prendergast. Vice President: Pat Arnott. Management firm and music publisher (Auto-Tunes, Dee Songs and Steeler Music/Fraze-songs). Estab. 1982. Represents individual artists, groups and songwriters, producers and engineers; currently handles 3 acts. Receives 15-25% commission. Reviews material for acts. "They are mostly self-contained. We do not solicit music, but are willing to listen."

How to Contact: Prefers cassette (or VHS ½" videocassette) with 3 songs and lyric sheet. Does not return unsolicited material. Reports in 2 months.
Music: Mostly rock, pop, metal and dance. Works primarily with rock/pop recording artists and songwriters. Current acts include Big House (rock band), Brighton Rock (heavy metal band/songwriters) and Nick Heyward (pop band/songwriter).
Tips: "Have a business attitude, style in presentation, sincerity, honesty, hunger. Include photo, contact information (with phone number) and brief history of songwriters/band and members involved."

GLENN HENRY ENTERTAINMENT AGENCY, 1304 Crestline, Santa Barbara CA 93105. (805)687-1131. Contact: Glenn Henry. Booking agency. Represents individuals and groups; currently handles 16 acts. Receives 10-15% commission. Reviews material for acts.
How to Contact: Query by phone to arrange personal interview. Prefers cassette with 3-6 songs. Artist may submit 8x10 promo pictures and/or credits. "Telephone first. If we can use act or band we'll request a video." SASE. Reporting time varies.
Music: Mostly rock, lounge rock and top 40/pop. Works with lounge and hotel bands with female vocalist if possible, piano singles, rock duos, trios, quartets. At present, needs pop rock band with female vocalist. Current acts include Nikki and the Runaways, Ca-mish-un, Asylum, City Limits, Road House Rockers, TKO, Rumors and Blue Moon.

BOB HINKLE MANAGEMENT/THE CHILDREN'S GROUP, 17 Cadman Plaza West, Brooklyn NY 11201. (718)858-2544. President: Bob Hinkle. Management firm. Represents individual artists, groups and songwriters. Currently handles 5 artists. Receives 15-25% commission. Reviews material for acts.
How to Contact: Call first and obtain permission to submit. Prefers cassette (or ¾" or VHS videocassette) with 3-5 songs and lyric sheet. Artist should send a videocassette of his/her performance. Does not return unsolicited material. Report in 1 month.
Music: Mostly pop, rock, country; also R&B, gospel and children's songs. Works primarily with recording bands, soloists and children's performers. Current acts include Classical Kids (series of readings by Sue Hammond to introduce classical music to kids), Red Grammar (children's performer) Dan Conley (children's performer) and Steven Schoenberg (concert pianist).
Tips: "Tailor writing to needs of artists without losing what makes your writing unique."

HITCH-A-RIDE MANAGEMENT, P.O. Box 1001, Florence KY 41022-1001. (606)371-5469. Manager: J.H. Reno. Management firm, booking agency and publishing company. Represents professional individuals, groups and songwriters; currently handles 5 acts. Receives 15% commission. Reviews material for acts.
How to Contact: Prefers cassette (or videocassette—"be natural") with 1-4 songs and lyric sheet. SASE. Reports in 1 month.
Music: Mostly modern country and light cross-over rock. Works primarily with vocalists. Current acts include Sheila Reno, Pam Hanna, Mike Tomlin and Jack Reno (country vocalists).

*DOC HOLIDAY PRODUCTIONS, 5405 Echo Pines Circle W., Fort Pierce FL 34951. (804)838-9552. Vice President: Judith Guthro. Management firm, booking agent, music publisher (BMI, ASCAP, SESAC) and record company (Tug Boat Records). Estab. 1985. Represents international individual artists, groups and songwriters; currently handles 47 acts. Receives 15-25% commission. Reviews material for acts.
How to Contact: Submit demo tape by mail. Unsolicited submissions are okay. Prefers cassette with 1 song and lyric sheet. Does not return unsolicited material. Reports in 2 weeks.
Music: Mostly country, pop and rock. Works primarily with vocalist dance bands. Current acts include Richie Balin (country singer/writer), Jon Washington (pop singer/writer) and Ronn Craddock (country singer).

*ADAM HURDLE ASSOCIATES, INC., P.O. Box 5181, Richmond VA 23220. (804)359-3578. Representative: David Hurdle. Management firm and booking agency. Represents local and international individual artists; currently handles 1 act. Receives 15% commission. Reviews material for acts.
How to Contact: Submit demo tape by mail. Unsolicited submissions are okay. Prefers cassette with 8-10 songs and lyric sheet. SASE. Reports in 2 weeks.
Music: Mostly country, swing era and contemporary. Current acts include Cheryl K. Warner (country-cross-over).
Tips: "Believe absolutely in yourself. Never quit trying. Be prepared emotionally/psychologically for rejection—rejection—rejection until Voila!"

*ILLUMINATI GROUP, 37 Bennett Village Terrace, Buffalo NY 14214-2201. (716)832-5894. Partner: Ron Weekes/Donnell Mueller. Management and public relations/total identity design for the entertainment industry. Represents solo artists, groups, TV, film and variety artists; currently handles 5 acts. Commission or retainer, depending on project.
How to Contact: Submit demo tape by mail. Unsolicited submissions are okay. "Do not call." Prefers professional quality cassette (VHS ¾" videocassette) with 4 songs and lyric sheet. SASE. Reports in 1 month. "Like to see headshots and any print press."
Music: Mostly top 40/pop, R&B and dance-house; also MOR, alternative and black contemporary. Works primarily with vocalists/instrumentalists.
Tips: "Know first what publicists do. Read Sherry Eaker's *Back Stage Handbook for Performing Artists*. Artists with no prior contract should have funding for promotion. High degree of professionalism and winning attitude vital. Read about power of imaging in Claude Bristol's book *The Magic of Believing*. We're interested in long-term relationships, not a flash in the pan. Prefer to deal through personal managers but will consider artists with knowledge of the business."

*IN TUNES, 519 Tilden Ave., Teaneck NJ 07666. (201)836-1315. Responsible Agent: Lynn W. Kloss. Booking agency and music publisher (Lucrative Music/BMI and Lucratunes/ASCAP). Estab. 1989. Represents international individual artists and songwriters; currently handles 3 acts. Commission negotiable. Reviews material for acts.
How to Contact: Write first and obtain permission to submit. Prefers cassette with up to 3 songs and lyric sheet. SASE. Reports in 1 month.
Music: Mostly folk and country; also R&B and some rock. Works primarily with original singer/songwriters with emphasis on lyrics; also arranges songwriting workshops. Current acts include Fred Koller (folk/country singer/songwriter/publisher).
Tips: "I primarily arrange songwriting workshops and concert dates for Fred Koller, author of *How to Pitch and Promote Your Songs* (a Writer's Digest book), but we're also looking for publishable material."

INTERMOUNTAIN TALENT, P.O. Box 942, Rapid City SD 57709. (605)348-7777. Owner: Ron Kohn. Management firm, booking agency and music publisher (Big BL music). Estab. 1978. Represents invididual artists, groups and songwriters; currently handles 25 acts. Receives 10-20% commission. Reviews material for acts.
How to Contact: Query. Prefers cassette with 3 songs and lyric sheet. Artist may submit videocassette. SASE. Reports in 3 weeks.
Music: Mostly rock; also top country/rock. Works with solo acts, show bands, dance bands and bar bands.Current acts include Hod Rod Dee Luxx, Doctor K and the Shantays (rock bands), Bold Lightning (rock), Night Thunder (variety), Hat Trick (rock) and Terrie McKenzie (solo artist).

ISLAND MANAGEMENT, Box 221, Albert Park, Victoria 3206 **Australia**. Phone: (03)7634100. Managing Director: Larry Tyler. Management firm and booking agency. Represents individual artists, groups and songwriters. Currently handles 4 acts. Receives 15-20% commission. Reviews material for acts.
How to Contact: Prefers cassette (VHS PAL videocassette) with 4 songs and lyric sheet. SAE and IRC. Reports in 1 month.
Music: Mostly pop, rock and R&B. Works primarily with recording artists with charting songs. Current acts include Spaniards (rock/pop group), Brian Mannix (pop singer), Uncanny X-Men (pop group), Bon Voyage (heavy rock & roll) and Leslie Avril (country).

J. BIRD ENTERTAINMENT AGENCY, 250 North Kepler Ave., Deland FL 32724. (904)734-9446. President: John R. Bird II. Management firm and booking agency. Estab. 1963. Represents local, regional and international individual artists, groups, songwriters and recording acts; currently handles 55 acts. Receives 15-25% commission. Reviews material for acts.
How to Contact: Submit demo tape by mail. Unsolicited submissions are OK. Prefers cassette (or VHS videocassette) with 2-3 songs and lyric or lead sheets. Does not return unsolicited material. Reports in 2 weeks.
Music: Mostly top 40, rock, pop and country; also R&B. Works primarily with dance bands and recording acts in concert format. Current acts include Greg Allman (recording act), The Drifters (nostalgia) and Molly Hatchet (concert act).
Tips: "J. Bird agency represents established, concert and copy bands solo and duo acts to national club circuit and national college concert circuit. Bands should have adequate equipment and transportation and perform either original concert material, period-nostalgia material, or current top 40. We stress professional promotional packages including: 8 × 10" photo, audio and video cassette tape."

JACKSON ARTISTS CORP., (Publishing Central), Suite 200, 7251 Lowell Dr., Shawnee Mission KS 66204. (913)384-6688. President: Dave Jackson. Management firm, booking agency (Drake/Jackson Productions), music publisher, (All Told Music/BMI, Zang/Jac Publishing/ASCAP, and Very Cherry/

ASCAP), record company and record producer. Represents artists, groups and songwriters; currently handles 32 acts. Receives 10-20% commission from individual artists and groups; 10% from songwriters. Reviews material for acts.

How to Contact: Query, arrange personal interview or submit demo. Prefers cassette (or VHS videocassette) with 2-4 songs and lead sheet. "Mark names of tunes on cassettes. May send up to 4 tapes. "Although it's not necessary, we prefer lead sheets with the tapes—send 2 or 3 that you are proud of. Also note what 'name' artist you'd like to see do the song. We do most of our business by phone." Will return material if requested with SASE. Reporting time varies.

Music: Mostly gospel, country and rock; also bluegrass, blues, easy listening, disco, MOR, progressive, soul and top 40/pop. Works with acts that work grandstand shows for fairs as well as bar bands that want to record original material. Current acts include "Ragtime Bob" Darch (songwriter/entertainer), The Tennesseans (gospel), Jill Jordon (country), Don Juan (country), Dixie Cadillacs (country/rock), Impressions (50's and 60's), Gary Adams Players (pop), The Five Scamps (jazz), Tracie Spencer, Paul & Paula and Bill Haley's Comet.

Tips: "Be able to work on the road, either as a player or have a group. Invest your earnings from these efforts in demos of your originals that have been tried out on an audience. And keep submitting to the industry."

JAM MANAGEMENT, Box 6588, San Antonio TX 78209. (512)828-1319. Production: Scudder Miller. Management firm and booking agency. Estab. 1970. Represents local, regional and international individual artists, groups and songwriters. Currently handles 3 acts. Commission varies. Reviews material for acts.

How to Contact: Submit demo tape by mail. Unsolicited submissions are okay. Prefers cassette with 3 songs and lyric sheets. Does not return unsolicited material. Reports in 2 weeks.

Music: Rock, country and pop. Works with all kinds of bands. Current acts include Scudder Moon (rock), S&M Hardware (songwriters) and Flash Cadillac (50's rock).

Tips: "Have good material, good attitude, be persistent."

ROGER JAMES MANAGEMENT, 10A Margaret Rd., Barnet, Herts EN4 9NP **England**. Phone: (01)440-9788. Professional Manager: Laura Skuce. Management firm and music publisher (R.J. Music/PRS). Estab. 1977. Represents songwriters. Receives 50% commission; reviews material for acts.

How to Contact: Prefers cassette with 3 songs and lyric sheet. Does not return unsolicited material.

Music: Mostly pop, country and "any good song."

JANA JAE ENTERPRISES, #520, 4815 S. Harvard, Tulsa OK 74135. (918)749-1647. Vice President: Diana Robey. Booking agency, music publisher (Jana Jae Publishing/BMI), and record company (Lark Record Productions, Inc.). Estab. 1979. Represents individual artists and songwriters; currently handles 12 acts. Receives 15% commission. Reviews material for acts.

Music: Mostly interested in country and pop; also classical and jazz instrumentals. Works with vocalists, bands, solo instrumentalists. Represents Jana Jae (country singer/fiddle player), Matt Greif (classical guitarist) and Sydni (solo singer).

JANC MANAGEMENT, Box 5563, Rockford IL 61125. (815)398-6895. President: Nancy Lee. Management firm, booking agency and record company. Represents individual artists, groups and songwriters; currently handles 2 acts. Reviews material for acts.

How to Contact: Prefers cassette (or VHS videocassette) with 4 songs and lyric sheet. SASE. Reports in 2 weeks.

Music: Mostly country (contemporary) and pop; also up-tempo songs, ballads and novelty. Works primarily with vocalists, dance bands and show bands. Current acts include George James and the Mood Express.

Tips: "Be very neat and professional with your submissions."

JMAR PRODUCTIONS, P.O. Box 2393, Beverly Hills CA 90213-2393. President: Jeff Rizzotti. Management firm and booking agency. Estab. 1969. Currently handles 7 acts. Receives 10% commission. Reviews material for acts.

How to Contact: Query by mail. Prefers cassette with 3-6 songs. SASE. Reports in 2 weeks.

Music: Mostly 60s renditions; also top 40, country, jazz and soul. Works primarily with vocalists and bar bands.

Tips: "Music from the heart goes to the heart. If the 'circulation' is right, you know it."

LAURA JOHN MUSIC, 355 W. Pleasantview Ave., Hackensack NJ 07601. Contact: Joe Cecere. Artist representative and music publisher. Estab. 1986. Represents individual artists, groups and songwriters; currently handles 4 acts. Receives 10-15% commission. Reviews material for acts.

Close-up

Bob Halligan
Songwriter
New York, New York

"I've spent the last four years of my life trying to dispel the notion that I only write heavy metal," says Bob Halligan. "I still occasionally do that, but I don't really focus on it anymore." A colleague once dubbed Bob "The Heavy Metal Carole King," a title that Bob says is a double-edged sword: "On the one hand, it describes me as an expert, but on the other hand it pigeonholes me as strictly heavy metal, which to a lot of people is not music. So some people figured I couldn't write 'real' music."

If anyone ever really doubted Bob's ability to write outside of the heavy metal genre, he has soundly proven them wrong with recent cuts on albums by performers like Cher and Michael Bolton. But, as he admits, his reputation was first made with metal. He has had over 80 covers in his career and has written or co-written songs for Judas Priest, Helix, Night Ranger, Blue Oyster Cult and—most recently—Kiss ("Rise to It" and "Read My Body") and Kix ("Don't Close Your Eyes").

"I fell into writing metal sideways. The first Judas Priest recording ('Take These Chains') happened by sheer chance. The song was played for them and they loved it. They recorded it in a much heavier style than I had demoed it. I discovered at that point that there was a dearth of songwriting ability in the heavy metal groups, and that, if I desired to create a niche for myself, I could—as a writer for these types of bands. So I set myself about the task of writing another song for Judas Priest, 'Heads Are Gonna Roll,' and sure enough, they went for that one too. I thought, 'Gee, there would appear to be a living in this.' "

Writing heavy metal differs in a number of ways from writing for other song markets, according to Bob. "You kind of use a different lexicon or dictionary. At one time I even wrote out my own little heavy metal lexicon. I went through the dictionary and picked out a lot of aggressive, obnoxious-sounding words and made a big list of them. Then, whenever I got stuck I'd go to the list. Another thing is that when you're writing metal, you're essentially writing for white teenage males, and rebellion is kind of the word of the day, you know. It's necessary that they be independent, anti-authoritarian, aggressive, not vulnerable. In other words, the speaker in the song can't be construed as a 'wimp'; he can't be waiting for the girl to make up her mind; he has to make up *his* mind—and sort of drag her along behind him, caveman-style. That's one of the reasons I don't fancy writing much heavy metal anymore; I don't find that a particularly edifying point of view."

Breaking into writing heavy metal is a little trickier than writing for some other genres, since the bands tend to want to do most of their own writing. "That's true with a lot of acts," says Bob, "but particularly with the metal guys." Bob got around that hurdle by offering to co-write with band members. "They like to be in on the writing," he says, "so I've found that co-writes are the best way to make something happen. They like to have their own artistic stamp on the song, and there is always the financial factor—people want to have a piece of something if they can. There is also the ego factor of wanting to see their names on the copyright. The totally outside-written song is absolutely the exception. All of the heavy metal bands, whether they can write or not, do."

Bob says that no matter what kind of writing you're doing, "if you're not obsessed you don't have a chance, because there is so much rejection. But if you are obsessed with the idea of writing songs successfully, eventually you will be successful. It really is as simple as that. The only way you can lose is if you quit."

— Mark Garvey

How to Contact: Prefers cassette (or videocassette). SASE. Reports in 1 month.
Music: Mostly country. Works with country singers and songwriters. Current acts include Bandit (original country band), Patti Davis (country singer/songwriter), Wayne Edwards (singer/songwriter) and Carol Sharer (singer-songwriter/violinist).
Tips: "We need good story songs for female lead singers."

DUSTY JONES MANAGEMENT CO., 139 E. Harding Rd., Springfield OH 45504. (513)399-6708. Owner: Robert T. "Dusty" Jones. Management firm and music publisher (Scramrock Music Co./ BMI). Estab. 1980. Represents full bands; currently handles 3-4 acts. Receives approximaterly 10% commission. Reviews material for acts.
How to Contact: Prefers cassette with 3 songs with lyric or lead sheets. "I am now dealing with songwriters and/or artists who have full bands only. I am looking for bands with high energy and outstanding showmanship and with a 'killer' look. Important: include a photo of the band." Does not return unsolicited material. Reports in 1-2 days.
Music: Mostly heavy metal, speed metal/thrash and hard rock. Works with rock and metal concert and bar bands. Represents Tracer (commerical metal band), Spike Opera (speed metal band) and Paragon (progressive metal band).
Tips: "I am looking for full bands with energetic and yet melodic original music. Also bands which are into their look as well as their music and stage show."

(KAM) EXECUTIVE RECORDS, 11 Shady Oak Trail, Charlotte NC 98210. (704)554-1169. Executive Director: Butch Kelly. Record company (KAM Executive Records/BMI). Estab. 1982. Represents local, regional and international individual artists, groups and songwriters. Currently handles 10 acts. Receives 15% commission. Reviews material for acts.
How to Contact: Write or call first and obtain permission to submit. Prefers cassette (or VHS videocassette) with 3-6 songs. Reports in 2 months.
Music: Mostly pop, R&B and rock; also rap and dance. Works primarily with vocalists and show or dance bands. Current acts include Lady Krush, Caro and Richard Kirkpatrick.

*KAUFMAN HILL MANAGEMENT, Suite 632 E, 410 S. Michigan Ave., Chicago IL 60605. (312)477-6644. Contact: Don Kaufman or Shawn Hill. Management firm (also Mozart Midnight Productions, Inc.) and record company (Vamp Records). Estab. 1982. Represents individual artists, groups and songwriters; currently handles 5 acts. Receives 20-25% commission. Reviews material for acts.
How to Contact: Prefers cassette (or VHS videocassette) with 2-6 songs and lyric sheet. Does not return any material. Reports in 1 month.
Music: Mostly R&B, pop, rock and rap. Works primarily with singer/songwriters, bands, groups, and vocalists. Current acts include Aponte (bilingual pop singer, songwriter), Kevin Irving (lead singer of Club Nouveau R&B) and Darkside (rap).
Tips: "Submit by mail. If you have what we need, we will be in touch."

BUTCH KELLY PRODUCTION, 11 Shady Oak Trail, Charlotte NC 28210. (407)554-1162. Executive Director: Butch Kelly. Management firm, booking agency, music publisher (Butch Kelly Production & Publishing), record company (KAM Executive Records) and Fresh Avenue Records. Estab. 1982. Represents local, regional and international individual artists, groups and songwriters. Currently handles 6 acts. Receives 15% commission. Reviews material for acts.
How to Contact: Submit demo tape by mail. Unsolicited submissions are okay. Write first and obtain permission to submit. Prefers cassette (or VHS videocassette) with 3-6 songs and lyric sheets. SASE. Reports in 6 weeks-2 months.
Music: Mostly uptempo dance, R&B and pop; also rap and rock. Works primarily with show bands and dance bands. Current acts include Tim Greene (R&B), Caro (R&B/pop), A. Brown (R&B), Flame (R&B/pop) and Kelly Montgomery (R&B/pop).
Tips: "Send up-tempo dance songs and pictures on Maxell tape for best sound."

HOWARD KING AGENCY, INC., 7050 Babcock Ave., North Hollywood CA 91605. President: Howard King. Management firm and booking agency. Estab. 1962. Represents artists, groups and songwriters. Receives 10-15% commission. Reviews material for acts.
How to Contact: Prefers cassette with maximum 3 songs, photo, publicity material and lyric sheet. SASE. Reporting time varies.
Music: Mostly top 40; also country, dance-oriented, easy listening, jazz, MOR, rock and pop. Works primarily with top 40 artist singles, duos and groups.

*****KINSELLA**, Juniper Hill, Warrington Rd., Mere, Cheshire WA16 0TE **England**. Phone: 0565-830336. FAX: (0565)830657. New Business Manager: Kevin P.D. Kinsella. Management firm and music publisher. Represents individual artists, groups and songwriters; currently handles 20 acts. Receives 25% commission. Reviews material for acts.
How to Contact: Write or call first to arrange personal interview. Prefers reel-to-reel. SAE and IRC.
Music: Mostly dance and pop. Represents Kimberly (dance/pop), Alison (dance/pop) and Sabina (rock).

*****JEFF KIRK**, 515 Inwood Dr., Nashville TN 37211. (615)331-0131. Owner/President: Jeff Kirk. Management firm and booking agency. Estab. 1981. Represents regional (Mid-South) individual artists; currently handles 1 act. Commission varies. Reviews material for acts.
How to Contact: Submit demo tape by mail. Unsolicited submissions are okay. Prefers cassette (VHS videocassette) with 1-3 songs and lyric or lead sheet. SASE. Reports in 6 weeks.
Music: Mostly jazz, pop and rock. Works primarily with jazz groups (4-6 members), instrumental and vocal. Current acts include Jeff Kirk Quartet (mainstream jazz) and New Vintage (jazz fusion).
Tips: "Please submit brief demos with as high audio quality as possible."

BOB KNIGHT AGENCY, 185 Clinton Ave., Staten Island NY 10301. (718)448-8420. President: Bob Knight. Management firm, booking agency, music publishing and royalty collection firm. Estab. 1971. Represents artists, groups and songwriters; currently handles 7 acts. Receives 10-20% commission. Reviews material for acts and for submission to record companies and producers.
How to Contact: "Phone calls accepted 6-9 p.m. (Eastern time)." Prefers cassette (or videocassette) with 5-10 songs and lead sheet "with bio and references. Send photos of artists and groups." SASE. Reports in 1 month.
Music: Mostly top 40/pop; also easy listening, MOR, R&B, soul and rock (nostalgia 50s and 60s). Works primarily with lounge groups, high energy dance, 50's acts and show groups. Current acts include The Elegants (oldie show); Gengo & Gregorio (top 40); and The AD-LIBS (oldie show).

HOWARD KNIGHT ENTERTAINMENT GROUP, 1609 Congress Rd., Eastover SC 29044. (803)776-8397. President: Howard A. Knight, Jr.. Management firm, booking agency, music publisher (Tenaline Music/ASCAP, Howard Knight Music/SESAC, record company (Pegasus Records) and public relations firm (Telstar Productions). Estab. 1969. Represents individual artists, groups and songwriters; currently handles 11 acts. Receives 10-25% commission. Reviews material for acts.
How to Contact: Prefers cassette (or videocassette if available) with 4 songs and lyric sheet. Does not return any material. Reports in 6 weeks.
Music: Mostly country, pop, rock; also gospel. Works primarily with vocalists and self-contained groups. Current acts include Jesse Blevins (country singer/writer), The Bandit Band (country group), Mundo Earwood (country singer/writer), Claude King (country singer/writer), Randy Chapman (country singer/writer), Julie Farris (country singer/writer), Billy Sloan (country singer/writer), Almost Nuts Band (country, group), Felix Rust (rock, singer/writer), William Wayne (country, singer/writer) and Chris Murphy (folk-country, singer/writer).
Tips: "Submit material about every 2 months."

*****S.V. KYLES & ASSOCIATES**, P.O. Box 8305, Houston TX 77288. (713)662-4196. Sr. Consultant: Sirron Kyles. Management firm. Represents international individual artists and groups; currently handles 5 acts. Receives 15-20% commission. Reviews material for acts.
How to Contact: Submit demo tape by mail. Unsolicited submissions are okay. Prefers cassette (VHS videocassette) with 3 songs. Does not return unsolicited material. Reports in 1 month.
Music: Mostly rock & roll, country and R&B; also pop and dance. Recent acts include Steppen Stone (rock), Aubrey Dunnham (jazz) and Vann (country).

L.D.F. PRODUCTIONS, P.O. Box 406, Old Chelsea Station, New York NY 10011. (212)925-8925. President: Mr. Dowell. Management firm and booking agency. Estab. 1982. Represents artists and choirs in the New York area. Currently handles 2 acts. Receives 20-30% commission.

How to Contact: Write first and obtain permission to submit. Prefers cassette (or videocassette— well-lighted, maximum 10 minutes) with 2-8 songs and lyric sheet. SASE. Reports in 1 month. "Do not phone expecting a return call unless requested by L.D.F. Productions."
Music: Mostly black gospel; also choral and church/religious. Works primarily with vocalists and choirs. Current acts include L.D. Frazier (gospel artist/lecturer); and Frazier's (gospel workshop choir).
Tips: "Those interested in working with us must be original, enthusiastic, persistent and sincere."

*LANDMARK DIRECTION COMPANY, INC., P.O. 132, Amelia OH 45102. (513)752-0611. President: James B. Williams. Management firm, booking agency, music publisher (Landmark Publishing/BMI) and record company (JAB Production Co., Inc.). Estab. 1987. Represents regional (Midwest) individual artists, groups and songwriters; currently handles 3 acts. Reviews material for acts.
How to Contact: Submit demo tape by mail. Unsolicited submissions are okay. Prefers cassette (VHS videocassette) with best 3 songs and lyric or lead sheets. SASE. Reports in 6 weeks.
Music: Mostly country, pop and R&B. Works primarily with individual and group recording artist/ road acts.
Tips: "Only send your best material, and send it only to *one* company at a time. Make your presentations brief and as described above. Have all your material copyrighted before submitting."

LANDSLIDE MANAGEMENT, 928 Broadway, New York NY 10010. (212)505-7300. Principals: Ted Lehrman and Libby Bush. Management firm, music publisher (KozKeeOzko Music) and record company (Silverado Records). Estab. 1978. Represents singers, singer/songwriters and actor/singers; currently handles 3 acts. Receives 15% commission. Reviews material for acts.
How to Contact: Submit demo tape and lyric sheet "of potential hit singles only—not interested in album cuts." SASE. "Include picture, resume and (if available) ½" videocassette if you're submitting yourself as an act." Reports in 6 weeks.
Music: Dance-oriented, MOR, rock (soft, pop), soul, top 40/pop and country/pop. Current acts include Cortes Alexander (soft rock), Deborah Dotson (soul/pop/cabaret) and Loretta Valdespino (pop).

LARI—JON PROMOTIONS, 627 Countryview, Columbus NE 68601. (402)564-7034. Owner: Larry Good. Music publisher (Lari-Jon Publishing Co./BMI) and record company (Lari-Jon Records). "We also promote package shows." Represents individual artists, groups and songwriters; currently handles 5 acts. Receives 15% commission. Reviews material for acts.
How to Contact: Prefers cassette with 5 songs and lyric sheet. SASE. Reports in 1 month.
Music: Mostly country, gospel and 50s rock. Works primarily with dance bands and show bands. Represents Larry Good (singer/writer), Busted Loose (country group), Linda Oberle (female artist), John Nace (singer/writer), Tommy Campbell (singer/songwriter) and Kent Thompson (singer).

*LAS VEGAS ENTERTAINMENT SERVICES, 8145E. Camelback Rd., #216, Scottsdale AZ 85251. (602)947-3734. President: A.J.Sagman. Booking agency. Estab. 1986. Represents local, regional or international individual artists, groups and songwriters; currently handles 20 acts. Receives 15% commission. Reviews material for acts.
How to Contact: Submit demo tape by mail. Unsolicited submissions are okay. Prefers VHS videocassette with 4 songs. Reports in 3 weeks. "Please send a self-addressed, stamped padded envelope if you'd like the tape returned."
Music: Mostly pop, R&B. Works primarily with big name or semi-name performers, soloists and dance bands. Current acts include Coasters, Shirelles and Tokens (oldies acts); and soloists (opening acts for big names).
Tips: "VHS video is the BEST piece of promo material to submit. Do not call."

*OVERTON LEE MANAGEMENT, 10051 Greenleaf, Santa Fe Springs CA 90670. (213)946-3193. President: Overton Lee. Management firm, music publisher (Boggy Depot/BMI) and record company (O.L. Records and New Act Records). Estab. 1980. Represents local and international individual artists, groups and songwriters; currently handles 5 acts. Receives 20% commission. Reviews material for acts.
How to Contact: Submit demo tape by mail. Unsolicited submission okay. Prefers cassette with 1-3 songs and lyric sheet. SASE. Reports in 3 months.
Music: Mostly country, gospel and rock & roll. Current acts include Touch of Country, Marcy Carr and Beau Dean.

DAVID LEFKOWITZ TALENT, 3470 Nineteenth St., San Francisco CA 94110. (415)777-1715. Contact: David Lefkowitz. Management firm and booking agency. Represents individual artists, groups and songwriters from nothern California; currently handles 5 acts. Receives 10-20% commission. Reviews material for acts.

How to Contact: Prefers cassette with 3-5 songs and lyric sheet. Does not return unsolicited material. Reports in 3 weeks.
Music: Mostly Alternative music, rock, pop and R&B. Works with modern rock bands. Represents Capture the Flag (modern rock band), Limbomaniacs (funk/rock band) and Primus (funk/thrash band).

*LEGION ARTISTS, 38 Music Sq. East, Nashville TN 37203. (615)255-8005. Agents: Joe Silver and Tommy Loomas. Management firm, booking agency. Estab. 1986. Represents individual artists and groups. Deals with artists from anywhere. Currently handles 5 acts. Receives 15-25% commission. Review material for acts.
How to Contact: Write first and obtain permission to submit. Prefers cassette or VHS videocassette with 3 songs and lyric sheets. Reports in 6 weeks.
Music: Interested in country, pop and rock. Represents Joe Silver (comedian), Bobby Lee Morgan (rock singer), and Fleming McWilliams (pop singer).
Tips: "Send the best work you have."

*LEMON SQUARE MUSIC, Box 671008, Dallas TX 75367-8008. (214)750-0720. Contact: Bart Barton. Production company. Represents artists, groups and songwriters; currently handles 7 acts. Reviews material for acts.
How to Contact: Query by mail, then submit demo tape. Prefers cassette with 2-4 songs. SASE. Reports in 1 month.
Music: Country and gospel. Works primarily with show bands. Current acts include Dania Presley (country), Freed (progressive country artist), Craig Solieau (comedy act), Audie Henry (progressive country singer), Susie Calvin (country), Billy Parker (traditional country) and Bev Marie (traditional country).

*LEROI AND ASSOCIATES, 104 Chapin Pkwy., Buffalo NY 14209. (916)884-6192. Secretary: Camille Hudson. Management firm. Estab. 1985. Represents individual artists and groups. Deals with artists from anywhere. Currently handles 3 acts. Receives 10-20% commission.
How To Contact: Submit demo tape by mail. Unsolicited submissions are OK. Prefers cassette with 4 songs. Does not return unsolicited material. Reports in 1 month.
Music: R&B and pop. Works mainly with vocalists. Current acts include Rick James, Val Young and Mary Jane Girls.

THE LET US ENTERTAIN YOU CO., 900 19th Ave. S., Suite 204, Nashville TN 37212-2125. (615)321-3100. Administrative Assistants: Carrie or Craig. Management firm, booking agency and music publisher (ASCAP/SESAC/BMI). Estab. 1968. Represents groups and songwriters; currently handles 50-60 acts. Receives 15% commission. Reviews material for acts.
How to Contact: Prefers cassette or videocassette and lyric sheet. Does not return unsolicited material.
Music: Mostly country, pop, R&B; also rock and new music. Works with all types of artists/groups/ songwriters. Current acts include C.N. Double (showband), Wizzards (dance/show band) and Boystowne (dance/rock).

LEVINSON ENTERTAINMENT VENTURES INTERNATIONAL, INC., Suite 650, 1440 Veteran Avenue, Los Angeles CA 90024. (213)460-4545. President: Bob Levinson. Management firm. Estab. 1978. Represents national individual artists, groups and songwriters; currently handles 6 acts. Receives 15-20% commission.
How to Contact: Write first and obtain permission to submit or to arrange personal interview. Prefers cassette (or VHS videocassette) with 6 songs and lead sheet. "Inquire first. Don't expect video to be returned unless SASE included with submission and specific request made." Does not return unsolicited material. Reports in 1 month.
Music: Rock, MOR, R&B and country. Works primarily with rock bands and vocalists.
Tips: "Should be a working band, self-contained and, preferably, performing own original material."

LIFE MUSIC MINISTRIES, INC., Box 302, Keystone Heights FL 32656. (904)473-4182 and (904)661-2678. Vice President: Penny Parker Dewberry. Management firm (gospel concerts) and music publisher (Life Music Ministries, Inc./BMI), record company (The Warehouse Recording Studio of Jacksonville, Florida) and record producer (Life Music Ministries, Inc.). Estab. 1983. Represents songwriters and musicians. Currently handles 6 acts. Receives 10-25% commission. Reviews material for acts, or available on consultant basis.
How to Contact: Write first and obtain permission to submit. Prefers cassette with minimum of 3 songs and lyric or lead sheets. SASE. Does not return unsolicited material. Reports "as soon as possible—depends on our workload."

Music: Gospel (contemporary or traditional). Works with gospel artists, gospel groups and gospel instrumental/vocal groups. Current acts include Jazz for Jesus (concert group, vocals/piano,bass, varied added instruments), Bill Chase (gospel songwriter), Matt Roy (Christian vocalist), Dean Dewberry (songwriter/vocalist/pianist), Penny Parker Dewberry (lyricist/keyboard bass/vocalist) and Karen Ruth Mosher/Johnson (gospel songwriter).
Tips: "The only time you fail is when you stop trying."

LINE-UP PROMOTIONS, INC., 9A, Tankerville Place, Newcastle-Upon-Tyne NE2 3AT **United Kingdom**. Phone: (091)2816449. FAX: 091-261-9745. Director: C.A. Murtagh. Management firm, booking agency, record company (On-Line Records), music publisher (On Line Records & Publishing) and record producer. Represents individual artists, groups and songwriters; currently handles 6-8 acts. Receives 15% commission. Reviews material for acts.
How to Contact: Prefers cassette (or videocassette) and lyric sheet. "Send full press kit, commitments and objective." Does not return unsolicited material. Reports in 1 month. "We're looking for professional acts who can entertain in city centres and unusual situations; e.g., tea dances, supermarkets, metro stations and traditional venues."
Music: Mostly acoustic pop, rock, new world, Afro and reggae. Works primarily with original groups (not MOR). Current acts include Moonlight Drive (rock), Fan Heater (post punk/new wave/psychedelic), Swimming Pool (fine art rock), Royal Family (post punk exploitative), Leg Theory (rock/pop), APU (Andean music) and The Light Programme (swing jazz).

LMP MANAGEMENT FIRM, Suite 206, 6245 Bristol Pkwy., Culver City CA 90230. Contact: Larry McGee. Management firm, music publisher (Operation Perfection, Inc.) and record company (Boogie Band Records Corp.). Represents individual artists, groups and songwriters; currently handles 36 acts. Receives 10-15% commission. Reviews material for acts.
How to Contact: Prefers cassette (or videocassette) with 1-4 songs and lead sheet. "Try to perform one or more of your songs on a local TV show. Then obtain a copy of your performance. Please only send professional quality material. Keep it simple and basic." Does not return unsolicited material. Reports in 2 months.
Music: Mostly pop-oriented R&B; also rock and MOR/adult contemporary. Works with vocalists and high energy self-contained groups with unique images with choreographed performances. "Current acts include Sheena-Kriss (self-contained band), Bill Sawyer (vocalist) and Allen Brothers (self-contained band).
Tips: "Do research on current commercial marketplace. Take the necessary steps, time, talent and money to present a professional product."

LOCONTO PRODUCTIONS, 10244 NW 47 St., Sunrise FL 33351. (305)741-7766. Contact: Phyllis Finney Loconto. Management firm. Estab. 1978. Represents 3 clients. Receives 5% commission. Reviews material for acts.
How to Contact: Prefers cassette with maximum 3 songs. "We are looking primarily for country artists and songs with strong hooks and crossover potential." SASE. Reports in 1 month.
Music: All types, including dance music, Latin and country; also bluegrass, children's, church/religious, country, easy listening, folk, gospel, MOR, and top 40/pop. Works primarily with country vocalists, country bands, MOR vocalists and bluegrass artists. Current acts include Bill Dillon, Rob Mellor, Jennifer Geiget, The Lane Brothers and Frank X. Loconto.
Tips: "Material must be 'top shelf.'"

LOGAN-GREGORY AND ASSOCIATES, 8404 Troubador Way, Chattanooga TN 37363. Road Manager: Blake Wilde. Private corporation. Estab. 1980. Represents only one act, Con Hurley. Receives 10% commission. Reviews material for acts.
How to Contact: Submit demo tape by mail. Unsolicited submissions are okay. Prefers cassette with 4 songs and lyric sheets. SASE. Reports in 1 month.
Music: Mostly country and R&B; also contemporary blues.
Tips: "We are only interested in material for Con Hunley, who has 5 albums with Warner Bros., MCA and Capitol. Listen to any of these and check out his style. He is a very strong singer and it will be worth your trouble if the song or songs are accepted."

LONDON MANAGEMENT, Regent House, 235/241 Regent Street, W1A2JT London **England**. Phone: (01)493-1610. Executive Booker: Phil Dale. Management firm and booking agency. Represents individual artists, groups, songwriters and comedy artists; currently handles "hundreds of acts." Receives 15-25% commission. Reviews material for acts.
How to Contact: Write first and obtain permission to submit. Prefers cassette (or VHS [British] videocassette). SAE and IRC. Reports in 3 months.
Music: Mostly blues, pop, MOR and rock. Works primarily with pop, rock, bar and house bands and concert acts. Current acts include "many top names."

*TOMMY LOOMAS, 38 Music Sq. E., Nashville TN 37203. (615)255-8005. Agent: Glen Horsley. Management firm. Estab. 1975. Represents individual artists and groups. Deals with artists from anywhere. Currently handles 3 acts. Receives 15-25% commission. Reviews material for acts.
How to Contact: Write first and obtain permission to submit. Prefers cassette (or VHS videocassette if possible). Does not return unsolicited material. Reports in 6 weeks.
Music: Country, rock and pop. Works most often with vocalists. Current acts include Joe Silver (comedian), Bobby Lee Morgan and Fleming McWilliams.

JEFFREY LOSEFF MANAGEMENT, Suite 205, 4521 Colfax Ave., N. Hollywood CA 91602. (818)505-9468. President: Jeffrey C. Loseff. Management firm. Represents local individual artists; currently handles 5 acts. Receives 15% commission. Reviews material for acts.
How to Contact: Write or call first and obtain permission to submit. Prefers cassette (or VHS videocassette) with 3 or more songs and lead sheet. SASE. Reports in 6 weeks.
Music: Mostly pop, jazz, cabaret, light rock; also blues. Works primarily with film and TV composers. Current acts include Sarah Coley (jazz vocalist), Bill Payne Duo (jazz instrumental) and Hayden Wayne (film, stage TV scoring).
Tips: "Have an ear for the public and present unique material."

*LOWELL AGENCY, 1556 2nd St., Cuyahoga Falls OH 44221. (216)928-1166. Contact: Leon Seiter. Booking agency. Estab. 1985. Represents regional (Midwest and Southeast) individual artists; currently handles 3 acts. Receives 10% commission. Reviews material for acts.
How to Contact: Submit demo tape by mail. Unsolicited submissions are okay. Prefers cassette with 4 songs and lyric sheet. SASE. Reports in 1 month.
Music: Mostly country. Works primarily with country vocalists. Current acts include Leon Seiter (country singer/entertainer/songwriter), Ford Nix (Bluegrass singer and 5 string banjo picker) and Tom Durden (country singer, co-writer of "Heartbreak Hotel").

RICHARD LUTZ ENTERTAINMENT AGENCY, 5625 0 St., Lincoln NE 68510. (402)483-2241. General Manager: Cherie Worley. Management firm and booking agency. Estab. 1964. Represents individuals and groups; currently handles 200 acts. Receives 15-20% minimum commission.
How to Contact: Query by phone. Prefers cassette (or videocassette) with 5-10 songs "to show style and versatility" and lead sheet. "Send photo, resume, tape, partial song list and include references. Add comedy, conversation, etc., to your videocassette. Do not play songs in full—short versions preferred." SASE. Reports in 1 week.
Music: Mostly top 40 and country; also dance-oriented and MOR. Works primarily with bar and dance bands for lounge circuit. "Acts must be uniformed." Current acts include Rainbow Express (variety) Debbie Fry (country) and Mark Selby & Sluggers (blues/jazz).

*M & M TALENT AGENCY INC., 146 Round Pond Lane, Rochester NY 14662. (716)723-0514. Contact: Carl Labate. Management firm, booking agency and record producer. Represents artists and groups; currently handles 5 acts. Receives 20% commission. Reviews material for acts.
How to Contact: Prefers cassette (or VHS or Beta videocassette) with minimum 3 songs and lyric sheet. May send video if available; "a still photo would be good enough to see the type of performance; if you are a performer, it would be advantageous to show yourself or the group performing live. Theme videos are not helpful." SASE. Reports in 3 weeks.
Music: Mostly top 40; also dance, rock and R&B. Works primarily with show bands, dance bands and barbands; also vocalists, and recording artists. Current acts include What's Up (top 40 dance), Margaret Wilson (R&B), Chesterfield Kings (new music/rock) and Zoot Suit (40s show).
Tips: "We seek serious people willing to work and take direction."

KEVIN MABRY ENTERPRIZES, 8 E. State, Milford Center OH 43045. (513)349-2971. Owner/Artist: Kevin Mabry. Management firm and booking agency. Represents local and regional artists, groups and songwriters; currently handles 1 act. Receives 10-15% commission. Reviews material for acts.
How to Contact: Prefers cassette or 7½ ips reel-to-reel with 4 songs and lyric sheet. Does not return unsolicited material.
Music: "Positive" country, contemporary Christian and MOR/pop. Works primarily with show bands, vocalists, country groups and contemporary Christian acts. Current acts include Kevin Mabry, Kevin Mabry & Liberty Street and Shenandoah V (variety).
Tips: "I'm looking for positive country songs with good message—mostly up-tempo. Also great contemporary Christian songs. Positive material is in demand."

MCFADDEN ARTIST CORPORATION, 818 18th Ave. S., Nashville TN 37203. (615)242-1500. Chairman: Jack McFadden. Management firm and music publisher (Music General Corp.). Represents individual artists and groups; currently handles 12 acts. Reviews material for acts.

How to Contact: Prefers cassette with 3-4 songs and lyric sheet. Does not return unsolicited material. Reports as soon as possible.
Music: Mostly country, country rock and pop/black. Current acts include Buck Owens, Lorrie Morgan, David Frizzell, Dean Dillon, Gene Watson, Ken Meeker, Jessie McQueen, Marty Haggard and Billy Ray Cyrus.

MAGIC MANAGEMENT AND PRODUCTIONS, 178-49 131st Ave., Jamaica, NY 11434. (212)978-3600. General Manager: Bryan P. Sanders. Management firm, booking agency and concert productions firm. Estab. 1987. Represents regional (New York tri-state) individual artists, groups and disc jockeys; currently handles 9 acts. Receives 15-20% commission. Reviews material for acts.
How to Contact: Write first and obtain permission to submit. Prefers cassette (or VHS videocassette) with minimum of 2 songs and lyric sheet. SASE. Reports in 2½ weeks.
Music: Mostly R&B, "Crossover Club Music" and rap; also "club DJ mixes," gospel and jazz. Works primarily with dance bands, vocalists, disk jockeys. Current acts include Perry Mason (rap songwriter), Big City Band/Mark Adams (R&B songwriter) and Supreme K/Kenneth Atwood (rap songwriter).
Tips: "Keep in mind that it's not necessarily the size of the company but what that company can do for you that makes the difference."

*MAGNUM MUSIC CORPORATION LTD., 8607-128 Avenue, Edmonton Alberta **Canada** T5E 0G3. (403)476-8230. Manager: Bill Maxim. Booking agency, music publisher (Ramblin' Man Music Publishing/PRO) and record company (Magnum Records). Estab. 1984. Represents international individual artists, groups and songwriters; currently handles 3 acts. Reviews material for acts.
How to Contact: Write first and obtain permission to submit. Prefers cassette with 3-4 songs. Does not return unsolicited material. Reports in 1 month.
Music: Mostly country and gospel. Works primarily with "artists or groups who are also songwriters." Current acts include Catheryne Greenly (country), Billy Jay (country) and Cormier Country (country).
Tips: "Prefers finished demos."

*MAINE-LY COUNTRY MUSIC, 212 Stillwater Ave., Old Town ME 04468. (207)827-2185. Owner/Manager: Jeff Simon. Booking agency, music publisher (Maine-ly Music/BMI, Maine-ly Country Music/SESAC) and record company (Maine-ly Country Records). Estab. 1988. Represents international individual artists, groups and songwriters; currently handles 2 acts. Receives 15-25% commission. Reviews material for acts.
How to Contact: Submit demo tape by mail. Unsolicited submissions are okay. Prefers cassette (or VHS videocassette) with 3-5 songs and lyric or lead sheet. SASE. Reports in 6 weeks.
Music: Mostly country-country rock, pop and gospel. Works primarily with country-country rock vocalists and dance bands. Current acts include Jeff Simon (vocalist/songwriter), Maine-ly Country (country-country rock band) and Allison Ames (vocalist/songwriter).
Tips: "Send demos, bio, picture, or videos (VHS format), think positively and be prepared to work."

MAINSTAGE MANAGEMENT INTERNATIONAL, INC., 22 Sprindrift Way, Annapolis MD 21403. (301)268-5596. Executive Vice President: Paul Bartz. Management firm and booking agency. Represents individual artists and groups; currently handles 24 acts. Receives 20% commission. Reviews material for acts.
How to Contact: Prefers cassette (or VHS videocassette) and lyric sheet. SASE. Reports in 1 month.
Music: Pop and MOR. Works primarily with vocalists. Current acts include Petula Clark.
Tips: "Please do not continually call to assess status of tapes."

*MAJESTIC PRODUCTIONS, P.O. Box 330-568, Brooklyn NY 11233-0016. (718)919-2013. President: Half Pint. Management firm and record company (Majestic Control Records). Estab. 1983. Represents international individual artists and groups; currently handles 4 acts. Reviews material for acts.
How to Contact: Write. Prefers cassette (or VHS videocassette) with 2 songs. SASE. Reports in 2 months.
Music: Mostly rap, urban and hip-house. Current acts include rap groups, solo artists and urban dance groups).

MAKOUL PRODUCTIONS, 1449 Hamilton St., Allentown PA 18102. (215)821-0906. Executive Producer: Tom Makoul. Management firm and concert producers. Estab. 1975. Represents local, regional and international individual artists and groups. Receives 15-25% commission. Reviews material for acts.
How to Contact: Submit demo tape by mail. Unsolicited submissions are okay. Prefers cassette (or ½″ VHS videocassette). SASE. Reports in 2 weeks.
Music: Mostly rock and pop. Works primarily with individual artists and album-oriented rock groups.
Tips: "Have material that is commercially viable and will fit into today's CHR and AOR formats."

DAVID MALDONADO MANAGEMENT, Suite 703, 1674 Broadway, New York NY 10019. (212)247-6888. Vice President, A&R: Juan Toro. Represents individual artists and groups; currently handles 9 acts. Pays 25% commission. Reviews material for acts.
How to Contact: Prefers cassette and lyric sheet. Does not return unsolicited material. Reports in 3 weeks.
Music: Mostly pop, pop/rock and light metal (glam-rock); also dance/pop. Works primarily with vocalists. Current acts include Ruben Blades (rock), Chrissy I-Eece (pop/dance), Marc Anthony (pop/dance), Menudo (pop rock) and Sa-Fire (dance).

ED MALHOIT AGENCY, Box 2001, Claremont NH 03743. (603)542-9494 or 542-8777. Agent: Ed Malhoit. Management firm and booking agency. Represents groups in eastern US; currently handles 16 acts. Receives 10-20% commission. Reviews material for acts.
How to Contact: Write first. Prefers cassette (or VHS videocassette) with minimum 5 songs. SASE. Reports in 1 month.
Music: Rock, show, dance and bar bands. Current acts include The Voice, 8084, Al Alessi Band and Skyler (all rock concert/club acts.)

MANAGEMENT VII, 1811 NE. 53rd St., Ft. Lauderdale FL 33308. (305)776-1004. Contact: Vic and Romona Beri. Management firm. Represents artists, groups and songwriters; currently handles 5 acts. Receives 10-20% commission. Reviews material for acts.
How to Contact: Prefers cassette with 3-10 songs and lyric sheet. SASE. Reports in 1 month.
Music: Country, crossover, and top 40/pop. Current acts include Dan Riley (country/pop/comedy guitar), Rain "Tribute to the Beatles" (Beatles type music), Frank Gorshin (impressionist) and Marsh & Adams (comedy team).

RICK MARTIN PRODUCTIONS, 125 Fieldpoint Road, Greenwich CT 06830. (203)661-1615. President: Rick Martin. Personal manager and independent producer. "Office of Secretary of the National Conference of Personal Managers." Represents groups, artists/songwriters, actresses/vocalists, and comedians/vocalists. Currently handles 7 acts. Receives 15-25% commission. "Occasionally, we are hired as consultants, production assistants or producers of recording projects." Reviews material for acts.
How to Contact: Prefers cassette (or VHS videocassette) with 2-4 songs. "Don't worry about an expensive presentation to personal managers or producers; they'll make it professional if they get involved." Artists should enclose a photo. SASE. "We prefer serious individuals who represent themselves professionally. You may call for report 10 days after submission."
Music: Mostly top 40, rock and dance; also easy listening and pop. Produces rock dance groups, female vocalists, songwriters and actress/vocalists (pop). Current acts include Babe (all female revue – top 40), Marisa Mercedes (vocalist/pianist/songwriter), Sabel (actress/vocalist), Robert Gordon (artist/songwriter), Robert and Steven Capellar and Festible (Caribbean Revue).
Tips: "Don't spend a lot of money on recordings, but be prepared to have some financial backing if attempting to be an artist. Depend on yourself for everything including, most importantly, creativity. Present material in the simplest way."

*MASTER TALENT, Suite D, 407 Church St., Vienna VA 22180. (703)281-2800. Owner/Agent: Steve Forssell. Booking agency. Estab. 1989. Represents local and regional (Northeast/Midwest) individual artists and groups; currently handles 4 acts. Receives 10-20% commission.
How to Contact: Write or call first and obtain permission to submit. Prefers cassette (or VHS/BETA videocassette) with 4+ songs and lyric or lead sheet. SASE. Reports in 2 weeks.
Music: Mostly hard rock/metal, progressive/alternative and R&B/dance; also variety/covers. Works primarily with hard rock groups. Current acts include Fraidy Cat (pop metal), Rob Wolf (hard pop) and D.T. & the Shakes (progressive/garage).
Tips: "Submit only best work when it's *ready*. We're looking for professionally managed groups/ artists with good publicist/promotion. Product in market is a plus."

*PHIL MAYO & COMPANY, P.O. Box 304, Bomoseen VT 05732. (802)468-5011. President: Phil Mayo. Management firm and record company (Thrust Records). Estab. 1981. Represents international individual artists, groups and songwriters. Receives 20% commission.
How to Contact: Submit demo tape by mail. Unsolicited submissions are okay. Prefers cassette (or VHS videocassette) with 3 songs and lyric or lead sheet. SASE.
Music: Mostly rock, pop and R&B; also gospel. Works primarily with dance bands, vocalists, rock acts.

*MC PROMOTIONS & PUBLIC RELATIONS, 8504 Willis Ave. #6, Panorama City CA 91402. (818)892-1741. Promotes local country artists. Receives 10% commission. Reviews material for acts.
How to Contact: Submit demo tape by mail. Unsolicited submissions are okay. Prefers cassette (or videocassette). SASE. Reports in 3 weeks.
Music: Mostly country. Works primarily with vocalists. Current acts include Diana Blair (singer/songwriter) and Dawna Kay (singer/songwriter).

*MEAN GREEN MANAGEMENT (ARTIST MANAGEMENT), Suite 260, 202 So. Lake Ave., Pasadena CA 91101. (818)584-0499. Manager: Mikel Hooks. Management firm. Estab. 1976. Represents international individual artists and groups; currently handles 3 acts. Receives 25% commission.
How to Contact: Submit demo tape by mail. Unsolicited submissions are okay. Prefers cassette (or VHS videocassette live or edited) with 6 songs and lead sheet. Does not return unsolicited material. Reports in 2 weeks.
Music: Mostly rap, R&B and pop; also rock, country and gospel. "We work most often with self-contained/dance bands; 5-7 piece bands." Current acts include Fast Forward (dance band), King T.L. Kor (rap) and UBK (rap).
Tips: "Submit only finished demos; only on 24 tracks (no 16 tracks). 5 to 6 tunes, picture and autobiography."

ALEX MELLON MANAGEMENT, Box 614, New Kensington PA 15068. (412)335-5152. President: Alex Mellon. Estab. 1978. Represents individual artists, groups and songwriters; currently handles 3 acts. Receives 20% commission. Reviews material for acts.
How to Contact: Prefers cassette with 3-4 songs and lyric sheet. Does not return unsolicited material. Reports in 3 weeks.
Music: Mostly pop, rock and country. Works primarily with pop acts and songwriters. Current acts include Shilly Shally (pop act), Modern Times (jazz band) and Stan Xidas (songwriter).

MENES LAW CORP., Suite 1600, 1901 Avenue of the Stars, Los Angeles CA 90067. (213)277-4895. Directors: Barry Menes and Paul I. Menes. Law firm handling business affairs and some limited management. Estab. 1982. Represents record companies, artists, groups, songwriters, video companies, agencies, personal managers and some publishing companies; currently handles over 100 acts. "Mostly paid by the hour, but on rare occasion we'll accept contingency over guarantee." Reviews materials for acts.
How to Contact: Prefers cassette (or short videocassette). Include biography. SASE. Reports in 1 month.
Music: Anything contemporary. Works primarily with individuals and bands with original materials.

GREG MENZA & ASSOCIATES, P.O. Box 7558, Marietta GA 30062-7558. (404)427-5335. FAX: 404-590-ROCK. Director: Greg Menza. Management firm, booking agency and concert producers. Represents artists, groups and songwriters; currently handles 20 acts. Receives 15-20% commission. Reviews material for acts.
How to Contact: Query by mail. Prefers cassette (or VHS videocassette) with 3-6 songs. "Professional quality only." Reports in at least 1 month. "Include SASE if you wish material returned. Send only high quality finished demos."
Music: Gospel, rock and country, "contemporary Christian rock bands and clean cut positive secular acts." Works primarily with contemporary Christian rock artists. Current acts include Larry Howard & The Sanctified Blues Band, Jerome Olds, Tami Gunden, DeGarmo & Key, DC Talk, The Newsboys, Whitecross, Jacob's Trouble, Rick Cua, Fred "Rerun" Berry, Pendleton Brown, Zion, Sacred Warrior and David Teems.

*METROPOLITAN TALENT AUTHORITY, 109 Earle Ave., Lynbrook NY 11563. (516)599-4157. President: J.C.. Management firm and consultants. Estab. 1985. Represents local and international individual artists, groups and songwriters; currently handles 1 act. Receives 15-25% commission. Reviews material for acts.
How to Contact: Submit demo tape by mail. Unsolicited submissions are okay. Prefers cassette and lyric sheet. SASE. Reports in 4-5 weeks.
Music: Mostly rock, nu-music and pop/rock/dance; also R&B, rap and hard rock. Works primarily with bands, songwriters, producers. Current acts include The Way Moves (Nu-music).
Tips: "We want quality artists with originality, vision and distinctive lead vocal. Imaginative—intelligent lyrics, memorable hooks and melodies. Also, artists must look great, present themselves well and have a positive image through their music and look."

MID-EAST ENTERTAINMENT INC., Suite 200, 553 S. Limestone, Lexington KY 40508. (606)254-3327. Agent: Robert Moser. Represents artists and groups; currently handles over 300 acts. Receives 10-20% commission. Reviews material for acts.

How to Contact: Prefers cassette with 3-6 songs, photo and songlist. Songs should have 1 verse, 1 bridge and 1 chorus. SASE. Reports in 1 month.

Music: Mostly top 40 and R&B; also country, dance-oriented, easy listening, jazz, rock, soul and pop. Works primarily with dance bands. Current acts include Paradox (top 40/rock), The Sensations (top 40/classics), Duos (top 40/oldies), Custom Sounds (variety), Hawkeye (50's-80's dance), City Heat (top 40/classics) and Nervous Melvin (college rock).

MIDNIGHT LIFE ASSOCIATES, Suite 271, 328 Flatbush Ave., Brooklyn NY 11238. (718)604-9435. General Partner: Christopher R. Owens. Management and consulting firm. Represents individual artists and groups; currently handles 4 acts. Receives negotiable commission. Reviews material for acts and one label (Black Moon Records, Inc.).

How to Contact: Prefers cassette (or VHS videocassette) and lyric sheet. SASE. Comments within 10 months.

Music: R&B, rap, pop, rock and blues. Works primarily with original-oriented groups with "interesting or danceable" material & pop vocalists with innovative styles. Affiliated with independent rap label (Black Moon Records, Inc.), and reviews material for that label.

THE GILBERT MILLER AGENCY, INC., Suite 243, 21243 Ventura Blvd., Woodland Hills CA 91364. (818)888-6363. Agent: Jeff Miller. Booking agency. Represents musical and variety/novelty acts; currently handles 2 bands. Receives 15% commission. Reviews material for acts.

How to Contact: Prefers record, CD or cassette on a record label, 8x10 photo. "MTV-quality videos accepted. Will only call if song or group is accepted. Accepted groups will be notified in 2 weeks. No kits will be returned."

Music: Mostly rock. Works primarily with heavy metal hard rock, new wave, nostalgia rock and new age groups. Current acts include Eric Bordon and Robby Krieger (classic rock), Axe, Retaliation, Terriff (heavy metal) and Perfect Stranger (new wave).

*MKM MUSIC PRODUCTIONS LTD., 703, 141 Somerset St. W., Ottowa, Ontario K2P 2H1 **Canada.** (613)234-5419. President: Michael Mitchell. Management firm. SOCAN (PROCAN and CAPAC). Estab.1982. Represents individual artists. Deals with Canadian artists. Currently handles 2 acts. Receives 20% commission. Review material for acts.

How to Contact: Submit demo tape by mail. Unsolicited submissions are OK. Prefers cassette with 3 songs and lyric sheet. SASE. Reports in 3 weeks.

Music: Folk and pop. Works with concert folk groups. Current acts include The Michael Mitchell Band and Joan MacIsaac.

MOMENTUM MANAGEMENT, 4859-D Jackson St., Riverside CA 92503. (714)351-1227. Professional Manager: Sterling Pounds. Management firm. Estab. 1988. Represents local groups; currently handles 2 acts. Receives 10-20% commission. Reviews material for acts. Specializes in professional development.

How to Contact: Prefers cassette or 7½ ips reel-to-reel (or VHS videocassette) with 3-4 songs and lyric sheets. May submit albums, EP, 12″ singles, etc. SASE. Retains all material for future reference.

Music: Mostly rock, pop and modern rock; also anything unique. Works primarily with local bands (mostly new talent). Current acts include The Feel (pop/rock) and The Remnant (pop/rock).

Tips: "Honesty works best. Artists shouldn't submit unless they are ready to hear the truth about their work."

MOONSTONE MUSIC LTD., 1 Winsford House, Luxborough Street, London W1M 3LD **United Kingdom.** Phone: (01)486-8491. FAX: (01)224-0423. Managing Director: Nicholas Webb. Music publisher (Moonstone Music/PRS-UK, ASCAP—US). Estab. 1982-83. Represents songwriters; currently handles 6 acts. Receives 20-50% commission. Reviews material for acts.

How to Contact: Prefers cassette (or videocassette if available) with 3-5 songs. "Moonstone only returns material if interested."

Music: Mostly new age, jazz/instrumental, rock; also acoustic guitar music. Current acts include Acoustic Alchemy (new age band), John Parsons (writer/producer/artist) and Nick Webb (writer/artist).

Tips: "We are looking for truly original material—well played and arranged."

MOORE ENTERTAINMENT GROUP, 11 Possum Trail, Saddle River NJ 07458. (201)327-3698. President: Barbara Moore. Estab. 1984. Represents individual artists and groups; currently handles 5 acts. Receives 10% commission. Reviews material for acts.

How to Contact: Prefers cassette (or videocassete if available) and lyric sheet. "Include photo and bio." SASE. Reports in 3 weeks.
Music: Mostly dance, rock, R&B and pop. Works primarily with vocalists. Current acts include Kerry Clark (rock/pop), Robin Trapp (dance music), Katani (R&B); Cheree (dance), Eddie Skuller (pop/rock), Lou Taylor (pop/rock) and Maria Brancassio (pop/dance).

DALE MORRIS AND ASSOCIATES, 818 19th Ave., S., Nashville TN 37203. (615)327-3400. Booking Agent: Barbara Hardin. Booking agency. Represents "Alabama."
How to Contact: Write first for submission policy.

MORRIS AND BRADLEY MANAGEMENT, #207, 50 Music Square W., Nashville TN 37203. (615)329-2593. Management firm and record company (Maxx Records). Estab. 1987. Represents individual artists and groups; currently handles 10 acts. Receives 20% commission. Reviews material for acts.
How to Contact: Prefers cassette (or VHS videocassette) with 3 songs and lyric sheet. Please submit SASE for returns. Does not return unsolicited material. Reports in 1 month.
Music: Mostly traditional country and country/rock; also R&B and pop. Works primarily with vocalists and groups. Current acts include Jill Jordan (country/MOR), Richard Fagan (country singer/songwriter) and Don Juan (country/MOR).
Tips: "Submit a clear cassette tape, a photo and brief bio."

*MOZART MIDNIGHT PRODUCTIONS, Suite 632-E, 410 S. Michigan Ave., Chicago IL 60605. (312)477-6644. President: Don Kaufman. Management firm. Estab. 1982. Represents international individual artists, groups and songwriters; currently handles 6 acts. Receives 20-25% commission. Reviews material for acts.
How to Contact: Submit demo tape by mail. Unsolicited submissions are okay. Prefers cassette with 3-10 songs and lyric sheet. Does not return unsolicited material. Reports in 1 month.
Music: Mostly dance-pop, light rock and R&B; also metal, ballads and rap. Works primarily with singer/songwriters. Current acts include Kevin Irving (lead singer of Club Nouveau), Aponte (composer/producer and vocalist) and Darkside (rap group).

*MURPHY'S LAW ENTERTAINMENT GROUP LTD., 246-14 54th Ave., Queens NY 11362. (718)224-6480. Manager: Jack Flanagan. Management firm, booking agency (ASCAP) and record company (Profile Records). Estab. 1989. Represents international individual artists and groups; currently handles 3 acts. Reviews material for acts.
How to Contact: Submit demo tape by mail. Unsolicited submissions are okay. Prefers cassette with any number of songs. Does not return unsolicited material. Reports in 3 weeks.
Music: Mostly rock, R&B and pop; also rap and reggae. Works primarily with rock groups and rap acts. Current acts include Murphy's Law (rock), Shutdown (rap and Chopper (pop).
Tips: "Just send it!"

*MUSIC, MARKETING & PROMOTIONS, INC., P.O. Box 22, South Holland IL 60473. (708)862-4198. President: Michael Haines. Management firm. Estab. 1987. Represents international individual artists, groups and songwriters; currently handles 3 acts. Receives 15-20% commission. Reviews material for acts.
How to Contact: Write or call first and obtain permission to submit. Prefers cassette (VHS videocassette) with 3-4 songs and lyric sheet. SASE. Reports in 3 weeks.
Music: Mostly rock, country and pop; also R&B. Works primarily with pop/rock bands, solo artists and songwriters. Current acts include John Kontol (singer/songwriter), Rick Anthony (country songwriter) and Face of Luxury (pop band).
Tips: "Send clear demos. We're most interested in the song, not the production, but it must be audible."

MUSIC SERVICES OF AMERICA, 252 Mennonite Rd., Collegeville PA 19426. (215)489-4631. President: Jim Femino. Record company (Road Records). Fezsongs, publishing branch (ASCAP). Estab. 1970. Represents individual artists, groups and songwriters; currently handles 15 acts. Receives 15-20% commission. Reviews material for acts.
How to Contact: Prefers cassette (or videocassette) with 3 songs and lyric sheet. Does not return unsolicited material. Reports in 4 weeks.
Music: Mostly country, rock, pop. Works primarily with singer/songwriters and original bands, including metal. Current acts include Jim Femino (writer/artist), Dennis Secfrudge (singer/songwriter) and Manatees (original dance music).

*MUSIC STAR AGENCY, INC. (INTERNATIONAL HEADQUARTERS), 106 Main St., Binghamton NY 13905. (607)772-0857. Attn: Talent Coordinator. Booking agency with 87 international offices. Represents US and Canadian artists "to be marketed worldwide primarily in hotels, top 40/rock clubs or military installations; concert venues. Currently handles more than 900 acts. Receives 20% commission. Reviews material for acts. Submits material to buyers, recording companies, production companies and managers.
How to Contact: Prefers cassette (or VHS videocassette) with 5 songs "that most represent your act, along with current promo package. In preparing videos, quality audio and video must be maintained throughout the tape. Adequate lighting and professional audio and video engineers will help. Keep the clips short and visually exciting."
Music: Mostly top 40 lounge, top 40 country, top 40 rock and oldies. Works primarily with top 40 touring hotel acts from solo entertainers to show bands. Current acts include Boxtops, Beatlemania, Jay & The Techniques and Vogues (top 40 show bands).
Tips: "Professional quality promotional materials (photos, tape, songlist, equipment list) are essential to securing good engagements for any act. A business-like approach to the music business is also essential.

MUSKRAT PRODUCTIONS, INC., 44 N. Central Ave., Elmsford NY 10523. (914)592-3144. Contact: Bruce McNichols. Estab. 1970. Represents individuals and groups; currently represents 23 acts. Deals with artists in the New York City area. Reviews material for acts.
How to Contact: Write first. Prefers cassette (or short videocassette) with 3 songs minimum. SASE. Reports "only if interested."
Music: "We specialize in old-time jazz, dixieland and banjo music and shows;" also old time, nostalgia, country and jazz. Works primarily with dixieland, banjo/sing-along groups to play parties, Mexican mariachi bands and specialty acts for theme parties, dances, shows and conventions. Current acts include Smith Street Society Jazz Band (dixieland jazz), Your Father's Mustache (banjo sing-along), Roaring 20s Revue (show and dance band), and Harry Hepcat and the Boogie Woogie Band (50s rock revival).

FRANK NANOIA PRODUCTIONS AND MANAGEMENT, 1999 N. Sycamore Ave., Los Angeles CA 90068. (213)874-8725. President: Frank Nanoia. Management and production firm. Represents artists, groups and songwriters. Produces TV specials and concerts. Currently handles 10 acts. Receives 15-25% commission. Reviews material for acts.
How to Contact: Prefers 7½, 15 ips reel-to-reel or cassette (or videocassette) with 3-5 songs and lyric and lead sheets. "Professional quality please. Check sound quality as well." Does not return unsolicited material. Reports "only if material is above average. No phone calls please."
Music: Mostly R&B and dance, also top 40/pop, jazz fusion, country, easy listening, MOR, gospel and soul. Works primarily with vocalists and show and bar groups. Current acts include Marc Allen Trujillo (vocalist/songwriter); Paramour (R&B show group), and Gilberto Duron (recoring artist). Current productions include "The Golden Eagle Awards," The Caribbean Musical Festival, and "The Joffrey Ballet/CSU Awards."

NASH ANGELES INC., Box 363, Hendersonville TN 37077. (615)824-8845. Manager: Wilson Frazier. Management firm and music publisher (BMI). Represents individual artists, groups and songwriters; currently handles 1 act. Receives 25% commission. Reviews material for acts.
How to Contact: Prefers cassette (or videocassette) with lyric sheet. Does not return unsolicited material. Reports in 1 month.
Music: Mostly country-pop, AOR, country and pop; also rock. Works primarily with vocalists. Current act is Eddie Reasoner (singer/songwriter).

NASHVILLE INTERNATIONAL ENTERTAINMENT GROUP, 116 17th Ave. S., Nashville TN 37203. (615)244-5357. President: Reggie M. Churchwell. Management firm (Reggie M. Churchwell Artist Management), record company (Phoenix Records, Inc.) and music publisher (Four Seasons Music/ASCAP, Sir Winston Music/BMI). Represents individual artists and groups; currently handles 5 acts. Publishing done with writer on 50/50 basis.
How to Contact: *Write first and obtain permission to submit.* Prefers cassette with 2-3 songs and lyric or lead sheets. SASE. Reports in 3 weeks.
Music: Mostly country, pop and gospel. Works primarily with vocalists. Current acts include Bruce Bright, Sonny Shroyer (Enos on Dukes of Hazzard), Howard Lips, Charlie Lamb, CATFISH and the Delta Rhythm Kings, Casey Stephens, and Vic Rorrer.

*JACK NELSON & ASSOCIATES, 5800 Valley Oak Dr., Los Angeles CA 90068. (213)465-9905. Assistant: Shawn Brogan. Management firm. Estab. 1981. Represents local, regional or international individual artists, groups and songwriters; currently handles 6 acts. Receives 15% commission. Reviews material for acts.

How to Contact: Call first and obtain permission to submit. Prefers cassette (or videocassette if available) with 2-4 songs and lyric sheets. SASE. Reports in 1 month.
Music: Currents acts include Jeffrey Osborne, Marlon Jackson and Kathy Sledge.

NEVADA MUSIC PRESENTATIONS, (formerly Nevada Talent and Booking), % Ward Johns and Sabian Simpson, Suite 101, 550 E. Plumb Lane, Reno NV 89502. (702)827-3648. Management firm and booking agency. Estab. 1981. Represents artists, groups and songwriters; currently handles 6-12 acts. "We represent all types of music to record labels and booking/management firms throughout the world." Currently handles 12 acts. Receives "5% consultants fee." Reviews material for acts.
How to Contact: Query by mail, arrange personal interview or submit demo tape. Prefers cassette (or VHS or Beta videocassette) with 4-10 songs and lyric sheet. "It's important to have VHS or Beta tape and a professional 16-24 track demo. Also send pictures and printed resume."
Music: Mostly pop/rock and new wave; also country and all other types. Works primarily with show and dance bands: rock groups, original jazz artists and original rock/pop/soul/R&B artists. Current acts include Geary Hanley (country), Ron Shirrel (country), Robin Baxter (rock), Jessica Hart (rock), Larry Elliot (MOR/rock), Michael Stosic (pop), Michael Shiflett (pop) and Rich Chaney (pop/C&W).
Tips: "Send new material with strong hooks. Although it is not mandatory, a videocassette is a big help for an artists marketing potential. We've music mortgage brokers helping find financial opportunities for booking agencies, management firms, and record labels as our secondary income resources."

NEW ARTIST'S PRODUCTIONS, 131 Connecticut Ave., N. Bay Shore NY 11706. Professional Department: Jeannie G. Walker. Management firm, record company and music publisher. Represents individual artists, groups and songwriters; currently handles 45-60 acts. Receives 20% commission. Reviews material for acts.
How to Contact: Prefers cassette (or professionally prepared videocassette) and lyric sheet; prefers professional videos. SASE. Reports in 8 weeks.
Music: Mostly pop, country and easy listening; also rock, gospel and blues. Works primarily with vocalists and dance bands. Current acts include Rory Bennett (night club act), Cherokee (vocalist & dance band), Mindset (dance band) and Anjel (vocalist).
Tips: "New Artist's Productions will listen to all newcomers in the music field. We will evaluate and give an honest opinion of their songs and help them produce, arrange or market the songs we feel show potential."

THE NEW MUSIC TIMES, INC., Box 8573, Albany NY 12208. (518)438-4815. President: Jeri Goldstein. Management firm and music publisher. Estab. 1976. Represents individual artists and songwriters; currently handles 3 acts. Receives 15-20% commission. Reviews material for acts.
How to Contact: Write first and obtain permission to submit. Prefers cassette with no more than 3 songs and lyric or lead sheets. SASE. Reports in 6 weeks.
Music: Mostly country, blues and gospel; also rock-a-billy and country-rock. Works primarily with country/folk vocalists and country bands with national touring experience. Current writers include Robin and Linda Williams, Cathy Fink and Marcy Marxer (country/folk/children).
Tips: "Looking for individual songs, not artists, at this time."

NEW STARS ENTERTAINMENT AGENCY, "Foxhollow," West End, Nailsea Bristol BS19 2DB **United Kingdom.** Proprietor: David Rees. Management firm and booking agency. Estab. 1983. Represents individual artists, groups, songwriters, comedians and specialty acts—all types. Currently handles over 200 acts. Receives 12½-15% commission. Reviews material for acts.
How to Contact: "Songwriters write and ask type of material we are presently seeking." Prefers cassette with 3 songs and lyric sheet. SAE and IRC. Reports in 1 month.
Music: Mostly MOR, pop, 60s style, country and rock. Works primarily with vocal guitarists/keyboards, pop groups, pub/club acts, guitar or keyboard duos. Current acts include Legend (duo), Ocean (four-piece group), Ricky Ford & The Cyclones, Sunsets and Venerina.
Tips: "Our business is mainly at venues wanting artists who perform well-known covers. Original material can be introduced during an evening as a feature, and this is often an easy way of getting people to accept it, rather than the 'take it' or 'leave it' attitude."

NEWALL ARTISTS AGENCY, Box 3038, Palos Verdes CA 90274. FAX: (213)541-5594. President: Christopher Schotts. Management firm and booking agency. Estab. 1988. Represents local, regional and international individual artists, groups and songwriters. Receives up to 25% commission. Reviews material for acts.

How to Contact: Submit demo tape by mail. Unsolicited submissions are OK. Prefers cassette with 3 or more songs of "very best material" and lyric sheet. SASE. Reports in 3 weeks.
Music: "Self-contained bands, vocalists, self-contained creative bands for new markets—mostly anything that opens my ears—must be potent."
Tips: "The NAA is a franchised Agency with the American Federation of Musicians—we will get your material heard by the labels."

NORTHSTAR MANAGEMENT INC., 33532 Five Mile Rd., Livonia MI 48154. (313)427-6010. President: Angel Gomez. Management firm. Estab. 1979. Represents local and international individual artists, groups and songwriters; currently handles 4 acts. Receives 10-25% commission. Reviews material for acts.
How to Contact: Submit demo tape by mail. Unsolicited submissions are OK. Prefers cassette with 3-5 songs. SASE. Reports in 4 weeks.
Music: Mostly rock, pop and top 40; also metal. Works primarily with individual artists, groups (bar bands) and songwriters. Current acts include Zoom Club (new music), Billy the Kid (rock), Zandallen (Top-40) and Hunter Brucks (rock).
Tips: "Think about what you're sending. Are you proud? If so, send it!"

N2D, Box 121682, Nashville TN 37212-1682. Contact: Douglas Casmus. Management firm and publisher (Breezeway Publishing Companies). Represents artists, groups, songwriters and comedians; currently handles 2 acts. Reviews material for acts.
How to Contact: Prefers cassette with 2 songs and lyric sheet. Does not return material. Reports only if interested.
Music: Country, rock and comedy. Current acts include David Murphy and Johnny Cobb (rock). "We've had songs recorded by Julio Iglesias, Ray Charles, John Denver, John Conlee, Dobie Gray and more."
Tips: "Looking for great songs—any format! Also open to crazy and novelty material."

NUTMEG MANAGEMENT, 2049 Silas Deane Highway, Rocky Hill CT 06067. (203)529-6405. Contact: Keith Beccia. Management firm. Estab. 1984. Represents local, regional and international individual artists, groups and songwriters; currently handles 2 acts. Reviews material for acts.
How to Contact: Submit demo tape by mail. Unsolicited submissions are OK. Prefers cassette with 4-5 songs and lyric sheet. Does not return unsolicited material. Reports in 6 weeks.
Music: Mostly rock, pop and R&B. Works primarily with vocal groups. Current acts include Felix Cavaliere (songwriter/performer) and Mark Putorti (singer/songwriter).

OAK STREET MUSIC, 301-140 Bannatyne Ave., Winnipeg, Manitoba R3B 3C5 **Canada**. Phone: (204)957-0085; FAX: (204)943-3588. C.E.O.: Gilles Paquin. Record label and music publisher. Estab. 1987. Roster includes performers, songwriters and musicians; currently handles 9 acts. Unsolicited material is accepted. Sister company, Direction Four Management, heads up the artist management division.
How to Contact: Prefers cassette (or VHS videocassette) with maximum 4 songs and lyric or lead sheet. "Something which shows the artists capabilities—doesn't need to be fancy. Be *factual*." SASE please.
Music: Primarily a family entertainment label, with interest also in the pop/rock genres. Current acts include Fred Penner (children's entertainer), Al Simmons (new age vaudevillian), Norman Foote (singer, songwriter, puppeteer) and Jeffrey Hatcher and The Big Beat (roots rock and roll group).

ON THE LEVEL MUSIC!, Rd. 3, 195A Dean St., Oswego NY 13827. (607)687-2323. President: Fred Gage. Management firm and booking agency. Estab. 1971. Represents individual artists, groups and songwriters; currently handles 12 acts. Receives 15-25% commission. Reviews material for acts.
How to Contact: Prefers cassette (or VHS videocassette) with 4 songs and lyric or lead sheets. For video: "Full length not needed, short clips only." SASE. Reports in 1 month.
Music: Mostly rock, pop and gospel. Works primarily with rock groups ("arena size to bar bands"). Current acts include Second Chapter of Acts (Christian rock), Wendy Talbot (folk), Disciple (rock), Jamie Norathomas (folk/rock), Terry Talbot (folk/rock), Toymakers Dream (Broadway type) and Tayra Antolick (show rock).
Tips: "Be great not just good and be hungry to make it."

OPEN DOOR MANAGEMENT, Suite 365, 15327 Sunset Blvd., Pacific Palisades CA 90272. (213)459-2559. President: Bill Traut. Associates: Kit Thomas, Carol Neu. Management firm and production company (Open Door Management and Bill Trut Productions). Represents artists, groups and songwriters; currently handles 8 acts. Receives 20% commission. "We are sometimes paid $200/hour as

consultants, and we also package with the artist on a 50/50 basis from time to time." Reviews material for acts.
How to Contact: Prefers cassette with 1-4 songs (or videocassette with 2-3 songs). SASE "with enough postage." Reports in 3 months.
Music: New A/C. Jazz, New Age and acoustic singer/songwriters. Artists include Eliza Gilkyson (New A/C singer/songwriter, Gold Castle Records); Steve Kujala (classical/jazz/fusion flute, Sonic Edge Records); and Oregon (jazz, new age group, Epic Records); and The Greene String Quartet (classical, jazz, pop group, Virgin classics).
Tips: "Quality is important to us, both of the music and of the presentation. Send a current photo and your credits along with your demos."

OPERATION MUSIC ENTERPRISES, 1400 E. Court St., Ottumwa IA 52501. (515)682-8283. President: Nada C. Jones. Management firm and booking agency. Represents artists, groups and songwriters; currently handles 4 acts. Receives 15% commission. Reviews material for acts.
How to Contact: Prefers cassette (or VHS videocassette) and lyric sheet. "Keep material simple. Groups - use *only group* members - don't add extras. Artists should include references. SASE. Reports in 2 months.
Music: Mostly country; also blues. Works primarily with vocalists, and show and dance groups. Current acts include Reesa Kay Jones (country vocalist and recording artist), John Richards Show, Country Class, Prairie Fire and Larry Gillaspie, the Rocky Mountain White Water Band and White River Country (country/bluegrass).

*ORACLE ENTERTAINMENT, 225 Lafayette St., #1109, New York NY 10012. (212)925-9599. President: George Gilbert, Vice President: Walter Winnick. Management firm. Estab. 1988. Represents local, regional or international individual artists, groups and songwriters; currently handles 3 acts. Receives 15-20% commission. Reviews material for acts.
How to Contact: Submit demo tape by mail. Unsolicited submissions are okay. Prefers cassette (or VHS or ¾" videocassette) with any number of songs. SASE. Reports in several weeks (depends on how busy we are at that time period).
Music: Mostly rock, pop and metal. Works primarily with national rock bands. Current acts include Meat Loaf, Jack Bruce and Marchello.
Tips: Submit as much (and as big a variety of) music as possible.

OREGON MUSICAL ARTISTS, P.O. Box 122, Yamhill OR 97148. (503)662-3309. Contact: Michael D. LeClair. Management firm and production agency. Estab. 1982. Represents artists, groups and songwriters; currently handles 3 acts. Receives 10-25% commission. Reviews material for acts.
How to Contact: Prefers cassette with 3-10 songs and lyric sheet (or videocasette). Does not return unsolicited material. Reports in 1 month.
Music: Mostly top 40/pop and R&B; also blues, church/religous, country, dance, easy listening, gospel, jazz, MOR, progressive, hard and mellow rock and soul. Works primarily with writers and bar bands "with excellent vocalists." Current acts include The Hoyt Brothers (easy country ballads), Lee Garrett (songwriter) and Boomer Band (50's bar band).

*ORIGINAL PROJECTS UNLIMITED, INC., 36 West 3rd Ave., Denver CO 80223. (303)722-9653. President: Lauri Day-Workman. Management firm (Orignal Projects Unlimited, Inc.). Estab. 1986. Represents international groups and producers/engineers; currently handles 3 acts. Receives 15-20% commission.
How to Contact: Submit demo tape by mail. Unsolicited submissions are okay. Prefers cassette with 3-4 songs, lyric sheet and photo/promotional/package. SASE. Reports in 4-6 weeks.
Music: Mostly rock, metal and pop; also alternative. Works primarily with rock and heavy metal bands; producers/engineers. Current acts include Strange Parade (rock/band), Killian Dare (rock/band) and Geoffrey Workman (producer/engineer).
Tips: "Must be original, hardworking and professional. Mostly interested in bands that promote themselves, believe in themselves and have some knowledge of the music business. Must be marketable."

OUT OF THE BLUE MANAGEMENT, 2315 Belgrave, Montreal Quebec H4A 2L9 **Canada**. (514)486-5699. Agents/Associates: Frank Farkas or Jocelyne Pepin. Management firm and music publisher (Freeride Music/CAPAC). Estab. 1989. Represents local, regional and international individual artists and groups; currently handles 3 acts. Receives 15% commission. Reviews material for acts.
How to Contact: Submit demo tape by mail. Unsolicited submissions are OK. Prefers cassette (or live performance on VHS videocassette) with 3 songs and lyric sheet. SASE. Reports in 1 month.
Music: Mostly commercial rock, pop/dance and R&B; also heavy metal. Works primarily with rock bands, dance bands and vocalists. Current acts include Dorion and The Freeriders, Justin Jordan and Riopel.

Tips: "Be honest and hardworking; there is always a light at the end of the line, so go for it."

PAINTER ASSOCIATES (RICHARD A. PAINTER MANAGEMENT & MARKETING), P.O. Box 111717, Nashville TN 37222-1717. (615)776-5185. President: Richard Allan Painter. Management and marketing firm and music publisher (R.A.P. Music). Estab. 1984. Represents individual artists, groups and songwriters; currently handles 1 act. Receives 20-30% commission. Reviews material for acts.
How to Contact: Write or call first and obtain permission to submit. Prefers cassette (or VHS ½″ videocassette) with 4 songs and lyric or lead sheets. SASE. Reports in 1 month.
Music: Mostly pop, rock and R&B; also adult contemporary, jazz/New Age. Current act is Trace Balin.
Tips: "Must possess songs that have hit potential for radio airplay. Must also possess stage appearance/presence/performance visually conducive to video/TV recording exposure. Prefers self-contained touring acts."

PARADISE PRODUCTIONS, Box 29367, Honolulu HI 96820. (808)924-3301. General Manager: Kathy Koran. Management firm and booking agency. Estab. 1971. Represents artists, groups and songwriters. Currently handles 25 acts. Receives minimum 15% commission. Reviews material for acts.
How to Contact: Prefers cassette (or VHS videocassette) with minimum 4 songs and lyric sheet. SASE. Reports in 1 week.
Music: Mostly rock, top 40/pop, soul, easy listening and Las Vegas style show groups; also dance-oriented, jazz, MOR, progressive, R&B and light rock. Works primarily with Las Vegas show groups, dance bands, vocalists and high energy rock concert groups. Current acts include Rod Young (Las Vegas show band), Triple X (concert rock group), Bobby Hutton (soul/pop show group) and Alexander Butterfield (soul/show/pop group).
Tips: "Topnotch polished material is what we need."

PARASOL PUBLICATIONS (U.K.), 17 Elm Grove Rd., Dinas Powys, Cardiff CF6 4AA South Wales, **United Kingdom** Phone: (0222)513723. Director: Colin Ryman. Mangement firm. Estab. 1985. Represents local and London based individual artists, groups and songwriters; currently handles 5 acts. Receives 25% commission. Reviews material for acts.
How to Contact: Prefers cassette (or videocassette) with 5 songs and lyric or lead sheets. SAE and IRC. Reports in 2 months.
Music: Mostly pop, MOR, musical show/themes, rock and 'new styles.' Works primarily with vocalists and pop bands. Current acts include Steve Johnson (singer/songwriter), Beaus Bohemians (7 piece red hot, culture shock rock band), Alienation (TV pop program session band), The Miracle Brothers (innovative, culty, free form pop band) and The P. Peeps (TV/cartoon/band).

JACKIE PAUL MANAGEMENT AND CONSULTANT FIRM, 559 Wanamaker Rd., Jenkintown PA 19046. (215)884-3308. FAX: (215)884-1083. President: Jackie Paul. Management firm (BMI/Terrance Moore Music, Inc.). Estab. 1985. Represents local and national artists, groups, producers and musicians. Currently handles 2 acts. Receives 15-30% commission. Reviews material for acts.
How to Contact: Submit demo tape by mail. Unsolicited submissions are okay. Call first and obtain permission to submit. Prefers cassette (or VHS videocassette) with 1-3 songs and lyric or lead sheets. "It's not mandatory but if possible, I would prefer a videocassette. "Do the best to help portray the image you represent, with whatever resources possible." SASE. Reports in 2-4 weeks.
Music: Mostly rap, pop and R&B/dance. Works primarily with vocalists. Current acts include Blue Eagle (pop singer/songwriter, drummer/producer) and Terrance T'Luv (R&B-dance singer/songwriter/producer).
Tips: "Be sincere, patient and willing to take advice."

PENTACHORD/PENTARCH MUSIC, 406-68 Water St., Vancouver, British Columbia V6B 1A4 **Canada**. (604)688-0077. Contact: Cliff Jones. Management firm, music publisher and record company (Penta Records). Estab. 1987. Represents individual artists, groups and songwriters. Reviews material for acts.
How to Contact: Call first and obtain permission to submit. Prefers cassette with 4 songs and lyric sheet. Does not return unsolicited material. Reports in 1 month.
Music: Mostly CHR and AC. Current acts include Boulevard, Paul Laine and the Scramblers.

PERFORMANCE GROUP, P.O. Box 40825, Washington DC 20016. (301)320-4137. President: Dennis Oppenheimer. Management firm. Estab. 1984. Represents local, regional and international individual artists, groups and songwriters; currently handles 8 acts. Receives 20% commission. Reviews material for acts.

How to Contact: Submit demo tape by mail. "Performance videso preferred." Unsolicited submissions are OK. Prefers cassette with 3-5 songs. SASE. Reports in 2 weeks.
Music: Mostly rock, pop and dance. Works primarily with vocalists and original bands. Current acts include Annie Haslam, Renaissance, Big Bang Theory, Judy Bats, Warzone, Niagara, Patricia Kaas and East is East.
Tips: "Include bio and photo."

PAUL PETERSON CREATIVE MANAGEMENT, 9005 Cynthia, #309, Los Angeles CA 90069. (213)273-7255. Contact: Paul Peterson. Management firm. Represents artists and groups from the Midwest and West Coast; currently handles 4 acts. Receives 20% commission. Reviews material for acts.
How to Contact: Prefers cassette (or ¾" or VHS videocassette) with 2-4 songs and lyric sheet. SASE. Reports in 3 weeks.
Music: Mostly pop/rock and rock; also jazz and top 40/pop. Works with rock bands doing original material. Current acts include Man About Town (pop/rock band), Second Language (modern rock), Brian Savage (jazz/new age) and Honky Tonk Angels Band (southern country/rock).

*PHIL'S ENTERTAINMENT AGENCY LIMITED, 889 Smyth Rd., Ottawa Ontario K1G 1P4 **Canada**. (613)731-8983. Booking agency. Estab. 1979. Represents artists and groups; currently handles 50 acts. Receives 10% commission. Reviews material for acts "occasionally."
How to Contact: Query by mail. Prefers cassette (or videocassette) with 4-7 songs. "Be sure the name of artist and date of completion are on the video." Does not return unsolicited material.
Music: Mostly country; also country/rock, MOR and "old rock 'n' roll." "We work with show bands, male and female vocalists, bar bands and dance bands on a regular basis." Current acts include Ralph Carlson (country/bluegrass), Neville Wells (country), Bruce Golden (country-country/rock), Herb Sherman, Gerry Allard, Lyoness and Judy Woodstock.
Tips: "Be professional and business-like. Keep agency supplied with up-to-date promo material and develop entertainment ability. Videotape your live performance, then give yourself an honest review."

*PHOENIX TALENT, LTD., 332 South Michigan 1847, Chicago IL 60604. (312)786-2024. President: Lou Johnson. Vice President: Paul Ramey. Management firm and booking agency (AF of M, AFTRA and SAG). Estab. 1986. Represents local, regional or international individual artists, groups and songwriters; currently handles 5 acts. Receives 10-15% commission. Reviews material for acts.
How to Contact: Call first and obtain permission to submit. Prefers cassette with 3 songs and lead sheets. SASE. Reports in 4 weeks.
Music: Mostly R&B, pop and rap; also gospel and jazz. Works primarily with singer/songwriters who have producer capabilities (R&B/dance). Current acts include Stanley Turrentine (sax), Peter Black (producer/artist) and Darryl Pandy (singer).
Tips: "Your material should always be studio quality and practically finished, with the fullest sound possible. Have a flair for what's happening now but still retain your individuality!"

PLACER PUBLISHING, Box 11301, Kansas City KS 66111. (913)287-3495. Owner: Steve Vail. Management firm, booking agency, music publisher (ASCAP) and record company (System Records). Estab. 1980. Represents local, regional and international individual artists, groups and songwriters. Currently handles 6 acts. Reviews material for acts.
How to Contact: Write or call first and obtain permission to submit. Prefers cassette or 7½ reel-to-reel (or VHS or Beta videocassette) with lyric sheets. Does not return unsolicited material. Reports in 6 weeks.
Music: Mostly new-age, progressive and jazz or fusion. Works primarily with esoteric or avant-garde groups or individuals. Current acts include David Sears and Darrel Datsun.
Tips: "Be creative. Please no mainstream tunes."

*PLATINUM GOLD MUSIC, 9200 Sunset Blvd. #1220, Los Angeles CA 90069. Managers: Steve Cohen/David Cook. Management firm, music publisher. ASCAP. Estab. 1978. Represents individual artists, groups and songwriters. Deals with local artists and regional artists (East or West coasts). Currently handles 3-4 acts. Receives 15-20% commission. Reviews material for acts.
How to Contact: Write or call first and obtain permission to submit. Prefers cassette (or VHS videocassette) with 3 songs and lyric sheets. Does not return unsolicited material.
Music: Mostly interested in contemporary R&B, dance/pop, hip hop/rap; also pop rock, hard rock and pop. Works most often with vocalists. Current acts include Troop (R&B vocal group) and Def Jef (rap/hip hop).
Tips: "No ballads. We do not look for potential; be prepared and professional before coming to us-and ready to relocate to West Coast if necessary."

PODESOIR INTERNATIONAL MANAGEMENT, Suite 3L, 211 West 56th St., New York NY 10019. (212)767-0520. Executive Administrator: June M. Allison. Management firm. Estab. 1986. Represents local, regional and international individual artists and groups. Currently handles 4 acts. Receives 20% commission. Reviews material for acts.
How to Contact: Submit demo tape and press package by mail. Unsolicited submissions are okay. Prefers cassette (or videocassette) with 3 songs and lyric or lead sheets. SASE. Reports in 3 weeks.
Music: Mostly R&B/rap, pop and rock. Current acts include Euro-K (rap trio), Craig Raymond (pop/rock), Trevor Jackson (R&B) and Romance & Romeo (rap duo).
Tips: "Be persistent and work hard on your craft."

*POWER STAR MANAGEMENT, 6981 N. Pirk Dr., #618, Pennsauken NJ 08109. (609)486-1480. President: Brian Kushner. Management firm (Power Star Management). Estab. 1981. Represents international individual artists and groups; currently handles 4 acts. Receives 20% commission. Reviews material for acts.
How to Contact: Submit demo tape by mail. Unsolicited submissions are okay. Prefers cassette (or VHS videocassette) with 4 songs and lyric sheet. SASE. Reports in 3 weeks.
Music: Mostly pop/dance, rock and R&B. Current acts include Britny Fox, Alisha and Tuff.

PPK AG, Wiesliacher 21, Zurich CH-8053 **Switzerland**. Phone: (01)383 77 55. FAX: (01)383 77 60. Director: Fritz Portner. Management firm and music publisher (PPK-Publishing). Represents individual artists, songwriters and producers; currently handles 3 acts. Receives 20% commission. Reviews material for acts.
How to Contact: Prefers cassette with 1-5 songs and lyric sheet. SAE and IRC. Reports in 5 weeks.
Music: Mostly country and R&B. Works primarily with vocalists and country bands. Current acts include John Brack, Angelika Milster and Che & Ray (all show and concert acts).

*PREMIER ARTISTS, 9 Dundas Ln., Albert Park, Victoria 3206 **Australia**. (03)699-9555. FAX: (03)695-7819. Booking agency. Estab. 1975. Represents groups; currently handles 100 acts. Receives 10% commission. Reviews material for acts.
How to Contact: Prefers cassette (or VHS videocassette) with 2 or 3 songs. Does not return unsolicited material. Reports in 2 weeks.
Music: Mostly rock and pop. Works primarily with rock bands. Current acts include John Farnham, Jimmy Barnes, Paul Kelly and the Messengers.

PRO TALENT CONSULTANTS, Box 1192, Clearlake Oak CA 95423. (707)998-1609. Coordinator: John Eckert. Management firm and booking agency. Estab. 1979. Represents individual artists and groups; currently handles 13 acts. Receives 15% commission. Reviews material for acts.
How to Contact: Prefers cassette (or VHS videocassette) with 4 songs and lyric sheet. SASE. Reports in 3 weeks.
Music: Mostly country, country/pop and rock. Works primarily with vocalists, show bands, and dance bands. Current acts include John Richards (country singer), Glenn Elliott Band (country group), Rock Soul Aggregation (rock group) and Just Us (country).
Tips: "Never give up if you're *honestly* interested in working in the show/music business. The music business is the greatest business to be in, but only the strongest performers who believe in themselves survive."

PROCESS TALENT MANAGEMENT, 439 Wiley Ave., Franklin PA 16323. (814)432-4633. Contact: Norman Kelly. Management firm. Estab. 1970. Represents artists and groups; currently handles 10 acts. Receives 10-15% commission. Reviews material for acts.
How to Contact: Write or call first and obtain permission to submit. Prefers 7½ ips reel-to-reel, cassette or 8-track cartridge with 2-6 songs. "Send your best songs and performances with photo, audiocassette and SASE. Reports in 2 weeks.
Music: Mostly country; also bluegrass, country, gospel, MOR, jazz and rock. Works primarily with vocalists, self-contained country shows and bar bands. Current acts include Remember When (vocal group, Sounds of the 1960's), and Tara Bailey (country singer).

THE RAINBOW COLLECTION, LTD., P.O. Box 300, Solebury PA 18963. (215)862-0849. President: Herb Gart. Management, production and publishing firm. Represents artists, groups and songwriters; currently handles 10 acts. Receives 20% commission. Reviews material for acts. Signs songwriters.
How to Contact: Prefers cassette (or VHS videocassette) with 3 songs. "Be true to the intent of the song, and don't hide the performer. Simple and straightforward preferred." Does not return unsolicited material. Reports in 6 weeks.

Music: Rock, pop, heavy metal, R&B, rap, country and dance-oriented. Works "almost exclusively with strong songwriters whether they are solo artists or bands." Current acts include Between the Sheets, Funhouse, Michael Purington, Mike Angelo & The Idols and Marc Berger Band.

Tips: "Don't necessarily worry about current trends in music. Just do what you do to the best of your ability. With our company the song is the thing even if production-wise it's in its infant stages. If you feel you have a great and unique talent, contact us."

THE RECORD COMPANY OF THE SOUTH (RCS), 5220 Essen Ln., Baton Rouge LA 70809. (504)766-3233. President: Cyril E. Vetter. Vice President: Andrew Vetter. Management firm, music publisher and record company. Represents artists, groups and songwriters; currently handles 5 acts. Receives 20-25% commission. Reviews material for acts.

How to Contact: "Not accepting submissions at this time".

Music: Country, R&B, rock, soul and top 40/pop. Works primarily with artists, bands and songwriters. Current acts include Irma Thomas (top 40/pop and R&B), Luther Kent (top 40/pop and R&B), and Butch Hornsby (country).

RED GIANT RECORDS AND PUBLISHING, 3155 South. 764 East., Salt Lake City UT 84106. (801)486-4210. President: Anthony Perry. Music publisher (Red Giant Records) and record company (Red Giant). Estab. 1982. Represents local, regional and international individual artists, groups and songwriters. Curently represents 4 artists and groups. Receives 10-15% commission. Reviews material for acts.

How to Contact: Submit demo tape by mail. Unsolicited submissions are OK. Prefers cassette (or ½ VHS videocassette) with 3-4 songs and lyric or lead sheets. Does not return unsolicited material. Reports in 4 weeks.

Music: Mostly jazz avant rock, country/R&B and R&B. Works primarily with instrumentalists, vocalists and bands. Current acts include John Herron (songwriter), Spaces (vocal group), Bombs Away (R&B) and Armed & Dangerous (R&B).

*REED SOUND RECORDS, INC., 120 Mikel Dr., Summerville SC 29485. (803)873-3324. Contact: Haden Reed. Management firm. Represents artists and groups; currently handles 3 acts. Receives 10% commission. Reviews material for acts.

How to Contact: Query by mail. Prefers cassette with 1-4 songs. SASE. Reports in 1 month.

Music: Mostly country; also church/religious, easy listening and gospel. Current acts include Becky Knowles and The Country Blues, Haden Reed (country songwriter), Vocalettes (gospel), and Country Blues (show band).

JOEY RICCA, JR.'S ENTERTAINMENT AGENCY, 408 S. Main St., Milltown NJ 08850. (201)287-1230. Owner/President: Joseph Frank Ricca, Jr. Management firm and booking agency. Estab. 1985. Represents individual artists, groups and songwriters; currently handles 75-100 acts. Receives 10-15% commission. Reviews material for acts.

How to Contact: Write or call to arrange personal interview. "We prefer that all material be copyrighted and that a letter be sent right before submitting material, but neither of these is essential." Prefers cassette or reel-to-reel (or videocassette) with 3-4 songs and lyric or lead sheets. Does not return unsolicited material. Reports in 6 weeks.

Music: Mostly love songs/ballads, songs for big band vocalists, and soft jazz/Latin; also good commercial material. Works with show bands, dance bands and bar bands. Current acts include Maria Angela, Donny "Z," Anthony Paccone, One Trak Mind and Diamond.

Tips: "Good lyrics and strong musical arrangements are essential if one of our vocalists are to select a song they would like to sing. No matter what others may think of your work submit the songs you like best that you wrote. They probably are great. I look for good love songs, ballads, and Broadway play type compositions. No metal please."

RIOHCAT MUSIC, 104 Walnut Trace, Hendersonville TN 37075. (615)824-1435. Contact: Robert Kayne. Management firm, booking agency, record company (Avita Records) and music publisher (Riohcat Music/BMI). Estab. 1975. Represents individual artists and groups; currently handles 4 acts. Receives 15-20% commission. Reviews material for acts.

How to Contact: Prefers cassette and lead sheet. Does not return unsolicited material. Reports in 6 weeks.

Music: Mostly contemporary jazz and fusion. Works primarily with jazz ensembles. Current acts include Jerry Tachoir Quartet, Marlene Tachoir, and Jerry Tachoir/Van Manakas Duo.

Tips: "Be organized, neat and professional."

A.F. RISAVY, INC., 1312 Vandalia, Collinsville IL 62234. (618)345-6700. Divisions include Artco Enterprises, Golden Eagle Records, Swing City Music and Swing City Sound. Contact: Art Risavy. Management firm and booking agency. Estab. 1960. Represents artists, groups and songwriters; currently handles 50 acts. Receives 10% commission. Reviews material for acts.
How to Contact: Write first and obtain permission to submit or to arrange personal interview. Prefers 7½ ips reel-to-reel or cassette (or VHS videocassette) with 2-6 songs and lyric sheet. SASE. Reports in 2 weeks.
Music: Mostly rock, country, MOR and top 40; also all other types. Current acts include Street Corner Symphony, Philthy McNasty, Fantasy, Billy-Peek, Jules Blatner, John Bartley, Sgt. Karter, Troppix, Sneakers, Seen, Catch and Inside Out.
Tips: Artists should be "well-dressed, polished and ambitious. VHS videotapes are very helpful."

RNJ PRODUCTIONS, INC., 11514 Calvert St., North Hollywood CA 91606. (818)762-6105. President: Rein Neggo, Jr. Management firm. Estab. 1974. Represents individual artists; currently handles 8 acts. Receives 10-25% commission. Reviews material for acts.
How to Contact: Prefers cassette with 3 songs and lead sheet. SASE. Reports in 1 month.
Music: Mostly adult contemporary, country, pop and folk. Works primarily with vocalists and concert artists. Current acts include Glenn Yarbrough, Arizona Smoke Review, Limeliters, Bill Zorn, Jon Benns and The Kingston Trio.

ROCK-A-BILLY ARTIST AGENCY, Box 4740, Nashville TN 37216. (615)865-4740. A&R Director: S.D. Neal. Management firm, booking agency and record company. Estab. 1974. Represents artists and groups; currently handles 20 acts. Receives 15% commission. Reviews material for acts.
How to Contact: Prefers cassette (or VHS videocassette if available) with 2-6 songs and lyric sheet. SASE. Reports in 3 weeks.
Music: Mostly R&B, rock and country; also all other types including rockabilly. Works primarily with vocalists. Current acts include Dixie Dee, Rhythm Rockers, Rufus Thomas, Richie Derwald, Mickey Finn Band and Greg Paul.

***ROCKEN DAVIE PRODUCTIONS**, P.O. Box 70, Brackettville TX 78832. (512)563-2759. Contact: Rocco Fortunato. Management firm. Estab. 1979. Represents regional (Southwest) individual artists and groups; currently handles 2 acts. Reviews material for acts.
How to Contact: Write first and obtain permission to submit. Prefers cassette with 3 songs and lyric sheet. Does not return unsolicited material. Reports in 1 month.
Music: Mostly country, country-pop and country-cross over; also Bluegrass and novelty. Works primarily with single vocalists and various vocal groups "2 to 4 voices."
Tips: "Material 'in the raw' is OK if you are willing to work with us to develop it."

***ROCKVILLE MUSIC MANAGEMENT**, Suite 200, 100 Merrick Rd., Rockville Centre NY 11570. (516)536-8341. Executive Director: James Citkovic. Management firm. Estab. 1989. Represents international individual artists, groups, songwriters and producers; currently handles 6 acts. Receives 5-30% commission. Reviews material for acts.
How to Contact: Submit demo tape by mail. Unsolicited submissions are okay. Prefers cassette (or VHS videocassette) with 1-4 songs and lyric sheet. SASE. Reports in 4-5 weeks.
Music: Mostly rock, pop and alternative; also R&B and dance. Current acts are Drew Miles (Nu Music/1990 pop rock), Naked Angels (power pop/rock dance) and Fighter Town (commercial rock).
Tips: "We want quality artists with originality, vision and distinctive lead vocal; imaginative lyrics, memorable hooks and melodies; and artists that project a positive image with their music, look and lyrics."

***SAMUEL ROGGERS & ASSOC.**, 1 West Loop South #100, P.O. Box 8305, Houston TX 77288. (713)683-2298 and (713)662-4196. Senior Consultant: Sirron Kyles. Management firm and booking agency. Estab. 1971. Represents local and international individual artists and groups. Receives 15% commission. Reviews material for acts.
How to Contact: Submit demo tape by mail. Unsolicited submissions are okay. Prefers cassette (or VHS videocassette if available) with 3 songs and lyric sheets. SASE. Reports in 3 weeks.
Music: Mostly rock, R&B and country; also gospel and comedy. Works primarily with concert acts. Current acts include Mickey Blu (R&B singer/songwriter), Seven South Seas (Polynesian singer/songwriter) and Night Rider (rock singer/songwriter).

***JAY B. ROSS & ASSOCIATES P.C.**, 838-40 W. Grand Ave., Chicago IL 60622. (312)243-7876. President: Jay B.Ross. Management firm and law firm. Estab. 1968. Represents local, regional or international artists, groups and songwriters. Reviews material for acts.

How to Contact: Prefers cassette (or videocassette if available) with three songs. Does not return submissions without SASE. Reports 2-6 weeks.
Music: Mostly R&B, urban dance and industrial (rock and dance); also rock/pop, heavy metal and gospel/blues. Works primarily with vocalists. Current acts include Sugar Blue, Gene "Duke of Earl" Chandler, Industrial Dance Force, 4 P.M. (Pale Males) RAP and Daughters of the Blues.
Tips: "Submit finished demos if possible, put your best song first."

*ROUND ROBIN, 101 Hurts Ln., Hendersonville TN 37075. (615)824-5900. FAX: (615)824-8800. Contact: Jim Pierce. Music publisher (Strawboss Music [BMI]) and record company (Round Robin Records). Represents one artist. Handles 3 acts. Receives 20% commission. Review material for acts.
How to Contact: Write or call first to arrange personal interview. Prefers cassette and lyric sheets. Does not return unsolicited material. Reports in 2 months.
Music: All types of country. Works primarily with single acts. Currents act include Arne Benoni (country), Lenny Valens (country/pop) and Blaine Dakota (country).

RUSCH ENTERTAINMENT AGENCY, 3588 N. Thomas Rd., Freeland MI 48623. (517)781-1553. President: Dean A. Rusch. Booking agency. Estab. 1970. Represents groups in Michigan; currently handles 250-300 acts. Receives 10-15% commission. Reviews material for acts. Is a member of the International Talent Artists Association.
How to Contact: Write first and obtain permission to submit. Prefers cassette (or VHS videocassette) with 3-10 songs and lyric sheet. SASE. Reports in 2 weeks.
Music: Mostly top 40/pop; also country, dance-oriented, MOR, easy listening and rock. Works primarily with dance bands. Current acts include Ceyx, Dedication, Harmony, Loose Change, Evergreen, Infinity (all dance bands), Nights Society Orchestra and the Uptown Review (dance band/10 p. orchestra), Skyline (band, horn), and Ovation (dance band).

RUSTRON MUSIC PRODUCTIONS, Send all artist song submissions to: 1156 Park Lane, West Palm Beach FL 33417. Main Office: 33 Whittier, Hartsdale, NY 10530. (914)761-3025. ("Main office does not review new material—only South Florida Branch office does."). Artists' Consultant: Rusty Gordon. Composition Management: Ron Caruso. Management firm, booking agency, music publisher (Rustron Music Publishers/BMI) and record producer (Rustron Music Productions). Estab. 1970. Represents individuals, groups and songwriters; currently handles 8 acts. Receives 10-25% commission for management and/or booking only. Reviews material for acts.
How to Contact: Query, arrange personal interview, or submit in person. Prefers cassette with 3-6 songs and lyric or lead sheet. SASE. Reports in 1 month.
Music: Blues (country and rock), country (rock, blues, progressive), easy listening (ballads), R&B, folk/rock (contemporary/topical), MOR (pop style), rock (folk/pop), top 40/pop and salsa/disco; also New Age. Current acts include: Marian Joy Ring (folk/jazz fusion), Janet Bratter (contemporary/topical folk), Sue Massek of The Reel World String Band (contemporary folk/country), Circle & Star (Jayne Reby & Bonnie Pedicord) (contemporary folk), Robin Plitt (historical/contemporary folk) and Marie Nofsinger (country folk).

SALT WORKS MUSIC, INC., 21 Fleetwood Ave., Jackson OH 45640-1806. (614)286-3420. (Branch: 4901 Yorkshire Rd., Nashville TN 37204). President: R.J. Elliot. Vice President: M.A. Morgan. Management firm and music publisher (Sojourner Music/BMI and Salt Creek Music/ASCAP). Estab. 1986.
How to Contact: "Requests and tapes should be sent to our Jackson, Ohio office." Prefers cassette or 7½ ips reel-to-reel with 3-4 songs and demo and lyric sheet. "We will not return tape unless postage paid envelope is provided." Reports in 3 weeks.
Music: Mostly country, country rock and gospel/religious; also pop and MOR. Works primarily with vocalists and songwriters. Current acts include Mike Morgan (vocalist/songwriter) and Walt Cook and Carl Angel (vocalists).

SANDCASTLE PRODUCTIONS, 236 Sebert Road, Forest Gate, London E7 ONP **England**. Phone (081)534-8500. Senior Partner: Simon Law. Management firm, music publisher (Sea Dream Music/PRS, Scarf Music Publishing and Really Free Music/PRS) and record company (Plankton Records,

The asterisk before a listing indicates that the listing is new in this edition. New markets are often the most receptive to unsolicited submissions.

Embryo Arts/Belgium and Gutta/Sweden) and record producers. Estab. 1980. Represents individual artists, groups and songwriters; currently handles 9 acts. Receives up to 10% commission. Reviews material for acts.

How to Contact: Prefers cassette with 3 songs and lyric sheet. SAE and IRC. Reports in 6 weeks.

Music: Mostly funk/rock, blues, rock and gospel. Works primarily with bands or artists with a Christian bias to their material. Current acts include Fresh Claim (funk rock), Medals (jazz/rock) and Solid Air (pop/rock).

Tips: "Have a commitment to communication of something real and honest in 'live' work."

WILLIAM SEIP MANAGEMENT, INC., P.O. Box 515, Waterloo, Ontario, N2J 4A9 **Canada**. (519)741-1252. President: William Seip. Management firm. Estab. 1978. Currently handles 4 groups. Receives 10-25% commission. Reviews material for acts.

How to Contact: Query by mail or phone, then arrange personal interview. Prefers cassette (or videocassette) with 1-3 songs. Provide bio and letter outlining direction and goals. SAE and IRC. Reporting time varies.

Music: Mostly commercial rock; also rock (heavy) and top 40/pop. Works with bar bands, concert acts and recording artists. Current acts include Helix (hard rock), Ray Lyell & the Storm (commerical rock) and Cherry Smash (hard rock).

SELECT ARTISTS ASSOCIATES, 7300 E. Camelback Rd., Scottsdale AZ 85251. (602)994-0471. Owner/Operator: Charles T. Johnston. Booking agency. Estab. 1967. Represents individual artists and groups; currently handles 35 acts. Receives 20% commission. Reviews material for acts.

How to Contact: Prefers cassette (or videocassette). SASE. Reports in 1 month.

Music: Mostly rock (top 40), pop and R&B. Works primarily with dance bands. Current acts include Corte, Unity, Righteous Brothers, Bill Medley, Torch, Pop Machine, Sister Max, Vinny Di John Band, Straight from the Heart, and Joey Navarro Project.

*770 MUSIC INC., Box 773, Bondi Junction, New South Wales 2022 **Australia**. Phone: (02)550-3719. A&R Representative: Mr. Nun. Management firm, booking agency, music publisher (770 Music), record company (770 Music) and record producer (770 Productions). Estab. 1980. Represents individual artists, groups and songwriters; currently handles 44 acts. Receives 25% commission. Reviews material for acts.

How to Contact: Prefers cassette (or VHS or Beta videocassette) with 10 songs and lyric or lead sheets. Does not return unsolicited material. Reports back in 3 months.

Music: Mostly triple crossover—country, rock and pop. Works primarily with dance bands, showbands and individual artists and songwriters. Current acts include Dynamic Hypnotics (pop), Urban Guerillas (rock), CCC (gospel/Christian), Beam Me Up Spock (dance), The Gary Who School (teenage top 100), Placebo, The Untouchables (heavy metal).

Tips: "Company Motto: The love you make equals the love you create."

*SHANKMAN DE BLASIO, INC., 2434 Main St., Santa Monica CA 90405. (213)399-7744. Manager/Talent Acquisition: Peter Houlahan. Management firm. Represents local, regional or international individual artists, groups and songwriters; currently handles 20 acts. Receives 15-20% commission. Reviews material for acts.

How to Contact: Write first and obtain permission to submit. Prefers cassette (or VHS videocassette "only if available") with 3 songs. SASE. Reports in 4 weeks.

Music: Mostly rock and pop; also folk, alternative, MOR and metal. Works primarily with jazz, folk artists, rock, movie scoring and pop artists. Current acts include David Foster (producer, songwriter, movie scorer), Syd Straw (folk/rock singer), Exene Cervenka, John Doe of "X" (alternative rock, post-punk) and Quarter Flash.

SHAPIRO & COMPANY, C.P.A. A Professional Corporation, Suite 620, 9255 Sunset Blvd., Los Angeles CA 90069. (213)278-2303. Certified Public Accountant: Charles H. Shapiro. Business management firm. Estab. 1979. Represents individual recording artists, groups and songwriters. Commission varies.

How to Contact: Write or call first to arrange personal interview.

Music: Mostly rock and pop. Works primarily with recording artists as business manager.

Tips: "We assist songwriters with deals including administration of publishing."

SHOE STRING BOOKING AGENCY, 696 The Queensway, Toronto Ontario M8Y 1K9 **Canada**. (416)255-5166. Contact: Armin Darmstadt. Management firm and booking agency. Represents local artists; currently handles 10 acts. Receives 15% commission. Reviews material for acts.

How to Contact: Write first and obtain permission to submit. Prefers cassette (or VHS videocassette) with 2-4 songs and lyric sheet. Does not return unsolicited material. Reports in 3 weeks.
Music: Mostly rock, R&B/pop and country/rock. Works primarily with vocalists and dance bands. Current acts include SAB, Gigalo and Pulsations.

*SHOW TIME TALENT AGENCY, Rt. 1 Box 942, Lynchburg VA 24502. (804)239-0336. President: Jerry Hollandsworth. Management firm. Estab. 1983. Represents individual artists. Currently handles 1 act. Reveiws material for acts.
How to Contact: Write first and obtain permission to submit. Prefers cassette with 4 songs and lyric and lead sheet. Does not return unsolicited material.
Music: Country and pop. Works with "high energy country bands." Acts include The Hollanders.

*SHOWTIME PRODUCTIONS, 120 North St., Bolivar MO 65613. (417)326-3244. Manager: Charley Ealy. Management firm. Estab. 1985. Represents individual artists. Currently handles 4 acts. Receives 20% commission. Reviews material for acts.
How to Contact: Prefers cassette. Does not return unsolicited material.
Music: Mostly country. Works primarily with vocalists. Current acts include Lisa Childress, George Howard Luce and K.C.Hackney.

SIDARTHA ENTERPRISES, LTD., Box 1414, East Lansing MI 48823. (517)655-4618. President: Thomas R. Brunner. Management firm and booking agency. Estab. 1968. Represents artists and groups; currently handles 5 acts. Receives 15-20% commission. Reviews material for acts.
How to Contact: "Always make phone contact first." Prefers cassette (or videocassette) with at least 4 songs and lyric sheet. SASE. Reports in 1 month.
Music: Rock and top 40/pop. Works primarily with bar bands and recording acts. Current acts include Kody Lee (rock), Sheer Threat (rock), Mariner (rock) and Rumolf (rock).

*SILVER CREEK PARTNERSHIP, P.O. Box 33, Pope Valley CA 94567. (707)965-2277. Managing Partner: Carla L. Forrest. Management firm, music publisher (Ohana Music Productions/ASCAP). Estab. 1988. Represents local and regional (Northern California) artists, groups and songwriters; currently handles 1 act. Receives 10% commission.
How to Contact: Submit demo tape by mail. Unsolicited submissions are OK. Prefers cassette with 3-4 songs and lyric and lead sheet. SASE. Reports in 3-4 weeks.
Music: Mostly rock, top 40/pop and dance; also R&B. Works primarily with vocalists/musicians. Current acts include WAKEA!
Tips: "Demos should be uncluttered with vocals upfront. Strong melody and 'hook.' "

SIMMONS MANAGEMENT CO., 10th Floor, 5 W. Hargett St., Raleigh NC 27601. (919)828-1277. FAX: (919)832-9101. President: Harry Simmons. Vice President: Debbie Cecil. Management firm. Represents producers, artists, groups and songwriters; currently handles 14 acts and 4 producers. Receives 15-20% commission. Reviews material for acts.
How to Contact: Prefers cassette (or VHS videocassette) with 3-6 songs and lyric sheet; also submit promotional material, photos and clippings. SASE. Reports in 6 weeks.
Music: Mostly modern pop; also modern rock, new wave, dance-oriented, MOR, R&B and top 40/pop. Works primarily with "original music recording acts or those that aspire to be." Current acts include Don Dixon (producer, songwriter and recording artist), Marti Jones (recording artist), The Woods (recording artists, songwriters), Heidi Rodewald/Danielle Faye (performers, songwriters), Dan Fredman (producer) and Rev. Billy C. Wirtz (recording artist), Jim Brock (recording artist) and Steve Haigler (producer).
Tips: "We are interested in strong songs; style is not so important."

BRAD SIMON ORGANIZATION, INC., 122 E. 57th St., New York NY 10022. (212)980-5920. President: Brad Simon. Represents individual artists, and musical groups; currently handles 30 acts. Receives 20% commission.
How to Contact: Prefers cassette (or VHS videocassette) with minimum 3 songs. SASE. Reports in 2 months.
Music: R&B/pop, easy listening, jazz, progressive, rock (all types) and top 40/pop (new adult comteporary). Works with artists and groups in contemporary rock, pop, jazz with strong commercial appeal and crossover potential, vocal and instrumental artists with strong performing and writing skills. Current acts include Tom Grant (pop/jazz), Max Roach (jazz), Kim Pensyl (pop/jazz), Special EFX (pop/jazz), and Ben Sidran (pop/jazz).
Tips: "Artists must have original and distinctive material with strong commercial appeal."

*SINGERMANAGEMENT, INC., Suite 1403, 161 West 54th St., New York NY 10019. (212)757-1217. President: Robert Singerman. Management firm. Estab. 1982. Represents local, regional or international individual artists and groups; currently handles 7 acts. Receives 15-20% commission. Reviews material for acts.

How to Contact: Submit demo tape by mail. Unsolicited submissions are okay. Prefers cassette (or VHS videocassette if available). Does not return unsolicited submissions.

Music: Mostly rock, country and R&B; also world music. Current acts include Fleshtones, L'il Queenie and David Halley.

T. SKORMAN PRODUCTIONS, INC., 4700 L.B. McLeod Rd., Orlando FL 32811. (305)843-4300. President: Ted Skorman. Management firm and booking agency. Estab. 1983. Represents groups; currently handles 40 acts. Receives 10-25% commission. Reviews material for acts.

How to Contact: "Phone for permission to send tape." Prefers cassette with 3 songs (or videocassette of no more than 15 minutes). "Live performance - no trick shots or editing tricks. We want to be able to view act as if we were there for a live show." Does not return unsolicited material. Reports in 1 month.

Music: Mostly top 40 and dance; also rock, MOR and pop. Works primarily with high-energy dance acts, recording acts, and top 40 bands. Current acts include Jadi (dance), No Ones Ark (dance), Image (dance), Savoir Faire (dance) and Raven Black and The End (recording artists).

Tips: "We have many pop recording acts, and are looking for commercial material for their next albums."

SKYLINE MUSIC CORP., Box 31, Lancaster NH 03584. (608)586-7171. President: Bruce Houghton. Management firm (Skyline Management), booking agency (Skyline Music Agency) and record company (Adventure Records). Estab. 1984. Represents individual artists and groups. Currently handles 15 acts. Receives 10-15% commission. Reviews material for acts.

How to Contact: Prefers cassette (or videocassette) with 3 songs. Does not return unsolicited material.

Music: Mostly rock, pop and dance. Works primarily with concert rock attractions and dance bands. Current acts include Foghat (rock), The Outlaws (rock), Toy Caldwell (rock), Blushing Brides, Rick Danko, Badfinger and Van Zant.

DAN SMITH AGENCY, Box 3634, Shawnee Mission KS 66203. (913)648-3906. Contact: Dan Smith. Management firm and booking agency. Estab. 1979. Represents artists, groups and songwriters in the Midwest. Currently handles 4 acts. Receives 10% commission. Reviews material for acts.

How to Contact: Prefers cassette with 3-5 songs and lyric sheet (or VHS videocassette) "Make sound quality clear and mixed well." SASE. Reports in 1 month.

Music: Mostly country rock, top 40, progressive and R&B; also bluegrass, blues, country, dance-oriented, folk, jazz, MOR and soul. Works primarily with dance, bar and concert bands. Current acts include Rick Harrelson Band (country rock), Crossroads (country rock), Dixie Cadillacs (country rock), and Blackwater (country rock).

Tips: "Have complete promo—bio, photo (glossy), song list, credits, etc."

SOPRO, INC., Box 227, Chicago Ridge IL 60415. (312)425-0174. Contact: Bud Monaco or Red Rose. Management firm and artist development firm. Represents artists and groups in the local region; currently handles 5 acts. Receives maximum 15-20% commission. Reviews material for acts.

How to Contact: Write first and obtain permission to submit. Prefers cassette with 3-6 songs and lead sheet. Does not return unsolicited material. Reports in 2 weeks if interested.

Music: Mostly rock, blues, dance-oriented and top 40; also R&B, MOR and progressive rock. Works primarily with concert rock, blues and dance-oriented bands. Current acts include Don Griffin and The Griff Band (rock/blues), The Midwest Expedition (rock), Jody Noa & The Sho'Nuff Blues Band (blues), Joe Jammer & The Kissing Bandits (rock/dance) and Tommy Biondo (rock).

SOUND '86 TALENT MANAGEMENT, P.O. Box 222, Black Hawk SD 57718. (605)343-3941. Management firm. Estab. 1974. Represents 10 artists and groups. Receives 5-10% commission. Reviews material for acts.

How to Contact: Query by mail or submit demo tape. Prefers cassette (or VHS videocassette-professional) with 3-8 songs and lyric sheet. SASE. Reports in 1 month.

Music: Mostly rock (all types); also bluegrass, country, dance, easy listening and top 40/pop. Works primarily with single artists. Current artists include Danny Wayne (songwriter), Jack Jenson and Black Hills Country Band.

SOUTHERN CONCERTS, 8665 Oakwood, Olive Branch MS 38654. (601)895-8333. President: Buddy Swords. Management firm, record company (SCR Records), record producer and music publisher (Buddy Swords Music and Swamp Fox Music). Represents artists; currently handles 5 acts. Receives 20% commission. Reviews material for acts.
How to Contact: Prefers cassette (or videocassette) with maximum 4 songs. Does not return unsolicited material. Reports in 1 week.
Music: Mostly country, rock and blues. Works primarily with groups at festivals, concerts and bars. Current acts include Jerry Lee Lewis and Wendel Adkins.

SOUTHERN NIGHTS INC., 2707 No. Andrews Ave., Ft. Lauderdale FL 33311. (305)563-4000. President: Dick Barten. Management firm and booking agency. Estab. 1976. Represents local and regional individual artists and groups; currently handles 35 acts. Receives 15-20% commission. Reviews material for acts.
How to Contact: Write or call first and obtain permission to submit. Prefers cassette (or VHS videocassette) with minimum of 4 songs and lyric or lead sheets."Keep videos simple—we are not interested in special effects on original material." SASE. Reports in 2 weeks.
Music: Mostly top 40/pop and rock. Works primarily with current top 40, high energy show and dance groups. Current acts include F/X (top 40 rock show), US#1 (touring top 40 dance act), Donna Allen (soul), Ruby Baker & Future and Starlight (top 40).
Tips: "Be prepared; send complete package of material and be ready to audition."

SP TALENT ASSOCIATES, Box 475184, Garland TX 75047. Talent Coordinator: Richard Park. Management firm and booking agency. Represents individual artists and groups; currently handles 7 acts. Receives negotiable commission. Reviews material for acts.
How to Contact: Prefers VHS videocassette with several songs. SASE. Reports back as soon as possible.
Music: Mostly rock, nostalgia rock, country; also specialty acts and folk/blues. Works primarily with vocalists and self-contained groups. Current acts include Joe Hardin Brown (country and western), Rock It! (nostalgia) and Renewal (rock group).
Tips: "Appearance and professionalism are *musts*!"

SPIDER ENTERTAINMENT CO., 5 Portsmouth Towne, Southfield MI 48075. President: Arnie Tencer. Vice President: Joel Zuckerman. Management firm. Estab.1977. Represents artists, groups and songwriters; currently handles 2 acts. Receives minimum 20% commission. Reviews material for acts.
How to Contact: Prefers cassette (or videocassette) with 3 songs. Does not return unsolicited material. Reports only if interested.
Music: Mostly rock and roll, contemporary pop, also top/40 pop. Works primarily with "rock bands with good songs and great live shows." Current acts include Gus Papas (rock singer and writer-guitarist) and Legal Tender (high energy "Detroit" rock band).
Tips: Artists "must have commercially viable material."

STAR ARTIST MANAGEMENT INC., 17580 Frazho, Roseville MI 48066. (313)778-6404. President: Ron Geddish. Chairman: Joe Sgroi. Executive V.P.: Tony Pasqualone. Director of Canadian Operations: Brian Courtis. Director of West Coast Operations: S.D. Ashley. Director of East Coast Operations: Nat Weiss. Management firm (business and personal). Estab. 1972. Represents solo rock performers and rock groups. Receives 5% (business management), 15-20% (personal management). Reviews material for acts.
How to Contact: Prefers cassette (or videocassette) with 2 songs. SASE. Reports in 3 weeks.
Music: Rock. Works primarily with new music and rock groups. Current acts include Elvis Hitler (Enigma/Restless Records), Robb Roy (rock, Nemperor Records) and His Name is Alive (4AD/Electra Records).

STARCREST PRODUCTIONS, INC., 209 Circle Hills Dr., Grand Forks ND 58201. (701)772-6831. President: George J. Hastings. Management firm and booking agency. Estab. 1970. Represents artists, groups and songwriters; currently handles 8 acts. Receives negotiable commission. Reviews material for acts. Receives 15% commission.
How to Contact: Query by mail. Prefers 7½ ips reel-to-reel or cassette with 2-10 songs with lyric and lead sheet. SASE. Reports in 1 month.
Music: Mostly country/gospel. Works primarily with vocalists and dance bands. Current acts include Mary Joyce (country/gospel), Swinging Doors (country/country rock), The Pioneers (country/country rock), The Teddy Bears (dance, show), George Hastings (songwriter) and Bob Angel (country songwriter).

STARSTRUCK PRODUCTIONS, 3057 Main Street, Buffalo NY 14214. (716)835-7625. FAX: (716)835-7701. General Manager: Tom McGill. Management firm and booking agency. Represents 24 groups. Receives 15-20% commission. Reviews material for acts.

How to Contact: Prefers cassette (or VHS videocassette) with 4-6 songs and lyric sheet. Please send current press kit with photo. Does not return unsolicited material.

Music: Mostly rock, pop, top 40. Works primarily with rock groups. Current acts include Only Humen (top 40 recording group, EMQ America Records), The Tweeds (rock/recording), Big Wheelie and The Hubcaps (nostalgia/touring act), Lady Five (rock), Silent Scream (rock) and Wright of Way (rock).

Tips: "Approach your career realistically. Overnight success stories are few and far between. Write solid, commercial material and be persistent."

*STILETTO MANAGEMENT, 6640 Sunset Blvd., Hollywood CA 90028. (213)467-9442. Manager: Eric Borenstein. Management firm. Estab. 1982. Represents local, regional or international individual artists, groups and songwriters; currently handles 17 acts. Receives 20% commission. Reviews material for acts.

How to Contact: Submit demo tape by mail. Unsolicited submissions are OK. Prefers cassette (or VHS videocassette if available) with 3 songs. Does not return unsolicited material.

AL STRATEN ENTERPRISES, 10303 Hickory Valley, Ft. Wayne IN 46835. President: Allan Straten. Management firm, booking agency, music publisher (Hickory Valley Music/ASCAP) and record company (Yellow Jacket Records). Represents individual artists and songwriters; currently handles 4 acts. Receives 10-20% commission. Reviews material for acts.

How to Contact: Prefers cassette with 3-4 songs and lyric sheet. SASE. Reports in 1 month.

Music: Mostly traditional and contemporary country – no rock. Works primarily with vocalists and writers. Current acts include April (vocalist), Mike Vernanglia (singer/songwriter), Roy Allan (vocalist/writer) and Sylvia Grogg (writer).

*STUBBLEFIELD ASSOCIATES, Suite 303, 595 E. Broad St., Columbus OH 43215. (614)365-9000. A&R: Brian Carter. Management firm. Estab. 1980. Represents local, regional or internationl individual artists and groups; currently handles 2 acts. Receives 15-25% commission. Reviews material for acts.

How to Contact: Call first and obtain permission to submit. Prefers cassette (or VHS videocassette if available) with 3 songs and lyric and lead sheet. SASE. Reports in 2 weeks.

Music: Mostly jazz, R&B and country. Works primarily with vocalists, jazz bands and groups. Current acts include Ed Clay (keyboardist) and Diane Meadows (vocals).

Tips: "Submit your best materials for consideration. Stay alert and be prepared to make a career decision."

SUNSET PRODUCTIONS, 117 W. 8th, Hays KS 67601. (913)625-9634. President: Mark Meckel. Management firm, booking agency and music publisher. Estab. 1974. Represents local, regional and international individual artists, groups and songwriters; currently handles 15 acts. Receives 15-20% commission. Reviews material for acts.

How to Contact: Submit demo tape by mail. Unsolicited submissions are OK. Prefers cassette with 3 songs and lyric sheet. Does not return unsolicited material. Reports in 3-4 weeks.

Music: Mostly rock, country and pop. Works primarily with bands on college circuit and in bars statewide. Current acts include The Heat (rock band), Jimmy Dee Band ('50s rock'n'roll) and Mark Selby (rock/folk singer, songwriter).

Tips: "Be willing to work with the producer. Take criticism in a constructive manner, be open to making changes."

THE T.S.J. PRODUCTIONS INC., 422 Pierce St., NE, Minneapolis MN 55413-2514. (612)331-8580. Vice President/Artist Manager: Katherine J. Lange. Management firm and booking agency. Estab. 1974. Represents artists, groups and songwriters; currently handles 1 international act. Receives 10-15% commission. Reviews material for acts.

How to Contact: Call or write first before sending package. Prefers "cassette tapes only for music audio (inquire before sending video), with 2-6 songs and lyric sheet." SASE. Reports in 2 weeks.

Music: Mostly country rock, symphonic rock, easy listening and MOR; also blues, country, folk, jazz, progressive, R&B and top 40/pop. Currently represents Thomas St. James (songwriter/vocalist).

Tips: "We will view anyone that fits into our areas of music. However, keep in mind we work only with national and international markets. We handle those starting out as well as professionals, but all must be marketed on a professional level, if we work with you."

TABITHA MUSIC, Sandpiper Ct., Harrington Ln., Exeter, HX4 8NS **England**. Phone: (0392)462294. FAX: (0392)462299. Managing Director: Graham Sclater. Management firm, music publisher and record company (Tabitha Records). Estab. 1975. Represents local, regional and international individual artists, groups and songwriters. Reviews material for acts.
How to Contact: Submit demo tape by mail. Unsolicited submissions are okay. Prefers cassette (or VHS videocassette if available) with 4 songs. SASE. Reports in 1 month.
Music: Mostly rock, pop and country; also R&B and folk. Works primarily with vocalists/groups. Current acts include Andy Ford (vocalist), Sovereign (R&B group) and Flic (pop group).

TALENT ATTRACTIONS, Box 8542, Asheville NC 28814. (704)253-4161. President: Larry Phillips. Management firm and booking agency. Represents artists, groups and songwriters; currently handles 5 acts. Receives 10% commission. Reviews material for acts.
How to Contact: Prefers cassette (or videocassette) with 1-5 songs and lyric or lead sheet. SASE. Reports in 30-50 days.
Music: Country, rock and top 40/pop. Works primarily with 4-6 piece groups and single vocal artists. Current acts include Natalie Nugent (vocalist and actress), Joe Berry (country, top 40/pop vocalist), Julie Ed (MOR and classic country), and Justice (top 40/pop, country band).
Tips: "At present I am only interested in original copyrighted songs. An inexpensive cassette is sufficient. If I like the songs, I will ask for a studio demo."

TALENT MASTER, P.O. Box 158558, Nashville TN 37215. (615)298-5070. President: Steve Bess. Booking agency. Estab. 1967. Represents artists and musical groups from Tennessee and surrounding states; currently handles 15 acts. Receives 15-20% commission. Reviews material for acts.
How to Contact: Prefers personal interview (artist/group only) or submit demo with good promo kit. Prefers live cassette (or videocassette) with 1-3 songs. "I look for professionalism in the presentation as well as for quality of song and overall performance ability." Does not return unsolicited material. Reports in 3 weeks.
Music: Country, dance, easy listening, MOR and rock (top 40, country). "The primary type of music I use most is country, but we are open to different types of music, especially on the cutting-edge." Works primarily with recording artists and dance and show bands. Current acts include Ray Griff, Larry G. Hudson, The Jordanaires, Charlie McCoy, A Tribute to Patsy Cline, and Daniele Alexander (all recording artists).

3L PRODUCTIONS, 3578 Silverplains Dr., Mississauga, Ontario L4X 2P4 **Canada**. (416)625-2165 or (416)238-2901. Manager: Gino Latini. Management firm and music publisher (Caras ITAA/CIRPA). Estab. 1985. Represents local and regional (Ontario) individual artist and groups; currently handles 5 acts. Receives 10-15% commission. Reviews material for acts.
How to Contact: Call first to arrange personal interview. Prefers cassette (or VHF videocassette) with 3 songs and lyric sheet. SASE and IRC. Reports in 1 month.
Music: Mostly rock, pop and R&B. Works primarily with dance band with good vocals, bar bands and recording bands. Current acts include Ten Seconds Over Tokyo (rock/pop), Tribal Son (new music), More Foreplay (rock) and Champions (classic rock).
Tips: "Be willing to work hard and be patient till the right break comes along."

*TIP TOP ATTRACTIONS/KAM MANAGEMENT, P.O. Box 1384, Mobile AL 36633. (205)432-7827. President: Kirke Weinacker. Management firm, booking agency, music publisher. Estab. 1985. Represents local, regional or international individual artists, groups, songwriters; currently handles 5 acts. Receives 10-20% commission. Reviews material for acts.
How to Contact: Submit demo tape by mail. Unsolicited submissions OK. Prefers cassette (or VHS videocassette if available) with 3-5 songs. SASE. Reports in 2 weeks.
Music: Mostly rock, R&B and pop. Works primarily with soloists and bands. Current acts include Mike Lawson (single), Tip Tops (show band) and Tribute (variety band).

A TOTAL ACTING EXPERIENCE, Suite 100, Dept. Rhymes-1, 14621 Titus St., Panorama City CA 91402. Agent: Dan A. Bellacicco. Talent agency. Estab. 1984. Represents vocalists, lyricists, composers, groups; currently handles 27 acts. Uses the services of in-house talent for scoring of motion pictures, television, videos, musicals, jingles, TV commercials, and material for major recording artists. Receives 10% commission. Reviews material for acts. Agency License: TA-0698.
How to Contact: Prefers cassette (or VHS videocassette) with 3-5 songs and lyric or lead sheets. Please include a revealing "self talk" at the end of your tape. "Singers or groups who write their own material must submit a VHS videocassette with photo and resume." SASE. Reports in 6-12 weeks only if interested.

Music: Mostly top 40/pop, jazz, blues, country, R&B, dance and MOR; also "theme songs for new films, TV shows and special projects."
Tips: "No calls please. We will respond via your SASE. Your business skills must be strong. Please use a new tape and keep vocals up front. We welcome young, sincere talent who can give total commitment, and most important *loyalty*, for a long-term relationship. We are seeking female vocalists a la Streisand or Whitney Houston, who can write their own material, for a major label recording contract. Your song's story line must be as refreshing as the words you skillfully employ in preparing to build your well-balanced, orchestrated, climactic last note! Try to eliminate old, worn-out, dull, trite rhymes. A new way to write/compose or sing an old song/tune will qualify your originality and professional standing."

*TRIED & TRUE MUSIC, P.O. Box 39, Austin TX 78767. (512)288-1698. Secretary: Jill McGuckin. Record company (Tried & True Music). Estab. 1986. Represents local individual artists; currently handles 2 acts. Receives 10% commission. Does not review material for acts.
How to Contact: Write first and obtain permission to submit. Prefers cassette with 4 songs and lyric sheets. Does not return unsolicited submissions. Reports in 3 months.
Music: Mostly county. Works primarily with songwriters/vocalists. Current acts include Jerry Jeff Walker and Chris Wall.

TRYCLOPS LTD., 115 New Barn Lane, Cheltenham, Glouchestershire GL52 3LQ **England.** Phone: 0242-234045. Director: Ian Beard. Booking agency, concert promotional company. Estab. 1971. Represents individual artists and groups; currently handles 12-15 acts. Receives 10-15% commission. Reviews material for acts.
How to Contact: Write or call first and obtain permission to submit. Prefers cassette (or VHS videocassette). Does not return unsolicited material. Reports in 2 weeks.
Music: Mostly rock, contemporary folk, pop; also R&B, jazz, new wave/new age. Works with very wide range of artists/acts from singer/songwriters to trios and jazz bands. No artists solely represented. Current acts include singer/songwriters Johnny Coppin, Steve Ashley and Dave Cartwright (not solely represented).

TSMB PRODUCTIONS, 736 N. Dupont Hwy., Dover DE 19901. (302)734-2511. Chief Executive Officer: Terry Tombosi. Music publisher (Terry Allen Publishing/BMI) and record company (TSMB Records). Estab. 1985. Represents individual artists, groups and songwriters; currently handles 10 acts. Receives 12.5% commission. Reviews material for acts.
How to Contact: Write to arrange personal interview. Prefers cassette or 15 ips reel-to-reel (or VHS videocasette) with 3 songs and lyric or lead sheet. "Good audio, good lighting (not lite show) a must." SASE. Reports in 6 weeks.
Music: Mostly R&B, rock, pop, country and new wave. Works primarily with vocalists and rock bands. Current acts include Hubcaps (R&B), The Cutters (60's) and Tony Cowan (soul).
Tips: "Follow directions. Be completely prepared. The standard things like demos, pictures, set lists, bios need to be ready but often they aren't."

UMBRELLA ARTISTS MANAGEMENT, INC., Box 20244, 443 Riddle Rd., #1, Cincinnati OH 45220. (513)861-1500. FAX: (513)861-1502. President: Stan Hertzman. Management firm. Represents artists, groups and songwriters; currently handles 5 acts.
How to Contact: Prefers cassette with 3 songs and lyric sheet. SASE. Reports in 1 month.
Music: Progressive, rock and top 40/pop. Works with contemporary/progressive pop/rock artists and writers. Current acts include The Bears (modern band); Rockhouse (modern rock band), He Said She Said (pop rock band), Pizoner (rock band) and Adrian Belew (artist/producer/songwriter/arranger whose credits include Frank Zappa, David Bowie, Talking Heads, Tom Tom Club, Cyndi Lauper, Laurie Anderson, Paul Simon and Mike Oldfield).

*UNDERCOVER MANAGEMENT CO., 4919 Murietta Ave., Sherman Oaks CA 91423. (818)995-1474. Managing Director: Jeff Gordon. Management firm. Record company (Gordon Records). Estab. 1985. Represents local, regional or international individual artists, groups, songwriters, "any good artist"; currently handles 1 act. Receives negotiable commission. Reviews material for acts.
How to Contact: Submit demo tape by mail. Unsolicited submissions are OK. Prefers cassette (or VHS videocassette if possible) with 2 or more songs and lyric sheet (if possible). SASE. Reports in 2-3 weeks.
Music: Mostly hard rock, dance and rap; also straight ahead rock, pop and R&B. Works primarily with hard rock groups. Current acts include Guardian (melodic hard rock band on Enigma/Capitol Records).
Tips: "Do not give up, and submit quality material."

URGENT RECORDS, P.O. Box 90754, Austin TX 78709-0754. (512)282-4036. Contact: A&R Director. Music publisher (BMI) and record company (Urgent). Estab. 1987. Represents nationally-known recording artists, groups and songwriters; currently handles 5 acts. Reviews material for acts.
How to Contact: Submit demo tape by mail. Unsolicited submissions are OK. Prefers cassette with 3 songs and lyric sheets. Does not return unsolicited material. Reports in 3 months.
Music: Mostly contemporary Christian; also pop. Current acts include Bob Bennett, Phillip Sandifer, Billy Crockett and Rob Frazier.
Tips: "Be totally committed and persistent."

*V.J.D. MANAGEMENT, 7 Ch. Taverney, 1218 Grand-Saconnex, Geneva **Switzerland**. Phone: (41)22.798.38.65. Fax: (41)22.798.15.23. Managing Director: José Dubey. Management firm and music publisher (Zero Problem Publishing/SUISA). Represents individual artists, groups and songwriters; currently handles 5 acts. Receives 20-30% commission. Reviews material for acts.
How to Contact: Write or call first and obtain permission to submit. Prefers cassette (or VHS PAL videocassette) with 5 songs. Does not return unsolicited material. Reports in 5 weeks.
Music: Mostly pop and rock. Current acts include Ho-Saí Pop (band), Dom Torsch (singer/songwriter/producer), Francie Conway (folk-rock singer), Chris Comet (producer) and Carolyn Foxx (vocalist).

VALEX TALENT AGENCY, and Pyramid Sound Records, P.O. Box 241, Ithaca NY 14851. (607)273-3931. Publishing President: John Perialas. Booking Vice President: Fred Johnson. Management firm, booking agency and music publisher. Estab. 1959. Represents artists, groups and songwriters in northeast US; currently handles 20 acts. Receives 15-25% commission. Reviews material for acts.
How to Contact: Prefers 7½ ips reel-to-reel or cassette with 3-6 songs and lead sheet. SASE. Reports in 1 month. "Songwriters please send cassettes or 7½ ips reel-to-reel in care of John Perialas, Copper John Music. After sending material allow appropriate time for material to be reviewed (2 weeks); then follow with call."
Music: Mostly top 40, rock and new wave; also country pop, dance, easy listening, MOR, R&B, rock, and pop. Works with vocalists, show, dance and bar bands. Current acts include Atlas (contemporary funk/rock), Charlie Starr (country rock), Bernie Milton (soul/R&B), Raven (heavy metal) and Kinetics (new wave).
Tips: "Don't give up. Push that extra mile."

VAN DYKE ENTERPRISES, Box 275, Hanover PA 17331. (717)632-4075. Manager: Steve Eck. Management firm, booking agency and record company (Aria Records). Estab. 1977. Represents local, regional and international individual artists; currently handles 3 acts. Receives 10-15% commission. Reviews material for acts.
How to Contact: Submit demo tape by mail. Unsolicited submissions are OK. Prefers cassette (or videocassette if available) with 4 songs and lyric sheet. Reports in 3 weeks.
Music: Mostly country, pop and rock. Works primarily with country. Current act includes Bruce Van Dyke (country), Westwind (country) and Sherwood Country (traditional country).
Tips: "We are looking for clean country ballads and up-tempo country songs."

*RICHARD VARRASSO MANAGEMENT, P.O. Box 387, Fremont CA 94537. (415)792-8910. Management firm. Represents local, regional or international individual artists, groups and songwriters; currently handles 2 acts. Receives 20% commission. Reviews material for acts.
How to Contact: Submit demo tape by mail. Prefers cassette. Does not return unsolicited material. Reports in 6 months.
Music: Current acts include Greg Kihn, Jimmy Lyon and Chaz Ross.

VELVETT RECORDING COMPANY, 517 W. 57th St., Los Angeles CA 90037. (213)753-7893. Manager: Aaron Johnson. Management firm and record company. Represents artists, groups and songwriters; currently handles 5 acts. Reviews material for acts.
How to Contact: Prefers cassette with 2-3 songs and lead sheet. SASE.
Music: Mostly blues and gospel; also church/religious, R&B, rock, soul and top 40/pop. Works primarily with show and dance bands and vocalists. Current acts include Arlene Bell (soul/top 40/pop artist), Chick Willis (blues artist), and Jay Harmon (top 40 singer).

VICTORY ARTISTS, 1054 Conifer Ln., Petaluma CA 94954. (707)762-4858. Director A&R: Shelly Trumbo. Management firm, music publisher (Light Force Music/ASCAP) and record company (Victory Label/Bay City Records/Frenze). Estab. 1985. Represents local, regional and international individual artists and groups; currently handles 6 acts. Receives 15% commission. Reviews material for acts.

How to Contact: Write first and obtain permission to submit. Prefers cassette (or VHS videocassette) with 3 songs and lyric sheets. "Good home video is OK. Tapes must be good quality cassettes." SASE. Reports in 8 weeks.

Music: Mostly pop/rock, power ballad material and contemporary Christian. Works primarily with female rock singers and female front with group. Current acts include Shelly T (rock vocalist with band), Jonathon Raupp (singer/songwriter) and Justin Sayre (rock act).

*VISION MANAGEMENT, 7958 Beverly Blvd., Los Angeles CA 90048. (213)658-8744. Owner/Artist Manager: Shelly Heber. Management firm. Represents local, regional or international individual artists and groups; currently handles 4 acts. Reviews material for acts.

How to Contact: Write or call first and obtain permission to submit. Prefers cassette with 3 songs maximum. SASE. Reports in 2 weeks.

Music: Mostly blues/rock and Anita Bakerish R&B. Works primarily with guitarists and vocalists. Current acts include Robbey Ford (guitarist/vocalist), Dave Alvin (guitarist/songwriter/vocalist) and Marilyn Scott (vocalist/songwriter).

Tips: "Present no more than three songs in as professional manner as possible."

*VISION MUSIC GROUP INC., Suite #"C", 435 Eastern Blvd., Baltimore MD 21221. (301)687-4100. FAX: (301)687-4102. President: Ernest W. Cash. Management firm, music publisher (Ernie Cash Music/BMI), record company (Confidential Records Inc.). Estab. 1988. Represents local, regional or international individual artists, groups, songwriters. Reviews material for acts.

How to Contact: Write or call first to arrange personal interview. Prefers cassette (or VHS videocassette if available) with any number of songs and lyric and lead sheet. SASE.

Music: Mostly country, pop and gospel; also contemporary, light rock and blues. Works primarily with individual country artists and groups. Current acts include Ernie Cash and Jimmy Peppers (country singer).

Tips: "Above all be honest with me and I will work with you. Please give me time to review your material and give it a justifiable chance with our music group."

VOKES BOOKING AGENCY, Box 12, New Kensington PA 15068-0012. (412)335-2775. President: Howard Vokes. Represents individual artists, country and bluegrass bands. For special occasions books nationally known acts from Grand Ole Op'ry, Jamboree U.S.A., Appalachian Jubliee, etc. Receives 10-20% commission.

How to Contact: New artists send 45 rpm record, cassette or LP. Reports back within a week.

Music: Country, bluegrass, old time and gospel; no rock or country rock. "We work mostly with traditional country bands and bluegrass groups that play various bars, hotels, clubs, lounges, or fund raising projects." Current acts include Howard Vokes & His Country Boys (country), Mel Anderson, A.J. Jenkins, Bunnie Mills, Morgan Ruppe, Bobby Yates, Wayne Copley, Shawn Lee, Luke Gordon and Norman Wade.

BEN WAGES AGENCY, 2513 Denny Ave., Pascagoula MS 39567. (601)769-7104 or FAX: (601)769-8590. Owner: B. Wages. Management firm and booking agency. Estab. 1978. Represents local, regional and international individual artists, groups and songwriters; currently handles 200 acts. Receives 10-15% commission. Reviews material for acts.

How to Contact: Submit demo tape by mail. Unsolicited submissions are OK. Prefers cassette (or videocassette). SASE. Reports in 4 weeks.

Music: Mostly country/nostalgia and rock. Works primarily with name acts and dance bands. Current acts include Percy Sledge, Ace Cannon and John Fred.

*LOUIS WALSH MANAGEMENT/BOOKING AGENCY, 1, The Elms, Grove House, Milltown Road, Dublin 6 **Ireland**. Phone: 619212 or 697025. Management firm and booking agency. Represents individual artists, groups and songwriters. Receives 10-20% commission. Reviews material for acts.

How to Contact: Prefers cassette (or VHS videocassette) with 2 songs and lyric or lead sheet. Reports in 3 weeks.

Music: Mostly pop, rock and country. Works primarily with pop singers, rock bands, dance bands and country and western. Currrent acts include Johnny Logan (singer/songwriter), Linda Martin (pop female singer), Dickie Rock (male vocalist) and Jump the Gun (pop/rock).

WESTWOOD ENTERTAINMENT GROUP, Suite 127, 1692 Oak Tree Rd., Edison NJ 08820. (201)548-6700. FAX: (201)548-6748. President: Victor Kaplij. Director of A&R: Kevin McCabe. Artist management agency (Westunes Music/ASCAP). Estab. 1985. Represents regional artists and groups; currently handles 1 act. Receives 15% commission. Reviews material for acts.

How to Contact: Prefers cassette with 3 songs and lyric sheet. SASE. Reports in 6 weeks.
Music: Mostly rock; also pop. Works primarily with singer/songwriters, show bands and rock groups. Current acts include The Pressures of Time (rock).
Tips: "Present a professional promotional/press package (3) song limit."

*ALAN WHITEHEAD & ASSOCIATES LTD., 2 Great Marlborough St., London W1V 1DE **United Kingdom.** Phone: (01)734-5018. Managing Director: Alan Whitehead. Management firm (Alan Whitehear Management), booking agency, music publisher (Good God Music/PRS) and record producer. Represents individual artists, groups and songwriters; currently handles 10 acts. Receives 15-20% commission. Reviews material for acts.
How to Contact: Prefers cassette (or VHS videocassette). SAE and IRC. Reports in 1 week.
Music: Mostly pop; also dance music. Works primarily with vocalists, pop duo and trios. Current acts include David Marcus (singer), Liquirice All Sorts (group) and Bimbo's (2 girl singing act).
Tips: "Have a polite and professional attitude."

SHANE WILDER ARTISTS' MANAGEMENT, Box 3503, Hollywood CA 90078. (818)508-1433. President: Shane Wilder. Management firm, music publisher (Shane Wilder Music/BMI) and record producer (Shane Wilder Productions). Represents artists and groups; currently handles 10 acts. Receives 15% commission. Reviews material for acts.
How to Contact: Prefers cassette (or videocassette) with 4-10 songs and lyric sheet. SASE. Reports in 1 month.
Music: Country. Works primarily with single artists and groups. Current acts include Mike Franklin (country recording artist), Teresa O'Dell (country artist), Denise Myatt, Craig Reynolds (songwriter), Wynn Hammons (country artist), Jane Tyler (actress), Melanie Ray (country singer and actress) and Jacklyn Palmer (film actress).
Tips: "Make sure your work is highly commercial. We are looking for strong female country songs for major artists. Material should be available for publishing with Shane Wilder Music, BMI."

WOLFTRACKS MANAGEMENT, Box 10205, Rockville MD 20895. (301)942-5420. Director: David J. Galinsky. Management firm. Estab. 1986. Represents local, regional and international individual artists and groups; currently handles 2 acts. Receives 15-20% commission. Reviews material for acts.
How to Contact: Submit demo tape by mail. Unsolicited submissions are OK. Prefers cassette (or videocassette) with 4 songs and lyric sheet. Does not return unsolicited material. Reports in 2-3 weeks.
Music: Mostly original hard rock, pop/dance and progressive. Current acts include Rob Wolf (guitarist/songwriter/singer), and Dean Ray (alternative rock).
Tips: "Hard work and talent will pay off."

RICHARD WOOD ARTIST MANAGEMENT, 42 Clinton Ave., Staten Island NY 10301. (718)981-0641. Contact: Richard Wood. Management firm. Estab. 1974. Represents musical groups; currently handles 2 acts. Receives 10-15% commission. Reviews material for acts.
How to Contact: Prefers cassette and lead sheet. SASE.
Music: Mostly dance, R&B and top 40/pop; also MOR. Works primarily with "high energy" show bands, bar bands and dance bands. Current acts include Sister and Brother (R&B/pop band).
Tips: "Please be versatile and able to make changes in material to suit the type of acts I book. Most of the material I receive only deals with love as a theme. Try to write to other subjects that are contemporary i.e. honesty, politics, peace in the world. Pay special attention to lyrics – try to go beyond the basics and paint pictures with the words."

WORLD CLASS TALENT, 1522 Demonbreun, Nashville TN 37203. (615)244-1964. Booking agency. Estab. 1983. Represents local, regional and international individual artists and groups; currently handles 15 acts.
How to Contact: Write first and obtain permission to submit or arrange personal interview. Prefers cassette (VHS videocassette) and lyric sheet. Does not return unsolicited material. Reports as soon as possible.
Music: Mostly country, gospel and pop. Work primarily with vocalists, band members and comedians. Current acts include Barbara Mandrell (country singer), Joe Napote (comedian) and Steve Hall (country singer/puppeteer/comedian).
Tips: "Get a major or top independent record deal then call for an appointment with one of our agents. Bring your best material. We're anxious to listen."

WORLD WIDE MEDIA, 9000 Sunset Blvd., #710, Los Angeles CA 90069. (213)274-0211. President: Grace Reinbold. Management firm. Estab. 1984. Represents local, regional and international groups; currently handles 3 acts. Receives 15-20% commission. Reviews material for acts.

How to Contact: Write and obtain permission to submit. Prefers cassette with 3-4 songs and lead sheet. Does not return unsolicited material. Reports in 2 weeks. Include bio and photo.
Music: Mostly rock, pop and heavy metal. Works primarily with aggressive rock bands. Current acts include The Royal Court of China (hard rock band), Richie Owens and Big Sky (contemporary rock).

*DOUGLAS A. YEAGER PRODUCTIONS, INC., 300 W. 55th St., New York NY 10019. (212)245-0240. President: Doug Yeager. Management firm and music publisher (Aixoise Music Co./ASCAP). Estab. 1971. Represents local, regional or national individual artists, groups and songwriters; currently handles 5 acts. Receives 10-25% commission. Reviews material for acts.
How to Contact: Prefers cassette with 4 songs and lyric sheets. SASE. Reports in 2 months.
Music: Mostly R&B ballads, R&B dance and pop ballads; also folk/pop, folk/political and gospel pop/rock. Works primarily with vocalists (pop/R&B/folk-rock). Currents acts include Richie Havens, Cliff Eberhardt (folk/rock), Michelle Pleeter (pop/R&B) and Josh White, Jr. (pop/gospel).
Tips: "Do not send songs that are less commercial (accessible) than what is being played today on commercial radio."

*ZAR MANAGEMENT, (formerly Masters Management), Dreilinden Str. 42, St. Gallen CH 9011 **Switzerland.** Holder: Victor Waldburger. Management firm, music publisher (Zar Musikveriag), record label and record producer. Estab. 1980. Represents individual artists, groups, songwriters and producers; currently handles 5 acts. Reviews material for acts. Receives 20% commission.
How to Contact: Write or call to submit or to arrange a personal interview. Prefers cassette (or European VHS videocassette). Reports only if interested.
Music: Mostly pop, dance,hard rock, heavy metal. Current acts include Taboo, Sultan and Kaboko.

ZEE TALENT AGENCY, 3095 Sinclair St., Winnipeg, Manitoba R2P 1Y6 **Canada.** (204)338-7094. President/Agent: Linda Zagozewski. Agent: Duncan Wilson. Booking agency. Estab. 1980. Represents groups; currently handles 22 acts. Receives 10-15% commission. Reviews material for acts.
How to Contact: Write first and obtain permission to submit. Prefers cassette (or videocassette). SAE and IRC. Reports in 2 weeks.
Music: Mostly rock, top 40 and country/rock; also variety and show music. Current acts include Misiqa, Maclean & Maclean and Get Back.

Managers and Booking Agents/'90-'91 changes

The following markets appeared in the 1990 edition of *Songwriter's Market* but do not appear in the 1991 edition. Those companies that did not respond to our request for an update of their listing may not have done so for a variety of reasons—they may be out of business, for example, or they may be overstocked with submissions.

Adoration, Inc. (asked to be deleted)
Ajaye Entertainment Corp. (asked to be deleted)
All Star Talent & Promotions (did not respond)
Don Anderson Production, Inc. (asked to be deleted)
Michael Anthony Agency (did not respond)
Pat Armstrong & Associates, Inc. (did not respond)
Ars Nova Management (moved; no forwarding address)
Artist Management International, Ltd. (asked to be deleted)
Artwork Management & Design (moved; no forwarding address)
Be-All and End-All (did not respond)
Big Picture Entertainment (did

not respond)
Wal Bishop Enterprises (did not respond)
Brinkworth Enterprises (did not respond)
Brusco Management Ltd. (did not respond)
BSA Inc. (did not respond)
Canadian Talent International (did not respond)
Capitol Booking Service, Inc. (asked to be deleted)
Marv Dennis & Associates, Inc. (asked to be deleted)
Steve Draper Enterprises (did not respond)
Encore Entertainment (asked to be deleted)
Entertainment Express Management and Productions (did not respond)
James Evans Management Co. (did not respond)
Falcon Productions (did not

respond)
Bobby Farrell International Management & Promotions (deleted)
Franklin Entertainment Group (asked to be deleted)
Peter Freedman Entertainment (did not respond)
Gail and Rice Productions (did not respond)
Gallin-Morey Associates (asked to be deleted)
Glo Gem Productions, Inc. (did not respond)
Gary Good Management (did not respond)
Great Plains Associates, Inc. (did not respond)
Liz Gregory Productions/Talent Agency (did not respond)
Bob Hale Talent/lj Productions (did not respond)
Geoffrey Hansen Enterprises,

Ltd. (did not respond)
IEA/International Entertainment Associates (did not respond)
Inside Music, Inc. (did not respond)
Invasion (did not respond)
It Management (did not respond)
JVS Productions (did not respond)
Key Artist Management & Entertainment Consultants (did not respond)
King Eugene Productions (did not respond)
La La La Productions (did not respond)
Lane-3 Productions (did not respond)
Stan Lawrence Productions (did not respond)
Buddy Lee Attractions (asked to be deleted)
Light Force Music/Victory Media Group (did not respond)
Majestic Artists, Inc. (did not respond)
Louis Marek Music Inc. (did not respond)
Masada Music, Inc. (did not respond)
Media Five Entertainment (did not respond)
Media Promotion Enterprises (did not respond)
Joseph C. Messina, Cartoon Records (did not respond)
Midcoast, Inc. (did not respond)
Mob Management (did not respond)
Monterey Peninsula Artists (asked to be deleted)
MSP (Mascara Snake Productions) (moved; no forwarding address)
Multi-Media Management (did not respond)
Music City Promotions (did not respond)
National Booking Agency of Dallas (did not respond)
Nelson Management (did not respond)
J.P. Newby (did not respond)
Not Rude Productions (did not respond)
The Office, Inc. (did not respond)

Dee O'Reilly Management, Ltd. (did not respond)
Orpheus Entertainment (did not respond)
Palmer Enterprises (did not respond)
Paper Clip Productions, Inc. (did not respond)
Pat Patton and Associates (did not respond)
Pietro Talent U.S.A. (did not respond)
Possibilities Unlimited, Inc. (did not respond)
Producers, Incorporated (asked to be deleted)
Propas Management Corporation (did not respond)
Quinto Productions/Records (did not respond)
Rainbow Collection Ltd. (did not respond)
Patrick Rains and Associates (asked to be deleted)
Ric Rac Inc. (did not respond)
Rice Management Group Inc. (did not respond)
Rich + Famous Management Inc. (did not respond)
Rightrack Management/Chaser Music (did not respond)
Rob-Lee Music (did not respond)
Rochester Talent Unlimited, Inc. (did not respond)
Rodanca Music (did not respond)
Rolling Thunder Productions (did not respond)
Nicholas Rubenstein Organization (did not respond)
Scott-Dean Agency (did not respond)
Segue Management (did not respond)
Shadowfacts Management (did not respond)
Mickey Sherman Artist Management & Development (did not respond)
Al Shotwell Management (did not respond)
Michael Skinner Productions (did not respond)
Southern Reign Management (did not respond)
Southern Talent International (did not respond)
Starmount Entertainment (did not respond)

Starplayer Attractions, Inc. (did not respond)
Bill Stein Associates Inc. (did not respond)
Ronald Stein Productions (did not respond)
Stinnette Entertainment Agency (did not respond)
Falcon Stuart Ltd. (did not respond)
Tabitha Music (did not respond)
The Talent Connection/Radioactive Mgmt. (did not respond)
Talent One Productions Inc. (moved; no forwarding address)
Tammi Artist Management (did not respond)
TAS Music Co./Dave Tasse Entertainment (did not respond)
TCR Productions (did not respond)
William Tenn Management (did not respond)
Bill Thomas Management (asked to be deleted)
Trend Records (R) (did not respond)
Triangle Talent, Inc. (did not respond)
23 West Entertainment, Inc. (did not respond)
Umpire Enterprizes (did not respond)
United Entertainment (did not respond)
Wallach Enterprises (did not respond)
Wide Country Music (did not respond)
Thomas Wiggins & Associates (did not respond)
Elmer Willett Associates (did not respond)
Winterswan (did not respond)
Wise Entertainment (did not respond)
The Erv Woolsey Company (did not respond)
World Wide Management (did not respond)
Wyatt Management Inc. (did not respond)
Zane Management, Inc. (did not respond)

Advertising, AV, and Commercial Music Firms

The field of advertising, audiovisual and commercial music production represents a whole different world—and market—for the songwriter. Music for advertising and commercial purposes encompasses not only television and radio jingles and background music, but also sound effects, music for use with educational projects, scoring of corporate or "industrial" films and AV presentations, and more.

Commercial music can be a very lucrative field for the songwriter who is energetic, has a gift for hook-filled melodies and is able to write in many different styles. One day you might be called upon to write a reggae-flavored jingle for a suntan oil, the next day you could be writing bluegrass for a clothing store or scoring a string quartet piece for a public radio promotional spot. It's a fast-paced business in which quick, high-quality work is expected. For every writer who can't handle the pace, there are ten more waiting to take his place. The good news is that if you can prove yourself among the ad executives—if your work is fast and good—you will never lack employment.

Advertising agencies

Advertising agencies work on assignment as their clients' needs arise. They work closely with their clients on broadcast campaigns. Through consultation and input from the creative staff, agencies establish a "feel" they believe commercials should project for a client's product or image. They seek jingles and music to stimulate the consumer to identify with a product and hum the commercial in his head—while paying the cashier for the product or service.

When listening to a demo, agencies are not looking for a finished product so much as for an indication of creativity and diversity. Most composers will put together a reel of excerpts of work from previous projects, or short pieces of music which show they can write in a variety of styles and arrange and produce different effects.

When contacting ad agencies, keep in mind that they are looking for music that can capture and hold an audience's attention in a very short time span (sometimes within 10 or 15 seconds). Your demo should be fast-paced and interesting. You should type on the label and/or indicate in your cover letter that you are the composer, to differentiate your tape from those of singers and musicians looking for jingle work.

Audiovisual firms

Audiovisual firms create a variety of products. Some provide the music for advertising agencies that do most of the work on an ad campaign themselves, but have a limited creative team or little experience in music production. Audiovisual firms also produce slide presentations, film and videos for sales meetings and other corporate gatherings. They also do films, videos and slide shows for education markets as well as for the entertainment field. Some produce feature motion pictures and television shows. How-to videos are available on nearly every subject and represent a market for clever songwriters to explore. Spoken-word videos, especially those for children, are increasing in popularity and often use background music to set the tone and complement the story or spoken message. Many audiovisual production houses have limited staffs and tight deadlines, and welcome ideas (and, ultimately, finished productions) from outside songwriters.

Sometimes when audiovisual producers need music for a production, they will turn to commercial music houses or music libraries simply because of time and budget considerations. But when they are searching for something fresh, original and unique, a competent and savvy songwriter will be called in to provide exactly what is needed—and be paid well for his efforts. All the audiovisual firms listed here have expressed an interest in receiving queries or submissions from outside writers. The key in submitting your demo is to demonstrate your versatility in writing specialized background music and themes. Listings for specific companies will tell what facet(s) of the audiovisual field they are involved in and what types of clients they serve.

Commercial music houses and music libraries

Commercial music houses are companies which are contracted (either by an advertising agency or the advertiser himself) to compose custom jingles. Since they are neither an advertising agency nor an audiovisual firm, their main concern is music. And they use a lot of it—some composed by inhouse songwriters and some contributed by outside writers.

Music libraries are a bit different in that their music is not custom composed for a specific client or advertising agency. What the music library provides is a vast collection of instrumental music in many different styles that, for an annual fee or on a per use basis, the customer can use however he chooses (most often in audiovisual and multi-media applications).

Like the other types of businesses in this section, music libraries often use the talents of outside composers.

Companies within this section which are either commercial music houses or music libraries will tell you that in boldface type within their listing.

Most of the companies listed here pay by the job, but some pay by the hour and others may negotiate a contract that includes royalty payments. Be sure you understand upfront exactly what is expected of you (number of songs, type of music, length of pieces, etc.) and know exactly how much and when you will be paid.

You may be asked to sell all rights or one-time rights, depending upon the particular job and needs of the client. All rights means the buyer can use your work any way he wants and for as long as he chooses. One-time rights means your material can only be used for one presentation, and all other uses must be renegotiated with you. A "buy-out" is when the writer is paid one flat fee and does not receive any additional money for future uses of his work.

Writing jingles and composing themes on assignment are not simple tasks. Commercial music production is an extremely demanding, highly competitive field. Especially in advertising, show that you can be creative in "selling" yourself as a writer. You can make a good impression on the executives you contact by finding an inventive way of calling attention to your demo package.

For additional names and addresses of advertising agencies (but no marketing information), refer to the *Standard Directory of Advertising Agencies* (National Register Publishing Company). Audiovisual firms are listed in the *Audiovisual Marketplace* (R.R. Bowker).

AD HOC MARKETING RESOURCES, INC., 145 West 28th St., New York NY 10025. (212)947-7100. Creative Director: Karen Hochman. Advertising agency. Clients include financial, travel, publishing and consumer products firms. Estab. 1983. Uses the services of independent songwriters/composers and lyricists for commercials for radio and TV. Commissions 3 composers and 2 lyricists/year. Pays by the job. Buys all rights and one-time rights.
How to Contact: Submit demo tape of previous work. Query with resume of credits or write to arrange a personal interview. Prefers cassette (or VHS videocassette). SASE. "We keep resume on file." Reports in 3 weeks.
Music: Uses all styles for commercials.
Tips: "Submit tape showing range of work. We prefer to work with the same people on a number of projects (i.e. people who we grow comfortable with)."

THE AD TEAM, 15251 NE 18th Ave., N. Miami Beach FL 33162. (305)949-8326. Vice President: Zevin Auerbach. Advertising agency. Clients include automobile dealerships, radio stations, TV stations, retail. Seeking background music for commercials and jingles. Uses the services of independent songwriters for jingles for commercials. Commissions 4-6 songwriters. Pays by the job.
How to Contact: Submit demo tape of previously aired work. Prefers cassette. SASE.
Music: Uses all styles of music for all kinds of assignments. Most assignments include writing jingles for radio and television campaigns.

*AIM, INC., 308 Pompano, Foster City CA 94404. (415)349-5555. President: James H. Fielen. Advertising agency. Clients include automotive, hotels and manufacturers. Estab. 1979. Uses the services of music houses and independent songwriters/composers for radio and TV commercials. Commissions 3 lyricists/year. Pays by the job. Buys all rights.
How to Contact: Submit demo tape of previous work; write to arrange personal interview. Prefers cassette. SASE, but prefers to keep material on file.

*AIR SOUND/PLUM PRODUCTIONS, 1116 Boylston St., Boston MA 02115. (617)282-0147. Studio Manager: Don O'Brien. Scoring service, jingle/commercial music production house and music sound effect library. Clients include musicians and ad agencies. Estab. 1980. Uses the services of independent songwriters/composers and lyricists for scoring of films, background music for documentaries, jingles for radio, TV and commercials for radio, TV. Commissions 4 composers and 2 lyricists/year. Pays by the job.
How to Contact: Submit tape demonstrating composition skill and manuscript showing music scoring skills. Prefers cassette with 2-3 songs and lead sheet. SASE. Reports in 2 weeks.
Music: Uses all types.
Tips: "Make yourself as versatile as possible—able to work in many idioms."

ALEXIS MUSIC INC. (ASCAP), MARVELLE MUSIC CO. (BMI), Box 532, Malibu CA 90265. (213)463-5998. President: Lee Magid. Music Publishing and Production Co. Clients include all types—record companies and advertising agencies. Estab. 1960. Uses the services of music houses, independent songwriters and producers for scoring of recordings, background music for film or video or theatre, jingles for commericials, commercials for radio and TV and manufacturers, events, conventions, etc. Commissions 5 composers and 5 lyricists/year. Pays by the job or by royalty. Buys all rights, publishing.
How to Contact: Submit demo tape of previous work or tape demonstrating composition skills or query with resume of credits. Prefers cassette (or VHS videocassette) with 3 pieces and lyric sheets. "If interested, we will contact you." SASE; keeps material on file only if needed. Include phone number and address on tape. Reports in 6 weeks.
Music: Uses R&B, gospel, jazz, Latin, Afro-Cuban, country; anything of substance.
Tips: "Send me a good demo, that can be understood so that we can judge. Send only one cassette."

ANCORA PRODUCTIONS, INC., 44 Bridge St., Corning NY 14830. (607)962-3170. Chief Executive Officer: Anthony Rocco. Audiovisual firm. Clients include Fortune 500 corporations. Uses services of music houses, independent songwriters/composers and lyricists for scoring of original music or background music for multi-image presentations. Commissions 2 composers and 1 lyricist/year. Pays $6,000-8,000/job. Buys all rights.
How to Contact: Submit demo tape of previous work or write or call first to arrange personal interview. Prefers cassette with minimum of 3 songs. Prefers to keep submitted work on file.
Music: Mostly upbeat for multi-image assignments.

ANDERSON COMMUNICATIONS, 2245 Godbyrd, Atlanta GA 30349. (404)752-9353. President: Al Anderson. Producer: Vanessa Vaughn. Advertising agency and syndication operation. Estab. 1971. Clients include major corporations, institutions and media. Uses the services of music houses for scoring and jingles for TV and radio commercials and background music for TV and radio programs. Commissions 5-6 songwriters or composers and 6-7 lyricists/year. Pays by the job. Buys all rights.
How to Contact: Call first and obtain permission to submit. Prefers cassette. SASE, but prefers to keep material on file. Reports in 2 weeks or "when we have projects requiring their services."
Music: Uses a variety of music for music beds for commercials and jingles for nationally syndicated radio programs and commercials targeted at the black consumer market.
Tips: "Be sure that the composition plays well in a 60 second format."

ANGEL FILMS COMPANY, Rt. One, Box 69, New Franklin MO 65274-9998. (314)698-3900. President: Arlene Hulse. Motion picture and record production company (Angel One Records). Estab. 1980. Uses the services of independent songwriters/composers, lyricists and in-house agency for scoring and background music for feature films, music videos, cartoons, television productions and records.

Commissions more than 12 composers and 12 lyricists/year. Payment depends upon budget; each project has a different pay scale. Buys all rights.
How to Contact: Submit demo tape of previous work or tape demonstrating composition skills; submit manuscript showing music scoring skills; query with resume of credits; or write to arrange personal interview. Prefers cassette (or VHS videocassette) with 3 pieces and lyric and lead sheet. "Do not send originals." SASE, but prefers to keep material on file. Reports in 3 weeks.
Music: Uses basically MOR, but will use anything but C&W and religious for record production, film, television and cartoon scores.
Tips: "We prefer middle of the road music, but are open to all types. We use a lot of background music in our work, plus we have our own record label, Angel One, that is looking for music to record. Don't copy other work. Just be yourself and do the best that you can. That is all that we can ask."

ANGLE FILMS, 1341 Ocean Ave., Suite 240, Santa Monica CA 90401. President: John Engel. Motion picture production company and freelance producer. Estab. 1985. Clients include advertising agencies and motion picture production/distribution companies. Uses the services of music houses and independent songwriters/composers for scoring of films and commercials for TV. Pays by the job or other arrangement "entirely dependent on production and company contracting us." Buys one-time rights.
How to Contact: Prefers cassette with 5 pieces and lyric sheet. Does not return unsolicited material; prefers to keep on file. Reports only if interested.
Music: Uses all genres for short drama and feature films.
Tips: "Submit large-orchestra pieces and arrangements and be patient."

APON PUBLISHING COMPANY, INC., Box 3082 Steinway St., Long Island City NY 11103. (718)721-5599. Manager: Don Zeemann. Jingle/**commercial music production house**, music sound effect library and background music. Clients include background music companies, motion picture industry and advertising agencies. Estab. 1957. Uses the services of own special suppliers for background music for every use of the industries, jingles for advertising agencies and commercials for radio and TV. Payment is negotiated. Buys all rights.
How to Contact: Send demo cassette with background music, no voices. Prefers cassette with 2-5 pieces. SASE, but prefers to keep material on file. Reports in 2 months.
Music: Uses only background music, no synthesizer life instruments.

NICOLAS ASTOR-GROUF ENTERPRISES, P.O. Box 3248 Yale Station, New Haven CT 06520. Vice President: Richard Whattey. Advertising agency and jingle/**commercial music production house**. Clients include commercial products. Uses the services of independent songwriters/composers and lyricists for jingles for radio and TV commercials. Commissions 25 composers and 25 lyricists/year. Pays statutory royalty. Buys all rights.
How to Contact: Submit demo tape of previous work or tape demonstrating composition skills. Prefers cassette (or VHS videocassette). SASE, but prefers to keep material on file. Reports in 6 weeks.
Music: Uses up-tempo for commercials.

ATLANTIC FILM AND VIDEO, 171 Park Lane, Massapequa NY 11758. (516)798-4106. Sound Designer: Michael Canzoneri. Motion picture production company. Clients include commercial. Estab. 1986. Uses the services of independent songwriters/composers and lyricists for background music for movies and commercials for TV. Commissions 1 composer and 1 lyricist/year. Pays $75-300/job. Buys one-time rights.
How to Contact: Submit demo tape of previous work or query with resume of credits. Prefers cassette or 7½ ips reel-to-reel. "Please specify what role you had in creating the music: composer, performer, etc." SASE, but prefers to keep material on file. Reports in 6 weeks.
Music: Uses jazz—modern, classical for films.
Tips: "Have patience and good songs."

AUDIO-VISUAL ASSOCIATES, 334 E. 31st St., Kansas City MO 64108. (816)931-4102. Contact: Don James. Clients include industrial firms. Uses services of songwriters for thematic scores in films and filmstrips. Payment negotiable. Buys all rights.

*AVID PRODUCTIONS, 235 E. 3rd Ave., San Mateo CA 94401. (415)347-3417. Producer: Chris Craig. Music sound effect library, scoring service, jingle/commercial music production house and video productions. Clients include corporate clients/independent producer. Estab. 1984. Uses the services of independent songwriters/composers for scoring of video production, corporate identity themes and jingles for video production. Commissions 1-2 composers/year. Pays $100-500/job. Rights negotiable.

Close-up

Ron McCroby
Songwriter/Jingle Writer/Performer
Chagrin Falls, Ohio

Photo by: George Remington

Ron McCroby whistles while he works. Literally. Using only his own breath and mouth (an instrument he has dubbed the "puccolo"), Ron performs solo and along with some of the world's greatest jazz and classical musicians at festivals and concerts around the globe. He has received many honors and much critical praise for his whistling and has appeared on television many times on shows like Merv Griffin, PM Magazine and Johnny Carson's Tonight Show. Besides his talents as a whistler, he is a composer, arranger, producer and prolific jingle writer.

Ron has been writing music for advertising for many years. His work has helped to sell products and services for companies such as Kenner Toys, Hillshire Farms, Wendy's and King's Island. Ron shares with *Songwriter's Market* some thoughts and advice about the business of jingle writing.

"There are big differences between songwriting and jingle writing. First, a jingle has to be memorable; it has to have a little hook in it someplace that sells the product. Lyric writing is very important to music for commercial applications because you have to know how to use the product name as many times as you can without being obnoxious about it. I have always tried to get the name of the product or company into the music track as soon as possible. And of course it's very important to have a melody that is easy to remember. I think it's much harder to write an effective jingle than it is to write a song. When you're writing a song, you don't have any time constraints; you're totally wide open to do as many verses or repetitive lyrics as you want. But with jingles you only have so much time – 30 seconds, generally, sometimes only 15. You have to be pretty sharp to do all that magic in 15 or 30 seconds and make it come off artistically sound, pleasing and memorable – and sell the product."

Ron says that, unlike regular songwriting, jingle writing requires the ability to write in many different styles. "A lot of writers who are unsuccessful in the jingle industry are those whose music all sounds the same. Whether they're writing something for a truck or for food, it all sounds the same. My own philosophy has always been to create a piece of music that is identified somehow with the product the company is trying to sell."

For songwriters hoping to become jingle writers, Ron suggests practicing by rewriting jingles that are already being aired. "Take something that's already out there and do it a different way; try it the way you would like to have it done. If you hear something on the air and think, 'I could do better than that,' do it. Take another approach at it."

"Just start writing," says Ron. "Prepare a few demo tracks of your stuff and play them for the creative directors at the ad agencies. Show them that you're a source and that you could produce for them."

– Mark Garvey

How to Contact: Write or call first to arrange a personal interview. Prefers cassette (or VHS/¾" videocassette) with 2 songs. Prefers to keep material on file. Reports in 4 weeks.
Music: Uses up-tempo, high-tech sounds for training tapes/corporate ID pieces.

BALL COMMUNICATIONS, INC., 1101 N. Fulton Ave., Evansville IN 47710. (812)428-2300. President/ Creative Director: Martin A. Ball. Audiovisual and television production and meeting production firm. Estab. 1960. Clients include Fortune 500 firms. Uses the services of lyricists and independent songwriters/composers for jingles, background music and theme songs. Commissions 4 songwriters and 4 lyricists/year. Pays $1,500-2,500/job. Buys all rights.
How to Contact: Prefers cassette, 7½ ips reel-to-reel (or ½" videocassette). Does not return unsolicited material; prefers to keep on file. Responds by letter or telephone. SASE. Reports in 1 month.
Music: All types. Uses theme songs/jingles.

TED BARKUS COMPANY, INC., 1512 Spruce St., Philadelphia PA 19102. (215)545-0616. President: Allen E. Barkus. Advertising agency. Uses the services of independent songwriters and music houses for jingles and background music for commercials. Commissions 1-3 songwriters/year. Pays by the job. Buys all rights.
How to Contact: Call to arrange personal interview or write to obtain permission to submit. Prefers cassette (or VHS videocassette) with 3-5 pieces. SASE, but prefers to keep material on file "when the style matches our objectives."
Music: Uses various styles of music depending upon client needs for "positioning concepts with musical beds, doughnut for inserted copy."
Tips: "Learn as much as possible about the product and who the consumer will be before starting a project. Understand that the commercial also has to work with the print and television media in terms of everything else the client is doing."

*BARRON HILLMAN & MELLNICK, INC., 80 Broad St., Boston MA 02110. (617)482-3883. Vice President/Creative Director: Capel States. Ad agency. Estab. 1959. Uses services of songwriters for jingles and background music. Commissions 3-4 songwriters/year and 2 lyricists/year. Payment negotiable. Buys all rights.
How to Contact: Query first or submit demo tape of previous work. Prefers reel-to-reel or cassette (or videocassette) with 5-10 songs. SASE, but prefers to keep material on file.
Tips: "Be updated at all times on trends in the marketplace—music styles in vogue, etc."

BEASLEY OVERCASH & MOORE, INC., Suite 805, 3100 Smoketree Ct., Raleigh NC 27609. (919)872-0050. Creative Director: Jim Moore. Broadcast Producer: Jerry Stifelman. Advertising agency. Clients include retail and business-to-business. Uses services of music houses and independent songwriters/ composers for background music for videos and training films and commercials for radio and TV. Commissions 4-5 composers/year. Pays by the job. Buys all rights.
How to Contact: Submit demo tape of previous work. Prefers cassette (or VHS videocassette) with 4-5 pieces. Does not return unsolicited material; prefers to keep on file. Reports in 2 months.
Music: Uses popular, jazz and classical for commercials and videos.
Tips: "Send memorable lyrics, hummable tunes. No clichés."

NORMAN BEERGER PRODUCTIONS, 3217 S. Arville St., Las Vegas NV 89102. (702)876-2328. Owner: Norman Beerger. Audiovisual firm and wilderness video producer/distributor. Estab. 1984. Clients include Reader's Digest, National Wildlife Federation, consumers, audio/video/book catalogs and retail. Uses the services of music houses and independent songwriters/composers for background music for wilderness exploration videos. Commissions 6 composers/year. Pays 1¢/minute/cassette royalty. Buys non-exclusive rights.
How to Contact: Submit demo tape of previous work. Prefers cassette (or ½" VHS videocassette). SASE, but prefers to keep material on file. Reports in 1 month.
Music: Uses new age, contemporary, synthesizer music for educational films.
Tips: "Submit demo tape. It will be returned."

*THE BERKSHIRE GROUP, P.O. Box 14, Simsbury CT 06070. (203)658-0012. Coordinator: Rebecca Brown. Advertising agency. Clients include business-to-business, sports and industrial. Estab. 1982. Uses the services of music houses for jingles and commercials for radio and TV. Pays per arrangement. "Buys rights as required."
How to Contact: Submit demo tape of previous work demonstrating composition skills. Prefers cassette with 2-4 songs. Does not return unsolicited material; prefers to keep on file. Reports in 2 weeks.
Music: Uses easy listening, up-tempo and pop for slide presentations and commercials.

RALPH BING ADVERTISING CO., 16109 Selva Dr., San Diego CA 92128. (619)487-7444. President: Ralph S. Bing. Estab. 1946. Advertising agency. Clients include those in the automobile business. Uses the services of music houses for jingles. Pays by the job as determined by the producer. Buys all rights. Commissions 1-2 composers and lyricists/year.
How to Contact: Write first and obtain permission to submit. Prefers cassette with 3-6 songs. SASE, but prefers to keep material on file. Reports "when and if needed."
Music: Easy listening.
Tips: "Go with current trends as they occur."

THE BLACKWOOD AGENCY, INC., (formerly J. Ronald Gaffé, Inc.), 1831 Newman Rd., Okemos MI 48864. (517)349-6770. Production Manager: Christine Gaffe. Advertising agency. Estab. 1979. Clients include financial and package goods firms. Uses services of music houses for scoring of commercials and training films, background music for slide productions, jingles for clients and commercials for radio and TV. Commissions 3 composers/year. Pays by the job. Buys all rights.
How to Contact: Submit demo tape of previous work. Prefers cassette (or ¾" videocassette) with 6-10 songs. SASE, but prefers to keep material on file.
Tips: "Give us good demo work."

BLAIR ADVERTISING, INC., a member of the Omnicom Group, 96 College Ave., Rochester NY 14607. (716)473-0440. President/Creative Director: John R. Brown. Advertising agency. Member of AFTRA, SAG, ASCAP. Serves consumer, financial and packaged good clients. Uses staff writers and independent songwriters for jingles. Commissions 15 songwriters and 2 lyricists/year. Pays $5,000-30,000/job.
How to Contact: Query. Prefers cassette with 3-5 songs. Does not return unsolicited material.
Music: "We're seriously interested in hearing from good production sources. We have some of the world's best lyricists and songwriters working for us, but we're always ready to listen to fresh, new ideas."

***BLATTNER/BRUNNER INC.**, 814 Penn Ave., Pittsburgh PA 15222. (412)263-2979. Marketing Services Coordinator: Traci Trainor. Clients include retail/consumer; service; high-tech/industrial. Estab. 1975. Uses the services of music houses and independent songwriters/composers for scoring of commercials and videos, background music for TV and radio spots, jingles for TV and radio spots and commercials for radio, TV. Commissions 2-3 composers/year. Pays by the job. Buys all rights or one-time rights, depending on the job.
How to Contact: Submit demo tape of previous work demonstrating composition skills. Write first to arrange personal interview. Prefers cassette (or VHS or ¾" videocassette) with 5-10 songs. SASE but prefers to keep submitted materials on file.
Music: Uses up-beat, "unique-sounding music that stands out" for commercials and industrial video.
Tips: "We're always interested in hearing new pieces."

BRADLEY COMMUNICATIONS, 1840 S. Bragaw, Anchorage AK 99508. (907)276-6353. Copywriter: Katie Hickey. Advertising/public relations agency. Clients include tourism and development. Estab. 1968. Uses the services of music houses for background music for informative videos and jingles and commercials for radio/TV. Buys one-time rights.
How to Contact: Submit demo tape of previous work which demonstrate composition skills. Prefers cassette or VHS or ¾" videocassette. SASE, but prefers to keep materials on file. Reports back "when need arises."
Music: Uses up-tempo and emotional music.

BRAUNCO VIDEO, INC., Box 236, Warren IN 46792. (219)375-3148. Producer: Magley Tocsin. Video production company. Estab. 1988. Clients include industrial manufacturing, service companies, factories, United Way agencies, entertainers, songwriters, etc. Uses the services of independent songwriters/composers and house studio bands for jingles and background music for corporate video presentations. Commissions 3-6 composers/year. Pays by the job. Buys all rights.
How to Contact: Submit demo tape of previous work or write to arrange personal interview. Prefers cassette or 15 ips reel-to-reel (or ¾" videocassette) with many pieces. "We have no use for lyric or vocals." Does not return unsolicited material.

Listings of companies within this section which are either commercial music production houses or music libraries will have that information printed in boldface type.

Music: Uses up-tempo, heavy metal, R&B with a bit of jazz influence and soft music for promotional corporate demos.
Tips: "Believe in yourself."

BROACH AND CO., Box 1139, Greensboro NC 27402. (919)373-0752. Creative Director: Allen Broach. Advertising agency. Clients include furniture, banking, and consumer goods firms. Estab. 1982. Uses the services of music houses and independent songwriters/lyricists for scoring, background music for commercials and videos, jingles for commercials and commercials for radio and TV. Commissions 1-5 composers and up to 3 lyricists/year. Buys all rights or one-time rights.
How to Contact: Submit demo tape of previous work or tape demonstrating compositional skills. Prefers cassette with 6-10 songs and lead sheet. Does not return unsolicited submissions; prefers to keep submitted material on file.

BROADCAST VIDEO, INC., 20377 N.E. 15th Ct., Miami FL 33179. (305)653-7440. Senior Audio Engineer: Scott Pringle. Film/video post production house. Clients include advertising agencies, film/video producers. Audio department established 1988. Uses the services of music houses, independent songwriters/composers and music libraries for scoring and background music for commercials, documentaries and corporate presentations; jingles for commercials; and commercials for radio and TV. Pays by the job. Rights negotiated with client.
How to Contact: Query with resume of credits or write first to arrange personal interview. Prefers cassette or 7.5 or 15 ips reel-to-reel (or any videocassette). SASE, but prefers to keep material on file. Reports in 1 month.
Music: "We use music for commercials the most, but use songwriters most often for lengthier programs—corporate, documentaries, etc."

BURKHARDT & CHRISTY ADVERTISING, INC., 221 East 48th St., New York NY 10017. (212)688-2222. Creative Director: Ron Burkhardt. Advertising agency. Clients include Bogner of America, Sony Corporation, BMW Motorcycles, New York Hilton and Bitter Automobile. Estab. 1986. Uses the services of music houses for background mostly for radio, jingles for TV and radio and commercials for radio and TV. Pays by the job or royalty. Buys all rights or one-time rights.
How to Contact: Contact Karen LePri. Prefers cassette. Does not return unsolicited material.
Music: Uses all styles for commercials. Leans to avant-garde, "cutting edge" work.
Tips: "Send a good tape with a follow up."

*BUTWIN & ASSOCIATES, INC., 8700 Westmoreland Ln., Minneapolis MN 55426. (612)546-0203. President: Ron Butwin. Clients include corporate and retail. Estab. 1977. Uses the services of music houses and independent songwriters/composers for scoring, background music, jingles and commercials for radio, TV. Commissions 2-5 composers/year. Pays varying amount/job. Buys all rights and one-time rights.
How to Contact: Submit demo tape of previous work. Write first to arrange personal interview. Prefers cassette, ¼" videocassette. "We are only interested in high-quality professional work." Does not return unsolicited material but prefers to keep material on file.
Music: Uses easy listening, up-tempo, pop and jazz for slide presentations and commercials.

CAEDMON, 10 E. 53rd St., New York NY 10022. (212)207-7000 or 1-800-223-0420. Editorial Assistant: Anne Gaudinier. Spoken word (story) recording company. Clients include schools, libraries, retail stores and wholesalers. Uses the services of independent songwriters for background music for spoken-word recordings. Pays by the job. Buys one-time rights.
How to Contact: Write first to obtain permission to submit. Prefers cassette. SASE. Reports in 2 months.
Music: Uses background music for children's recordings and dramatic recordings.

CALDWELL VAN RIPER, 1314 N. Meridian, Indianapolis IN 46202. (317)632-6501. Executive Creative Director: Jeffrey Leiendecker. Advertising agency and public relations firm. Serves industrial, financial and consumer/trade clients. Uses jingles and background music for commercials. Commissions 25 pieces/year.
How to Contact: Submit demo tape of previously aired work or submit tape showing jingle/composition skills. Prefers standard audio cassette. SASE. Reports "as soon as possible."

CALF AUDIO, 157 Gray Rd., Ithaca NY 14850. (607)272-8964. President: Haines B. Cole. Vice President: J. Todd Hutchinson. Producer/Engineer: Alfred B. Grunwell. Assistant Engineer: Margaret T. Baker. Professional audio analysis and design; 24 track recording studio; audiovisual firm and **music/sound effects library**. Estab. 1977. Uses the services of music houses and independent songwriters/

composers for background music, jingles and radio and TV commercials and audiovisual presentations. Pays by the job. Buys all rights.

How to Contact: Submit demo tape of previous work; write to arrange personal interview. Prefers cassette or 15 ips reel-to-reel with 3-5 pieces. Send "full documentation." Does not return unsolicited material; prefers to keep on file. Reports in 3 weeks.

Music: Uses contemporary pop for educational films, slide presentations and commercials.

Tips: "Assimilate but don't duplicate works from the past. Take direction well."

CANARY PRODUCTIONS, Box 202, Bryn Mawr PA 19010. (215)825-1254. President: Andy Mark. Music library. Estab. 1984. Uses the services of music houses and independent songwriters for background music for AV use, jingles for all purposes, and commercials for radio. Commissions 10 composers/year. Pays $500-1,000 for 10 cuts of full length music, or on consignment per composition. "No songs, please!"

How to Contact: Prefers cassette with 5-10 pieces. SASE. Reports in 2 weeks.

Music: All styles, but concentrates on industrial. "We pay cash for produced tracks of all styles and lengths. Production value is imperative. No scratch tracks accepted."

CANTRAX RECORDERS, 2119 Fidler Ave., Long Beach CA 90815. (213)498-6492. Owner: Richard Cannata. Recording studio. Clients include anyone needing recording services (i.e. industrial, radio, commercial). Estab. 1980. Uses the services of independent songwriters/composers and lyricists for scoring of jingles, soundtracks, background music for slide shows and films, jingles for radio, commercials for radio and music demos and music videos. Commissions 10 composers and 12 lyricists/year. Pays by the job. Buys all rights.

How to Contact: Submit demo tape of previous work demonstrating composition skills. Prefers cassette or 7½/15 ips reel-to-reel (or VHS videocassette) with lyric sheets. "Indicate noise reduction if used. We prefer reel to reel." SASE, but prefers to keep material on file. Reports in 2 weeks.

Music: Uses jazz, New Age, rock, easy listening and classical for slide shows, jingles and soundtracks, etc.

Tips: "Send a 7½/15 ips reel for us to audition; you must have a serious, professional attitude."

*CAPITAL ASSOCIATED INDUSTRIES, INC., 2900 Highwoods Blvd., Raleigh NC 27604. (919)878-9222. Associate: John Yarboro. Audiovisual firm, scoring service, jingle/commercial music production house, music sound effect library and audio for video; video production. Clients include major industrial, other business organization. Estab. 1963. Uses the services of animated graphics. Commissions 2 composers and 2 lyricists/year. Pays $500 and up/job. Buys one-time rights.

How to Contact: Prefers cassette, 15 or 30 ips reel-to-reel, ½ VHS; ¾ videocassette with enough songs to show style. SASE. Prefers to keep material on file, "if we are interested."

Music: Uses all kinds of music for all kinds of assignments.

*CAPITOL PRODUCTION MUSIC, 6922 Hollywood Blvd., #78, Hollywood CA 90028. (213)461-2701. Managing Director: Ole Georg. Scoring service, jingle/commercial music production house, music sound effect library. Clients include broadcast, corporate/industrial, theatrical, production/post-production houses. Uses the services of independent songwriters/composers for 35-70 minutes of music beds for CD library. Commissions 6 composers/year. Pays by the job. Buys all rights.

How to Contact: Submit demo tape of previous work demonstrating composition skills. Query with resume of credits. Prefers cassette with 5 songs. Does not return unsolicited material but prefers to keep on file. "No report unless we have interest."

Music: Uses hot pop, "big acoustic" corporate industrial, atmospheric.

Tips: "Material most likely to be considered is that with heavy dynamics and strong edit-points."

CENTER ONE VIDEO PRODUCTIONS INC., 1706-D Capital Cir. N.E., Box 3749, Tallahassee FL 32308. (904)656-7000. President: David W. Murray. Vice President: David Murray, Jr. Audiovisual firm and video production company. Clients include state agencies, private corporations, advertising agencies, and TV programs. Uses services of music houses and independent songwriters/composers for background music for jingles, and special commercial spots and commercials for TV. Commissions 1-2 composers/year. Pays by the job. Buys all rights.

How to Contact: Submit demo tape of previous work; query with resume of credits. Prefers cassette or 7½ IPS reel-to-reel (or VHS or ¾" videocassette) with 6-8 pieces. SASE, but prefers to keep materials on file. Reports in 1 month.

Music: Uses modern, jazz, easy listening for corporate image, commercials and special TV programs. No heavy rock.

Tips: "We don't need many, if any, songs with words; mostly just music."

CENTRA ADVERTISING COMPANY, #35 Maryland Plaza, St. Louis MO 63108. (314)367-5900. Broadcast Services Manager: Linda Schumacher. Advertising agency. Estab. 1983. Clients include packaged goods and public service firms. Uses the services of music houses, independent songwriters and lyricists for commercials for radio and TV. Buys all rights.
How to Contact: Submit demo tape of previous work. Prefers cassette. Does not return unsolicited material. Prefers to keep material on file.
Music: Uses up-tempo for TV and radio commercials.

*CGI ADVERTISING, 297 North St., Hyannis MA 02601. (508)775-8500. Creative Director: John R. Ulren. Advertising agency. Clients include financial, computer, retail. Estab. 1985. Uses the services of music houses and independent songwriters/composers for jingles and commercials for radio, TV. Commissions 4-5 composers/year. Pays $2-5,000/job. Buys all rights, one-time rights.
How to Contact: Submit demo tape of previous work demonstrating composition skills. Prefers cassette (or VHS videocassette) with 3-10 songs. SASE but prefers to keep material on file. "Will respond when need arises."
Music: Uses varying styles for commercials.
Tips: "High quality, reasonable price; show me something original."

*CHANNEL ONE VIDEO TAPE INC., 3341 NW 82nd Ave., Miami FL 33122. (305)592-1764. General Manager: Jay P. Van Dyke. Video production house, **music library.** Estab. 1969. Clients include commercial, industrial, medical and network programs. Uses music library for commercials for TV and industrials, medical, programs. Pays by the job or "yearly fee." Buys all rights.
How to Contact: Submit demo tape of previous work. Prefers 7½ ips reel-to-reel. Does not return unsolicited material; prefers to keep on file. Reports if interested.
Music: Uses all styles of music for all kinds of assignments.

CHAPMAN RECORDING STUDIOS, 228 W. 5th, Kansas City MO 64105. (816)842-6854. Contact: Chuck Chapman. Custom music and production. Estab. 1973. Clients include video producers, music producers, musicians and corporations. Uses the services of independent songwriters/composers and arrangers for background music for video productions; jingles for radio, TV, corporations; and commercials for radio and TV. Commissions 4 composers and 4 lyricists/year. Buys all rights.
How to Contact: Call to arrange submission of tape demo. Prefers cassette. SASE, but prefers to keep material on file. Reports in 2 months.
Music: Uses all styles, all types for record releases, video productions, and TV and radio productions; and up-tempo and pop for educational films, slide presentations and commercials.

*CHASE/EHRENBERG & ROSENE, INC., 211 E. Ontario, Chicago IL 60611. (312)943-3737. Executive Vice President: John Rosene. Advertising agency. Clients include retailers and national manufacturers. Estab. 1942. Uses the services of music houses, independent songwriters/composers and needle drop for scoring of commercials and commercials for radio, TV. Commissions 1 or 2 composers/year. Pays by the job. Buys all rights.
How to Contact: Submit demp tape of previous work demonstrating composition skills. Write or call first to arrange personal interview. Prefers cassette. Does not return unsolicited material but prefers to keep on file.
Music: Uses up tempo, rock, pop for commercials.

CHIAT/DAY/MOJO ADVERTISING, 320 Hampton Dr., Venice CA 90291. (213)314-5000. President/ Executive Director: Lee Clow. Creative Director: Steve Rabosky. Serves health care, packaged food, home loan, automotive, electronics and motorcycle clients. Uses background music in commercials. Commissions 1 piece/year. Pays by the job.
How to Contact: Submit demo tape of previously aired work. Prefers 7½ ips reel-to-reel. SASE. Reports "as soon as possible."

CINEVUE, P.O. Box 428, Bostwick FL 32007. (904)325-5254. Director/Producer: Steve Postal. Motion picture production company. Estab. 1955. Serves all types of film distributors. Use the services of independent songwriters/composers and lyricists for scoring of and background music for movies and commercials. Commissions 10 composer and 5 lyricists/year. Pays by the job. Buys all rights or one-time rights.
How to Contact: Query with resume of credits or write to arrange personal interview. Prefers cassette or reel-to-reel with 10 pieces and lyric or lead sheet. SASE, but prefers to keep material on file. Reports in 2 weeks.
Music: Uses all styles of music for features (educational films and slide presentations).

CLASSIC VIDEO, INC., 5001 East Royalton Rd., Broadview Hts. OH 44133. (216)853-8377. Producer: Bob Anderson. Jingle/production house, video programming and commercial producer. Estab. 1983. Uses independent songwriters for background music for commercials, jingles and music themes. Commissions 20-30 songwriters and 5-10 lyricists/year. Pays $200-1,500/job. Buys all rights.
How to Contact: Submit demo tape of previously aired work. Prefers cassette or 7½ ips reel-to-reel with various pieces and lyric or lead sheets. "Please include basic structure and references." Does not return unsolicited material; prefers to keep on file.
Music: "High tech electronic sounds for music backgrounds for high tech industrials, and commercials for radio/TV consumer products."
Tips: "Be flexible in musical style, rates and turn around time."

CLEARVUE, INC., 6465 N. Avondale, Chicago IL 60631. (312)775-9433. President: William O. McDermed. Audiovisual firm. Serves the educational market. Estab. 1969. "We only produce for ourselves." Uses the services of independent songwriters. Commissions 3 songwriters or composers/year. Pays by the job.
Music: "We are seeking music programs for the educational market and programs for the teaching of music."

COAKLEY HEAGERTY, 1155 N. 1st St., San Jose CA 95112. (408)275-9400. Creative Director: Susan Rivera. Advertising agency. Estab. 1966. Clients include consumer, business to business and high tech firms. Uses the services of independent songwriters, lyricists and music houses for background music for commercials and jingles. Commissions 25 songwriters/year. Pays $3,000-20,000/job. Buys all rights.
How to Contact: Submit demo tape of previously aired work. Prefers cassette or 7½ ips reel-to-reel with 8-10 pieces. Does not return unsolicited material; prefers to keep material on file. Reports in 2 weeks.
Music: All kinds of music for jingles and music beds.
Tips: "Send a tape with current samples of commercials only with a price list and whether or not you'll do spec work."

COMMUNICATIONS FOR LEARNING, 395 Massachusetts Ave., Arlington MA 02174. (617)641-2350. Executive Producer/Director: Jonathan L. Barkan. Audiovisual and design firm. Clients include multinationals, industry, government, institutions, local non-profits. Uses services of music houses and independent songwriters/composers for scoring and background music for audiovisual and video soundtracks. Commissions 1-2 composers/year. Pays $2,000-3,000/job. Buys one-time rights.
How to Contact: Submit demo tape or tape demonstrating composition skills. Prefers cassette or 7½ or 15 ips reel-to-reel (or ½" or ¾" videocassette). SASE, but prefers to keep material on file. "For each job we consider our entire collection." Reports in 2 months.
Music: Uses all styles of music for all sorts of assignments.
Tips: "Please don't call. Just send good material and when we're interested, we'll be in touch."

*COMMUNIPLEX SERVICES INC., 2081 Seymour Ave., Cincinnati OH 45237. (513)731-6300. President: Steven Reece. Advertising agency. Clients include consumer businesses. Estab. 1976. Uses the services of independent songwriters/composers for jingles and commercials for radio, TV. Commissions 3 composers and 2 lyricists/year. Pays by the job. Buys all rights.
How to Contact: Submit demo tape of previous work. Prefers cassette (or ¾" videocassette) with 4 songs and lyric and lead sheet. SASE but prefers to material on file.
Music: Uses pop for commercials.

CONNELLY & CO. INC., 15155 91st Ave. N., Maple Grove MN 55369. (612)420-5720. President: Steve Connelly. Advertising agency and consultant. Clients include Fortune 500 firms. Estab. 1988. Uses the services of music houses, independent songwriters/composers and lyricists for background music for video presentations and jingles for radio. Commissions 3 composers and 3 lyricists/year. Pays $1,000-4,000/job. Buys all rights.
How to Contact: Submit demo tape of previous work or tape demonstrating composition skills. Prefers cassette (or ¼" videocassette) with 5 songs. Does not return unsolicited material. Prefers to keep material on file. Reports in 2 weeks.
Music: "Depends on assignment. Don't send a lot—just your best."

CONTINENTAL PRODUCTIONS, Box 1219, Great Falls MT 59403. (406)761-8816. Production Sales/ Marketing: Duke Brekhus. Video production house. Clients include advertising agencies, business, industry and government. Uses the services of independent songwriters/composers for TV commercials and non–broadcast programs and jingles for TV commercials. Commissions 1-6 composers/year. Pays $85-500/job. Buys all rights or one-time rights.

How to Contact: Write or call first and obtain permission to submit. Prefers cassette (or ½" VHS videocassette). SASE, but prefers to keep on file. Reports in 2 weeks.
Music: Uses contemporary music beds and custom jingles for TV and non-broadcast video.
Tips: "Songwriters need to build a working relationship by providing quality product in short order at a good price."

T. COOKE PRODUCTIONS, INC., 955 Gardenview Off-Pkwy., St. Louis MO 63141. President: Thomas Cooke. Audiovisual firm and motion picture production company. Clients include Fortune 500 industrial/consumer products companies. Uses services of independent songwriters/composers, lyricists and music houses for scoring of industrial video/film, background music for A/V programs. Commissions 4-6 composers/year. Pays $3,000-6,000/job. Buys all rights.
How to Contact: Submit demo tape of previous work or query with resume of credits. Prefers cassette with 6 songs. SASE, but prefers to keep material on file.
Music: Uses music to sell, hype, motivate for slide presentations, corporate image videos, and live industrial stage shows.

*CORPORATE COMMUNICATIONS INC., Main St., Box 854, N. Conway NH 03860. (603)356-7011. President: Kimberly Beals. Advertising agency. Estab. 1983. Uses the services of music houses, independent songwriters/composers for background music, jingles and commercials for radio/video. Commissions 2-3 composers/year. Pays by the job. Buys all rights, one-time rights.
How to Contact: Submit demo tape of previous work demonstrating composition skills and manuscript showing scoring skills. Query with resume of credits. Prefers cassette (or ½" videocassette) with 5 songs. Does not return unsolicited material; prefers to keep on file. Reports in 1-2 weeks.
Music: Uses varying styles of music for varying assignments.

*CORPORATE DESIGN ASSOCIATES, 4676 Barranca, Irvine CA 92714. Account Manager: Steven Byrne. Advertising agency. Clients include business and consumer. Estab. 1975. Uses the services of music houses and independent songwriters/composers for radio commercials and cable. Commissions "several" composers/year. Pays by the job. Buys all rights or one-time rights.
How to Contact: Send a letter. Does not return unsolicited material.

*COVENANT PRODUCTIONS—ANDERSON UNIVERSITY, 1100 E. 5th St., Anderson IN 46012. (317)641-4345. Operation Director: Scott Fritz. Teleproduction house. Clients include corporate/industrial; some religious; some broadcast. Estab. 1985. Uses the services of music houses, independent songwriters/composers for scoring of TV programs/productions, background music for TV programs/productions and commercials for radio, TV. Commissions 5 composers/year. Pays by minute of used music $10-100/minute. Buys all rights, one-time rights.
How to Contact: Submit demo tape of previous or tape demonstrating composition skills. Prefers cassette or 15 ips reel-to-reel (or ¾" Betacam or VHS videocassette, if scored) with 3-5 songs. SASE, but prefers to keep material on file. Reports in 2 weeks.
Music: Uses music beds—easy listening, jazz, up-tempo for commercials and documentaries.
Tips: "Avoid a 'generic' sound."

CREATIVE ASSOCIATES, 626 Bloomfield Ave., Verona NJ 07044. (201)857-3444. Production Coordinator: Susan Graham. Audiovisual firm. Clients include commercial, industrial firms. Estab. 1975. Uses the services of music houses and independent songwriters/composers for scoring of video programs, background music for press tours and jingles for new products. Pays $300-5,000+/job. Buys all or one-time rights.
How to Contact: Submit demo tape of previous work demonstrating composition skills or query with resume of credits. Prefers cassette or ½" or ¾" VHS videocassette. SASE, but prefers to keep material on file.
Music: Uses all styles for many different assignments.

*CREATIVE AUDIO PRODUCTIONS, 326 Santa Isabel Blvd., Laguna Vista, Port Isabel TX 78578. (512)943-6278. Owner: Ben McCampbell. Jingle/commercial music production house. Serves ad agencies, broadcast stations (TV and radio), video/film production houses and advertisers. Uses the services of lyricists for jingles for commercials and commercials for radio and TV. Commissions 1 composer and 2 lyricists/year. Pays $200-500/job. Buys one-time rights.
How to Contact: Submit demo tape of previous work or write first to arrange personal interview. Prefers cassette with 3-5 songs and lyric sheet. Does not return unsolicited material; prefers to keep on file. Reports in 1 month.
Music: Uses pop, up-tempo, reggae for commercials.

CREATIVE HOUSE ADVERTISING, INC., Suite 301, 30777 Northwestern Hwy., Farmington Hills MI 48018. (313)737-7077. Executive Vice President/Creative Director: Robert G. Washburn. Advertising agency and graphics studio. Serves commercial, retail, consumer, industrial, medical and financial clients. Uses the services of songwriters and lyricists for jingles, background music for radio and TV commercials and corporate sales meeting films and videos. Commissions 3-4 songwriters/year. Pays $50-100/hour or $1,500-5,000/job depending on job involvement. Buys all rights.
How to Contact: Query with resume of credits or submit tape demo showing jingle/composition skills. Submit cassette (or ¾" videocassette) with 6-12 songs. SASE, but would prefer to keep material on file. "When an appropriate job comes up associated with the talents/ability of the songwriters/musicians, then they will be contacted."
Music: "The type of music we need depends on clients. The range is multi; contemporary, disco, rock, MOR and traditional."

CREATIVE SOUND STUDIOS, 601 N. 6th St., Allentown PA 18102. (215)439-8004. Studio Manager: Andrea Czarnecki. Audiovisual firm and jingle/**commercial music production house**. Serves advertising agencies/direct clients. Estab. 1977. Uses the services of independent songwriters/composers for jingles, commercials for radio and TV and A/V soundtracks. Commissions 2 composers and 2 lyricists/year. Pays $700 + /job. Buys all rights.
How to Contact: Submit demo tape of previous work. Prefers cassette with any number of songs. SASE, but prefers to keep material on file. Reports in 1 month.
Music: Uses jingles and industrial music.
Tips: "Forward a demo and letter of introduction."

CREATIVE SUPPORT SERVICES, 1950 Riverside Dr., Los Angeles CA 90039. (213)666-7968. Contact: Michael M. Fuller. **Music/sound effects library**. Clients include audiovisual production houses. Estab. 1978. Uses the services of independent songwriters and musicians for background music for audiovisuals and commercials for radio. Commissions 3-5 songwriters and 1-2 lyricists/year. Pays by the job or by royalty. Buys exclusive distribution rights.
How to Contact: Write or call first. Prefers cassette "chrome or metal only" or 7½ ips reel-to-reel with 3 or more pieces. Does not return unsolicited material; prefers to keep on file. "Will call if interested."
Music: Uses "industrial music predominantly, but all other kinds or types to lesser degree."
Tips: "Target your market. Lower your monetary expectations. Remember the risks that have to be incurred to buy someone's music."

CRESTON ASSOCIATES, LTD., 123 East 54th St., New York NY 10022. (212)486-7764. President: Diane T. Creston. Advertising agency. Clients include fashion, toys, medical firms. Estab. 1987. Uses the services of music houses and independent songwriters/composers for background music for sales film and commercials for TV. Commissions 3-4 composers/year. Pays $250 + /job, "depending on the job." Buys all rights or one-time rights.
How to Contact: Submit demo tape of previous work or tape demonstrating composition skills (indicate as such); query with resume of credits. Prefers cassette with 6-8 songs. "No phone calls. Be specific about your role in the material, i.e. writing, arranging." SASE, but prefers to keep material on file.
Music: Uses up-tempo, rock and pop for educational films and commercials.
Tips: "Submit a professional tape and material. We will maintain a file and call songwriters when needed."

CRESWELL, MUNSELL, FULTZ & ZIRBEL, Box 2879, Cedar Rapids IA 52406. (319)395-6500. Executive Producer: Terry Taylor. Advertising agency. Serves agricultural, consumer and industrial clients. Uses songwriters and music houses for jingles and background music in commercials and multi-image soundtracks. Commissions 7-8 songwriters for 15 pieces/year. Pays by the job. Buys rights on talent residuals.
How to Contact: Submit demo tape of previously aired work. Prefers 7 or 15 ips reel-to-reel or cassette with 7-8 songs maximum. Does not return unsolicited material. Reports "when we want figures on a job."
Music: All types. Likes to hear a good range of music material. Will listen to anything from "small groups to full orchestration."
Tips: "Create unique, recognizable melodies."

*CROSS KEYS ADVERTISING, 329 S. Main St., Doylestown PA 18901. President: Laura Thompson. Advertising agency. Clients include retail, industrial and commercial. Estab. 1981. Use the services of music houses and independent songwriters/composers for background music, jingles and commercials for radio and TV. Commissions 3-4 composers/year. Pays by the job. Buys all rights.

How to Contact: Submit demo tape of previous work. Prefers cassette. Does not return unsolicited materials; prefers to keep on file.
Music: Uses all styles for commercials.

R.J. DALE ADVERTISING INC., 500 N. Michigan Ave., #2204, Chicago IL 60611. (312)644-2316. Executive Vice President: William Stewart. Advertising agency. Clients include H&BA Manufacturers, retail bank, lottery, food, distilled spirits manufacturers. Estab. 1979. Uses the services of music houses and independent songwriters/composers for background music for sales meetings and commercials for radio and TV. Commissions 5 composers/year. Pays by the job. Buys all rights or two-year rights.
How to Contact: Submit demo tape of previous work showing range of ability. Prefers cassette (or ¾″ U-matic videocassette). SASE, but prefers to keep material on file.
Music: Uses pop, jazz, fusion and R&B for commercials.

*dbF A MEDIA COMPANY, P.O. Box 2458, Waldorf MD 20604. (301)843-7110. President: Randy Runyon. Advertising agency, audiovisual firm and audio and video production company. Clients include business and industry. Estab. 1981. Uses the services of music houses, independent songwriters/composers and lyricists for background music for industrial videos, jingles for radio and TV and commercials for radio and TV. Commissions 5-12 composers and 5-12 lyricists/year. Pays by the job. Buys all rights.
How to Contact: Submit demo tape of previous work. Query with resume of credits. Prefers cassette or 7½ IPS reel-to-reel (or VHS videocassette) with 5-8 songs and lead sheet. SASE, but prefers to keep material on file. Reports in 6 weeks.
Music: Uses up-tempo contemporary for industrial videos, slide presentations and commercials.
Tips: "Keep us up to date with your current projects."

DD&B STUDIOS INC., 401 S. Woodward, Birmingham MI 48009. (313)642-0640. Director of Creative Services: Rick Stawinski. Audiovisual firm. Clients include Fortune 500 businesses. Uses the services of music houses, independent songwriters/composers and lyricists for scoring of soundtracks, background music for slide shows and jingles and commercials for radio and TV. Commissions 10-15 composers and 10-15 lyricists/year. Pays by the job. Buys all rights.
How to Contact: Submit demo tape of previous work and written resume. Prefers cassette (or ¾″ or VHS videocassette) with 3-4 pieces; lyric or lead sheet optional. Does not return unsolicited material; prefers to keep on file. Responds "when a project exists that could use the submitted talent."
Music: Uses light rock, synthesized scores, SFX for industrial and commercial assignments.
Tips: "Be aware of what your competition is doing—be unique! Send updated demo tapes on a regular basis."

DE WOLFE MUSIC LIBRARY, 25 W. 45th St., New York NY 10036. (212)382-0220. Vice President: Mitchel J. Greenspan. **Music sound effect library and jingle/commercial music production house.** Clients include advertising agencies, industrials, production companies, etc. Uses the services of independent songwriters/composers for background music for commercials, TV, radio, cable, films, etc. Buys all rights or negotiable rights.
How to Contact: Query with resume of credits or submit tape demonstrating composition skills. Prefers cassette or 15 or 7½ ips reel-to-reel (or ¾″ videocassette). SASE, but prefers to keep material on file. Reports in "several weeks."
Music: Uses all kinds of music for all kinds of assignments.

*DECKER, DECKER AND FREAS INC., 4 East 43rd St., New York NY 10017. (212)599-6040. Executive Vice President and Creative Director: Lenwood W. Freas. Advertising agency, motion picture production company and marketing communications. Clients include publishing, cable networks, product launches. Estab. 1983. Uses the services of music houses, independent songwriters/composers and lyricists for background music for videos, radio, promotion, etc., jingles for new products, advertising and programming, commercials for radio and TV, and videos, music videos, packaging for client promo. Commissions 5-10 composers and 5-10 lyricists/year. Buys varying rights.
How to Contact: Query with resume of credits. "Do not submit anything other than name, music style and info which can be put in our computer retrieval file." Does not return unsolicited material; prefers to keep on file.
Music: Uses all types, from jazz to pop to rock to classic for advertising, promotion, videos, film and broadcast.
Tips: "Give us your permanent address, phone, resume and a short list of music you love to do. A sense of price would help but is not necessary."

DELTA DESIGN GROUP, INC., 409 Washington Ave., Greenville MS 38701. (601)335-6148. President: Noel Workman. Advertising agency. Serves industrial, health care, agricultural and retail commercial clients. Uses the services of songwriters for jingles. Commissions 3-6 pieces/year. Pays $500-2,500/job. Buys "rights which vary geographically according to client. Some are all rights; others are rights for a specified market only. Buy out only. No annual licensing."
How to Contact: Submit demo tape showing jingle/composition skills. Prefers 7½ ips reel-to-reel with 3-6 songs. "Include typed sequence of cuts on tape on the outside of the reel box." SASE. Reports "when services are needed."
Music: Needs "30- and 60-second jingles for agricultural, health care, auto dealers and chambers of commerce."

DISK PRODUCTIONS, 1100 Perkins Rd., Baton Rouge LA 70802. (504)343-5438. Director: Joey Decker. **Jingle/production house.** Estab. 1982. Clients include advertising agencies, slide production houses and film companies. Uses independent songwriters/composers and lyricists for scoring of TV spots and films and jingles for radio and TV. Commissions 7 songwriters/composers and 7 lyricists/year. Pays by the job. Buys all rights.
How to Contact: Prefers cassette or 7½ ips reel-to-reel (or ½" videocassette) and lead sheet. Does not return unsolicited material; prefers to keep on file. Reports "immediately if material looks promising."
Music: Needs all types of music for jingles, music beds or background music for TV and radio, etc.
Tips: "Advertising techniques change with time. Don't be locked in a certain style of writing. Give me music that I can't get from pay needle-drop."

DSM PRODUCERS ENT PUBLISHING COMPANY, 161 W. 54th St., New York NY 10019. (212)245-0006. Vice President, National Sales Director: Doris Kaufman. Scoring service, jingle **commercial music production house** and original stock library called "All American Composers Library" record producers. Clients include networks, corporate, advertising firms, film and video, book publishers (music only). Estab. 1979. Uses the services of independent songwriters/composers and "all signed composers who we represent" for scoring of film, industrial films, major films—all categories; background music for film, audio cassettes, instore video—all catagories; jingles for advertising agencies and commercials for radio and TV. Commissions 10 composers and 1 lyricist/year. Pays royalty.
How to Contact: Submit tape demonstrating composition skills. Prefers cassette (or VHS videocassette) with 2 songs and lyric or lead sheet. "Keep the vocals up in the mix—use a large enough return envelope to put in a standard business reply letter." SASE. Reports in 6 weeks.
Music: Uses dance, new age, country and rock for adventure films and sports programs.

ROY EATON MUSIC INC., 595 Main St., Roosevelt Island NY 10044. (212)980-9046. President: Roy Eaton. Jingle/**commercial music production house.** Clients include advertising agencies, TV and radio stations and film producers. Estab. 1982. Uses the services of independent songwriters/composers and lyricists and scoring of TV commercials and films, background music for TV programs, jingles for advertising agencies and commercials for radio and TV. Commissions 10 composers and 1 lyricist/year. Pays $50-3,000/job. Buys all rights.
How to Contact: Submit demo tape of previous work. Prefers cassette with 3-5 pieces. Does not return unsolicted material; prefers to keep on file. Reports in 2 months.
Music: Uses jazz fusion, new age and rock/pop for commercials and films.
Tips: "Submit what you do best."

CHARLES EDELSTEIN ADVERTISING, INC., 92 Austin Dr., Holland PA 18966. (215)355-5015. President: Charles Edelstein. Advertising agency. Estab. 1971. Uses the services of independent songwriters, lyricists and music houses for jingles and background music. Commissions 5 composers and 5 lyricists/year. Pays $500 and up/job or $75/hour. Buys all rights.
How to Contact: Write first and obtain permission to submit. Prefers cassette. SASE.
Music: Uses all styles of music for various kinds of assignments.

EDUCATIONAL INSIGHTS, 19560 S. Rancho Way, Dominguez Hills CA 90220. (213)637-2131. Director of Development: Dennis J. Graham. Audiovisual firm. =Clients include schools and parents of young children. Uses the services of music houses and independent songwriters for scoring of children's plays, learning programs and music education materials. Commissions 4 composers/year. Pays by the job or 5% royalty. Buys all rights.
How to Contact: Submit demo tape of previous work. Prefers cassette. SASE. Reports in 1 month.
Music: Needs "music for young children, especially educational in nature."

Listings of companies in foreign countries have the name of the country in boldface type.

EFFECTIVE LEARNING SYSTEMS, INC., 5221 Industrial Blvd., Edina MN 55435. (612)893-1680. Director of Marketing: James W. Griswold. Audio cassette publishers. Clients include general public. Estab. 1972. Uses the services of music houses and independent songwriters/composers for background music for self-help audio cassettes (foreground also). Commissions 1 or 2 composers/year. Pays by the job. Buys unlimited useage, exclusive rights for self-help tapes.
How to Contact: Submit demo tape of previous work. Prefers cassette with at least 4 pieces. "Include fee requirements with sample." SASE. Reports in 4 weeks.
Music: Uses many styles, if good quality, but emphasis on new age/relaxation styles for self-help audio cassettes background; subliminal audio cassettes foreground.
Tips: "Only send professional-sounding demo with realistic fee requirements. Listen to "Love Tapes®" series for examples of acceptable music to date."

THE EFX COMPANY, 2300 S. 9th St., 136A, Arlington VA 22204. (703)486-2303. Operations Manager: Kelly Muchoney. Audiovisual firm. Clients include corporate and commercial video production, graphics and animation. Estab. 1982. Uses the services of independent songwriters/composers for scoring of instructional films, background music for corporate and commercial videos, jingles for TV/in house corporate videos and commercials for TV. Commissions 20 composers/year. Pays by the job or depending upon instruments/studio. Buys rights depending upon assignment.
How to Contact: Submit demo tape of previous work and tape demonstrating composition skills. Prefers cassette (or VHS or ¾ videocassette) with 3-5 pieces and lyric sheets. SASE. Reports in 3 weeks.
Music: Uses contemporary instrumentals, CHR, AOR and MOR for educational films and commercials.

*ELITE VIDEO PRODUCTIONS, 1612 East 145h St., Brooklyn NY 11229. (718)627-0499. President: Kalman Aeines. Motion picture production company. Clients include industrial. Estab. 1978. Uses the services of music houses and independent songwriters/composers for background music for narration and commercials for TV. Commissions 5 composers/year. Pays $500-2,500/job. Buys all rights.
How to Contact: Submit demo tape of previous work. Prefers cassette. "Call first." Does not return unsolicited material; prefers to keep materials on file. Reports back in 2 weeks. Assignments include work on educational films.

DON ELLIOTT PRODUCTIONS, 15 Bridge Rd., Weston CT 06883. (203)226-4209. (New York office: 67 Park Ave., New York NY 10016. (212)679-5670.) Vice President in Charge of New Material: Doriane Elliott. Scoring service. Clients include advertising agencies, CBS Records, Arista Records. Uses the services of independent songwriters and lyricists for scoring of films and albums; background music for commercials; and jingles for radio and TV. Commissions for jingles only. Payment and rights purchased depend on the job.
How to Contact: Submit demo tape of previous work or tape demonstrating composition skills. Prefers cassette. Does not return unsolicited material; prefers to keep on file. Reports in 2 weeks.
Music: Looking for music for jingles or original music. "Presently, we are leaning toward more new albums. We have a 24-track, fully equipped studio."

*ENSEMBLE PRODUCTIONS, P.O. Box 2332, Auburn AL 36831. (205)826-3045. Owner: Barry J. McConatha. Audiovisual firm and video production/post production. Clients include corporate, governmental and educational. Estab. 1984. Uses services of music houses and independent songwriters/composers for scoring of documentary productions, background music for corporate public relations and training videos, jingles for public service announcements, and for montage effects with A/V and video. Commissions 2-5 composers/year. Pays $100-500/job, $25/hour or by the composition $50-500. Buys all rights and one-time rights.
How to Contact: Submit demo tape of previous work. Submit demo tape demonstrating composition skills. Needs are sporadic, write first if submission is to be returned. Prefers cassette or 7½/15 IPS reel-to-reel (or VHS videocassette) with 3-5 songs. "Most needs are upbeat industrial sound but occasional mood setting music also. Inquire for details." Does not return unsolicited material; prefers to keep on file. Reports in 3-5 weeks "if solicited."
Music: Uses up-beat, industrial, new age, and mood for training film. PR, education and multi-media.
Tips: "Stay away from disco sound!"

ENTERTAINMENT PRODUCTIONS, INC., Box 554, Malibu CA 90265. (213)456-3143. President: Edward Coe. Motion picture and television production company. Estab. 1972. Clients include motion picture and TV distributors. Uses the services of music houses and songwriters for scores, production numbers, background and theme music for films and TV and jingles for promotion of films. Commissions/year vary. Pays by the job or by royalty. Buys all rights.

How to Contact: Query with resume of credits. Demo should show flexibility of composition skills. "Demo records/tapes sent at own risk—returned if SASE included." Reports by letter in 1 month, "but only if SASE is included."
Tips: "Have resume on file. Develop self-contained capability."

*ETV, P.O. Box 31, FDR Station, New York NY 10150. (212)755-7322. Contact: J. Edwards. Motion picture production company. Estab. 1960. Uses the services of music houses and lyricists for scoring and background music.
How to Contact: Submit demo tape of previous work, tape demonstrating composition skills or manuscript showing music scoring skills. Prefers cassette with lyric and lead sheets. Does not return unsolicited submissions. Reports 6 months.
Music: Uses jazz and pop rock for educational films, slide presentations, commercials, etc.

*RICHARD R. FALK ASSOC., 1472 Broadway, New York NY 10036. (212)221-0043. President: Richard Falk. Public Relations. Clients include national companies, shows and stars. Estab. 1940. Uses the services of lyricists for promotions. Commissions 2 composers and 3 lyricists/year. Pays $100/job. Buys one-time rights.
How to Contact: Send a simple flyer on some past credits, nothing too involved. SASE. "If accompanied by SASE, replies immediately."

FANCY FREE MUSIC, 300 Hempstead Turnpike West Hempstead NY 11552. (516)538-7786. Creative Director: Joe Orlando. Scoring service, jingle commercial music production house and music sound effect library. Clients include advertising agencies, A/V houses, film editors and independent producers. Estab. 1979. Uses the services of independent songwriters/composers and lyricists and music programmers for scoring of commercials, A/V programs, background music for slide shows, jingles for radio and TV and commercials for radio and TV. Commissions 4 composers and 1 lyricist/year. Pays $100-750/job. Buys all rights.
How to Contact: Submit demo tape of previous work or write or call to arrange personal interview. Prefers cassette or 7½ ips reel-to-reel with 4-6 songs and lyric sheets. SASE for return. Prefers to keep material on file. Reports in 4 weeks.
Music: Uses classical, pop, R&B, jazz and MOR for A/V films, slide shows, TV/radio commercials and songs.
Tips: "Make your demo tape as contemporary as possible. Innovative sounds, strong hooks, tight lyrics."

FERGUSON & ASSOCIATES ADVERTISING, 76 W. Main St., Rexburg ID 83440. (208)356-9381. Producer/Director: Brad Shaw. Advertising agency. Estab. 1971. Clients include Diet Center, Inc. (in-house agency). Uses independent songwriters, lyricists and music houses for background music for commercials, jingles and motivational, promotional and training audiovisual presentations. Commissions 2-3 songwriters and 1-2 lyricists/year. Pays by the job. Buys all rights.
How to Contact: Submit demo tape of previously aired work. Prefers cassette (or ¾" videocassette). Does not return unsolicited material; prefers to keep on file. Reports "as jobs occur."
Music: Easy listening, country, pop and rock for jingles, music beds, TV, promotional films and exercise music.
Tips: "Send regular, recent, short but top-quality demos."

FILM AMERICA, INC., 3132 Randolph Rd. NE, Atlanta GA 30345. (404)261-3718. President: Avrum Fine. Motion picture editing house. Clients include advertising agencies, corporate audiovisual producers and film/tape producers. Uses the services of music houses and independent songwriters for scoring of industrial films/TV spots; lyricists for jingles for TV spots, commercials for TV and theater trailers. Commissions 3 composers and 3 lyricists/year. Pays by the job. Buys all rights.
How to Contact: Submit demo tape of previous work. Prefers cassette (or VHS videocassette). Does not return unsolicited material; prefers to keep on file. Reports in 4 weeks.
Music: "All contemporary idioms."

*FILM CLASSIC EXCHANGE, 143 Hickory Hill Circle, Osterville MA 02655. (508)428-7198. Vice President: Elsie Aikman. Motion picture production company. Clients include motion picture industry/TV networks and affiliates. Estab. 1916. Uses the services of music houses, independent songwriters/composers and lyricists for scoring, background music, jingles and commercials for motion pictures, TV movies, TV shows and specials. Commissions 10-20 composers and 10-20 lyricists/year. Pays by the job. Buys all rights or one-time rights.
How to Contact: Submit demo tape of previous work. Prefers cassette (or VHS videocassette). SASE but prefers to keep material on file. Reports in 3-weeks to 2 months.
Music: Uses pop and up-tempo for theatrical films/TV movies.
Tips: "Be persistent. Keep us informed of new projects."

GARY FITZGERALD MUSIC PRODUCTIONS, Suite B29, 37-75 63rd St., Woodside NY 11377. (718)446-3857. Producer: Gary Fitzgerald. Scoring service, **commercial music production house and music/sound effects library**. "We service the advertising and record community." Estab. 1987. Uses the services of independent songwriters, vocalists, lyricists and voice-over talent for scoring of TV, radio and industrials; background music for movies; jingles for TV, radio and industrials; and commercials for radio and TV. Commissions 4-5 composers and 4-5 lyricists/year. Pays per project. Rights purchased depends on project.
How to Contact: Submit demo tape of previous work or tape demonstrating composition skills. Prefers cassette. Does not return unsolicited material; prefers to keep on file. "A follow-up call must follow submission."
Music: Uses all styles of music.
Tips: "Always submit what you feel is your strongest work. Be persistent."

FLYNN/WRIGHT, INC., 2928 Ingersoll, Des Moines IA 50312. (515)243-2845. Writer/Producer: Sam Cohen. Estab. 1985. Serves wide range of clients including food, financial, industrial, agricultural and retail; client list available on request. Uses services of music houses for jingles, background music for commercials and music score for AV (very occasionally). Commissions 1-3 songwriters and 1-3 lyricists/year. Pays $2,400-10,000/job. Rights negotiable.
How to Contact: "Telephone first then follow up with mailed information." Prefers reel-to-reel or cassette with any number songs. SASE, but prefers to keep material on file.
Music: Primarily interested in jingles.
Tips: "Don't rely on mailing demo. Follow up. Have a good product and a good track record; do free piano demos. Send a variety of finished pieces."

*FOCUSED AUDIO, 30 Berry St., San Francisco CA 94107. (415)777-3108. Vice President Operations: Rob Grace. Audiovisual firm, jingle/commercial music production house. Clients include TV, film, corporate and ad agencies. Estab. 1979. Uses the services of music houses, independent songwriters/composers for scoring for films/TV, background music for corporate video, jingles for commercials and commercials for radio and TV. Commissions 5 composers and 2 lyricists/year. Pays $5,000/job; $50/hour.
How to Contact: Submit demo tape of previous work demonstrating composition skills and query with resume of credits. Prefers cassette with 4 or more songs and lyric sheet. SASE, but prefers to keep material on file. Reports in 1 month.
Music: Uses varied musical styles for TV commercials and educational films.
Tips: "Put your best foot forward . . . follow through with the attitude that someone will want your music."

FOREMOST FILMS AND VIDEO, INC., 7 Regency Dr., Holliston MA 01746. (508)429-8046. President: David Fox. Video production company. Estab. 1983. Serves consumer and corporate/industrial clients. Uses the services of independent songwriters, lyricists and music houses for corporate and industrial videos. Commissions 1-2 composers and 1-2 lyricists/year. Buys all rights.
How to Contact: Submit demo tape of previous work. Prefers cassette, CD or 7½ ips reel-to-reel (or ½" or ¾" videocassette) with 2-3 pieces and lyric or lead sheet. SASE. Reports within weeks.
Music: Styles of music used and kinds of assignments depend on specific jobs.
Tips: "Be patient, the market fluctuates so much for video production. Call every few months just to keep in touch. This keeps your name fresh in my mind."

FREDRICK, LEE & LLOYD, 235 Elizabeth St., Landisville PA 17538. (717)898-6092. Vice President: Dusty Rees. Jingle/**commercial music production house**. Clients include advertising agencies. Estab. 1976. Uses the services of independent songwriters/composers and staff writers for jingles. Commissions 2 composers/year. Pays $650/job. Buys all rights.
How to Contact: Submit tape demonstrating composition skills. Prefers cassette or 7½ ips reel-to-reel with 5 jingles. "Submissions may be samples of published work or original material." Does not return unsolicited material. Reports in 2 weeks.
Music: Uses pop, rock, country and MOR.
Tips: "The more completely orchestrated the demos are, the better."

*FREED & ASSOCIATES, Mill Centre, 3000 Chestnut Ave., Baltimore MD 21211. (301)243-1421. Senior Writer/Broadcast Producer: Steven L. Schiff. Advertising agency. Clients incluse a variety of retail and non-retail businesses. Estab. 1960. Uses the services of music houses and independent songwriters/composers for background music for television commercials, jingles for TV/radio commercials and commercials for radio and TV. Commissions 4-5 composers and 2-4 lyricists/year. Pays $2,000-10,000/job. Buys all rights or one-time rights, depending on the project.

How to Contact: Submit demo tape of previous work. Prefers cassette (or ½" or ¾" videocassette). Does not return unsolicited material; prefers to keep on file. Reports in 1 month.
Music: Uses varying styles for commercials and corporate videos.

PAUL FRENCH AND PARTNERS, 503 Gabbettville Rd., LaGrange GA 30240. (404)882-5581. Contact: Ms. Gene Ballard. Audiovisual firm. Uses the services of music houses and songwriters for musical scores in films and original songs for themes; lyricists for writing lyrics for themes. Commissions 20 composers and 20 lyricists/year. Pays minimum $500/job. Buys all rights.
How to Contact: Submit demo tape of previous work. Prefers reel-to-reel with 3-8 songs. SASE. Reports in 2 weeks.

FRENCH & ROGERS, INC., 5455 Corporate Dr., Troy MI 48098. (313)641-0010. Producer: Renae Garver. Advertising agency. Clients include industrial firms. Estab. 1966. Uses the services of independent songwriters/composers for scoring of video tape productions. Commissions 1 composer/year. Pays negotiated rate by the job. Buys all rights.
How to Contact: Submit demo tape of previous work. Prefers cassette with 3 or more songs. Does not return unsolicited material; prefers to keep material on file.
Music: Uses up-tempo, jazz for trade show tapes and product demonstrations.

*FRONTLINE VIDEO, INC., 243 12th St., Del Mar CA 92014. (619)481-5566. Production Manager: Alicia Reed. Television and video production company. Clients include sports programming, in surfing, skateboarding, boardsailing; medical patient education; and various industrial clients. Estab. 1983. Uses the services of independent songwriters/ composers for background music for sports programming and industrial clients; intros, extros. Commissions 5 composers/year. Pays by the composition $150 per cut.
How to Contact: Submit demo tape of previous work. Prefers cassette. Does not return unsolicited material, but prefers to keep material on file. "We contact artists on an 'as needed' basis when we're ready to use one of their pieces or styles."
Music: Uses up-tempo, jazzy, rock. "We buy works that come to us for national and international TV programming."
Tips: "Background music for surfing and other sports is our biggest area of need. Current-sounding, driving pieces in rock or jazzy styles are appropriate. We don't have time to respond to every submission, but if your tape is here at the right time and we like it, we'll contact you."

GARDINER—A MARKETING COMPANY, Box 30, Salt Lake City UT 84110. (801)364-5600. Vice President/Creative Director: Gordon A. Johnson. Advertising agency. Estab. 1949. Clients include medical, high tech, financial, retail and industrial firms. Uses independent songwriters and music houses for jingles and background music. Commissions 1-3 songwriters/composers per year. Pays $5,000/job average. Buys all rights; "unlimited buyout per market."
How to Contact: Accepts "demo tapes of established music houses only." Prefers cassette or 7½ ips reel-to-reel (or ¾" or VHS videocassette) with 5 or more pieces. SASE, but prefers to keep material on file. Reports if needed.
Music: Mostly MOR, novelty, uptempo contemporary—all styles of music for jingles and scoring for TV commercials.
Tips: "We prefer full cuts of music. Don't think of it as a 'jingle' but more as a 'song.' Lyrics need to be clear."

JAN GARDNER AND ASSOCIATES, Suite 229, 3340 Poplar, Memphis TN 38111. (901)452-7328. Production Director: Danny Umfress. Advertising agency. Uses services of songwriters and lyricists for jingles. Commissions 2 songwriters and 2 lyricists/year. Pays by the job. Buys all rights.
How to Contact: Submit demo tape of previous work. Prefers 7½ ips reel-to-reel or cassette with 3-12 songs. SASE, but prefers to keep material on file.
Music: "We have a wide range of clients and needs."

GEER DUBOIS ADVERTISING INC., 114 Fifth Ave., New York NY 10011. (212)741-1900 ex. 277. Executive Producer: Paul Mavis. Advertising agency. Clients include national, regional and local advertisers. Estab. 1935. Uses the services of music houses and independent songwriters/composers for scoring of TV and radio commercials, background music, jingles and commercials for radio and TV. Commissions 25 composers/year. Pays $750-3,000/job. Buys all rights.
How to Contact: Submit demo tape of previous work; query with resume of credits; write to arrange personal interview or contact Laura Hatton at the above address. Prefers cassette (or ¾" videocassette). "Keep it short with brief samples of your work." SASE, but prefers to keep material on file. "Unless there's a specific job, I don't have the time to report back on submissions."

Music: Uses all styles—depending on the commercial—for commercials only.
Tips: "Send a cassette or ¼" videotape with 8-10 samples of your best work with a short letter telling us who you are."

A GENTLE WIND, Box 3103, Albany NY 12203. (518)436-0391. Producer: Jill Person. Children's entertainment recording company. Clients include schools, libraries and retail stores. Estab. 1981. Uses the services of independent songwriters/composers. Pays standard royalty.
How to Contact: Submit demo tape of songs for (not about) children. Prefers cassette. Does not return unsolicited material. Reports in 3 months.
Music: Uses all styles.

*GILLESPIE ADVERTISING, INC., International Corporate Center, P.O. Box 3333, Princeton NJ 08543. (609)799-6000. Associate Creative Director: Dave Shea. Advertising agency. Clients include NBA basketball team, national yogurt franchise chain, shopping malls, several banks, a swimwear company, a chain of drug stores plus several industrial and business to business accounts. Estab. 1974. Uses the services of music houses and independent songwriters/composers for scoring of TV spots and sales videos, jingles for radio & TV and commercials for radio and TV. Commissions 4 composers/year. Pay varies by the job.
How to Contact: Submit demo tape of previous work. Write or call first to arrange personal interview. Prefers cassette (or ½" videocassette) with 5-10 songs. Does not return unsolicited material; prefers to keep on file.
Music: Uses all types for commercials and videos.
Tips: "Never underestimate the power of your demo!"

GLYN/NET, INC., 12 Floor, 155 W. 23rd St., New York NY 10011. (212)691-9300. Vice President Production: Dawn Salvatore. Motion picture and video production company. Clients include major corporations. Uses the services of music houses, independent songwriters and lyricists for scoring of and background music for films and TV shows. Commissions 2-3 composers/year. Pays by the job. Buys all rights or one-time rights.
How to Contact: Prefers cassette (or ¾" videocassette). Does not return unsolicited material. Reports in 3 weeks.
Music: All types.

GOODMAN ASSOCIATE, (formerly Okovic/Goodman Productions), 718 S. 22nd St., Philadelphia PA 19146. (215)546-1448. President: Robert M. Goodman. Motion picture production company. Estab. 1985. Clients include advertising agencies and corporate and industrial firms. Uses the services of independent songwriters/composers and recording studios for scoring of films and commercials for radio and TV. Commissions 4-6 composers/year. Pays by the job. Negotiates for either all rights or one-time use with a non-resale clause for a stated period.
How to Contact: "Please call us to determine if the services you can offer would be of use in our business." Prefers cassette (or VHS videocassette). SASE. "For a specific assignment we call within 2 weeks; otherwise, the samples will be kept on file."
Music: Uses all styles of music for corporate sales marketing and promotional films, commercials and documentaries.
Tips: "Be aware of the fact that music for film is of secondary importance. Don't overwrite."

GREEN ADVERTECTS, INC., 1500 Forest Ave., Richmond VA 23229. (804)282-4622. President: Francis Green. Advertising agency. Estab. 1970. Uses the services of independent songwriters, lyricists and music houses for jingles and background music for commercials. Buys local rights only. Pays by the job.
How to Contact: Submit demo tape of previously aired work. Prefers cassette. Does not return unsolicited material; prefers to keep on file.
Music: Up-tempo and classical for jingles.
Tips: "We are currently looking for a car care or carwash jingle. We can use something previously produced for others."

DENNIS R. GREEN AND ASSOCIATES, INC., Suite 110, 29355 Northwestern Hwy., Southfield MI 48034. (313)352-0700. President: Dennis R. Green. Advertising agency. Estab. 1973. Clients include retail and industrial firms. Uses the services of music houses for jingles for radio and television and commercials for radio and TV. Commissions 6 composers/year. Pays $1500-2500/job. Buys all rights.
How to Contact: Submit a demo tape of previous work or query with resume of credits. Prefers cassette or 7.5 ips. reel to reel (or VHS videocassette) with 6-10 songs. SASE, but prefers to keep submitted material on file. Reports back in two weeks.

Music: All kinds, depending on clients' needs.
Tips: "Send a demo reel and keep in touch."

HERB GROSS & CO., 18 Harvard St., Rochester NY 14607. (716)244-3711. President: Herb Gross. Consumer advertising specialist. Uses services of songwriters for jingles and movies. Commissions 6 songwriters/year. Pays $1,500-8,000/job; "depending on total authorized budget."
How to Contact: Submit demo tape of previous work. Prefers cassette with 3-6 songs. SASE, but prefers to keep material on file.
Music: Needs "60-second radio spots, 30- and 10-second TV spots. Uptempo, contemporary styles. Long form industrial videos. All styles of music, classical, comedy, laid back, country, etc."

GRS, INC., 13300 Broad St., Pataskala OH 43062. (614)927-9566. Manager: S.S. Andrews. Teleproduction facility. Estab. 1969. Varied clients. Uses the services of music houses and independent songwriters/composers for jingles and background music. Pays by the job. Buys all rights.
How to Contact: Submit demo tape of previous work. Prefers cassette. Does not return unsolicited material; prefers to keep on file.
Music: All styles for commercials.
Tips: "Follow our instructions exactly."

HEPWORTH ADVERTISING CO., 3403 McKinney Ave., Dallas TX 75204. (214)526-7785. President: S.W. Hepworth. Advertising agency. Estab. 1952. Serves financial, industrial and food clients. Uses services of songwriters for jingles. Pays by the job. Buys all rights.
How to Contact: Call first and obtain permission to submit or submit demo tape of previously aired work. Prefers cassette. SASE. Reports as need arises.

*HEROD ADVERTISING, INC., 3200 Troup Hwy., #339, Tyler TX 75701. (214)593-2362. President: Dan P. Herod. Advertising agency, audiovisual firm and music sound effect library. Clients include full service, banks, retail, industrial and music industry. Estab. 1954. Uses the services of music houses for background music for commercials, audiovisual presentations, jingles for commercials and commercials for radio and TV. Commissions 4-5 composers/year. Pays by the job. Buys shared rights.
How to Contact: Submit demo tape of previous work. Prefers cassette or 7½ or 15 ips reel-to-reel with 3-4 songs and lyric sheet. SASE, but prefers to keep material on file. Reports in 2-3 weeks.
Music: Uses modern contemporary and country western for films, commercials and audiovisual.
Tips: "Send demo tapes of previous or new work."

HEYWOOD FORMATICS & SYNDICATION, 1103 Colonial Blvd., Canton OH 44714. (216)456-2592. Owner: Max Heywood. Advertising agency and consultant. Clients include radio, television, restaurants/lounges. Uses the services of music houses and record companies and writers for background music for video presentation and industrial, and commercials for radio and TV. Payment varies per project.
How to Contact: Submit demo tape of previous work. Prefers cassette or 7½ or 15 ips reel-to-reel (or VHS/Beta videocassette). SASE.
Music: Uses pop, easy listening and CHR for educational films, slide presentations and commercials.

HILLMANN & CARR INC., 2121 Wisconsin Ave. NW, Washington DC 20007. (202)342-0001. President: Alfred Hillmann. Vice President/Treasurer: Ms. Michal Carr. Audiovisual firm and motion picture production company. Estab. 1975. Clients include corporate, government, associations and museums. Uses the services of music houses and independent songwriters/composers for scoring of films, video productions, PSA's and commercials for radio and TV. Commissions 2-3 composers/year. Payment negotiable.
How to Contact: Query with resume of credits, or submit demo tape of previous work or tape demonstrating composition skills, or write to arrange personal interview. Prefers cassette or 7½ ips reel-to-reel (or ¾" VHS or Beta videocassette) with 5-10 pieces. Does not return unsolicited material; prefers to keep on file only when interested. Reports in 1 month. SASE.
Music: Uses contemporary, classical, up-tempo and thematic music for documentary film and video productions, multi-media exposition productions, public service announcements.

HOME, INC., 731 Harrison Ave., Boston MA 02118. (617)266-1386. Director: Alan Michel. Audiovisual firm and video production company. Clients include cable television, nonprofit organizations, pilot programs, entertainment companies and industrial. Uses the services of music houses and independent songwriters/composers for background music for videos and TV commercials. Commissions 2-3 songwriters/year. Pays $50-300/job. Buys all rights or one-time rights.

How to Contact: Query with resume of credits, or submit demo tape of previous work. Prefers cassette with 6 pieces. SASE, but prefers to keep material on file. Reports as projects require.
Music: Mostly synthesizer. Uses all styles of music for educational videos.
Tips: "Plan to develop a working relationship for the long term."

HUDSON VALLEY MOTION PICTURE, VIDEO, STILL AND THEATRICAL SOCIETY, 67 Maple St., Newburgh NY 12550. (914)561-5866. Producer/Researcher: Richard Suraci. Advertising agency, audiovisual firm, scoring service, jingle/**commercial music production house,** motion picture production company and **music sound effect library.** Clients include corporate, industrial, motion, broadcast firms. Estab. 1987. Uses services of music houses, independent songwriters/composers and lyricists for scoring, background music and jingles for various projects and commercials for radio and TV. Pays by the job, by royalty or by the hour. Buys all rights or one-time rights.
How to Contact: Submit demo tape of previous work or tape demonstrating composition skills, submit manuscript showing music scoring skills, query with resume of credits or write to arrange personal interview. Prefers cassette (or ½", ¾", or 1" videocassette) with as many songs as possible and lyric or lead sheets. SASE, but prefers to keep material on file. Reports ASAP.
Music: Uses all types of music for all types of assignments.

*INNOVATIVE VIDEO ASSOCIATES, Suite 7, 415 Commerce Ln., Berlin NJ 08009. (609)768-5006. President: Lawrence Chatman. Audiovisual firm. Clients include industrial and commercial businesses. Estab. 1984. Uses the services of independent songwriters/composers for background music for industrial. Commissions 1-2 composers/year. Buys one-time rights.
How to Contact: Submit demo tape of previous work. Prefers cassette. SASE, but prefers to keep submitted materials on file. Reports in 2 months.
Music: Jazz and pop.

INTERMEDIA, 2720 Turner St., Victoria B.C. V8T 4V1 **Canada.** (604)389-2800. Fax: (604)389-2801. President: A.W. (Tony) Reynolds. Motion picture production company. Clients include industrial, educational, broadcast and theatrical. Estab. 1980. Uses the services of independent songwriters/composers for scoring of TV shows and films, jingles for commercials and commercials for radio and TV. Commissions 2-3 composers/year. Pays by the job. Buys all, one-time or varying rights.
How to Contact: Submit demo tape of previous work. Prefers cassette. SASE, but prefers to keep material on file. Reports in 2 weeks.
Music: Uses up-tempo, pop, jazz and classical for theatrical films, educational films and commercials.
Tips: "Be professional and competitive—current standards are very high."

INTERNATIONAL MEDIA SERVICES, INC., 718 Sherman Ave., Plainfield NJ 07060. (201)756-4060. President: Stuart Allen. Audiovisual firm, motion picture and television production company. Clients include schools, businesses, advertising and entertainment industry. Uses the services of music houses, songwriters/composers and lyricists for scoring of corporate and broadcast programs, background music for television and film, jingles for cable TV and broadcast spots, and commercials for radio and TV. Commissions 30 composers and 25 lyricists/year. Pays "per contract or license." Buys all rights or one-time rights.
How to Contact: Query with resume of credits or arrange personal interview. 'We accept no unsolicited material, contact required first." Prefers 7½ ips reel-to-reel, cassette (or ¾" videocassette) with 4-10 songs. SASE.
Tips: "Stay with professional and high quality material. Be persistent. Have a good broadcast quality demo. Follow-up periodically."

*INTERNATIONAL MOTION PICTURE'S LTD., Box 30260, Bakersfield CA 93385-1260. Producer: Judge A. Robertson. Audiovisual firm, scoring service, and motion picture production company. Services include original songs and themes for multi-image and motionpicture. Uses the services of independent songwriters/composers for the scoring of soundtracks and commercials for radio and TV. Commissions 3 composers/year. Pays by the job. Buys all rights.
How to Contact: Write first and obtain permission to submit. Prefers cassette, reel-to-reel (or videocassette) with 2 pieces. Does not return unsolicited material; prefers to keep on file. Response time varies.
Music: Uses all styles of music for motion pictures, etc.

IZEN ENTERPRISES, INC., 26 Abby Dr., E. Northport NY 11731. (516)368-0615. President: Ray Izen. Video services. Clients are various. Estab. 1980. Uses the services of music houses, independent songwriters/composers and lyricists for scoring of customized songs and background music. Commissions 2 composers and 2 lyricists/year. Pay is open. Buys all rights.

How to Contact: Submit demo tape of previous work. Prefers cassette or VHS videocassette. SASE, but prefers to keep material on file.

JASEN, NAVARRO & FOSTER, (formerly Jasen Advertising & Marketing), 14502 N. Dale Mabry, Tampa FL 33618. (813)960-4444. Creative Director: Abel Navarro. Advertising agency. Clients include business, medical, industrial and retail firms. Uses the services of music houses, independent songwriters/composers and lyricists for background music for radio and TV commercials, jingles and commercials for radio and TV. Commissions 3 composers and 3 lyricists/year. Pays by the job. Buys all rights.
How to Contact: Submit demo tape of previous work. Prefers cassette. Does not return unsolicited material; prefers to keep material on file.
Music: Uses up-tempo, pop and jazz for jingles.

THE JAYME ORGANIZATION, 25825 Science Park Dr., Cleveland OH 44122. (216)831-0110. Creative Supervisor: Debbie Klonk. Advertising agency. Uses the services of songwriters and lyricists for jingles and background music. Pays by the job. Buys all rights.
How to Contact: Query first; submit demo tape of previous work. Prefers cassette with 4-8 songs. SASE. Responds by phone as needs arise.
Music: Jingles.

K&R'S RECORDING STUDIOS, 28533 Greenfield, Southfield MI 48076. (313)557-8276. Contact: Ken Glaza. Scoring service and jingle/**commercial music production house.** Clients include commercial, industrial firms. Services include sound for pictures (music, dialogue). Uses the services of independent songwriters/composers for scoring, background music, jingles, commercials for radio and TV, etc. Commissions 4 composers/month. Pays by the job, royalty or hour. Buys all rights.
How to Contact: Write or call first to arrange personal interview. Prefers cassette (or ¾″ or VHS videocassette) with 5-7 pieces minimum. "Show me what you can do in 5 to 7 minutes." SASE. Reports in 1 week.
Music: "Be able to compose with the producer present."

KAUFMANN ADVERTISING ASSOCIATES, INC., 1626 Frederica Rd., St. Simons Island GA 31522. (912)638-8678. President: Harry Kaufmann. Advertising agency. Clients include resorts and cable TV. Estab. 1964. Uses the services of independent songwriters/composers and lyricists for scoring of videos, background music for videos, radio, TV, jingles for radio and commercials for radio and TV. Commissions 0-2 composers and 0-2 lyricists/year. Pays by the job.

*KELLIHER/SAMETS, 130 S. Willard St., Burlington VT 05401. (802)862-8261. Associate C.D. Andrew Yavelow. Marketing communications firm. Clients include consumer, business-to-business, trade, public service; local, regional, national. Estab. 1977. Uses the services of music houses and independent songwriters/composers for scoring of commercials, background music for commercials, industrial, jingles for commercial, commercials for radio and TV. Commissions 6 composers/year. Pays $100-2,000/job. Buys all rights.
How to Contact: Submit demo of previous work. Submit tape demonstrating composition skills. "Do not call." Prefers cassette (or VHS videocassette) with lead sheet. Does not return unsolicited material; prefers to keep on file. "Will call if needed."
Music: Uses folk, new age, jazz, classical, blues, funk, be-bop, swing, gospel, impressionist and expressionist.
Tips: "No interest in 'over produced' sound; looking for creativity and toe-tapping; ability to convey *mood*; *no* show-biz."

KEN-DEL PRODUCTIONS INC., First State Production Center, 1500 First State Blvd., Wilmington DE 19804-3596. (302)999-1164. Estab. 1950. A&R Director: Shirley Kay. General Manager: Ed Kennedy. Clients include publishers, industrial firms and advertising agencies. Uses services of songwriters for slides, film scores and title music. Pays by the job. Buys all rights.
How to Contact: Submit demo of previous work. Will accept audio or video tapes. "We prefer to keep tapes on file for possible future use." Reports in 1 month.

 The asterisk before a listing indicates that the listing is new in this edition. New markets are often the most receptive to unsolicited submissions.

*KEY PRODUCTIONS, INC., Box 2684, Gravois Station, St. Louis MO 63116. President: John E. Schroeder. Audiovisual firm. Estab. 1964. Clients include churches, colleges, church schools, industry and festivals. Uses services of songwriters for stage and educational TV musical dramas, background music for filmstrips, some speculative collaboration for submission to publishers and regional theatrical productions. Commissions "10 pieces/year, but selects up to 50 songs." Pays $50 minimum/job or by 10% minimum royalty. Buys one-time rights or all rights.
How to Contact: Query with resume of credits or submit demo tape showing flexibility of composition skills. "Suggest prior fee scales." Prefers cassette with 3-8 pieces. SASE. Reports in 1 month.
Music: "We almost always use religious material, some contemporary Biblical opera, some gospel, a few pop songs, jazz, blues, folk-rock and occasionally soul."
Tips: "Enclose typed lyrics in sequence with the demo cassette recording."

*KIMBO EDUCATIONAL UNITED SOUND ARTS, INC., 10-16 N. 3rd Ave., Box 477, Long Branch NJ 07740. (201)229-4949. Producers: James Kimble or Amy Laufer. Audiovisual firm and manufacturer of educational material: records, cassettes and teacher manuals and guides. Clients include schools and stores selling teachers' supplies. Uses the services of music houses, songwriters and educators for original songs for special education, early childhood, music classes, physical education and pre-school children; lyricists for lyrics to describe children's activities centering on development of motor skills, language, forms or related educational skills. Commissions 5-7 pieces and 5-7 lyricists/year. Pays by the job or royalty. Buys all rights.
How to Contact: Submit demo tape of previous work, tape demonstrating composition skills, manuscript showing music scoring skills or lead sheet with lyrics. Prefers cassette with 1-12 songs. "Upon receipt of a demo tape and/or written material, each property is previewed by our production staff. The same chances exist for any individual if the material is of high quality and we feel it meets the educational goals we are seeking." Reports in 2 months. Free catalog available.
Music: "Contemporary sounds with limited instrumentation so as not to appear too sophisticated nor distracting for the young or special populations. Lyrics should be noncomplex and repetitive."

SID KLEINER MUSIC ENTERPRISES, 10188 Winter View Dr., Naples FL 33942. (813)566-7701 and (813)566-7702. Managing Director: Sid Kleiner. Audiovisual firm. Serves the music industry and various small industries. Uses the services of music houses, songwriters and inhouse writers for background music; lyricists for special material. Commissions 5-10 composers and 2-3 lyricists/year. Pays $25 minimum/job. Buys all rights.
How to Contact: Query with resume of credits or submit demo tape of previously aired work. Prefers cassette with 1-4 songs. SASE. Reports in 5 weeks.
Music: "We generally need soft background music, with some special lyrics to fit a particular project. Uses catchy, contemporary, special assignments for commercial/industrial accounts. We also assign country, pop, mystical and metaphysical. Submit samples—give us your very best demos, your best prices and we'll try our best to use your services."

KTVU RETAIL SERVICES, Box 22222, Oakland CA 94623. (415)874-0228. TV station and retail Marketing Director: Richard Hartwig. Retail TV commercial production firm. Estab. 1974. Clients include local, regional and national retailers. Uses the services of music houses, independent songwriters/ composers, lyricists and music libraries for commercials for radio and TV. Commissions 50+ composers and 4 lyricists/year. Pays by the job. Buys all rights.
How to Contact: Submit demo tape of previous work. Prefers cassette or 7½ ips reel-to-reel with 6 pieces. SASE, but prefers to keep material on file.
Music: All styles for TV and radio commercials.

LA BOV AND BEYOND MUSIC PRODUCTION, Box 5533, Ft. Wayne IN 46895. (219)420-5533. Creative Director: Cheryl Franks. President: Barry La Bov. Scoring service and **commercial music production house**. Clients include advertising agencies, film production houses and A/V firms. Uses the services of independent songwriters/composers and lyricists for scoring and background music for films, TV and audiovisual projects; jingles and commercials for radio and TV. Commissions 4-10 composers and 2-5 lyricists/year.
How to Contact: Submit demo tape of previous work, tape showing composition skills or manuscript showing music scoring skills. Prefers cassette, 7½ or 15 ips reel-to-reel (or VHS videocassette) with 5-10 pieces. SASE, but prefers to keep material on file. Reports in 3 weeks. "We will call when tape has been received and evaluated."
Music: Uses all styles of music for all kinds of assignments from commercials to songs. "We look for positive, eager writers who strive to create unique, outstanding music."
Tips: "Try new approaches and work to keep a fresh sound. Be innovative, conceptually strong, and positive."

*LANE AUDIO PRODUCTIONS, INC., 1507 Wesley, Springdale AR 72764. President: Richard Eby. Jingle/commercial music production house and general recording studio. Clients include corporate clients (J.B. Hunt, IBM), local agencies and business (jingles). Estab. 1988. Uses the services of independent songwriters/composers, lyricists and voice talent (singing and spoken), musicians for background music for various projects, jingles for local businesses and commercials for radio and TV. Commissions 4-8 composers and 2-4 lyricists/year. Pays $75-400/job or 20-50% royalty. Buys all rights, one-time rights and percentage of rights.
How to Contact: Submit demo tape of previous work. Submit tape demonstrating composition skills. Prefers cassette or 7.5 or 15 IPS reel-to-reel with 3-5 songs and lyric sheet. "Most useful to us right now is easy listening instrumental but we will listen to anything." Does not return unsolicited material; prefers to keep on file. Reports in 2 weeks.
Music: Uses all types for commercials, production music on training tapes, etc.

LANE & JOHNSON, 4466 Laclede Pl., St. Louis MO 63108. (314)533-0010. Creative Director: George Johnson. President: Carla Lane. Audiovisual firm, scoring service and music contractor. Estab. 1976. Clients include business, industry, government, agricultural conglomerates and hospitals. Uses the services of independent songwriters and arrangers for bed music. Commissions 2 or 3 composers/year. Pays by the job. Buys all rights.
How to Contact: Query with resume of credits; submit tape of previous work or tape demonstrating composition skills or manuscript showing music scoring skills. Prefers cassette with any number of songs. SASE. Reports in 2 weeks.
Music: Depends on client's needs.

LANGE PRODUCTIONS, 7661 Curson Terrace, Hollywood CA 90046. (213)874-4730. Production Co-ordinators: Anita Horner. Medical video production company. Clients include doctors, hospitals, corporations. Estab. 1987. Uses services of independent songwriters/composers for scoring and background music for medical videos. Commissions 6 composers/year. Pays by the job, $300-700. Buys all rights.
How to Contact: Submit demo tape of previous work. SAE, but prefers cassette. Prefers to keep materials on file. Reports in 3 weeks.

*LAPRIORE VIDEOGRAPHY, 86 Allston Ave., Worcester MA 01604. (508)755-9010. Owner: Peter Lapriore. Video production company. Clients include business, educational and sports. Estab. 1985. Uses the services of music houses and independent songwriters/composers for background music for industrial productions and commercials for TV. "We also own a music library." Commissions 2 composers/year. Pays $1,000/job. Buys all rights, one-time rights and limited use rights.
How to Contact: Submit demo tape of previous work demonstrating composition skills. Prefers cassette or VHS videocassette with 5 songs and lyric sheet. Does not return material, but prefers to keep material on file. Reports in 2 weeks.
Music: Uses medium, up-tempo and classical for marketing, educational films and commercials.

CHRISTOPHER LARDAS ADVERTISING, Box 1440, New York NY 10101. (212)688-5199. President: Christopher Lardas. Advertising agency. Clients include manufacturers of packaged items. Estab. 1960. Uses the services of music houses, independent songwriters/composers and lyricists for commercials for radio and TV. Commissions 3 composers/year. Pays on a fee basis. Buys all rights.
How to Contact: Submit demo tape of previous work or tape demonstrating composition skills. Prefers cassette. Does not return unsolicited material; prefers to keep material on file. Reports in 3 weeks.
Music: Uses up-tempo, pop and jazz for commercials.

LEDFORD PRODUCTIONS, INC., Box 7363, Furnitureland Station, High Point NC 27264-7363. (919)431-1107. President: Hank Ledford. Audiovisual firm and advertising firm. Clients include banks, manufacturers of heavy duty equipment and luxury items and Fortune 500 companies. Uses music houses for background music for video/slide shows and radio commercials. Commissions 25 pieces or songs/year. Pays by the job. Buys all rights or one-time rights.
How to Contact: Submit demo tape of previous work. Prefers cassette (or ¼" VHS videocassette). Does not return unsolicited material; prefers to keep on file.
Music: Uses music for videos, slide presentation-industrial/product introductions.

LEISURE-FOR-PLEASURE, 5 Burcot Avenue, Wolverhampton West Midlands WV 12SB **England**. Phone: (0902) 52194. Chairman: John B. Thomas. Advertising agency, audiovisual firm and scoring service. Estab. 1980. Uses the services of music houses, independent songwriters/composers and lyricists for background music, jingles and commercials for radio and TV. Commissions 2 composers and 2 lyricists/year. Pays by the job. Buys all rights.

How to Contact: Submit tape demonstrating composition skills or manuscript showing music scoring skills, or write or call to arrange personal interview. Prefers cassette (or videocassette) with 2 songs and lyric or lead sheet. SAE and IRC. Does not return unsolicited material; prefers to keep on file. Reports in 1 month.
Music: Uses easy listening music for educational films.

S.R. LEON COMPANY, INC., 132 South St., Oyster Bay NY 11731. (516)922-0031. Creative Director: Max Firetog. Advertising agency. Serves industrial, drug, automotive and dairy product clients. Uses jingles and background music for commercials. Commissions vary. Rights purchased are limited to use of music for commercials.
How to Contact: Submit demo tape of previously aired work. Prefers cassette. No length restrictions on demo.
Music: Uses all types.

LEWIS, GILMAN & KYNETTE, INC., 200 South Broad St., Philadelphia PA 19102. (215)790-4100. Broadcast Business Manager: Valencia Tursi. Advertising agency. Serves industrial and consumer clients. Uses music houses for jingles and background music in commercials. Pays creative fee asked by music houses.
How to Contact: Submit demo tape of previously aired work. "You must send in previously published work. We do not use original material." Prefers cassette. Will return with SASE if requested, but prefers to keep on file.
Music: All types.

LIGHT PRODUCTIONS, 1915 Webster, Birmingham MI 48009. (313)642-3502. Producer: Terry Luke. Audiovisual firm. Estab. 1974. Clients include corporations, industrial, motivational, New Age, churches and educational institutions. Uses the services of music houses and independent songwriters/composers for jingles, background music for TV commercials, slide presentations and training videos. Commissions 4-15 songwriters and 2-3 lyricists/year. Pays $100-3,000/job or $4-65/hour. Buys all rights or one-time rights.
How to Contact: Write or call first and obtain permission to submit; submit demo tape of previous work. Prefers cassette (or VHS videocassette). SASE, but prefers to keep material on file. Reports in 3 weeks.
Music: Uses up-tempo, rock, spiritual, easy listening and inspirational for slide presentations, training videos and artistic video-MTV.
Tips: "Be creative and upbeat."

*LOTT WALKER ADVERTISING, 2648 Ridgewood Rd., Jackson MS 39216. (601)981-9810. Art Director: John C. Abbate. Advertising agency. Clients include financial, healthcare, telecommunications. Estab. 1976. Uses the services of music houses and independent songwriters/composers for jingles for commercials for radio and TV. Commissions 1-2 composers and 1-2 lyricists/year. Pays by the job. Buys all rights and one-time rights.
How to Contact: Submit demo tape of previous work. Prefers cassette. "Let us know your rates." Does not return unsolicited material; prefers to keep on file.
Music: Uses all types of music for all kinds of assignments.

WALTER P. LUEDKE & ASSOCIATES, INC., Eastmoor Bldg., Suite One, 4223 E. State St., Rockford IL 61108. (815)398-4207. Secretary: Joan Luedke. Advertising agency. Estab. 1959. Uses the services of independent songwriters/composers and lyricists for background music for clients, jingles for clients and commercials for radio and TV. Commissions 1-2 composers and 1-2 lyricists/year. Pays by the job. Buys all rights.
How to Contact: Write first to arrange personal interview. Prefers cassette. "Our need is infrequent, best just let us know who you are." SASE, but prefers to keep material on file. Reports in 1 week.
Music: Uses various styles.

LUNA TECH, INC., 148 Moon Dr., Owens Cross Roads AL 35763. (205)725-4224. Chief Designer: Norman A. Plaisted. Fireworks company. Clients include theme parks, municipalities and industrial show producers. Estab. 1969. Uses music houses, independent songwriters and client music departments for scoring of music for fireworks displays. Commissions 1-2 composers/year. Pays $500-3,000/job. Buys all rights or one-time rights.
How to Contact: Query with resume of credits or submit demo tape of previous work. Prefers cassette (or VHS videocassette) with 1-5 pieces. Does not return unsolicited material; prefers to keep on file. Reports in 1 month; will call if interested.

Music: "Music for fireworks choreography: dynamic, jubilant, heraldic, bombastic, original."
Tips: "Send us a demo tape showing your composition skills and tailored as much as possible toward our needs."

MCCAFFREY AND MCCALL ADVERTISING, 8888 Keystone Crossing, Indianapolis IN 46240. (317)574-3900. Associate Creative Director: William Mick. Advertising agency. Serves consumer electronics, technical ecucation, retail and commercial developers. Estab. 1984. Uses the services of music houses for scoring, background music and jingles for radio and TV commercials. Commissions 3 composers/year; 1 lyricist/year. Pays $3,000-5,000/job. Buys all rights.
How to Contact: Submit demo tape of previous work and write to arrange personal interview. Prefers cassette (or ¾" videocassette) with 6 songs. SASE, but prefers to keep submitted materials on file.
Music: High-energy pop, sound-alikes and electronic for commercials.
Tips: "Keep in touch, but don't be a pest about it."

McCANN-ERICKSON WORLDWIDE, Suite 1900, 1360 Post Oak Blvd., Houston TX 77056. (713)965-0303. Creative Director: Jesse Caesar. Advertising agency. Serves all types of clients. Uses services of songwriters for jingles and background music in commercials. Commissions 10 songwriters/year. Pays production cost and registrated creative fee. Arrangement fee and creative fee depend on size of client and size of market. "If song is for a big market, a big fee is paid; if for a small market, a small fee is paid." Buys all rights.
How to Contact: Submit demo tape of previously aired work. Prefers 7½ ips reel-to-reel. "There is no minimum or maximum length for tapes. Tapes may be of a variety of work or a specialization. We are very open on tape content; agency does own lyrics." SASE, but prefers to keep material on file. Responds by phone when need arises.
Music: All types.

McDONALD DAVIS & ASSOC., 250 W. Coventry Ct., Milwaukee WI 53217. (414)228-1990. Vice President/Creative Director: Steve Preston. Advertising agency. Uses music houses for background music for commercials. Commissions 15 composers and producers/year. Pays $1,000-3,000/job. Buys all rights.
How to Contact: Write to arrange personal interview or submit demo tape of previously aired work or tape demonstrating composition skills. Prefers cassette (or ¾" videocassette) with 10 pieces and resume of credits. Does not return unsolicited material; prefers to keep on file. "We report in 1 week on solicited material."
Music: Uses all styles of music for post-scoring television commercials.

MADDEN & GOODRUM, 4301 Hillsboro Rd., Nashville TN 37215. (615)292-4431. Executive Vice President/Creative Director: Mil Leonard. Advertising agency. Estab. 1970. Serves retail, service businesses and manufacturers. Uses independent songwriters and music houses for jingles and background music for commercials. Commissions 4-6 composers and 4-6 lyricists/year. Pays by the job. Buys all rights or one-time rights.
How to Contact: "Send a demo; send address and phone number." SASE. Reports "when we need them."
Music: Needs vary.

LEE MAGID INC., (Alexis Music Inc., Marvelle Music Co.) Box 532, Malibu CA 90265. (213)463-5998. President: Lee Magid. Audiovisual firm, scoring service and motion picture production company. Clients include publishing, business, industry, theatrical and educational firms. Uses the services of songwriters, lyricists and composer/arrangers for scoring, themes and background music for films and videos, jingles and commercials for radio and TV. Commissions 10-15 songwriters/composers and 10 lyricists/year. Buys all rights. Pays by the job or by royalty.
How to Contact: Send resume of credits or submit tape demonstrating composition skills. Prefers cassette (or videocassette) with maximum 3 songs (or 3 minutes). "I would make direct contact with songwriter/composer and designate preference and style." SASE. Reports in 1 month.
Music: Mostly pop, rock and R&B; also gospel, jazz and country. Vocals and/or instrumental.
Tips: "Use your instincts. Write songs for visual and musical memory effect. Try to become an innovator. Think ahead."

MALLOF, ABRUZINO & NASH MARKETING, 477 E. Butterfield Rd., Lombard IL 60148. (708)964-7722. President: Ed Mallof. Advertising agency. Estab. 1980. Works primarily with auto dealer jingles. Uses music houses for jingles. Commissions 5-6 songwriters/year. Pays by the job. Buys all rights.
How to Contact: Submit demo tape of previous work. Prefers cassette with 4-12 songs. SASE; but prefers to keep material on file. Reports "when we feel a need for their style."
Tips: "Submit good driving music with clever lyrics."

*MANN ADVERTISING, 466 Hanover St., Box 3818, Manchester NH 03105. (603)625-5403. Broadcast Producer: Terrence Toland. Advertising agency. Clients include retail/industrial/hi-tech. Estab. 1974. Uses the services of music houses for background music for industrial videos and commercials for radio and TV. Pays $3,000-7,000/job. Buys all rights and one-time rights.
How to Contact: Submit demo tape of previous work. Prefers cassette (or VHS videocassette) with 3-7 songs. SASE, but prefers to keep material on file. Reports in 2 weeks.
Music: Uses up tempo, easy listening, jazz for commercials, slide shows, industrial videos.
Tips: "Present clean clear work—make it your best work *only*."

THE MARKETING CONNECTION, Suite 100, 7616 Southland, Orlando FL 32809. (407)855-4321. Vice President, Sales: Leon Lebeau. Audiovisual firm. Uses services of music houses, independent songwriters/composers, lyricists and recording studios for scoring of A/V sound tracks and videos, walk-in music for shows, jingles for videos (non-commercial) and sound effects. Commissions 2-3 composers and 1-2 lyricists/year. Pays by the job, $30-50/hour or local studio rates. Buys all rights or one-time rights.
How to Contact: Submit demo tape of previous work; call first to arrange personal interview. Prefers cassette (or ¾″ or ½″ videocassette) or 7½ ips reel-to-reel. "New material only." SASE, but prefers to keep material on file. Reports in several weeks.
Music: Uses up-tempo, pop and jazz for educational and training films and slide presentations.

*MASTER MANAGEMENT MUSIC, 1626 W. Wilcox St. #242, Los Angeles CA 90028. (213)871-8054 ex. 516. President/CEO: George Van Heel. Advertising agency, jingle/commercial music production house, promotion/production company and music publishing company (BMI). Estab. 1987. Uses the services of music houses, independent songwriters/composers and lyricists for scoring, background music and jingles for campaigns and commercials for radio/TV. Commissions 1 composer/year; 1 lyricist/year. Pays $5,000/job. Buys all rights.
How to Contact: Write first to arrange personal interview. "No personal deliveries; by appointment only!" Prefers cassette or VHS videocassette with 3 songs and lyric and lead sheets. "All songs must be patriotic." Does not return unsolicited submissions; prefers to keep materials on file. Reports in 2 months.
Music: Pop/rock style for campaigns, educational and music videos.

MAXWELL ADVERTISING INC., 444 W. Michigan, Kalamazoo MI 49007. (616)382-4060. Creative Director: Jess Maxwell. Advertising agency. Uses the services of lyricists and music houses for jingles and background music for commercials. Commissions 6-8 lyricists/year. Pays $4,000-20,000/job. Buys all rights or one-time rights.
How to Contact: Submit demo tape of previously aired work or tape demonstrating composition skills. Prefers cassette (or VHS videocassette). SASE, but prefers to keep material on file.
Music: Uses various styles of music for jingles and music beds.

*MEDIA CONSULTANTS, P.O. Box 130, Sikeston MO 63801. (314)472-1116. Owner: Richard Wrather. Advertising agency. Clients are varied. Estab. 1979. Uses the services of music houses and independent songwriters/composers for scoring of and background music for industrial video and commercials for radio and TV. Commissions 10-15 composers and varied number of lyricists/year. Pays varying amount/job. Buys all rights.
How to Contact: Submit a demo tape of previous work. Submit tape demonstrating composition skills. Prefers cassette (or ½″ or ¾″ videocassette). Does not return unsolicited material; prefers to keep on file.
Music: Uses all styles of music for varied assignments.

MEDIA GROUP TELEVISION, 7th Ave. and 23rd Sts., Moline IL 61265. (309)764-6411. Media Manager: Curt Shaffer. Video production company. Estab. 1976. Clients include advertising agencies, cable systems, TV stations, corporate offices, retailers, industrial plants, etc. Uses the services of independent songwriters and music houses for jingles, background music for commercials and background for industrial training, etc. Pays by the job. Buys all rights.
How to Contact: Submit demo tape of previous work. Prefers cassette with 5 pieces. Prefers to keep material on file. Reports in 3 weeks.
Music: "Specifically looking for an up-tempo jingle to use in chiropractic commercials across the US."

MEDIA PRODUCTIONS, 2095 N. Andrews Ext., Pompano Beach FL 33069. (305)979-6467. General Manager: Jim Haney. Motion picture, TV and post-production company. Clients include advertising agency and commercial production company. Uses the services of music houses and independent songwriters/composers for TV commercials. Commissions 2 composers and 2 lyricists/year. Pays $200-2,000/job. Buys all rights.

How to Contact: Submit tape demonstrating composition skills or manuscript showing music scoring skills. Prefers 7½ ips reel-to-reel (or ¾" videocassette) with 4-8 songs and lyric sheet. SASE, but prefers to keep material on file. Reports in 2 months.
Music: Uses up-tempo and pop music for commercials.

ARTHUR MERIWETHER INC., 1529 Brook Dr., Downers Grove IL 60515. (312)495-0600. Producer: Mark Lemermano. Audiovisual firm. Clients include business, industry and advertising agencies. Uses the services of music houses and independent songwriters for background music for filmstrips, slides, audio tapes, videotapes and radio commercials. Uses lyricists for corporate meeting themes. Payment negotiable. Buys all rights.
How to Contact: Submit demo tape of previous work, or query with resume of credits. Prefers cassette or 7½ ips reel-to-reel. Does not return unsolicited material; prefers to keep on file. Reports as soon as possible.

METROTAPE PRODUCER SERVICES INC., 3423 South Blvd., Charlotte NC 28209. (704)525-2306. Audio engineer: Mike Robinson. Audiovisual firm. Serves corporate clients. Uses the services of music houses and independent songwriters/composers for background music for audiovisual and multi-image productions, and commercials for radio. Commissions 1-2 composers/year. Pays by the job or by royalty. Buys all rights and one-time rights.
How to Contact: Submit demo tape of previous work or write or call to arrange personal interview. Prefers cassette (or VHS or ¾" videocassette). SASE, but prefers to keep material on file. Reports ASAP.
Music: Uses up-tempo, mid-tempo, jazz and classical music for slide presentations.

*JON MILLER PRODUCTION STUDIOS, 7249 Airport Rd., Bath PA 18014. (215)837-7550. Executive Producer: Jon Miller. Audiovisual firm, jingle/commercial music production house and video production company. Clients include industrial, commercial, institutional and special interest. Estab. 1970. Uses the services of music houses, independent songwriters/composers and lyricists for scoring of themes and background music and background music for audio and video production and live presentations. Commissions 5-10 composers and 1-5 lyricists/year. Pays by the job. Buys all rights or one-time rights.
How to Contact: Submit demo tape of previous work. Query with resume of credits and references. Prefers cassette with 7 songs and lyric or lead sheets. Does not return unsolicited material; prefers to keep on file. Reports in 2-3 weeks.
Music: Uses up tempo and title music introduction music for industrial marketing and training videos.
Tips: "Provide professional product on time and within budget. Keep communication open."

MITCHELL & ASSOCIATES, 7830 Old George Town Rd., Bethesda MD 20814. (301)986-1772. President: Ronald Mitchell. Advertising agency. Serves food, high-tech, transportation, financial, real estate, automotive and retail clients. Uses independent songwriters, lyricists and music houses for background music for commercials, jingles and post-TV scores for commercials. Commissions 3-5 songwriters and 3-5 lyricists/year. Pays $3,000-10,000/job. Buys all rights.
How to Contact: Submit demo tape of previously aired work. Prefers cassette or 7½ ips reel-to-reel. Does not return unsolicited material; prefers to keep on file.
Music: "Depends upon client, audience, etc."

MONTEMAYOR Y ASOCIADOS, 70 N.E. Loop 410 #870, San Antonio TX 78216. (512)342-1990. Creative Director: Olga Bernal Uriegas. Advertising agency. Clients include automotive, product (soft drink/beer), fast food, financial firms. Estab. 1983. Uses the services of music houses, independent songwriters/composers and lyricists for scoring of television audio, jingles for products and commercials for radio and TV. Commissions 5 composers and 5 lyricists/year. Pays by the job. Buys all rights or yearly buy-outs.
How to Contact: Submit demo tape of previous work. Prefers cassette (or ½" or ¾" videocassette). Properly label demo with name, address and telephone number. Does not return unsolicited material; prefers to keep material on file. Reports in 2 months.
Music: Uses all styles with Latin flavor for all types of assignments.

*MONTEREY BAY PRODUCTION GROUP, Suite 204, 563 Arthur Rd., Watsonville CA 95076. (408)722-3132. Owner/Manager: Denise V. Collins. Video production services. Clients include industrial business and broadcast. Estab. 1985. Uses the services of independent songwriters/composers for scoring of promotional, educational and commercial videos. Commissions 3-10 composers/year. Pays by the job.

How to Contact: Submit demo tape of previous work. Query with resume of credits. Prefers cassette (or VHS videocassette) with 5 songs. Prefers to keep material on file. Reports in 1 month.
Music: Uses all types for promotional, training and commercial.

MOTIVATION MEDIA, INC., 1245 Milwaukee Ave., Glenview IL 60025. (708)297-4740. Production Manager: Glen Peterson. Audiovisual firm, video, motion picture production company and business meeting planner. Estab. 1969. Clients include business and industry. Uses the services of songwriters and composers "mostly for business meetings and multi-image production"; lyricists for writing lyrics for business meeting themes, audience motivation songs and promotional music for new product introduction. Commissions 3-5 composers/year. Payment varies. Buys one-time rights.
How to Contact: Query with resume of credits; or submit demo tape of previous work. Prefers cassette with 5-7 songs. Responds when the need arises.
Music: Uses "up-beat contemporary music that motivates an audience of sales people."
Tips: "Keep in touch—let us know what new and exciting assignments you have undertaken."

MTC PRODUCTION CENTER, (formerly American Video Factory), 4150 Glencoe Ave., Marina Del Rey CA 90292. (213)823-8622. Music Composer: Emilio Kauderer. Scoring service and jingle/**commercial music production house**. Clients include advertising, corporate, entertainment and other businesses. Uses the services of independent songwriters/composers for background music for commercials, feature films, industrials, jingles and commercials for radio and TV. Commissions 5 composers and 5 lyricists/year. Pays by the job. Buys all rights.
How to Contact: Write or call first to arrange personal interview. Prefers cassette. SASE. Prefers to keep submitted materials on file. Reports in 2 weeks.
Music: Uses jazz, classical, new age, pop and up-tempo.

MULTI IMAGE PRODUCTIONS, 8849 Complex Dr., San Diego CA 92123. (619)560-8383. Sound Editor/Engineer: Jim Lawrence. Audiovisual firm and motion picture production company. Serves business, corporate, industrial, commercial, military and cultural clients. Uses music houses, independent songwriters/composers/arrangers and lyricists for scoring of industrials, corporate films and videos; background music for AV, film, video and live shows; and jingles and commercials for radio and TV. Commissions 2-10 composers and 2-5 lyricists/year. Pays $500+/job. Buys all rights.
How to Contact: Query with resume of credits or write to obtain permission to submit. Prefers 7½ or 15 ips reel-to-reel with 2-5 pieces. Does not return unsolicited material; prefers to keep on file. Reports in 6 weeks.
Music: Uses "comtemporary, pop, specialty, regional, ethnic, national and international" styles of music for background "scores written against script describing locales, action, etc. We try to stay clear of stereotypical 'canned' music and prefer a more commercial and dramatic (film-like) approach."
Tips: "We have established an ongoing relationship with a local music production/scoring house with whom songwriters would be in competition for every project; but an ability to score clean, full, broad, contemporary commercial and often 'film score' type music, in a variety of styles would be a benefit."

*MUSIC LANE PRODUCTIONS, Box 3829, Austin TX 78764. (512)447-3988. Owner: Wayne Gathright. Music recording, production and jingle/commercial music production house. Estab. 1980. Serves bands, songwriters and commercial clients. Uses the services of music houses and independent songwriters/composers for jingles and commercials for radio and TV. Pays by the job. Buys one-time rights.
How to Contact: Submit demo tape of previous work or tape demonstrating composition skills; or query with resume of credits. Prefers cassette. Does not return unsolicited material; prefers to keep on file. Reports in 6 weeks.
Music: Uses all styles.

MUSIC MASTERS, 2322 Marconi Ave., St. Louis MO 63110. (314)773-1480. Producer: Greg Trampe. **Commercial music production house** and **music/sound effect library**. Estab. 1976. Clients include multi-image and film producers, advertising agencies and large corporations. Uses the services of independent songwriters/composers and lyricists for background music for multi-image and film, jingles and commercials for radio and TV. Commissions 6 composers and 2 lyricists/year. Pays $100-2,000/job. Buys all rights.
How to Contact: Query with resume of credits or write and obtain permission to submit. Prefers cassette or 7½ or 15 ips reel-to-reel (or Beta or VHS videocassette) with 3-6 pieces. SASE, but prefers to keep material on file. Reports in 1 month.
Music: "We use all types of music for slide presentations (sales & motivational)."
Tips: "Resume should have at least 3 or 4 major credits of works completed within the past year. A good quality demo is a must."

MYERS & ASSOCIATES, Suite 203, 3727 SE Ocean Blvd., Stuart FL 34996. (407)287-1990. Senior Vice President: Doris McLaughlin. Advertising agency. Estab. 1973. Serves financial, real estate, consumer products and hotel clients. Uses music houses for background music for commercials and jingles. Commissions 2-3 songwriters/year and 2-3 lyricists/year. Pays by the job. Buys all rights.
How to Contact: Submit demo tape of previously aired work. Prefers cassette. Does not return unsolicited material; prefers to keep on file.
Music: Uses "various styles of music for jingles, music beds and complete packages depending on clients' needs."

MYSTIC OAK RECORDS, 1727 Elm St., Bethlehem PA 18017. (215)865-1083. Project Coordinator: Heather Lynne. Production company. Serves independent clients and marketing firms. Uses the services of independent songwriters/composers and lyricists for jingles and commercials for radio and TV. Commissions 20 composers and 5 lyricists/year. Pays by the job. Rights vary by contract.
How to Contact: Submit demo tape of previous work or query with resume of credits. Prefers cassette (or VHS videocassette) with 3 songs. Does not return unsolicited material; prefers to keep on file.
Music: Uses easy listening, up-tempo and pop for educational films and commercials.

FRANK C. NAHSER, INC., 18th Floor, 10 S. Riverside Plaza, Chicago IL 60606. (312)845-5000. Contact: Dick Cohen. Advertising agency. Serves insurance, telecommunications, toys, bicycles, hotels, and other clients. Uses the services of independent songwriters/composers, lyricists and music houses for scoring of television commercials, background music for commercials for radio and TV and music for industrial/sales presentations and meetings. Commissions 6-10 songwriters and 4 lyricists/year. Pays $5,000-15,000 for finished production or varying royalty. Buys one-time rights.
How to Contact: Submit demo tape of previous work. Prefers cassette. Does not return unsolicited material; prefers to keep on file. "No phone calls, please. When a cassette is submitted we listen to it for reference when a project comes up. We ignore most cassettes that lack sensitivity toward string and woodwind arrangements unless we know it's from a lyricist."
Music: "We mostly use scores for commercials, not jingles. The age of the full sing jingle in national TV spots is quickly coming to an end. Young songwriters should be aware of the difference and have the expertise to score, not just write songs."
Tips: "The writing speaks for itself. If you know composition, theory and arrangement it quickly becomes evident. Electronic instruments are great tools; however, they are no substitute for total musicianship. Learn to read, write, arrange and produce music and, with this book's help, market your music. Be flexible enough to work along with an agency. We like to write and produce as much as you do."

HENRY NASON PRODUCTIONS, 1900 Superfine Ln., Wilmington DE 19802. (302)656-7646. Producer: Leslie Maxwell Henson. Audiovisual firm. Clients include corporate and industrial firms. Estab. 1972. Uses the services of music houses and independent songwriters/composers for background music for corporate production. Pays by the job and by the hour. Buys all rights or one-time rights.
How to Contact: Submit demo tape of previous work or query with resume of credits. Prefers cassette (or ¾" videocassette). SASE, but prefers to keep material on file.

*NATIONAL TELEPRODUCTIONS, INC., P.O. Box 1804, W. Palm Beach FL 33402. (407)689-9271. Producer: Robert Peterson. Motion picture and television production company. "70% of our work is programming for national television release; the balance is corporate and international business." Estab. 1975. Uses music houses and independent songwriters/composers for scoring of background music for television programming, documentaries and corporate/industrial presentations and commercials for TV. Commissions 10-15 composers/year. Pays $3-15,000/job. Rights purchased vary by project.
How to Contact: Submit demo tape of previous work. Prefers cassette. SASE, but prefers to keep submitted material on file. Only reports back if the individual is being considered for an assignment.
Tips: "Keep your sample tape current!"

NEW AGE SIGHT & SOUND, 120 Interstate N. Pkwy E., #164, Atlanta GA 30339. (404)956-7956. Studio Manager: Dean Gleason. Jingle/**commercial music production house**; audio for video and record production. Uses the services of MIDI synthesists and music houses for background music for video and commercials for radio. Commissions 3-5 composers/year. Pays by the job or per hour (bid). Buys one-time rights or all rights.
How to Contact: Submit demo tape of previous work or write or call to arrange personal interview. Prefers cassette (or VHS videocassette) with 3-5 pieces. Does not return unsolicited material; prefers to keep on file. Reports if needed.
Music: Uses up-tempo and jazz for video demonstrations, overviews and training.
Tips: "Knowledge of MIDI is helpful."

NEW & UNIQUE VIDEOS, 2336 Sumac Dr., San Diego CA 92105. (619)282-6126. Contact: Pat Money. Video production company. Clients include home video market—general public. Estab. 1981. Uses the services of music houses and independent songwriters/composers for background music for videotape productions. Commissions 3 composers and 3 lyricists/year. Pays by the job, by royalty or by the hour. Buys all rights.
How to Contact: Query with resume of credits. Prefers cassette. Does not return unsolicited material; prefers to keep on file.
Music: Uses easy listening, up-tempo and jazz for educational films and action/adventure, nature and love stories.
Tips: "We are growing, so be patient."

NOBLE ARNOLD & ASSOCIATES, 1501 Woodfield Rd., Suite 202 N, Schaumburg IL 60173. (708)605-8808. Creative Director: John Perkins. Advertising agency. Clients include communication and health care firms. Estab. 1970. Uses the services of independent songwriters/composers for jingles. Commissions 1 composer and 1 lyricist/year. Pays by the job. Buys all rights.
How to Contact: Submit demo tape of previous work. Prefers cassette. Does not return unsolicited material. Reports in 4 weeks.

NORTHLICH STOLLEY LAWARRE, INC., 200 West Fourth St., Cincinnati OH 45202. (513)421-8840. Broadcast Producer: Judy Merz. Advertising agency. Clients include banks, hospitals, P&G, Cintas, Mead Paper. Estab. 1949. Uses the services of independent songwriters and music houses for jingles and background music for commercials. Commissions 3-5 composers/year. Pays by the job. Rights purchased varies.
How to Contact: Submit demo tape of previous work, tape demonstrating composition skills or query with resume of credits. Prefers cassette. SASE, but prefers to keep materials on file.
Music: Uses all kinds for commercials.

***NOTCH/BRADLEY**, 801 Vine, Chattanooga TN 37403. (615)756-8647. Creative Director: Doug Cook. Advertising agency. Clients include healthcare, tourism, et. al. Estab. 1984. Uses the services of independent songwriters/composers and lyricists for commercials for radio and TV. Commissions 10 composers and 5 lyricists/year. Pays $1,000-1,500/job. Buys all rights.
How to Contact: Submit demo tape of previous work. Prefers cassette (or ½" videocassette) with 5-7 songs. Does not return unsolicited material; prefers to keep on file. Reports in 2-4 weeks.
Music: Uses mood pieces—relaxed to high drama—primarily for commercials.
Tips: "We're open to different approaches, avoid generic stuff."

OMNI COMMUNICATIONS, 655 W. Carmel Dr., Carmel IN 46032-2669. (317)844-6664. President: W. H. Long. Television production and audiovisual firm. Estab. 1978. Serves industrial, commercial, and educational clients. Uses the services of music houses and songwriters for scoring of films and television productions; background music for voice overs; lyricists for original music and themes. Commissions varying number of composers and lyricists/year. Pays by the job. Buys all rights.
How to Contact: Query with resume of credits. Prefers reel-to-reel, cassette (or videocassette). Does not return unsolicited material. Reports in 2 weeks.
Music: Varies with each and every project; from classical, contemporary to commercial industrial.
Tips: "Submit good demo tape with examples of your range to command the attention of our producers."

ON-Q PRODUCTIONS, INC., 618 Gutierrez St., Santa Barbara CA 93103. (805)963-1331. President: Vincent Quaranta. Audiovisual firm. Clients include corporate accounts/sales conventions. Uses the services of music houses, independent songwriters/composers and lyricists for scoring of and background music for media productions and TV commercials. Commissions 1-5 composers and 1-5 lyricists/year. Pays by the job. Buys all rights or one-time rights.
How to Contact: Submit demo tape of previous work. Prefers cassette or 15 ips reel-to-reel (or VHS videocassete). SASE, but prefers to keep material on file. Reports in 1 month.
Music: Uses up-tempo music for slide and video presentations.

***PAISANO PUBLICATIONS/EASYRIDERS HOME VIDEO**, Box 3000, Agoura Hills CA 91364. (818)889-8740. Producer/Director: Rick Schmidlin. Home video and TV productions. Clients include consumer/motorcycle enthusiasts. Estab. 1971. Uses the services of music houses, independent songwriters/composers and pre-recorded bands for scoring of video and TV, background music for video and TV, jingles for radio spots and commercials for radio and TV. Commissions 2-3 composers/year. Pays $100/minute of usage. Buys all rights.

How to Contact: Write first to arrange personal interview. Prefers cassette (or VHS/¾" videocassette). SASE, but prefers to keep material on file. Reports in 1-2 months.
Music: Uses rock/country/contemporary.
Tips: "Harley riders a plus."

*PHD VIDEO, 143 Hickory Hill Cir., Osterville MA 02655. (508)428-7198. Acquisitions: Violet Atkins. Motion picture production company. Clients include business and industry, production and post-production video houses and ad agencies. Estab. 1985. Uses the services of music houses, independent songwriters/composers and lyricists for scoring and background music for commercials, home video and motion pictures and jingles for TV commercials. Commissions 10-12 composers and 10-12 lyricists/year. Pay is negotiable. Buys all rights preferably or one-time rights in certain circumstances.
How to Contact: Submit demo tape of previous work. Prefers cassette (or VHS videocassette). SASE but prefers to keep material on file. Reports in 2-4 weeks.
Music: Uses up-tempo and pop for commercials, motion pictures and TV shows.
Tips: "Be persistent. Constantly send updates of new work. Update files 1-2 times per year if possible. We hire approximately 25% new composers per year. Prefer to use composers/lyricists with 2/3 years track record."

PHILADELPHIA MUSIC WORKS, INC., Box 947, Bryn Mawr PA 19010. (215)825-5656. President: Andy Mark. Jingle producers/**music library producers**. Uses independent songwriters and music houses for background music for commercials and jingles. Commissions 200 songwriters/year. Pays $200/job. Buys all rights.
How to Contact: Call first and obtain permission to submit. Prefers cassette. "We are looking for quality jingle tracks already produced, as well as instrumental pieces between 2 and 3 minutes in length for use in AV music library." Does not return unsolicited material. Reports in 4 weeks.
Music: All types.
Tips: Looking for "knowledge of the jingle business and what works as background music for audiovisual presentations, such as slide shows, video training films, etc."

PHOTO COMMUNICATION SERVICES, INC., 6410 Knapp NE, Ada MI 49301. (616)676-1499; 676-1454. President: Lynn Jackson. Audiovisual firm and motion picture production company. Serves commercial, industrial and non-profit clients. Uses services of music houses, independent songwriters, and lyricists for jingles and scoring of and background music for multi-image, film and video. Negotiates pay. Buys all rights or one-time rights.
How to Contact: Submit demo tape of previous work, tape demonstrating composition skills or query with resume of credits. Prefers cassette or 15 ips reel-to-reel (or VHS videocassette). Does not return unsolicited material; prefers to keep on file. Reports in 6 weeks.
Music: Uses mostly industrial.

PHOTO COMMUNICATIONS CORP., 815 Greenwood Ave., Jenkintown PA 19046. (215)572-5900. Senior Writer/Marketing Coordinator: Ken Raichle. Audiovisual production company. Estab. 1970. Serves corporate, industrial, educational, business-to-business and pharmaceutical clients. Uses services of music houses, independent songwriters/composers and lyricists for scoring and background music for videos and multi-image programs. Commissions 1-2 composers and 1-2 lyricists/year. Pays by the job. Buys all rights or one-time rights; other rights sometimes.
How to Contact: Submit demo tape of previous work demonstrating composition skills or query with resume of credits. Prefers cassette with 4-5 pieces and lyric sheet. Sometimes returns unsolicited material with SASE; prefers to keep material on file.
Music: Uses up-tempo, dramatic, pop, classical, MOR, new age and electronic music for educational films, slide presentations, videos, corporate overviews, etc.
Tips: "Be flexible, creative and versatile."

MICHAEL POLLACK PRODUCTIONS, 34 Hills Dale, Coram NY 11727. (516)698-2526. President: Michael Pollack. Jingle/**commercial music production house** and record production. Clients include recording artists/industry music needs. Estab. 1978. Uses the services of independent songwriters/composers for background music for film. Commissions 6-10 composers and 3-5 lyricists/year. Pays by royalty. Buys one-time rights.

Listings of companies within this section which are either commercial music production houses or music libraries will have that information printed in boldface type.

How to Contact: Submit demo tape of previous work or write or call first to arrange personal interview. Prefers cassette. SASE, but prefers to keep material on file. Reports in 3 weeks.
Music: Uses new wave and rock for slide presentations and commercials.

POLLICK AND ASSOCIATES, 3003 N. Central, Phoenix AZ 85012. (602)230-7557. Producer: Allison Day. Advertising agency. Clients include health care, automotive aftermarket and newspapers. Estab. 1986. Uses the services of music houses for scoring of commercials for radio/TV. Commissions 4-10 composers/year; 4-10 lyricists/year. Pays $2,000/job. Buys all rights.
How to Contact: Submit demo tape of previous work. Prefers cassette or ¾" videocassette. Does not return unsolicited material; prefers to keep materials on file.
Music: Up-tempo, jazz and classical for commercials.

POP INTERNATIONAL CORPORATION, Box 527, Closter NJ 07624. (201)768-2199. Producers: Arnold De Pasquale and Peter DeCaro. Motion picture production company. Estab. 1973. Clients include "political campaigns, commercial spots, business and industry concerns as a production service; feature films and documentaries as producers." Uses services of music houses and songwriters for "mood purposes only on documentary films. However, Pop International Productions does conceptualize major theatrical and/or album musical projects." Commissions commercial and soundtrack pieces for entertainment specials. Commissions 4-5 composers and 3-4 lyricists/year. Pays by the job; or by royalty. Rights are negotiable.
How to Contact: Submit demo tape of previously aired work. Prefers cassette with 2-4 songs. "We review tapes on file, speak with agents and/or referrals, then interview writer. Once committee approves, we work *very* closely in pre-production." SASE. Reports in 3 weeks.
Music: Uses "mood music for documentaries, occasionally jingles for spots or promotional films or theme music/songs for dramatic projects (the latter by assignment only from producers or agencies). Some material is strictly mood, as in documentary work; some is informative as in promotional; some is motivating as in commercial; some is entertaining as in theatrical/TV."
Tips: "Be persistent and very patient. Try to get an agent, use demos and build a reputation for working very closely with scriptwriters/producers/directors."

*PPI (PETER PAN INDUSTRIES), PARADE VIDEO, CURRENT RECORDS, COMPOSE RECORDS, 88 St. Frances St., Newark NJ 07105. (201)344-4214. Product Manager: Marianne Eggleston. Video, record label, publishing. Clients include songwriters, music and video. Estab. 1928. Uses the services of music houses, independent songwriters/composers, lyricists, produces video and music for scoring, background music, jingles and commercials for radio and TV. Commissions 100's of composers and lyricists/year. Pays by the job, royalty and per agreement. Rights negotiable.
How to Contact: Submit demo tape and manuscript showing previous work, composition and scoring skills. Query with resume of credits. Prefers cassete or ½ or ¾ videocassette with 3 songs and lyric sheet. Also include a picture and bio of the artist. SASE. Prefers to keep material on file "if we like it for possible reference when we're looking for new materials."
Music: Uses all musical styles including childrens and health and fitness.
Tips: "Make sure presentation is professionally put together. Names and addresses on all packages and materials."

PREMIER VIDEO, FILM AND RECORDING CORP., 3033 Locust St., St. Louis MO 63103. (314)531-3555. President: Wilson Dalzell. Secretary/Treasurer: Grace Dalzell. Audiovisual firm, album producer and motion picture production company. Estab. 1931. Uses the services of songwriters for jingles and scoring and original background music and lyrics to reinforce scripts. Commissions 6-10 pieces and 5-10 lyricists/year. Pays by the job or by royalty. Buys all rights and "occasionally one-time rights with composer retaining title."
How to Contact: Query with resume of credits. Prefers 7½ or 15 ips reel-to-reel or cassette with any number of songs. SASE. Reports "as soon as possible with a short note using self-addressed envelope enclosed with submitted work informing talent they are on file for future reference."
Music: "As we serve every area of human development, all musical art forms are occasionally used."
Tips: "A limited need for music makes freelance writers a necessity. Be flexible. Have a simple, precise portfolio. Be sure your resume is direct, to-the-point and includes an honest review of past efforts. Be patient."

PREMIUM COMMUNICATIONS OF AMERICA, (formerly Expanding Images), 36A Mauchly, Irvine CA 92718. President: Robert Eissfeldt. Audiovisual firm. Clients include medical, insurance, finance, automotive and industrial firms. Estab. 1973. Uses the services of music houses, independent songwriters and lyricists for background music for multi-media shows, commercials for TV and industrial video productions. Pays by the job. Commissions 3 composers and 2 lyricists/year. Pays by the job. Buys all rights or one-time rights.

How to Contact: Prefers cassette. SASE, but prefers to keep material on file.
Music: All types.

*PRICE WEBER MARKETING COMMUNICATIONS, INC., P.O. Box 99337, Louisville KY 40223. (502)499-9220. Producer/Director: J.M. Hannan. Advertising agency and audiovisual firm. Estab. 1967. Clients include Fortune 500, consumer durables, light/heavy industrials and package goods. Uses services of music houses, and independent songwriters/composer for scoring, background music and jingles for industrial and corporate image films and commercials for radio and TV. Commissions 6-8 composers/year. Pays by the job ($500-2,000). Buys all rights or one-time rights.
How to Contact: Submit demo tape of previous work demonstrating composition skills. Prefers cassette with 10 pieces. "Enclose data sheet on budgets per selection on demo tape." Does not return unsolicited material; prefers to keep on file. "We report back only if we use it."
Music: Uses easy listening, up-tempo, pop, jazz and classical for corporate image industrials and commercials.
Tips: "Keep us updated on new works or special accomplishments. Work with tight budgets of $500-2,000. Show me what you're best at—show me costs."

PRO/CREATIVES, 25 W. Burda Place, Spring Valley NY 10977. President: David Rapp. Advertising and promotion agency. Serves consumer products and services, sports and miscellaneous clients. Uses background music in TV and radio commercials. Payment negotiable.
How to Contact: Query with resume of credits. SASE.

PROFESSIONAL MEDIA SERVICES, Suite 205, 18530 Beach Blvd., Huntington Beach CA 92648. (714)964-0542. Owner: Roy Moosa. Advertising production firm. Clients include "corporate promos and TV commercials." Estab. 1982. Uses the services of independent songwriters for scoring of commercials, corporate presentations, background music for training tapes, jingles for TV and commercials for radio and TV. Commissions 2 composers/year. Pays by the job. Buys all rights.
How to Contact: Query with resume of credits. Prefers cassette or reel-to-reel (or videocassette). Does not return unsolicited material; prefers to keep on file. Reports "as needed."
Music: "Upbeat background" music.
Tips: "Keep a video resume of your work."

*PULLIN PRODUCTIONS LTD., 822 5th Ave. SW, Calgary, Alberta T2P 0N3 **Canada**. (403)234-7885. Production Manager: Chris Pullin. Clients include business and industry. Uses the services of music houses, songwriters and lyricists for "original songs and themes for multi-image, motion picture and multi-media." Commissions 4 composers and 2 lyricists/year. Pays minimum $500/job. Buys all rights.
How to Contact: Submit demo tape (or videocassette) of previous work. Prefers reel-to-reel with 4-10 songs but "any format is OK." Does not return unsolicited material. "Contact is made only if interested."
Music: Looking for "strong themes for any number of instruments/vocals (single instrument to full orchestra). Requirements for each job are very carefully specified."

QUALLY & COMPANY INC., Huron Plaza, 30 East Huron #2502, Chicago IL 60611. (312)944-0237. President/Creative Director: Robert Qually. Advertising agency. Uses the services of music houses, independent songwriters/composers and lyricists for scoring, background music and jingles for radio and TV commercials. Commissions 2-4 composers and 2-4 lyricists/year. Pays by the job, by royalty sometimes. Buys various rights depending on deal.
How to Contact: Submit demo tape of previous work or query with resume of credits. Prefers cassete (or ¾" Beta videocassette). Prefers to keep material on file.
Music: Uses all kinds of music for commericals.

BILL QUINN PRODUCTIONS, 710 Cookman Ave., Asbury Park NJ 07712. (201)775-0500. Production Manager: Bill Newman. Audiovisual firm and motion picture production company. Estab. 1983. Clients include corporate and production companies. Uses the services of independent songwriters/composers and music houses for scoring of original productions and industrial films, background music for client accounts, commercials for radio and TV and video/film production. Commissions 15-20 composers/year. Pays by the job or approximately $25/hour. Buys one-time rights or all rights.
How to Contact: Submit demo tape of previous work or query with resume of credits. Call first to arrange personal interview. Prefers cassette. Will return unsolicited material accompanied by an SASE, but prefers to keep on file. "We respond by phone whenever we find music that fits a particular need."
Music: "We don't use one type of music more than another because our client list is rather lengthy and extremely varied. We use rock, pop, MOR, C&W, etc. Most often we commission music for TV and radio commercials. Interested in doing business with people in the New York and New Jersey area."

Tips: "Be flexible, able to work quickly and possess a working knowledge of all types of music."

RAMPION VISUAL PRODUCTIONS, 316 Stuart St., Boston MA 02116. (617)574-9601. Director/Camera: Steven V. Tringali. Motion picture production company. Estab. 1982. Clients include educational, independent producers, corporate clients and TV producers. Uses the services of independent songwriters/composers for jingles, background music and scoring to longer form programming. Commissions 6 composers/year. Pays by the job. Buys all rights.
How to Contact: Submit demo tape of previous work or query with resume of credits. Prefers cassette with variety of pieces. SASE. Does not return unsolicited material; prefers to keep material on file. Reports in 4 weeks.
Music: Uses all styles for corporate, educational and original programming.

REED PRODUCTIONS, INC., Box 977, Warsaw IN 46580. (219)267-4199. President: Howard Reed. Audiovisual firm and motion picture production company. Serves medical-industrial clients. Uses the services of music houses, independent songwriters/composers and lyricists for background music for audiovisual and video and commercials for TV. Commissions 1 composer and 1 lyricist/year. Pays $100-500/job. Buys all rights or one-time rights.
How to Contact: Submit demo tape of previous work. Prefers cassette (or VHS videocassette). SASE. Reports in 3 weeks.
Music: Uses traditional music for industrial, medical, audiovisual and video projects.

RHYTHMS PRODUCTIONS, P.O. Box 34485, Los Angeles CA 90034. A&R Department: R.S. White. Children's records, cassettes and videos. Clients include educational and childrens' markets. Estab. 1955. Uses the services of independent songwriters/composers for children's concept albums. Commissions 1-2 composers/year. Pays by royalty. Buys all rights.
How to Contact: Submit tape demonstrating composition skills. Prefers cassette. SASE. Reports in 2 months.
Music: Uses cassettes with educational content, activity or storybook and cassette.
Tips: "We buy completed master tapes."

*RICHTER PRODUCTIONS, INC., 330 W. 42nd St., New York NY 10036. (212)947-1395. President: Robert Richter. Motion picture production company. Clients include public and commercial TV, government agencies and nonprofit organizations. Uses services of music houses, songwriters and composers/arrangers for film scores and background music. Commissions 2 pieces/year. Pays by the job. Buys all rights or one-time rights.
How to Contact: Submit demo and resume of previously aired work. Prefers cassette with 2-5 songs on demo. SASE. "Also, put name, return address and phone number on the tape itself." Reporting time varies "according to our business rush."
Music: "We have varying needs—but usually we need music for already edited film."

RTG MUSIC, 130 E. 6th St., Cincinnati OH 45202. (513)381-0506. Creative Director: John Henry. **Music production company.** Estab. 1976. Clients include network television, advertising agencies, audiovisual producers and large corporations. Uses the services of lyricists, composers, arrangers, musicians and singers for pre- and post-scoring of video and film, jingles and commercials for radio and TV. Pays by the job. Buys all rights.
How to Contact: Write first to arrange personal interview. Submit resume and demo tape of previous work or compositions, or a video tape showing music scoring skills. Prefers cassette (or ¼" videocassette). "Tapes cannot be returned." Prefers to keep material on file. Do not call.
Music: All styles.
Tips: "Pay attention to details, make your demo and resume sound and look the best possible, and keep trying. Personal references help a lot. Be yourself. Write what you like, not what you think someone wants to hear."

*RUFFCUT RECORDING, 6472 Seven Mile, South Lyon MI 48178. (313)437-3058. Production Manager: J.D. Dudick. Jingle/commercial production house. Clients include advertising agencies and industrial accounts. Estab. 1990. Uses the services of independent songwriters/composers for background music for industrial films, jingles for local and national accounts and commercials for radio and TV. Commissions 5-10 composers/year. Pays by the job ($100-2,500) or by royalty (10-20%. Buys one-time rights.
How to Contact: Submit tape demonstrating composition skills. Prefers cassette with 3-5 songs and lyric sheets. Does not return unsolicited material; keep material on file. Reports in 2-4 weeks.
Music: "All styles that are creative and unique" for commercials/radio, film presentations.
Tips: "Don't worry about the production; keep it catchy with a melody you will hum to."

CHUCK RUHR ADVERTISING (formerly Ruhr/Paragon, Inc.), 1221 Nicollett Mall, Minneapolis MN 55403. (612)332-4565. Creative Director: Bill Johnson. Advertising agency. Serves consumer and industrial clients; client list available on request. Uses the services of songwriters and music houses for jingles and background music. Commissions 4-5 songwriters and 1-2 lyricists/year. Pays by the job. Initial fee negotiated, after that pays union scales. Pays residuals for subsequent use of material. Rights purchased are negotiable.
How to Contact: Submit demo tape of previous work. Prefers cassette. Reports "when needed."
Music: Uses background music and "originals befitting the message."
Tips: "Be original and be flexible. Study the best examples."

CHARLES RYAN ASSOCIATES, Box 2464, Charleston WV 25329. (304)342-0161. Director of Advertising Services: Tad Walden. Advertising agency. Clients in a variety of areas. Uses the services of music houses, independent songwriters/composers and lyricists for scoring, background music, jingles and commercials for radio and TV. Commissions 6-10 composers and 2-3 lyricists/year. Pays by the job. Buys all rights.
How to Contact: Submit demo tape of previous work or tape demonstrating composition skills; query with resume of credits; or write to arrange personal interview. Prefers cassette with 15-20 songs. Does not return unsolicited material; prefers to keep on file.
Music: Uses easy listening, pop, jazz, classical for educational films, slide presentations and commercials.

S.A. PRODUCTIONS, INC., 330 W. 58th St., New York NY 10019. (212)765-2669. President: Stan Applebaum. Scoring service, **commercial music production house** and **music/sound effect library**. Clients include motion picture production companies and advertising agencies, Broadway, music publishing and industrials. Estab. 1968. Uses the services of independent composers for scoring, background music, and composers/lyricists for jingles for national radio and TV commercials and industrials. Pays by the job. Buys all rights, one-time rights or negotiates rights purchased.
How to Contact: Query with resume of credits, or submit demo tape of previous work or tape demonstrating composition skills or manuscript showing music scoring skills, or write to arrange personal interview. Prefers cassette or 15 or 7½ ips reel-to-reel with 5-10 pieces. SASE, but prefers to keep material on file. Reports in 1 month.
Music: Uses all styles of music for various kinds of assignments.
Tips: "Be original with interesting harmonic and melodic development, and lyrics that are inventive and interesting."

SCHEMBRI VISION, 2156 Story Ave., Bronx NY 10473. (212)863-2986. Manager: Sal Schembri, Jr. Jingle/**commercial music production house**. Advertising agency. Serves retail and industrial clients. Uses the services of independent songwriters/composers for background music and jingles for TV commercials. Pays $250/job. Buys one-time rights.
How to Contact: Submit demo tape of previous work. SASE. Reports in 3 weeks.
Music: Uses easy listening and rap music for commercials.

KEN SCHMIDT CO. INC., 111 E. Wisconsin, Milwaukee WI 53202. (414)224-0210. Vice President/Creative Director: Wayne Rettig. Serves business-to-business clients. Uses the services of music houses and independent songwriters/composers for background music for industrial video/film, jingles and commercials for radio and TV. Commissions 2-3 composers/year. Pays by the job or by royalty. Buys all rights.
How to Contact: Submit demo tape of previous work or write to arrange personal interview. Prefers cassette. SASE, but prefers to keep material on file. Reports in several weeks.
Music: Uses up-tempo music for slide presentations and commercials.

SCHOENBACK ADVERTISING, INC., 1111 Park Ave., Baltimore MD 21201. (301)728-5566. Contact: Sarah Kelly. Advertising agency. Uses music houses for jingles, background music for TV commercials/films/tapes, and radio commercials. Commissions 5-10 composers/year. Pays by the job. Buys all rights or one-time rights.
How to Contact: Submit demo tape of previously aired work. Prefers cassette or reel-to-reel (or ¾" VHS videocassete). Does not return unsolicited material.
Music: Mostly advertising jingles.

WILSON SCOTT ASSOCIATES, INC., 425 S. Fairfax, Los Angeles CA 90036. (213)934-6150. Creative Directors: Brien Scott and Michael Wilson. Advertising agency. "We are a full service ad agency." Estab. 1986. Uses the services of music houses, independent songwriters/composers for background music, jingles and commercials for radio and TV. Commissions 2 composers and 1 lyricist/year. Pays by the job or by the hour. Buys all rights or one-time rights.

How to Contact: Submit demo tape of previous work or tape demonstrating composition skills or write first to arrange personal interview. Prefers cassette (or ¾" videocassette) with 1-8 songs. SASE, but prefers to keep material on file.
Music: Uses music for commercials.

TAMARA SCOTT PRODUCTIONS, 19062 Two Bar Rd., Boulder Creek CA 95006. Production Manager: Tamara Scott. Audiovisual firm, scoring service, motion picture production company and **music/sound effects library**. Clients include industrial firms. Uses the services of music houses, independent songwriters, lyricists and musicians for background music and scoring of film; jingles and commercials for radio and TV; and multi-image productions. Commissions 10-20 composers and 10-20 lyricists/year. Pays $150-1,000/job, $35/hour or by royalty. Buys all rights or one-time rights.
How to Contact: Submit tape demonstrating composition skills, or query with resume of credits. Prefers cassette or reel-to-reel (or videocassette). Does not return unsolicited material; prefers to keep on file. Reports "as needed."
Music: Positive, motivational, inspirational music.

SEASIDE PRODUCTIONS, (formerly Dune Productions), P.O. Box 93, Sea Isle City NJ 08243. Producer: Gregory C. Guarini. Scoring service and jingle/**commercial music production house**. Clients are mostly businesses and bands in Delaware Valley. Estab. 1987. Uses the services of independent songwriters/composers and lyricists for "management and publishing." Commissions varying number of composers and lyricists/year. Pays by the job or by royalty. Rights purchased "depend on situation."
How to Contact: Query with resume of credits, submit tape demonstrating composition skills or write to arrange personal interview. Prefers cassette (or VHS videocassette) with 4 songs and lyric or lead sheet. SASE, but prefers to keep material on file. Reports in 2 weeks.
Music: Uses all styles of music for all kinds of assignments.

*SEATTLE MOTION PICTURE SERVICE, 4717 Aurora N., Seattle WA 98013. Manager: Dick Pappas. Audiovisual firm, motion picture production company and music/sound effect library. Estab. 1962. Uses original music for scoring of films, background music for tapes and productions, jingles and commercials for radio and TV. Pays by the job, by royalty or per hour. Buys all rights or one-time rights.
How to Contact: Write or call first and obtain permission to submit. Accepts cassette or reel-to-reel (or videocassette). Does not return unsolicited material; prefers to keep on file. Reports in 3 weeks.
Music: Uses up-tempo and classical music for all kinds of assignments.

SHIMER VON CANTZ, Bourse Bldg., Philadelphia PA 19106. (215)627-3535. Creative Directors: Michael Carestil and Zsu Zsa Johnson. Advertising agency. Clients include hi-tech, health, financial and industrial companies. Estab. 1969. Uses the services of independent songwriters and music houses for jingles, background music for commercials and corporate videos. Commissions 4 songwriters/year. Pays $400-800/job. Buys all rights.
How to Contact: Submit demo tape of previously aired work. Prefers cassette. "Put name and phone number on tape and indicate cost of production." SASE, but prefers to keep material on file. Reports "if the submitted demo seems appropriate to a job."
Music: "Mostly up-tempo music for jingles."

SILVER BURDETT & GINN, 250 James St., CN 018, Morristown NJ 07960. (201)285-8002. Music Editor: Donald Scafuri. Publisher of textbooks and records for kindergarten through 8th grade. Estab. 1864. "Our books and records are sold directly to schools and are evaluated and chosen for use according to the adoption procedures of a particular school district." Uses the services of music houses, songwriters and lyricists for original songs for children K-8; lyricists for translating foreign lyrics into a singable English version and "writing original lyrics to a folk tune or a melody composed by someone else." Commissions 0-20 lyricists and 0-20 pieces/year. Pays $55-75 for lyrics and arrangements; up to $400 for original compositions (reprint rights plus statutory record royalty). Buys one-time rights for educational use.
How to Contact: Submit lead sheets of previous work. Prefers cassette. SASE. Reports in 1 month. Free catalog available.
Music: "We seek virtually any kind of song that is suitable both in words and music for children to sing. We are particularly interested in songs that are contemporary pop or folk-like in style. We are also interested in choral compositions for upper grades."
Tips: "Become acquainted with teachers and students in elementary or junior high classrooms. Find out what music they are presently using and what they would like to use."

SINGER ADVERTISING & MARKETING, INC., 1035 Delaware Ave., Buffalo NY 14209. (716)884-8885. Senior Vice President: Marilyn Singer. Advertising agency. Clients include health care, professional football, travel service and industrial. Estab. 1969. Uses the services of music houses for background

music for slide presentations, industrial videos, jingles for health care and professional footbal and commercials for radio and TV. Commissions 1 composer and 2-3 lyricists/year. Pay varies.
How to Contact: Submit demo tape of previous work. Prefers cassette or 15 ips reel-to-reel or ½" videocassette. SASE. Reports in weeks.
Music: Uses up tempo pop, New Age Jazz for commercial jingles and slide presentations.
Tips: "Study our client list and their current work and then submit."

SITTASON-CO. INC., 303 Greenup St., Covington KY 41012. (606)581-8100. Production Director: Linda Steele. Advertising agency. Clients include retail and industrial firms. Uses the services of music houses and independent songwriters/composers for commercials for radio and TV and music beds for audiovisual productions. Commissions 0-3 composers/year. Pays $500-1,500/job. Buys all rights.
How to Contact: Submit demo tape of previous work. Prefers cassete (or VHS videocassette). "No phone calls prior to submission of demo cassette by mail." SASE, but prefers to keep material on file.
Music: Uses up-tempo and pop (60-second radio donuts and 30- and 10-second TV music beds) for slide presentations and commercials.

*SOLO SPORTS VIDEO, P.O.Box 357, Dana Point CA 92629. Owner: Craig Peterson. Motion picture production company. Clients include in-house productions. Estab. 1985. Needs scoring and background music.
How to Contact: Query with resume of credits and postcard inquiring about upcoming needs. Prefers cassette with 3 songs. Contact by mail first. SASE. Prefers to keep material on file. Reports in 4-6 weeks.
Music: Uses variable musical styles for 60 to 90 minute movies.

ROBERT SOLOMON AND ASSOCIATES ADVERTISING, Suite 1000, 505 N. Woodward, Bloomfield Hills MI 48013. (313)540-0660. Copywriter/Producer: Jackie Purtan. Advertising agency. Clients include "food service accounts, convenience stores, retail accounts and small service businesses." Uses independent songwriters, lyricists and music houses for jingles and special presentations. Commissions 1-10 songwriters and 1-10 lyricists/year. Pays by the job. Buys all rights.
How to Contact: Submit demo tape of previously aired work. Prefers cassette or 7½ ips reel-to-reel with 1-5 pieces and lyric or lead sheets. "Submissions must be up-to-date and up to industry standards." Does not return unsolicited material; prefers to keep on file.
Music: "MOR, pop or rock jingles describing specific products or services."
Tips: "Please make sure all information presented is CURRENT!"

SONIC IMAGES PRODUCTIONS, INC., 4590 MacArthur Blvd. NW, Washington DC 20007. (202)333-1063. Vice President/Director of Video Services: Jolie Barbiere. Audiovisual firm, scoring services, **commercial music production house**, motion picture production company, **music/sound effect library** and CD-I development. Clients include independent producers, government, entertainment, associations, etc. Uses the services of music houses, independent songwriters/composers and lyricists for scoring of video and film productions; background music for art/experimental films and videos; jingles, public service announcements and radio and TV commercials. Commissions 2-4 composers and 1-2 lyricists/year. Pay varies. Buys all rights.
How to Contact: Submit demo tape of previous work or tape demonstrating composition skills. Prefers cassette (or ¾" VHS or Beta videocassette). "Include a resume." Does not return unsolicited material; prefers to keep on file. Reports if interested.
Music: Uses all commercial and classical styles of music for all kinds of assignments.
Tips: "We look for a clean professional product. Our clients demand it!"

SORIN PRODUCTIONS, INC., Freehold Executive Center, 4400 Route 9 S., Freehold NJ 07728. Contact: Production Coordinator. Audiovisual firm. Serves corporate and industrial clients. Uses services of music houses and independent songwriters/composers for background music for industrials. Commissions 1-3 composers and 1-3 lyricists/year. Pays by the job. Buys all rights.
How to Contact: Query with resume of credits. "No submissions with initial contact." Does not return unsolicited material; prefers to keep solicited materials on file. Reports in 1 month.
Music: Uses up-tempo and pop for audio, video and slides.

*SOTER ASSOCIATES INC., 209 North 400 W., Provo UT 84601. (801)375-6200. President N. Gregory Soter. Advertising agency. Clients include financial, health care, municipal, computer hardware and software. Estab. 1970. Uses services of music houses, independent songwriters/composers and lyricists for background music for audiovisual presentations and jingles for radio and TV commercials. Commissions 1 composer, 1 lyricist/year. Pays by the job. Buys all rights.
How to Contact: Submit tape demonstrating previous work and composition skills. Prefers cassette or VHS videocassette. Doesn ot return unsolicited submissions; prefers to keep materials on file.

SOUND CITY PRODUCTIONS, INC., Suite C, 911 18th Ave. S., Nashville TN 37212. (615)321-5955. President: Gary D. Caudel. Motion picture and video production company. Serves entertainment industry and general clients. Uses the services of independent songwriters/composers for jingles for TV commercials and songs. Pays 10% royalty and expenses; payment varies. Rights purchased vary.
How to Contact: Query with resume of credits. Prefers cassette (or VHS, 8mm or ¾" videocassette) with 2-4 pieces and typed lyric or lead sheet. SASE, but prefers to keep material on file.
Music: Uses all types of music for television programs, experimental video art, movies and videos.

*SOUND WRITERS PUBLICATIONS, INC., 223 Washington St., Newark NJ 07102. (201)642-5132. Marketing Director: Vladia Dv. Advertising agency, audiovisual firm and jingle/commercial music production house. Clients include major labels and large corporations. Estab. 1980. Uses the services of independent songwriters/composers and lyricists for scoring of jingles and TV commercials. Commissions 10 composers/year; 15 lyricists/year. Buys all rights and one-time rights.
How to Contact: Submit demo tape of previous work. Prefers cassette or ¾" videocassette. "We have a no return policy on all material." Prefers to keep material on file. Reports back in 4 weeks.
Music: Uses all types of music for commercials, training tapes and music videos.
Tips: "We don't like big egos."

SPARTRONIX VIDEOSERVICES, 476 Lancaster Pike, Frazer PA 19355. (215)647-2800. President: Dick Spahr. Audiovisual firm and video production/post production house. Estab. 1965. Clients include primarily industrial and corporate accounts. Uses the services of music houses and independent songwriters/composers for scoring of sales, point of purchase displays, industrial and corporate training programs (videos) and radio and TV commercials. Commissions 6 composers/year. Negotiates pay. Buys all or one-time rights, depending on project.
How to Contact: Submit demo tape of previous work. Prefers cassette (or ¾" or VHS videocassette). Will keep material on file. Reports in 1 month after interest shown by clients.
Music: Uses up-tempo, bright, hi-tech synth music for TV spots (broadcast and cable) and corporate and industrial, sales and training, and annual report videos.
Tips: "Buy Songwriter's Market!"

SPECTRUM SOUND STUDIOS, INC., 1634 SW Alder, Portland OR 97205. (503)248-0248. Contact: Music Director. Jingle/**commercial music production house, music sound effect library** and broadcast production. Estab. 1973. Clients include advertising agencies, corporations and music businesses. Uses the services of independent songwriters/composers for scoring of in-house corporate video, jingles for commercial production and commercials for radio and TV. Commissions 8 composers and 2 lyricists/year. Pays by the job. Rights are up to client.
How to Contact: Submit demo tape of previous work or query with resume of credits. Prefers cassette or 15 ips reel-to-reel (or ¾" videocassette). SASE. Reports in 1 month.
Music: Uses all styles of music for all kinds of assignments.

*SPIVACK ADVERTISING, INC., 7 Church Lane, Baltimore MD 21208. (301)484-9510. President: Irvin Spivack. Advertising agency. Clients include retail, financial and business-to-business. Estab. 1979. Uses the services of music houses for jingles for commercials for radio. Pay is negotiable.
How to Contact: Submit demo tape of previous work. Prefers cassette. Does not return unsolicited material.
Music: Generally up-tempo, but it really depends on clients.

EDGAR S. SPIZEL ADVERTISING, INC., 1782 Pacific Ave., San Francisco CA 94109. (415)474-5735. President: Edgar S. Spizel. Advertising agency, public relations firm and TV/radio production firm. Estab. 1950. Clients include public transportation, developers, retail, sports, auto and broadcast businesses. Uses the services of independent songwriters for background music in commercials. Buys all rights.
How to Contact: Query. Prefers cassette with 3-5 songs. Does not return unsolicited material.
Tips: "Stay in touch. While we seldom use music, when we do we don't like to scrounge. We like to have a selection at our fingertips."

*STAN & LOU, INC., 3013 Fountainview, #155, Houston TX 77057. (713)977-5000. Creative Director: Lou Congelio. Advertising agency. Clients include all aspects business's and retail outlets. Estab. 1988. Uses the services of music houses for scoring of video productions, background music for video productions, jingles for radio and TV commercials. Pay thru music house. Buys all rights and one-time rights.
How to Contact: Submit demo tape of previous work. Write first to arrange personal interview. Prefers cassette. SASE, but prefers to keep material on file.
Music: Uses all types music for all types assignments.

STARWEST PRODUCTIONS, INC., Studio A, 4910 Fox St., Denver CO 80216. President: Steven Pettit. Audiovisual firm and jingle **commercial music production house**. Clients include Fortune 500 companies to mom and pop shops. Estab. 1979. Uses the services of music houses and independent songwriters/composers for commercials for radio and TV. Commissions 2 composers and 2 lyricists/year. Pays $2,000/job. Buys all rights and rights with royalties.
How to Contact: Submit demo tape of previous work or query with resume of credits. Prefers 7½ ips reel-to-reel with 5-10 songs. SASE, but prefers to keep material on file. Reports in 1 month.
Music: Uses up-tempo music for slide presentations and live performances.
Tips: "Make my foot tap."

STATION BREAK PRODUCTIONS, 40 Glen St., Suite 1, Glen Cove NY 11542. (516)759-7005. Producer: Stephen Meyers. Advertising agency and jingle/**commercial music production house**. Clients include ad agencies, retail businesses, hotels, restaurants, corporate and special projects. Estab. 1985. Uses the services of independent songwriters/composers and singers, voice overs for commercials for radio and TV. Commissions 2 composers and 1 lyricist/year. Pays by the job. Buys all rights.
How to Contact: Submit demo tape of previous work or write to arrange personal interview. Prefers cassette with 4 pieces. Does not return unsolicited material; prefers to keep material on file. Reports in 1 month.
Music: Uses pop, classical and dance for industrial and commercials.
Tips: "Send your best work to date. Start with your strongest style."

STONE & ADLER, 1 E. Wacker Dr., Chicago IL 60601. Sr. Vice President/Executive Creative Director: David Moore. Advertising agency and direct marketing firm. Estab. 1966. Serves industrial, consumer and financial clients. Uses music houses for background music in commercials. Commissions 1-2 pieces/year. Pays according to budget. Usually buys one-time rights.
How to Contact: Submit demo tape of previously aired work. Prefers reel-to-reel or cassette. Returns material if requested with SASE, but prefers to keep tape on file.
Music: All types. "Be versatile, cost-effective."

*STRAUCHEN ASSOCIATES, INC., 3388 Erie Ave., Cincinnati OH 45208. (513)871-5353. President: Stephen H. Strauchen. Advertising agency. Clients include financial, food, business-to-business and insurance. Estab. 1981. Uses the services of music houses and independent songwriters/composers for scoring of commercial jingles and sales films and background music for radio, TV and audiovisual presentations. Commissions 3-4 composers/year; 1 lyricist/year. Pays $500-1,000/job or $20-30/hour. Buys all rights.
How to Contact: Submit demo tape of previous work. Prefers cassette, 7½ ips reel-to-reel or VHS videocassette. SASE, but prefers to keep materials on file.
Music: Easy listening, up-tempo, pop and jazz.
Tips: "Be specific regarding rates, use rights, etc."

SULLIVAN & FINDSEN ADVERTISING, 2165 Gilbert Ave., Cincinnati OH 45206. (513)281-2700. Director of Broadcast Production: Kirby Sullivan. Advertising agency. Clients include consumer and business-to-business firms. Uses the services of music houses, independent songwriters/composers and lyricists for scoring, background music, jingles and commercials for radio and TV. Commissions 3 composers and 3 lyricists/year. Pays by the job. Buys all rights.
How to Contact: Submit demo tape of previous work. Prefers cassette. Does not return unsolicited material; prefers to keep material on file. "We report back when we need some work."
Music: Uses all styles for commercials.

TALCO PRODUCTIONS, 279 E. 44th St., New York NY 10017. (212)697-4015. President: Al Lawrence. Audiovisual firm, TV and motion picture production company. Clients include corporate, nonprofit and educational organizations. Uses the services of music houses and independent songwriters/composers and lyricists for scoring and background music for film and TV, and radio. Commissions 2-3 composers and 0-2 lyricists/year. Pays by the job. Buys all rights.
How to Contact: Query with resume of credits. SASE for reply. "Do not submit demo unless request is made!"
Music: Uses easy listening, up-tempo, pop, jazz, classical, adult contemporary and rock for educational films and documentaries.

TEEMAN/SLEPPIN ENTERPRISES INC., 147 W. 26 St., New York NY 10001. (212)243-7836. President: Bob Teeman. Vice President: Stu Sleppin. Management, motion picture and music video production company. Clients include artists, film companies, TV stations and corporate sponsors. Uses the services of independent songwriters/composers and lyricists for scoring of TV shows and films and original songs. Commissions 3 composers and 3 lyricists/year. Pays by the job. Rights negotiable.

How to Contact: Submit demo tape of previous work or write to arrange personal interview. Prefers cassette (or VHS or ¾" videocassette). SASE, but prefers to keep material on file. Reports in 2 months.
Music: Uses pop and dance for original songs tied into a film or campaign.

*TELECINE SERVICES & PRODUCTION LTD., 23 Seapoint Ave., Monkstown, Co. Dublin Ireland. 353-01-808744. FAX: (353)01-808679. Director: Anabella Nolan. Audiovisual firm and video production house. Estab. 1977. Clients include advertising and commercial business. Uses the services of songwriters and music houses for original songs for TV commercials and audiovisual and video programs; lyricists for writing lyrics for commercials and conference themes. Commissions 5 songwriters/composers and 3 lyricists for 20 pieces/year. Pays $5,000/job. Buys all rights or rights within one country.
How to Contact: Query with resume of credits or submit tape demonstrating composition skills. Prefers 15 ips reel-to-reel or cassette with 3-10 songs. SAE and IRC. Reports in 1 month.
Tips: "Understand our marketing needs; know the difference between European and U.S. tastes."

*TEXAS AFFILIATED PUBLISHING COMPANY, "STREETPEOPLES WEEKLY NEWS", P.O. Box 270942, Dallas TX 75227-0942. (214)634-2220. Contact: Editor. Advertising agency and newspaper publisher. Clients are varied. Estab. 1977. Uses the services of independent songwriters/composers for commercials for radio and TV. Pays negotiable amount. Buys all rights and one-time rights.
How to Contact: Write first to arrange personal interview. "No phone calls please. Send *no* originals, include SASE for returns. Our current project is about the problems of the 'homeless.' Persons writing songs about this may want to send for a copy of 'Streetpeoples Weekly News' to get an idea of what's involved. Send $2 to cover handling/postage." Prefers to keep materials on file. Reports in 3 weeks.
Music: Uses easy listening, up-tempo for commercials.

*CHRISTOPHER THOMAS/MULLER JORDAN WEISS, Suite 1101 7777, Bonhomme, St. Louis MO 63105. (314)725-4992. Writer/Producer: Laura Tomlinson. Advertising agency. Clients include consumer, business-to-business, agricultural. Estab. 1955. Uses the services of music houses and independent songwriters/composers for commercials for radio and TV. Commissions 1 composer every 2 or 3 years. Pays by the job. Buys all rights.
How to Contact: Submit demo tape of previous work. Prefers cassette (or ¾" videocassette) with 4-5 songs. Does not return unsolicited material; prefers to keep on file. Reports in 3 weeks.
Music: Uses up-tempo for commercials.

*TOP OF THE MOUNTAIN PUBLISHING/POWELL PRODUCTIONS, Suite 123, 11701 S. Belcher Rd., Largo FL 34643. (813)530-0110. FAX: (813)536-3681. Administrator: Dr. Tag Powell. Publisher of books, audio-cassettes and seminars (producer). Clients include domestic and foreign distributors of books and audiocassettes. Estab. 1980. Uses independent songwriters/composers for background music for subliminal audiocassettes and New Age type music audiocassettes. Pays by the job. Buys all rights.
How to Contact: Submit demo tape of previous work. Prefers cassette with 5-7 songs. Does not return material. Prefers to keep submitted materials on file. "Responds when the need arises."
Music: Uses New Age instrumental.
Tips: "Call first to let us know you are submitting material."

TPS VIDEO SVC., Box 1233, Edison NJ 08818. (201)287-3626. President: R.S. Burkt. Audiovisual firm, motion picture production company and **music/sound effects library**. Clients include AT&T, IBM and Xerox (industrial firms). Uses the services of independent composers and arrangers for scoring of industrials, background music and jingles for radio and TV commercials. Does not buy songs. Commissions 20-100 composers/year. Pays by the job. Buys all rights or one-time rights.
How to Contact: Submit demo tape of previous work demonstrating composition skills. Prefers cassette. SASE for response. Reports in 3 weeks.
Music: Considers all types of music for advertising.

*TRAYNOR, BREEHL & GLAZEN ADVERTISING, 1250 Old River Rd., Cleveland OH 44113. (216)241-7200. FAX: (216)241-4126. Advertising agency. Clients include consumer, retail. Estab. 1972. Uses the services of music houses, independent songwriters/composers and arrangers for jingles for radio/TV spots and commercials for radio and TV. Commissions 6-10 composers/year. Pays $1,500-6,000/job. Buys all rights.
How to Contact: Submit demo tape of previous work. Prefers cassette (or ¾ videocassette) with 5-7 songs. Does not return unsolicited material; prefers to keep on file.
Music: Uses pop, jazz, classical and esoterica for commercials.
Tips: "Put your best foot forward. Lead off with a song you are willing to be judged on."

TRI VIDEO TELEPRODUCTION, (main office) Box 8822, Incline Village NV 89450. (702)323-6868. In California: Suite C, 1615 5th St., Davis CA 95616. (916)758-5335. Director: Jon Paul Davidson. Corporate television production firm. Clients include corporate accounts, primarily in health care and telecommunications. Estab. 1978. Uses the services of music houses and independent songwriters/composers for scoring of logo soundbeds and intro/conclusions and background music for transitions and presentations. Commissions 3-4 composers/year. Pays $500-2,000/job. Buys all rights and/or one-time rights.

How to Contact: Query with resume of credits. Prefers cassette with 1-3 pieces. SASE, but prefers to keep material on file. "We do not report back. We will use on-file tapes to demo to clients when making selection. If your work is what client likes and is appropriate, we will contact you."

Music: Uses easy, up-tempo and classical for educational and industrial.

Tips: "The corporate market is quite varied. Needs are of every type. Just keep in touch. We do lots of custom work rather than volume, so number of projects is small each year."

TULLY-MENARD, INC., 2207 S. Dale Mabry, Tampa FL 33629. (813)253-0447. Broadcast Producer: Robert A. Ackroyd. Advertising agency. Estab. 1960. Clients include a fast food restaurant, supermarket, theme park, retailers, manufacturers, car dealer. Uses the services of songwriters and music houses for TV and radio commercials, jingles, background music and film and AV soundtracks. Payment negotiable, "dependent on project, budget and needs." Buys all rights.

How to Contact: Write or call for permission to submit demo tape of previous work. Prefers cassette or 7½ ips reel-to-reel with 5-8 songs. SASE, but prefers to keep material on file. "We research our file at the onset of need to determine candidates and parameters, then obtain bids and demos."

Music: "Broadcast and off-line; jingles and music tracks. Institutional jingles for a wide variety of clients."

Tips: "Stay current with today's sound, but be different—give it your own personality. Listen carefully to the parameters we give you, and if you don't quite grasp what we're looking for, ask! Provide the same package services as major music houses but with more originality and ingenuity."

*TULLYVISION STUDIOS, 465 Main St., Tullytown PA 19007. (215)946-7444. Producer: Michelle A. Powell. Audiovisual firm. Clients include corporate/industrial. Estab. 1983. Uses the services of music houses and independent songwriters/composers for marketing, training and corporate image videotapes. Commissions 3 composers/year. Pays $500/job. Buys all rights or one-time rights.

How to Contact: Submit demo tape of previous work. Query with resume of credits. Prefers cassette or ¾" VHS videocassette with 3 songs. SASE, but prefers to keep submitted materials on file. Reports in 3 weeks.

Music: Uses up-tempo and pop for educational films and slide presentations.

27TH DIMENSION INC., Box 1149, Okeechobee FL 34973-1149. (800)634-0091. President: John St. John. Scoring service, jingle/**commercial music production house** and **music sound effect library**. Clients include A/V producers, video houses, recording studios and radio and TV stations. Estab. 1986. Uses the services of independent songwriters/composers for scoring of library material and commercials for radio and TV. Commissions 10 composers/year. Pays $100-1,000/job; publishing (performance fees). "We buy the right to use in our library exclusively." Buys all rights except writer's publishing. Writer gets all performance fees (ASCAP or BMI).

How to Contact: Submit tape demonstrating composition skills or call. Prefers cassette. "Call before sending." Does not return unsolicited material; prefers to keep on file. SASE. Reports in 1 week.

Music: Uses industrial, pop jazz, sports, contemporary and new age for music library.

Tips: "Follow style instructions carefully."

UNITED ENTERTAINMENT PRODUCTIONS, 4024 State Line, Kansas City KS 66103. (913)262-3555. Operations Manager: Dave Maygers. Recording studio, artist management, publishing company and record company. Estab. 1972. Serves musical groups, songwriters, and ad clients. Uses the services of independent songwriters, lyricists and self-contained groups for scoring of album projects, background music for ads and industrial films, jingles and commercials for radio and TV. Pays negotiable royalty. Buys all rights or one-time rights.

How to Contact: Submit demo tape of previous work demonstrating composition skills. "Send cassette of material and lyric sheet when applicable." Does not return unsolicited material; prefers to keep material on file.

Music: "Rock, pop, R&B, jazz, country to be used in music projects."

USAV COMMUNICATIONS GROUP, Box 51620, New Berlin WI 53151. (414)796-2000. President: Jeffery Smale. Audiovisual firm. Clients include major manufacturers and service organizations. Estab. 1969. Uses services of independent songwriters/composers for jingles for business shows. Commissions 2 composers and 2 lyricists/year. Pays $7,500-15,000/job. Rights purchased vary.

How to Contact: Submit demo tape of previous work. Prefers cassette (or Betacom, VHS or ¾" videocassette). Does not return unsolicited material; prefers to keep on file.
Music: Uses all types of music for meeting presentations, slide and/or video programs.

VIDEO ARTS, Box 433, Manasquan NJ 08736. (201)223-5999. Producer: Nicholas G. Kuntz. **Music sound effect library.** Clients include professional video production companies and cable TV industry. Estab. 1987. Uses the services of independent songwriters/composers for background music for video productions and advertising and commercials for TV. Pays by the job. Buys all rights.
How to Contact: Submit demo tape of previous work. Prefers cassette with 3-5 songs. "All work must be composed and recorded via MIDI and, if selected, MIDI files must be provided. The library to be marketed will be entirely in MIDI format. All styles will be considered." Does not return unsolicited material; prefers to keep on file. "Reports back on submissions only if selected."
Music: Uses all styles (must be written using MIDI) for background music for video production and cable advertisements.
Tips: "Know MIDI and be able to work in the format."

*VIDEO I-D, INC., 105 Muller Rd., Washington IL 61571. (309)444-4323. Manager, Marketing Services: Gwen Wagner. Post production/teleproductions. Clients include industrial and business. Estab. 1978. Uses the services of professional library music for video production pieces and commercials. Buys all rights.
How to Contact: Submit demo tape of previous work. Prefers cassette or VHS videocassette with 5 songs and lyric sheet. SASE, but prefers to keep submitted materials on file. Reports in 3 weeks.
Music: "Musical styles depend upon client preference."

*VINEBERG COMMUNICATIONS, Suite B-800, 61-20 Grand Central Pkwy., Forest Hills NY 11375. (718)760-0333. President: Neil Vineberg. Jingle/commercial music production house. Clients include TV/film producers. Estab. 1986. Uses the services of independent songwriters/composers and lyricists for background music for TV/film, corporate videos/film and commercials for radio and TV. Commissions 5 composers and 2 lyricists/year. Pays by the job. Buys all rights and one-time rights.
How to Contact: Submit demo tape of previous work. Submit tape demonstrating composition skills. Query with resume of credits. Write first to arrange personal interview. Prefers cassette (or VHS videocassette) with 4 songs and lead sheet (if possible). "No calls. Write only." SASE, but prefers to keep material on file. Reports in 1 month.
Music: Uses all except classical.

*VIP VIDEO, Film House, 143 Hickory Hill Cir., Osterville MA 02655. (508)428-7198. President: Jeffrey H. Aikman. Audio visual firm. Clients include business, industry and television stations. Estab. 1983. Uses the services of music houses, independent songwriters/composers and lyricists for scoring of multi-image productions, background music for videotapes and motion pictures and jingles for TV commercials. Commissions 15-20 composers and 15-20 lyricists/year. Pays by the job, amounts vary depending on the length and complexity of each project. Buys all rights, preferable but can handle one-time rights for special projects.
How to Contact: Submit demo tape of previous work. Prefers cassette with 1-2 songs. SASE but prefers to keep material on file unless specifically stated. Reports in 3 weeks.
Music: Uses easy listening, pop and up-tempo for feature films, TV series, TV pilots and background for videotapes. Currently working or scoring series of 26 feature length silent films. If project is successful, this series will be added to at the rate of 13 per year.

VISION FILM GROUP, INC., 72 Princess St. 2nd Fl., Winnipeg, Manitoba R3B 1K2 **Canada**. (204)942-6215. President: Al Rosenberg. Audiovisual firm, motion picture and music video production company. Estab. 1985. Clients include industrial and entertainment firms. Uses the services of music houses, independent songwriters/composers and lyricists for background music for audiovisual and videos, and TV commercials. Commissions 3-5 composers and 2-4 lyricists/year. Pays $100-500/job. Buys all rights or one-time rights.
How to Contact: Submit demo tape of previous work, or tape demonstrating composition skills. Prefers cassette (or Beta videocassette). Does not return unsolicited material; prefers to keep on file. Reports in 2 weeks.
Music: Uses rock, contemporary, new age, up-tempo, unpublished music for videos, marketing programs, audiovisual presentations and commercials.
Tips: "Currently looking for fresh material for a rock musical for TV and video—as well as touring."

*VTI COMMUNICATIONS FOR BUSINESS, 919 N. Michigan Ave., Chicago IL 60611. (312)440-1800. Vice President Media Group: David Foote. Audiovisual firm. Clients include corporate communications. Uses the services of independent songwriters/composers and lyricists for scoring and background

music for multi-image and video corporate programs. Commissions 3-5 composers and 2-3 lyricists/ year. Pays $200-3,500/job. Buys all rights, one-time rights or rights per project and application.
How to Contact: Submit demo tape of previous work or tape demonstrating composition skills, or write first to arrange personal interview. Prefers cassette with 3-5 pieces. "We get requests for popular sound-a-likes with lyrics changed." Does not return unsolicited material; prefers to keep on file. Reports only if there is a need.
Music: Uses up-tempo, pop and jazz for "infomercials," audiovisuals and corporate videos (marketing).
Tips: "Must be flexible on price, understand what our client wants, be creative."

*BEN WAGES AGENCY, 2513 Denny Ave., Pascagoula MS 39567. (601)769-7104. FAX: (601)769-8590. Owner/President: Ben Wages. Advertising agency, management firm, booking agency and record company (Sea Coast Recording). Estab. 1978. Uses the services of independent songwriters, lyricists and music houses for jingles and background music for commercials. Pays by the job, by royalty or per hour. Buys all rights or one-time rights. Depends on particular situation.
How to Contact: Write or call to arrange personal interview or submit demo tape of previously aired work. Prefers cassette (or VHS videocassette). SASE, but prefers to keep material on file. Reports in 4 weeks.
Music: "Country is predominantly used. Assignments are most often commercial jingles."
Tips: "Be as professional as possible when submitting material and be thorough. Neatness is always a plus. Would advise sending copyrighted material only. Include as much info as possible."

WEBER, COHN & RILEY, 444 N. Michigan Ave., Chicago IL 60611. (312)527-4260. Executive Creative Director: C. Welch. Advertising agency. Serves real estate, business, financial and food clients. Estab. 1960. Uses music houses for jingles and background music for commercials. Commissions 2 songwriters and 2 lyricists/year. Pays $500 minimum/job. Buys all rights or one-time rights, "open to negotiation."
How to Contact: Write a letter of introduction to creative director. SASE. "We listen to and keep a file of all submissions, but generally do not reply unless we have a specific job in mind." Songwriters may follow up with a phone call for response.
Music: "We use music for a variety of products and services. We expect highly original, tight arrangements that contribute to the overall concept of the commercial. We do not work with songwriters who have little or no previous experience scoring and recording commercials."
Tips: "Don't aim too high to start. Establish credentials and get experience on small local work, then go after bigger accounts. Don't oversell when making contacts or claim the ability to produce any kind of 'sound.' Producers only believe what they hear on sample reels. Produce a sample reel that's professional and responsive to today's needs. Present a work that is creative and meets our strategies and budget requirements."

*WESTERN PUBLISHING COMPANY, INC., 1220 Mound Ave., Racine WI 53404. (414)633-2431. Manager, Youth Electronics: Virginia Clapper. Children's publisher. Distributes entertainment products through mass market channels. Estab. 1907. Uses the services of music houses, independent songwriters/composers and lyricists for scoring of and background music for songs, short films and storytelling audio cassettes. Commissions 2-3 composers and 4-5 lyricists/year. Pays by the job. Buys all rights. Work for hire arrangement preferred.
How to Contact: Submit demo tape of previous work. Wirte first to arrange personal interview. Prefers cassette (or VHS videocassette) with 2-6 songs and lead sheets. SASE, but prefers to keep submitted materials on file. Reports in 6 weeks.
Music: Uses children's songs for film scores; book and tape audio productions.
Tips: "Expect to be employed on a work for hire basis, allowing straight buy-out of all rights."

*WESTON WOODS STUDIOS, 389 Newtown Turnpike, Weston CT 06883. Production Manager: Paul R. Gagne. Audiovisual firm, motion picture production company. Estab. 1955. "We produce films and audio visual products based on children's picture books." Clients include educational/institutional market and home market video. Uses services of independent composers and copyists for scoring of short films and filmstrip soundtracks. Commissions 3-5 composers/year. Pays by the job, $600 minimum. Buys all rights.
How to Contact: Submit demo tape of previous work, tape demonstrating composition scores or query with resume of credits. Write to arrange personal interview. Prefers cassette. "Write only; we cannot accept telephone queries." Does not return unsolicited material. Prefers to keep material on file.
Music: Uses serious non-commercial scoring for acoustic instruments (synth OK) in classical, folk, or ethnic styles for educational films and filmstrips of children's stories; no driving rhythm tracks; no songs, please especially "kiddie songs."

*WHITE PRODUCTION ARCHIVES, INC., 604 Davis St., Evanston IL 60201. (708)328-2221. President: Matthew White. Motion picture production company. Produce home video entertainment programs. Estab. 1987. Uses the services of independent songwriters/composers for scoring of offbeat documentaries; videogame tapes. Pays by the job. Buys all rights.
How to Contact: Submit demo tape of previous work. Prefers cassette. Does not return unsolicited material. Prefers to keep submitted materials on file.
Music: Uses material for home videos.

SANDY WILBUR MUSIC, INC., 48 E. 43rd St., 7th Floor, New York NY 10017. (212)949-1190. Jingle/commercial music production house. Clients include advertising agencies, film producers and corporate clients. Uses the services of singers, arrangers, players (primarily MIDI keyboards) for scoring of TV and film, and jingles and commercials for radio and TV. Commissions 2 composers and 2 lyricists/year. Pays by the hour "depending upon what the job is." Buys all rights.
How to Contact: Call first for permission to submit. Prefers cassette (or VHS videocassette) with 3 pieces limit. Does not return unsolicited material; prefers to keep on file. Reports in 1 month.
Music: Uses R&B, rock, jazz, pop, top 40 for commercials, educational films, etc.
Tips: "We're primarily interested in singers, arrangers, players and programmers, but if a songwriter has one or more of these skills, I will listen. This is a competitive business. Apply only if you believe you are different or better than what's out there. Be patient—if I feel you are right for the company, I'll get back to you."

*WINMILL ENTERTAINMENT THE CULVER STUDIOS, 9336 W. Washington Blvd., Culver City CA 90232. (213)202-3308. Manager/Music Videos: Daniel Zirilli. Motion picture and music video production company. Clients include record labels and major motion picture studios. Estab. 1987. Uses the services of music houses and independent songwriters/composers for scoring of motion pictures, background music for motion pictures, commercials for TV and music videos for special accounts (i.e. fashion etc.). Commissions 2 composers/year. Pay commensurate with film budget allocation. Rights bought depends on project.
How to Contact: Query with resume of credits. SASE. Report back depends on project deadline and needs.
Music: Music depends upon the project.
Tips: Patience, persistence and talent.

*EVANS WYATT ADVERTISING, 5151 Flynn Parkway, Corpus Christi TX 78411. (512)854-1661. Owner: E. Wyatt. Advertising agency. Clients are general/all types. Estab. 1975. Uses the services of music houses and independent songwriters/composers for background music for soundtracks, jingles for advertising and commercials for radio and TV. Commissions 8-10 composers/year. Pays by the job. Buys all rights.
How to Contact: Submit demo tape of previous work. Submit tape demonstrating composition skills. Query with resume of credits. Write first to arrange personal interview. Prefers cassette. SASE, but prefers to keep material on file. Reports in 2 months.
Music: Uses all types for commercials plus videos mostly.
Tips: :"Make it *easy* to judge your work! Be sure you've got the talent you claim and present it clearly. If we don't like your pitch immediately, chances are we won't like your work."

YARDIS CORPORATION, 9138 West Chester Pike, Upper Darby PA 19082. (215)789-2200. President: Ray Rosenberg. Advertising agency. Clients include travel, financial, car dealers, tour operators. Estab. 1946. Uses the services of music houses and independent songwriters/composers for background music for video presentations, jingles for various spots and commercials for radio and TV. Payment depends on circmstances. Rights purchased depends on circumstances.
How to Contact: "Call; go from there." Prefers cassette (or VHS videocassette). Does not return unsolicited material; prefers to keep material on file.
Music: Uses various styles for various assignments.

GREG YOUNGMAN MUSIC, P.O. Box 8102, Long Beach CA 90808. (213)425-9597. Creative Director: Jo Nance. Advertising agency, jingle/**commercial music production house** and **sound effect library**. Serves all types of clients—local, regional, national levels. Uses the services of independent songwriters/composers and lyricists for background music for audiovisual projects, jingles and commercials for radio. Commissions 12 composers and 12 lyricists/year. Pays $500-10,000/job. Buys all rights.
How to Contact: Submit demo tape of previous work or tape demonstrating composition skills. Prefers cassette or 7½ or 15 ips reel-to-reel. Prefers to keep material on file. Reports in 1 month.
Music: Uses all types for radio commercials and station ID.
Tips: "Be creative, magical and don't be afraid to take chances. *Carefully* listen to radio and TV commercials."

ZM SQUARED, 903 Edgewood Lane, Box C-30, Cinnaminson NJ 08077. (609)786-0612. Estab. 1971. Clients include colleges, schools, businesses and audiovisual producers. Uses the services of songwriters "for themes for our no-needledrop music library, background for audiovisual presentations and jingles. We prefer to work with composer/arranger/performer and use primarily background music." Commissions 5 composers/year. Pays 10-35% royalty. Buys all rights.

How to Contact: Submit demo tape of previous work. Prefers cassette with 4-6 songs. SASE. Reports in 3 weeks. Free catalog available.

Music: "We require a variety of background music—educational and industrial for general use with audiovisual programs."

Tips: "Know what we want and be able to produce what you write."

Advertising, AV, and Commercial Music Houses/ '90-'91 Changes

The following markets appeared in the 1990 edition of *Songwriter's Market* but do not appear in the 1991 edition. Those companies that did not respond to our request for an update of their listing may not have done so for a variety of reasons—they may be out of business, for example, or they may be overstocked with submissions.

Allerice Video (did not respond)

Arztco Pictures, Inc. (did not respond)

Atlantis Audio/Video Production (asked to be deleted)

Bachner Productions, Inc. (did not respond)

Beckman Associates (did not respond)

Bell & Roberts (did not respond)

Ron Berns & Associates (did not respond)

Blank Tape Systems (did not respond)

Dick Bronson, Inc. (asked to be deleted)

Carter Advertising Inc. (moved; no forwarding address)

Walter Cauf Associates (moved; no forwarding address)

Channel 3 Video (did not respond)

Cine Design Films (did not respond)

CLI Productions (did not respond)

Communications Concepts (did not respond)

The Creative Dept. Advertis

ing Inc. (did not respond)

Creativity Unlimited Press (did not respond)

John Crowe Advertising Agency (did not respond)

Davidoff and Partners, Inc. (did not respond)

Della Femina, McNamee WCRS (did not respond)

Devine Videoworks Corp. (asked to be deleted)

DMA Productions (did not respond)

DRGM (did not respond)

Filippone Sound & Video (did not respond)

Furman Films, Inc. (did not respond)

Glasshouse Pictures Limited (did not respond)

Image Associates, Inc. (did not respond)

Innerquest Communications Corp. (did not respond)

Kid Kirk Productions (did not respond)

K-Larrco (deleted)

Laguna Video Productions (did not respond)

Al Paul Lefton Co. (did not respond)

Media People, Inc. (did not respond)

Arthur Mills Associates, Inc. (did not respond)

Music Factory Enterprises, Inc. (did not respond)

Network Music, Inc. (did not respond)

Ogilvy & Mather/New Zealand (did not respond)

Pyramid Productions (did not respond)

Carl Schurtz Music (did not respond)

Shaffer Shaffer Shaffer, Inc. (did not respond)

Sorgel Studios Inc. (did not respond)

Souvenirs of Hawaii (did not respond)

Studio M Productions Unltd. (did not respond)

TPS Video Svc. (did not respond)

TRF Production Music Libraries (did not respond)

Vandor Advertising Group (deleted)

Videosmith Inc. (did not respond)

Wilson Communications, Ltd. (out of business)

Wire Duck (did not respond)

Yardis Corporation (did not respond)

Play Producers and Publishers

Works in musical theater, unlike drama or humor, are most commonly products of collaboration. And because of the nature of the musical (the meshing of music and script into a single, unified work), this type of theater is more difficult to successfully develop and produce. Although collaboration is not an absolute for a good musical, the best of musical theater has been written by the combination of playwright and composer.

How does one go about finding a suitable partner? Check the drama departments at local colleges—scan bulletin boards, talk to professors and maybe even take a few classes. Also join a local theater group. Among the actors and directors you make contact with, there will certainly be a struggling playwright who is also looking for a collaborator.

Listed in this section are many playhouses and publishers devoted to developing new plays and musicals. They receive hundreds of submissions annually from playwrights and songwriters, but only a few are chosen for production. So, whether working alone or collaboratively, there are important steps you should take to broaden your knowledge of the field and improve the chances of your work being selected for publication or production.

First, learn as much as possible about the theater: its history, what's already been produced, current trends, and other important information. Find out about the genre by attending (and reading) plays and musicals, reading theater magazines and discussing related topics with people in your theater group. All this will help you be well-rounded, more in touch with the theater world and, ultimately, a more versatile writer and/or composer.

When writing a musical, keep in mind the value of a simple, inexpensive production, but at the same time envision a work with expandability. Professional casts can handle complex songs and arrangements—most local and regional theaters (the major marketplace) cannot. Financially, rising production costs have prompted theater directors and producers, even on Broadway, to seek shows with simpler sets and smaller casts. Although some directors agree that this may reduce a playwright's creative scope, it's just not feasible for smaller theaters to handle elaborately designed works. This doesn't mean you should create a 2-character, bare-stage play. Instead, provide flexibility and give the piece room for embellishments that seem natural to the work, but are not essential. A musical should be an outline, not a blueprint, which is followed by contribution from the director, choreographer and all involved. In short, it is beneficial to create a musical that may be further developed, not one that has to be condensed.

Finally, research markets to determine which theaters and publishers are most apt to be interested in your musical. It would be nice to immediately shoot for Broadway, but this simply is an unrealistic goal. Many nonprofessional groups—dinner theaters, children's theaters, community playhouses and college and high school drama departments—provide excellent outlets for musicals.

The following listings provide information you will need to submit to the theater, producer and/or play publisher right for YOU. Remember to follow submission instructions meticulously.

THE ACTING COMPANY, P.O. Box 898, Times Sq. Station, New York NY 10108. (212)564-3510. Play producer. Estab. 1972. Produces 2-3 plays/year. "Have done musicals in the past. We are a national touring company playing universities and booking houses." Pays by royalty or negotiated fee/commission. Submit through agent only. SASE. Reports in 12 weeks.

Musical Theater: "We would consider a wide variety of styles—although we remain a young, classical ensemble. Most of our classical plays make use of a lot of incidental music. Our company consists of 17 actors. All productions must be able to tour easily. We have no resident musicians. Taped sound is essential. Actors tend to remain active touring members for 2-3 seasons. Turnover is considerable. Musical ability of the company tends to vary widely from season to season. We would avoid shows which require sophisticated musical abilities and/or training."

*ALLEGHENY HIGHLANDS REGIONAL THEATRE, 526 West Ogle St., Ebensburg PA 15931. (814)472-4333. Artistic Director: Mark Hirschfield. Play producer. Estab. 1974. Produces 7 plays and 3 musicals (1 new musical)/year. "Rural audience, many elderly, many families; we have 2 spaces—a 200 seat arena (4 shows) and a 600 seat proscenium (3- shows)." Pays $75-150/performance. Query with synopsis, character breakdown and set description. SASE. Reports in 3 months.
Musical Theatre: "Small cast, full-length musicals, preferably orchestrated for no more than 6 musicians. Anything set in Pennsylvania about Pennsylvanians is of particular interest. Also interested in musicals for children, either one-act or full-length. Roles for children are a plus. We have difficulty finding men to audition. Few mens roles are a plus. No more than 19-20 including chorus, no more than 2-3 settings. We had original music scored for scene changes and intermission music for *She Stoops To Conquer*. Perhaps some underscoring for a mystery would be fun."
Productions: *Oklahoma!*, by Rodgers & Hammerstein; *Cabaret*, by Kander & Ebb; and *George M*, by George M. Cohan.

THE ALPHA THEATRE PROJECT, INC., 720 South Hamilton, 317 Court, Saginaw MI 48605. (517)790-1005. Executive Producer: Lee-Perry Belleau. Play producer. Estab. 1981. Produces 14 plays and 6 musicals (1-2 new musicals)/year. "We produce mainly for young audiences, although we do produce a 6 show season of musicals and plays for general audiences as well." Pays $15-75/ performance royalty or $500-2,000 by outright purchase.
How to Contact: Query first. Does not return unsolicited material. Reports in 6 months.
Musical Theater: Children's musicals, 40-50 minutes in length with 3-5 characters (for touring); adult full-length musicals and revues for our mainstage stock season, 4-6 characters. Also very interested in topics dealing with social concerns of children (abuse, divorce, drugs, war, etc.). Small casts of 5 or less for mainstage (general audiences); casts of 3 or less for touring theatre for youth. No religious material. Would consider original music for use in a play being developed.
Productions: *Unraveling Your Mitten*, by Paul Langford (Michigan History); *Gershwin and Gershwin*, by staff (music of Gershwin); and *Free Beer and Bowling*, by staff (music of '60's).
Tips: "It takes time to develop a project then schedule it for performance. In other words, don't expect to be produced overnight!"

AMAS MUSICAL THEATRE INC., 1 E. 104th St., New York NY 10029. (212)369-8000. Managing Director: Jeffrey Solis. Founder/Artistic Director: Rosetta Lenoire. Produces 3 original musicals/year. Presents 2 children's theater productions and one summer tour. "AMAS is a multi-racial theater, dedicated to bring all people—regardless of race, creed, color or religion—together through the performing arts." Does not pay for manuscripts but "provides a top quality New York showcase with a good record of commercial pick-ups." Submit script with cassette tape of score (or partial score) with SASE.
Musical Theater: Musicals only. "All works to be performed by multi-racial casts. Musical biographies especially welcome. Cast size should be under 13 if possible, including doubling. Because of physical space, set requirements should be relatively simple. We do not want to see material with explicit sex or violence or very strong language. Prefer themes of love, joy and togetherness."
Productions: *Bubbling Brown Sugar*; *Bingo*, by Hy Gilbert, George Fischoff and Ossie Davis (Negro baseball leagues); *Dazy*, by Phillip Rose; *Hot Sake*; *Prime Time*, by Johnny Brandon; and *Step Into My World*, by Miki Grant.
Tips: "A good melody line is important, ideally one that children and adults can hum and sing. Lyrics should tell a story; avoid repetition."

*AMELIA MAGAZINE, 329 "E" St., Bakersfield CA 93304. (805)323-4064. Editor: Frederick A. Raborg, Jr. Play publisher. Estab. 1983. Publish 1 play/year. General audience; one-act plays published in AMELIA Magazine. Best play submitted is the winner of the annual FRANK MCCLURE One-Act Play Award. Submit complete manuscript and score per contest rules by postmark deadline of May 15. SASE. Reports in 6-8 weeks. "We would consider publishing musical scores if submitted in clean camera-ready copy—also single songs. Payment same as for poetry—$2-25 plus copies."

AMERICAN LIVING, History Theater, Box 2677, Hollywood CA 90078. (213)876-2202. President and Artistic Director: Dorene Ludwig. Play producer. Estab. 1975. Produces 2-5 plays/year. All over U.S., but mostly Southern California—conventions, schools, museums, universities, libraries, etc. Pays by royalty.

How to Contact: Query first. SASE. Reports in 6 months.
Musical Theater: "We only use primary source, historically accurate material: in music — *Songs of the Civil War* or *Songs of the Labor Movement*, etc. — presented as a program rather than play would be the only use I could foresee. We need music historians more than composers."
Tips: "Do not send fictionalized historical material. We use primary source material only."

AMERICAN STAGE FESTIVAL, P.O. Box 225, Milford NH 03055. (603)673-4005. Literary Manager: Austin Tichenor. Regional theater. Estab. 1974. Produces 17 plays and 3 musicals (1 new musical)/ year. 500 seat theater, Broadway-sized stage, summertime audience. Pays 4-7% royalty.
How to Contact: Submit script and tape of songs with SASE. Do not submit score. Reports in 6 months.
Musical Theater: "We are interested in musicals that tell a story, in which songs make a dramatic contribution. Particularly interested in a return to popular song formats, used dramatically, not nostalgically." Cast and musicians should not total more than 15. Musicals should use traditional song forms.
Productions: *Peg O' My Heart*, by David Heneker (musical comedy); *The Last of the Souhegans*, by Andrew Howard (musical comedy); and *Feathertop*, by Skip Kennon (musical comedy).
Tips: "Be willing to learn from your audience."

*ARAN PRESS, 1320 S. Third St., Louisville KY 40208. (502)636-0115. Editor/Publisher: Tom Eagan. Play publisher. Estab. 1983. Publishes 40-50 plays, 1-2 musicals and 1-2 new musicals/year. Professional, college/university, community, summer stock and dinner theater audience. Pays 50% royalty or book royalty 10%. Query first. SASE. Reports in 2 weeks.
Musical Theater: "The musical should include a small cast, simple set for professional, community, college, university, summer stock and dinner theater production."
Productions: *Comedy of History*, by Dick W. Zylstra (musical history); *The Big Dollar*, by Herschel Steinhardt (real estate business); and *Caribbean Blue*, by Jonathan Lowe (tropical island revolution).

ARENA PLAYERS REPERTORY THEATRE, 296 Route 109, East Farmingdale NY 11735. (516)293-0674. Producer: Frederic De Feis. Play producer. Produces 30 plays/year. Plays performed in a "professional, arena-style repertory theater playing to a broad cross-section of teenagers to senior citizens, drawn from all over Long Island as well as Manhattan." Pays royalty averaging $600-1,200. Query with synopsis. SASE. Reports in 1 month.
Musical Theater: "We are particularly interested in full-length intimate musicals which can be mounted with minimal orchestration and are well-suited to production in a small, arena-style theater."
Productions: *Umbrellas of Cherbourg*, by Demy; and *I Love My Wife*, by Michael Stewart and Cy Coleman.

ARKANSAS REPERTORY THEATRE, 601 Main, P.O. Box 110, Little Rock AR 72203. (501)378-0445. Contact: Lynn Frazier. Play producer. Estab. 1976. Produces 9-12 plays and 2 musicals/year. "We perform in a 345-seat house." Pays 5-10% royalty or $75-150 per performance.
How to Contact: Query with synopsis, character breakdown and set description. SASE. Reports in 3 months.
Musical Theater: "Small casts are preferred. We like issue-oriented pieces and prefer shows to run 1:45 to 2 hours maximum. Simple is better; small is better, but we would consider more complex shows. We aren't interested in children's pieces, puppet shows or mime. We always like to receive a tape of the music with the book."
Productions: *On the Verge*, by Eric Overmyer; *A Walk in the Woods*, by Lee Blessing; *Golden Shadows Old West Museum*, by Larry King; and *Pageant*, by Michael Rice.

ARKANSAS STATE UNIVERSITY-BEEBE CAMPUS, Box H, Beebe AR 72012. (501)882-6452. Director of Theater: L.R. Chudomelka. Play producer. Produces 6 plays (3 musicals)/year. Plays are performed in a "600 seat theater (proscenium) in a city of 4,000, 30 miles from metropolitan area of more than 200,000." Pays $35-100/performance. Submit complete manuscript and score. SASE. Reports in 2 weeks.
Musical Theater: "Material should be within the ability of traditional community college with traditional and non-traditional students: simple dancing, innovative and traditional, not over-sophisticated (somewhat family oriented). Variety of music styles and balanced major role shows — no 'star' shows. Flexible cast size, props, staging, etc. We do not want extremes, unnecessary profanity or 'operatic' material."
Productions: *Something's Afoot*, by McDonald/Vos/Gerlach (mystery); *Happy Time*, by Nash/Kander/ Ebb (family relations); and *Damn Yankees*, by Abbott/Wallop/Adler/Ross (baseball).
Tips: "Music should be singable and vary in style. Songs should be an intricate part of the show and not just put in for spectacle. Major roles should be balanced between 4 or 5 characters, rather than one-character shows with chorus."

ASOLO STATE THEATER FOR THE PERFORMING ARTS, 5555 N. Taxiami Trail, Sarasota FL 34243. (813)351-9010. Contact: Literary Manager. Play producer. Produces 8 plays (1 musical)/year. Plays are performed at the Asolo Theater (325-seat proscenium house) or by the Asolo Touring Theater (6-member company touring the Southeast). Pays 5% minimum royalty. "We no longer accept unsolicited manuscripts or tapes. Inquiries should be made in the form of a letter, a one-page synopsis, and a self-addressed, stamped postcard." SASE.

Musical Theater: "We want small non-chorus musicals only. They should be full-length, any subject, with not over 10 in the cast. There are no restrictions on production demands; however, musicals with excessive scenic requirements may be difficult to consider."

Productions: *Dames at Sea*, by Haimsohn/Miller/Wise; *The Drunkard*, by Herrod/Manilow; and *Man with a Load of Mischief*, by Clifton/Tarver.

BAKER'S PLAYS, 100 Chauncy St., Boston MA 02111. (617)482-1280. Editor: John B. Welch. Play publisher. Estab. 1845. Publishes 18-25 plays and 3-5 new muscials/year. Plays are used by children's theaters, junior and senior high schools, colleges and community theaters. Pays 50-80% royalty. Submit complete manuscript, score and cassette tape of songs. SASE. Reports in 3 months.

Musical Theater: "Seeking musicals for teen production and children's theatre production. We prefer large cast, contemporary musicals which are easy to stage and produce. Plot your shows strongly, keep your scenery and staging simple, your musical numbers and choreography easily explained and blocked out. Originality and style are up to the author. We want innovative and tuneful shows but no X-rated material. We are very interested in the new writer and believe that, with revision and editorial help, he can achieve success in writing original musicals for the non-professional market." Would consider original music for use in a play being developed or in a pre-existing play.

Publications: *Adventures of Daredevil Dan*, by Tim Kelly, Ole Kittleson and Arne Christianson (40's-50's radio adventure); and *Joseph*, by Earl Reimer and Marshall Laurence (The Biblical Joseph Story).

BERKSHIRE PUBLIC THEATRE, P.O. Box 860, 30 Union St., Pittsfield MA 01202. (413)445-4631. Artistic Director: Frank Bessell. Play producer. Estab. 1976. Produces 9 plays (2 musicals)/year. "Plays are performed in a 285-seat proscenium thrust theatre for a general audience of all ages with wide-ranging tastes." Pays negotiable royalty or negotiable amount per performance. Query first. SASE. Reports in 6 weeks.

Musical Theater: Seeking musicals with "no more than 3 acts (2½ hours). We look for fresh musicals with something to say. Our company has a flexible vocal range. Cast size must be 2-50, no more, with a small orchestra (up to 8)." Would also consider original music "for a play being developed and possibly for existing works."

Productions: *Good Time Rock & Roll*, by The Musical Beach Party, Tommy De Frantz (surfing R&R); *Hollywood Primitive*, by Frank Bessell (love, innocence and discovery); and *Lysistrata*, by Alice Spatz (modern adaptation of the Greek).

Tips: "We are a small company. Patience is a must. Be yourself—open, honest. Experience is not necessary but is helpful. We don't have a lot of money but we are long on nurturing artists! We are developing shows with commercial prospects to go beyond the Berkshires, i.e., a series of rock music revues is now in its fifth year."

*BRISTOL RIVERSIDE THEATRE, P.O. Box 1250, Bristol PA 19007. (215)785-6664. Artistic Director: Susan D. Atkinson. Play producer. Estab. 1986. Produce 5 plays, 2 musicals/year (1 new musical every 2 years). "New 302-seat proscenium Equity theater with audience of all ages from small towns and metropolitan area." Pays by royalty 6-8%. Submit complete manuscript, score and tape of songs. SASE. Reports in 6 months.

Musical Theatre: "No strictly children's musicals. All other types with small to medium casts and within reasonable artictic tastes. Prefer one-set; limited funds rectrict. Does not wish to see anything catering to prurient interests."

Productions: *The Robber Bridegroom*, by Alfred Uhry/R. Waldman (E. Welty novella - 1790s Missis-sippi delta); *A Day in Hollywood/A Night*, by Frank Lazarus/D. Vosburgh (1930s Hollywood); and *Sally Blane, World's Greatest Girl Detective*, by David Levy/Leslie Eberhard (spoof of teen detective genre).

Tips: "He or she should be willing to work with small staff, open to artistic suggestion, and aware of the limitations of newly developing theaters."

CALIFORNIA MUSIC THEATRE, Ste 400M, 2500 E. Colorado, Pasadena CA 91107. (818)792-0776. Artistic Director: Gary Davis. Play producer. Estab. 1986. Produces 4 plays and 4 musicals (1 new musical)/year. "Plays produced at Pasadena Civic Auditorium. Proscenium-3,000 seats. Base of 13,000 subscribers/average of 25,000 per production." Pays by royalty. Submit complete manuscript, score and tape of songs. SASE. Reports in 3 months.

Close-up

John Welch
Editor
Baker's Plays
Boston, Massachusetts

For John Welch and Baker's Plays, honesty is the main ingredient of a successful play or musical production.

That honesty is reflective of the plays and musicals that Welch currently seeks for the play publisher—realistic, real-life productions dealing with contemporary issues and focusing on the human experiences of everyday life.

In particular, Welch looks for material geared toward teen audiences. "A number of years ago, we decided that the high school market needed to be given the opportunity to deal with the materials on the stage which are more contemporary, dealing with real issues," says Welch. "So we developed a piece entitled 'Voices From the High Schools,' and it has become enormously successful. It was tied with 'Grease' for the second most popular play to be produced by high schools." The play deals with suicide, teen pregnancy, alcoholism and drugs. Viewing a play with such issues "opens up the opportunities for teachers, administrators and, in particular, parents, to discuss these issues with the kids," he says, which contributes to a positive learning experience.

An ideal submission, says Welch, is a manuscript and/or musical score that has been audience tested, although he stresses that this is not a requirement. "It can start off as a read through," he says. And Baker's reviews everything submitted—a musical or play does not need to be submitted through an agent.

Once a work is accepted for publication, Baker's negotiates a contract. The company circulates 55,000 catalogs per year, listing all new and backlist musicals and plays. From that catalog, high school drama departments, community theaters and others order the work for their respective group to produce. Baker's then collects the monies inhouse and splits with the authors. The leasing of production rights varies from a one-act of $15 for the first performance and $10 for each repeat performance to a musical, which may go for $75 for the first performance and $50 for each performance thereafter.

Welch advises those who are interested in being published to "have realistic production values in mind." Also, a composer or writer should not be too proud or inflexible about their work. "The artist must get the material on its feet. I tell them that they can't fall in love with the play through the typewriter," he says. "The process of developing the play is a unique one because the ideas and words come from the creator and are placed in someone else's mouth. When the transfer of words occurs, the writer must remember that the material is not so select and so wonderful that others can't have the opportunity to invest their response." Feedback from those involved can improve a play immensely, Welch says.

He concludes by mentioning that theater is not wholly intellectual—the basis of theater must be emotional. "When you're asking someone else to find an emotional connection, it can expand the play - and it can be a collaboration of the writer, the musician, the actor and all involved. This collaboration is what makes theater so wonderful."

—Brian C. Rushing

Musical Theater: "Our audience is rather conservative."
Productions: *Babes in Toyland*, by Toby Bluth (new adaptation); *Stike Up the Band*, by Gershwin/Kaufman; and *Drood*, by Rupert Holmes.
Tips: "Please understand that we place great importance on lyrics. If it doesn't read well, we do not pursue the piece beyond the initial reading."

WILLIAM CAREY COLLEGE DINNER THEATRE, William Carey College, Hattiesburg MS 39401. (601)582-6218. Managing Director: O.L. Quave. Play producer. Produces 2 plays (2 musicals)/year. "Our dinner theater operates only in summer and plays to family audiences." Payment negotiable. Submit complete manuscript and score. SASE. Reports as soon as possible.
Musical Theater: "Plays should be simply-staged, have small casts (8-10 maximum), and be suitable for family viewing; two hours maximum length. Score should require piano only, or piano, electric piano and drums."
Productions: *Ernest in Love*; *Rodgers and Hart: A Musical Celebration*; and *Side by Side*, by Sondheim.

THE CAST THEATRE, 804 El Centro Ave., Los Angeles CA 90038. (213)462-9872. Literary Manager: Diana Gibson. Play producer. Estab. 1974. Produces 20 plays and 1-2 musicals (1-2 new musicals)/year. Pays 5% royalty.
How to Contact: Prefer line reading at the theatre. It is better that playwright is in attendance. SASE. Reports in months.
Musical Theater: "We want adult topics. We want a cast size no larger than 12 people. We have a small stage."
Productions: *Back Home—A Los Angeles Musical*, by Kirby Tapper, Bob Schrack (Los Angeles' clichés); and *'Tis Pity She's a Whore*, by Robert Priar (original musical version).

*CENTENARY COLLEGE, THEATRE DEPARTMENT, Shreveport LA 71134-1188. (318)869-5011. Chairman: Robert R. Buseick. Play producer. Produces 6 plays (1-2 new musicals)/year. Plays are presented in a 350-seat playhouse to college and community audiences. Submit manuscript and score. SASE. Reports in 1 month.
Productions: *Steel Magnolias*; *Annie*; *Moliere*; *Baby, A Day in Hollywood/A Night in the Ukraine*; *A Little Shop of Horrors*; and *Jerry's Girls*, by Todd Sweeney.

CHARLOTTETOWN FESTIVAL, Box 848, Charlottetown, Prince Edward Island C1A 7L9 **Canada**. Artistic Director: Walter Learning. Play producer. Produces 4 plays, 4 musicals and 1-2 new musicals/year. Plays are performed for "a large general audience in our 1100-seat festival theater, 187-seat Mackenzie theater, or 100-seat cabaret theater." Pays 4-12% royalty. Submit complete manuscript, score and tape of songs. SAE and IRC. Reports in 4 months.
Productions: *Anne of Green Gables*, by Harron and Campbell (family); *Are You Lonesome Tonight*, by Alan Bleasdale (mature audiences); and *Alexandra: The Last Empress*, by Cliff Jones.

CIRCA' 21 DINNER PLAYHOUSE, P.O. Box 3784, Rock Island IL 61204-3784. (309)786-2667. Producer: Dennis Hitchcock. Play producer. Estab. 1977. Produces 1-2 plays, 4-5 musicals (2 new musicals)/year. Plays produced for a general audience. Two children's works per year, concurrent with major productions. Pays by royalty. Query with synopsis, character breakdown and set description or submit complete manuscript, score and tape of songs. SASE. Reports in 8 weeks.
Musical Theater: "For children's musicals we prefer 2-act, 1½ hour limit with cast of no more than 10, piano and percussion accompaniment, and limited scenic requirements. Folk or fairy tale themes. Works that do not condescend to a young audience yet are appropriate for entire family. We're also seeking full-length, small cast musicals suitable for a broad audience." Would also consider original music for use in a play being developed.
Productions: *A Chorus Line*, by James Kirkwood/Marvin Hamlisch; *Oklahoma*, by Rodgers and Hammerstein; *Mame*, by Jerry Herman; and *Hansel and Gretel*, with orignal music by John Luebker.
Tips: "Small, upbeat, tourable musicals (like *Pump Boys*) and bright musically-sharp children's productions (like those produced by Prince Street Players) work best. Keep an open mind. Stretch to encompass a musical variety—different keys, rhythms, musical ideas and textures."

 The asterisk before a listing indicates that the listing is new in this edition. New markets are often the most receptive to unsolicited submissions.

CIRCLE IN THE SQUARE THEATRE, 1633 Broadway, New York NY 10019. (212)307-2700. Literary Advisor: Seth Goldman. Play producer. Estab. 1951. Produces 3 plays/year; occasionally produces a musical. Pays by royalty. Query with a letter, 1-page synopsis and script sample (10 pages). Reports in 6 months.
Musical Theater: "We are looking for original material with small cast and orchestra requirements. We're not interested in traditional musical comedies." Will consider original music for use in a play being developed or in a pre-existing play at the option of the director.
Production: *Pal Joey.*

*CITIARTS/THEATRE CONCORD, 1950 Parkside Dr., Concord CA 94519. (415)671-3065. Artistic Director: Richard H. Elliott. Play producer. Estab. 1973. Produces 8 plays and 4 musicals (0-4 new musicals)/year. "CitiArts/Theatre Concord is the resident theater in the 203-seat Willows Theatre, a proscenium stage, in Concord, located in suburban San Francisco." Pays 5-12% royalty, or terms negotiated.
How to Contact: Submit complete manuscript and score. SASE. Reports in 2 months.
Musical Theater: "Full-length musicals addressing contemporary themes or issues, small to mid-size cast (maximum 15 characters) with maximum 15 instruments. Topics which appeal to an educated suburban and liberal urban audience are best. Maximum 15 cast members, 15 musicians, prefer unit set (we have no fly loft or wing space)." "We often commission original scores for straight plays. Composer should send resume and recorded example of work with scores if possible."
Productions: *Six Women with Brain Death*, by Mark Houston (women's issues); *A . . . My Name is Alice*, by Various (women's issues); and *Cinderella*, by Rogers & Hammerstein (children's show).
Tips: "Be prepared and believe in your material."

CITY THEATRE, 315 S. Bellefield Ave., Pittsburgh PA 15213. (412)624-5041. Resident Dramaturg: Scott Cummings. Play producer. Estab. 1974. Produces 4 plays/year. "Plays are performed in an intimate 117 seat Thrust-Stage Theatre to an adventurous subscriber base." Query with synopsis, character breakdown and set description. Does not return unsolicited material. Reports in 2-3 weeks for query; 3-4 months for script.
Musical Theater: "We want sophisticated plays with music. We prefer a small cast with no more than 10 (including musicians) and single set because we have thrust stage capabilities only. We don't want traditional, large cast musical comedies."
Productions: *Painting It Red*, by Steven Dietz (modern romance); *Lovers and Keeper*, by Irene Fornes (failed romance); and *Maybe I'm Doing It Wrong*, by Randy Newman (musical review).

*CLEVELAND PUBLIC THEATRE, 6415 Detroit Ave., Cleveland OH 44102. (216)631-2727. Director of Playwright Development: Linda Eisenstein. Play producer. Estab. 1983. Produces 6 plays plus 12 staged readings; much performance art, 1-2 musicals and 1 new musical/year. "We are a progressive urban loft theater (80-150 seats) with audiences that are adult and sophisticated—mix of yuppies, artists, radicals and punks." Pays $25-100 per performance. Query with synopsis, character breakdown (sample song tape optional) or submit complete ms, score and tape of songs. SASE. Reports in 3-6 months.
Musical Theater: "We seek progressive, political, alternative and outrageous musicals. Also music for our performance art and sound festivals—cutting edge experimental. Don't expect a realistic set—we do mostly 3-quarter and arena, with no fly space. We don't want to see fluff or traditional Broadway fare, would-be Broadway fare or traditional children's plays." "A writer must think weird; don't watch TV." "We use several local composers (Cleveland) to write our 'incidental' music."
Production: *Star Wares: The Next Generation*, by James Levin and Linda Eisenstein (political satirical rock opera); *The Rocky Horror Show*, by Richard O'Brien (transvestite horror spoof); *Chickalena & the End of the World*, by Caroline Van Ausdal (abstract children's folk opera) and *Ripped Van Winkle* by San Francisco Mime Troupe (political satire—touring).
Tips: "If you live in the area, come and work as a volunteer in our Festival of New Plays or other artist outreach. We are particularly committed to local artists."

*DAVID J. COGAN, Suite 36M, One Lincoln Plaza, 20 W. 64th St., New York NY 10023. Contact: David Cogan. Play producer. Produces 1 play/year. Produces musical comedy, straight comedy and drama in New York. Pays on a royalty basis, or buys script outright for $5,000 maximum. Query. SASE. Reports in 1 month.
Musical Theater: Interested only in completed projects.
Productions: *A Raisin in the Sun*, by Hannesbury (drama); and *The Odd Couple*, by Neil Simon (comedy).

CREATIVE PRODUCTIONS, INC., 2 Beaver Pl., Aberdeen NJ 07747. (201)566-6985. Director: Walter L. Born. Play producer. Estab. 1970. Produces 3 musicals (1-2 new musicals)/year. "Our audience is the general community with emphasis on elderly and folks with disabilities. We use local public school theater facilities." Pays by royalty or per performance, as required by broadway rental houses. Query with synopsis, character breakdown and set description. Does not return unsolicited material. Reports in 1 month.

Musical Theater: "We want family type material (i.e. *Brigadoon, Charlie Brown*) with light rock to classical music and a maximum running time of two hours. The subject matter should deal with older folks or folks with disabilities. We have no flying capability in facility; cast size is a maximum 10-12; the sets are mostly on small wagons, props aren't anything exotic; the orchestra is chamber size with standard instruments. We don't want pornographic material or children's shows. We want nothing trite and condescending in either the material or the treatment. We like the unusual treatment well-structured and thought out, with minimal sets and changes. We can't handle unusual vocal requirements. We prefer an integrated piece with music a structural part from the beginning."

Productions: *Taking My Turn*, by Robert H. Livingston (retired folks); *Land Beyond Forever*, by Lorna Hope (the color wheel); and *Drummer I Must March to*, by Susan Dunn (the journey into darkness [blindness] by a young college woman).

*CREATIVE THEATRE, 102 Witherspoon St., Princeton NJ 08540. (609)924-3489. Artistic Director: Eloise Bruce. Play producer. Estab. 1969. Produces 5 plays, all with music (1 new musical)/year. "Plays are performed for young audiences grades K-6. The plays are always audience participation and done in schools (45 minute format)." Pays a fee for writing and production sans royalty for two seasons. Then per performance royalty fee. Query first or query with synopsis, character breakdown and set description. SASE. Reports in 1 month.

Musical Theater: "Audience participation plays, 45 minutes in length, 4-6 performers, usually presentational style. Topics can range from original plots to adaptations of folk and fairytales. Staging is usually in the round with audience of no more than 300/seating on the floor. No lighting and usually piano accompaniment. Actor is focus with strong but very lean set and costume design." Does not wish to see plays without audience participation.

Productions: *The Legend of Sleepy Hollow*, adaptation by Bernice Bronson (ghost story); *Where Snow Falls Up*, by Mark Schaeffer/Rita Asch (holiday story); and *Nightingale*, by John Urquart/Rita Grossberg (fairytale).

Tips: "Develop child centered work which encourages the imaginations of the audience and is centered in child play."

CREEDE REPERTORY THEATRE, P.O. Box 269, Creede CO 81130. (719)658-2541. Producing/Artistic Director: Richard Baxter. Play producer. Estab. 1966. Produces 6 plays and 1 musical/year. Performs in 187-seat proscenium theatre; audience is primarily tourist base from Texas, Oklahoma, New Mexico and Colorado. Pays 7% royalty. Query first. SASE. Reports in 1 year.

Musical Theater: "We prefer historical western material with cast no larger than 11. Staging must be flexible as space is limited."

Productions: *Baby Doe Tabor*, by Kenton Kersting (Colorado history); *A Frog in His Throat*, by Feydeau, adapted by Eric Conger, (French farce); and *Tommyknockers*, by Eric Engdahl, Mark Houston and Chris Thompson (mining).

Tips: "Songwriter must have the ability to accept criticism and must be flexible."

*DEEP ELLUM THEATRE GROUP/UNDERMAIN THEATRE, Box 141166, Dallas TX 75214. (214)748-3082. Literary Manager: Lisa Schmidt. Play producer. Estab. 1983. Produces 5 plays and 1 musical/year. "We draw an audience with a wide age range who seek to be intellectually challenged." Pays 6% royalty.

How to Contact: Submit complete manuscript and score. SASE. Reports in 1 month.

Musical Theater: "We seek experimental or innovative scripts. We usually produce plays under 2 hours in length. We work with a resident company of 6 actors. We prefer plays with a cast under 10. The theater seats 80. Stage design is flexible; proscenium, thrust, etc., but little space for more the 5-6 musicians. We don't want to see anything we consider to be ordinary musical comedy (i.e. anything vaguely like *Me and My Gal, Annie* or *Westside Story*. We stress great acting over great singing. We generally use only a piano, percussion, keyboard and guitar. We would consider a new musical score for an existing play for example, we developed in house a musical score for *Disgrace*, which was performed live nightly."

Productions: *Disgrace*, by John O'Keefe (sexual captivity); *Goose and Tomtom*, by David Rabe (dream world gangsters); *Vinegar Tom*, by Caryl Churchill (witch trials).

DELAWARE THEATRE COMPANY, P.O. Box 516, Wilmington DE 19899. (302)594-1104. Artistic Director: Cleveland Morris. Play producer. Estab. 1978. Produces 1 play and 1 musical/year; number of new musicals depends on season. Plays are performed for a general audience at Delaware Theatre Company, a 300-seat auditorium with thrust stage. Pays 5-12% royalty. Query with synopsis, character breakdown and set description. SASE. Reports in 6 months.

Musical Theater: "We are interested in general adult material, suitable to be performed along with few straight plays in a subscription series." Cast limitation, 12; orchestra size, 5; moderate sets, props, etc. Would consider original music for use in a play being developed or for use in a pre-existing play.
Productions: *Cash Flow*, by D.B. Gilles (drama); *Three Guys Naked from the Waist Down*, by Rupert/Colker (musical); and *The Foreigner*, by Larry Shue (comedy).
Tips: "Submit a piece ready for fast production; we do not have a sufficiently long rehearsal period for major revisions."

DEPARTMENT OF THEATRE, MICHIGAN STATE UNIVERSITY, East Lansing MI 48824-1120. (517)353-5169. Producer/Director: Dr. Jon Baisch. Produces 7-10 plays and 4-6 musicals (1-2 new musicals), 4-6 large scale and small revue musicals/year. Payment negotiable. "Our audiences are students, faculty, and members of the Lansing community. We use 8 theatres, ranging from 100 to 2,500 seats, including proscenium, platform, arena, and cabaret theatre types. We stage everything from large-scale productions with orchestra and large casts to small-cast, intimate shows and cabaret entertainment. We seek both adult and children's shows, all types for a variety of audiences. We often use original music composed by faculty or students in MSU's School of Music. They are available to us for the whole term of rehearsal and production." Performance rights negotiable. Query with synopsis and production specifications. SASE. Reports in 1 month.
Musical Theater: "We are interested in all types of new musicals. However, we are espcially interested in small cast revues and book shows for cabaret and summer theatre productions, and unusual material for our small arena and studio theatres."
Productions: *South Pacific, Wonderful Town* and *Pirates of Penzance*.
Tips: "Write a good, modern show. Either write a good story or find one to adapt. The public—much of it—still wants a story."

STEVE DOBBINS PRODUCTIONS (formerly Illustrated Stage Company), 25 Van Ness Ave., San Francisco CA 94102. Executive Director: Mike Lojkoviz. Play producer. Estab. 1978. Produces 4 plays and 1 new musical/year. Plays performed for San Francisco Bay Area audiences. Pays 5% royalty. Query with synopsis, character breakdown, set description and tape of songs. SASE. Reports in 3 months.
Musical Theater: "We seek all types of material as long as the ideas are new. No formula scripts." Would consider original music for use in a play being developed.
Productions: *Dylan Thomas*, by Kevin Reilly (life of the poet); *Doo Wop*, (Black musical); *Dan White Incident*, by Steve Dobbins (actual recreational of the Dan White case); and *With Relish*, by Morris Bobrow (food).
Tips: "Write to us explaining your idea."

THE DRAMATIC PUBLISHING COMPANY, 311 Washington St., Woodstock IL 60098. (815)338-7170. Music Editor: Dana Smith. Play publisher. Publishes 35 plays (3-5 musicals)/year. Estab. 1885. Plays used by community theaters, little theaters, high schools, colleges, stock and professional theaters, churches and camps. Pays standard royalty. Submit complete manuscript, score and tape of songs. SASE. Reports in 5 months.
Musical Theater: Seeking "children's musicals not over 1¼ hours, and adult musicals with 2 act format. No adaptations for which the rights to use the original work have not been cleared. If directed toward high school market, large casts with many female roles are preferred. For professional, stock and community theater small casts are better. Cost of producing a play is always a factor to consider in regard to costumes, scenery and special effects." Would also consider original music for use in a pre-existing play "if we or the composer hold the rights to the non-musical work."
Publications: *Ginger*, book, lyrics by Ronald Alexander, music by Diane Leslie (musical comedy); *Charlotte's Web*, (E.B. White's Story) book by Joseph Robinette, music and lyrics by Charles Strouse; and *Cotton Patch Gospel*, music lyrics score by Harry Chapin, book by Tomkey and Russell Tveyz (contemporary retelling of books of Matthew and John).

EAST WEST PLAYERS (EWP), 4424 Santa Monica Blvd., Los Angeles CA 90029. (213)660-0366. Managing Director: Michele Garza. A non-profit professional theatre. Estab. 1965. Produces 4-5 plays and 1 musical (new musicals occasionally, "but welcomes submissions")/year. "The primary mission of EWP is to produce new plays by Asian American playwrights, but we also do one musical per year and western plays.80% Asian American audience, 20% mixed." Pays by outright purchase, $500-750, more if production is extended beyond normal 6-week run. Submit complete manuscript, score and tape of songs. SASE. Reports in 2 months.
Musical Theater: "We want contemporary themes—Asian and Asian American focus. Nothing too cute. We welcome musicals that have a small to medium size cast. Age ranges of actors should be early 20's to early 60's only. No children's musicals. It would be wonderful if the writer could create a musical based on an Asian or Asian American theme (M. Butterfly, Pacific Overtures, etc.). We would consider original music for use in a play being developed or for use in a pre-existing play. Many

of our plays involve music/sound effects. Music is used as a directorial emphasis or trasition tool."

Productions: *The Fantasticks*, by Tom Jones/Harvey Schmidt (a boy, a girl); *Laughter and False Teeth*, by Hirashi Kashiwagi (internment camps); and *Webster Street Blues*, by Warren Kubota (70's youth play in San Francisco's Japantown).

Tips: "Be creative and more specifically, find out what kind of plays we do before submitting your work to us."

ECCENTRIC CIRCLES THEATRE, 400 W. 43rd St., #4N, New York NY 10036. (212)564-3798. Artistic Director: Rosemary Hopkins. Play producer. Estab. 1978. Produces 3 plays and 1 new musical/year. "Plays and musicals are preformed at a designated theatre rented by ECT. Audience is generally all ages, and from New York." Query with synopsis, character breakdown and set description. SASE. Reports in 6 weeks. "We have a small set and small cast. We are open to all topics and styles including children's musicals. We don't want puppet shows."

Productions: *Natural Causes*, by Lilian Lieblich (new comedy).

Tips: "Be open for comments and changes and adapt to a small budget and small theatre situation."

ELDRIDGE PUBLISHING CO., INC., P.O. Box 216, Franklin OH 45005. (513)746-6531. Editor: Nancy S. Vorhis. Play publisher. Estab. 1906. Publishes 20 plays and 2-3 musicals/year. Seeking "large cast musicals which appeal to students. We like variety and originality in the music, easy staging and costuming. We serve the school and church market, 4th grade through 12th; also Christmas musicals for churches." Would also consider original music for use in a play being developed; "music could make an ordinary play extraordinary." Pays 35% royalty, $150-500 for outright purchase or 10% copy sales. Submit tape with manuscript if at all possible. SASE. Reports in 3 months.

Productions: *Dogs!*, by Hamlett/Simpson (homeless dogs); *6 Myths of Christmas*, by Linda Pou (animals at the manger); and *Spring Is Not So Far*, by Allen/Elizabeth Snair (children rescue spring).

Tips: "We prefer musicals be test produced. Have your church youth group or your child's class perform it, if possible. That way you'll work out any bugs before we even see it."

EMPIRE STATE INSTITUTE FOR THE PERFORMING ARTS (ESIPA), Empire State Plaza, Albany NY 12223. (518)443-5222. Literary Manager: James Farrell. Play producer. Produces approximately 5 plays (2 new musicals)/year. Plays performed for student audiences grades K-12, family audiences and adult audiences. Two theaters: main theater seats 950 with full stage, studio theater seats 450 with smaller stage. Pay negotiable. Submit complete manuscript and tape of songs. SASE. Reports in 3-4 months.

Musical Theater: Looking for "intelligent and well-written book with substance, a score that enhances and supplements the book and is musically well-crafted and theatrical. Length: up to 2 hours. Could be play with music, musical comedy, musical drama or opera. Excellence and substance in material is essential. Cast could be up to 25; orchestra size up to 15. No incomplete scripts and scores."

Productions: *Pied Piper*, by Adrian Mitchell/Dominic Muldowney (musical adaptation of the classic tale); *The Snow Queen*, by Adrian Mitchell/Richard Peaslee (musical adaptation of the Andersen fairy tale).

Tips: "There is a great need for musicals that are well-written with intelligence and substance which are suitable for family audiences."

THE EMPTY SPACE THEATRE, P.O. Box 1748, Seattle WA 98111-1748. (206)587-3737. Literary Manager: Kurt Beattie. Play producer. Estab. 1974. Produces 5 plays and varying number of new musicals/year. "We have a subscription audience, mainly composed of professionals. We produce in our own theatre." Pays by royalty. Query with synopsis, character breakdown and set description. SASE. Reports in 4 months.

Musical Theater: "We want broadly comic, satirical or political pieces and all musical idioms, from classical to whatever is the current end of the musical spectrum. We have no limitations, though we rarely produce more than one large cast show per year. We don't want old-fashioned show biz yawners, or yuppie angst. We regularly employ composers/sound designers."

Productions: *Laughing Wild*, by Christopher Durang; *Etta Jenks*, by Marlane Meyer; and *Speed-The-Plow*, by David Mamet.

Tips: "Avoid musical-comedy formulae."

*ENCORE PERFORMANCE PUBLISHING, P.O. Box 692, Orem UT 84057. (801)225-0605. Editor: Michael C. Perry. Play publisher. Estab. 1979. Publishes 5-12 plays (including musicals)/year. "We are interested in plays which emphasize strong family values and play to all ages of audience." Pays by royalty; 50% performance, 10% book. Query with synopsis, character breakdown and set description then submit complete manuscript, score and tape of songs. SASE. Reports in 6 weeks to 3 months.

Musical Theater: Musicals of all types for all audiences. Can be original or adapted. "We tend to favor shows with at least an equal male/female cast." Do not wish to see works that can be termed offensive or vulgar. However, experimental theater forms are also of interest.
Productions: *Children of the Universe*, by Paul Morse (child self-worth); *Let It Ring!*, by Margaret Smoot, K. Newell Dayley and Michael McLean (patriotic musical); and *Gammer Gurtons Needle*, by Vern Adix (1 hour version of classic).
Tips: "Always write with an audience in mind."

*GEOF ENGLISH, PRODUCER, Saddleback College, 28000 Marguerite Pkwy., Mission Viejo CA 92692. (714)582-4763. Performing Arts Director: Geofrey English. Play producer for musical theater. Produces 9 musicals (six new musicals)/year. Community audience of mostly senior citizens. Pays by royalty and performance. Submit complete manuscript, score and tape of songs. SASE. Reports in 2 months.
Musical Theater: Looking for mainly family musicals. Have no limitations am open to options. It is important that music must be sent along with scripts. Best not to call. Just send materials.
Productions: *Mrs. Warren's Profession*, by George Bernard Shaw; *Night Must Fall*, by Emlyn Williams; and *Shooting Stars*, by Molly Newman.
Tips: "Submit materials in a timely manner—usually at least one year in advance."

*ENSEMBLE THEATRE OF CINCINNATI, 1127 Vine St., Cincinnati OH 45210. (513)421-3556. Artistic Director: David A. White III. Play producer. Estab. 1986. Produces 6 plays (3 new musicals in 5 years)/year. "We are dedicated to the development of new works. We produce a 6 show season in a beautifully renovated 130-seat 3/4 thrust theater." Pays $600-1,000 outright purchase.
How to Contact: Submit complete manuscript, score and tape of songs. SASE. Reports in 2 months.
Musical Theater: Adult-oriented, risk-taking, simple set, cast of 6-10, with a simple orchestration. Material should be submitted in September or October for consideration for upcoming season.
Productions: *Gifts of the Magi*, by Randy Counts (adult Christmas); *20 Years Ago Today*, by David A. White III (adult rock); *Telme Tales*, by Kate Dahlgren (children's adventure).

*THE FIREHOUSE THEATRE, 11 and Jackson, Omaha NE 68102. (402)346-6009. Artistic Director: Dick Mueller. Play producer. Estab. 1972. Producer 6 plays and 1-2 musicals/year. General audience. Pays royalty. Query with synopsis, character breakdown and set description. Submit complete ms, score and tape of songs. SASE.
Musical Theater: General interest. "We are a small house of 289 seats. Budget is what limits the scale of production."
Productions: *Shakespeare And The Indians*, by Dale Wasserman, *Battle Hymn* and *Red Dawg*, by Leland Ball.

FLORIDA STUDIO THEATRE, 1241 N. Palm Ave., Sarasota FL 34236. (813)366-9017. Director of New Play Development: Carolyn Michal. Play producer. Produces 2 plays and 2 musicals/year. "Florida Studio Theatre is a professional, non-profit theatre. It seats 165 and has limited technical abilities. The audience is generally comprised of well-educated people over 50 years of age. FST subscribers expect innovative, contemporary theatre." Pays by royalty. "Workshop productions receive $200 honorarium." Query with synopsis, character breakdown and set description. SASE. Reports in 2 months on queries, 7 months on manuscripts.
Musical Theater: "FST is looking for smaller cast musicals and cabaret musicals. We prefers innovative or off-beat shows. The stage is small. There is no pit. In the past we have had a 3 person musical combo. Send letter of inquiry first with SASE. A tape included with the script and score is helpful." Would also consider original music for use in pre-existing play. "Two of the straight plays we are putting on in the future will have original music underscoring."

*SAMUEL FRENCH, INC., 45 W. 25th St., New York NY 10010. (212)206-8990. Editor: Lawrence Harbison. Play publisher. Estab. 1830. Publishes 90-100 plays and 5-6 new musicals/year. Amateur and professional theaters. Pays 80% of amateur royalties; 90% of professional royalties. Query first, then submit complete ms and tape of songs. SASE. Reports in 6 weeks to 8 months.
Musical Theater: "We publish primarily successful musicals from the NYC stage." Don't submit large-cast, big "Broadway" musicals—which haven't been done on Broadway.
Productions: *Starmites*, by Keating and Ross; *Me and My Girl*, by various; and *Mail*, by Colker and Rupert.

*THE WILL GEER THEATRICUM BOTANICUM, Box 1222, Topanga CA 90290. (213)455-2322. Artistic Director: Ellen Geer. Play producer. Produces 3 plays (1 musical)/year. Plays are performed in "large outdoor amphitheater with 60'x 25' wooden stage. Rustic setting." Pays by royalty or per performance.

Query with synopsis, character breakdown and set description. SASE. Submit scripts from September through December.

Musical Theater: Seeking social or biographical works, children's works, full length or 1 act musicals with cast of up to 10 equity actors (the rest non-equity). Requires "low budget set and costumes. We emphasize paying performers." Would also consider original music for use in a play being developed. Does not wish to see "anything promoting avarice, greed, violence or apathy."

Productions: *Dory! A Musical Portrait!* (adapted from writings of Dory Previn); *Women and Other People* (adapted women's writing and lyrics); *Americana* (adapted writings of great poets, politicians and characters in American history); and *Pie In The Sky*, lyrics and music by Peter Alsop.

Tips: "Reach us with idea and show enthusiasm for theater."

GEORGE STREET PLAYHOUSE, 9 Livingston Ave., New Brunswick NJ 08901. (201)846-2895. Associate Artistic Director: Wendy Liscow. Producing Director: Gregory Hurst. Produces 7 plays, including 1 musical and 1 new musical/year. "We are a 367-seat thrust theater and 100-seat black box, working under a LORT C-contract with a 5,500 subscriber base." Fees vary. "Each situation is handled individually." Query with synopsis, character breakdown and set description. SASE. Reports in 2 months.

Musical Theater: Seeking musical adaptations. "We are interested in a variety of themes and formats. We aren't seeking to limit the things we read."

Productions: *Greetings*, by Tom Dudzick; *Pendragon*, by Laurie Hutzler; and *Forgiving Typhoid Mary*, by Mark St.Germain (all new plays).

*GREAT AMERICAN CHILDREN'S THEATRE COMPANY, 304 E. Florida, Milwaukee WI 53204. (414)788-2188. Managing Director: Annie Jurczyk. Play producer. Estab. 1976. Produces 1 or 2 plays and 1 musical/year. Has done new musicals in the past. Audience is school age children. Pays a negotiable royalty. Query with synopsis, character breakdown and set description. Does not return unsolicited material. Reports as quickly as possible, "depending on our workload."

Musical Theater: Children's musicals. Average cast size is 13. No adult productions. "We have used original music as background for our plays."

Productions: *Charlie & the Chocolate Factory*, by Roald Dahl (children's story); *Charlotte's Web*, by Joseph Robinette (children's story); and *Cinderella*, by Moses Goldberg (children's story).

Tips: "Persevere! Although we don't use a lot of musicals, we will consider one that is of excellent quality."

GREEN MOUNTAIN GUILD, Box 659, Pittsfield VT 05762. (802)746-8320. Managing Director: Marjorie O'Neill-Butler. Play producer. Estab. 1971. Produces 10 plays (6 musicals)/year. Produces plays for a summer theater audience in Killington, Vermont. Pays $75 minimum/performance. Query with synopsis. Send script and cassette with music. SASE. Reports in 1 month.

Musical Theater: "We are looking for musicals with a small cast, a good story line, well-developed characters, songs and music that come naturally out of the story and music that works with piano and drums only." No frivolous material. Prefers one-set shows.

Productions: *Jenny Lind*, by David Harvey (an original play); *Sweeney Todd*, by Stephen Sondheim; *Student Prince*, by Sigmund Romberg; *Naughty Marietta*, by Victor Herbert; and *Hello Dolly*, by Jerry Herman.

HERITAGE ARTISTS AT THE MUSIC HALL, Box 586, Cohoes NY 12047. (518)235-7909. Producing Director: Robert W. Tolan. Play producer. Estab. 1982. Produces 6 plays and 6 musicals (1-3 new musicals)/year. "We perform a subscription series of small and/or principal musicals in the 250-300 seat Cohoes Music Hall." Pays negotiable royalty per performance. Submit synopsis, character breakdown and tape. SASE. Reports in 8 weeks.

Musical Theater: Seeking "adult themes, plays with music, review/cabaret shows and children's musicals." Requires "smaller casts."

Productions: *Baby*, by Pearson, Maltby, Shire (parenthood); *Billy Bishop Goes to War*, by John Gray, Eric Peterson (WWI air ace); *The Wonder Years*, by David Levy, et.al. (baby boom); and *Theda Bara and the Frontier Rabbi*, by Johnston and Hochhauser (silent film era).

HEUER PUBLISHING CO./ART CRAFT PUBLISHING CO., Box 248, Cedar Rapids IA 52406. (319)364-6311. Publisher: C. Emmett McMullen. Play publisher. Estab. 1928. "We sell exclusively to junior and senior high school groups throughout the U.S. and Canada; individually, some church and related groups." Pays by royalty or by outright purchase. Query with synopsis, character breakdown and set description. SASE. Reports in 2 months.

Musical Theater: "We prefer comedies with a large number of characters. All material must be suitable for high school production and be within the scope of high school actors. We do not publish individual music. All music should be within the play material."

HIP POCKET THEATRE, 1627 Fairmount Ave., Ft. Worth TX 76104-4237. (817)927-2833. Producer: Diane Simons. Play producer. Produces 10 plays/year (4 new musicals). Estab. 1977. "Our audience is an eclectic mix of Ft. Worth/Dallas area residents with multi levels of incomes and backgrounds. Payment varies according to type of script, reputation of playwright, etc." Query with synopsis, character breakdown and set description; "please include tape if possible." Reports in 1 month.
Musical Theater: "We are not interested in cabaret revues, but rather in full-length pieces that can be for adults and/or children. We tend to produce more fanciful, whimsical musicals (something not likely to be found anywhere else), but would also consider political pieces. Basically, we're open for anything fresh and well-written. We require no more than 15 in a cast, and a staging would have to adapt to an outdoor environmental thrust stage." Would also consider original music for use in a play being developed.
Productions: *R. Crumb Comix*, by Robert Crumb (underground cartoons and comic strips from the 60's and 70's); *Molemo!*, by Johnny Simons and Douglas Balentine (autobiographical memory journey); and *Shazam!*, by Johnny Simons and Douglas Balentine (original musical serialization of the Captain Marvel stories)..
Tips: "Think creative, complex thoughts and musical visions that can be transformed into reality by creative, visionary musicians in theaters that rarely have the huge Broadway dollar Star Wars extravaganza, and infinitely harder to pull off. Cast size must be kept to a minimum (no more than 15)."

JEWISH REPERTORY THEATRE, 344 E. 14th St., New York NY 10003. (212)674-7200. Director: Ron Avni. Associate Director: Edward M. Cohen. Play producer. Estab. 1974. Produces 5 plays and 1-2 new musicals/year. Pays 6% royalty. Submit complete manuscript, score and tape of songs. SASE. Reports in 4 weeks.
Musical Theater: Seeking "musicals in English relating to the Jewish experience. No more than 8 characters. We do commission background scores for straight plays."
Productions: *Kumi—Leml* (musical farce); *The Special* (musical comedy); and *The Shop on Main Street* (musical drama).

*KAWARTHA FESTIVAL, P.O. Box 161, Lindsay, Ontario K9V 4S1 **Canada**. Artistic Director: Brian Tremblay. Play producer. Estab. 1964. Produces 6 plays, 1 musical and 1 new musical/year. "Ours is a 'vacation' audience. The plays are produced at the Academy Theatre (682 seats)." Pays 10% royalty. Query first. SASE.
Musical Theater: "Two-act material is what we look for. Light in nature with a small cast. Nothing over 6 performers. Nothing of a heavy nature or with a large cast."
Productions: *Noel & Gertie*, by Tom Kneebone (musical review) and *Mercer Beaucoup*, by Jack Northmore (musical review).
Tips: "Allow at least one year advance on project."

THE LAMB'S THEATRE CO., 130 W. 44th St., New York NY 10036. (212)997-0210. Literary Manager: Carlotta Scarmack. Play producer. Estab. 1984. Produces 3-4 plays and 1 or 2 new musicals/year. Plays are performed for "the off-Broadway theatre audience, also group sales including school programs from New York public high schools and colleges in the area." Pays 6% royalty. Query with synopsis, character breakdowns and set description. SASE. Reports in 6 months.
Musical Theater: "We are looking for full length musicals that are entertaining, but moving, and deal with serious issues as well as comic situations. No one act plays. Large-cast epics are out. Both our spaces are intimate theatres, one an 85-seat black box space and one a 385-seat proscenium. Material with explicit sex and nudity and plays which require large amounts of obscene language are not appropriate for this theatre. We require a small orchestra in a musical." Would also consider original music for use in a play being developed; "we have hired a composer for music in our current production:*St. Hugo of Central Park*."
Productions: *Godspell* by Stephen Schwartz (gospel of Matthew); *Johnny Pye & The Foolkiller* by R. Courts/M. St. Germain (original musical based on Stephen V. Benet short story); *The Gifts of the Magi* by R. Courts/M. St. Germain (original musical based on O. Henry short stories).

*LOS ANGELES DESIGNERS' THEATRE, P.O. Box 1883, Studio City CA 91614-0883. (818)769-900 or (213)650-9600. Artistic Director: Richard Niederberg. Play producer. Estab. 1970. Produces 20-25 plays, 8-10 musicals/year. Plays are produced at several locations, primarily Studio City, California. Pays by royalty. Submit complete manuscript, score and tape of songs, character breakdown and set descriptions. Video tape submissions are also accepted. SASE. Reports in 3 months but faster if cassette of show is included with script.
Musical Theater: "We seek out controversial material. Street language okay, nudity is fine, religious themes, social themes, political themes are encouraged. Our audience is very 'jaded' as it consists of TV, motion picture and music publisher executives who have 'seen it all.' " Does not wish to see bland, "safe" material. We like first productions. "In the the cover letter state in great detail the proposed

involvement of the songwriter, other than as a writer (i.e. director, actor, singer, publicist, designer, etc.). Also, state if there are any liens on the material or if anything has been promised."
Productions: *Offenbach in the Underworld*, by Frederick Grab (biography w/can-can); *Is Nudity Required*, by Stephen Oakley (comedy); and *Wonderful World of Waiver?* (backstage musical). Also *Vine Street*, by H.D. Parkin III (street musical with film/video elements); and *Hostages* (political musical).
Tips: "Send me a script and a cassette, and be obsessed with your desire to see your show be a success."

*JAN McART'S CABARET THEATRE, P.O. Box 4866, Key West FL 33040. (305)296-2120. General Manager: M. Scott Stander. Play producer. Estab. 1979. Produces 2 play and 4 musicals (1 new musical)/year. "We are in a tourist town—anything goes." Payment for each submission is negotiable.
How to Contact: Submit complete manuscript, score and tape of songs. SASE. Reports in 1 month.
Musical Theater: "We are open for anything (we produce all different types of theater. We do prefer small casts."
Productions: *Prince of Central Park*, by Evan Rhodes (New York—Broadway-Belasco); *Daddy's All Pupose*, by Tom Rothchild (family African princess); *Americas her Name*, by Gene Bone and Howard Fenton (tribute to America), original cast recording.

*DON AND PAT MACPHERSON, 461 Parkway, Gatlinburg TN 37738. (615)436-4039. Co-owners/ producers: Don MacPherson and Pat MacPherson. Play producer. Estab. 1977. Produces 2 musicals/ year. Plays are performed at Sweet Fanny Adams Theatre, Gatlinburg, Tennessee to tourist audience. Pays $100-200/week. Query with synopsis, character breakdown and set description. SASE. Reports in 1 month.
Musical Theater: Produce musicals that are funny, fast—in fact, silly; musical farces. Theater is 1890 style so shows should fit that period. Have done many westerns. Cast size limited to 7 or 8 with 2 musicians. Stage very small. Use old-time backdrops forsets. Shows should be no longer than 90 minutes. Does not wish to see shows that would not fit 1890s style—unless it had a country theme.
Productions: *Phantom of the Opry*, by Don & Pat MacPherson/J. Lovensheimer (spoof of *Phanton of the Opera*); *Life & Times of Billy Kincaid*, by MacPherson/Lovensheimer (western); and *Not Quite Snow White*, by MacPherson/Lovensheimer (fairytale).
Tips: "See a production at Sweet Fanny Adams."

MAGNIFICENT MOORPARK MELODRAMA AND VAUDEVILLE CO., 45 E. High St., Moorpark CA 93021. (805)529-1212. Producer: Linda Bredemann. Play producer. Estab. 1982. Produces 7 plays and 6-7 new musicals/year. "Our audience is family and church groups, ages 2 to 90." Pays by royalty, outright purchase or per performance. Submit complete manuscript, score and tape of songs. SASE. Reports in 12 months.
Musical Theater: "We want plays set in any era, but must have a villain to boo—hero to cheer— heroine to ahh. Each act should run no more than 1 hour with a 2 act maximum. We want family- oriented comedies only. Cast should be no more than 20. We have a small stage (30×30). We don't want obscene, vulgar or off-color material. We want up beat music—can be popular songs or old time."
Productions: *Robin Hood*, by Tim Kelly; *Cinderella Meets the Wolfman*, by Tim Kelly (fairy tale); and *Sourdough*, by Dexter Fisch (Western).
Tips: "Have fun. Make the characters memorable, lovable and believable. Make the music tuneful and something to hum later."

MANHATTAN THEATRE CLUB, 453 W. 16th St., New York NY 10011. (212)645-5590. Director of Script Department: Kate Loewald. Artistic Associate: Jonathan Alper. Play producer. Estab. 1971. Produces 9 plays and sometimes 1 musical/year. Plays are performed at the Manhattan Theatre Club before varied audiences. Pays negotiated fee. Query with synopsis, "5-10 page libretto and lyric sam- ple." SASE. Reports in 6 months.
Musical Theater: "Small cast, original work. *No* historical drama, verse drama or children's plays." Will consider original music for use in a play being developed or in a pre-existing play.
Productions: *Real Life Funnies*, by Alan Menken and Howard Ashman (topical New York City); *Livin' Dolls*, by Scott Wittman and Marc Shaiman; *Ain't Misbehavin'*, by Fats Waller and Richard Maltby; *On the Swing Shift*, by Michael Dansicker and Sarah Schlesinger; *Urban Blight*, by Richard Maltby, Jr., David Shire and others; and *1-2-3-4-5*, by Maury Yeston and Larry Gelbart.

MERIWETHER PUBLISHING, LTD. (CONTEMPORARY DRAMA SERVICE), 885 Elkton Dr., Colorado Springs CO 80907. (303)594-4422. Editor/President: Arthur Zapel. Play publisher. Estab. 1968. Pub- lishes 35 plays and 5-10 musicals (5 new musicals)/year. "We publish musicals for church school elementary, middle grade and teens. We also publish musicals for high school secular use. Our musicals are performed in churches or high schools." Pays 10% royalty or by negotiated sale from royalties. "Sometimes we pay a royalty to a limited maximum." Query with synopsis, character breakdown and set description or submit script with cassette tape of songs. SASE. Reports in 2 months.

Musical Theater: "We are always looking for good church/school musicals for children. We prefer a length of 15-20 minutes, though occasionally we will publish a 3-act musical adaptation of a classic with large casts and sets. We like informal styles, with a touch of humor, that allow many children and/or adults to participate. We like musicals that imitate Broadway shows or have some name appeal based on the Classics. Box office appeal is more critical than message—at least for teenage and adult level fare. Musical scripts with piano accompaniments only. We especially welcome short, simple musicals for elementary and teenage, church use during the holidays of Christmas and Easter. We would like to know of arrangers and copyists."

Productions: *Bicycles Built For Two*, by Peg Kehret and Art Wiggins (comedy); *The Velveteen Rabbit*, by Larry Nestor and Gary Peterson (children's show); and *A Maiden's Plight*, by Eric Stonerook (melodrama-comedy).

Tips: "Keep the music manageable for unprofessional performers. Keep music book costs to a minimum in terms of arrangements and copy or engraving expenses. We will look only at materials that are neatly presented and of professional quality. Anything not completely developed is returned immediately. If the musician can provide a camera-ready music score we are more inclined to publish the work. The competition with Broadway name musicals is great. New musicals must have competitive appeal."

*MILWAUKEE REPERTORY THEATER, 108 E. Wells St., Milwaukee WI 53202. (414)224-1761. Dramaturg: Robert Meiksins. Play producer. Estab. 1954. Produces 17 plays, 3-4 musicals (1-2 new musicals)/year. "The space is a 106 seat cabaret with a very small playing area (8x28)." Pays by royalty. Send script and/or cassette. SASE. Reports in 3-4 months.

Musical Theater: "Cast size must be limited to 3 singers/performers with minimum movement. Suitable for cabaret. Must appeal to a broad adult audience and should not run longer than 1 hour. We also seek to explore a multi-cultural diversity of material."

Productions: *A Little Tom Foolery*, by Tom Lehrer (political satire); *Jukejointjammin*, by R. Meiksins & B. Roberts (1930s jazz); and *A Gershwin Serenade*, by Larry Deckel (musical retrospective).

MUSIC-THEATRE GROUP INC., 735 Washington St., New York NY 10014. (212)924-3108. Managing Director: Diane Wondisford. Music-theatre producer. Produces 6 music-theatre pieces/year. Plays are performed "off-broadway in New York City; for summer audiences in Stockbridge, MA." Pays negotiable royalty or fees. Query with synopsis, character breakdown, set description and tape of music. SASE.

Musical Theater: "We don't actually seek developed properties, but examples of people's work as an indication of their talent in the event that we might want to suggest them for a future collaboration. The music must be a driving element in the work. We generally require not more than 10-12 in cast and a small band of 4-5."

Productions: *Cinderella/Cedrillon*, based on the opera by Jules Massenet; and *Juan Darien*, by Julie Taymor and Elliot Goldenthal.

MUSICAL THEATRE WORKS, INC., 440 Lafayette St., New York NY 10003. (212)677-0040. Literary Manager: Brook Randolph Garrett. Produces new musicals exclusively. Estab. 1983. 14 productions have transferred to Broadway, off-Broadway and regional theater. Produces 3-4 new musicals and 12-16 readings each season. Productions and readings are held at the Theatre at Saint Peter's Church, Citicorp Center. No payment for productions.Submit complete script, cassette tape of songs and SASE. Reply in 2-4 months.

Musical Theater: "We are seeking full-length book/avant-garde musicals which have never been produced. Fourteen cast maximum. Full, but modest productions in 164-seat modern off-Broadway theater for metropolitan NYC audience. Only completed projects will be considered for development."

Productions: *Midsummer Nights*, by Kevin Kuhn and Bryan D. Leys (a 60's Laguna Beach send-up of Shakespeare's fantasy); *Goose! Beyond the Nursery . . .*, by Mark Frawley, Scott Evans and Austin Tichenor (musical revue of Mother Goose characters dealing with the modern neuroses of the 90's); *Sugar Hill*, by Louis St. Louis, Roberto Fernandez and Tony Walsh (a musical drama chronicling the struggles of mother, daughter and grandaughter of a Harlem show business family).

NATIONAL MUSIC THEATER CONFERENCE, O'Neill Theater Center, 234 West 44th St., #901, New York NY 10036. (212)382-2790. Artistic Director: Paulette Haupt. "The Conference develops new music theater works." Estab. 1978. Develops 3-4 musicals each summer. "The O'Neill Theater Center is in Waterford, Connecticut. The audiences for the staged readings of works-in-progress are a combination of local residents, New York and regional theater professionals." Pays a stipend, room and board, and all costs of the workshops are covered. Query first. SASE. Response within 4 months.

Musical Theater: "The Conference is interested in all forms of music theater. Staged readings are presented with script in hand, minimal props, piano only. There are no cast limitations. We don't accept works which have been previously produced by a professional company."
Productions: *Hannah ... 1939*, by Bob Merrill; *The Real Life Story of Johnny de Facto*, by Douglas Post; *The Pig of Molette* by Sheldon Harnick and Thomas Shepard; and *Gunmetal Blues*, by Scott Wentworth, Marion Alder and Craig Bohmler.

*NATIONAL MUSIC THEATER NETWORK, INC., #1111, 1457 Broadway, New York NY 10036. (212)382-0984. President: Timothy Jerome. Service to evaluate new musical works and publish a catalogue of recommended works to play producers. "Our catalogue of recommended works is targeted to approximately 5,000 regional theaters and musical producers interested in presenting new works. Our 'sampler' series concerts feature excerpts from recommended works for the NYC area. In 1990-91 we will present 15 'sampler' concerts of recommended works. Producers contact us for creators' works. We contact creators and creators contact producers." Submit complete mansucript, score and tape of songs. Writers are required to "fill out our submission form plus $30 fee." SASE. Reports in 6 months.
Musical Theater: "We accept all styles. Take the time to present your materials neatly. We accept only *completed* musicals and operas, i.e. script/score/tape."
Tips: "Use us as a resource to help you market your work."

*THE NEW CONSERVATORY CHILDREN'S THEATRE COMPANY & SCHOOL, 25 Van Ness, San Francisco CA 94102. (415)861-4914. Executive Director: Ed Decker. Play producer. Estab. 1981. Produces about 5 plays and 1 or 2 musicals (1 new musical)/year. Audience includes families and community groups; children ages 14-19. "Performance spaces are 50-150 seat theater, but we also tour some shows. Pays $25-35 per performance. If we commission, playwright receives a commission for the initial run and royalties thereafter; otherwise playwright just gets royalties."
How to Contact: Query with synopsis, character breakdown and set description. SASE. Reports in 3 months.
Musical Theater: "We seek innovative and preferably socially relevant musicals for children and families, with relatively small cast (stage is small), in which all roles can be played by children. We have a small stage, thus cannot accomodate plays casting more than 10 or 12 people, and prefer relatively simple set requirements. Children cast are in the 9-19 age range. We do not want mushy, cute material. Fantasy is fine, as is something like Sendak & King's *Really Rosie*, but nothing gooey." "We are very interested in using original music for new or existing plays. Songwriters should submit a resume and perhaps a tape to let us know what they do."
Productions: *Consensus*, by Dylan Russell (American family); *Get Real!*, by Doug Holsclaw (AIDS education, age 9-12); *Kegger*, by Megan Terry (teen alcohol use).
Tips: "Be flexible, able to revise and open to suggestions!"

NEW THEATRE, P.O. Box 650696, Miami FL 33265. (305)595-4260. Executive Artistic Director: Rafael de Acha. Play producer. Estab. 1986. Produces 10 plays and 2 musicals (2 new musicals)/year. Audience is mixed urban South Florida, with median age of 35, mostly upper-class white and Hispanic. Pays by royalty. Query with synopsis, character breakdown and set description. SASE. Reports in 3 months.
Musical Theater: "Specifically small, revue-style musicals, such as *Brecht on Brecht*; *Side by Side*; *Oh, Coward*, etc. Also interested in experimental work along the lines of *Three Postcards*, etc. We perform in a 70-seat black box theater, with modest production values." Would consider original music for use in a play being developed, but "that kind of work requires the composer to be involved very heavily. We often use incidental music specially composed for a play and have also commissioned original works."
Productions: *Feiffer's People*, by Jules Feiffer (satire); *Dear Liar*, by Jerome Kilty (biographical play); *Spoon River Anthology*, by Edgar Lee Masters (play with music) and *You are Here*, by Susan Westfall and Bernard Harding.
Tips: "Keep lines of communication open."

NEW TUNERS THEATRE, Theatre Building, 1225 Belmont, Chicago IL 60657. (312)929-1367. Associate Producer: George Gorham. Play producer. Estab. 1968. Produces 3 musicals (3 new musicals)/year. "We play to mixed urban and suburban audiences. We produce in a 148-seat theater in the Theatre Building." Pays 6-12% royalty.

"How to Use Your Songwriter's Market" (at the front of this book) *contains comments and suggestions to help you understand and use the information in these listings.*

How to Contact: Submit complete manuscript and tape of songs. Score not necessary. SASE. Reports in 6 months.

Musical Theater: "We look at all types of musical theater, both traditional as well as more innovative forms. We have less interest in opera and operetta, but we will consider. We have no interest in children's theater. Fifteen is the maximum cast size we can consider and less is decidedly better. We work with a younger (35 and under) company of actors.

Productions: *A Change in the Heir*, by George Gorham and Daniel Sticco (Mark Twain short story); *Future of American Musical Theater*, by Charles Strouse (back-stage gossip); and *Charlie's Oasis Museum & Bar*, by Jane Boyd and Gregg Opelka (group effort to save a favorite bar); *Babes in Barns*, by John Carroll, Charlotte Samples and John Sparks (Mickey & Judy spoof).

Tips: "Go to the theater, study what uses music has served in the best of the musical theater. We see too many writers all making the same mistakes."

*NEW VIC SUPPER THEATRE, 755 S. Saginaw, Flint MI 48502. (313)235-8866. Executive/Artistic Director: Patricia Victor. Play producer. Estab. 1981. Produces 8-10 plays and 2-3 musicals/year. Audience is a wide range of dinner theater patrons from old to young. Half of the audience is generated by group sales. Perform on small proscenium with thrust. Query with synopsis, character breakdown and set description. SASE. Reports in six months.

Musical Theater: "We will look at most any style or topic of musical; 20-25 is top end of cast size. Staging is detailed but limited because of smaller stage. We will try and accommodate most shows." Will consider adding original music to an already existing show. Last season added original music to a production of Moliere's *The Miser*.

Productions: *1940s Radio Hour*, by Walton Jones; *Joseph and the Amazing Technicolor Dreamcoat*, by Andrew Lloyd Weber & Tim Rice; and *Olymus On My Mind*, by Barry Harmon & Grant Sturale.

Tips: "We have a pretty strong following that has built up with us in our eight years of existence. They are an older audience primarily, but getting younger all the time. Excessive swearing and strong sexual content should be avoided."

NEW VOICES: A WRITER'S THEATRE, 551 Tremont St., Boston MA 02116. (617)357-5667. Artistic Director: Stanley Richardson. Play producer. Conducts 12-20 readings, 4-5 studio proscripts and music."

NEW YORK THEATRE WORKSHOP, 18th Floor, 220 W. 42 St., New York NY 10036. (212)302-7737. Artistic Director: James C. Nicola. Play producer. Produces 4 mainstage plays and approximately 50 readings/year. "Plays are performed in the Perry Street Theatre, Greenwich Village. Audiences include: subscription/single ticket buyers from New York area, theater professionals, and special interest groups. Pays by artistic fees, approximately $5,400 total annually." Query with synopsis, character breakdown and set description. SASE. Reports in 3 months.

Musical Theater: "As with our non-musicals, we seek musicals of intelligence and social consciousness that challenge our perceptions of the world and the events which shape our lives. We favor plays that possess a strong voice, distinctive and innovative use of language and visual imagery. Integration of text and music is particularly of interest. Musicals which require full orchestrations would generally be too big for us. We prefer 'musical theater pieces' rather than straightforward 'musicals' per-se. We often use original music for straight plays that we produce. This music may be employed as pre-show, post-show or interlude music. If the existing piece lends itself, music may also be incorporated within the play itself. Large casts (12 or more) are generally prohibitive and require soliciting of additional funds. Design elements for our productions are of the highest quality possible with our limited funds—approximately budgets of $10,000 are allotted for our productions."

Productions: *The Waves*, adopted from Virginia Woolf's novel. Music and lyrics by David Bucknam. Text and direction by Lisa Peterson; and *My Children! My Africa*, by Athol Fugard.

Tips: "Submit a synopsis which captures the heart of your piece; inject your piece with a strong voice and intent and try to surprise and excite us."

*NORTH CAROLINA BLACK REPERTORY COMPANY, 610 Coliseum Dr., Winston-Salem NC 27106. (919)723-2266. Executive/Artistic Director: Larry Leon Hamlin. Play producer. Estab. 1979. Produces 4 plays and 2 musicals (1 new musical)/year. "Musicals are produced primarily for a Black audience but should also appeal to the general public. Performance in a 540 seat proscenium theater." Pays by royalty, by outright purchase or per performance. Query with synopsis, character breakdown and set description. Tape recording of songs should also be included. SASE. Reports in 4 months.

Musical Theatre: "Full length musicals are desired, even musicals for children. As well as being entertaining, musicals should support improving the quality of life for all humanity, offering solutions or alternatives to problems. The company prefers a cast of no larger than 15, but is not limited to that number." Will consider original music for a play in development or pre-existing play that would be used to set mood or enhance dramatic moments.

Productions: *Celebration*, by Larry Leon Hamlin (blues vs. gospel); *Night Voices*, by Ricardo Pitts-Wiley (friendship); and *Don't Bother Me, I Can't Cope*, by Micki Grant (humanity).
Tips: "Constant communication is important. Keeping Artistic Director aware of career progress."

*NORTHSIDE THEATRE COMPANY OF SAN JOSE, 848 E. William St., San Jose CA 95116. (408)288-7820. Artistic Director: Richard T. Orlando. Play producer. Estab. 1979. Produces 6 plays and 1 musical (1 new musical)/year. "Family entertainment, plays are performed at the Olinder Theatre." Pays by royalty. Query with synopsis, character breakdown and set description. SASE. Reports in 3 weeks.
Musical Theatre: "Classic family plays (with a twist or different concept)." Cast size: 10-15. Sets: Unit in concept with simple additions. Staging: proscenium with thrust. Small 90 seat theater fully equipped. "We are interested in new ideas and approaches. Production should have social relevancy." Will consider using original music for already existing plays. "Example: the underscoring of a Shakespeare piece. Next season we are doing *A Midsummer Nights Dream* and *A Christmas Carol*."
Productions: *A Christmas Carol*, by Charles Dickens (seasonal); *After the Rain*, by John Bowen (future civilization); and *Voices from the High School*, by Peter Dee (youth and their lives).
Tips: "Be aggressive, sell your idea and be able to work within the budget and limitations that the artistic director is confined to."

ODYSSEY THEATRE EMSEMBLE, 2055 S.Sepulveda Blvd., Los Angeles CA 90025. (213)477-2055. Literary Manager: Jan Lewis. Play producer. Estab. 1969. Produces 9 plays and 1-2 new musicals/year. "Our audience is predominantly over 35, upper middle-class, audience interested in eclectic brand of theater which is challenging and experimental." Pays by royalty (percentage to be negotiated). Query with synopsis, character breakdown and set description. Query should include resume(s) of artist(s) and tape of music. SASE. "Unsolicited material is not read or screened at all." Reports on query in 2 weeks; manuscript in 6 months.
Musical Theater: "We want nontraditional forms and provocative, unusual, challenging subject matter. We are not looking for Broadway-style musicals. Comedies should be highly stylized or highly farcical. Works should be full-length only and not requiring a complete orchestra (small band preferred.) Political material and satire are great for us. We're seeking interesting musical concepts and approaches. The more traditional Broadway-style musicals will generally not be done by the Odyssey. If we have a work in development that needs music, original music will often be used. In such a case, the writer and composer would work together during the development phase. In the case of a preexisting play, the concept would originate with the director who would select the composer."
Productions: *Symmes' Hole*, by Randolph Dreyfuss (search for the center of the earth); *Spring Awakening*, by Frank Wedekind (sexual awakening in youth); and *McCarthy*, by Jeff Goldsmith (Senator Joe McCarthy).
Tips: "Stretch your work beyond the ordinary. Look for compelling themes or the enduring questions of human existence. If it's a comedy, go for broke, go all the way, be as inventive as you can be."

OFF CENTER THEATRE, 1501 Broadway, New York NY 10036. (212)768-3277. Producer: Abigail McGrath. Play producer. Estab. 1968. Produces varying number of plays and new musicals/year. The plays are performed "off-Broadway." Pays percentage of box office receipts after initial expenses have been recouped. Submit complete manuscript, score and tape of songs. SASE. Reports in 1 month.
Musical Theater: Socially relevant. Not children/young audiences. Issue oriented, small cast.
Productions: *Just for Fun – The Music of Jerome Kern* (revue); *Biting the Apple*, by Tony McGrath and Stanley Seidman (revue); and *Hello, This Is Barbara, I'm Not in Right Now . . .* , by Barbara Schottenfeld (singles in New York City).
Tips: "Must be in New York City area for a length of time to work on a piece during readings and/or workshop – without guarantee of production."

OLD GLOBE THEATRE, Box 2171, San Diego CA 92112. (619)231-1941. Literary Manager: Mark Hofflund. Artistic Director: Jack O'Brien. Produces 12 or 13 plays/year, of which a varying number are musicals. "This is a regional theater with three spaces: 600-seat proscenium, 225-seat arena and large outdoor summer stage. We serve an national audience base of over 260,000." Query with synopsis and letter of introduction, or submit through agent or professional affiliation. No unsolicited material please. Reports in 6 months.
Musical Theater: "We look for skill first, subject matter second. No prescribed limitations, though creators should appreciate the virtues of economy as well as the uses of extravagance. Musicals have been produced on all three of our stages."
Productions: *Into The Woods*, by Stephen Sondheim and James Lapine; *Kiss Me Kate; A . . . My Name is Alice; Suds; Pump Boys and Dinettes; Marry Me a Little; White Linen*, by Stephen Metcalfe; and the premiere of *Heartbeats*, by Amanda McBroom.
Tips: "Craft comes first." (". . . and you still need a good book").

OMAHA MAGIC THEATRE, 1417 Farnam St., Omaha NE 68102. (402)346-1227. Artistic Director: Jo Ann Schmidman. Play producer. Estab. 1968. Produces 8 performance events with music/year. "Plays are produced in our Omaha facility and on tour throughout the midwest. Our audience is a cross-section of the community." Pays standard royalty or commissions. Query with synopsis, character breakdown and set description. SASE. Reports in 3 months.

Musical Theater: "We want the most avant of the avant garde—plays that never get written, or if written are buried deep in a chest because the writer feels there are not production possibilities in this nation's theatres. Plays must push form and/or content to new dimensions. The clarity of the playwright's voice must be strong and fresh. We don't want standard musical plays, naturalism, or realism. We should consider original music as sound structure and for lyrics."

Productions: *Headlights*, music by Luigi Waites & Frank Fongi, lyrics by Megan Terry (literacy in America); *Walking Through Walls*, music John J. Sheehan and Mark Nelson, lyrics by Jo Ann Schmidman and Megan Terry (walls we build around ourselves, courage, absolute truth); and *Babes Unchained*, music by John J. Sheehan, book and lyrics by Schmidman & Terry (struggle to achieve a greater sense of freedom).

THE OPEN EYE: NEW STAGINGS, 270 W. 89th St., New York NY 10024. (212)769-4143. Artistic Director: Amie Brockway. Play producer. Estab. 1972. Produces 9 one-acts, 5-6 full length or new stagings for youth; varying number of new musicals. "Plays are performed in a well-designed and pleasant theater seating 115 people." Pays on a fee basis or by commission. "We are pleased to accept unsolicited play manuscripts under the following conditions: 1) The script must be clean (no pencil marks, magic markers, paste overs, etc.). 2) It must be bound. 3) A self-addressed stamped envelope must be enclosed for each manuscript's return. Also keep in mind: the best time for submission is from April through July. We receive many scripts, and reading takes time. Please allow three to six months for a response. Please do not send synopses of your plays. Instead, please consider carefully whether you think your play is something New Stagings should read, and if it is, send the complete script."

Musical Theater: "New Stagings is committed to innovative collaboration and excellence in performance of both classic and new material, presenting the finest of professional talents—established artists and relative newcomers alike. We produce plays which invite us as artists and audience to take a fresh look at ourselves and the world of which we are a part. We seek to involve the performers and the audience in the live theater experience. And we are making a concerted effort to reach new audiences, young and old, and of all ethnic backgrounds. New Stagings for Youth is a not-for-profit professional theater company whose aim is to develop new theater audiences by producing plays for children and young people. New Stagings Lab offers opportunities to performing artists (directors, playwrights, actors, dancers, musicians) to develop new theater pieces through a program of rehearsed readings and workshops. Our stage is roughly 20' x 25' which limits the size of the set, cast and other related details and also, we do not have the height for a fly system. We seldom do political or propaganda related plays. We frequently use music to enhance a script, as well as performing plays with music in them, and also musicals. We believe in using various forms of art (music, movement) in most of our productions."

Productions: *The Nightingale*, by William Electric Black, composed by Elliot Sokolov (based on Hans Christian Anderson tale); *The Odyssey*, by Amie Brockway, composed by Elliot Sokolov (based on Homer's tale); and *The Sun Gets Blue*, by William Electric Black, composed by Paul Shapiro (Harlem in a black-out).

Tips: "Come see our work."

*OZARK ACTORS THEATRE, P.O. Box K, Rolla MO 65401. (314)364-9523. Artistic Director: F. Reed Brown. Play roducer. Estab. 1987. Produces 3 plays and 1 musical/year. South-central Missouri is a rural (primarily agricultural) area. O.A.T. is located in Rolla, which houses the Univesity of Missouri-Rolla. Pays by royalty. Query with snyopsis, character breakdown and set description. SASE. Reports in 2-3 months.

Musical Theatre: "Virtually any subject is desired. We look for shows/musicals that will fit into a summer stock season. Musicaltheatre. No opera." Primarily small casts (not to exceed 15). Relatively small (unit) sets. Without major technical requirements. "O.A.T. does not wish to produce material which might be viewed controversial. Such as strong sexual, racial or political views. No strong language." Will consider original music for work already in progress. "We produced an original work entitled *Voices* with writings by Van Gogh, Thoreau, Emily Dickenson, Ann Frank and Helen Keller. The score composer is Alan Johnson."

Productions: *Voices*, compiled by Fred Brown, music by Alan Johnson (life, death, criticism); *I Do! I Do!*, by Schmidt/Jones (marriage); and *The Boys Next Door* by Tom Griffin (the mentally handicapped).

PAPER MILL PLAYHOUSE, Brookside Dr., Milburn NJ 07041. (201)379-3636. Executive Producer: Angelo Del Rossi. Contact: Maryan F. Stephens, Literary Advisor. Play producer. Produces 2 plays and 4 musicals (1 new musical)/year. "Audience based on 40,000 subscribers; plays performed in 1,192-seat proscenium theatre." Pays negotiable royalty or will option play under Dramatist Guild. "A synopsis of book plus tape of songs should be submitted first. Scores not necessary. Letter of introduction should accompany each submitted synopsis." SASE. Letter in 2 weeks, response in 6 months.

Musical Theater: Seeking "traditional Broadway sized musicals — either original or adaptations. One act plays are not considered. Developing works can be submitted to our musical workshop series. No cast size limitations — minimum of 5 characters usually to maximum size of 40-45." No nudity, profanity, etc.

Productions: (1989-90 Season) *42nd Street*, by Harry Warren, Al Dubin, Michael Steward and Mark Bramble; *Rhythm Ranch*, by Hal Hackady and Fred Stark; *The Cocktail Hour*, by A.R. Gurney; *Steel Magnolias*, by Robert Harling; *Fanny*, by S.N. Behrman, Joshua Logan and Harold Rome; *Mikado Inc.*, by Robert Johanson, Jane Waterhouse and Albert Evans.

Tips: "New musicals are sought for our Musical Theatre Project development program, which includes a series of staged readings and laboratory (workshop)."

PENNSYLVANIA STAGE COMPANY, 837 Linden St., Allentown PA 18101. (215)434-8570. Production Manager: Peter Wrenn-Meleck. Play producer. Estab. 1979. Produces 7 plays (1 new musical)/season "when feasible." "We are a LORT D theatre with a subscriber base of approximately 6,000 people. Plays are performed at the Pennsylvania Stage Company in the J.I. Rodale Theatre." Payment is negotiated on an individual basis. Query with synopsis, character breakdown, set description and a tape of the music. "Please do not send script first." SASE. Reports in 2 months.

Musical Theater: "We are interested in full-length musicals which reflect the social, historical and political fabric of America. We have no special requirements for format, structure or musical involvement. We ask that once submission of a musical has been requested, that it be bound, legibly typed and include SASE. Cast limit of 10, but we prefer cast limit of 8. One set or unit set. Ours is a 274 — seat house, there is no fly area, and a 23-foot proscenium opening."

Productions: *Just So*, by Mark St. Germain (based on Rudyard Kipling's *Just So Stories*); *Shim Sham*, by Johnny Brandon and Eric Blau (Buddy Bradley, an American tap and jazz choreographer); *Feathertop*, by Bruce Peyton and Skip Kennon (Nathaniel Hawthorne short story); *Song of Myself*, by Gayle Stahlhuth, Gregory Hurst and Arthur Harris.

Tips: "Consider the importance of what the musical has to say. Book and lyrics should have equal weight — lyrics should further the plot rather than arrest it."

PIONEER DRAMA SERVICE, P.O. Box 22555, Denver CO 80222. (303)759-4297. Play publisher. Publishes 7 plays (3 new musicals)/year. Estab. 1963. "Plays are performed by junior high and high school drama departments, church youth groups, college and university theatres, semi-professional and professional children's theatres, parks and recreation departments." Query with synopsis, character breakdown and set description. SASE. "No unsolicited manuscripts." Reports in 6 weeks. Playwrights paid by royalty (10% sales) or by outright purchse ($200-500).

Musical Theater: "We seek full length children's musicals, high school musicals and one act children's musicals to be performed by children, secondary school students, and/or adults. As alway, we are seeking musicals easy to perform, simple sets, many female roles and very few solos. Must be appropriate for educational market. Developing a new area, we are actively seeking musicals to be produced by elementary schools — 20 to 30 minutes in length, with 2 to 3 songs and large choruses. We are not interested in profanity, themes with exclusively adult interest, sex, drinking, smoking, etc. Several of our full-length plays are being converted to musicals. We edit them, decide where to insert music and then contact with someone to write the music and lyrics."

Productions: Published *Tied to the Tracks*, by Tim Kelly, Arne Christiansen and Ole Kittleson (musical melodrama); *Little Luncheonette of Terror*, by Tim Kelly, Bill Francoeur and Steve Fendrical (full-length musical comedy); and *The Magical Pied Piper*, by Richard and Pauline Kelvin (children's musical).

Tips: "If one has a musical to publish, send letter of inquiry with plot synopsis, number of male and female characters, number of sets or set changes, approximate duration and production history. Also send complete music score and tape, if possible."

PLAYERS PRESS, INC., P.O. Box 1132, Studio City CA 91604. (818)789-4980. Associate Editor: Marjorie Clapper. Vice President: Joe W. Witt. Play publisher. Estab. 1965. Publishes 13-14 plays/year. Plays are used primarily by children but also by adults. Pays 25% royalty or negotiable outright purchase. Submit complete manuscript, score and tape of songs. SASE. Reports in 3 months.

Musical Theater: "We will consider all submitted works. Presently children's musicals are in demand. When cast size can be flexible (describe how it can be done in your work) it sells better."
Publications: *Rumplestiltskin*, by William Alan Landes; and *Nessie*, by William Hezlep (both children's plays).
Tips: "When submitting, it is best to send a clean, clear sounding tape with music. We do not publish a play or musical which has not been produced."

PLAYHOUSE ON THE SQUARE, 51 S. Cooper, Memphis TN 38104. (901)725-0776. Executive Producer: Jackie Nichols. Play producer. Produces 12 plays (4 musicals)/year. Plays are produced in a "260-seat proscenium resident theater." Pays $500 for outright purchase. Submit complete manuscript and score. SASE. Reports in 4 months.
Musical Theater: Seeking "any subject matter—adult and children's material. Small cast preferred. Stage is 26' deep by 43' wide with no fly system." Would also consider original music for use in a play being developed.
Productions: *Gypsy*, by Stein and Laurents; *The Spider Web*, by Agatha Christie (mystery); and *A Midsummer Night's Dream*, by William Shakespeare.

PLAYWRIGHTS HORIZONS, 416 West 42nd St., New York NY 10036. (212)564-1235. Director: Ira Weitzman. Literary Manager/Musical Theater Program Director. Play producer. Estab. 1971. Produces about 6 plays and 2 new musicals/year. "A general New York City audience." Pays by fee/ royalty. Send script and tape (not necessarily complete). SASE. Reports in 6 months.
Musical Theater: "No revivals or children's shows; otherwise we're flexible. We can't do a Broadway-size show. We generally develop work from scratch; we're open to proposals for shows, and ideas from bookwriters or songwriters. We have frequently commissioned underscoring and incidental music."
Productions: *Lucky Stiff*, by Lynn Ahrens/Stephen Flaherty (musical comedy); *The Heidi Chronicles*, by Wendy Wasserstein (play); and *Driving Miss Daisy*, by Alferd Uhry (play).

*PUERTO RICAN TRAVELING THEATRE, Suite 148, 330 W. 42nd St., New York, NY 10036. (212)354-1293. Producer: Miriam Valle. Play Producer. Estab. 1967. Publishes 4 plays and 1 new musical/year. Primarily an Hispanic audience. Playwrights are paid by stipend.
How to Contact: Submit complete manuscript and tape of songs. SASE. Reports in 6 months.
Musical Theater: "Small cast musicals that will appeal to Hispanic audience. Musicals are bilingual; we work in Spanish and English. We need simple sets and props and a cast of about 8, no more. Musicals are generally performed outdoors and last for an hour to an hour and 15 minutes."
Productions: *Chinese Charades*, by Manuel Perralras, Sergio Garcia and Saul Spangenberg (domestic musical); *El Jardin*, by Carlos Morton, Sergio Garcia (Biblical musical); and *Lady With A View*, by Eduardo Ivan Lopez and Fernando Rivas (Statue of Libery musical).
Tips: "Deal with some aspect of the contemporary Hispanic experience in this country."

THE REPERTORY THEATRE OF ST. LOUIS, 130 Edgar Rd., St. Louis MO 63119. (314)968-7340. Associate Artistic Director: Susan Gregg. Play producer. Estab. 1966. Produces 9 plays and 1 or 2 musicals/ year. "Mainstream regional theatre audience. We produce all our work at the Loretto Hilton Theatre." Query with synopsis, character breakdown and set description. Does not return unsolicited material. Reports in 8 months.
Musical Theater: "We want plays with a small cast and simple setting. No children's shows or foul language. After a letter of inquiry we would prefer script and demo tape."
Productions: *The Merry Wives of Windsor Texas*, by John Haber, Shakespeare (the Shakespearean play gone crooked).

*ROUND HOUSE THEATRE, 12210 Bushey Dr., Silver Spring MD 20902. (301)217-6770. Artistic Director: Terry Whiddon. Play producer. Estab. 1977. Produces 5 plays/year. "We serve Montgomery County as well as all of the Washington D.C. metropolitan area; subscribers are generally over 45— upper middle class." Pays by royalty. Query with synopsis, character breakdown and set description. Does not return unsolicited material. Reports in months.
Musical Theater: "Small scale full-length musicals with contemporary issues and sensibilities . . . challenging our audiences in content, style, format, etc. Also, ½ hour musicals for school tours (elementary). Cast of 2-7 . . . minimal orchestration approach. We are in a modified thrust theater seating 220, so the plays that work best are intimate in nature (no fly space)."
Productions: *Emerald City*, by David Williamson (greed); *Italian American Reconciliation*, by John Patrick Shandley (love/relationships); and *Of Mice and Men*, by John Steinbeck (homelessness/despair).
Tips: "Begin with a good story—and let the music and lyric grow out of it . . . but don't let them grow past something we can do."

PHILIP ROGER ROY PRODUCTIONS, INC., 324 Fitzwater St., Philadelphia PA 19147. (215)925-3769. Producer/President: Philip Roger Roy. Play producer. Estab. 1972. Produces 1 play and 1-3 musicals/ year. "We play to cabaret or dinner theater audiences in Philadelphia, Toronto and on tour throughout North America." Pays 3-6% royalty. Submit complete manuscript, score and tape of songs. Does not return unsolicited material.
Musical Theater: "We want new musicals to run under 2 hours with small casts of 4-6, for cabaret or dinner theaters with a stage of about 12×20'."
Productions: *Let My People Come,* by Earl Wilson Jr. (sexual revolution); *You're It!,* by Earl Wilson Jr. (the theater); *Groucho: A Comic Play,* by Ron McCloskey (Groucho Marx).

*SALOME: A JOURNAL FOR THE PERFORMING ARTS, 5548 N. Sawyer, Chicago IL 60625. (312)539-5745. Editor: Effie Mihopoulos. Play publisher and magazine publisher. Estab. 1975. Plays and individual songs are published in the magazine. Pays by a copy of the magazine. Query with synopsis, character breakdown and set description, or submit complete ms, score and tape of songs. SASE. Reports in 1 month.
Musical Theater: Seeks eclectic plays and music. "Good quality is the only criterion." Published *Jean Le Baptiste,* by Kirby Olson (2 characters interacting in a bar).

*SEATTLE GROUP THEATRE, 3940 Brooklyn Ave. NE, Seattle WA 98105. (206)685-4969. Artistic Director: Rubén Sierra. Estab. 1978. Produces 6 plays and 1-2 musicals (1 new musical)/year. 200 seat intimate theater; 10' ceiling limit; 35' wide modified thrust; 3 piece band. Pays 6-8% royalty. Query with synopsis, character breakdown and set description. Does not return unsolicited material.
Musical Theater: "Multicultural themes; relevant social issues, (race relations, cultural differences, war, poverty, women's issues, homosexuality, physically challenged, developmentally disabled). Address the issues that our mission focuses on." Past musicals include *A-My Name is Alice, Rap Master Ronnie, Jacques Brel is Alive, Stealing, Voices of Christmas.* Cast size of 10 maximum.
Productions: *Growing up Queer in America,* by Chris Cinque (a lesbian story); *The Boys Next Door,* by Tom Griffin; *For Colored Girls Who Have Considered Suicide,* by Ntozake Shange; *Spiderwoman Theater* and *The Independence of Eddie Rose.*

*SHENANDOAH PLAYWRITES RETREAT (A PROJECT OF SHENAN ARTS, INC.), Rt. 5, Box 167-F, Staunton VA 24401. (703)248-1868. Director of Playwriting and Screenwriting Programs: Robert Graham Small. Play developer. Estab. 1976. Develops 12-15 plays/year. Pays fellowships. Query first. Does not return unsolicited material.
Productions: *Ascension Day,* by Michael Henry Brown (Nat Turner's rebellion); *Thursday's Child,* by Julie Jensen (forty something and pregnant); and *Cable Affair,* by Tom Dunn (business ethics).

GEOFFREY SHERMAN/PRODUCING ARTISTIC DIRECTOR, 441 W. 26th St., New York NY 10001. (212)645-4940. Literary Manager: Rebecca Kreinen. Play producer. Produces 5 plays/year. "We are an off-Broadway theatre, supported by subscribers and grants. We operate in a 137-seat house." Submit synopsis, tape and SASE. Response time varies from 3-6 months.
Musical Theater: "Our five play season is aimed exclusively for adult audiences and any sort of children's musicals or puppet shows would be inappropriate. Other than that, the only criteria we demand is excellence. We cannot handle a cast size larger than 7. We have a large space that is flexible to a certain extent. We are also interested in developing works that we feel have potential."
Productions: *Moms,* by Alice Childress (Moms Mabley); *Crackwalker,* by Judith Thompson (Canadian drama); *No Way to Treat a Lady,* by Douglas Cohen, (musical of Goldman novel).
Tips: "Interested in international flavor; also multi-cultural works and/or political relevance."

SOUTH WESTERN COLLEGE, 900 Otay Lakes Rd., Chula Vista CA 92010. (619)421-6700. Artistic Director: W. Virchis. Play, mime and performance art work producer. Estab. 1964. Produces 6 plays and 2 musicals (1 new musical)/year. Query with synopsis. SASE. Reports in 3 weeks.
Productions: *Evita* (world college premiere); *Wiz* (black musical); *Jesus Christ Superstar* (rock opera); *Pancho Diablo* (Chicano); *Nine* (musical); *Leader of the Pack* (musical); *Laguna,* by Vic Bemeil; *Plymouth Rock,* by Scott Busath; and *Nightshriek* (world premier, rock musical based on MacBeth).

STAGE ONE, 425 W. Market St., Louisville KY 40202. (502)589-5946. Producing Director: Moses Goldberg. Play producer. Estab. 1946. Produces 8-10 plays and 0-2 new musicals/year. "Young people ages 5-18." Pays 3-6% royalty, $1,500-3,000 outright purchase or $25-75 per performance. Submit complete manuscript and tape of songs. SASE. Reports in 4 months.
Musical Theater: "We seek stageworthy and respectful dramatizations of the classic tales of childhood, both ancient and modern. Ideally, the plays are relevant to young people and their families, as well as related to school curriculum. Cast is rarely more than 12."

Productions: *Diary of Anne Frank*, by Goodwin & Hacket (young girl); *Velveteen Rabbit*, by Fairbank (toy rabbit); *Wind in the Willows*, by Goldberg (animals); *Cinderella* by Goldberg/Cornett (fairy tale); and *Vasiliga*, by Goldberg/Corcoran (fairy tale).

Tips: "Stage One accepts unsolicited manuscripts that meet our artistic objectives. Please do not send plot summaries or reviews. Include author's resume, if desired. In the case of musicals, a cassette tape is preferred. Cast size is not a factor, although, in practice, Stage One rarely employs casts of over 12. Scripts will be returned in approximately 3-4 months, if SASE is included. No materials can be returned without the inclusion of a SASE. Due to the volume of plays received, it is not possible to provide written evaluations."

STOREFRONT THEATRE, Ste 209, 213 SW Ash, Portland OR 97209. (503)224-9598. Music Director: Teddy Deane. Play producer. Estab. 1969. Produces 5-9 plays, 2-3 musicals and 1-2 new musicals/year. Plays are performed for general adult audiences. "We have a 150-seat theatre, regularly lease a 350-seat theatre and lease others according to productions. We have had as many as 5 shows running simultaneously both in Portland and in Seattle (3 of which were musicals)." Pays by royalty or special arrangement. Query with synopsis, character breakdown, set description and tape of songs. SASE. Reports as soon as possible.

Musical Theater: "We seek imaginative, unusual, non-mainstream, original musicals on any topic and in any style with strong characters and an incredibly well-written book. If your plot doesn't hang together, don't hang it on us. We try not to exclude any subject matter in soliciting material, however, our audience is primarily made up of adults who come to us either for intellectual stimulation or a fairly off-beat good time. Small casts and sets get preferential treatment for budgetary reasons, however, we will consider a cast of up to 14 persons. We use small accompaniment ensembles (up to 5 players) only. In terms of structure, musicals we use are either long one acts of about 1½ hours to 1¾ hours or conventional 2 acts with an overall length of 2¼ hours."

Productions: *Angry Housewives*, by Chad Henry/A.M. Collins (contemporary); *Babes on Burnside*, by Teddy Deane (review).

SYRACUSE TALENT COMPANY, INC., 100 Southfield Dr., Fayetteville NY 13066. (315)637-3733. Producing Director: Christine Lightcap. Play producer. Produces approximately 3 plays and 7 musicals/year. Performs mainstage at Civic Center, in Syracuse, New York and Central New York dinner theatres including (4) productions (3 musicals, 1 non-musical) in July and August at 3 Rivers Inn. "We want comedies, musicals, not too heavy." Pays royalty or per/performance. Submit complete manuscript, score and tape of songs. SASE. Reports in 2 weeks.

Musical Theater: Seeking an "entertaining comedy with unit set for dinner theatre or unit set with insets for Civic Center. Dinner theatre cast size 2-10; Civic Center 20 or less. No fly space. No heavy material." Musical requirements: dinner theatre and Civic Center: piano, drums and bass, to 8 pieces. Would consider original music for use in a play being developed or for use in a pre-existing play with permission.

Productions: (July-August '88) *Annie, Get Your Gun*; *West Side Story*; *Mousetrap* and *Grease*.

TADA!, 120 West 28th St., New York NY 10001. (212)627-1732. Artistic Directors: Janine Nina Trevens and James Learned. Play producer. Estab. 1984. Produces 2-4 plays and 2-4 musicals (1-3 new musicals)/year. "TADA! is a company producing works performed by children ages 6-17 for family audiences in New York City. Performances run approximately 30-35 performances. Pays by royalty or negotiable commission. Query with synopsis and character breakdown or submit complete manuscript, score and tape of songs. SASE. Reports in 2 months.

Musical Theater: "We want various styles and contemporary topics particularly. Must be children playing children, not playing adults. Play can be any length – ½ hour-1 hour plus. Our plays are usually large cast, ensemble pieces. We are not interested in treatments of well-known fairy tales. We are interested in the developmental process. If we like the work, we are likely to work closely with the authors throughout rehearsals and performances."

Productions: *Wide-awake Jake*, by Robby Merkin (composer), Faye Greenberg (lyricist) and Alice Elliott (book) (boy's adventures learning how to sleep); *Once a Year on Christmas Eve*, by Jeremy Beck (a town inhabited by children celebrates a unique Christmas); and *Maggie and the Pirate*, by Winnie Holzman and David Evans (a girl and her pet cricket).

Tips: "When writing for children don't condescend. The subject matter should be appropriate but the music/treatment can still be complex and interesting."

THEATRE FOR YOUNG AMERICA, 7204 W. 80th St., Overland Park KS 66204. (913)648-4604. Artistic Director: Gene Mackey. Play producer. Estab. 1977. Produces 8 plays (2-3 musicals)/year. For children, preschool to high school. Pays $15-70/performance. Query with synopsis. SASE. Reports in 1 month.

Musical Theater: 1-1½ hour productions with small cast oriented to children and high-school youths. "A clear, strong, compelling story is important; a well known title is very important."
Productions: *Androcles and the Lion*, by Aurand Harris and Glen Mack; *Little Lulu*, by Chad Henry (musical for young audience); *The Hare and the Tortoise*, by Cheryl Benge and Gene Mackey (adapted from Aesop's fable); *Tom Sawyer*, by Michael Dansicker and Sarah Marie Schlesinger (adapted from Mark Twain's novel); and *Chicken Little*, by Gene Mackey (book), and Chery Benge (music).

*THEATRE OFF PARK, 224 Waverly Pl., New York NY 10014. (212)627-2556. Artistic Director: Albert Harris. Play producer. Estab. 1974. Produces 2-3 plays, variable number of musicals (1 new musical)/ year. "We reach a broad audience of primarily middle-income, multi-ethnic and -racial patrons. Our audiences include many seniors and other Manhattanites from all walks of life." Pays by fee, approximately $1,500/work. Query with synopsis, character breakdown and set description. SASE. Reports in 6 months.
Musical Theater: "We desire to produce new musicals of many styles and lengths which give light to a diversity of social issues and lifestyles. We also encourage adaptations or revivals of rarely produced or never performed works of recognized authors. Cast limit is 8. We simply require originality and sophistication in style and presentation.Some projects envisioned would require an original incidental score."
Productions: *I Could Go On Lip-Synching!*, by John Epperson/Justin Ross (fictional biography of a rising performer); *Mademoiselle Colombe*, by Albert Harris from Jean Anonilh (musical-Paris 1890s); *Stardust The Mitchell Parish Musical*, by Albert Harris/Lyrics by Mitchell Parish/Music by Duke Ellington, Glenn Miller, Hoagy Carmichael, etc. (revue).
Tips: "Find a showcase for your work in New York which we may attend or secure the services of a New York agent who is familiar with our work and will submit for you."

THEATRE TESSERACT, 820 E. Knapp St., Milwaukee WI 53202. (414)273-PLAY. Producer/Artistic Director: Sharon McQueen. Play producer. Estab. 1984. 5 productions/year, of which 1-2 are musicals. Playwrights paid by royalty (5-8%). "Performance spaces vary greatly but generally seat 150. We have 1,000 season subscribers and single ticket buyers of every age range and walk of life." Pays $30-50 per performance. Submit complete manuscript, score and tape of songs with at least one professional letter of recommendation. SASE.
Musical Theater: "We produce Broadway and off-Broadway style material, preferring slightly controversial or cutting edge material (i.e. *March of the Falsettos*). We have never produced a work that has not been successful in some other theatrical center. We are very limited financially and rarely stage shows with more than 6 in the cast. Props, sets and costumes should be minimal. We have no interest in children's theatre, mime shows, puppet shows, etc. We have never yet used original music for our plays. We may consider it, but there would be little if any money available for this purpose."
Productions: *Billy Bishop Goes to War*, by John Gray/Eric Peterson (World War I flying ace); *A . . . My Name is Alice*, by various writers (women's themes); and *Damn Tango*, by Helena Dynerman (European translation of 17 tangos with cast of 17 singer/dancers).

*THEATRE THREE, P.O. Box 512, Port Jefferson NY 11777. (516)928-9202. Associate Artistic Director: Jerry Friedman. Theater. Estab. 1969. Produces 16 plays and 3 musicals/year. Main stream Long Island audience. Plays produced in our Victorian theater on Main Street in Port Jefferson. Contracts are negotiated on per play basis.
How to Contact: Query with synopsis, character breakdown and set description. SASE. Reports in 3 months.
Musical Theater: Open to many types. Children's musicals as well. No puppet shows. Single sets, smaller casts more desirable.
Productions: *La Cage Aux Folles*; *Singin' in the Rain*; and *Follies*.

THEATRE WEST VIRGINIA, P.O. Box 1205, Beckley WV 25802. (800)666-9142. General Manager: Johanna Young. Play producer. Estab. 1955. Produces 7-9 plays and 2-3 musicals/year. "Audience varies from main stream summer stock to educational tours to dinner theater." Pays 5% royalty or $25 per performance. Query with synopsis, character breakdown and set description; should include cassette tape. SASE. Reports in 2 months.
Musical Theater: "Theatre West Virginia is a year-round performing arts organization that presents a variety of productions including community performances such as dinner theater, *The Nutcracker* and statewide educational programs on primary, elementary and secondary levels. This is in addition to our summer, outdoor dramas of *Hatfields & McCoys* and *Honey in the Rock*, now in their 29th year." Anything suitable for secondary school tours and/or dinner theater type shows. No more than 7 in cast. Play should be able to be accompanied by piano/synthesizer.

Productions: *Thomas Jefferson Still Survives*, by Nancy Moss (historical); *Frogsong*, by Jean Battlo (literary/historical); *Guys & Dolls*, by Frank Loesser; *Grease* (currently in production), by Jim Jacobs and Warren Casey; and *Murder at the Howard Johnsons*, by Ron Clark/Sam Bobrick (comedy).

*THEATRE-IN-THE-SCHOOLS, INC., #32, 220 East 4th, New York NY 10009. Executive Director: Timothy Jeffryes. Play producer. Estab. 1983. Produces 2 plays/year. "We perform in schools through-out America—currently non-musicals, but we're interested in expanding." Pays 5-8% royalty or $500-1,000 for outright purchase.
How to Contact: Query with synopsis, character breakdown and set description. SASE. Reports in 10 weeks.
Musical Theater: "For ages 5-17, including history, folktales, current social issues. The text must be paramount to the songs—that is, plot should not generally be revealed through songs. Also, songs should be easy to sing. Cast size is ideally 2, with numerous character changes (as many as 10 charac-ters), but we will consider shows with 4 actors. Show must be simple enough to set up in 15 minutes." Does not wish to see shows which do not involve audience directly. "Show must involve the audience somewhat. 4th wall can be intermittently put up and removed. Some songs can be sung with the audience. Music must be playable on a tape recorder, not live."
Productions: *Legends of Ancient America*, by William S. Leavengood (legends); *Road to the Constitu-tion*, by William S. Leavengood (constitution); *More Stories*, by Tim Jeffryes (folktales).
Tips: "Give the audience the benefit of the doubt as far as comprehension goes."

THEATREVIRGINIA, 2800 Grove Ave., Richmond VA 23221-2466. (804)367-0840. Literary Manager: Bo Wilson. Play producer. Estab. 1955. Produces 5-9 plays (2-5 musicals)/year. "Plays are performed in a 500-seat LORT-C house for the Richmond-area community." Payment subject to negotiation. "Please submit synopsis, sample of dialogue and sample of music (on cassette) along with a self-addressed, stamped letter-size envelope. If material seems to be of interest to us, we will reply with a solicitation for a complete manuscript and cassette. Response time for synopses is 4 weeks; response time for scripts once solicited is 5 months."
Musical Theater: "We do not deal in one-acts or in children's material. We would like to see full length, adult musicals. There are no official limitations. We would be unlikely to use original music as incidental/underscoring for existing plays, but there is potential for adapting existing plays into musicals."
Productions: *West Side Story*, by Bernstein/Sondheim/Laurents (love story among gangs); *Man of La Mancha*, by Wasserman/Darion/Leigh (Don Quixote/oppression); *The Amen Corner*, by James Bal-dwin, (family struggle in gospel setting); and *A Wireless Christmas*, by Wilson/Burgler/Liebman (an original musical about a radio station at Christmas).
Tips: "Read plays. Study structure. Study character. Learn how to concisely articulate the nature of your work. A beginning musical playwright, wishing to work for our company should begin by writing a wonderful, theatrically viable piece of musical theatre. Then he should send us the material requested in our listing, and wait patiently."

THEATREWORKS, 1305 Middlefield Rd., Palo Alto CA 94301. (415)424-9441. Literary Manager: Les-lie Martinson. Play producer. Estab. 1970. Produces 12 plays and 5 musicals (2 new musicals)/year. Theatrically-educated suburban area bordering Stanford University 30 miles from San Francisco and San Jose—3 mainstages and 2 second stage performance spaces. Pays per contract.
How to Contact: Submit complete manuscript, score or sample songs and tape of songs; synopses and character breakdowns helpful. SASE. Reports in 4-6 months.
Musical Theater: "We use original songs and music in many of our classics productions, for instance specially composed music ws used in our production of the *The Tempest* for Ariels song, the pagent song, the storm and the music of theisles. We are looking both for full-scale large musicals and smaller chamber pieces. We also use original music and songs in non-musical plays. No ancient Roman, ancient Greek or biblical settings please!"
Productions: 1989-1991 productions include: *Go Down Garvey* (world premiere); *Galileo* (2nd pro-duction in residence); *Into the Woods*; *Big River*; *Oliver*; *Candide*; *The Tempest* (with original songs); *The Miser* (with original songs), *No Way to Treat a Lady* (composer in residence); *Rags*; *Peter Pan* and *Lady Day at Emerson's Bar and Grill*.
Tips: "Write a great musical. We wish there were more specific 'formula,' but that's about it. If it's really terrific, we're interested."

THEATREWORKS/USA, 890 Biway, New York NY 10003. (212)677-5959. Literary Manager: Barbara Pasternack. Play producer. Produces 10-13 plays, all are musicals (3-4 new musicals)/year. Audience consists mainly of children and families. Pays 6% royalty and aggregate of $1500 commission-advance against future royalties.

How to Contact: Query with synopsis, character breakdown and sample scene and song. SASE. Reports in 6 months.

Musical Theater: "One hour long, 5-6 adult actors, highly portable, good musical theater structure; adaptations of children's literature, historical or biographical musicals, issues, fairy tales—all must have something to say. We demand a certain level of literary sophistication. No kiddy shows, no camp, no fractured fables, no shows written for school or camp groups to perform. Approach your material, not as a writer writing for kids, but as a writer addressing any universal audience. You have one hour to entertain, say something, make them care—don't preach, condescend. Don't forget an antagonist. Don't waste the audience's time. We always use original music—but most of the time a project team comes complete with a composer in tow.

Productions: *The Play's The Thing*, by Robert Waldman and Thomas West (Shakespeare and Co.); *Footprints on the Moon*, by Art Perlman and Jeff Lunden (early days of space exploration); *The Velveteen Rabbit*, by James Still and Jimmy Roberts (picture book); *Jekyll and Hyde*, book and lyrics by David Crane and Marta Kaufmann, music by Michael Sklopf; *Harold and the Purple Crayon*, music by Jon Ehrlich, lyrics by Robin Pogrebin and Jon Ehrlich, book by Jane Shepard.

Tips: "Write a good show! Make sure the topic is something we can market! Come see our work to find out our style."

*UNIVERSITY OF ALABAMA NEW PLAYWRIGHTS' PROGRAM, P.O. Box 870239, Tuscaloosa AL 35487-0239. (205)348-5283. Director/Dramarturg: Dr. Paul Castagno. Play producer. Estab. 1982. Produces variable number of plays. University audience. Pays by arrangement. Submit complete ms, score and tape of songs. SASE. Reports ASAT—usually 1-2 months.

Musical Theater: Any style or subject (but no children's or puppet plays). No cliché or "standard" musicals. No limitations—just good theater. Drama with music.

Tips: "Experiment with new ideas/forms, plays/musicals with dance; scripts for dance."

WALNUT STREET THEATRE COMPANY, 825 Walnut St., Philadelphia PA 19107. (215)574-3584. Literary Manager: Ernest Tremblay. Play producer. Estab. 1982. Produces 10 plays and 2 musicals (1 new musical)/year. Plays produced on a mainstage with seating for 1,052 to a family audience; and in studio theatres with seating for 79-99 to adult audiences. Pays by royalty or outright purchase. Query with synopsis, character breakdown, set description, and ten pages. SASE. Reports in 5 months.

Musical Theater: "Adult Musicals. Plays are for a subscription audience that comes to the theatre to be entertained. We seek musicals with lyrical non-operatic scores and a solid book as well as revues. We are looking for a small musical for springtime and one for a family audience at Christmas time. We would like to remain open on structure and subject matter and would expect a tape with the script. Cast size: around 30 equity members (10 for smaller musical); preferably one set with variations." Would consider original music for incidental music and/or underscore. This would be at each director's discretion.

Productions: *Mike*, by Jose Fernandez, Jacques Levy and Steven Margoshes (New York's High School of Performing Arts); and *Fame*, by Thomas Meehan, Mitch Leigh and Lee Adams (Mike Todd).

Tips: "Our budget allows very little development time in-house, so the project must be in a state of near-completion before we would consider it."

WASHINGTON JEWISH THEATRE, 6125 Montrose Rd., Rockville MD 20852. (301)881-0100. Artistic Director: Laurie Wagner. Play producer. Estab. 1984. Produces 3-5 plays/year; 50% of productions are musicals (1-2 new musicals)/year. "We are looking for new plays that have some type of Jewish theme. These themes may include biographical plays, plays with Jewish characters in leading roles, World War II plays, etc." Pays by royalty.

How to Contact: Submit complete manuscript, score and tape of songs. SASE.

Musical Theater: "We like musicals with simple sets and few characters. We have no restrictions on style, but topics must in some way conform to the concept of Jewish theater. Our usual running time is 120 minutes including intermission."

Productions: 1990-91 Season: *Isn't It Romantic*, by Wendy Wasserstein; *First Nights*, by James Glossman and Stephen Randay (a commissioned musical); *A Thousand Clowns*, by Herb Gardner; and *Another Antigone*, by A.R. Gurney.

WATERLOO COMMUNITY PLAYHOUSE, Box 433, Waterloo IA 50704. (319)235-0367. Managing Director: Charles Stilwill. Play producer. Estab. 1917. Produces 12 plays (1-2 musicals)/year. "Our audience prefers solid, wholesome entertainment, nothing risque or with strong language. We perform in Hope Martin Theatre, a 368-seat house." Pays $15-150/performance. Submit complete manuscript, score and cassette tape of songs. SASE.

Musical Theater: "Casts may vary from as few as 6 people to 54. We are producing children's theater as well. We're *especially* interested in new adaptations of classic children stories."
Productions: *Barnum*; *Little House On The Prairie*, by Patricia Stilwill and Ken Ostercamp; *Camelot*; *You're A Good Man Charlie Brown*; *West Side Story*; and *Fiddler*.
Tips: Looking for "new adaptations of classical children's stories or a good Christmas show."

*the WEST BANK DOWNSTAIRS THEATRE BAR, 311 W. 42nd St./Theatre Row, New York NY 10036. (212)695-6909. Managing Director: Rowan Joseph. Play producer. Estab. 1983. Produces about 400 plays and 50 musicals (40 new musicals)/year. Our audience is basically a heavy entertainment industry crowd. We also draw a mostly upscale, young (mid 20's-30's), educated, politically aware group. Pays per performance; varies with house size. Submit complete ms, score and tape of songs. SASE. Reports in 4-5 months.
Musical Theater: "We present small 'mini-musicals' or shortened versions of full-length works. Topics may vary but all material should be geared for an adult theater crowd. We will look at rock works as well as standard and contemporary style musicals. We do *not* present children's musicals or puppet show musicals. Everything is simple, simple, simple. The focus should be on the product, not on the production. Our theater is basically a standard black box theater space with a bar attached to it. We have a simple 6 dimmer board and a decent sound board. We have a very astute audience with good imaginations. A suggestion goes a long way. Writers should have their own voices. If a work is well-written, even if we may not agree with its point of view or particularly like it we would still (and do still) present it. We are not here to judge, we're here to support new voices."
Productions: *The Czar of Rock & Roll*, by Rusty Magee and Lewis Black (life of Dean Reed); *Exmass*, by Mark Houghtaling and Brad Smith Lewis Black (a contemporary morality miracle play with music; *Tiny Dancer*, by Paul Scott Goodman (life and family and career in New York City).
Tips: "Only send along your absolute best material in a clean, well-structured professional manner and hope it's right for the space."

WEST COAST ENSEMBLE, Box 38728, Los Angeles CA 90038. (213)871-8673. Artistic Director: Les Hanson. Play producer. Estab. 1982. Produces 6 plays (1-2 new musicals)/year. "Our audience is a wide variety of Southern Californians. Plays will be produced in one of our two theatres on Hollywood Boulevard." Pays by royalty. Submit complete manuscript, score and tape of songs. SASE. Reports in 6 months.
Musical Theater: "There are no limitations on subject matter or style. Cast size should be no more than 12 and sets should be simple. If music is required we would commission a composer, music would be used as a bridge between scenes or to underscore certain scenes in the play."
Productions: *Losing Venice*, by John Clifford (futility of war); *The Club*, by Eve Merriam (the inequity of gender); and *Coming of Age* (original musical), by Tony Tanner (growing older and staying young).
Tips: "Submit work in good form and be patient. We look for musicals with a strong book and an engaging score with a variety of styles."

JENNY WILEY THEATRE, Box 22, Prestonsburg KY 41653-0022. (606)886-9274. General Manager: Tedi Vaughn. Play producer (Jenny Wiley Drama Association, Inc./JWDA). Produces 3 musicals plus 1 new musical/year. Plays are performed for "tourist audience, middle-income (20-25,000 average attendance in summer) in Jenny Wiley State Resort Park Amphitheatre." Pays outright purchase of $4,000-6,000, by royalty or per performance. "Additional payment in ensuing years of performance is variable." Query. SASE. Reports in 3 weeks.
Musical Theater: Seeking "family oriented shows not exceeding 2 hours performance time. The works should not call for more than 20 in the ensemble. Twentieth century setting works best, but historical works with music are strongly considered. Musicals should deal with Appalachia or Kentucky historical figures. Shows are produced outdoors — beware of flashy spectacle at outset of show (while it's still daylight). It must be, at its basis, family entertainment." Would also consider original music for use in play being developed "either as performance music (score and vocal), as part of a musical theater production, or as background (underscoring)."
1990 Productions: *Jenny Wiley Story*, by Daniel A. Stein (historical with music); *Joseph & the Amazing Technicolor Dreamcoat*; *How To Succeed in Business Without Really Trying*; and *Grease*.
Tips: "Present a scenario/synopsis for consideration. If we are interested, we will give aid in developing it (and funding it if it falls under our funding resource availabilities). We would like to develop quality works with appropriate music that deal with historical themes or Appalachian tales. At present we need music for the Jenny Wiley Story. We want exciting original music based on colonial period music or adaptations of music of that period."

WILMA THEATER, 2030 Sansom St., Philadelphia PA 19103. (215)963-0249. Artistic Producing Director: Jiri Zizka; Artistic Producing Director: Blanka Zizka. Play producer. Produces 4-5 plays (1-2 musicals)/year. Plays are performed for a "sophisticated, adventurous, off-beat and demanding audience," in a 100-seat theater. Pays 6-8% of gross income. Submit synopsis, score and tape of songs. SASE. Reports in 10 weeks.

Musical Theater: Seeks "innovative staging, universal issues, political implications and inventive, witty approach to subject. We emphasize ensemble style, group choreography, actors and musicians overlapping, with new, inventive approach to staging. Do not exceed 4-5 musicians, cast of 12, (ideally under 8), or stage space of 30x20." Also interested in plays with music and songs.

Productions: *Hairy Ape*, by O'Neil (search for self-identity); *The Mystery of Irma Zep* by Charles Ludlum; *Incommunicado*, by Tom Dulak; *Marat/Sade* (basic questions of human existence); and *Three Guys Naked From the Waist Down* (worship of success).

WOOLLY MAMMOTH THEATRE CO., 1401 Church St., Washington DC 20005. (202)393-3939. Literary Manager: Martin Blank. Play producer. Estab. 1978. Produces 3-4 plays/year. Submit complete manuscript and score and tape of songs. SASE. Reports in 8 weeks.

Musical Theater: "We do unusual works. We have not done a musical, but are open to the idea. 8-10 in cast. We do not wish to see one acts. Be professional in presentation."

Productions: *Christmas on Mars*, *Aunt Daw and Limon* and *Sharon and Billy*.

Tips: "Just keep writing! Too many people expect to make it writing one or two plays. I don't think a writer is up to speed until the fifth or sixth work!"

WORCESTER FOOTHILLS THEATRE CO., 074 Worcester Center, Worcester MA 01608. (508)754-3314. Literary Manager: Greg DeJarnett. Play producer. Estab. 1974. Produces 7 plays and 1 or 2 musicals (indefinite new musicals)/year. "General audience, multi-generational. Plays are produced at Worcester Foothills Theatre, a 349 seat Proscenium stage. Pays by negotiable royalty. Query with synopsis, character breakdown and set description. SASE. "Reports back in 4 weeks for synopsis, 3-4 months for scripts."

Musical Theater: "Full length preferred, one acts considered. Any style or topic. No gratuitous sex, violence or language. Generally a cast of 8-10 and a single set but these are not rigid restrictions."

Productions: *Dames at Sea*, by George Haimsohn/Robin Miller; and *Tom Foolery*, by Cameron Mackintosh/Robin Ray, *1940's Radio Hour* by Walton Jones; *Viva Vaudeville*, by Marc Smith (vaudeville show); and *Little Shop of Horrors*, by Howard Ashman/Alan Menken.

Play Producers/'90-'91 Changes

The following markets appeared in the 1990 edition of *Songwriter's Market* but do not appear in the 1991 edition. Those companies that did not respond to our request for an update of their listing may not have done so for a variety of reasons—they may be out of business, for example, or they may be overstocked with submissions.

The American Playwright's Theatre (moved; no forwarding address)
Arrow Rock Lyceum Theatre (did not respond)
Bailiwick Repertory (did not respond)
California Music Theatre (did not respond)
The Coterie Theatre (did not respond)
The Cricket Theatre (did not respond)
The Downstairs Cabaret (did not respond)
Los Angeles (Inner City) Cultural Center (did not respond)
McCarter Theatre (did not respond)

Harland D. Meltzer (did not respond)
Mixed Blood Theatre Co. (did not respond)
Myers Mountaineer Dinner Theatre (moved; no forwarding address)
Negro Ensemble Company (moved; no forwarding address)
Organic Theater Company (asked to be deleted)
Richard Rose — American Stage Festival (did not respond)
San Diego Repertory Theatre (did not respond)
Second Stage Theatre (did not respond)
Soho Repertory Theatre (did

not respond)
Spotlight Repertory Theatre Assocs. Inc. (did not respond)
Robert Turoff/Golden Apple Dinner Theatre (did not respond)
University of Victoria, Theatre Department (did not respond)
Upstairs Dinner Theatre (did not respond)
Cedric Vendyback (asked to be deleted)
Wabash College Theater (did not respond)
Wisdom Bridge Theatre (did not respond)
Women's Project and Productions (did not respond)

Over the past two years, Fine Arts has proven to be one of the fastest-growing sections of *Songwriter's Market*. This year we welcome over 80 new markets to this category.

The fine arts market is very different from most of the other markets in this book. The song selection and marketing concerns that weigh on the minds of pop music industry professionals in New York, Los Angeles and Nashville really do not apply to the markets found in this section.

Most of the listings found here are interested in hearing new works of a "serious," or "classical" nature—arranged for the symphony orchestra or some configuration thereof. They are all interested in high-calibre works that they can "premiere" for their local audiences. Most of these companies and organizations are not-for-profit, so you cannot expect to make much, if any, money from them. Though the pay is low, most composers are thrilled just to have their work performed by an orchestra and enjoyed by an audience. A successfully premiered work may lead to performances of the piece by other orchestras or commissions for future works. Some orchestras, if they decide to perform your work, will pay your expenses to attend rehearsals and/or the premiere performance of your work.

Most of the listings in this section give explicit instructions about what kinds of music they are interested in, the instrumentation and level of difficulty their players can handle and how to submit your work to them. Be sure to follow their submission instructions closely. Don't hurt your chances by sending anything but your best compositions, and be professional when contacting the musical directors. More names and addresses (but no marketing information) of fine arts companies can be found in the annual *Musical America Directory* (ABC Consumer Magazines).

*AFTER DINNER OPERA CO., INC., 23 Stuyvesant St., New York NY 10003. (212)477-6212. Executive Director: Dr. Richard Flusser. Opera Company. Estab. 1949. Members are professionals. Performs 30 concerts/year including 4 new works. Concert hall "varies from 200 seats to 900 seats." Pays $0-500/performance. "Send SASE with postage, or materials cannot be returned. Do not send your only copy. Mail to: Dr. Richard Flusser (H140), After Dinner Opera Co., Inc., Queensborough Community College, 222-05 56th Ave., Bayside, NY 11364-1497. We report to all submissions in May of every year."
Music: "Seeks piano vocal scores with indications of instruments from 2-17, chamber size operas from 10 minutes long to 2 hours; no more than 10 singers. Especially interested in 3 character operas under one hour in length. Also interested in operas for children. No gospel or heavy metal rock." Performances: H.H. Beach's Cabildo (one act opera), William Grant Still's *Troubled Island* (opera) and Seymour Barab's *Fair Means or Foul* (children's opera).
Tips: "Start with an interesting, singable libretto. Make sure that you have the rights to the libretto."

*THE AMERICAN BOYCHOIR, Lambert Dr., Princeton NJ 08540. (609)924-5858. Music Director: James H. Litton. Professional Boychoir. Estab. 1937. Members are highly skilled children. Performs 125 concerts/year including 25-30 new works. Commissions 3-5 composers or new works/year. Performs community concerts and for local concert associations, church concert series and other bookings. Pays by commission. Query first. SASE. Reports in 6 months.
Music: "Dramatic works for boys voices (age 10-14); 15 to 20 minutes short opera to be staged and performed throughout the USA." Choral pieces, either in unison, SSA, SA or SSAA division; unaccompanied and with piano or organ; occasional chamber orchestra. Pieces are usually sung by 26 to 50 boys. Composers must know boychoir sonority.
Performances: Ned Porem's *Who Has Seen The Wind* (song cycle for boys' voices); Daniel Pinkham's *Angels are Everywhere* (song cycle for boys' voices); and Milton Babbitt's *Glosses* (motet for boys' voices).

*ARLINGTON SYMPHONY, 933 N. Glebe Rd., Arlington VA 22203. (703)528-1817. Music Director: David Sz. Pollitt. Symphony orchestra. Estab. 1945. Members are professionals and amateurs. Performs 7-9 concerts/year including 1-2 new works. Commissions 1 composer or new work/year. "Concert hall seats 1,400, audience is mostly older." Payment arrangements vary. Query first. SASE.
Music: "We are generally looking for a piece for first half of a program—15 or 20 minutes long. We are full symphony size; moderate difficulty is OK."
Performances: Dan Gawthrop's *Three Nocturnes*; Marcus Uzilevsky's *Folk Symphony for Sara*; and Doug Jackson's *Concentric Shades*, all orchestral (world premieres).
Tips: "Be good and be persistent."

*ASHLAND SYMPHONY ORCHESTRA, P.O. Box 13, Ashland OH 44805. (419)289-5115. General Manager: James E. Thomas. Symphony orchestra. Estab. 1970. Members are professionals and amateurs. Performs 5 concerts/year. "We usually perform in a hall which seats 729. For larger events there is another which seats 1,100. Audience comes from local university-oriented community and surrounding area." Submit complete score. SASE. Reports in 6 months.
Music: "For full symphony orchestra all styles, with caution for extremely contemporary orchestration and arrangements."
Performances: Verdi's *Requiem* (orchestral/choral/soloists); Tchaikovsky's *Piano Concerto #1* (piano with orchestra); and Brahms' *Symphony #2* (symphony).

BALTIMORE OPERA COMPANY, INC., 527 N. Charles St., Baltimore MD 21201. (301)727-0592. Artistic Administrator: James Harp. Opera company. Estab. 1950. Members are professionals. Performs 16 concerts/year. "The opera audience is becoming increasingly diverse. Our performances are given in the 3,000-seat Lyric Opera House." Pays by outright purchase. Submit complete score and tapes of piece(s). Reports in 1-2 months.
Music: "Our new General Director, Mr. Michael Harrison, is very much interested in presenting new works. These works would be anything from Grand Opera with a large cast to chamber works suitable for school and concert performances. We would be interested in perusing all music written for an operatic audience."
Performances: Verdi's *Otello* (opera), Rossini's *Il Barbiere di Siviglia* (opera) and R. Strauss' *Salome* (opera).
Tips: "Opera is the most expensive art form to produce. Given the current economic outlook, opera companies cannot be too avant garde in their selection of repertoire. The modern operatic composer must give evidence of a fertile and illuminating imagination, while also keeping in mind that opera companies have to sell tickets!"

BILLINGS SYMPHONY, 104 N. Broadway, Billings MT 59101. (406)252-3610. Music Director: Dr. Uri Barnea. Symphony orchestra, orchestra and chorale. Estab. 1950. Members are professionals and amateurs. Performs 10 concerts/year including 5-8 new works. Audience: mostly adults. Hall: Alberta Bair Theater (capacity 1,418). Pays by royalty or outright purchase. Query first. SASE. Reports in 4 months.
Music: Any style. Traditional notation preferred.
Performances: Ellen Taaffe Zwilich's *Images* (two pianos and orchestra), Allen Vizzutti's *Snow Scenes* (trumpet and orchestra) and Graham Whettam's *An English Suite* (orchestra).
Tips: "Write *good* music. Make sure score and parts are legible and ready for use (rehearsal numbers, other instructions, etc.)."

*THE BOSTON MUSICA VIVA, Suite 203, 295 Huntington Ave., Boston MA 02115-4401. Manager: David Chambless Worters. Chamber music ensemble. Estab. 1969. Members are professionals. Performs 12-20 concerts/year including 6-10 new works. Commissions 3-5 composers or new works/year. "We perform our subscription series in a hall that seats 300, and our audience comes from Boston, Cambridge and surrounding areas. Frequent tours have taken the ensemble across the U.S. and the world." Pays by commission. Submit complete score and tapes of piece(s). Does not return unsolicited material. Reports in months.
Music: "We are looking for works for: flute, clarinet, percussion, piano, violin, viola, cello plus vocalist (or any combination thereof). Made for no more than ten performers. We're looking for exciting avant garde music. We don't particularly want to see anything on the pop side."
Performances: HK Gruber's *Cello Concerto in One Movement* (chamber concerto); Paul Earls' *Eliot-ime* (chamber work); and Kathryn Alexander's *Song of Songs* (song cycle).

*BRECKENRIDGE MUSIC INSTITUTE, Box 1254, Breckenridge CO 80424. (303)453-9142. Executive Director: Pamela G. Miller. Chamber orchestra with ensembles: brass, woodwind and string quartets and a vocal quartet. Estab. 1980. Members are professionals. Performs more than 30 concerts/year including several new works. Commissions 1 composer or new work/year. "We perform our main season in a tent—we are in a resort area, so our audiences are a mix of local citizens and visitors." Chamber orchestra concerts: 300-400 people; chamber ensemble recitals: 85-150 people; choral/orchestra concert: 450 people. "Our contracts include remarks, notes and commissioned work." Query first. Does not return unsolicited material. Usually reports in months, but depends on the time of year the work is submitted.

Music: "Typically, we try to premiere an orchestral piece each year and highlight the composer's other work during a 4-5 day composer-in-residence program. We need *chamber* orchestra or ensemble music only—nothing for more instrumentation." Doesn't want to see "pops."

Performances: Jean Berger's *Two Psalms for Choir, Solo Voices and 2 Pianos* (chamber orchestra world premiere); Cecil Effinger's *Capriccio for Chamber Orchestra* (world premiere); and William Schmidt's *Miniatures for Chamber Orchestra* (world premiere).

Tips: "Be flexible and affable—and you'll have a *great* stay in the Colorado Rockies during a week in July!"

*BREMERTON SYMPHONY ASSOCIATION INC., 535B 6th St., P.O. Box 996, Bremerton WA 98310. (206)373-1722. Music Director: Joseph Levine. Sympnony orchestra. Estab. 1942. Members are amateurs. Performs 8 concerts/year including a varying number of new works. The audience is half seniors, half adult. 1,200-seat hall in Bremerton High School; excellent acoustics. Query first.

Music: "Should be good for competent community orchestras."

Tips: Contact Joseph Levine, (206)283-5553; 2917 W. Eaton, Seattle, WA 98199.

*BRONX ARTS ENSEMBLE, % Golf House Van Cortlandt Park, Bronx NY 10471. (212)601-7399. Artistic Director: William Scribner. Symphony orchestra and chamber music ensemble. Estab. 1972. Members are professionals. Performs 90 concerts/year including 10 new works. "Performs concerts at colleges and various historic sites in the Bronx; also in halls in Manhattan." Pays per performance. Query first. SASE.

Music: Seeks "primarily chamber music or orchestral. No pops or jazz."

Performances: Meyer Kupferman's *Images of Chagall* (1987 world premiere); David Chesky's *Trumpet Concerto* (1988, solo trumpet and orchestra, New York premiere); and Roberto Sierra's *El Mensajero de la Plata* (1988 chamber opera).

*CABRILLO MUSIC FESTIVAL, 9053 Soquel Dr., Aptos CA 95003. Executive Director: Michael Stamp. Contemporary/classical music festival. Estab. 1963. Members are professionals. Performs 12 concerts/year. "Our audience consists of people interested in contemporary classical music. We perform in a variety of halls including churches, theaters and outdoor concert sites." Commissioning of new works for a fee. Query first. Submit complete score and tapes of piece(s). SASE. Reports in 2 months.

Performances: Lou Harrison's *Grand Duo* (World Premiere, chamber music for violin and piano); Chinary Ung's *Inner Voices* (West Coast Premiere, full orchestra); and Gordon Mumma's *Than Particle* (percussion and computer).

Tips: "Scores should be sent to CMF Composers Project, % Larry Duckles, 16 Gibbs Ct., Irvine CA 92715. All scores should be sent priority mail. California composers who wish to submit orchestral scores for reading during the 1991 Festival should do so by 12/31/90. Composers must be able to verify that they have been residents of CA for at least one year."

CANADIAN CHILDREN'S OPERA CHORUS, #215, 227 Front St. E., Toronto **Canada** M5A 1E8. (416)366-0467. Manager: Suzanne Bradshaw. Children's vocal ensemble. Estab. 1968. Members are amateurs. Performs 2-3 concerts/year. Performs choral Christmas concert in a church with candlelight; spring opera production often at Harbourfront, Toronto. Pays by outright purchase; "CCOC applies to Ontario Arts Council or the Canada Council for commission fees." Query first. SAE and IRC.

Music: "Operas of approximately 1 hour in length representing quality composers. In addition, the portability of a production is important; minimal sets and accompaniment. CCOC prefers to engage Canadian composers whose standards are known to be high. Being a non-profit organization with funding difficulties, we prefer piano accompaniments or just a few instruments."

Performances: Derek Holman's *Sir Christëmas* (20-minute choral suite with 5 instruments); Harry Somers' *A Midwinter Night's Dream* (1-hour opera) and Gian Carlo Menotti's *Chip and His Dog* (30-minute opera), all commissioned by CCOC.

CANADIAN OPERA COMPANY, 227 Front St. E, Toronto ON M5A 1E8 **Canada**. (416)363-6671. Artistic Planning Coordinator: Sandra J. Gavinchuk. Opera company. Estab. 1950. Members are professionals. 60 performances including a minimum of 1 new work/year. Commissions maximum of 3 composers or new works/year. "New works are done in the Texaco Opera Theatre, which seats approximately 400." Pays by contract. Submit complete score and tapes of piece(s). SASE.

Music: Vocal works, preferably operatic in nature. 6 singers, 1 hour in duration and 5 orchestral players. "Do not submit works which are not for voice. Ask for requirements for the Composers In Residence program."

Performances: Denis Gougeon's *The Expensive Embarrassment* (music theater); John Oliver's *Guacamayo's Old Song and Dance* (opera/musical theater), Peter Koprowski's *Dulcitius: Demise of Innocence* (music theater); and Andrew MacDonald's *The Unbelievable Glory of Mr. Sharp* (music theater).

Tips: "We have a Composers-In-Residence program which is open to Canadian composers or landed immigrants 40 years of age or under."

*CAPITAL UNIVERSITY CONSERVATORY OF MUSIC OPERA/MUSICAL THEATRE, 2199 E. Main St., Columbus OH 43209-2394.. (614)236-6122. Director, Opera/Musical Theatre: William Florescu. College opera/musical theater program. Estab. 1970. Members are students. Performs 2-4 stage works/year including 1-2 new works. Commissions 1 composer or new work/year. "The audience is basically a community arts audience and family and friends of performers. Mees Hall Auditorium (cap. 1,100) is where we perform big, standard works. The Toledo Room (cap. 255) is where we perform chamber and experimental works. Both of these halls are to be upgraded and renovated in the next year-and-a-half." Pays by royalty or $50-150 per performance. Submit complete score and tapes of piece(s). SASE. Reports in 3-4 weeks.

Music: "I am seeking music theater pieces, particularly of a 'chamber' nature. I am open to a wide variety of musical styles, although the music should be singable for undergraduates; piano or small ensemble accompaniment. Ideally, pieces should be for 4-6 performers, most of whom will be able to tackle a wide variety of musical styles. Ideal length for works should be 15 minutes to 45 minutes. I am not particularly interested in 'rock' pieces, although if they work theatrically, I would certainly consider them."

Performances: Chris Becker's (a Capital student) *Satie* (music theater piece); Gustav Holst's *The Wandering Scholar* (chamber opera); and Milton Granger's *The Proposal* (chamber opera).

Tips: "If a composer is interested in writing for the situation we have here at Capital, I would suggest he or she either write or call me to *specifically* discuss a project. This will help both sides bring the performance about."

CARSON CITY CHAMBER ORCHESTRA, P.O. Box 2001, Carson City NV 89702-2001. (702)883-4154. Conductor: David C. Bugli. Amateur community orchestra. Estab. 1984. Members are amateurs. Performs 5 concerts including 1 new work/year. "Most concerts are performed for about 250 listeners in the Carson City Community Center Auditorium, which seats 840. However, the mid-December concerts have audiences as large as 700. We have no provisions for paying composers at this time but may later." Query first. Reports in 2 months.

Music: "We want classical, pop orchestrations, orchestrations of pre-Bach music for modern orchestras, concertos for violin or piano, holiday music for chorus and orchestra (children's choirs available), music by women, music for brass choir. Most performers are amateurs, but there are a few professionals who perform with us. Available winds: 2 flutes and flute/piccolo, 2 oboes (E.H. double), 3 clarinets in B flat, 1 bass clarinet, 2 bassoons, 3 horns, 4 trumpets, 3 trombones, 1 tuba. Strings: 8-8-3-3-2. Avoid rhythmic complexity (except in pops); no 12-tone music that lacks melodic appeal. Composers should contact us first. Each concert has a different emphasis. Note: Associated choral group, Carson Chamber Singers, performs several times a year with the orchestra and independently."

Performances: David Bugli's *State of Metamorphosis* (overture). Premieres to date include an overture and arrangements of Christmas and popular tunes.

Tips: "Our orchestra members will do their best efforts for you if the music is clear, cohesive, legible and capable of being put together in 6-8 rehearsals."

CARSON-DOMINQUEZ HILLS SYMPHONY, % Music Dept. California State University, Dominquez Hills, Carson CA 90747. (213)516-3947. Music Director: Dr. Frances Steinen. Symphony orchestra. Estab. 1973. Members are professionals and amateurs. Performs 4-5 concerts/year including 2-3 new works. Concerts performed in University Theatre (485 seats), Community Center (1000 seats) and an annual July 4th "Pops" Concert in Olympic Velodrome (10,000 attendance). Pays $100-200 for outright purchase or $25-200/performance. Query first, then submit complete score and tape of pieces. SASE.

Music: "Especially interested in women composers or ethnic minorities." Seeks arrangements for July 4th concert and annual children's concerts. 60-65 performers maximum. Does not wish to see "highly esoteric contemporary music or music which requires numerous unusual instruments."

Performances: Zwillich's *Symphony No. 1*.

*CASCADE SYMPHONY ORCHESTRA, 9630 214th Pl. S.W., Edmonds WA 98020. (206)778-6934. Director/Conductor: Robert Anderson. Symphony orchestra. Estab. 1962. Members are professionals and amateurs. Performs 4-5 concerts/year including 2-3 new works. "Audience is knowledgeable with a variety of backgrounds and interests—excellent cross-section. Perform in a rather old auditorium

seating 950." Submit complete score and tapes of pieces. SASE. Reports in 6 weeks.
Music: "Music should be suitable for symphony orchestra. Nothing over 20 minutes."
Performances: Paul Creston's *Dance Overture* (various dance rhythms); and Daniel Barry's *Sound Scapes* (Premiere based on ostenatos).

*CENTER FOR CONTEMPORARY OPERA, 475 Riverside Dr., 936, New York NY 10115. (212)870-2010. Director: Richard Marshall. Opera. Estab. 1982. Members are professionals. Performs 3 concerts/year; all are new works. 247-seat theater. Pays royalties. Submit complete score and tapes of pieces. SASE.
Music: "Looking for full-length operas. Limited orchestras and choruses. Orchestra—not over 25."
Performances: Sullivan's *Dream Play* (opera); Britten's *The Prodigal Son* (opera) and Beesau's *My Heart is in the Highlands* (stage premiere, opera).

*CHAMBER MUSIC IN YELLOW SPRINGS, INC., Box 448, Yellow Springs OH 45387. (513)767-1458. President; Bruce Bradtmiller. Chamber music presenting organization. Estab. 1981. Members are volunteer staff. Performs 5 concerts/year. "Have commissioned a composer once in 1989. The audience is very enthusiastic and quite knowledgeable in chamber music. The hall is a church, seating 280 with excellent acoustics." Pays $5,000 for outright purchase. Query first.
Music: "We are interested in innovative chamber music; however the composer should approach us with an ensemble identified. We are a chamber music presenting organization. We rarely present groups with more than 6 performers." Does not wish to see popular music.
Performances: Rick Sowash's *Anecdotes and Reflections* (instrumental, chamber work, violin, cello, piano, clarinet).
Tips: "We book primarily on the quality of ensemble. A composer should make an arrangement with a top-notch group and approach us through the ensemble's agent."

CHICAGO CHAMBER ORCHESTRA, 410 S. Michigan Ave., Chicago IL 60605. (312)922-5570. Music Director: Dr. Dieter Kober. Chamber orchestra. Estab. 1952. Members are professionals. Performs 25 concerts/year including 4-5 new works. Commissions 1 composer/year. Payment varies by director's discretion. Query, submit complete score and tapes of pieces, or submit through agent. SASE.
Music: Seeking compositions "not longer than 20 minutes for chamber orchestra. Pieces must not require many rehearsals and must not exceed 30 performers. We do not wish to see pop or electronic music."
Performances: Vazgen Muradian's *Concerto for Contrabassoon*, Ada Belle Marcus' *Brevities* (piano, chamber orchestra) and Franz Berwald's *Concerto for Violin in C# minor*.
Tips: "Have clean-looking score and parts."

*CHORUS OF WESTERLY, 22 High St., Westerly RI 02891. (401)596-8664. Music Director: George Kent. Community chorus. Estab. 1959. Members are professionals and amateurs. Performs 12 concerts/year including 1-2 new works. "4 'major works' concerts/year and 2 'pops' concerts/year. Summer pops reaches audiences of 28,000." Pays by outright purchase. Submit complete score and tapes of pieces. Reports in 3 weeks.
Music: "We normally employ a full orchestra from Boston. Major works desired—although 'good' pops charts considered."
Performances: Brahm's *Requim* and Holst's *Choral Symphony*.

*CINNABAR OPERA THEATER, 3333 Petaluma Blvd. N., Petaluora CA 94952. (707)763-8920. Artistic Director: Marvin Klebe. Opera company. Estab. 1974. Members are professionals. Performs 35 concerts/year. "Audience is ⅓ local, ⅓ Sonoma county, ⅓ greater San Francisco Bay area; theater is converted mission revival schoolhouse seating 99-150; no orchestra pit." Pays by arrangement with composer. Query first. SASE.
Music: "Our musical taste can best be described as eclectic. We produce full-length and one-act works; small orchestrations are preferred. Small casts are preferred. We are interested in works appropriate for opera singers who are also actors."

*CITY SUMMER OPERA BOX A-44, 50 Phelan Ave., San Francisco CA 94112. (415)239-3132. Music Department: Madeline Mueller. Opera company. Estab. 1987. Members are professionals and amateurs. Performs 8 concerts/year including 1 new work. Seats 300. Chamber orchestra of 30 performers or less. Pays by royalty. Submit complete score and tape of pieces. SASE. Reports in 3 months.
Music: "Contemporary operas suitable for young singers (some young professionals) and a chorus of amateurs. Level of difficulty must be appropriate for young voices and not too complicated musically. Must have large cast (65 approximately). Prefer text in English. Angular lines, difficult harmonies not appropriate. Dramatic works preferred—with interesting story or 'message.' Must be interesting musically but not too complex for our students."

Performances: Zigron's *Sweeney Agonistes* (chamber opera); Virgil Thomson's *Mother of Us All* (opera); and Kurtweill's *Mahogany* (opera).

*THE CLEVELAND PLAY HOUSE, P.O. Box 1989, Cleveland OH 44106. (216)795-7000. Literary Manager: Roger T. Danforth. Professional theater. Estab. 1915. Pays by royalty. Agent submission only. Reports in 4 months.
Music: Seeks only musical theater.
Tips: "Find agent to submit."

*COCKPIT IN COURT, 7201 Rooseville Blvd., Baltimore MD 21237. (301)522-1269. Managing Director: F. Scott Black. Community theater. Estab. 1973. Performs 8 concerts/year including 1 new work. "Audience is the Metropolitan-Baltimore community. Our theater is a 420 seat proscenium." Pays by royalty. Query first. SASE. Reports in 6 weeks.
Music: Seeks "Broadway show music."
Performances: Robert Macht's *Circles in the Sand*; Meredith Wilson's *Music Man* and Jerry Herman's *Milk and Honey* (all musicals).

COMMONWEALTH OPERA INC., (formerly Project Opera, Inc.) 160 Main St., Northampton MA 01060. (413)586-5026. Artistic Director: Richard R. Rescia. Opera company. Estab. 1977. Members are professionals and amateurs. Performs 4 concerts/year. "We perform at the Academy of Music at Northampton in an 800 seat opera house. Depending on opera, audience could be family oriented or adult." Pays by royalty. Query first. SASE. Reports in months.
Music: "We are open to all styles of opera. We have the limitations of a regional opera company with local chorus. Principals come from a wide area. We look only at opera scores."
Performances: Humperdinck's *Hansel and Gretel* (opera); Puccini's *Turandot* (opera); and Verdi's *La Traviata* (opera).
Tips: "Innovation that combines ease of production with new set, scenic and lighting techniques to produce effective opera at reasonable cost should somehow be built into the music."

*COMMUNITY FINE ARTS CENTER, 400 C St., Rock Springs WY 82901. (307)362-6212. Director: Allen Keeney. Orchestras. Estab. 1946. Members are amateurs and professionals. Performs 2 concerts/year. "We lean toward orchestras for more classical orientated people. Performances are held in the Rock Springs High School Auditorium with seating capacity of 800 seats." Pays $5,000-12,500/performance. Query first. Does not return unsolicited material. Reports in 1 month.
Music: "We prefer blues and symphony arrangements. No rock."
Performances: Eugene Ballet's *Cinderella* (ballet); Montana Repertory Theatre's *Out West, the Last Place* (musical theater); Charles Dickens' *Christmas Carol* (musical theater).

*CONCORDIA: A CHAMBER SYMPHONY, 330 Seventh Ave., New York NY 10001. (212)967-1290. Manager: Pat Ryan. Symphony orchestra. Estab. 1984. Members are professionals. Performs 5 concerts/year including 5-6 new works. Commissions 5 composers or new works/year. "Lincoln Center, Alice Tully Hall. Audiences between 28 and 50 years, mostly." Pays contest winner's prize and copying. Query first. SASE. Reports in 4 months.
Music: "Seeks jazz-influenced works for chamber symphony, 9-12 minutes, 2,2,2,2/2,210/strings percussion.
Performances: Laura Karpman's *Switching Stations* (jazz fusion); and Michael Daugherty's *Snap*.

*CONNECTICUT CHORAL ARTISTS, 90 Main St., New Britain CT 06051. (203)224-7500. Artistic Director: Richard Coffey. Professional concert choir. Estab. 1974. Members are professionals. Performs 10-15 concerts/year including 2-3 new works. "Mixed audience in terms of age and background; perform in various halls and churches in the region." Payment "depends upon underwriting we can obtain for the project." Submit complete score and tapes of pieces. SASE. Reports in 6 months.
Music: Seeking "works for mixed chorus of 36 singers; unaccompanied or with keyboard and/or small instrumental ensemble; text sacred or secular/any langauge; prefers suites or cylical works, total time not exceeding 15 minutes. Performance spaces and budgets prohibit large instrumental ensembles.

 The asterisk before a listing indicates that the listing is new in this edition. New markets are often the most receptive to unsolicited submissions.

Works suited for 750-seat halls are preferable. Substantial organ or piano parts acceptable. SCORES SHOULD BE VERY LEGIBLE IN EVERY WAY. Though not a requirement, we find that works with sacred texts get wider coverge."

Performances: Bernstein's *Missa Brevis (1988* regional premiere; based upon his *The Lark*); Frank Martin's *Mass for Double Chorus (1928* (regional premiere); Villa-Lobos' *Magdalena (1948* performed 1987 revival at Lincoln Center and recorded for CBS).

Tips: "Use conventional notation and be sure manuscript is legible in every way. Recognize and respect the vocal range of each vocal part. Work should have an identifiable *rhythmic* structure."

*DALLAS CHAMBER ORCHESTRA, Sammons Center for the Arts, 3630 Harry Hines, Dallas TX 75219. (214)520-3121. Music Director: Ronald Neal. Chamber orchestra. Estab. 1978. Members are professionals. Performs 30 concerts/year. Query first. Does not return unsolicited material.

Music: "Style—not contemporary; music for string orchestra only."

*DENVER CHAMBER ORCHESTRA, #1360, 1616 Glenarm Pl., Denver CO 80202. (303)825-4911. Orchestra Manager: Ellen Plunkett. A chamber orchestra with 35 pieces. Estab. 1968. Members are professionals. Performs 25 concerts/year including 2 new works. Commissions 1 composer or new work/year. "We play in a 500-seat auditorium in an arts complex and at The Paramount Theatre in Denver which seats 2,000. We usually pay the composer's air fare and room and board for the performance; sometimes an additional small stipend." Query first. SASE. Reports in 2 weeks.

Music: Seeks "pieces orchestrated for 35-40 instruments. No pop, symphonic."

Performances: Edward Smaldone and Otto Luening's *Dialogue*.

Tips: "Submit a query, which we will submit to our music director, Joan Fallelte."

*DENVER YOUNG ARTISTS ORCHESTRA, 1415 Larimer, Denver CO 80202. (303)571-1935. Executive Director: Peggy Atkinson. Youth orchestra. Estab. 1977. Members are amateurs-students. Performs 3 concerts/year including 1 new work. Boettcher Concert Hall seats 2,600 in main concert hall in Denver: "Supporters of our orchestra comprise the audience." Query first or contact Music Director. We do not return unsolicited material. Pays by outright purchase.

Music: "Pieces that will challenge our youth orchestra but that are within their capabilities, both musically and numerically." Symphonic only.

Performances: William Hill's *Mountain Thunder* (symphonic).

Tips: "We are doing our first commissioned piece this year so we are not ready to commit to how we will handle payment in the future. Reasonable price—willingness to work with youth orchestra (our budget is quite small)."

DIABLO VALLEY PHILAHARMONIC, 321 Golf Club Rd., Pleasant Hill CA 94523. (415)685-1230, Ext. 454. Conductor: Fredric Johnson. Symphony orchestra. Estab. 1974. Members are both professionals and amateurs. Performs 5 concerts/year including 2 new works. Sometimes commissions 1 composer, new work/year. "We perform in a 400-seat hall to a California audience. They'll go for anything new or unique if we don't overload them (i.e. quantity)." Pays through ASCAP. Submit complete score or complete score and tapes of piece(s). SASE.

Music: "Music must be for full romantic orchestra, without extra parts (harp, piano, English horn, Kazoo)—it's too expensive. Pieces should be of reasonable difficulty for about 65 musicians."

Performances: Marilyn Shufro's *Ciudades: Toledo y Seville* (orchestra); Earle Browne's *Modules* (orchestra); and Aaveneinen's *Rain* (suite for accordian/strings).

Tips: "Our orchestra is formed at the beginning of the season; it's tough to get the good musician in mid-season, so please avoid extra or exotic instruments."

EASTERN NEW MEXICO UNIVERSITY, Station 16, Portales NM 88130. (505)562-2736. Director of Orchestral Activities: Robert Radmer. Symphony orchestra, small college-level orchestra with possible choral collaboration. Estab. 1934. Members are students (with some faculty). Performs 5 concerts/year including up to 2 new works. "Our audience are members of a college community and small town. We perform in a beautiful, acoustically fine 240-seat hall with a pipe organ." Pay is $3,000 for outright purchase. Query first, submit complete score and tapes of piece(s), submit complete score or submit through agent only. SASE. Reports in 2 months.

Music: "Pieces should be 12-15 minutes; winds by 2, full brass. Work shouldn't be technically difficult. Organ, Harpsichord, piano(s) are available. We are a small college orchestra; normal instrumentation is represented but technical level uneven throughout orchestra. We have faculty available to do special solo work. We don't want 12-tone or works over 25 minutes. We like to see choral-orchestral combinations and writing at different technical levels within each family, i.e., 1st clarinet might be significantly more difficult than 2nd clarinet."

Performances: Poulenc's *Gloria* (choral/orchestra), Meyers' untitled work (as yet) (overture) and Morton Gould's *American Salute* (overture).

Tips: "I would like to see a choral/orchestral score in modern idiom for vocal solo(s), a chamber choir and large chorus used in concertino/ripeno fashion, with a 'Beethovenized' orchestra with full brass and percussion, featuring first chair players."

EUROPEAN COMMUNITY CHAMBER ORCHESTRA, 2, Five Bells, Offwell, Devon EX14 95B **United Kingdom.** Phone: (44)404 83 701. General Manager: Ambrose Miller. Chamber orchestra. Members are professionals. Performs 60 concerts/year. Commissions 2 composers or new works/year. Perform regular tours of Europe, also Americas and Asia, including major venues. Pays $500/performance. Query first. SASE and IRC. Reports in 3 months.

Music: Seeking compositions for strings, 2 oboes and 2 horns with a duration of about 15 minutes.

Performances: Patricia Saunders' *Four Pieces* (strings), Celedonio Romero's *Concierto Malaga* (guitar and chamber orchestra) and Jane O'Leary's *The Petals Fall* (strings, oboes and horns).

Tips: "Write something short and not too difficult, so it is easy to program."

*FAIRFAX SYMPHONY ORCHESTRA, P.O. Box 1300, Annandale VA 22003. (703)642-7200. Composer-in-Residence: Anthony Stark. Symphony orchestra. Estab. 1957. Members are professionals. Performs 50 concerts/year including 2 new works. "We perform at two halls: George Mason University's Concert Hall which seats 1939; and The Kennedy Center Concert Hall which seats 2759." Pays by commission. Query first. SASE. Reports in 2-3 months.

Music: "All styles appropriate to symphony orchestra (106 players) or chamber orchestra (50 players). Do not want pop music."

Performances: Ellen Taafe Zwilich's *Cello Symphony*; David Stock's *Symphony in One Movement*; and Nicholas Maw's *Spring Music*.

*FLORIDA SPACE COAST PHILHARMONIC, INC., Box 3344, Cocoa FL 32924 or 2150 Lake Dr., Cocoa FL 32926. (407)632-7445. General Manager: Alyce Christ. Artistic Director and Conductor: Maria Tunicka. Philharmonic orchestra and chamber music ensemble. Estab. 1986. Members are professionals. Performs 7-14 concerts/year. Concerts are performed for "average audience – they like familiar works and pops. Concert halls range from 600 to 2,000 seats." Pays 10% royalty (rental); outright purchase of $2,000; $50-600/performance; or by private arrangement. Query first; submit complete score and tape of piece(s). SASE Reports ASAP; "our conductor tours frequently thus we have to keep material until she has a chance to see and hear it."

Music: Seeks "pops and serious music for full symphony orchestra, but not an overly large orchestra with unusual instrumentation. We use about 60 musicians because of hall limitations. Works should be medium difficulty – not too easy and not too difficult – and not more than 10 minutes long." Does not wish to see avante-garde music.

Tips: "If we would commission a work it would be to feature the space theme in our area."

FUNDACION TEATRO DEL LIBERTADOR, Av. Velez Sarsfield 365, 5000 Córdoba **Argentina.** Phone: (051) 227201. Principal Conductor: Carlos Giraudo. Youth orchestra. Members are amateurs. Performs 20 concerts/year including 10 new works. Commissions 2-3 composers or new works/year. Concerts are performed for university and high school students. Submit complete score and tapes of pieces. SAE and IRC.

Music: Seeking "post romantic, impressionist, or contemporary works, 8-12 minutes in length with the following orchestration: 3-3-3-1/2-3-2-1/10-10-8-4-2.Harp. 2 Percussion."

Performances: Stravinsky's *Berceuse/Finale Firebyrd*, Moussorsky's *The Great Kizu Entrance* and Faure's *Masque et Bergamasque*.

*GRAND TETON MUSIC FESTIVAL, P.O. Box 490, Teton Village WY 83025. (307)733-3050. Music Director: Ling Tung. Symphony orchestra and chamber music ensemble. Estab. 1962. Members are professionals. Performs 40 concerts/year. Commissions 1-3 new works/year. "Concerts are aimed at people interested in wide variety of classical music. Concert hall is an enclosed, all-wood structure seating approximately 700." Pays weekly honorarium plus travel expenses. Query first. Does not return unsolicited material. Reports in 6 months.

Music: "For the most part, the Festival performs standard repertoire. New music is usually restricted to small ensembles (less than 10 players), although occasionally, if a noted composer is involved, the orchestra will perform a large scale work. Generally less than 10 players, no restriction on difficulty. No musical theater or opera."

Performances: Joan Tower's *Petroushskates* (quintet: flute, clarinet, violin, cello and piano); John Harbison's *Woodwind Quintet*; George Crumb's *Gnomic Variations* (solo piano).

GREAT FALLS SYMPHONY ASSOCIATION, Box 1090, Great Falls MT 59403. (406)453-4102. Music Director and Conductor: Gordon J. Johnson. Symphony orchestra and chamber music ensemble. Estab. 1959. Members are professionals and amateurs. Performs 7 concerts (2 youth concerts)/year including 2-3 new works. Commissions 1 composer or new work/year. "Our audience is conservative. Newer music is welcome; however, it might be more successful if it were programatic." Plays in Civic Center Auditorium seating 1,850. Pays outright purchase of $1,000. Submit complete score and tapes of pieces. SASE.
Music: "Compositions should be for full orchestra. Should be composed ideomatically for instruments avoiding extended techniques. Duration 10-20 minutes. Avoid diverse instruments such as alto flute, Wagner tuben, saxophones, etc. Our orchestra carries 65 members, most of whom are talented amateurs. We have a resident string quartet that serves as principals. Would enjoy seeing a piece for quartet solo and orchestra. Send letter with clean score and tape (optional). We will reply within a few weeks."
Peformances: Bernstein's *Chichester Psalms* (choral and orchestra); Hadkinson's *Boogie, Tango and Grand Tarantella* (bass solo); and Milhand's *Le Boef Sur le Toit* (orchestral).
Tips: "Music for orchestra and chorus is welcome. Cross cues will be helpful in places. Work should not require an undue amount of rehearsal time (remember that a concerto and symphony are probably on the program as well)."

*GREATER NASHVILLE ARTS FOUNDATION, 111 Fourth Ave. S., Nashville TN 37201. (615)259-6374. Program Coordinator: Steve Carson. Community arts organization. Estab. 1982. Performs 52 concerts/year "in art galleries and shopping malls; places where we can reach the general public of Nashville, which is our constituency, as we are affiliated with the Metropolitan Nashville Arts Commission." Pays union scale or better per performance. Query first. Does not return unsolicited material. Reports in 2 months.
Music: "We program performances of all kinds of music, from classical to country, jazz to rock."
Tips: "Work should have a multi-level appeal."

GULF COAST SYMPHONY, Box 4303, Biloxi MS 30535. (205)666-9554. Music Director: Andrew Harper. Symphony orchestra. Estab. 1962. Members are professionals and amateurs. Performs 4 concerts/year including 2 new works. Commissions variable number of composers or new works/year. Saenger Theater in Biloxi seats about 900. Children's Concert and Pops Concert in Biloxi Coliseum seats 2,700. Query first. Submit complete score and tapes of piece(s). We do not return unsolicited submissions. Reports in 6 months.
Music: Classical, pops, children's pieces. Winds triplicate. Be careful of exposed writing for 2nd violin and viola. Do not wish to see unaccompanied choral pieces, vocal solo or aria with piano accompaniment. Pieces should contain melodic interest. For children's pieces, a narrator or involvement of audience.
Performances: M. Rot's *Overture* (orchestral); L. Zanirelli's *Lexicon of Beasties* (children's concert); and R. Peck's *The Thrill of the Orchestra* (children/youth concert).

*HAUTBOIS PRODUCTIONS, #5R, 162 W. 75th St., New York NY 10023. (212)580-8133. Director: Ethan Bauch. Presents classical music for private functions. Estab. 1978. Members are professionals. Concerts include 2-8 new works/year. Commissions 2 composers or new works/year. Audiences consist of classical music lovers. Most concerts given in living rooms throughout the NYC area. Pays $500 and up for outright purchase. Query first. SASE. Reports in 2 months. Trios to 8-10. Does not want to see experimental work. "Our audiences are mainly conservative and used to baroque, classical and romantic styles."
Music: Lyrical, non-"avant garde" chamber works—various ensembles (strings, woodwinds or combinations thereof).

*HELSINKI PHILHARMONIC ORCHESTRA, Finlandia Hall, SF-00100 Helsinki **Finland**. Phone: +358 0 40 241. Managing Director: Mr. Reijo Jyrkiäinen. Philharmonic orchestra. Members are professionals. Performs 80 concerts/year including 4-6 new works. Comissions 2-3 composers or new works/year. Audience is mainly subscribers of symphony concerts. Finlandia Hall has 1,700 seats. Pays $3,000-5,000 for outright purchase. Submit complete score and tapes of piece(s). Reports in 2 months.
Music: "We seek modern music for symphony orchestra and chamber orchestra. Mostly interested in symphonic but also light music possible, no length limitations; symphony orchestra 4444 6441 13 2 strings. No pop, rock or country."

*HIGH DESERT SYMPHONY ORCHESTRA, P.O. Box 1255, Victorville CA 92392. (619)247-6966. Music Director: K.C. Manji. Symphony orchestra. Estab. 1969. Members are both amateurs and professionals. Performs 8 concerts/year; 2 new works/year. Plays in a 500 seat auditorium. Community-based audience; middle class incomes. "Composers usually not paid." Submit complete score and tapes of piece(s). SASE. Reports back in 2 months.

Music: "Syle: American nationalistic; length: up to 30 minutes. Level of difficulty must be intermediate/advanced, depending on amount of rehearsal time. Right now I would appreciate anything that would stress ensemble blending and be fairly tonal in color. This is an orchestra in the process of rebuilding and going forward."

Tips: "Send legible score and parts with clear directions either in music or in prose."

*THE PAUL HILL CHORALE (AND) THE WASHINGTON SINGERS, 5630 Connecticut Ave., NW, Washington DC 20015. (202)364-4321. Music Director: Paul Hill. Vocal ensemble. Estab. 1967. Members are professionals and amateurs. Performs 8-10 concerts/year including 2-3 new works. Commissions one new composer or work every 2-3 years. "Audience covers a wide range of ages and economic levels drawn from the greater Washington, DC metropolitan area. Kennedy Center Concert Hall seats 2,700." Pays by outright purchase. Submit complete score and tapes of pieces. SASE. Reports in 2 months.

Music: Seeks new works for: 1)large chorus and symphony orchestras; 2)chamber choir and small ensemble.

Performances: Argento's *Peter Quince at the Clavier*; Rorem's *An American Oratorio*; and Luboff's *A Choral Extravaganza*.

Tips: "We are always looking for music that is high quality and accessible to Washington audiences."

*HOUSTON YOUTH SYMPHONY & BALLET, P.O. Box 56104, Houston TX 77256. (713)621-2411. Orchestra Operations Manager: Jesse P. Johnson. Symphony orchestra. Estab. 1947. Members are students. Performs 6 concerts/year. "Performs in Jones Hall: 3,000 seat concert hall; Cullen Performance Hall: 1,000 seat concert hall for general audiences." Query first. SASE. Reports in 2 months.

Music: Uses full orchestra music suitable for players age 7-14. "We have two full orchestras, string orchestra."

Performances: Barber's *V/N Concerto, School for Scandal*; Shostakovich's *Symphony #5*; and Sammartini's *Symphony for Strings*.

*HUNTSVILLE YOUTH ORCHESTRA, P.O. Box 7223, Huntsville AL 35801. (205)536-2219. Music Director: Frederick R. Mayer. Chamber music ensemble and youth orchestra. Estab. 1961. Members are students. Performs 4-8 concerts/year including 0-2 new works. Commissions 0-1 composers or new works/year. Audience is mainly family adults of performers, students, musicians and music educators. Perform at Von Braun Civic Center Concert Hall; 1,600 seats. "Acoustically excellent." Payment individually arranged. Submit complete score and tapes of piece(s) or send representative works, score and tape. "We prefer to keep copies of scores and tapes on file." Reports in 3 weeks initially; 6 months for final decision.

Music: No longer than 3-15 min; Instrumentation: 3-2-2(1)-2, 4331, Perc (3) pro, strings. "Works possessing good rhythmic motion and drive; with dramatically contrasting sections. Areas of tonal centricity helpful. Good parts for all (when possible) and great parts for a few in typically strong instruments. NYSMA Grade 2-3 and 4-6. Must have relatively strong audience appeal on single listening."

Performances: Les Fillmer's *Finale from "Quadlibet"* (full orchestra) and Joann Forman's *(Ballet in Progress)* (full orchestra).

Tips: "Beautiful sounds, that have something to say. Excitement, contrast; challenging, worthwhile parts for young players."

IDAHO STATE – CIVIC SYMPHONY, P.O. Box 8099, Pocatello ID 83209. (208)236-3479. Music Director/Conductor: Dr. Thom Ritter George. Symphony orchestra. Estab. 1934. Members are professionals and amateurs. Performs 12 concerts/year. "Audience varied, ranges from highly musically educated to little background in music; in general, prefer music with which they have some familiarity. The symphony performs in Goranson Hall, on the campus of Idaho State University – seats 444, good acoustics. We consider converted works by composers scoring for full orchestra. The majority of our activities are oriented to the classical music audience." Pays by outright purchase or per performance. Query first. Does not return unsolicited material

Performances: Griffes' *Poem for Flute and Orchestra*; Edouard Lalo's *Symphonie Espagnole*; and Sibelius' *Symphony No. 2 in D Major, OP. 43.*

Tips: "Write a work which is structurally sound and score idiomatically for the symphony orchestra."

*INTER SCHOOL ORCHESTRAS OF NEW YORK, 125 E. 87 St., New York NY 10128. (212)410-9823. Conductor: Jonathan Strasser. Youth orchestra. Estab. 1972. Members are amateurs. Performs 6 concerts/year. "Varied churches to major halls like Carnegie or Alice Tully. Varied audiences." Pays for outright purchase. Does not return unsolicited material.

Music: Orchestra of 50 (advanced) of 30 strings, horns and trumpets—intermediate group of 50. Cheval works or works with huge orchestration. "Composers should realize that players are 18 and younger so works should not be outrageously complicated or difficult."

Performances: Gordon Jacob's *Concerto for Trombone* (full orchestra); Carl Kudik's *Gerald McBoing Boing* (narrated work with violas, celli, winds [single] 2 trumpets and 23 percussion instruments); and Samuel Baker's *Adagio for Strings*.

Tips: "Remember that we are an educational, music making organization seeking to give the youngsters in our orchestras the best learning and performing experiences kpossible. We wish to stretch their experience but not present them with impossibilities."

*ISRAEL SINFONIETTA BEER SHEVA, 12 Derech Hameschachrerim, Beer Sheva 84 299 **Israel**. Phone: (57)31616. Managing Director: Mr. Leor Segal. Chamber orchestra. Members are professionals. Performs 120 concerts/year including 5 new works. Commissions 1 new composer or new works/year. "Our Beer Sheva audience is a serious but rather conservative one. Concerts are performed in a small hall seating 400 people. In other locations, throughout Israel, audiences are more broad-minded; halls seat 600-800 people." Pays by agreement. Query first; "it is wise to check before sending score to ensure that orchestration is suitable for our orchestra." SAE and IRC. Reports in 3 months.

Music: Seeking pieces with "orchestration: 7/6/5/5/2; 2/2/2/2 2/2/0/0 and percussion. No limitation on difficulty."

Performances: Aharon Harlap's *A Child's World* (suite).

*ITHACA OPERA ASSOCIATION, 109 E. Seneca St., Ithaca NY 14850. (607)272-0168. Music Director: Edward Murray. Opera company. Estab. 1949. Members are professionals and amateurs. Performs 20-30 concerts/year. Opera company mainstage productions are performed in small, three-quarter round setting; winter touring production is performed in large auditorium settings. In addition to mainstage productions, maintains a small ensemble company which performs in schools and for civic organizations throughout area, so site specs vary. Pays by royalty or per performance. Query first. SASE. Reports in months.

Music: "We seek works for children; we are always on the lookout for pieces that are fun for children as well as educational, or works that are essentially family-oriented, that include choruses of children or adolescents. We are limited by small performing specs; we need works with set requirements that allow us to take the show on the road easily."

Performances: Richard Wargo's *The Music Shop* (one-act opera); Gian Carlo Menotti's *Amahl and The Night Visitors* (one-act opera); and Tom Jones' *The Fantasticks* (music theater piece).

Tips: "We are especially interested in works that involve kids as well as entertain them! An availability for 'Meet the Composer' days would be an added draw."

*JACKSON SYMPHONY ORCHESTRA, P.O. Box 3429, Jackson TN 38303. (901)427-6440. Executive Director: Dr. Carol L. Quin. Symphony orchestra. Estab. 1961. Members are professionals. Performs more than 60 concerts/year including 3 new works. Commissions 1 composer or new work/year. "The audience is a conservative group with an average age of 50. The hall seats 2,000. Four concerts on the season are 'classical,' three are 'Cabaret' with table seating and dinner." Composer is paid by prize for composition competition. Query first. SASE.

Music: "Music should be melodic, not complicated. No more than 60 performers. Do not send strange requests for instrumentation."

Tips: "Write a letter about the piece—send instrumentation list and description with length."

JOHNSON CITY SYMPHONY ORCHESTRA, P.O. Box 533, Johnson City TN 37604. (615)926-8742. Symphony orchestra. Estab. 1969. Members are professionals and amateurs. Performs 7 concerts/year including 2 new works. Commissions 1 composer or new work/year. "We perform in a 1903 Victorian theater which seats 648." Pays $1,500 outright purchase. Query first. Does not return unsolicited material. Reports in 1 month.

Music: "We have done 3 minute pieces for strings, brass or winds; up to 45 minute pieces for full orchestras. We can perform pieces of moderate difficulty—strings 10-10-6-4-3, 2 oboes max, 1 English horn max, 3 trombones, 1 tuba."

Performances: Lewis Songer's *MacRae Meadow* (brass piece, 3 min.); Martin Herman's *Up a Tree* (storyteller and orchestra) and Alan Murchie's *Daen for Brass and Woodwinds*.

Tips: "Music should not be too atonal. Should be something with market interest and have local color."

*KENTUCKY OPERA, 631 S. Fifth St., Louisville KY 40202. (502)584-4500. Opera. Estab. 1952. Members are professionals. Performs 22 concerts/year. Performs at Whitney Hall, The Kentucky Center for the Arts, seating is 2,400; Bomhard Theater, The Kentucky Center for the Arts, 620; Macauley

Theater, 1,400. Pays by royalty, outright purchase or per performance. Submit complete score and tapes of piece(s). SASE. Reports in 6 months.
Music: Seeks opera—1 to 3 acts with orchestrations. No limitations.
Performances: Daniel Dutton's *The Stone Man* (1 act opera); Philip Glass' *The Fall of the House of Usher* (2 act opera).

KITCHENER-WATERLOO CHAMBER ORCHESTRA, Box 937, Waterloo ON N2J 4C3 **Canada**. (519)744-3828. Music Director: Graham Coles. Chamber Orchestra. Estab. 1985. Members are professionals and amateurs. Performs 8 concerts/year including some new works. "We perform at St. John's Lutheran Church (seats 500), Humanities Theatre, University of Waterloo (seats 1,200). We perform mainly baroque and classical repertoire, so that any contemporary works must not be too dissonant, long or far fetched." Pays by music rental and performing rights fees only. Submit complete score. "It's best to query first so that we can outline what not to send. Include: complete CV—list of works, performances, sample reviews." SASE. Reports in 4 weeks.
Music: "Musical style must be accessible to our audience and players (3 rehearsals). Length should be under 20 minutes. Maximum orchestration 2/2/2/2 2/2/0/0 Timp/1 Percussion Harpsichord/organ String 4/4/3/3/1. We have limited rehearsal time, so keep technique close to that of Bach-Beethoven. We also play chamber ensemble works—octets, etc. We do not want choral or solo works."
Performances: John Weinzweig's *Divertimento I* (flute and strings); Peter Jona Korn's *4 Pieces for Strings* (string orch.); and Graham Coles *Variations on a Mozart Rondo* (string orch.).
Tips: "If you want a first-rate performance, keep the technical difficulties minimal."

*KNOX-GALESBURG SYMPHONY, Box 31 Knox College, Galesburg IL 61401. (309)343-0112, ext. 208. Music Director: Bruce Polay. Symphony orchestra. Estab. 1951. Members are professionals and amateurs. Performs 7 concerts/year including 1-4 new works. Audiences are middle to upper middle class plus college students. Hall is 927 seat renovated vaudeville hall with excellent acoustics. Pays $50-200 per performance. Query first. Submit complete score and tapes of pieces. SASE. Reports in 5 weeks.
Performances: Polay's *Perspectives*; Lenoke's *Tribute to the Duke*; and Julstrom's *Adagio* (all orchestral).
Tips: "Send neat, easy to read scores."

*L.A. SOLO REPERTORY ORCHESTRA, 7242 Louise Ave., Van Nuys CA 91406. (818)342-8400. Music Director: James Swift. Symphony orchestra. Estab. 1968. Members are professionals and amateurs. Performs 6 concerts/year including 7 new works. Commissions 1 composer or new work/year. "General audience. Hall of Liberty: 1,400 seats, Van Nuys Jr. High School auditorium: 800 seats." Pay is negotiated. Submit complete score and tapes of pieces. SASE. Reports in 6 weeks.
Music: "20th century symphonic, particularly with solo instruments. Many composers extend development to point of boredom, so we reserve right to cut or perform single movements. Use of odd instruments or greatly extended sections tends to inhibit performance. No hard rock—even when intended for large orchestra."
Performances: Rowan Taylor's *Symphony #35*; (4 mvt symphony); Martin Selbrede's *Concerto for Trumpet & Trombone* (3 mvt Premiere); and Rocco Di Giovanni's *Aria for Solo Clarinet and Orchestra* (concertpiece Premiere).
Tips: "Edit the work! Keep the moderately sophisticated audience in mind. Compose for audience enjoyment if you want your work repeated!"

LAKESIDE SUMMER SYMPHONY, 236 Walnut Ave., Lakeside OH 43440. (419)798-4461. Conductor: Robert L. Cronquist. Symphony orchestra. Members are professionals. Performs 8 concerts/year. Perform "Chautauqua-type programs with an audience of all ages (2-102). Hoover Auditorium is a 3,000-seat auditorium." Query first. SASE.
Music: Seeking "classical compositions for symphony composed of 50-55 musicians. The work needs to have substance and be a challenge to our symphony members. No modern jazz, popular music or hard rock."
Performances: Richard's Nanes' *Prelude, Canon & Fugue* (classical).

*LAMARCA AMERICAN VARIETY SINGERS AND IMAGE, 2424 W. Sepulveda Blvd., Torrance CA 90501. (213)325-8708. Director/Manager: Priscilla LaMarca. Vocal ensembles. Estab. 1979. Members are professionals and amateurs. Performs 20 concerts/year including 5-10 new works. Commissions 2 composers or new works/year. Performs at major hotels, conventions, community theaters, fundraising events, cable television, community fairs, Disneyland. Submit complete score and tapes of pieces. SASE. Reports in 2 months.

Music: "Seeks 3-10 or 15 minute medleys; a variety of musical styles from Broadway—pop styles to humorous specialty songs. Top 40 dance music, Linda Ronstadt-style to Whitney Houston. Light rock and patriotic themes. Also interested in music for children. No heavy metal or anything not suitable for family audiences."
Performances: Norris Community Theatre *USA Medley* (show-theatrical).
Tips: "Make sure the lyrics fit the accents of the music.[Be-caúse, not Bé-cause]. Make sure there is continuity of the song's meaning throughout. Keep the beat about 120-140 bpm. and no lengthy instrumental interludes."

LEXINGTON PHILHARMONIC SOCIETY, 161 N. Mill St., Arts Place, Lexington KY 40507. (606) 233-4226. Music Director: George Zack. Symphony orchestra and chamber music ensembles. Estab. 1961. Performs 35-40 concerts/year including 12-15 new works. Members are professionals. Commissions 1-2 composers or new works/year. Series includes "8 serious, classical subscription concerts (hall seats 1,500); 15-outdoor pops concerts (from 1,500 to 5,000 tickets sold); 3-5 run-out concerts (½ serious/ ½ pops); and 10 children's concerts (hall seats 1,500)." Pays via ASCAP and BMI, rental purchase and private arrangements. Submit complete score and tape of pieces. SASE.
Music: Seeking "good current pops material and good serious classical works. No specific restrictions, but overly large orchestra requirements, unusual instruments and extra rentals help limit our interest."
Performances: Zwillich's *Celebration* (overture); Crumb's *A Haunted Landscape* (tone poem); and Corigliano's *Promenade* (overture).
Tips: "When working on large-format arrangement, use cross-cues so orchestra can be cut back if required. Submit good quality copy, scores and parts. Tape is helpful."

*LINCOLN YOUTH SYMPHONY ORCHESTRA, 720 S. 22nd St., Lincoln NE 68510. (402)473-0248. Music Director: Dr. Brian Moore. Youth orchestra. Estab. 1956. Members are amateurs. Performs 3 concerts/year. "The audience is made up of parents, friends, University teachers and teachers from the schools and a general audience." Pays by outright purchase. Query first. SASE. Reports in 2 weeks.
Music: "Needs orchestral compositions of moderate difficulty—new music/contemporary styles are welcomed. Orchestra is full winds and strings."
Performances: Schubert's *Unfinished*; Percy Grainger's *Walking Song* (winds only); and Shastakovich's *Cello Concerto* (solo).
Tips: "Call and talk to us first."

LITHOPOLIS AREA FINE ARTS ASSOCIATION, 3825 Cedar Hill Rd., Canal Winchester OH 43110. (614)837-8128. Series Director: Virginia E. Heffner. Performing Arts Series. Estab. 1973. Members are professionals and amateurs. Performs 5-6 concerts/year including 1 or 2 new works. "Our audience consists of couples and families 35-65 in age range and several senior citizens. Our hall is acoustically excellent and seats 400. It was designed as a lecture-recital hall in 1925." Composers "may apply for Ohio Arts Council Grant under the New Works category." Pays 1-2% royalty, $66/performance. Query first. SASE. Reports in 4 weeks.
Music: "We prefer that a composer is also the performer and works in conjunction with another artist, so that they could be one of the performers on our series. Piece should be musically pleasant and not too dissonant. It should be scored for small vocal or instrumental ensemble. Dance ensembles have difficulty with 15' high 15' deep and 27' wide stage. We do not want avant-garde or obscene dance routines. No ballet (space problem). We're interested in something historical—national, or Ohio emphasis would be nice. Small ensembles or solo format is fine."
Tips: "Personally talk to me first and then I can show you our performance hall. Through ORACLE, we might be able to black-book you."

*THE LOUISVILLE ORCHESTRA, 609 W. Main St., Louisville KY 40202. (502)587-8681. Music Director: Lawrence Leighton Smith. Symphony orchestra. Estab. 1937. Members are professionals. Performs 100 concerts/year including 6 new works. Commissions 2 composers or new works/year. Master-Works classical subscription concerts are performed in the 2,400-seat Whitney Hall of the Kentucky Center for the Arts. "Our audience varies in age from University students to seniors and comes from the areas surrounding Louisville in Kentucky and Indiana." Pays by commission. Submit complete score and tapes of piece(s). Does not return unsolicited material. Reports in months. Planning done year in advance of performance.
Music: "All styles appropriate to symphony orchestras. No chamber works, pop music or lead sheets." Orchestration for standard symphony orchestra. No pop music/pop vocal/New Age. Enclose a tape of performance or keyboard realization.
Performances: Chinary Ung's *Inner Voices* (orchestra/symphonic); William Bolcom's *Commedia for "Almost" 18th Century Orchestra*; Ezra Laderman's *Sanctuary* (symphonic); Joan Tower's *Silver Ladders* (symphonic).

THE LYRIC OPERA OF DALLAS, Suite 818, 8111 Preston Rd., Dallas TX 75225. (214)368-2183. Artistic Director: John Burrows. Music Theatre Company. Estab. 1982. Members are professionals. Performs 3-4 concerts/year including 3 new works in 6 years. "The Majestic Theatre in downtown Dallas is a beautifully restored Victorian building, seating 1,500. There are excellent stage facilities and a good orchestra pit." Query first or submit complete score and tapes of piece(s). SASE. Reports in 3 weeks; 2 months if submitted between April and August.
Music: "We want stageworks for not in excess of 35 onstage performers, and 30 orchestra musicians. The only other limitation is that all performances are in English. We don't want works demanding exceptional scenic demands or very large forces. The Lyric Opera of Dallas is known for performing a high proportion of comedic material, and has no tradition of presenting esoteric works."
Performances: Robert Rodriguez *The Ransom of Red Chief* (one-act opera); Leonard Bernstein *Candide* (comic operetta, SW premier of opera version); and Alan Strachan/Benny Green's *Cole* (revue of life and compositions of Cole Porter).

***MANITOBA CHAMBER ORCHESTRA**, 202-1317A Portage Ave., Winnipeg Manitoba R3G OV3 **Can-ada**. (204)783-7377. General Manager: Rita Manzies. Chamber orchestra. Estab. 1972. Members are professionals. Performs 10 concerts/year including 2 new works. "Audiences are generally profession-als—also many young people. We perform two series—one in a church (seats 1,000) and the other in a hotel (seats 250). Candlelight concerts in the hotel are more casual." Pays by commission. Query first. SASE.
Music: Seeks "music for string orchestra and one solo instrument. Limitations: 22 strings; no pop music."
Performances: Chan Ka Nin's *Treasured Pastun Leisure Pleasure* (orchestral); and Jerome Summers' *Caprice* (strings and wind).

***MARSHALL UNIVERSITY SYMPHONY ORCHESTRA**, 400 Hal Greer Blvd., Huntington WV 25755. (304)696-6417. Director of Instrumental Ensembles: Michael McArtor. Symphony orchestra. Estab. 1962. Members are professionals and amateurs. Performs in 4 concerts/year including 1-2 new works. Pays $500-1,000 for outright purchase. Query first. SASE. Reports in 2 months.
Music: Seeks "all styles. Not to exceed 20 minutes-chamber orchestra and full orchestra. Medium difficulty is our current rating."
Performances: Beethoven's *Overture to Egmont*; Mozart's *Serenade No. 4*; Holst's *St. Paul's Suite*; and Haydn's *Symphony No. 92* (all overtures).
Tips: "Create a *playable* work for a growing string department."

***MILWAUKEE YOUTH SYMPHONY ORCHESTRA**, 929 N. Water St., Milwaukee WI 53202. (414)272-8540. Music Coordinator: Susan Chandler. Youth orchestra. We also have a Junior Wind Ensemble. Estab. 1956. Members are students. Performs 3-4 concerts/year including 1-2 new works. "Our groups perform in Uihlein Hall at the Performing Arts Center in Milwaukee. The audiences usually consist of parents, music teachers and other interested community members. We usually are reviewed in either the Milwaukee Journal or Sentinel." Query first. SASE.
Tips: "Be sure you realize you are working with students and not professional musicians. The music needs to be technically on a level students can handle."

MISSOURI SYMPHONY SOCIETY, P.O. Box 1121, Columbia MO 65205. (314)875-0600. Artistic Direc-tor and Conductor: Hugo Vianello. Symphony orchestra, chamber music ensemble, youth orchestra and pops orchestra. Estab. 1970. Members are professionals. Performs 23 concerts/year including up to 8 new works. Commissions one composer or new work/year. "Our home base is a 1,200-seat reno-vated 1928 movie palace and vaudeville stage. Our home audience is well-educated, including profes-sionals from Columbia's five hospitals and three institutions of higher education. Our touring program reaches a broad audience, including rural Missourians and prison inmates. We are proud that 1991 represents our 20th performance season. We hope to do a world premier at each of our eight home series concerts to celebrate this anniversary." Pays through ASCAP and BMI. Submit complete score (and if available, tapes of pieces). SASE. Reports in 8 weeks.
Music: "We want good orchestral (chamber) music of any length—2222/2200/timp/strings/piano. There are no limitations on difficulty."
Performances: Marshall Fine's *Missouriana* (premiere, chamber orchestra); Norman Dello Joio's *New York Profiles* (chamber orchestra); and Richard Nanes' *Symphony for Strings*.

MOHAWK TRAIL CONCERTS, P.O. Box 843, Greefield MA 01302. (413)774-3690. Managing Director: Jeanne Donado. Chamber music presenter. Estab. 1970. Members are professionals. Performs approx-imately 20 concerts/year including 2-3 new works. "Audience ranges from farmers to professors, chil-dren to elders. Concerts are performed in churches and town halls around rural Franklin County,

Massachusetts." Pays by performance. Query first. Does not return unsolicited material. Reports in months.

Music: "We want chamber music, generally not longer than 30 minutes. We are open to a variety of styles and orchestrations for a maximum of 8 performers. We don't want popular, rock or theater music."

Performances: Michael Cohen's *Fantasia for Flute Piano and Strings* (chamber); William Bolcom's *Nes Songs* (piano/voice duo); Alice Parker's *Songs for Eve* (chamber).

Tips: "We are looking for artistic excellence, a committment to quality performances of new music, and music that is accessible to a fairly conservative (musically) audience."

*MORAVIAN PHILHARMONIC OLOMOUC, Nám. míru 23, Olomouc, CSSR 772 00 **Czechoslovakia**. Phone: 28971. Contact: S. Macura. Chamber music ensemble and philharmonic orchestra. Members are professionals. Performs 60 concerts/year including 20 new works. Commissions 1-2 composers or new works/year. "Audience of a university town of considerable historic tradition." Concerts are performed in a hall seating about 800, "neoclassicist style." Pays per performance in Czech crowns. Submit complete score with tapes of pieces. SAE and IRC. Reports in 3 weeks.

Music: Maximum 15 minutes, any style, large orchestra or interesting concerto music (soloist accompanied by large orchestra or chamber ensemble-strings). "Special emphasis on melody."

Performances: Vacek Miloš' *Symfonie č.2*, Matěj Josef's *Kytička*; and Parsch Arnošt *Poeme.Koncert pro cimbál*.

Tips: "Wait until the piece starts simmering in your mind; do not write just for the sake of writing something."

MUSIC PROGRAMS: LOS ANGELES COUNTY MUSEUM OF ART, 5905 Wilshire Blvd., Los Angeles CA 90036. (213)857-6115. Music Programs Coordinator: Cheryl Tiano. Presenting organization. Estab. 1971. Members are professionals. Performs 100 concerts/year including 35 new works. "Usually, the audience is, to some extent, educated in either the classics or arts. The hall seats 600." Pays $350-12,000 per performance. Submit program proposal and tape. SASE. Reports in 3 months.

Music: "We want small groups, electronics, computers, chamber ensembles, outstanding solo artists and jazz. We require good credentials. We don't present dance music (usually). Rap, disco, country, etc . . . are not appropriate for this venue; however, sometimes there is a fine line between art and entertainment. Submit a written program proposal (what they would play), tapes of prior performances, and follow through with phone calls.

Performances: Donald Martino's *From the Other Side* (chamber ensemble); Roberto Sierra's *Invocaciones* (percussion/soprano); and Jack Vees *Child Bride* (cello/computer).

Tips: "For this venue, composers either function as performers as well (playing their own works), or are associated with an ensemble, in some way, that is willing to present the composer's work as part of the ensemble's program."

*MUSIC THEATRE OF ARIZONA, 918 S. Park, Tempe AZ 85281. (602)829-0008. Artistic Director: Ron Newcomer. Music theater production company. Members are professionals and amateurs. Performs 3-7 concerts/year including 1-2 new works. "Performs in three venues: 3,000 seat concert hall (Grady Garmage on ASU's campus) a 7,000 seat concert hall (Sundome) and an 800 seat theater (Herberger) where new works performed here." Pays by royalty (varies). Submit complete score and tapes of pieces. SASE. Reports in 3 months.

Music: "New musical theater works, preferably small casts—any style, from country to jazz, pop, etc. Small casts up to 15 preferred due to Lort contract demands. No hard rock or material you would consider inappropriate for general public. Suggestive material is fine, vulgar is another thing. Stick to *musical theater* format."

Performances: Rodgers & Hammerstein's *The King & I* (musical); Maltby & Shine's *Starting Here Starting Now* (musical revue); Charles Strouse's *Annie* (musical); and Nancy Loeds' *Scrooge: A Musical Ghost Story* (premiere musical).

Tips: "Be flexible and willing to share and blend with the creative effort, without giving up your initial intent. Share and compromise instead of becoming stubborn or closed to any new idea or thought."

*MUSIC TODAY, 129 W. 67th St., New York NY 10023. (212)362-8060. Director: Andrew Berger. Chamber music ensemble. Estab. 1980. Members are professionals. Performs 3 concerts/year including 3-5 new works. Commissions 1-2 composers or new works/year. "We perform in Merk Concert Hall, seating 450 people. We are trying to attract a large, diverse audience of serious music listeners. Pays by royalty and commissioning grants where available. Query first by mail, please, with resume and letter." SASE. Reports in 3 months.

Music: "Seeks works for conductor and chamber ensemble of varied instrumentation from 6 to 22 players. We are particularly interested in crossover and semi-theatrical pieces. We are not interested in pop music per se."

Performances: Xavier Rodriguez's *Tango* (chamber with vocal soloist); Larry Bell's *Piano Concerto*; and Christopher Rouse's *Rotae Passionis* (chamber with clarinet solo).

Tips: "Write good music. We are especially interested in considering scores from women and minorities although decisions are made strictly according to the quality of the work."

*NASHVILLE OPERA ASSOCIATION, 1900 Belmont Blvd., Nashville TN 37212. (615)292-5710. General Director: Kyle Ridout. Opera company. Estab. 1981. Members are professionals and amateurs. Performs 4 concerts/year. "Tennessee Performing Arts Center (Jackson Hall) has 2,400 seats and Tennessee Performing Arts Center (Polk Theatre) has 1,100 seats." Pays by outright purchase. Submit complete score and tapes of pieces. SASE. Reports in 1 month.

Music: Seeks opera and music theatre pieces, sometimes accept one-acts."

Performances: Donizetti's *Lucia di Lammermoor*; Sullivan's *The Mikado*; and Verdi's *Il Travatore* (opera).

Tips: "Be willing to work through the score by subjecting the work to readings/workshop."

*NATIONAL ASSOCIATION OF COMPOSERS/USA, Nacusa Box 49652, Los Angeles CA 90049. (213)541-8213. President: Marshall Bialosky. Chamber music ensemble and composers' service organization. Estab. 1932. Members are professionals. Performs 6-9 concerts/year—all new works. Usually performed at universities in Los Angeles and at a mid-town church in New York City. Paid by ASCAP or BMI, NACUSA does not pay composers. Must join the organization to receive services. SASE. Reports in 3 months.

Music: Chamber music for five or fewer players; usually in the 5 to 20 minute range. "Level of difficulty is not a problem; number of performers is solely for financial reasons. We deal in serious, contemporary concert hall music."

NATIONAL SINFONIETTA, 23451 Roanoke, Oak Park MI 48237. (313)546-4814. Music Director: Burton A. Zipser. Sinfonietta (64 member orchestra). Estab. 1982. Members are professionals. Performs 22 concerts/year. Concerts are performed in a hall with 1,660 seats, excellent acoustics and pipe organ for an audience of high school humanities students and senior citizens. Pays $500/performance; "We have performing rights society memberships (ASCAP, BMI, SESAC). Query or submit complete score and tapes of pieces. "Composers must be American." SASE. Reports in 3 months.

Music: Seeking compositions with "a maximum length of 25-30 minutes, with the following orchestration: 3-3-3-3 4-3-3-1 percussion (not more than 5), harp, piano (sax if required). We have only 10 hours of rehearsal time. Shorter works (with chorus, concerti) may be submitted. Only submit pieces that have previously been performed in public—no premieres. These works will be performed on national/cable public TV—they should be accessible, representative and interesting. Since many people will be introduced to the composer for the first time, he or she should submit something that won't discourage future interest."

Performances: David Owens' *Psalm* (string orchestra).

Tips: "Write music which creates positive emotional reactions, is colorful in sound and does not assault the ear."

*NEBRASKA CHAMBER ORCHESTRA, 749 NBC Center, Lincoln NE 68508. (402)477-0366. General Manager: Peggy Chesen. Chamber orchestra. Estab. 1976. Members are professionals. Performs 6 concerts/year including 6 new works. "We perform in two halls; one seats 850 and the other seats 2,250. Our audience is primarily 30 years or older in age, a minimum of a Bachelors Degree in education and a minimum income of $25,000. Our audience comes from metropolitan Lincoln and surrounding areas." Pay by individual arrangements. Query first. SASE.

Music: "We want all styles appropriate to a chamber orchestra and accessible for the Nebraska audience. Lengths can vary but prefer approximately 30 minute pieces. NCO standard instrumentation: 2-2-2-2 2-2 timpani, strings (65442). No excessively difficult works due to limited rehearsal time."

Performances: Loris Tjeknavorian's *Concerto for Guitar and Orchestra, "Zareh" Op. 39* (concerto); Russell Peck's *Amber Waves for Brass Quartet and Orchestra* (miniature classical symphony); and Michael Torke's *Ash (1988)*.

NEW YORK CITY OPERA EDUCATION DEPARTMENT, New York State Theater, Lincoln Center, New York NY 10023. (212)870-5635. Administrative Director: Nancy Kelly. "The company produces a total of 110 educational programs/year and one fully staged children's opera each season for elementary, junior high and high school students. Different introductory programs cover opera, operetta, musical comedy and other forms of music theater. The programs are performed in the schools by professional singers with piano accompaniment. Schools must pay a set fee per performance. Query first.

Music: "We look for operas that are appropriate in subject matter for school-age children and theatrical enough to hold the students' attention. Works should be no longer than 1 hour in length in order to fit into class schedules. The limitations of school stages dictate minimal scenic and technical requirements. The total performing ensemble (singers and musicians) should not exceed 9."

Performances: *Opera Adventure, American Patchwork, On Broadway!* and a newly commissioned opera, *East of the Sun, West of the Moon* by Robert Dennis and Stephen Phillip Policoff.

*THE NEW YORK CONCERT SINGERS, 401 East 80th St., New York NY 10021. (212)879-4412. Music Director/Conductor: Judith Clurman. Chorus. Estab. 1988. Performs 2-3 concerts/year including new works. Commissions 1 composer or new work/year. "Audience is mixture of young and old classical music 'lovers.' Chorus performs primarily at Menkin Concert Hall, NYC." Pays at completion of work. Query first or send score and tape with biographical data. SASE.

Music: Seeks music "for small professional ensemble, with or without solo parts, a cappella or small instrumental ensemble. Not for large orchestra and chorus (at this stage in the group's development). Looking for pieces ranging for 7-20 minutes."

Performances: Ned Rorem's *Homer: Three Scenes from the Iliad* (30 minutes/chorus/soloist/8 instruments); Richard Hundley's *Ball* (12 minutes/chorus/soloists from chorus/4 hand PN.); and Leonard Bernstein's *Missa Brevis* (15 minutes/chorus/2 percussionsists).

Tips: "When choosing a piece for a program I study both the text and music. Both are equally important."

*NORFOLK CHAMBER MUSIC FESTIVAL/YALE SUMMER SCHOOL OF MUSIC, 96 Wall St., New Haven CT 06520. (203)432-1966. Summer music festival. Estab. 1941. Members professionals and amateurs; the students in the festival are almost professionals. Performs 12 concerts, 14 recitals including 3-6 new works. Commissions 0-1 composer or new work/year. The 1,200-seat Music Shed was built in 1906 by architect Eric K. Rossiter. The interior is lined with California redwood, the floor is wooden and the ceiling is a peaked cathedral, which creates wonderful acoustics." Pays a commission fee (set fee). Submit complete score and tapes of piece(s). SAE. Reports in 1 month.

Music: "Chamber music of combinations, particularly for strings, woodwinds, brass and piano. There are 1-2 chamber orchestra concerts per season which include the students and feature the festival artists. Other than this, orchestra is not a medium featured, rather, chamber ensembles are the focus."

Performances: Ronald Roseman's *Woodwind Quintet* (performance); Robert Nagel's *Brass Trio* (performance); and Joan Panetti's *Brass Quintet* (premiere).

*NORTH ARKANSAS SYMPHONY ORCHESTRA, P.O. Box 1243, Fayetteville AR 72702. (501)521-4166. Music Director: Carlton Woods. Symphony orchestra, chamber music ensemble, youth orchestra and community chorus. Estab. 1954. Members are professionals and amateurs. Performs 20 concerts/year including 3 or 4 new works. "General audiences—currently perform in churches and schools in six area cities." Pays $200-500/performance. Query first. SASE.

Music: Seeks "audience pleasers—rather short (10'-15'); and full orchestra pieces for subscription (classical) concerts. Orchestra is 60-70 members."

Performances: Robert Mueller's *Deep Earth Passing*; and Will Gay Bottje's *Sounds from the West Shore.*

*THE NORTHSHORE SYMPHONETTE, 17005 191st Ave., Woodinville WA 98072. (206)788-3404. Conductor: Dr. Stafford Miller. Chamber string orchestra. Estab. 1986. Members are professionals and amateurs. Performs 4 concerts/year. "Audience is members of the community. We play at Chateau Ste. Michelle, a local winery." No payment. Query first. SAE. Reports in 2 weeks.

Music: Open to all submissions. Music must be of medium difficulty. "We are a 14-piece string orchestra but we add other instruments as required. Music submitted should be of medium difficulty and be understandable by the musicians and audience. As we are a very low-budget orchestra, I can offer no promise of payment." Submit music within the limits of instrumentation of medium difficulty.

Performances: *Faure Requiem* (with added instrumentation); Mozart's *Three Divertimenti*; Tchaikovsky's *Serenade For Strings*; and Bach's *Brandenburg Concerto #4*.

Tips: "Present music that is within the possibilities of performance. It must be playable. It must have the possibility of being understood by the audience. Manuscript must be correct and readable. Write for yourself, of course, but make an attempt to communicate with your listeners. Music need not be extremely difficult to be good."

*OLD STOUGHTON MUSICAL SOCIETY, P.O. Box 794, Stoughton MA 02072. (617)344-5993. President: Joseph M. Klements. Community chorus. Estab. 1786. Members are amateurs. Performs 2 concerts/year. "Audience is general public." Query first. Does not return unsolicited material. Reports in 6 weeks.

Music: Seeks "choral compositions by American (preferably New England) composers. We have an extensive collection of materials from early American singing schools but have broadened repertoire to early and modern American composers. Chorus size less than 40, with 1-20 accompanists. Level of difficulty should be geared to accomplished amateurs."
Performances: E.A. Jones' *Easter Oratorio*; Everett Titcomb's *Christmas Story* (cantata); and Leo Sowerby's (anthems).

OPERA IN THE SCHOOLS, 4015 Spotswood Trail, San Antonio TX 78230. (512)699-8791. Director: Evelyn Troxler. Opera company: children's operas. Members are professionals. Performs 150 concerts/year including 1 new work. Commissions 1 composer/year. "Operas are performed for children, grades Kindergarten through 8. We perform in auditoriums, classrooms, gymnasiums, etc." Pays $30-40/performance. Submit complete score. SASE. Reports in 1 month.
Music: Seeking "operas for young audiences with a good bit of dialogue, not to exceed 30 minutes. Four to five soloists, no chorus. Accompaniment suitable for piano, synthesizer, flute, clarinet and percussion (any or all of them). No more than 5 singers and 5 in the orchestra. Any level of difficulty. Special emphasis should be on story lines (comedy especially). Must be good theatre as well as good music. Story must be full of adventure, not scary but fun; lines need to have comedy, music must be tuneful."
Performances: Rea's *The Wizard's Ring* and *The Enchanted Flute* (children's pieces) and Englebert Humperdinck's *Hansel and Gretel* (30 minute version).
Tips: "Find a good libretto, one which permits a lot of imagination in the staging."

*OPERA ON THE GO, 184-61 Radnor Rd., Jamaica Estates NY 11432. (718)380-0665. Artistic Director: Jodi Rose. American opera chamber ensemble. Estab. 1985. Members are professionals. Performs about 30 operas/year; all new works. "We perform primarily in schools and community theaters. We perform only American contemporary opera. It must be lyrical in sound and quality as we perform for children as well as adults. We prefer pieces written for children based on fairy tales needing 4 to 6 singers." Pays $20 per performance. Query first then submit complete score and tapes of piece(s). SASE. Reports if requested within weeks on submissions; if unsolicited, about 2-3 months.
Music: Need works in all age groups including adults. For older ages the pieces can be up to 60 minutes. Rarely use orchestra. "Keep the music as short as possible since we do a prelude (talked) and postlude involving the children's active participation and performance. If it is totally atonal it will never work in the schools we perform in."
Performances: Edith Hemenway's *Goldilocks and the 3 Bears* (opera for N-3 grade); Mark Bucci's *Sweet Betsy From Pike* (opera for 6 grade-adult); and Seymour Barub's *Fair Means or Foul* (opera for grades 3-8).
Tips: "Be flexible. Through working with children we know what works best with different ages. If this means editing music to guarantee its' performance, don't get offended or stubborn."

*OPERAWORKS, 170 W. 73rd St., New York NY 10023. (212)873-9531. President: Joel Casey. Chamber opera company. Estab. 1984. Members are professionals. Performs 4-6 concerts year; 2-3 new works/year. Symphony hall has 1,200 seats. Submit complete score and tapes of pieces. SASE. Reports in 4-6 weeks.
Music: Chamber opera. Small orchestral arrangement preferred, especially the use of synthesizer or recorded sound.

ORANGE COUNTY OPERA, INC., P.O. Box 1470, Sunset Beach CA 90742. (213)592-2017. Artistic Director: Christopher Webb. Educational opera company. Estab. 1976. Members are professionals. Performs 300 concerts/year. "We are an educational opera company that performs in schools in Los Angeles and Orange Counties. We perform at the schools with an average audience of 300 per performance. We are interested in 30 minute operas." Payment open to negotiation. Query first. SASE. Reports in 2 months.
Music: "We want lyrical opera in English. We have done 30 minute versions of *Hansel and Gretel, Daughter of the Regiment, Act I—Tales of Hoffman*. We want to show off opera as another art form kids do not see or hear often. We want piano accompaniment and lively, humorous music and story. The maximum number of performers should be 5 plus accompanist. Singers are professional level. We don't want avant-garde, atonal music. We want very singable music. Our goal is to entertain with excellent voices, story and music. We would like a show with both male and female singers, fast-paced; perhaps queries about specific ideas we could address better."
Performances: Mollicone's *The Starbird* (one act opera).
Tips: "Show opera to be a wonderful visual and aural experience. Excite the kids—make them want to see and hear more. We would love to have a new work for our company and introduce young audiences to modern opera. We want a story line that will appeal to those audiences and create an interest in opera and musical theater/live theater."

*OREGON SYMPHONY, 711 SW Alder, Portland OR 97205. (503)228-4294. Director of Concert Operations: Peggie Schwarz. Symphony orchestra. Estab. 1896. Members are professionals. Performs 125 concerts/year including 3-4 new works. Commissions varying number of new works. "Classical concerts are attended predominantely by 35-60 year olds. Hall seats 2,776 — renovated vaudeville house." Pays by commission — flat fee negotiable. Submit complete score and tapes of pieces. SASE.
Music: "Classical orchestrations: 16-14-12-10-8; pops: 12-10-8-8-6; jazz: 3333-5331 3 perc, 1 tmp, 1 harp, 1 keyboard. No country. Send a list of other orchestras with whom you have performed."
Performances: Schiff's *Slow Dance* (symphonic w/jazz flavor); and Singleton's *Shadows* (symphonic w/jazz flavor).

*PENSACOLA CIVIC BAND, 1000 College Blvd., Pensacola FL 32504. (904)484-1800. Director: Don Snowden. Community band. Estab. 1971. Members are professionals and amateurs. Performs 6 concerts/year. "Our audience varies in age and we play in a 300 seat auditorium." Query first. SASE.
Music: Popular medleys of Broadway shows and other familiar popular music. Standard instrumentation. No limit on difficulty.

*PHOENIX SYMPHONY ORCHESTRA, 3707 N. 7th St., Phoenix AZ 85014. (602)277-7291. Assistant Conductor: Mark R. Smith. Symphony orchestra. Estab. 1947. Members are professionals. Performs 130 concerts/year including 15 new works. Commissions 2 composers or new works/year. "Various halls, primarily Phoenix Symphony Hall, Grady Gammage Center on Arizona State University campus (designed by Frank Lloyd Wright), and Scottsdale Center for the Arts. Patrons of all ages." Pays by outright purchase, per performance or commission. "Fee depends upon size and duration." Query first. SASE. Reports in 3 months.
Music: Seeks "serious orchestra works, pops, children's works, chamber orchestra. No theater pieces for concert (except children's)."
Performances: Elfman's *Batman Suite* (symphonic); Richardson's *Oboe Concerto* (chamber orchestra/solo); and Neikrug's *Violin Concerto* (symphonic/solo).
Tips: "Manuscript should be extremely neat. Score professional in appearance. Include duration and tape (cassette) if available."

PICCOLO OPERA COMPANY, 18662 Fairfield Ave., Detroit MI 48221. (313)861-6930. Executive Director: Marjorie Gordon. Opera company. Estab. 1962. Members are professionals. Performs 5-50 concerts/year including 1 new work. Commissions 1 composer or new work/year. Concerts are performed for a mixed audience of children and adults. Pays by royalty or outright purchase. Query or submit complete score and tapes of pieces. Does not return unsolicited material.
Music: "Musical theater pieces, lasting about one hour, for adults to perform for adults and/or youngsters. Peformers are mature singers with experience. The cast should have few performers (up to 10), no chorus or ballet, accompanied by piano or orchestra. Skeletal scenery. All in English."
Performances: Humperdinck's *Hansel & Gretel* (opera); Barab's *Little Red Riding Hood* (opera); and Gilbert & Sullivan's *Festival of Highlights* (concert).

*PLYMOUTH MUSIC SERIES OF MINNESOTA, 1900 Nicollet Ave., Minneapolis MN 55403. (612)870-0943. Managing Director: Jeanne Patterson. Choral orchestral performing society. Estab. 1969. Members are professionals and amateurs. Performs 5 concerts including 1-2 new works. Audience is generally all ages from late 20s. Comes from entire Twin Cities metro area. "We perform in Ordway Music Theatre, Orchestra Hall, Cathedrals in both Minneapolis and St. Paul." Pays commission fee. Query first. SASE. Reports in months.
Music: All styles appropriate to a choral/orchestral society except pop or rock. "Text used is of special concern. If the work is over ½ hour, the use of soloists is preferred."
Performances: Peter Schickele's *Oedipus Tex* (fully-staged opera); Libby Larsen's *Coming Forth Into Day* (dramatic 1-hour work for narrator, baritone and soprano soloist, chorus and orchestra); and Aaron Copland's *The Tender Land* (semi-staged opera).
Tips: "Be patient. We have a very small staff and are constantly behind in reviewing scores. Tapes are very helpful."

*PRO ARTE CHAMBER ORCHESTRA OF BOSTON, #187, 105 Charles St., Boston MA 02114. (617)661-7067. Chair, New Works Committee: Anne Black. Symphony orchestra. Estab. 1978. Members are professionals. Performs 8 concerts/year including 4 new works. Commissions 2 composers or new works/year. "We have an average audience of about 700, approximately 340 subscription seats, age range attending is from 17 to 75, the average is 47, income categories in the middle to lower middle income range. Hall seats 1250, small stage, on university campus." Paid only if grant or individual support can be found. Query first. SASE. Reports in 6 months.

Music: "Styles range from baroque to modern, but original; some jazz, some minimilist, open to suggestions. Length of no longer than 15 minutes. Orchestration size of 2222 2200 tmp+1 perc. (moderate on percussion equipment capacity). Strings 7.6.4.3.2. Level of difficulty not a problem, forces to be utilized must be strictly enforced as stated above."

Performances: Linda Bouchard's *Fanorev* (short, minimilistic); Jay A. Gach's *I Ponentino* (medium length, somewhat dissonant); and Jan Swafford's *Chamber Sinfonietta* (concertino/ripieno utilized medium length, jazzy).

Tips: "Resonable forces without lots of percussion, medium length, not too dissonant, no sound equipment, interesting individual style."

*QUEENS OPERA, 313 Bay 14th St., Brooklyn NY 11214. (718)256-6045. General Director: Joe Messina. Opera company. Estab. 1961. Members are professionals. Performs in 9 concerts/year. SASE. Reports in 1 month.

Music: "Operatic scores and songs, small orchestra."

Performances: Puccini's *Madama Butterfly*; Strauss' *Die Fledermaus*; and Puccine's *La Boheme*.

*THE RIDGEFIELD YOUTH ORCHESTRA, 700 N. Salem Rd., Ridgefield CT 06877. (203)438-3785. Music Director, Conductor: Dr. Charles Spire. Youth orchestra. Estab. 1971. Members are students. Performs 6 concerts/year including 3 new works. Audience is the general public, parents and students. Concert hall has 1,000 seats. Pays $400 for outright purchase. Query first. SASE. Reports in 2 weeks.

Music: Modern, serious, light. Level 6-difficult. 100 performers including standard symphony plus saxaphone. "Composer should involve soloists from all sections of the orchestra."

Performances: Dvorak's *Symphony No. 9* (serious); *Music Man Symphonic Impressions* (light); Curten's *The Phantom of the Opera* (light).

*SALT LAKE SYMPHONIC CHOIR, P.O. Box 45, Salt Lake City UT 84110. (801)466-8701. Manager: Richard Taggart. Professional touring choir. Estab. 1949. Members are professionals and amateurs. Performs 4-15 concerts/year including 1-3 new works. "We tour throughout U.S. and Canada for community concert series, colleges and universities. Pay is negotiable. Query first. Does not return unsolicited material. Reports in 3 months.

Music: Seeking "4- to 8-part choral pieces for a 100-voice choir—from Bach to rock."

*SAN DIEGO SYMPHONY ORCHESTRA, 1245 7th Ave., San Diego CA 92101. (619)699-4200. Artistic Administrator: Bert Harclerode. Symphony orchestra. Estab. 1927. Members are professionals. Performs 85 concerts/year including 100 new works. Symphony Hall: 2,255-seat downtown facility (renovated Fox movie theater) used October-May; 3,600-seat outdoor facility with combination cabaret talbe and gallery seating used from June-September. Pays through ASCAP or BMI. Submit complete score and tapes of pieces. SASE.

Music: "Orchestral music desired. 85-piece symphony orchestra. No chamber orchestra/music."

Performances: Joseph Schwantner's *Long Before the Winde* (Praeludium for orchestra).

Tips: "Submit works and tapes; information is then given to Executive Director, then to Music Director for consideration."

*SARASOTA OPERA ASSOCIATION, 61 N. Pineapple Ave., Sarasota FL 34236. (813)366-8450. Artistic Director: Victor De Renzi. Opera company. Estab. 1959. Members are professionals. Performs 22 opera performances/year. Commissions 1 new work/year maximum. "Our main season of four productions is for a community audience. The opera house has 1,033 seats. We also do children's operas in schools, which may occasionally include original works." Pays royalty (whatever dictated by publisher). Submit complete score and tapes of piece(s). SASE. Reports in 3-4 months.

Music: "For mainstage productions, we use only standard repertoire. However, for the Youth Opera, we use contemporary children's operas. We prefer approximately 45 minutes long, piano accompaniment and few characters, (e.g., 3-4, including a pianist) so as to be able to tour. We want things that are lyrical and singable. Nothing extremely atonal. An emphasis on whimsical material that is appropriate for children is preferred."

Performances: Barab's *The Toy Shop* (children's opera); Davies' *Cinderella* (children's opera); Breedon's *The Frog Prince* (children's opera); and Barab's *Little Red Riding Hood* (children's opera).

Tips: "Be a good grantwriter!"

SAULT STE. MARIE SYMPHONY ORCHESTRA, 801 Prospect, Sault Ste. Marie MI 49783. (906)635-2265. Music Director: Dr. John Wilkinson. Symphony orchestra. Estab. 1972. Members are professionals and amateurs. Performs 5 full orchestra concerts/year, 25-30 other. "Our audience is conservative. Our performance hall seats 964." Query first. SASE. Reports in 2 months.

Music: "We have traditional orchestra size 2222/4231/2, plus strings. String 88552. We want pieces of length (5-15 minutes) in approachable styles. We have 45-50 performers. Pieces should be of moderate difficulty (or less!). Engage the listener; make it playable."
Performances: Ridout-Quesnel's *Colas et Colinette* (light overture); S. Glick's *Elegy* (elegy); and J. Weinzweig's *The Red Ear of Corn* (ballet suite).

SEAWAY CHORALE AND ORCHESTRA, INC., 2450 Middlefield Rd., Trenton MI 48183. (313)676-2400. Conductor, Executive Director: David M. Ward. Auditioned chorus and orchestra. Estab. 1975. Members are professionals and amateurs. Performs 5 major concerts/year (4 new works/year). Commissions 0-2 composers or new works/year. "We perform in halls, some church settings and high school auditoriums—large stage with orchestra pit. Our audience is ecumenically, financially, racially, socially, musically, multi-generation and a cross section of our area." Pays by negotiation. Query first by telephone or mail. SASE. Reports in 8 weeks.
Music: "We want 3-minute ballads for orchestra and chorus (for subscription concerts); sacred music, either accompanied or a cappella; Christmas music for chorus and orchestra. We have three performing groups: Voices of the Young—4th through 8th grades (40 members); Youth Sings—9th through 12th grades (a show choir, 24 members); Chorale—adults (70 members). Charismatic Christian music is not high on our priority list. Country music runs a close second. Our major concerts which draw large audiences utilize light selections such as show music, popular songs and music from movies. We present two concerts each year which we call Choral Masterpieces. These concerts include music from master composers of the past as well as contemporary. Our choral masterpieces concerts require Biblical or secular thoughts that are well-conceived musically."
Tips: "Music for adult chorale and orchestra—Christmas or general. Also music for children's chorus with orchestral accompaniment. Find an arts agency which will underwrite a high percentage of the cost of works which you might consider sending us for perusal. We are a nonprofit organization."

*SHAW FESTIVAL THEATRE, Box 774, Niagara-on-the Lake, Ontario L0S 1J0 **Canada.** Director of Music: Christopher Donison. Theater company. Estab. 1962. Members are professionals. Commissions 1-5 composers or new works/year. "We have the stages and draw our audience from everywhere in the world, with an obvious emphasis on the New York/Ontario area." Payment is negotiable. Contact by query first and submit complete score and tapes of piece(s). Does not return unsolicited material.
Music: "Intelligent, sophisticated, widely-based, innovative and yet pragmatic, both electronic and conventionally scored."
Performances: Murray Shaffer's *Patria* (opera) and Christopher Donison's *Peter Pan* (theater score).

*THE SINGERS FORUM, 31 West 21st St., New York NY 10010. (212)366-0541. Administrator: Denise Galon. Vocal school and presenting organization. Estab. 1978. Members are professionals and amateurs. Performs more than 50 concerts/year including 2 new works. Commissions 2 composers or new works/year. 99 and 75 seat performance space with varied audience. Pay through donations from patrons. Query first. SASE. Reports in 6 weeks.
Music: "All popular music, art songs, full musicals, small operas with minimal orchestration." No rock. "I'm always looking for works to fit our current voices."
Performances: *The Cabaret* (blues, jazz and pop); *Broadway: Then and Now* (scenes and music); and *Zeitgeist* (retrospective).
Tips: "Think of the voice."

SINGING BOYS OF PENNSYLVANIA, P.O. Box 206, Wind Gap PA 18091. (215)759-6002. Director: K. Bernard Schade, Ed. D. Vocal ensemble. Estab. 1970. Members are professional children. Performs 120 concerts/year including 2-3 new works. Commissions 1-2 composers or new works/year. "We attract general audiences: family, senior citizens, churches, concert associations, university concert series and schools." Pays by outright purchase $500-750. Query first. SASE.
Music: "We want music for commercials, music for voices in the SSA or SSAA ranges sacred works or arrangements of American folk music with accompaniment. Our range of voices are from G below middle C to A (13th above middle C). Reading ability of choir is good but works which require a lot of work with little possibility of more than one performance are of little value. We don't want popular songs which are not arranged for SSA or SSAA choir. We sing very few popular songs except for special events. We perform music by composers who are well-known composers and do works by living composers, but ones who are writing in traditional choral forms. Works of music which have a full orchestral score are of interest. The orchestration should be fairly light, so as not to cover the voices. Works for Christmas have more value than some other, since we perform with orchestras on an annual basis."
Performances: Arwel Hughes' *Paul Revere* (choral work with piano and percussion); *Appalachian Suite* (choral work with piano accompaniment, arr. by Schade); and Arthur Harris' *Christmas* (choral work with piano or orchestral).

Tips: "Come to hear the group sing in person!"

SOUTHWESTERN COLLEGE/WINFIELD COMMUNITY ORCHESTRA, 100 College, Winfield KS 67156. (316)221-4150, ext. 300. Conductor: Diane S. Mathie. Symphony orchestra and chamber music ensemble. Members are students and amateurs. Performs 3 concerts/year. Concerts performed for a well-educated audience in Richardson auditorium (seats 700). Pays per performance. Query first. SASE. Reports in 1 month.
Music: "We seek bright, short-overture type works, approximately 5-7 minutes."
Performances: Bizet's *Carmen Suite #1*; Brahms', *Hungarian Dance #5 + 6*; and LeVelle's *Mansfield Overture* (composed by senior composition major).
Tips: "In order to compose for our group, one must learn the strengths and weaknesses of each member of the orchestra. We consist of amateur musicians and 30% college student musicians."

SUSQUEHANNA SYMPHONY ORCHESTRA, P.O. Box 485, Forest Hill MD 21050. (301)838-6465. Music Director: Sheldon Bair. Symphony orchestra. Estab. 1978. Members are amateurs. Performs 5 concerts/year including 2 new works. "We perform in 2 halls. One is more intimate, 953 seats, mediocre acoustics, the other is larger (999 seats) with fine acoustics. Our audience encompasses all ages." Composers are normally not paid, just ASCAP or BMI royalties. Query first or submit complete score. SASE. Reports in 2 months.
Music: "We desire works for large orchestra any length, in a 'conservative 20th century' style. The music director appreciates a good tune. We are a community orchestra, so the music must be within our grasp. Violin I to 7th position by step only; Violin II—stay within 3rd position, english horn and harp are ok. We don't want avant-garde music."
Performances: Dr. James McVoy's *Spring Fancies* (3 movement character pieces); Robert Palmer's *Symphony No. 2* (3 movements, neo-classic); and David Finko's *Viola Concerto* (one movement concerto, 20th century Russian composer).

*TORONTO MENDELSSOHN CHOIR, 60 Simcoe St., Toronto, Ontario M5J 2H5 **Canada**. 1(416)598-0422. Manager: Michael Ridout. Vocal ensemble. Members are professionals and amateurs. Performs 15 concerts/year including 1-3 new works. "Most performances take place in Roy Thomson Hall. The audience is reasonably sophisticated, musically knowledgeable but with moderately conservative tastes." Pays by royalty or by direct commission (does not result in ownership of the work). Submit complete score and tapes of pieces. SASE.
Music: All works must suit a large choir (180 voices) and standard orchestral forces or with some other not-too-exotic accompaniment. Length should be restricted to no longer than ½ of a nocturnal concert. The choir sings at a very professional level and can sight-read almost anything. "Works should fit naturally with the repertoire of a large choir which performs the standard choral orchestral repertoire."
Performances: Mahler's *Symphony #8*; (choral-orchestral); Honneger's *King David* (choral-orchestral and narrator; and Orff's *Carmina Burana* (choral-orchestral).

*UNIVERSITY MUSICAL SOCIETY OF THE UNIVERSITY OF MICHIGAN, Burton Tower, Ann Arbor MI 48109-1270. (313)747-1174. Executive Director: Kenneth C. Fischer. Presenting organization. Estab. 1879. Performers are professionals. Presents 45 concerts/year including 2 new works. Commissions 1-2 composers or new works/year. "Diverse audience drawn from throughout Ann Arbor and Southeast Michigan. 3 halls: Hill Auditorium (4,173); Rackham Auditorium (1129); Power Center (1414)." Pays by commissioning fees. Query first. SASE. Reports in weeks.
Music: "UMS is part of several commissioning consortia with other major presenters. We are in a position to form partnerships with artists, managers, composers and presenters to commission new works and to guarantee multiple performances."
Performances: Donald Bryant's *Genesis* (30-minute piece for chorus, orchestra, soloists and children's chorus); and William Bolcom's sonata for cello and piano for Yo-Yo Ma and Emanuel A.
Tips: "We like to approach our commissions as a collaboration between the consortium presenters, the artist, the artist's manager and the composer. Getting all the parties involved at the beginning helps assure a timely completion of the commission and successful multiple performance."

*UNIVERSITY OF HOUSTON OPERA THEATRE, School of Music, Houston TX 77204-4893. (713)749-4370 or 749-1116. Director of Opera: Buck Ross. Opera/music theater program. Members are professionals, amateurs and students. Performs 3-4 concerts/year including 1 new work. Performs in a proscenium theater which seats 1,100. Pit seats approximately 40 players. Audience covers wide spectrum, from first time opera-goers to very sophisticated." Pays by royalty. Submit complete score and tapes of piece(s). SASE. Reports in weeks.

Music: "We seek music that is feasible for high graduate level student singers. Chamber orchestras are very useful. No more than 2½ hours. We don't want serial pieces, aleatoric or children's operas."
Performances: Mozart's *La Finta Giardiniera* (opera); Mary Carol Warwick's *Twins* (opera); and Kurt Weill's *The Tsar Has His Photograph Taken* (opera).

*UNIVERSITY OF SOUTHERN MISSISSIPPI SYMPHONY ORCHESTRA, Box 5081, Hattiesburg MS 39406. (601)266-5687. Music Director: Jay Dean. Symphony orchestra. Estab. 1922. Members are college students. Performs 8 concerts/year including 2 new works. Commissions 1 composer or new work/year. Payment negotiable. Submit complete score or score and tapes of piece(s). SASE. Reports in 2 months.
Music: All serious symphonic music. Should be suitable for university level players.

UTAH ARTS FESTIVAL, 168 W 500 N., Salt Lake City UT 84103. (801)322-2428. Assistant Director: Robyn Nelson. Annual 5 day arts festival. Estab. 1977. "We present 50-52 performances of music and dance/year. We have an outdoor festival with a week long attendance of 80,000 with 3 stages, seating 1,500-5,000." Pays per performance. Query first. SASE. Reports in 3 weeks.
Music: "We support new music along the lines of Morton Subotnick, John Zorn, Steve Reich, etc. We present everything from traditional folk/acoustic, reggae, blues, jazz and new music. We aren't looking for rock & roll, rap, heavy metal or New Age."
Performances: By Daniel Lentz & Group, Phillip Glass, Michael Brecker, Morton Subotnick and Anthony Davis.
Tips: Contact us with tape and press materials.

VALLEY CIVIC ORCHESTRA, 1700 Spartan Dr., Elgin IL 60123. (708)888-7389. Music Director/Conductor: Mark G. Rachelski. Chamber Orchestra. Estab. 1983. Members are professionals and amateurs. Performs 4-5 concerts/year including 2 new works. Commissions 1-2 composers or new works/year. "Our audience size is approximately 500. We perform in Schaumburg Prairie Center for the Arts (seats 750) and various community halls and churches." Pays up to $200 outright purchase or up to $100 per performance. Submit complete score or send SASE. Reports in 2 months.
Music: "We want works for small orchestra—classical and pops orchestrations, concertos, modern works, voice and orchestra, opera, chorus and orchestra. Winds doubled. We have some limited range extremities. Traditional notation should predominate."
Performances: Mark Rachelski's *Concert Overture*; Robert Muczynski's *Dovetail Overture*; and Claude Debussy's *Children's Corner Suite*.
Tips: "To begin composing: listen to orchestrations as often as possible, especially live performances. Try to write for a specific group and learn its requirements and limitations.."

VALLEY YOUTH ORCHESTRA ASSOCIATION, 18111 Nordhoff St.—MUSC, Northridge CA 91330. (818)885-3074. Music Director: H. Wesley Kenney. Symphony orchestra, youth orchestra and chamber orchestra. Estab. 1970. Performs 8 concerts/year including 2 new works. Members are amateurs and students. "Audience is comprised of parents of members, many senior citizens, other students and professional people. Halls are either Reseda High School (seats about 1,350) or a campus theater (seats 400 with large stage)." Pays outright purchase of $100-200, $100-200/performance, or negotiated amount. Submit complete score (full score only) and tape of pieces. SASE. Reports in 3 weeks.
Music: "We are seeking pieces of approximately 10-12 minutes in length written for full symphony orchestra, with brass sections of 2-3 horns, 3 trumpets, 1-3 trombones for the Junior Orchestra and full brass for the Senior. We will consider pieces for solo instrument or voice and orchestra. Style is less a concern than accessibility, and there should be something about the piece that will teach them something useful. For the Youth Orchestra, accessibility is often extremely important. If the group can understand the piece within the first rehearsal, they will work harder to perform their best because they enjoy it. But don't make the piece without challenge, or they will become bored with it before it can be perfected."
Performances: Chamber orchestra: Ginostefa's *Variacoines Concertantes* (variation for orchestra); senior orchestra: Schumann's *Symphony #3 in E-flat* (symphony); and junior orchestra: Brahms' *Tragic Overture, op. 81* (overture).
Tips: "Learn the limitations of the instruments, and rudiments of orchestral balance. In addition, be very specific with what sound is desired. A dot tells a lot, but never enough."

VEREINIGTE BÜHNEN/OPERNHAUS, Kaiser Josef Platz 10, Graz 8010 **Austria**. Phone: 0316/826451. Operndramaturgie: Dr. Monica Pirklbauer, Brigitte Bartz. Opera house. Members are professionals. Performs 8 operas/year including 1 new work. Operas are performed in our opera house with 1271 seats, both season tickets and open performances; or in studio with 240 seats, young audience." Submit complete score and tapes of pieces. SAE and IRC.

Music: "We would primarily like to find something for our studio, some kind of chamber opera for an orchestra of 10 members maximum and between 1 and 6 singers."

Performances: Otto M. Zykan's *Der Auszälreim* (opera, written 1986) and Friedrich Cerha's *Der Rattenfänger* (opera, written in 1987).

*VIRGINIA BEACH ORCHESTRAL ASSOCIATION, #285 780 Lynnhaven Pkwy., Virginia Beach VA 23452. (804)468-7677. Director Operations/Artistic Consultant: J.L. Kreger. Pops orchestra. Estab. 1983. Members are professionals. Performs 42 concerts/year including 7 new works. Commissions 4-6 composers or new works/year. "We perform in a hall that seats 972. Our audience varies and comes from metropolitan Virginia Beach and surrounding areas."Pays by outright purchase. Query first. SASE.

Music: "We want styles appropriate to pops orchestra, 8-12 minutes in length. 2222 4331 T 2P harp (optional), keyboard (optional). No limit on difficulty."

Performances: Kreger's "Visions" (ballet); Fluck's *Tribute to Tommy* (orchestra) and *Autumn Leaves* (piano & orchestra).

Tips: "Be open for suggestions!"

*WARMINSTER SYMPHONY ORCHESTRA, 524 W. Pine St., Trevose PA 19047. (215)355-7421. Music Director/Conductor: Gil Guglielmi, D.M.A. Community symphony orchestra. Estab. 1966. 12 "pros" and amateurs. Performs 4 concerts/year including perhaps 1 new work. We *try* for to commission one composer or new work/year. Audience is blue collar and upper middle-class. The concert hall is a local junior high school with a seating capacity of 710. "We operate on a small budget. Composers are not paid, or paid very little (negotiations)." Composer should contact Dr. Guglielmi. Does not return unsolicited material. Reports in months.

Music: Romantic style. Length: 10 minutes to a full symphony. Orchestration: full orchestra with no sound effects, synthesizers, computers, etc. "We play from Mozart to Tschaikovsky." "Performers: we have a maximum of about 60 players. Level of difficulty: medium advanced—one grade above a good high school orchestra. We rehearse 2 hours a week so that anything written should take about 20 minutes a week rehearsal time to allow rehearsal time for the remaining selections." "As stated above, the Philadelphia Orchestra which is only one half hour away plays avant-garde, contemporary music much better than we do. Our musicians and our audiences are middle-of-the-road." "The composer should write in *his* style and not try to contrive a piece for us. The orchestra has a full string section, 4 horns, 3 clarinets, 3 flutes, 2 bassons, 3 trumpets, 2 oboe, 1 English horn, 3 trombones, 1 tuba, 1 harp and a full percussion section."

Performances: Al Maene's *Perla Bella* (mini symphony); David Finke's *The Wailing Wall* (tone poem).

Tips: "Do not expect the Philadelphia Orchestra. My musicians are primarily lay-people who are dedicated to the performance of good music. What they lack in expertise they more than make up in practice, work and dedication."

WAYNE CHAMBER ORCHESTRA, 300 Pompton Rd., Wayne NJ 07470. (201)595-2694. Manager: Sheri Newberger. Chamber orchestra. Estab. 1986. Members are professionals. Performs 4 concerts/year. Regional audience from North Jersey area. Attractive and modern concert hall seating 960 patrons. Query with bio first. SASE.

Music: "We are looking for new American music for a 40-piece orchestra. Our only method of funding would be by grant so music may have to tie in with a theme. Although we have not yet performed new works, we hope to in the future."

Performances: Diamond's *Concerto for Chamber* (orchestra); Barber's *Adagio for Strings*; Fine's *Serious Song*.

WHEATON SYMPHONY ORCHESTRA, (formerly Wheaton Summer Symphony) 1600 E. Roosevelt, Wheaton IL 60187. (708)668-8585. Manager: Donald C. Mattison. Symphony orchestra. Estab. 1959. Members are professionals and amateurs. Performs 3 concerts/year including 1 new work. Composers are paid $100-200/performance. Query first. SASE. Reports in 2 months.

Music: "This is a *good* amateur orchestra that wants pieces in a traditional idiom. No avant garde, 12-tone or atonal material. Pieces should be 20 minutes or less and must be prepared in 3 rehearsals. Instrumentation is woodwinds in 3s, full brass 4-3-3-1, percussion, etc."

Performances: Jerry Bilik's *Aspects of Man* (4-section suite), Walton's *Variations on a Theme of Hindeminth's* and Augusta Read Thomas' *A Crystal Planet*.

*YOUTH ORCHESTRA OF GREATER FORT WORTH, 4401 Trail Lake Drive, Fort Worth TX 76109. (817)923-3121. General Manager: Freda Wise. Youth orchestra. Estab. 1965. Members are amateurs. Performs 5-10 concerts/year including a few new works. "Audiences are parents, families, teachers, musicians, community members. Orchestra hall has 385 seats; Ed Landrteh Auditorium has 1200 seats

(2 levels). Pays by outright purchase. Query first then submit complete score and tapes of pieces. SASE.

Music: Seeks "challenging, but possible, for advanced teen-aged musicians. 8-10 (possibly longer) minutes in length—full orchestra winds in threes; four trumpets; four trombones; tuba, six percussion, keyboard. No chamber pop."

Performances: Borodin's *Symphony No. 2*; Bizet's *Carmen Suite No. 1*; and Giannini's *Symphony No. 2* (all orchestral).

*ZION CHAMBER ORCHESTRA, Dowie Memorial Drive, Zion IL 60099. (312)872-4803. Music Director: Timothy C. Allen. Chamber orchestra. Members are professionals and amateurs. Performs 12 concerts/year including occasional new works. Audience is "low-middle class—middle class mostly. 522-seat auditorium, modern, effective acoustically, but a little dry for music." Submit complete score and tape of pieces. Does not return unsolicited material.

Music: "Instrumentation for chamber group—full complement of brass, winds, strings. Not interested in dissonance at this time. Prefers medium level difficulty."

Performances: D. Dickering's *Our Inurement* (serial. . .anti abortion); A. Koetz's *Sweet Hour of Prayer* (sacred, traditional); and Mendelsohn, Bach, Mozart, Brahms, Ives, Prokofiev, etc.

Fine Arts/'90-'91 Changes

The following markets appeared in the 1990 edition of *Songwriter's Market* but do not appear in the 1991 edition. Those companies that did not respond to our request for an update of their listing may not have done so for a variety of reasons—they may be out of business, for example, or they may be overstocked with submissions.

Anchorage Opera (did not respond)
Arts Council of Greater Kingsport (did not respond)
Asheville Symphony Orchestra (did not respond)
Atlanta Pops Orchestra (did not respond)
Atlanta Symphony Orchestra (did not respond)
Augsburg Choir (Augsburg College) (did not respond)
Baylor University Symphony Orchestra (did not respond)
Berkeley Symphony Orchestra (did not respond)
The Brooklyn Philharmonia Chorus, Inc. (did not respond)
The Calcutta School of Music (did not respond)
Capital Area Youth Symphonies (did not respond)
Chamber Orchestra of Albuquerque (did not respond)
Chatauqua Chamber Singers, Community Music Project (did not respond)
Colorado Children's Chorale (did not respond)
De Paul University (School of Music) (did not respond)

Emanuel County Arts Council (did not respond)
The Florida Orchestra (did not respond)
Georgetown Symphony Orchestra (did nòt respond)
Georgia State University Orchestra (did not respond)
Greater Trenton Symphony Orchestra (did not respond)
Guild Opera Company (did not respond)
Indianapolis Museum of Art (did not respond)
Kingsport Symphony Orchestra (did not respond)
The Lancaster Festival (did not respond)
Lehigh Valley Chamber Orchestra (did not respond)
Marian Civic Light Opera (did not respond)
MT3, Inc. (did not respond)
Musical Arts Association (did not respond)
Nebraska Jazz Orchestra Inc. (did not respond)
The Oakland Youth Chorus (did not respond)
Opera Northwest (did not respond)
Opera Pacific (did not respond)

Oratorio Society of New York (did not respond)
Pacific Chorale (did not respond)
Perry County Council of the Arts (did not respond)
PFL Management (did not respond)
Philadelphia College of Bible (did not respond)
Pierrot Plus Chamber Orchestra (did not respond)
Plainfield Symphony Orchestra (did not respond)
San Fernando Valley Symphony (did not respond)
Triangle Music Theater Associates (did not respond)
The Tulsa Philharmonic (did not respond)
Tuscawaras Philharmonic (did not respond)
UCI Symphony Orchestra (did not respond)
University of Tampa Collegiate Chorale (did not respond)
Waco Symphony Orchestra Association (did not respond)
West Coast Chamber Orchestra (did not respond)
Williamsburg Symphonia (did not respond)

Services & Opportunities

Organizations

A songwriting organization can be a songwriter's best friend. Whether local, statewide or national in scope, such an organization can provide helpful information and much-needed encouragement to novice and seasoned writers alike. Breaking in as a songwriter need not be the lonely, one-man-against-the-system undertaking it is often imagined to be. Among other things, a songwriting organization can provide you with: a place to meet collaborators; a forum for having your work heard and critiqued in a constructive way; the chance to pitch your material to music industry professionals (and get advice on making your pitches more effective); the latest music industry news as it relates to songwriters; tips on publishers, artists and record companies who are looking for material; and, perhaps most importantly, the opportunity to expand your network of friends and acquaintances in the music business.

Most organizations offer regular meetings of the general membership and occasional special events such as seminars and workshops to which music industry people are invited — to share their experience and perhaps listen to and critique demo tapes. There are songwriting organizations all over the United States. If you can't find one within an easy distance from your home, you might consider joining one of the national groups. These groups, based in New York, Los Angeles and Nashville, welcome members from across the nation and keep them involved and informed through newsletters and magazines, regular meetings, and large yearly get-togethers. They are an excellent way for writers who feel "stranded" somewhere in the middle of the country to keep up contacts and get their music heard in the major music centers.

In each of the following listings, organizations describe what they have to offer. Write to any that interest you for further information.

*AKRON'S SONGWRITERS WORKSHOP, 625 Hillsdale Ave., Akron OH 44303. (216)836-8065/666-7249. Director: Glenn Peterhansen. Estab. 1986. Serves songwriters and musicians. "Members are from 14 to 85 years old. Interests go from rap to 40's big band. All levels of writers, performers, hobby to full time pro. Members are interested in learning more about the music business and improving their writing and performing skills. We promote, encourage and educate the writing, recording and performaning artists of our area. "We offer a chance to meet other writers/musicians, exchange ideas and information about the music industry." Offers performance opportunities, field trips, newsletter, workshops and critique sessions with local/regional writers. Applications accepted year-round. "No dues at this time. A normal admission ($2-5) is charged for some events. Some workshops are $20-25. **Tips:** "We have a mailing list of some 1,500 local artists/writers and an active membership of only 75 at any one time. We encourage anyone to join our monthly meetings or showcases and take a step toward being a better writer. We are also working on an outlet for local video air play and developing a radio show 'The Band Next Door.' "

*AMERICAN CHORAL DIRECTORS ASSOCIATION, P.O. Box 6310, Lawton OK 73506. (405)355-8161. Estab. 1959. Serves musicians. "From college age students to the oldest senior adults. Members are those who are interested in learning, teaching, performing, composing and publishing choral music. Must be a student of, teacher of or conductor of choral music. We encourage the finest in choral music and promote its development in all ways, including performance, composition, publication and research. Provides an opportunity for songwriter to know names of potential markets. ACDA has membership of almost 16,000." Offers competitions, instruction, lectures, library, newsletter, performance opportunities, workshops and annual division or national conventions. Applications accepted year-round. Membership fee is: Active Member-$35, Retired Member-$10, Student Member-$10, Foreign Member-$60, Industry Member-$100, Institutional Member-$75 and Life Member-$1,000.

*AMERICAN COLLEGE OF MUSICIANS, P.O. Box 1807, 808 Rio Grande, Austin TX 78767. (512)478-5775. President: Richard Allison; Vice President: Julia Amada George. Estab. 1929. Serves musicians, teachers and students. Any musician/teacher (age 18 and older) can apply for membership. "The primary function of the American College of Musicians/National Guild of Piano Teachers is to establish definite goals and awards for piano students of all levels and grades. These goals attempt to prevent aimless drifting and give music study some definite direction and provide a measurement for progress. Non-competitive yearly auditions are held. Our organization sponsors a yearly composition contest. Guild auditions allow the programming of contemporary music. Our organization stresses a piano curriculum encompassing the best of piano literature and stressing the programming of American compositions." Accepts applications throughout the year. Annual membership dues are $22 (1990-91). "The American College of Musicians/National Guild of Piano Teachers is the largest organization of piano teachers in the world (US and 17 foreign countries). Guild piano auditions are held in over 840 centers in the US alone. Our teacher/student membership is over 115,000/year."

AMERICAN COUNCIL FOR THE ARTS, 1285 Avenue of the Americas, 3rd Floor, New York NY 10019. (212)245-4510. Contact: Membership Dept. "We are the leading private national nonprofit organization that serves all the arts." Members are state, regional and community arts agencies, arts centers, performing arts organizations, museums, libraries, parks and recreation departments, professional arts managers and artists and individuals interested in supporting the arts. Services include advocacy for the arts at the federal, state, and local levels; arts management training conferences and seminars; *Vantage Point* magazine featuring articles about major issues facing the arts today; *ACA Up Date*, a monthly up-to-the-minute news bulletin; ACA Books (publisher and distributor of books on the arts); a research library of 10,000 books and documents; and reference and information services. Memberships include individual membership (from $35-100) and institutional membership (from $150-250), depending on services and benefits desired.

AMERICAN FEDERATION OF MUSICIANS (AFM), Suite 600, 1501 Broadway, New York NY 10036. (212)869-1330. Membership available to all qualified musicians and vocalists in the United States and Canada. "The American Federation of Musicians of the United States and Canada is the largest entertainment union in the world and exists solely for the advancement of live music and the benefit of its 250,000 members. In addition to enhancing employment opportunities for members, the AFM aids members in negotiating contracts; enforces employers' observance of working conditions and wage scales; processes traveling members' claims at no cost to members; protects musicians from unfavorable legislation at the federal, state and local levels; negotiates pension, welfare and retirement benefits; offers instrument insurance to members; offers free job referral service to members who are seeking employment with traveling groups; and keeps membership informed of happenings in the business through its publication *International Musician*. Members also receive numerous benefits provided by each local chapter. Initiation fees and local dues vary; a small percentage of work dues are contributed by members. Write for further information or contact AFM local nearest you."

*AMERICAN LISZT SOCIETY, 210 Devonshire Dr., Rochester NY 14625. (716)586-9922. Membership Secretary: Reginald Gerig, 1328 Naperville Rd., Wheaton IL 60187. Estab. 1964. Serves musicians and those interested in music. Members may be any age and have interests in any area of music. Main purpose is to promote "annual music festivals in the US and abroad, residencies at universities, publications and international exchanges." Offers instruction, lectures, performance opportunities, newsletters and festivals. Membership fees vary. "The Festivals are presented at universities, centers for the arts, Library of Congress and colleges in different states every year. The ALS has 3 chapters which present additional programs. They are in Florida, Massachusetts and Connecticut. The Journal of ALS (JALS) is listed in the New Groves and is acclaimed internationally. The ALS Archives are kept at the Library of Congress. The ALS is a nonprofit organization."

AMERICAN MUSIC CENTER, INC., Suite 1001, 30 W. 26th St., New York NY 10010-2011. (212)366-5260. Executive Director: Nancy Clarke. Estab. 1939. For composers and performers. Members are American composers, performers, critics, publishers, and others interested in contemporary concert music and jazz. Offers newsletter, circulating library of contemporary music scores, advice on opportunities for composers and new music performers; disseminates information on American music. Purpose is to encourage the recognition and performance of contemporary American music. Members receive the twice-yearly *AMC Newsletter*, professional monthly "Opportunity Updates," eligibility for group health insurance, and the right to vote in AMC elections.

*AMERICAN MUSICIANS UNION INC., 8 Tobin Ct., Dumont NJ 07628. (201)384-5378. President and Treasurer: Ben Intorre. Estab. 1947. Serves musicians. vocalists and all age groups, all ethnic groups, music from gay 90's to contemporary, ballroom music, banquets, weddings, rock, disco, western, Latin, standards, etc. "We assist musicians in their efforts to perform and serve the public. We offer membership in a union, life insurance, meetings and union publication. "Applicant must be a musician, vocalist or manager. Disc-jockeys are not eligible." Offers newsletter and performance opportunities. Applications accepted year-round. Annual $27 dues; $10 initiation. Services include life insurance ($2,000 to age 65, reduced insurance to age 70) and advertisements in Quarternote are usually free to members. "We have locals in the U.S., in New Jersey, Minnesota, Michigan, etc."

*AMERICAN ORFF-SCHULWERK ASSOCIATION INC., P.O. Box 391089, Cleveland OH 44139. (216)543-5366. Executive Secretary: Cindi Wobig. Estab. 1969. Serves musicians and music educators; preschool, kindergarten and classroom teachers; music therapists; church musicians; college students and retired music educators. Offers library workshops, annual conference and quarterly publication. Chapters located in most states.

AMERICAN SOCIETY OF COMPOSERS, AUTHORS AND PUBLISHERS (ASCAP), 1 Lincoln Plaza, New York NY 10023. (212)595-3050. Director of Membership: Paul S. Adler. Membership Department Staff: Debra Cain, Jonathon Love, Debbie Rose, Leotis Clyburn, Lisa Schmidt and Marcy Drexler. Members are songwriters, composers, lyricists and music publishers. Applicants must "have at least one song copyrighted for associate membership; have at least one song commercially available as sheet music, available on rental, commercially recorded, or performed in media licensed by the Society (e.g., performed in a nightclub or radio station) for full membership. ASCAP is a membership-owned, performing right licensing organization that licenses its members' nondramatic musical compositions for public performance and distributes the fees collected from such licensing to its members based on a scientific random sample survey of performances." Primary value is "as a clearinghouse, giving users a practical and economical bulk licensing system and its members a vehicle through which the many thousands of users can be licensed and the members paid royalties for the use of their material. All monies collected are distributed after deducting only the Society's cost of doing business." **Tips:** "The Society sponsors a series of writers' workshops in Los Angeles, Nashville and New York open to members and nonmembers. Grants to composers available to members and nonmembers. Contact the membership department in New York or the following branch offices: 6430 Sunset Blvd., Los Angeles CA 90028; 2 Music Square W., Nashville TN 37203; 52 Haymarket, London SW1Y4RP, **England**."

AMERICAN WOMEN COMPOSERS, INC., Suite 409, 1690 36th St. NW, Washington DC 20007. (202)342-8179. Executive Assistants: Susan H. Fleer and Claudia Bezaka. Estab. 1976. Serves songwriters and musicians. Members are women and men who wish to further compositions written by American women: composers, performers and musicologists. We have a national membership with large concentrations in New York, California, Massachusettes, Illinois and Washington DC metropolitan areas. There are currently two chapters: Midwest (in Chicago) and New England (in Massachusetts). Eligibility requirements are to pay dues and complete application form. Since we are a support organization, we do not limit ourselves to just the professionals. We promote compositions by American women through our concerts and publications and circulating library. The primary value in this organization for a songwriter is free publicity. If songs are performed we mention in our newsletters; music placed in our library is circulated; newsletters provide information on competitions, grants and opportunities for composers in all musical media. Offers library, newsletter, performance opportunities and contact with others interested in women's music. Applications accepted year-round. Annual dues: composer/songwriter, $30; other professionals, $30; senior citizens/students, $15; Associate Members, $20.

ARIZONA SONGWRITERS ASSOCIATION, Box 678, Phoenix AZ 85001. (602)973-1988. Membership Director: Joanne Sherwood. Serves songwriters and musicians. "Membership is open to anyone wanting to learn the craft and business of songwriting. Our members are people of all ages (17-75 years), interested in all kinds of music (country, rock, R&B, top 40, novelty, jingles). In addition to songwriters, members are studio owners, lyricists, and working bands doing original material. We offer educational and promotional activities, and teach the business of songwriting from A-Z. Members have the chance to meet professionals and get first-hand advice and critiques on their songs on a monthly basis."

Offers competitions, instruction, lectures, newsletter, performance opportunities, social outings and workshops. Open mike night on the first Tuesday of each month. "We offer a yearly seminar with panels and critique sessions made up of Los Angeles and Nashville professionals from all walks of the business. ASA gets invitations to co-sponsor song contests, perform at public events, do radio and TV spots and have special performance weeks featuring the best of our songwriter/performers. We're getting good press for our meetings and activities. Several members have had cuts from songs picked up at meetings. Local and national airplay received by several members." Applications accepted year-round. Annual dues are $25 per year.

ARTS MIDWEST/REGIONAL JAZZ PROGRAM, Suite 310, 528 Hennepin Ave., Minneapolis MN 55403. (612)341-0755. Senior Program Director: Janis Lane-Ewart. Estab. 1985. Serves composers, musicians, dancers, actors and visual artists. "Arts Midwest is a not-for-profit arts organization which fosters and promotes the development of the arts in the Midwest. We are a resource for musicians (songwriters), and other artists in the region which includes the states of Illinois, Indiana, Iowa, Michigan, Minnesota, North Dakota, Ohio, South Dakota, and Wisconsin. Arts Midwest generates opportunities for artists and arts organizations, extending, enriching and complementing the programs and services of the member state arts agencies. The Jazz Program is but one of the programs of Arts Midwest. The Jazz Program produces technical assistance workshops, conferences and seminars; publishes a quarterly jazz newsletter (free); maintains a data base for the regional jazz community; and publishes a series of technical assistance how-to booklets. Other programs include the Performing Arts Touring Program, the Visual Arts Program, Services Program, and computer services." Applications are accepted throughout the year; however, "there are specific deadline periods for several of our funding programs, including the Performing Arts Touring Program, Meet the Composer, Visual Arts Fellowships, etc." Offers members competitions, lectures, performance opportunities, fellowships, workshops, touring programs and newsletter. ·

*ATLANTA SONGWRITERS ASSOCIATION, INC., 3121 Maple Dr., Atlanta GA 30305. (404)266-2666. Contact: Membership Chairman. Estab. 1979. Serves songwriters, musicians and music industry professionals. Songwriters of all styles of music; music industry professionals who support songwriters. Open to songwriters and non-songwriters. Membership open to any geographic location. Current members throughout Southeast. "We are an educational and service organization." Offers competitions, field trips, newsletter, performance opportunities, social outings, workshops and sell books on songwriting. Applications accepted year-round. Membership fee is regular, $35; deluxe, $50; corporate, $100.

*BRITISH LIBRARY NATIONAL SOUND ARCHIVE, 29 Exhibition Rd., London SW7 2AS **England**. Phone: (071)589-6603. FAX: (071)823-8970. Serves songwriters, musicians and anyone interested in recorded sound. Estab. 1955. "We answer the needs of researchers interested in all aspects of recorded sound. The primary value of our organization is the availability to listeners of recordings of all kinds (¾ million discs, 50,000 hours of tapes, etc.)." Offers lectures, library and listening facilities. "The National Sound Archive is a unique resource centre for the study of all kinds of music, recorded speech and theatre, and wildlife sounds; it is a prime source for broadcasters, film-makers, theatre companies, advertising agencies, the record industry and the general public. The Archive holds copies of almost all United Kingdom current commercial records (including compact discs), as well as a vast catalogue of recordings from as early as the 1890s. The Archive houses a wide range of broadcast materials, including duplicates of BBC Sound Archives recordings. There are also thousands of hours of unique unpublished recordings and a growing collection of videos. The National Sound Archive is one of the most extensive sources of information about recording in the world. It is up to our users to exploit this resource in whatever way suits their needs. Access can also be arranged at the Archive to over 90,000 musical scores."

CALIFORNIA COUNTRY MUSIC ASSOCIATION, P.O. Box 6116, Fullerton CA 92631. (714)738-1157. Executive Director: Gary Murray. Serves songwriters, musicians and country music fans and business. "Our members are of all ages, from the very young to the very old. They come from a wide variety of vocations, talents and professions. Their common interest is Country Music. A preferred geographic location would be the state of California, although a member may live out of state. All musicians, artists, and songwriters are eligible to compete in our chapter and statewide award shows, as long they have not charted on a major chart list in the last two years. The main purpose of this organization is to support, sponsor, organize, inform, and promote all facets of Country Music and entertainment. Our organization works together with the aspiring artist. We recognize, support and award their talents throughout the state and within our chapters. This organization cooperates with and supports country music radio stations, country music publications, charitable organizations, and the country music industry. We are a non-profit organization and our motto is 'God, country and country music.' Country music people are our number one concern." Offers competitions, instruction, lectures, newsletter, performance opportunities, social outings, workshops, showcases and award shows. Applications accepted year-round. Membership fee is $20/year.

*CANADA COUNCIL/COUNSEIL DES ARTS DU CANADA, P.O. Box 1047, Ottowa, Ontario K1P 5V8 **Canada**. (613)237-3400. Information Officer: Lise Rochon. Estab. 1957. Serves songwriters and musicians. "Individual artists must be Canadian citizens or permanent residents of Canada, and must have completed basic training and/or have the recognition as professionals within their fields. The Canada Council's objectives are to foster and promote the arts in Canada by offering financial assistance to professional Canadian artists and arts organizations. The Canada Council offers grants to professional musicians to pursue their own personal and creative development." Applications are not accepted throughout the year. "There are specific deadline dates for the various programs we administer." Call or write for more details.

CANADIAN COUNTRY MUSIC ASSOCIATION, Suite 102, 833 The Queensway, Toronto, Ontario M82 521 **Canada**. (416)252-1025. Executive Director: Sheila Hamilton. Estab. 1976. Members are songwriters, musicians, producers, radio station personnel, managers, booking agents and others. Offers newsletter, workshops, performance opportunities and annual awards. "Through our newsletters and conventions we offer a means of meeting and associating with artists and others in the industry. During our workshops or seminars (Country Music Week), we include a songwriters' seminar. The CCMA is a Federally chartered, non profit organization, dedicated to the promotion and development of Canadian Country Music throughout Canada and the world and to provide a unity of purpose for the Canadian Country Music industry. We are now involved with the *Music Copyright Action Group* and the main objective of the group is to get the government of Canada to revise the copyright act. We are similar to the CMA in the United States, with approximately 1,000 members (some from the US)." Send for application.

CANADIAN MUSICAL REPRODUCTION RIGHTS AGENCY LIMITED (CMRRA), 56 Wellesley St. W., Suite 320, Toronto, ON M5S 2S3 **Canada**. (416)926-1966. General Manager: David A. Basskin. Estab. 1975. Serves songwriters and copyright owners or administrators of musical compositions (composers, authors and music publishers). "Eligibility requirements a songwriter/musician must meet for membership: must own the copyright or have administration rights in one or more musical compositions for the territory of Canada. The organization's main purpose is to license the reproduction rights of copyright musical works and to collect and distribute the royalties collected to the rights owners on the basis of the licenses. The primary value in this organization for a songwriter is the administration and protection of their copyrights and the collection of royalties due to them." Offers instruction. Applications accepted year-round. "There are no membership fees or annual dues. For administering the copyright owner's work, CMRRA retains a 5% commission on revenues collected for mechanical rights and 10% for synchronization rights. Where money is received from a foreign society, CMRAA distributes it to its member clients at a 3% charge. CMRRA is the principal mechanical rights agency in Canada. It was primarily responsible for securing passage of amendments to Canada's *Copyright Act* abolishing the compulsory licence and statutory rate for songs used by record companies. This action permitted the royalty rate for recorded songs to rise for the first time in over 64 years."

CENTRAL OPERA SERVICE, Metropolitan Opera, Lincoln Center, New York NY 10023. (212)957-9871. Executive Director: Maria F. Rich. Estab. 1954. Members are songwriters, musicians and opera/music theatre producers. "Central Opera Service maintains an extensive library of reference books and domestic and foreign music periodicals, and the most comprehensive operatic archive and music theatre in the United States. COS draws on these unique resources to supply information to its members." Offers quarterly COS Bulletin (which includes a section "Attention Composers and Librettists"), and offers conferences. Publishes directories of opera/music theatre companies in the U.S. and Canada. Publishes directory of opera and musical premiere's world-wide and U.S. Applications accepted year-round. Membership fee is $20/year for an individual, $50/year for a company.

CHORUS AMERICA, 2111 Sansom St., Philadelphia PA 19103. (215)563-2430. Executive Director: Kenneth Garner. Estab. 1977. Serves musicians and choruses. Members are well-established and newly-organized ensembles of all types, as well as conductors, music directors, professional singers, teachers, students, libraries and music-related firms (all ages spread throughout the United States, Puerto Rico and Canada). All interested persons are eligible. The main purpose of this organization is to promote the professional quality and growth of vocal ensembles and to encourge greater appreciation and enjoyment of vocal music by all segments of American society. The primary value in this organization for a songwriter is the performance opportunity and exposure of their works. Offers competitions, newsletters, performance opportunities, workshops, technical assistance, consultations and grants: American Choral Works Performance Program. Applications deadline November 1. Annual dues: students, professional singers, board members of member organizations $25; conductors, voice teachers $50; organizations (choruses, ensembles, other) $60 minimum. Music-related Firms, $200; Libraries (subscribers to voice only) $20.

*COASTAL SONGWRITERS ASSOCIATION, 20 Capitol St., Savannah GA 31404. (912)336-0000. President: Jimmy Barefoot. Estab. 1982. Serves songwriters and musicians. From 17 years to 71 years old. "No one is turned away that is sincere." Offers competitions, field trips, instruction, lectures, library, newsletter, performance opportunitites, social outings and workshops. Application accepted year-round. Membership fee is a one time fee of $25, then $3/month.

COMPOSERS, ARRANGERS AND SONGWRITERS OF KANSAS, 117 W. 8th St., Hays KS 67601. (913)625-9634. Administrator: Mark Meckel. Serves songwriters, musicians, arrangers and lyricists. Membership open to "anyone desiring information on the business of songwriting, copyrights or marketing—from professional musicians to housewives. Our purpose is to help members get songs placed with publishing and record companies." No eligibility requirements other than "a desire for a career in the music industry." Applications accepted year-round.

*COMPOSERS GUILD, Box 586, 40 N. 100 West, Farmington UT 84025. (801)451-2275. President: Ruth Gatrell. For composers and songwriters. "We are a nonprofit organization working to help the composer/songwriter. Each year we sponsor classes, workshops, seminars, showcases/concerts and a composition contest, with cash prizes and winning numbers eligible for performance at the Composers Guild Spectacular. A songwriter benefits from joining Composers Guild through lower contest and seminar/class fees, (contest entries for members are $5—non-members are $15); through seminars, workshops and classes, most of which are taped for those who cannot attend; the challenge to write new music for the contest and concerts—we have an 'Americana' and a 'New Sounds for Christmas' concert each year in addition to the 'Spectacular,' featuring contest winners; through association with others with similar interests and from news from the field, as made available to the Guild."

*COMPUTER MUSIC ASSOCIATION, Box 1634, San Francisco, CA 94101. (817)566-2235. President: Larry Austin. Estab. 1978. Serves songwriters, musicians and computer music specialists. Membership includes a broad spectrum of composers, scientists, educators and hobbyists. The function of this organization is "to serve the interests of computer music practitioners and sponsor annual computer music conferences." Primary value in this organization is "music technology information." Offers lectures, performance opportunities, workshops and newsletters to members. Applications are accepted throughout the year. Membership fee is $32/year.

CONNECTICUT SONGWRITERS ASSOCIATION, Box 2995, New Haven CT 06515. (203)776-2277; (203)272-5889. Executive Director: Martha Theon. "We are an educational, nonprofit organization dedicated to improving the art and craft of original music. We offer a monthly newsletter (subscription rate is $15 per year/12 issues), monthly seminars and song critique sessions, performing opportunities at songwriter showcases, song screening service, discounts, awards and social outings." No eligibility requirements. Ages range from 12 to 70. Applications accepted year-round. Annual membership categories are: Individual $40, Student and Senior Citizen $20, Organizations $60, Sustaining $100, Benefactor $250, Lifetime $500. ("All memberships include newsletter subscription and are tax deductible to the extent allowed by law.")
Tips: "Members can learn about the music business, improve their songcrafting skills, gain performing opportunities and make collaboration contacts."

*COUNTRY MUSIC FOUNDATION LIBRARY & MEDIA CENTER, 4 Music Sqare E., Nashville TN 37203. (615)256-1639. Estab. 1964. Serves country music researchers. "We have no membership program. We are a research library, open by appointment to someone with serious research needs in country music (past hits, lyrics, biographies, etc.), weekdays 9 to 5 central time." Offers library.

COUNTRY MUSIC SHOWCASE INTERNATIONAL, INC., Box 368, Carlisle IA 50047. (515)989-3679. President: Harold L. Luick. Vice President: Barbara A. Lancaster. "We are a non-profit, educational performing arts organization for songwriters and entertainers. The organization produces on a regular basis a stage show which is available to community groups, civic organizations, and other non-profit organizations such as fairs and festivals that wish to raise funds or sponsor country music events of this type. Our members perform in these shows, and through constructive criticism and workshops we help to teach all performers the art of showmanship and musicianship. Workshops and seminars are also offered on songwriting and all phases of the music industry. The organization produces educational videos on all the above subjects and offers a nationally-distributed newspaper. To all supporting songwriter, artist, musician and fan club memberships we offer tip sheets and information on songwriting, lyric writing, management and booking, raising funds for your business, how to incorporate public relations and publicity, how to organize a fan club, merchandising and how to market a record of

Close-up

Kayte Devlin
President
Connecticut Songwriters Association
New Haven, Connecticut

Photo by: Dee Crandell

Proud of past successes and excited about big plans for the Connecticut Songwriters Association, Kayte Devlin looks to the 90s as a time of more growth and prosperity.

For the past 10 years, CSA has provided programs for aspiring and experienced songwriters to help them improve and polish their talent. Now, says Devlin, "CSA is coming into its own. "The last couple of years we've done really well. We've had many excellent programs . . . we've increased our membership and gotten better at everything." This has "laid a groundwork for bigger and better things for CSA," says Devlin, who serves as president of the organization.

Devlin stresses that the goal of the organization, a nonprofit educational group, is to "improve the art and craft of original musical and lyrical composition" by providing special services to music's artisans and craftsmen. CSA boasts an active roster of 200 members, most of whom write songs as a hobby. "Most of our members are not pursuing a professional career; they just want to write and improve their writing," Devlin says. "Some have had their songs published, but our main focus is to provide an opportunity for our members to have their songs heard and critiqued, no matter what they want to do with them."

This year CSA has already hosted several big-name songwriters, including Dan Hartman and Jeff Franzell. Hartman produces Tina Turner, Rick Astley and Dusty Springfield, and has a few hit songs himself. Franzell is an accomplished jazz and pop pianist, but is best known for co-writing "Don't Rush Me," recorded by Taylor Dayne, which reached no.2 on the pop charts. In addition, the organization recently hosted SESAC, and invites BMI and ASCAP to speak on the business of songwriting every year.

Despite frequent appearances by top professionals in the music business, CSA maintains a "personal" environment by offering internal creative workshops coordinated by CSA members themselves. Workshop topics include group collaboration, song rewriting, demo production and creating good lyrics, to cite a few examples. "We also get back to the basics of songwriting. . . . .and working on the art of songwriting is the most special thing we do with our members," says Devlin.

CSA not only serves as a songwriter's information source and support group, it also offers programs for young people. In the 1990-91 school year, CSA will actually go into the school system to teach special music classes. Devlin notes that music and lyrics are "valuable ways for children to express themselves," and since many CSA performers work with children as a career, it's natural for the group to offer musical education to the kids in area schools. In keeping with the educational mission of CSA, the organization has started a music scholarship program for school-age youngsters.

Devlin says, "If you surround yourself with people who have similar interests in music and who want to learn more about songwriting, it's a very positive thing. . . . and in the end everyone benefits and learns from each other."

—Brian C. Rushing

your song. All this plus 46 other music business subjects are available (free of charge) with all paid memberships. Upon receipt of membership payment, we send members a list of all the subjects they can chose from, and by returning their choices along with an SASE, we will send the information to them. They can chose different subjects all year long as long as they are paid up. We also send out up-dates on new subjects as they come along. We feel songwriters should belong to our organization because we feel we can help them self-educate and grow in the process because we offer song critique service (by mail, your SASE) at no charge to members. They can submit 1 song per month, and we will evaluate it as to its commercial potential, how they might improve it, or get it used or published. We offer constructive criticism and honest opinions. Songs that meet our professional standards are referred to publishing companies, producers and A&R people for possible use in recordings. We maintain that an entertainer, musician or songwriter should associate with the people who know more then they do; otherwise, they cannot learn or improve themselves. For free information and brochure on organization, send SASE." Membership fee is $20/year for supporting songwriter, artist or musician; $20/year for supporting fan club; $20/year for supporting patron.

*DALLAS SONGWRITERS ASSOCIATION, 2932 Dyer St., Dallas TX 75205. (214)691-5318. President: Barbara McMillen. Estab. 1988. Serves songwriters and lyricists of Dallas/Ft. Worth metroplex. Adults: ages 18-65, country rock, show, dance, pop, MOR, etc. Dallas/Ft. Worth area songwriters/lyricist who are 18 yrs. and older who are or aspire to be professional. To provide songwriters an opportunity to meet other songwriters, share information, find co-writers and support each other through group discussions at monthly meetings. To provide songwriters an opportunity to have their songs heard and critiqued by peers and professionals by playing cassettes and providing an open mike at monthly meetings and by offering quarterly contests judged by publishers. To provide songwriters opportunities to meet other music business professionals by inviting guest speakers to monthly meetings. To provide songwriters opportunities to learn more about the craft of songwriting and the business of music by presenting mini workshops at each monthly meeting. "We offer a chance for the songwriter to learn from peers and industry professionals and an opportunity to belong to a supportive group environment to encourage the individual to continue his/her songwriting endeavors." Offers competitions, field trips, instruction, lectures, library, newsletter, performance opportunities, social outings and workshops. Applications accepted year-round. Membership fee is $15.

*THE DRAMATISTS GUILD, INC., 234 W. 44th St., New York NY 10036. (212)398-9366. Membership includes over 7,000 playwrights, composers, lyricists and librettists nationwide. "As the professional association of playwrights, composers, and lyricists, the Guild protects the rights of all theater writers, and improves the conditions under which they work. Additionally, the Guild encourages and nurtures the work of dramatists in the U.S. through its program of seminars and workshops. To be a member of The Dramatists Guild, you must have completed a dramatic work (a one-act or full-length play or component part- book, music or lyrics- of a musical) whether produced or not. The Guild offers many services and activities, including use of the Guild's contracts and a royalty collection service; The Hotline, a nationwide toll-free phone number for business or contract problems; an annual marketing directory with up-to-date information on grants, agents, producers, playwriting contests, conferences and workshops; two publications — *The Dramatists Guild Quarterly* and *The Dramatists Guild Newsletter*; access to group health insurance and access to Guild's newsroom."

FEDERATION INTERNATIONAL DES ORGANISATIONS DE FESTIVALS (F.I.D.O.F.), #105, 4230 Stansbury Ave., Sherman Oaks CA 91423. (818)789-7569. FAX: (818)784-9141. Secretary General: Prof. Armando Moreno. Estab. 1967. Serves songwriters, musicians, festival and events managers and organizers. Members are of all ages from and from 62 countries around the world. "We coordinate dates of festivals, and coordinate the interests of all involved with festivals and cultural events (artists, songwriters, record, TV, video, publishing and other companies from around the world, as well as press)." Offers competitions, field trips, instruction, lectures, library, newsletter, performance opportunities, social outings, workshops, annual meetings on international and national levels, exhibition opportunities, being jurors in events, etc. Applications accepted year-round. Annual membership fee is $200 US dollars.

*FORT BEND SONGWRITERS ASSOCIATION, P.O. Box 117, Richmond TX 77469. Coordinator: Terry Jude Miller. Estab. 1989. Serves "any person, amateur or professional, interested in songwritingor music. Our members write pop, rock, country, rock-a-billy, gospel, R&B; children's music and musical plays." "Open to all, regardless of geographic location or professional status." "The FBSA provides its membership with help to perfect their songwriting crafts by conducting workshops, seminars, publishing a monthly newsletter and holding songwriting and vocal performance competitions and showcases. The FBSA provides instruction for beginning writers and publishing and artist tips for the more accomplished writer." Offers competitions, field trips, instruction, lectures, newsletter, performance opportunities, workshops and collaboration opportunities. Applications accepted year-round. Membership fee is $20 per year, which includes a free subscription to our newsletter." "The FBSA promotes the growth of songwriting, music and entertainment industries throughout North America. Our goal is to help as many people as possible become successful songwriters."

*HAWAIIAN ISLANDS COUNTRY MUSIC, P.O. Box 75148, Hon HI 96836. (205)685-0738. Owner: Maitai. Estab. 1977. Serves songwriters, musicians and entertainers. Members are anyone who loves music. Main purpose is to promote the emerging aspiring artist. Offers competitions, lectures, performance opportunities, workshops and promotion/management. Applications are accepted year-round. Memberships fee is $20.

THE HYMN SOCIETY IN THE UNITED STATES AND CANADA, (formerly The Hymn Society of America). Box 30854, Texas Christian University, Fort Worth TX 76129. (817)921-7608. Executive Director: W. Thomas Smith. Estab. 1922. Serves hymn text and tune writers. "Our members are church musicians, clergy, hymn writers and institutional libraries. The main purpose is to promote hymn singing, sponsor hymn writing, and foster hymnological research. Members will acquire skills in writing congregational hymns." Offers competitions, lectures, library, newsletters, performance opportunites, workshops and annual conferences. Applications accepted year-round. Membership fee and annual dues: $30.

INDIANAPOLIS SONGWRITERS, Box 44724, Indianapolis IN 46244-0724. (317)257-9200. Secretary: Liz Efroymson. Estab. 1983. Purpose is "to create an affiliation of serious-minded songwriters, promote the artistic value of the musical composition, the business of music, and recognition for the songwriter and his craft." Sponsors quarterly newsletter, monthly meetings, periodic showcases and periodic seminars and workshops. "The monthly critiques are helpful for improving songwriting skills. The meetings offer opportunities to share information concerning publishing demos, etc. In addition, it provides opportunity for members to meet co-writers." Membership fee of $20 per year.

INTERNATIONAL BLUEGRASS MUSIC ASSOCIATION (IBMA), 326 St. Elizabeth St., Owensboro KY 42301. (502)684-9025. Executive Director: Steve Kirkland; Director of Membership Services and Public Relations: Art Menius. Estab. 1985. Serves songwriters, musicians and professionals in bluegrass music. "IBMA is a trade association composed of people and organizations involved professionally and semi-professionally in the bluegrass music industry, including performers, agents, songwriters, music publishers, promoters, print and broadcast media, local associations, recording manufacturers and distributors. Voting members must be currently or formerly have been involved in the bluegrass industry as full or part-time professionals. A songwriter attempting to become professionally involved in our field would be eligible. We promote the bluegrass music industry and unity within it. IBMA publishes bi-monthly *International Bluegrass*, holds an annual trade show/convention during September in Owensboro, represents our field outside the bluegrass music community, and compiles and disseminates databases of bluegrass related resources and organizations. The primary value in this organization for a songwriter is having current information about the bluegrass music field and contacts with other songwriters, publishers, musicians, and record companies." Offers newsletter, performance opportunities, social outings, workshops, liability insurance, rental car discounts, consultation, and databases of record companies, radio stations, press, organizations and gigs. Applications accepted year-round. Membership fee for a non-voting patron $15/year; for an individual voting professional $35/year; for an organizational voting professional $100/year.

INTERNATIONAL FAN CLUB ORGANIZATION, Box 177, Wild Horse CO 80862. (719)962-3543. Co-Presidents: Loudilla Johnson, Loretta Johnson and Kay Johnson. For songwriters, musicians and performers and their fan club presidents. Members are fan club presidents, and/or artists/songwriters, etc. Applicants must be involved in the field of country music. An artist must have a fan club—"we assist them in setting up the fan club although we do not personally manage each individual operation for them." Purpose is to promote/publicize country music in an effort to spread good will, understanding and enjoyment of it around the world. "We hold an annual overseas showcase (London), plus dinner/show/business meetings/showcases in Nashville, annually in conjunction with Fan Fair. We believe fan clubs are a vital part of any entertainer's life." Offers competitions, instruction, newsletter, performance opportunities, social outings, workshops, business meetings, overseas tours and showcases.

INTERNATIONAL LEAGUE OF WOMEN COMPOSERS, Box 670, S. Shore Rd., Pt. Peninsula, Three Mile Bay NY 13693. (315)649-5086. Chairperson: Elizabeth Hayden Pizer. Estab. 1975. Serves (women) composers of serious concert music. "Members are women composers and professional musicians, music libraries, institutions and organizations. Full composer membership is open to any woman composer whose seriousness of intent has been demonstrated in one or more of the following ways: (1) by any single degree in composition (if the degree is not recent, some evidence of recent activity should be offered), (2) by holding a current teaching position at the college level, (3) by having had a serious work published, (4) by having had a work performed at a recognized symposium or by professional musicans, or, (5) by submitting two compositions to the Executive Board for review, exhibiting competence in scoring for chamber ensemble. Admission is governed neither by stylistic nor regional bias; however, primarily educational music is not considered sufficient. The ILWC is devoted to creating and expanding opportunities for, and documenting information about, women composers of serious music. This organization will help songwriters stay informed of various career/ performance opportunties; plus, allow them to participate in projects spear-headed by ILWC." Offers competitions, newsletter and performance opportunities. Applications accepted year-round. Annual dues are $20 for individuals; $10 for students/senior citizens; $30 for institutions/organizations.

INTERNATIONAL SONGWRITERS ASSOCIATION LTD., 37b New Cavendish St., London WI **England**. Phone: (01)486 5353. Membership Department: Anna M. Sinden. Serves songwriters and music publishers. "The ISA headquarters is in Limerick City, Ireland, and from there it provides its members with assessment services, copyright services, legal and other advisory services, and an investigations service plus the magazine for one yearly fee. Our members are songwriters in more than fifty countries worldwide, of all ages. There are no qualifications, but members under 18 are not accepted. We provide information and assistance to professional or semi-professional songwriters. Our publication, *Songwriter*, which was founded in 1967, features detailed exclusive interviews with songwriters and music publishers, as well as directory information of value to writers." Offers competitions, instruction, library and newsletter. Applications accepted year-round. Membership fee for European writers is £13.90; for non-European writers, it is US $20.

KANSAS SONGWRITERS ASSOCIATION, 117 W. 8th, Hays KS 67601. (913)625-9634. President: Mark Meckel. Serves songwriters and musicians. "The purpose of our organization is to help songwriters get songs recorded/published." Offers library for members. No membership fee.

*KERRVILLE MUSIC FOUNDATION INC., P.O. Box 1466, Kerrville TX 78029-1466. (512)257-3600. Executive Director: Rod Kennedy. The Kerrville Music Foundation was "founded in 1975 for the promotion and preservation of both traditional and new American music and has awarded more than $25,000 to musicians over the last 15 years through open competitions designed to encourage excellence in songwriting. Six new folk award winners are annually invited to share 20 minutes of their songs at the Kerrville folk festival with one selected to perform on the main stage the next year." Opportunities include: The Emerging Songwriters Competition at the NAPA Valley Folk Festival— Oct. 6 (award winners on Oct. 7) and the Rising Stars Songwriters Competition at Columbia River Folk Festival in Spokane, WA—July 21 (award winners on July 22).

KEYBOARD TEACHERS ASSOCIATION INTERNATIONAL, INC., 361 Pin Oak Lane, Westbury NY 11590. (516)333-3236. President: Dr. Albert DeVito. Estab. 1963. Serves musicians and music dealers/ keyboards. "Our members are music teachers, music dealers, music publishers, especially keyboard/ piano/organ. Active members must be teachers. We also have Friend Members who are not teachers. The main purpose of this organization is to keep keyboard teachers informed of what is happening in their field, students evaluation, teacher certification, etc. The primary value in this organization for a songwriter is being in contact with keyboard players, publishers and dealers." Offers evaluations of students, instruction, newsletter and workshops. Applications accepted year-round. Membership fee is $22.50 (1989-90).
Tips: "Each student in auditions receives a certificate according to grade level. It is a great experience for them with the encouragement given."

*THE LAMBDA PERFORMING ARTS GUILD OF AMERICA®, P.O. Box 14131, Denver CO 80214. Director: Sharon R. Smith-Fliesher. Estab. 1987. "Serving actors, musicians, vocalists, songwriters, playwrites and directors. Operated by and for lesbians. We are a nonprofit organization. No salaries are paid. We have a Board of Directors. Our board members donate time and services to the organization for the purpose of legitimizing the talents of lesbians. Applications for membership are accepted year-round. All appilcations are reviewed by our membership committee, prior to an applicant being

The asterisk before a listing indicates that the listing is new in this edition.

notified of acceptance. We offer copyright services, referrals to publishers, recording companies, agents, managers and producers. We publishe a newsletter twice annually. In the newsletter we feature artists, update information on performances regionally, nationally and internationally. Free classified listings to good standing members. Paid advertising for non-members and establishments purchasing blocked space. We offer two types of membership: Associate $25 (unpublished/amateur) and Full $50 (published/professional)."

THE LAS VEGAS SONGWRITERS ASSOCIATION, Box 42683, Las Vegas NV 89116-0683. (702)459-9107. President: Betty Kay Miller. Estab. 1980. "We are an educational, non profit organization dedicated to improving the art and craft of the songwriter. We offer quarterly newsletters, monthly general information meetings, workshops three times a month and seminars held quarterly with professionals in the music business. Dues are $20 per year." Members must be at least 18 years of age.

THE LOS ANGELES SONGWRITERS SHOWCASE (LASS), Box 93759, Hollywood CA 90093. (213)654-1665. Co-Directors: Len H. Chandler Jr. and John Braheny. General Manager: Stephanie Perom. "The Los Angeles Songwriters Showcase (LASS), is a nonprofit service organization for songwriters, founded in 1971 and sponsored by Broadcast Music, Inc. (BMI). LASS also provides counseling, and conducts classes and seminars. At our Wednesday night Showcase, we feature Cassette Roulette, in which a different publisher every week critiques songs submitted on cassette that night; and Pitch-A-Thon, in which a different producer or record company executive every week screens songs for his/her current recording projects and/or acts for their labels. The Showcase takes place every Wednesday night in front of an audience of songwriters and the music industry guests; there is no prescreening necessary. LASS also produces an annual Songwriters Expo in October." General membership: $120/year. Professional membership: $150/year. Included in both "general" and "professional" membership benefits are: priorities to have tapes listened to first at Pitch-A-Thon sessions; discounts on numerous items such as blank tapes, books, demo production services, tapes of Songwriters Expo sessions and other seminars; discounts on admission to the weekly showcase; career counseling (in person or by phone) and a subscription to the LASS 'Musepaper," a magazine for songwriters (also available to non-members for $17 bulk rate/$27 first class). Professional membership is available to general members by invitation or audition only and features special private pitch-a-thon sessions and referrals.
Tips: "Members may submit tapes to the weekly cassette roulette and pitch-a-thon sessions from anywhere in the world and be sent the recorded comments of the industry guests for that week. Most of the record companies, publishers and producers will not accept unsolicited material so our Wednesday night showcase is the best way to get your material heard by these music industry professionals."

LOUISIANA SONGWRITERS ASSOCIATION, P.O. Box 80425, Baton Rouge LA 70898-0425. (504)292-1387. Vice President, Membership: Janice Calvert. President: Butch Reine. Serves songwriters. "LSA is a support group of songwriters who are interested in helping each other and sharing their abilities. Our membership is not limited to age, music style, ethnic group or musical ability. We have members in their teens, as well as retired persons in our group. LSA was organized to educate and promote songwriting in Louisiana and help develop a market for our writers in Louisiana. We do have members outside of Louisiana, however. LSA has a membership of over 200 members. Have completed first songwriting contest, Louisiana Hot Sounds — Country Edition. We plan to continue the contest on an annual basis, adding additional categories as we go along. If you are interested in songwriting you qualify to belong to LSA. Many of us are unable to relocate to major music centers due to responsibilities to jobs and families. Through songwriting organizations like LSA, we are able to work together as a group to establish a line of communication with industry professionals while developing economically, a music center in our area of the country." Offers competitions, lectures, library, newsletter, performance opportunities, workshops, discounts on various music related books and magazines, and discounts on studio time. General membership is $30/year. "Our fiscal year runs June 1-May 31 of the following year. If a new member joins after January 1st, membership dues are $15 until June 1 of that year."

LOUISVILLE AREA SONGWRITERS' COOPERATIVE, P.O. Box 16, Pewee Valley KY 40056. President: Paul M. Moffett. Estab. 1986. Serves songwriters and musicians of all ages, races and all music genres. "The Louisville Area Songwriters' Cooperative is a not-for-profit corporation dedicated to the development and promotion of songwriting. Membership is open to any person in the Louisville area (and beyond) who is interested in songwriting. We offer a songwriter showcase on the first Saturday of each month, an open stage on Mondays at the *Rudyard Kipling*, a series of tapes of songs by members of the cooperative, meetings, speakers, the LASC newsletter, a songwriting contest, referral for collaboration, promotion and song plugging to local, regional and national recording artists and occasional bookings for performing members." Applications accepted year-round. Dues are $20/year.

MEMPHIS SONGWRITERS' ASSOCIATION, 1857 Capri, Memphis TN 38117. (901)763-1957. President: Juanita Tullos. Estab. 1973. Serves songwriters, musicians and singers. Age limit: 18 years and up. No specific location requirement. Must be interested in music and have the desire to learn the basics of commercial songwriting. "We instruct the potential songwriters on how to structure their songs and correctly use lyrics, commercially. We critique their material. We help them obtain copyrights, give them a chance to expose their material to the right people, such as publishers and A&R people. We hold monthly workshops, instructing members in the Commercial Music Techniques of songwriting. We have an annual Songwriters Showcase where their material is performed live for people in the publishing and recording professions and the general public. We have an annual Shindig, for bands and musicians and an annual seminar." Offers competitions, instruction, lectures, newsletter, performance opportunities and workshops. Applications accepted year-round. Annual dues: $15.
Tips: "Our association was founded in 1973. We have a charter, by laws and a board of directors (8). All directors are professionals in the music field. We are a non-profit organization. No salaries are paid. Our directors donate their services to our association. We have a president, vice president, secretary, treasurer, music instructor and consultant, production manager, assistant production manager, and executive director.

MIDWEST SONGWRITERS ASSOCIATION, INC., Rt. 5, Box 463, Marion IL 62959. (618)995-9072. Executive Director: Ron Gibson. Estab. 1985. Serves songwriters. Members are country, rock, pop, blues and gospel writers." The two main purposes of MSA are camaraderie and unification—others are to educate the songwriter regarding the music industry, low-cost demo's, and an opportunity to perform. The primary value in this organization will be to improve songwriting skills. Members have the opportunity to participate in monthly trips to Nashville, Tennessee to promote MSA member songs. These trips are paid for in part by grants received by MSA. It is my opinion that any aspiring songwriter can gain education and improve songwriting skills by being a member of a songwriter group." Offers instruction, newsletter, performance opportunities, social outings and workshops. $25 annual dues.
Tips: "Fund raising and grant applications are major functions of our non-profit organization. We recently were awarded $2,100 for MSA activities. I am a marketing/training consultant and would be available to instruct other songwriting groups how to apply for grants and foundation awards."

MISSOURI SONGWRITERS ASSOCIATION, INC., 693 Green Forest Dr., Fenton MO 63026. (314)343-6661. President: John G. Nolan, Jr. Serves songwriters and musicians. No eligibility requirements. "The MSA (a non-profit organization founded in 1979) is a tremendously valuable resource for songwriting and music business information outside of the major music capitals. Only with the emphasis on education can the understanding of craft and the utilization of skill be fully realized and in turn become the foundation for the ultimate success of MSA members. Songwriters gain support from their fellow members when they join the MSA, and the organization provides 'strength in numbers' when approaching music industry professionals." As a means toward its goals the organization offers: "(1) an extremely informative quarterly newsletter; (2) Annual Songwriting Contest; prizes include: album and cassette release of winners, publishing contract, free musical merchandise and equipment, free recording studio time, plaque or certificate; (3) Annual St. Louis Original Music Celebration featuring live performances, recognition, showcase, radio simulcast, videotape for later broadcast, awards presentation; (4) seminars on such diverse topics as creativity, copyright law, brainstorming, publishing, recording the demo, craft and technique, songwriting business, collaborating, etc.; (5) workshops including song evaluation, establishing a relationship with publishers, hit song evaluations, the writer versus the writer/artist, the marriage of collaborators, the business side of songwriting, lyric craft, etc; (6) services such as collaborators referral, publisher contacts, consultation, recording discounts, musicians referral, library, etc. The Missouri Songwriters Association belongs to its members and what a member puts into the organization is returned dynamically in terms of information, education, recognition, support, comradery, contacts, tips, confidence, career development, friendships, and professional growth." Applications accepted year-round. Tax deductible dues are $30/year.

MUSICIANS CONTACT SERVICE, 7315 Sunset Blvd., Hollywood CA 90046. (213)851-2333. Estab. 1969. For musicians and bands seeking each other in the greater Southern California area. "Provides 24-hour computerized call-in gig line of working bands needing players. Also for composers and lyricists seeking each other for collaboration on a national level. Detailed resumes are sent to songwriters, which are mailed back to the office, condensed, and compiled into one large listing of hundreds of collaborators seeking each other. These are sent all over the U.S. An updated list costs $25 for a one year listing."

Listings of companies in foreign countries have the name of the country in boldface type.

MUSICIANS NATIONAL HOT LINE ASSOCIATION, 277 East 6100 South, Salt Lake City UT 84107. (801)268-2000. Estab. 1980. Serves songwriters and musicians. "Members are musicians and those involved in related musical occupations. Our goal is to help musicians find bands to join, to help bands find musicians and gigs, and to help songwriters find work in a band or group." Offers newsletter and computer search file. Applications accepted year-round. Membership fee is $20/year.

Tips: "The Musicians National Hot Line Association is a non-profit organization dedicated to helping musicians. Those interested in more, detailed information may call (1-801-268-2000) or write (Musicians National Hot Line Association, PO Box 57733, Salt Lake City, UT 84157) for a free brochure."

*NASHVILLE ENTERTAINMENT ASSOCIATION, 7 Music Circle N., Nashville TN 37203. (615)256-4435. Executive Director: Connie Westfall. Estab. 1980. Serves songwriters, musicians and all areas of entertainment industry. All ages welcome; members should be affiliated with the entertainment industry. Promotes Nashville as a total entertainment center. We offer songwriter showcases and seminars. Offers lectures, newsletter, performance opportunities and workshops. Applications accepted year-round. $45 annual dues for U.S.A.; $50 annual dues for international.

NASHVILLE SONGWRITERS ASSOCIATION, INTERNATIONAL (NSAI), Suite 200, 1025 16th Ave. S, Nashville TN 37212. (615)321-5004. Executive Director: Pat Huber. Serves both professional and beginning songwriters. Members in all states and several foreign countries. "Our purpose is to gain recognition for the songwriter, to serve any purpose toward this recognition and to pursue this on a worldwide basis." Applicants may apply for 2 memberships; "active membership is having had at least one song published with an affiliate of BMI, ASCAP or SESAC. An associate membership is for the yet-to-be-published writer and others interested in the songwriter." Offers information, instruction, lectures, newsletter, seminars, symposiums, workshops, showcases, performance opportunities, songwriter concerts in various parts of the U.S., and awards. Applications accepted year-round. Annual dues $50; lifetime $500.

NATIONAL ACADEMY OF POPULAR MUSIC – SONGWRITERS' HALL OF FAME, 875 3rd Ave., 8th Floor, New York NY 10022. (212)319-1444. Managing Director: Christina Malone. Projects Director: Bob Leone. Estab. 1969. The main purpose of the organization is to honor great songwriters and support a Hall of Fame museum. Activities include: songwriting workshops, music industry panels, songwriter showcases. Offers newsletter. "Informally, our projects director helps members to network with each other. For example, publisher/members looking for material are put in touch with writer/members; collaborations are arranged. Nowhere else on the East Coast can a writer learn more about the craft of songwriting, the business of songwriting and the world of songwriting, in general. And nowhere are there more opportunities to meet with all types of music industry professionals. Our activities are available to all of our members, so networking is inevitable." Membership is open to everyone, but consists primarily of songwriters, publishers and other music industry professionals who are eligible to vote in annual inductee election. Annual awards dinner. Applications accepted year-round. Membership fee is $25/year.

NATIONAL ACADEMY OF SONGWRITERS (NAS), Suite 780, 6381 Hollywood Blvd., Hollywood CA 90028. (213)463-7178. Director of Services: Steve Schalchlin. A nonprofit organization dedicated to the education and protection of songwriters. Estab. 1973. Offers group legal discount; toll free hotline; *SongTalk* newspaper with songwriter interviews, collaborators network and tipsheet; plus Los Angeles based SongTalk seminar series featuring top names in songwriting, song evaluation workshops, song screening sessions, open mics and more. "We offer services to all songwriter members from street-level to superstar: substantial discount on books and tapes, song evaluation through the mail, health insurance program, and SongPitch service for qualifying members. Our services provide education in the craft and opportunities to market songs. The Academy is also active in addressing political issues affecting the profession. We produce the TV show *Salute to the American Songwriter*. Memberships: General – $75; Professional – $120; Gold – $200."

*NATIONAL ACADEMY OF SONGWRITERS/MIDWEST CHAPTER, 20 N. 4th St., Minneapolis MN 55401. (612)371-9401. President: Tom Lieberman. Serves songwriters. Songwriters, both professional and amateur, 18-45 years of age; wide range of musical styles represented. Monthly meeting in Minneapolis mostly benefits metro area members but there are no specific eligibility requirements. To help songwriters of all levels improve their skills through education and critiques by other songwriters. Monthly critique sessions provide necessary feedback and allow songwriters to meet other songwriters. Offers competitions, instruction, lectures, newsletter, social outings and workshops. Applications accepted year-round. $60 annual dues.

*NATIONAL ASSOCIATION FOR CAMPUS ACTIVITIES (NACA), Box 6828, Columbia SC 29260. (803)782-7121. Director of Convention and Member Services: Louis A. Ross. Estab. 1960. Serves songwriters, musicians and all types of talent, school and university activities programs. "Our members are 1170 colleges and universities across the U.S. and Canada and more than 550 firms in entertainment or related services for the campus activities market. Songwriters/musicians must join NACA to participate in our conventions, conferences, listings, mailing lists, etc. or be handled by an agency that is a member of NACA. NACA provides assitance for member institutions to establish and produce quality campus activities programming by providing education, information, and resources for students and staff to facilitate cooperative consumer efficiency and marketplace effectiveness. The primary value in this organization for a songwriter is: access to the college market for performance or personal appearance exposure; graphics assistance for one-stop shopping approach to posters, brochures, album design; advertising opportunities; outlet to agencies dealing with college market." Offers instruction, lectures, library, newsletter, performance opportunities, workshops, magazine, directory, conferences and conventions. Applications accepted May 1-April 30. National membership—$380 (annual); Regional membership—$190 (annual).

THE NATIONAL ASSOCIATION OF COMPOSERS/USA, Box 49652, Barrington Station, Los Angeles CA 90049. (213)541-8213. President: Marshall Bialosky. Estab. 1932. Serves songwriters, musicians and classical composers. "We are of most value to the concert hall composer. Members are serious music composers of all ages and from all parts of the country, who have a real interest in composing, performing, and listening to modern concert hall music. The main purpose of our organization is to perform, publish, broadcast and write news about composers of serious concert hall music—mostly chamber and solo pieces. Composers may achieve national notice of their work through our newsletter and concerts, and the fairly rare feeling of supporting a non-commercial music enterprise dedicated to raising the musical and social position of the serious composer." Offers competitions, lectures, performance opportunities, library and newsletter. Applications accepted throughout the year. $15 membership fee; $35 for Los Angeles and New York chapter members.
Tips: "Ninety nine percent of the money earned in music is earned, or so it seems, by popular songwriters who might feel they owe the art of music something, and this is one way they might help support that art. It's a chance to foster fraternal solidarity with their less prosperous, but wonderfully interesting classical colleagues at a time when the very existence of serious art seems to be questioned by the general populace."

*NATIONAL ASSOCIATION OF RECORDING MERCHANDISERS (NARM), Suite 307, 3 Eves Dr., Marlton NJ 08053. (609)596-2221. Director, Membership Development: Lynn Henley. Serves manufacturers, distributors, retailers of recorded music. "Companies are members; examples are: major and independent record labels, major and independent distribution companies, rack jobbers, one stops, chain and independent retail outlets (who sell records, CDs, audio/visual cassettes), and companies which provide a product or service to the record industry (e.g., computer hard/software, fixtures, packaging, pressing plants). NARM markets music via merchandising/P-O-P materials, provides educational seminars, has lobbyists in Washington, provides a forum for communication for the various segments of the music industry, and has an annual convention."

*NATIONAL ASSOCIATION OF SCHOOLS OF MUSIC, 11250 Roger Bacon Dr., Reston VA 22090. (703)437-0700. Executive Director: Samuel Hope. Assistant Director: Karen P. Moynahan. Estab. 1924. Serves songwriters, musicians and anyone interested in music in higher education. Individual Membership in NASM is open to everyone. The major responsibilities of the National Association of Schools of Music are the accreditation of post-secondary educational programs in music. In addition, NASM publishes books and reports, holds an annual meeting and other forums and provides information to the general public about educational programs in music. Offers a newsletter. Applications accepted year-round.

*NATIONAL BAND AND CHORAL DIRECTORS HALL OF FAME, 519 N. Halifax Ave., Daytona Beach FL 32118. (904)252-0381. Director: Dr. Watie Riley Pickens. Estab. 1985. Serves choral directors. Members are "high school and college choral directors and other nationally recognized choral directors. The main purpose of our organization is to recognize, honor and promote the profession of Band and Choral Directors." Offers competitions; clearing house for band and choral directors. Applications are accepted by invitation only. There are no annual fees or dues.

*NATIONAL FEDERATION OF MUSIC CLUBS, 1336 N. Delaware St., Indianapolis IN 46202. (317)638-4003. Executive Secretary: Patricia Midgley. Estab. 1898. Serves songwriters and musicians. "All ages—in 3 catagories: junior, student, senior (also affiliate groups). Must become a member in the state where you live. We promote good music in all areas, American music and American composers." Competitions and performances. Offers competitions, lectures, newsletter, performance opportunities, social outings, workshops board meetings and conventions. Applications accepted year-round.

*NATIONAL HIGH SCHOOL BAND INSTITUTE, 519 N. Halifax Ave., Daytona Beach FL 32118. (904)252-0381. Director: Dr. Watie Riley Pickens. Serves musicians. Members are high school band directors. "Professional high school band directors who have had national recognition are invited to submit their candidacy for nomination to the N.H.S.B.D. Hall of Fame. The main purpose of our organization is to recognize, honor and promote the profession of marching band directors." Offers competitions, instruction, lectures, library, newsletter, performance opportunities and National High School Band Directors Hall of Fame. Applications are accepted by invitation only. There are no annual fees or dues.

*NATIONAL JAZZ SERVICE ORGANIZATION, P.O. Box 50152, Washington DC 20004-0152. (202)347-2604. Contact: Eugene Holley/Willard Jenkins. Estab. 1985. Serves songwriters musicians, jazz educators and programs. Members include jazz musicians, enthusiasts, related organizations, schools, jazz media and state arts agencies. The NJSO is a not-for-profit public benefit corporation founded in 1985. The purpose of NJSO is nuture the growth of and enhancement of jazz music as an American art form. The NJSO functions as a consultant and referral service for the jazz community. NJSO provides help through their Technical Assistance program. The songwriter would have untold access of resources available through out Technical Resource Program. His or her membership would further enhance the status of jazz as an art in the United States. Offers instruction, newsletter and Technical Assistance Program. Membership fee $25-100. "We are in the process of putting together a comprehensive jazz database consisting any and all institutions, musicians and individuals involved with jazz."

NATIONAL SCHOOL ORCHESTRA ASSOCIATION, NSOA Service Office, 345 Maxwell Dr., Pittsburgh PA 15236-2067. Executive Secretary: Norman Mellin. Estab. 1958. Serves musicians and educators. "We support instrumental music teachers dedicated to the development of school orchestra programs: NSOA sponsors an annual composition contest with a $500 prize. Membership is not required." Offers competitions, instruction, newsletter, workshops and composition contest. Write for contest information.

*NECMA NORTHEAST COUNTRY MUSIC ASSN., P.O. Box 766, Altamont NY 12009. (518)854-3030. President: Kathy Bain. Estab. 1985. Serves songwriters, musicians and country music fans. "There are 3 classes of membership: professional—musicians, singers, songwriters who earn part or all of their livelihood off country music; organizational—talent agencies, recording studios, publishing companies, music stores, etc.; and *associate*—fans or any other persons who support country music. Members are generally from the Northeast—NY, MA, CT, VT, NH, RI, PA, NJ, WV, OH, MD; but will welcome other members from other areas and organizations who are promoting country music and wish to exchange ideas. Our main purpose is to preserve and promote country music, to help its membership through newsletters, seminars and workshops, to promote goodwill with other organizations who are helping country music. Offers competitions, instruction, lectures, newsletter, performance opportunities, social outings and workshops. Applications accepted year-round. Annual dues $10 professional, $5 social, $25 organizational. NECMA is a member of CMA.

NEW DRAMATISTS, 424 W. 44th St., New York NY 10036. (212)757-6960. Service organization dedicated to the development of playwrights. "We sponsor a composer-librettist studio each year where 5 of our writers work with 5 selected composers." For information about the studio and New Dramatists call (212)757-6960.

NEW ENGLAND SONGWRITERS/MUSICIANS ASSOCIATION, 2 Roland Kimball Road, Freeport, MA 04032. (207)865-1128. Director: Peter C. Knickles. Serves songwriters and musicians. "Our members are all ages, people actively and seriously interested in songwriting and the business of music. We are a trade organization for people in the music business, providing networking opportunities with over 300 members. The primary value in membership for a songwriter is learning how to function as a business." Offers competitions, field trips, instruction, lectures, newsletter, peformance opportunities, social outings, workshops, consulting, $1,000 grants, directories, free monthly meetings with professional industry guest speakers, and demo critiques monthly. Applications accepted year-round. Annual dues are $40.
Also *The Music Business Seminar*: A weekend seminar presented in 24 different cities each year. Designed to teach the individual involved in music how to profit from their craft. Entering our 4th year. Cost: $295. For a free 12 pp. brochure, contact: Peter C. Knickles, 2 Roland Kimball Rd., Freeport, MA 04032. (207)865-1128.

*NEW JERSERY AND PENNSYLVANIA SONGWRITERS ASSOC., 226 E. Lawnside Ave., Westmont NJ 08108. (609)858-3849. President and Founder: Bruce M. Weissberg. Estab. 1985. Serves songwriters and musicians. Members are all ages 16-80, all types of music, from central NJ to Wildwood, NJ to Philadelphia area. Must be serious about songwriting. Provides networking, information center and promotional center for workshops and guest speakers. "Primary value is that it enables musicians to network with other songwriters in the area." Offers lectures, library, newsletter, performance opportunities and workshops. Applications accepted year-round. $20/year, $15/year out of Philadelphia, NJ areas. "Our group is always interested in new ideas, new interested guest speakers and a true professional type of atmosphere."

*THE NEW YORK SINGING TEACHERS' ASSOCIATION, 317 W. 93rd St., Apt. 3B, New York NY 10025. (212)662-9338. Register: Lawrence Chelsi. Estab. 1906. Serves musicians and vocalists. Voice teachers of all ages and backgrounds (Actives). Voice coaches, composers, conductors, language coaches, speech teachers and others who support singers, professional singers (all above—Associates). Arts education relating to singing. Conducts monthly meetings, awards prizes in three competitions; two for classical singers, one for music theater singers, gives awards to professionals for career excellence, holds public symposia on important musical/vocal topics annually. A songwriter has to understand the voice in order to write for it effectively. This organization provides experts in all fields of voice, allowing for colleagues to exchange information and ideas. Offers competitions, lectures, performance opportunitites (limited), social outings, workshops meetings and symposia on specific topics. Applications accepted October through May. $25 per year for active members, payable upon application. $20 per for associate members payable upon application. We have several committees which are always open to new ideas and new members. The organization is the oldest and largest independent group of voice teachers in the United States (and maybe in the world).

*NORTH FLORIDA CHRISTIAN MUSIC WRITERS ASSOCIATION, P.O. Box 10394, Jacksonville FL 32247. (904)786-2372. President: Jackie Hand. Estab. 1974. Serves songwriters, musicians and anyone who promotes Christian music. Christians of any age or sex involved with anyone who writes, performs or promotes Christian music. "We help the songwriter get his music in the best possible form, offer planned concerts to present his work, publish his music in our song books and help with copyright information." Provides fellowship with other writers and performers. Offers competitions, field trips, instruction, newsletter, performance opportunities, social outings, workshops, ctirique—annual songwriting contest for members only. Applications accepted year-round. $15 yearly (individual); $20 (husband wife team).

NORTHERN CALIFORNIA SONGWRITERS ASSOCIATION, Suite 211, 855 Oak Grove Ave., Menlo Park CA 94025. (415)327-8296. Executive Director: Ian Crombie. Serves songwriters and musicians. Estab. 1979. "Our 1,200 members are lyricists and composers from ages 16-80, from beginners to professional songwriters. Our purpose is to provide the education and opportunities that will support our writers in creating and marketing outstanding songs. NCSA provides support and direction through local networking and input from Los Angeles and Nashville music industry leaders, as well as valuable marketing opportunities. We offer opportunities and education for songwriters. Most songwriters need some form of collaboration, and by being a member they are exposed to other writers, ideas, critiquing, etc." No eligibility requirements. Offers annual Northern California Songwriting Conference, monthly visits from major publishers, songwriting classes, seminars conducted by hit songwriters ("we sell audio tapes of our seminars—list of tapes available on request"), a monthly newsletter, monthly performance opportunities and workshops. Applications accepted year-round. Dues: $50/year.
Tips: "NCSA's functions draw local talent and nationally recognized names together. This is of a tremendous value to writers outside a major music center. We are developing a strong songwriting community in Northern California. We serve the San Jose, Monterey Bay, East Bay and San Francisco area and we have the support of some outstanding writers and publishers from both Los Angeles and Nashville. They provide us with invaluable direction and inspiration."

NSAI-WVSM SONGWRITERS WORKSHOP, RR #4, Box 112, Liberty IN 47353. (317)458-6152. Coordinator: Ann Hofer. Serves songwriters and musicians. Estab. 1981. "Our members are songwriters of all ages who are members of the Nashville Songwriters Association International. Some are interested in all aspects of the music business and others just songwriting. We have artists, musicians, lyricists, and melody writers. We meet the first Thursday of the month in the Liberty, Indiana High School Band room at 7:00 p.m. We meet September through May. Summer is for performing shows and outings. Our purpose is to assist our members with finding co-writers, keep them informed on publishers accepting material, help them make demo contacts, provide list of record companies, and to educate them on the ever-changing music and songwriting business. We are available to assist the songwriter in any way we can; we are dedicated to his/her needs. We believe that believing in yourself is the beginning of your dream coming true, and we want to encourage songwriters to do just that: believe in themselves." Offers competitions, instruction, lectures, library, performance opportunities, social outings, workshops and monthly critique sessions. Applications accepted year-round. Members pay $50/year to Nashville Songwriters Association International—no local dues.

OHIO SONGWRITERS ASSOCIATION, Suite #30, 27801 Euclid Ave., Euclid OH 44132. (216)731-SONG. President: J.N.A. Wunderle. Serves songwriters, musicians and related craftspeople (lyricists, arrangers, sound engineers, producers, vocalists, etc.). "Members of the OSA encompass young adults to senior citizens, at all ranges of musical and theoretical advancement, from professionals to amateurs who have written their first song and don't know what to do next. Prospective members are required to submit cassette tape with samples of their material, up to 3 pieces." Purpose is "to preserve and promote the creation of original music through education and opportunity." Services include marketing and copyright assistance, recording time, professional arrangement, lead sheets, career consultation, independent record production, music lessons, printing/artwork/logo designs, legal counsel with staff music attorneys, secretarial services, copyist, engineering/studio musicians/vocalists, practice space rental, collaboration pool, musicians referral service, band/musicians engagement listings, competitions, lectures, library, newsletter, performance opportunities, educational/video tape rental library, numerous books on songwriting and the music industry at 15% discount to members; educational/audio cassettes on songwriting in the music industry; OSA has weekly classes in songwriting and monthly seminars on the art and craft of songwriting in the music business; (professional members may open an account with OSA and make monthly payments, interest-free, on their recording projects. Members are eligible for substantial discounts on studio time at Sessions, Inc., 16-track state of the art recording studio offering digital mixdowns. Applications accepted year-round. Annual membership fee is $40.
Tips: "The main goal of OSA is to help songwriters get their 'creative ideas' to the market place. OSA seminars have included nationally known songwriters, representatives of ASCAP and BMI, professional studio engineers, music industry professionals with proven track records, presenting invaluable information to amateur and professional songwriters. OSA has its own independant label, Hall of Fame of Records, Tapes and Compact Discs, and their own publishing company, Tower City Publishing".

OHIO SONGWRITERS ASSOCIATION, 3312 Petzinger Rd., Columbus OH 43232. (614)235-2669. President: William Michael Kimmle. Estab. 1985. Serves songwriters, musicians and lyricists. Members are all ages and from any occupation, with an interest in arranging, recording or scoring, Offers competitions, instruction, lectures, newsletter, performance opportunities, social outings, workshops and professional advice on how to keep a good attitude in a business of ups and downs. Applications accepted year-round. Annual dues: $50.

PACIFIC NORTHWEST SONGWRITERS ASSOCIATION, Box 98324, Seattle WA 98198. (206)824-1568. "We're a non-profit association, and have served the songwriters of the Puget Sound area since 1977. Our focus is on professional songwriting for today's commercial markets. We hold monthly workshops and publish a quarterly newsletter. Our workshops are a great place to meet other writers, find collaborators, critique each other's songs, and share news and encouragement. Our members get immediate contact with hundreds of the biggest national artists, producers, publishers and record companies. Members also get free legal advice from our staff attorney. All this for only $25 per year. We welcome new members. If you have any questions, just give us a call."

*PACIFIC SONGWRITERS ASSOCIATION, Box 15453, 349 W. Georgia, Vancouver, BC V6B 5B2 **Canada.** (604)872-SONG. Estab. 1983. Serves songwriters. All ages, from teens to retired people; writers of music, lyrics and both; also industry people interested in understanding the craft of songwriting. "To inform and promote songwriting and songwriters in the Pacific area; our main activity is a monthly song evaluation session called The Song Works, and 6 times/year we publish the magazine *Hook Line & Singer*." "Access to professional panels for song evaluation and information; opportunity to meet other writers and industry people; a resource place for information." Offers lectures and workshops. Applications accepted year-round. Renewals are based on your 12-month anniversary. $40/year, includes subscription to *Hook Line & Singer*. Subscription only $10.

*PENNSYLVANIA ASSOCIATION OF SONGWRITERS, COMPOSERS, P.O.Box 4311, Allentown PA 18105. (215)433-6787. President: John Havassy. Estab. 1979. Serves songwriters and musicians. "Teens to 40's mostly rock and new music." "Open to anyone interested in finding a better, easier, faster way to further needs of songwriters." "We offer a venue for original music performances." Offers performance opportunities. Applications accepted year-round. $10 yearly. "Any performing songwriters should send tape and bio and other promotional materials for consideration for bookings. Our organization runs the Airport Music Hall in Allentown."

PITTSBURGH SONGWRITERS ASSOCIATION, 408 Greenside Ave., Canonsburg PA 15317. (412)745-9497. President: Frank J. DeGennaro. Estab. 1983. Serves songwriters. "Any age group is welcome. Current members are from mid-twenties to mid-fifties. All musical styles and interests are welcome. Country and pop predominate the current group; some instrumental, dance, rock and R&B also.

WOULD YOU USE THE SAME CALENDAR YEAR AFTER YEAR?

Of course not! If you scheduled your appointments using last year's calendar, you'd risk missing important meetings and deadlines, so you keep up-to-date with a new calendar each year. Just like your calendar, *Songwriter's Market*® changes every year, too. Many of the buyers move or get promoted, rates of pay increase, and even record companies' needs change from the previous year. You can't afford to use an out-of-date book to plan your marketing efforts!

So save yourself the frustration of getting submissions returned in the mail, stamped MOVED: ADDRESS UNKNOWN. And of NOT submitting your songs to new listings because you don't know they exist. **Make sure you have the most current marketing information by ordering *1992 Songwriter's Market* today.** All you have to do is complete the attached post card and return it with your payment or charge card information. Order now, and there's one thing that won't change from your *1991 Songwriter's Market* — the price! That's right, we'll send you the 1992 edition for just $19.95. *1992 Songwriter's Market* will be published and ready for shipment in September 1991.

Let an old acquaintance be forgot, and toast the new edition of *Songwriter's Market.* Order today!

(See other side for more books for songwriters)

MORE BOOKS FOR SONGWRITERS!

BUSINESS REPLY MAIL
FIRST CLASS MAIL PERMIT NO. 17 CINCINNATI, OHIO

POSTAGE WILL BE PAID BY ADDRESSEE

Writer's Digest Books

1507 DANA AVENUE
CINCINNATI OH 45207-9965

NO POSTAGE
NECESSARY
IF MAILED
IN THE
UNITED STATES

Composers and lyricists in group. Our organization wants to serve as a source of quality material for publishers and other industry professionals. We assist members in developing their songs and getting their works published. Also, we provide a support group for area songwriters, network of contacts and collaboration opportunities. We offer field trips, instruction, lectures, library and social outings. Annual dues are $25. We have no initiation fee."

POP RECORD RESEARCH, 17 Piping Rock Dr., Ossining NY 10562. Director: Gary Theroux. Estab. 1962. Serves songwriters, musicians, writers, researchers and media. "We maintain archives of materials relating to music, TV, film with special emphasis on recorded music (the hits and hitmakers 1877-present): bios, photos, reviews, interviews, discographies, chart data, clippings, films, videos, etc." Offers library and clearinghouse for accurate promotion/publicity to biographers, writers, reviewers, the media. "There is no charge to include publicity, promotional or biographical materials in our archives. Artists, writers, composers, performers, producers, labels and publicists are always invited to add or keep us on their publicity/promotion mailing list with career data, updates, new releases and reissues of recorded performances, etc. Fees are assessed only for reference use by researchers, writers, biographers, reviewers, etc."

*RECORDING INDUSTRY ASSOCIATION OF AMERICA, 1020 19th St., NW Suite 200, Washington DC 20036. Director, Member Services: John H. Ganoe. Estab. 1952. Serves recording companies. RIAA membership is corporate. Members include U.S.-based manufacturers of sound recordings. Membership in RIAA is not open to individuals. RIAA has extensive programs on behalf of our industry in the areas of government relations, public relations and anti-piracy enforcement. RIAA also coordinates industry market research and is the certifying body for gold and platinum records. We will provide, upon request, samples of RIAA publications, including our industry sourcebook, newsletter and annual statistical overview. Dues are corporate, and computed in confidence by an outside auditing firm.

ROCKY MOUNTAIN MUSIC ASSOCIATION, Suite 210 Union Station, 1701 Wynkwop St., Denver CO 80202. (303)355-7426. President: Deb Garrison. Serves songwriters and others in music community. Estab. 1986. Membership: 300 and growing. "Our membership ranges from age 18 to 79. Requirements are only that members demonstrate a keen interest in songwriting, music composition and/or performance. One purpose of this organization is to provide an outlet for songwriters in all genres, and to become an 'umbrella' for a Rocky Mountain music industry. We strive to aid our songwriting members in learning the craft of writing songs, and developing contacts within the music industry. We provide discounts at various recording studios, music stores and performances, and a songwriter's and musician's network. We endeavor to provide musicians and songwriter's with exposure that they would otherwise not have an opportunity to experience within this region." Offers lectures, performance opportunities, library, musical directory, social outings, newsletter and workshops. Applications taken year-round for annual May membership dues. 2 major events/year: Music Explosion, Music Awards Celebration and All Star Jam Music Fest, which showcases talent to major record labels. "We also offer 4 specialized technical workshops and have monthly meetings at 6:30 p.m. on first Monday of each month at the Days Inn, 1150 E.Colfax."
Tips: "A songwriter should belong to our organization so that trips to Nashville, New York or Los Angeles become unneccessary. There is a definite Rocky Mountain sound that deserves to be heard."

S.C. COUNTRY MUSIC ASSOCIATION, 1609 Congress Rd., Eastover SC 29044. (803)776-8397. President: Howard A. Knight, Jr. Estab. 1989. Serves songwriters, musicians and fans. "Members are country music professionals-singers, songwriters, musicians; country music fans; business such as music stores, western wear stores, night clubs, radio stations etc. Must be interested in helping to promote country music throughout S.C. and the country. Affiliated with Country Music Associations of America. We sponsor a lot of events which benefit songwriters, such as Writers Night. We have members who are looking for songs to record. Offers competitions, instruction, lectures, library, newsletter, performance opportunities, social outings, workshops and concerts. Applications accepted year-round. Annual dues are $15 for fans, $25 for music professionals and $50 for businesses.

SAN FRANCISCO FOLK MUSIC CLUB, 885 Clayton, San Francisco CA 94117. (415)661-2217. Serves songwriters, musicians and anyone who enjoys folk music. "Our members range from age 2 to 80. The only requirement is that members enjoy, appreciate and be interested in sharing folk music. As a focal point for the San Francisco Bay Area folk music community, the SFFMC provides opportunities for people to get together to share folk music, and the newsletter *The Folknik* disseminates information. We publish 2 songs an issue (6 times a year) in our newsletter, our meetings provide an opportunity to share new songs, and at our camp-outs there are almost always songwriter workshops." Offers library, newsletter, informal performance opportunities, social outings and workshops. Applications accepted year-round. Membership fee is $5/year.

SANTA BARBARA SONGWRITERS' GUILD, Box 2238, Santa Barbara CA 93120. (805)687-7360. President: Mike Crolius. Estab. 1983. "The Guild is beneficial to the songwriter because it serves to help a person's songwriting ability. Also, it helps to open doors to music industry professionals, which, otherwise, would be closed to them. The Guild is a non-profit organization for aspiring songwriters, performers, those interested in the music industry, and anyone interested in original music. Our members are able to meet other songwriters, to learn more about the craft of songwriting, to get their songs heard, and to network. The Guild sponsors monthly cassette tape presentations called Songsearches to L.A. publishers, with drawings held for studio time and gift certificates. Also sponsored are monthly workshops; plus classes and lectures on music in film and TV, studio recording, music business contracts and copyright law, record production, song marketing, music composition, lyric writing and vocal techniques, in addition to a directory of local music services and organizations. Discounts available to members include the following: blank tapes, books that deal with a wide range of pertinent music industry information, studio time at local recording studios, equipment and supplies at local music stores." Membership is $35/year.

SESAC INC., 156 W. 56th St., New York NY 10019. (212)586-3450; 55 Music Square E., Nashville TN 37203. (615)320-0055 Executive Vice President and Chief Executive Officer: Vincent Candilora. Vice President: Dianne Petty, Nashville. Serves writers and publishers in all types of music who have their works performed by radio, television, nightclubs, cable TV, etc. Purpose of organization is to collect and distribute performance royalties to all active affiliates. "Prospective affiliates are requested to present a demo tape of their works which is reviewed by our Screening Committee." For possible affiliation, call Nashville or New York for appointment.

SOCIETY FOR THE PRESERVATION AND ENCOURAGEMENT OF BARBER SHOP QUARTET SINGING IN AMERICA, INC. (S.P.E.B.S.Q.S.A., INC.), 6315 Third Ave., Kenosha WI 53140-5199. (414)654-9111. Membership Manager: Ron Rockwell. Estab. 1938. Serves songwriters, musicians and world's largest all male singing organization. "Members are from teenage to elderly. All are interested in vocal harmony (4 singing, barbershop style). The main purpose of this organization is to perpetuate and preserve the musical art form known as Barbershop Harmony. We are always looking for new songs that will adapt to barbershop harmonization and style." Offers competitions, instruction, lectures, library, newsletter, performance opportunities, social outings and workshops. "A week-long 'Harmony College' is presented each year, open to over 700 men. Instruction in all areas of music: vocal techniques, arranging, song writing, show production, chorus directing, etc. A 'Young Men In Harmony' program is offered, especially designed to appeal to young high school boys. Approved by MENC and ACDA. Our publishing program, which at present offers over 600 songs, is arranged in the barbershop style. The Society offers the opportunity for songwriters to have their music arranged and published." Applications accepted year-round. Membership is usually in local chapters with dues about $52 annually. A chapter-at-large membership, The Frank H. Thorne Chapter, is available at $40 annually.

SOCIETY OF COMPOSERS, AUTHORS AND MUSIC PUBISHERS OF CANADA (SOCAN), (formerly Performing Rights Organization of Canada Limited (PROCAN), Head Office (PROCAN): 41 Valleybrook Dr., Don Mills, Ontario M3B 2S6 **Canada**. (416)445-8700. FAX: (416)445-7108. Head Office (CAPAC): 1240 Bay Street, Toronto, Ontario, M5R 2C2 **Canada**. (416)924-4427. FAX: (416)924-4837. Chief Executive Officer: Jan Matejcek. (415)445-8700. Chief Operating Officer: Michael Rock (416)924-4427. In March, 1990, CAPAC and PROCAN merged to form a single, new Canadian performing rights society. The purpose of the society is to collect music user licence fees and distribute performance royalties to composers, authors and music publishers. The SOCAN catalogue is licensed by ASCAP and BMI in the United States.

THE SOCIETY OF INTERNATIONAL SONGWRITERS & COMPOSERS, Sovereign House, 12 Trewartha Rd., Praa Sands, Penzance, Cornwall TR20 9ST **England**. Phone: (0736)762826. FAX: (0736)763328. Secretary: C.A. Jones. Serves songwriters, musicians, record companies, music publishers, etc. "Our members are amateur and professional songwriters and composers, musicians, publishers, independent record publishers, studio owners and producers. Membership is open to all persons throughout the world of any age and ability, from amateur to professional. The society gives advice and services relating to the music industry. A free magazine is available upon request with an SAE or 3x IRC's. We provide contact information for artists, record companies, music publishers, industry organizations; free copyright service; *Songwriting & Composing Magazine*; and many additional free services." Applications accepted year-round. Annual dues are £15 in the U.K.; £18 in E.E.C. countries; £20 overseas. (Subscriptions in pounds sterling only).

*SOCIETY OF SINGERS INC., 1741 N. Ivar, #118, Hollywood CA 90028. (213)469-4956. Director/Membership Chairman: Ray Charles or Secretary: Dotti Irwin. Estab. 1986. Serves professional singers. "20-80 yrs., singers, songwriters, musicians, actors, business people, composers, any member of the general public. Anyone sympathetic to the goals of the Society of Singers. You do not have to be a singer to join." Our main purpose is to establish a retirement residence facility for ALL singers, and to help any member who has derived his or her primary income as a professional singer for at least 5 years. We maintain a special fund from which monies are disbursed to defray the financial burden of medical and other expenses placed on singers (who are qualified applicants) in times of crisis. Offers newsletter, social outings, sponsored public performances, member's parties. Applications accepted year-round. Minimum of $75 annual dues, upwards.

SONGWRITERS & LYRICISTS CLUB, %Robert Makinson, Box 023304, Brooklyn NY 11202-0066. Director: Robert Makinson. Estab. 1984. Serves songwriters and lyricists. Currently has 60 members. Gives information regarding songwriting: creation of songs, reality of market, collaboration, disc jockeys and other contacts. Only requirement is ability to write lyrics or melodies. Beginners are welcome. The primary benefits of membership for the songwriter are opportunities to collaborate and assistance with creative aspects and marketing of songs through publications and advice. Offers newsletter and assistance with lead sheets and demos. Applications accepted year-round. Dues are $24/year, remit to Robert Makinson. Write with SASE for more information. "Plan and achieve realistic goals. If you have a great song, we'll make every effort to help promote it."

SONGWRITER'S AND POET'S CRITIQUE, 2804 Kingston Ave., Grove City OH 43123. (614)875-5352. President: Patricia A. Adcock. Estab. 1985. Serves songwriters, musicians, poets, lyricists and performers. "We provide information, encouragement and help with the critiquing, networking and pairing of collaborators." Offers field trips, instruction, lectures, library, performance opportunities, social outings, workshops and critiquing sessions. Applications accepted year-round. Annual dues are $12. "We're a talented and diverse group; some of our members are published and recorded writers, and we invite all songwriters, musicians, and poets in the Columbus area to visit and share their creativity."

SONGWRITERS ASSOCIATION OF WASHINGTON, Suite 632, 1377 K St. NW, Washington DC 20005. (703)768-4688. President: Marcy Freiberg. Estab. 1979. "S.A.W. is a non-profit organization committed to providing its members with the means to improve their songwriting skills, learn more about the music business and gain exposure in the industry. S.A.W. sponsors various events to achieve this goal, such as workshops, seminars, meetings, showcases and the mid-Atlantic song contest. S.A.W. publishes *S.A.W. Notes*, a bi-monthly newsletter containing vital information on changes in the business markets for demos, free classifieds to members and upcoming events around the country. For more information regarding membership write or call.

THE SONGWRITERS GUILD OF AMERICA, #702, 50 Music Square West, Nashville TN 37203. (615)329-1782. Assistant Regional Director: Tameron Hedge. Serves songwriters. "The Guild is a voluntary national songwriters' association run by and for songwriters. It is made up of three categories of membership: Associate (unpublished) Members, Regular (published) Members, and Special Associate Members (heirs of deceased songwriters). We represent a wide range of writers in every category of music from Burt Bacharach to Johnny Cash, Bob Dylan to Barbra Streisand, Henry Mancini to Quincy Jones. Any person with an interest in the songwriting profession is eligible for membership. All applications for membership are reviewed by our Membership Committee before an applicant is notified of acceptance." The Guild offers a variety of services which include legal and accounting services for writers, legislative support on issues which affect songwriters and educational programs; also lectures (Ask-A-Pro), newsletter (local and national), performance opportunities (critique), social outings (membership meeting), workshops, group medical and life insurance plan, catalog administration program and estate planning. Applications accepted year-round. Membership fees are: Associate Membership (unpublished) — $45/year; Full Membership (published) — a graduated scale ranging from $55 to $350 annually, depending on the amount of royalties collected by The Guild from songwriter's publishers during the prior year; Special Associate Members (heirs) — $45 to $300 annually depending on the amount of royalties collected.

THE SONGWRITERS GUILD OF AMERICA, Suite 306, 276 Fifth Ave., New York NY 10001. (212)686-6820. West Coast: 6430 Sunset Blvd., Hollywood CA 90028. (213)462-1108. Nashville: United Artists Tower, 50 Music Square West, Nashville TN 37203. (615)329-1782. Founded as the Songwriters' Protective Association in 1931, name changed to American Guild of Authors and Composers in 1958, and expanded to AGAC/The Songwriters Guild in 1982. Effective 1985, the organizational name is The Songwriters Guild of America. "The Songwriters Guild of America is the nation's largest, oldest, most respected and most experienced songwriters' association devoted exclusively to providing songwriters with the services, activities and protection they need to succeed in the business of music." President: George David Weiss. Executive Director: Lewis M. Bachman. National Projects Director: George Wurzbach. West Coast Regional Director: Aaron Meza. Nashville Regional Director: Kathy Hyland. "A full member must be a published songwriter. An associate member is any unpublished songwriter with a desire to learn more about the business and craft of songwriting. The third class of membership comprises estates of deceased writers. The Guild contract is conceded to be the best available in the industry, having the greatest number of built-in protections for the songwriter. The Guild's Royalty Collection Plan makes certain that prompt and accurate payments are made to writers. The ongoing Audit Program makes periodic checks of publishers' books. For the self-publisher, the Catalogue Administration Program (CAP) relieves a writer of the paperwork of publishing for a fee lower than the prevailing industry rates. The Copyright Renewal Service informs members a year in advance of a song's renewal date. Other services include workshops in New York and Los Angeles, free Ask-A-Pro rap sessions with industry pros (see Workshops), critique sessions, collaborator service and newsletters. In addition, the Guild reviews your songwriter contract on request (Guild or otherwise); fights to strengthen songwriters' rights and to increase writers' royalties by supporting legislation which directly affects copyright; offers a group medical and life insurance plan; issues news bulletins with essential information for songwriters; provides a songwriter collaboration service for younger writers; financially evaluates catalogues of copyrights in connection with possible sale and estate planning; operates an estates administration service; and maintains a non-profit educational foundation (The Songwriters Guild Foundation)."

THE SONGWRITERS GUILD OF AMERICA, Suite 317, 6430 Sunset Blvd., Hollywood CA 90028. (213)462-1108. West Coast Director: B. Aaron Meza. Estab. 1931. Serves songwriters. Collects writers' royalties from publishers. "The Songwriters Guild of America is a protective and advisory agency for songwriters. The Guild represents authors and composers all over the world covering all phases of music: pop, R&B, rock, folk, country, jazz, theatre, classical, motion picture and television scores, as well as commercials. A full member must be a published songwriter. An associate member is any unpublished songwriter with a desire to learn more about the business and craft of songwriting. The third class of membership comprises estates of deceased writers. Offers songwriting contract, instruction, lectures, newsletter, royalty collection service, collaboration service, group life and medical insurance, monthly ASK-A-PRO sessions and workshops. Applications are accepted throughout the year. Annual dues are $45 for associate members and $55-350 for full members, depending on royalties collected by the Guild."

*SONGWRITERS OF OKLAHOMA, 211 W. Waterloo Rd., Edmond OK 73034. (405)348-6534. President: Harvey Derrick. Estab. 1983. Serves songwriters and musicians, professional writers, amateur writers, college and university faculty, musicians, poets and others from labor force as well as retired individuals. Age range is from 18 to 90. "Must be interested in writing and composing and have a desire to help others in any way possible. We have members from coast to coast. We offer workshops, critique sessions, contests, civic benefits, education of members on copyrights, contracts, publishers, demos, record companys, etc. as well as a sounding board of peers, education, comraderie and sharing of knowledge." Offers competitions, field trips, instruction, lectures, library, newsletter, performance opportunities, social outings and workshops. Applications accepted year-round. Membership fee is $15/year.

SONGWRITERS OF WISCONSIN, Box 874, Neenah WI 54957-0874. (414)725-1609. Secretary: Tony Ansems. Estab. 1983. Serves songwriters. "Membership is open to songwriters writing all styles of music. Residency in Wisconsin is recommended but not required. Members are encouraged to bring tapes and lyric sheets of their songs to the meetings, but it is not required. We are striving to improve the craft of songwriting in Wisconsin. The primary value of membership for a songwriter is in sharing ideas with other songwriters, being critiqued and helping other songwriters." Offers competitions, field trips, instruction, lectures, newsletter, performance opportunities, social outings, workshops and critique sessions. Applications accepted year-round. $7.50 subscription fee for Newsletter.

SOUTHWEST VIRGINIA SONGWRITERS ASSOCIATION, Box 698, Salem VA 24153. President: Sidney V. Crosswhite. (703)389-1525. Vice President: Robert W. Arrington. Estab. 1982. Non-profit, tax exempt organization which sponsors monthly newsletter, mail-in critique service for out-of-town members at no charge, and monthly meetings featuring song critiques, guest speakers and workshops. Also offers library, field trips and social outings. Purpose is "to increase, broaden, and expand the knowledge of each member and to support, better, and further the progress and success of each member in songwriting and related fields of endeavor through meetings, workshops, correspondence, and any other educational means available." Must submit application and be approved by Board of Directors. One-time initiation fee is $15. Dues are $12/year. "Every *serious* songwriter should belong to a local and a national organization. It's important to be around other songwriters on a regular basis."

THE TENNESSEE SONGWRITERS ASSOCIATION, Box 2664, Hendersonville TN 37077. (615)824-4555. Executive Director: Jim Sylvis. Serves songwriters. "Our membership is open to all ages and consists of both novice and experienced professional songwriters. The only requirement for membership is a serious interest in the craft and the business of songwriting. Most of our members are local, but we also accept out-of-state memberships. Our main purpose and functon is to educate and assist the songwriter, both in the art/craft of songwriting and in the business of songwriting. In addition to education, we also provide an opportunity for camaraderie, support and encouragement, as well a chance to meet co-writers. Our members often will play on each others' demo sessions. We also critique each others' material and offer suggestions for improvement, if needed. We offer the following to our members: 'Pro-Rap'—once a month a key person from the music industry addresses our membership on their field of specialty. They may be writers, publishers, producers and sometimes even the recording artists themselves. 'Pitch-A-Pro'—once a month we schedule a publisher, producer or artist who is currently looking for material, to come to our meeting and listen to songs pitched by our members. Annual Awards Dinner—honoring the most accomplished of our TSA membership during the past year. Tips—letting our members know who is recording and how to get their songs to the right people. A *Tennessee Songwriters Association Handbook*—available to members for $12.50 and to non-members for $15, which deals with every aspect of the music business. Other activities—a TSA summer picnic, parties throughout the year, and opportunities to participate in music industry-related charitable events, such as the annual Childrens Christmas Caravan benefit, which the TSA proudly supports." Applications accepted year-round. Membership runs for one year from the date you join. Membership fee is $25/year.

TEXAS MUSIC ASSOCIATION, #34, 504 W. 24th St., Austin TX 78705. (512)447-2744. Secretary/Treasurer: Steve Scearce. Estab. 1981. Local chapters in Austin, Dallas, San Antonio and Houston. Serves songwriters, musicians and all music industry professionals. Voting members must have significant professional involvement in the music industry; non-voting (associate) membership is open to everyone who supports Texas music. The TMA is the principal trade association for the Texas music industry, offering educational and professional development programs, newsletters, awards programs and lobbying for the industry's interests. Networking with professionals working in other fields of the music business (such as publishers, managers, agents, publicists, studio personnel, etc.) Offers lectures, newsletter, workshops, group health and equipment insurance, credit union, discount long distance phone service. Applications accepted year-round. General membership (voting) $50/yr. Company membership (voting) $150/yr. (All full-time employees qualify for benefits.) Associate membership (nonvoting) $25/yr. "TMA members are also eligible for discounted registration fees at the annual South By Southwest Music and Media Conference in Austin. Songwriters can benefit from TMA membership by taking advantage of our many member services, our networking opportunities, and our educational and professional development programs."

TEXAS SONGWRITERS ASSOCIATION, P.O. Box 1285, Chandler TX 75758. (214)849-2287. Executive Director: Shirley Horton Hutchins. Estab. 1986. Serves songwriters. "Our members are people of all ages, interested in all categories of music—any person interested in songwriting, whether professional or pre-professional, who will support the goals of TSA. Our organization assists those interested in songwriting through educational and informational programs and workshops and offers career guidance throughout all stages of individual development. We provide guidance and encouragement in all aspects of songwriting, from craft techniques to business and industry preparation." Offers instruction, lectures, newsletter, performance opportunities, social outings and workshops. Applications accepted year-round. General membership fee is $40; annual dues are $40.
Tips: "The informed songwriter stands a better chance of succeeding in the highly complex field of songwriting. TSA workshops inform writers, both on craft and business."

*THEATRICAL ENTERTAINMENT OF ACTORS & MUSICIANS, Box 30260, Bakersfield CA 93385. President: Judge A. Robertson. "Our purpose is to advance, educate, encourage, protect and promote overlooked creative talent. We help you help yourself to become a professionally paid artist by producing the creative aspects of songwriters, actors, and artists, and by providing performance opportunities. We notify publishers that demo tapes have been pre-screened by T.E.A.M. Our media showcase is in coproduction with Superstar Productions, Element Records, International Motion Pictures, Ltd., and Element Movie and Music (BMI)." Applications accepted year-round; one-time $55 fee and annual membership fee of $25.

TULSA SONGWRITERS ASSOCIATION, INC., P.O. Box 254, Tulsa OK 74101-0254. (918)660-2035. President: Sam Fox. Estab. 1983. Serves songwriters and musicians. Members are age 18-65 and have interests in all types of music. Main purpose of the organization is "to create a forum to educate, develop, improve, discover and encourage songwriting in the Tulsa area." Offers competitions, lectures, performance opportunities, field trips, social outings, instruction, newsletter and workshops. Applications accepted year-round. Dues are $25/year.
Tips: "We hold a monthly 'Writer's Night' open to the public for performance of original songs to expose the many talented writers in Tulsa."

UNITED SONGWRITER'S ASSOCIATION, 6429 Leavenworth Rd., Kansas City KS 66104. (913)788-7716. President: Victor J. Stoway. Vice President: Steven D. Caldwell. Treasurer: Patricia Winegar. Estab. 1987. Serves songwriters and musicians. "Members run the full spectrum of ages, with interest in every aspect of the music business. We help songwriters achieve the recognition they deserve; combining the talents of the members makes this possible. Members may also make contact with people in the music business. Copyright information, collaborating information, songwriting tips and the lowest prices on demo fees and cassette tapes are some of the benefits the members derive. We also have a song catalog, song critique workshops, open door invitation to two of Kansas City's record companies, and a 20-40% discount at some of the local music stores. USA is a non-profit association. The plans are in the works for USA to perform for charity fund-raising benefits. We would like for USA to be known as a friend to all the songwriters of the world." Offers field trips, instruction, lectures, library, newsletter (bi-monthly), performance opportunities, social outings and workshops (bi-monthly). Membership fee is $15/year.

UTAH SONGWRITERS ASSOCIATION, Box 71325, Salt Lake City UT 84107. (801)265-1110 or (801)964-1227. Estab. 1985. Serves songwriters and musicians. Interest lies mainly in country and folk music, along with pop, bluegrass and contemporary music. Writers are interested in learning how to get their music published. We offer monthly workshops for the songwriters in our area, monthly showcases where writers can perform original material for the public, an annual seminar where writers can meet and talk with major publishers and producers, and an annual songwriting contest. Our goal is to help educate the songwriters in this area and to let them know there is a support group willing to listen to their music and offer advice." Annual events sponsored by Utah Songwriters Association include: Intermountain Songwriters Seminar (May or June), and Intermountain Songwriting Competition (Oct. 15 through Jan. 2 of each year). Winner of the songwriting competition wins a free trip to Nashville to attend the Nashville Songwriters Assn. Spring Symposium in March or a trip to L.A. to attend the Songwriters Workshop in October. The trip is funded by entry fees of $10 for first song, $5 for each additional song. Membership dues are $25.

VOLUNTEER LAWYERS FOR THE ARTS, 3rd Floor, 1285 Avenue of the Americas, New York NY 10019. (212)977-9270. Estab. 1969. Contact: Staff Attorney. Serves songwriters, musicians and all performing, visual, literary and fine arts artists and groups. Offers legal assistance and representation to eligible individual artists and arts organizations who cannot afford private counsel. Also sells manuals and guides on arts-related issues. In addition, there are affiliates nationwide who assist local arts organizations and artists. Offers conferences, lectures, seminars and workshops.

WYOMING COUNTRY MUSIC FOUNDATION, Sussex Route, Kaycee WY 82639. (307)738-2303. President and Founder: Helen D. Ullery. Estab. 1983. Festival Coordinator: Sally and Fred Rogers, Box 43, Chugwater WY 82210. (307)422-3434. Serves songwriters and musicians. Members include "youth, amateurs, professionals, pioneers, country and gospel/country songwriters, musicians and vocalists. No eligibility requirements. Our purpose is to promote country music and country music performers, showcase talent, educate members, and coordinate our annual festival each summer." Offers competitions, lectures, performance opportunities, social outings, newsletter, workshops and annual songwriters contest. "Our songwriter contest is held each spring. Contest deadline is May 30, 1989. Entry is $10/song; 50% of entry fees goes back as prizes to winners. Entrants can not have been in top 50 in charts in the last 10 years. Final review is done in Nashville." Membership fee is $25; festival registration is $15. For membership application and a copy of contest rules send SASE to WCMF address above.

Workshops provide the opportunity to get together with musicians and songwriters with interests similar to yours. Many workshops concentrate on helping you improve your craft, others will give you valuable feedback on your material as well as expert evaluations and advice from music industry professionals.

Many workshops take place in the major music centers: New York, Los Angeles and Nashville. But there is a growing number of local and regional organizations that are putting together their own workshops and inviting music industry people to participate. As you look through this section, you will notice that almost every area of songwriting or performing interest is represented by some kind of workshop. There are programs for pop songwriters and performers, musical theater enthusiasts, jazz musicians and classical performers.

Look through this section for the workshops that appeal to you and write to them for further information.

APPLE HILL SUMMER CHAMBER MUSIC FESTIVAL, Apple Hill Center for Chamber Music, Box 217, E. Sullivan NH 03445. (603)847-3371. Student Recruitment and Special Projects Coordinator: Harriet Feinberg. "Apple Hill welcomes 45-50 students of all ages and abilities to each of four summer music sessions for coaching by the Apple Hill Chamber Players and distinguished guest faculty artists and opportunities to perform chamber music of all periods. Musicians may choose from three short sessions (10 days each), in which participants are assigned to 2 or 3 ensembles coached every day for 1½ hours; or the long session (1 month), in it's entirely of half-long segments (2 weeks each) which is a more in-depth program including improvisation, theory, composition, rock etudes. There is only one composition elective, during the long session. Programs are offered June-August. 55 musicians participate in each workshop. Participants are amateur and professional individual instrumentalists, singers and ensembles. Participants are selected by demo tape submissions. Send for application. Suggested application deadline: May 15th. There is a $25 application fee. Total cost for the short sessions: $760; total cost for long session: $1,800, or 2 weeks: $1010. Programs take place on a 70-acre New England farm. Includes the Louise Shonk Kelly Concert Barn, home of countless rehearsals, student performances and festival concerts; general meeting place and dining hall/bathroom facilities; rehearsal barn; faculty and student cabins; tennis courts."

*ASH LAWN-HIGHLAND SUMMER FESTIVAL, Rt. 6, Box 37, Charlottesville VA 22901. (804)293-9539. Director of Programs: Judy Walker. Estab. 1978. 4 Music At Twilight programs—classical or contemporary concerts. Opera series in repertoire with orchestra. Summer only. June, July and August. Festivals last summer only in Charlottesville VA. 12 songwriters/musicians participate in each festival. Participants are amateur and professional individual vocalists, ensembles, individual instrumentalists and orchestras. Participants are chosen by audition. Auditions are held in February in New York and Washington D.C. Send for application. Closing date: January 15.

*BAROQUE 28 (1990), Foundation for Baroque Music, 165 Wilton Rd., Greenfield Ctr. NY 12833. (518)893-7527. Pres. and Artistic Director: Robert Conant. Estab. 1959. To promote historically in-formed performances of music of the 17th and 18th centuries. Period instruments are used for the most part. Occasional performances of new music for early instruments. Workshops take place in July and August and last 3 weeks. Performance practice workshops are planned for the future. Maximum of 20 musicians participate in each workshop. Participants are professionals. "Write a letter. We are not presenters, but produce our own concerts with a regular pool of musicians. The main venue is our Baroque Festival Studio, seating 100 in Greenfield Center. Excellent acoustics for chamber music."

BMI-LEHMAN ENGEL MUSICAL THEATRE WORKSHOP, 320 W. 57th St., New York NY 10019. (212)586-2000. Director of Musical Theatre: Norma Grossman. Estab. 1961. "BMI is a music licensing company, collecting royalties for affiliated writers. We have departments to help writers in jazz, concert and pop writing." Offers programs "to musical theatre composers, librettists and lyricists. The BMI-Lehman Engel Musical Theatre Workshops were formed in an effort to refresh and stimulate professional writers, as well as to encourage and develop new creative talent for the musical theatre." Each workshop meets one afternoon a week for two hours at BMI, New York. Participants are professional songwriters, composers, playwrights and librettists. "BMI-Lehman Engel Musical Theatre Workshop Showcase presents the best of the workshop to producers, agents, record and publishing company execs, press people and agents for possible option and production." Applicants should call for application. Tape of 3 compositions required with application. Librettists should submit excerpts from works published, produced or in progress. No entry fee.

BROADWAY TOMORROW PREVIEWS, % Broadway Tomorrow Musical Theatre, Suite 53, 191 Claremont Ave., New York NY 10027. Artistic Director: Elyse Curtis. Estab. 1983. Purpose is the enrichment of American theatre by nurturing *new musicals.* Offers series in which composers present scores of their new musicals in concert. 2-3 composers/librettists/lyricists of same musical and 1 musical director/pianist participate. Participants are professional singers, composers and opera/musical theatre writers. Submission is by audio cassette of music, script if completed, synopsis, cast breakdown, resume, reviews, if any, acknowledgement postcard and SASE. Participants selected by screening of submissions. Programs are presented in fall and spring at Tower Theatre with possibility of full production of works presented in concert. No entry fee.

*CALGARY INTERNATIONAL ORGAN FESTIVAL, Calgary Centre for Performing Arts, 205 8th Ave., SE, Calgary, Alberta T2G 0K9 **Canada**. Phone: (403)294-7455. Project Assistant: Patricia Abernathy. Estab. 1980. To promote the Carthy Organ and organ music in general. Workshops and master classes are included in the festival. Offers competition for organists 35 years or younger, winners of major competitions or organists recommended by teachers on an invitation basis. Every four years beginning October 13-19, 1990. Festival lasts one week and takes place in Calgary, Alberta, Canada. Participants are amateur and professional instrumentalists. Performers selected by invitation only. A number of hotels are centrally available around the Centre. The large portion of the event centers around the Jack Singer Concert hall.

*CHICAGO JAZZ FESTIVAL, City of Chicago, Mayor's Office of Special Events, City Hall Rm. 703, 121 N. LaSalle St., Chicago IL 60602. (312)744-3315. Coordinator: Penny Tyler. Estab. 1979. "World's largest free outdoor jazz festival. Present jazz in all of it's forms, free to the public." Festival takes place the 4 days of Labor Day weekend at Petrillo Band Shell, Grant Park. 200 songwriters/musicians participate. Participants are professional jazz vocalists, bands, ensembles, vocal groups, composers, individual instrumentalists and orchestras. Participants are selected by audition (tape, not live) send tape and bio with photo. Individuals or groups are hired by Festival.

*COMPOSER/LIBRETTIST STUDIO, New Dramatists, 424 W. 44th St., New York NY 10036. (212)757-6960. Assistant to the Artistic Director: Beth Nathanson. Estab. 1984. Teams composers with playwrights in two-week workshop. Offered annually. Seminar starts the day after Labor Day in September and lasts two weeks at New Dramatists/New York City. Approximately 5 songwriters/musicians participate. Participants are vocalists, composers, opera/musical theater writers and playwrights. Submit demonstration tape. Send resume, bio, a cassette tape of one or more compositions that you have done for one or more voices and an SASE for return of your material. Deadline: June 15. Housing is available/piano/support services-administrative and artistic. Offers networking through New Dramatists.

COMPOSERS' INSTITUTE, The Festival at Sandpoint, Box 695, Sandpoint ID 83864. (208)265-4554. Executive Director: Timothy Hunt. Estab. 1989. Programs offered summer only (July 24-August 17), last 3 weeks each, staggered and take place at Schweitzer Mountain Resort (Sandpoint). 98 songwriters/musicians participate. Participants are professional individual vocalists, bands, ensembles, composers and individual instrumentalists. Participants are selected by demo tape submissions. Send for application. Closing dates for application are April 15-May 1. Registration fee: $25. Costs are all-inclusive and include room and board. Prices range from $1,000-1,400. Housing at Overniter lodge at Schweitzer Mountain Resort. Meals at the Saint Bernard Restaurant, also at Schweitzer.

*C-SC OPERA WORKSHOP, Culver-Stockton College, Division of Fine Arts, Canton MO 63435. (314)288-5221. Director of Opera Workshop: Dr. Carol Fisher Mathieson. "C-SC Opera Workshop provides students with experience in chamber opera through study and performance. We do one-act, small-cast chamber operas which require no chorus." Workshops offered annually, lasting 1 month (usually in February or March) with 1-4 performances. Performers are usually college students (3-8 per workshop) and occasional guests. "The experimental theatre at Culver-Stockton College seats 50. It can be used as a thrust or round stage. There is no curtain nor is there fly space. Lighting is minimal. We will present the works of composers of chamber opera which are within the ability range of our students (undergraduate) and require a small cast with no chorus. Keyboard or small wind ensemble accompaniment is necessary. Ours is a small workshop which aims at introducing students to the art of chamber opera. Our students are undergraduates; Culver-Stockton College is a liberal arts college. If a work is useful to our workshop, it will also be marketable to other small colleges, undergraduate workshops at universities and some civic groups. We are a church-related school, affiliated with the Christian church (Disciples of Christ), and would provide a testing ground for works marketable to church dramatic groups, too."

*DIRECTOR'S WORKSHOP, Shaw Festival Theatre, Box 774, Niagara on the Lake, Ontario L0S 1J0 **Canada**. (416)468-2153. Music Director: Christopher Dowison. Estab. 1985. Showcases readings by professionals of new plays directed by developing directors. Offered in August for 1 month at Shaw Festival Academy. Participants are professional songwriters, composers, opera/musical theater writers, playwrights and directors. Contact by mail. Closing date for application is June. Costs vary. Workshop is mainly theater and drama oriented.

THE DU MAURIER LTD. OTTAWA JAZZ FESTIVAL, P.O. Box 3104, Station D, Ontario K1P 6H7 **Canada**. (613)594-3580. Managing Director: Karen Dalzell. Estab. 1981. The Festival features ten days of jazz music (and some blues) on primarily outdoor stages. It is a celebration of jazz designed to introduce new audiences, and to promote less known artists. Everyday beginning at noon and running until three a.m., we run a number of series, each with an emphasis on a scene (e.g. local, national, international) or an approach (duo, solo, piano, etc.). Thirteen different series run daily so that all jazz approaches are covered in the festival." 400-500 professional vocalists, instrumentalists, bands, ensembles and vocal groups participate in each event. Performers are selected by demo tape submissions. "Programming committee reviews all submissions. Send us a letter of proposal along with any recorded material, bio, reviews, etc. All proposals should be into the Festival office by early April for consideration, as the Festival is always in late July. The 1990 edition will mark the tenth anniversary of the Festival. Dates are July 13 to 22nd." No entry fee.

*THE ELORA FESTIVAL, P.O. Box 990, Elora, Ontario N0B 1S0 **Canada**. (519)846-0331. Artistic Director: Noel Edison. Estab. 1970. "The Elora Festival is a choral music festival taking place in the picturesque and historic village of Elora, Ontario during two weeks and three weekends in the summer." Offered in the summer. Festival concerts range from 1 to 3 hours each. in the Village of Elora, Ontario and surrounding communities. 1 to 100 songwriters/musicians participate. Participants are professional songwriters, individual vocalists, bands, ensembles, vocal groups, composers, individual instrumentalists, orchestras, opera/musical theater writers and international artists. Audition in person. Performers selected by invitation only. Submit demonstration tape. Audition location is at the discretion of the Artistic Director pending his travel schedule. Usually held in Elora, Ontario. Phone direct or write to the Artistic Director, % of the Elora Festival. Accomodation provided, billeting throughout community.

FIREFLY FESTIVAL FOR THE PERFORMING ARTS, 202 S. Michigan, Lower Level, South Bend IN 46601. (219)288-3472. Executive Director: Carol Weiss Rosenberg. Estab. 1981. "This is a performing arts series. We present concerts, dance, musicals, plays, pops, jazz, 50s—a great variety. We employ musical groups—everything from pops orchestras to folk musicians to chamber ensembles as part of the performing arts series. The possibility for original works exists. Firefly offers diverse performing arts—pops, jazz, dance, theater, musical theater, chamber, opera, operetta; different arts each season. Some of these programs include original arrangements or compositions or entire new works. Concerts are performed on weekends from the end of June to early August. Most performances are in the evening, 8:00 p.m.-10:30 p.m. EST at St. Patrick's County Park. Participants are amateur and professional composers, individual vocalists, individual instrumentalists, bands, orchestras, ensembles, opera/musical theatre writers, vocal groups, dancers, and actors. Participants are selected by information accrued from booking conventions, performances seen, and tapes and promotional materials sent to the Firefly Festival. Contact us by phone or send materials. We're happy to hear of performers and/ or receive materials, tapes any time; our big push for booking is in the Fall."

*GRAND TETON MUSIC FESTIVAL, P.O. Box 490, Teton Village WY 83025. (307)733-3050. Music Director: Ling Tung. Estab. 1962. "Purpose is to present a wide variety of classical music over a seven week summer season. The Festival engages a resident company of approximately 130 professional musicians to perform orchestral music, chamber music and contemporary music." Offered in July and August and last 7 weeks in Teton Village, Wyoming. 130 songwriters/musicians participate. Participants are professional composers and individual instrumentalists. Participants are selected by audition in person, performers selected by invitation, submit demonstation tape and referral. Auditions are held either during the season in Wyoming or in Philadelphia (where the music director lives during the winter). Contact Ling Tung, 2373 Terwood Dr., Huntingdon Valley, PA 19006. Closing date for application month before Festival. Festival musicians are housed in condominiums. Rehearsals and concerts take place in the Festival's 700-seat concert hall. "The Festival presents a weekly series of concerts devoted to contemporary music, each one centered around a specific composer who is invited to take part, either as performer, commentator, or both. All inquiries form musicians and composers should be directed to the music director."

GROVE SCHOOL OF MUSIC, 14539 Sylvan St., Van Nuys CA 91411. (818)904-9400. Contact: Kevin Stevenson or John Cheas. Workshops are offered for guitarists, bassists, synthesists, recording engineers, drummers, keyboardists, vocalists, and brass and reed players. "The Grove School of Music offers a wide range of workshops at various proficiency levels; Music and Midi classes, film and video programs, harmony and ear training classes, professional instrumentals program, and demo and master production workshops. Our instructors are all working, well-respected professionals on the caliber of Doug Thiele, Jack Smalley and John D'Andrea. Details on classes, instructors and procedure are available through the admissions office in brochure form. Four 10-week terms/calendar year. Average class size is 15. Classes range from $80-200 covering five to ten 2-hour sessions. Some classes require texts or materials that are not included in the tuition fee. Complete classroom facilities. GSM offers year long, full-time programs for arrangers/composers, vocalists, players, recording engineers and synthesizer programmers. The school also offers the Composition and Musicianship Program (COMP) for a student wishing a primary career as a songwriter. The course includes instruction in record producing, the record industry and publishing. Students can obtain in-depth experience in all styles of song composition and learn concepts about the lyrical and compositional aspects of songwriging. Many of our students have won song contests, accepted positions at major publishing companies or trade magazines and have had songs recorded by such artists as the Surf Punks and Jefferson Starship. Applicants must be interviewed for placement prior to enrolling. Certain classes require auditions. Request current catalog by mail or telephone."

GUELPH SPRING FESTIVAL, Edward Johnson Music Foundation, Box 1718, Guelph, Ontario N1H 6Z9 **Canada**. (519)821-3210. Artistic Director: Simon Streatfeild. Estab. 1968. "We are basically a 3-4 week festival of the performing arts, with an emphasis on professional performers. We strive to bring together the best international and Canadian talent, to promote emerging Canadian talent and new music. We promote opera, chamber music, choral music, and some jazz. We regularly commission new works. In addition to concerts, the Edward Johnson Music Competition is for student musicians from Wellington County and Waterloo Region. A national vocal competition is held every five years for Canadian singers. Cash scholarships and awards are given." Festival lasts for 3-4 weeks in May. Participants are professional composers, vocalists, instrumentalists, bands, orchestras, choirs, ensembles, opera/musical theatre writers and vocal groups.

*HAMPDEN-SYDNEY MUSIC FESTIVAL, Box 25, Hampden-Sydney College, Hampden-Sydney VA 23943. (804)223-4381 ext. 304. Executive Director: James C. Kidd. Estab. 1982. "The music festival is devoted exclusively to chamber music through 4 Artist Concerts, and through a professional training program, the Musicians' Coaching Program. We offer two weeks of chamber music ensemble coaching by the resident artist-teachers as well as master-classes by instrument (piano, violin, winds, cello)." Festival lasts two weeks and takes place on Hampden-Sydney College campus from May 27-June 10, 1990. 8 artist-teachers, 30 in coaching program participate in each workshop. Participants are both amateur and professional individual instrumentalists. Performers selected by invitation only. Submit demonstration tape for Coaching Program. April 1, 1990. Entry fee: $500 for 2 wks. The $500 fee covers all expenses for the coaching program. Individual tickets for the 4 Artist Concerts range from $7 to $10. Participants in the Coaching Program are housed in the college's newest dormitories and all participants eat family-style in the college's dining hall. The Crawley Forum is the site of all concerts. "Special weekend programs are available on each of the two weekends which provide housing, food and concert tickets for 2 Artist Concerts."

HAYSTACK PROGRAM IN THE ARTS, Portland State University, Box 751, Portland OR 97207. (503)725-4081. Estab. 1969. Offers programs for writers, artists, musicians, amateur and professional songwriters, singers, composers, individual instrumentalists and choral conductors during summer only. Workshops last 1-2 weeks and take place in Cannon Beach, Oregon during June, July and August. 150-200 songwriters/musicians participate in each event. "Haystack is a summer-long program with short courses in writing, visual arts and music. The program is planned around the theme of arts and the environment, giving recognition to the special qualities gained from total immersion in educational activity with interspersed recreation. If you want an opportunity for growth and challenge, a chance to explore a new facet of yourself, a place to enhance your skills, and time to mingle with instructors and participants, Haystack is the place for you! The city of Cannon Beach and nearby communities have a variety of housing facilities. The area also has limited camp sites and trailer spaces available. Upon registration, all participants receive a map of Cannon Beach, a housing listing, and lists of supplies and facilities. Contact us at the above address or by phone: in Portland (503)725-4081, toll-

free in Oregon 1-800-452-4909 ext. 4081, or toll-free outside Oregon 800-547-8887 ext. 4081."
Tips : "We offer one and two week music workshops offered by leading musicians and teachers. Instruction is individualized and based on the student's current skill level."

*INTERNATIONAL CHORAL KATHAUMIXW, Powell River Academy of Music, Box 334, Powell River, British Columbia, V8A 5C2 **Canada**. (604)483-3346. Administrator: Terry Sabine. Estab. 1984. Purpose is "to present a children, youth and adult choral festival and competition; to provide a musical and educational experience for participants; to encourage understanding and goodwill by bringing together choirs from various parts of the world; to create a forum for choral conductors and singers; and to exhange information, musical expertise, repertoire and techniques. Programs include the Kathamixw International Conducting Course. Six participants rehearse and perform, attend symposia and concerts in conjunction with the Kathaumixw Festival. Prizes are given for various competitions, including: children's choirs, youth choir, adult choirs, chamber ensembles, contemporary choiral music, junior, youth and adult solos. The festival is held biennially in July for a duration of 5 days in Powell River, B.C. Canada. 1200 musicians participate in the festival. Participants are amateur vocalists, ensembles and vocal groups. Participants are selected by demo tape submissions. Send for application. Closing date is November. An entry fee of $50 is assessed (1990). Festival is held in the Powell River Complex. Concerts and competitions are held in the Theatre and Great Hall (arena). Overseas visitors are billeted; North American choirs stay in hotels and dorms."

*KERRVILLE FOLK FESTIVAL, Kerrville Festivals, Inc., P.O. Box 1466, Kerrville TX 78029. (512)257-3600. Founder/President: Rod Kennedy. Sponsors songwriters school, guitar school and new folk concert competition. Programs held in late spring, late summer and fall. Festivals last 8 days and are held outdoors at Quiet Valley Ranch. Around 110 acts participate. Performers are professional instrumentalists, songwriters and bands. Participants selected by auditioning in person or submitting demo tape, by invitation only. Send cassette, promotional material and list of upcoming appearances. "Songwriters/guitar schools are $90 and include breakfast, instructors, camping on ranch, fish fry and concert. Rustic facilities—no hookups. Food available at reasonable cost."

*LAKE OSWEGO FESTIVAL OF THE ARTS, P.O. Box 368, Lake Oswego OR 97034. (503)636-3634. Director: Joan Sappington. Estab. 1963. Purpose is to bring a variety of work in the visual and performing arts to the Portland Metropolitan area. A 3-day event with 3 or 4 performances of jazz, ensemble and classical instrument soloists. Offered annually in late June. Festival lasts 3 days. Festival performances presented in 200 seat theater or in outdoor park (3-4,000).

THE LEHMAN ENGEL MUSICAL THEATRE WORKSHOP, Suite 215, 1605 N. Cahuenga Blvd., Hollywood CA 90028. (213)465-9142. Co-Director: John Sparks. Estab. 1971. Held at Los Angeles Music Center 5 nights a week monthly (September through May), a series of workshops offered for development of musical theatre authors and projects. "First-year members do assignments designed to develop creative and critical faculties by performing and critiquing each others' works. In subsequent years, composers, lyricists and book writers work on their own projects, bringing work in as often as they wish and as time allows for critique." Size of group varies from 20-120 songwriters/musicians participate. Book writers, songwriters, composers, lyricists and opera/musical theatre writers are eligible. Members are amateur and professional and are selected from material submitted. Application fee is $25 ($100 per year) which applies to dues, if accepted. Send for brochure and application. Deadline is first week of August. "We conduct readings of completed works using limited funds provided, in part, by the NEA, to cover costs of copying scripts and music, fees for rehearsal pianists, etc."

MUSICAL THEATRE WORKS, INC., 440 Lafayette St., New York NY 10003. (212)677-0040. Literary Manager: Brook Randolph Garrett. Estab. 1983. "We develop and produce new works for the musical theatre: informal readings, staged readings and full productions of new musicals." Functions year-round. Participants are amateur and professional composers and songwriters and opera/musical theater writers. Participants are selected through a critique/evaluation of each musical by the Literary Manager and his staff. To contact, send completed script, cassette and SASE to the above address.

NATIONAL ACADEMY OF SONGWRITERS (NAS), Suite 780, 6381 Hollywood Blvd., Hollywood CA 90028. (213)463-7178. Staff Members: Steve Schalchlin, and Dan Kirkpatrick. "Offers programs for songwriters including Publishers' Evaluation Workshops, SONGTALK seminar series featuring top names in songwriting, lyric writing, demo production and more." Attendance: up to 30/workshop. Length: 2-4 hours/workshop. Membership is $75/year, professionals $120/year; Gold membership $200/year. Send for application. "NAS is a nonprofit membership organization dedicated to the protection and education of songwriters. NAS also provides a bimonthly newsletter containing tipsheet *Open Ears* and collaborators' network."

NEW MUSICALS PROJECT, Columbia College, 72 E. 11th, Chicago IL 60605. (312)663-9462. Managing Director: Mary M. Badger. Estab. 1986. Promotes musical theater. "This project is really geared toward the writing process, not production or publication, although it can include a production. Songwriters may participate if we can match them with a playwright. Musicians may participate only as they are needed for a particular project, i.e. pit band, recording." Participants are professional composers, bands, songwriters, singers and opera/musical theater writers. Participants are selected through in-person auditions and demo tape submissions. Submit script, outline, synopsis and demo tape. The project is year round and submissions are accepted at any time.

*NORDIC FEST, % Decorah Area Chamber of Commerce, P.O. Box 364, Decorah IA 52101. (319)382-3990. Contact: President of Nordic Fest. Estab. 1966. "A cultural celebration of the Scandanavian-American heritage common to most people in our area." Various performances both inside and outside. Strolling minstrals, yearly opera, street dancing. Festival is held in Decorah, Iowa and takes place the last full weekend in July (July 27-29, 1990) and lasts 3 days. The participants are both amateur and professional individual vocalists, bands, vocal groups, individual instrumentalists, orchestras and opera/musical theater writers. Participants are selected by in person audition at Luther College — Decorah, Iowa. Contact David Greedy, % Luther College, (319)382-2000.

*NORFOLK CHAMBER MUSIC FESTIVAL/YALE SUMMER SCHOOL, 96 Wall St., New Haven CT 06520. (203)432-1966. Manager: Sharon D. Moore. Estab. 1941. The Norfolk Festival/School offers training and performances including a 2-week seminar in June specializing in a particular ensemble medium, followed by a 6-week intensive chamber music session. The Festival/School is geared towards the standard chamber music ensembles; string quartets, woodwind quintets, brass quintets and ensembles including piano. Each year there is a 2-week seminar focuses on one specific instrument. Each student receives an Ellen Battell Stoeckel scholarship which covers all costs except for administrative fees (covers room, board, faculty, music etc.) Offered summer only mid-June through mid-August. One workshop lasts 2-weeks, one lasts 6-weeks. Workshops are held in Norfolk, CT (upper Northwest part of CT). 65-80 songwriters/musicians participate. Participants are both amateurs and professionals (leans toward the young professional) ensembles and individual instrumentalists. Participants are selected by audition in person, submit demonstration tape. Auditions are held in New Haven, CT — early to mid-March each year, Rochester, NY; Oberlin, OH; Chicago, IL; San Francisco, CA. Send for application or call (203)432-1966. Closing date for application is early to mid-February (some exceptions may apply). Application fee $25. 2-week session usually runs between $180-280 and covers administrative fees; all other costs (except transportation) are covered by the Ellen Battell Scholarship. 6-week session runs between $550-600 and also covers administrative fees, all other costs covered by scholarship. Students are housed in the town of Norfolk with host families in groups of 1 to 3 per home. The festival takes place on the beautiful 75-acre Ellen Battell Stoeckel Estate which includes the 1,200-seat Music Shed, various barns and cabins for practice and coachings.

*OCTOBER FEST OF CHAMBER MUSIC, Mohonk Mountain House, Lake Mohonk, New Paltz NY 12561. (914)255-1000. Assistant Manager of Advertising, Guest and Public Relations: Michelle E. DuBois. In 1976, the Octoberfest program was started at the Mohonk Mountain House. "Purpose: Octoberfest is a theme program which offers amateurs and professionals the chance to play in a relaxed,beautiful atmosphere." Octoberfest is lead by Alice Smiley and is offered annually. 100 musicians participate. Participants are amateur and professional individual instrumentalists and orchestras. Submit demonstration tape and résumé. Call and request an October Fest brochure. Closing date for application is month before or until all positions are filled. Fee $20. The hotel rates include 3 meals a day and use of the hiking trails. Tax and service charge are added. Hotel resort located in the Shawangunk Mountains of the Hudson Valley on a lake with hiking, tennis, golf, cross-country skiing, skating, horseback riding, etc. Located 7 miles off the NYS Thruway Exit 18. 90 miles from NYC.

SONGCRAFT SEMINARS, 441 East 20th Street, New York NY 10010. (212)674-1143. Estab. 1986. Year-round classes for composers and lyricists conducted by teacher/consultant Sheila Davis, author of *The Craft of Lyric Writing* and *Successful Lyric Writing*. The teaching method, grounded in fundamental principles, incorporates whole-brain writing techniques. The objective: To express your unique voice. All courses emphasize craftsmanship and teach principles that apply to every musical idiom — pop,theatre, or cabaret. For details on starting dates, fees, and location of classes, write or call for current listing.
Successful Lyric Writing: A 3-Saturday Course. Three 6-hour classes on the fundamental principles of writing words for and to music. Required text: *Successful Lyric Writing*. Held three times a year at The New School. Limited to 12.
Successful Songwriting A one-day Seminar/Workshop/Critique designed for composers as well as lyrics. Topics covered include: music forms, melody writing, plot development, guidelines on figurative language and whole-brain writing. Attendees receive "Keynotes on Successful Songwriting," a digest

of seminar theory. Held at colleges and songwriting associations around the country.

Song by Song by Sondheim: A one-day seminar focused on the elements of fine craftsmanship exemplified in the words and music of Stephen Sondheim, America's pre-eminent theater writer. Significant songs are played and analyzed from the standpoint of form, meter, rhyme, literary devices, and thematic development. Attendees are helped to apply these elements to their own writing. Held in April and November at The New School.

Whole-Brain Creativity: A one-day workshop that puts you in touch with your thinking writing style through an understanding of split hemispheric specialization. While having fun doing exercises to access each quadrant of the brain, you'll acquire new tools for increased creativity and successful songwriting. Limited to 10.

Successful Lyric Writing Consultation Course: This course, an outgrowth of the instructor's book, covers the same theory and assignments as The Basics Course. Participants receive critiques of their work by the book's author via 1-hour phone sessions.

SONGWRITER SEMINARS AND WORKSHOPS, 928 Broadway, New York NY 10010. (212)505-7332. President: Ted Lehrman. Vice President: Libby Bush. Estab. 1975. Offers programs for songwriters: introduction to pop songwriting; advanced workshop; and at-home songwriter workshop. Cycles begin in September and February. Approximately 10 in each songwriter workshop. Each cycle lasts eight weeks. "Our programs stress the craft and business realities of *today's* pop music industry. We guide our members in the writing of the hit single song (both lyrics and music) for those recording artists who are open to outside material. We also share with them our considerable experience and expertise in the marketing of commercial pop music product. Our instructors, Ted Lehrman and Libby Bush, both members of ASCAP, have had between them more than 80 songs recorded and commercially released here and abroad. They continue to be highly active in writing and placing pop songs for publication. Industry guests (record producers, record company, A&R people, publishers etc.) frequently attend workshop sessions." Workshops: Pop Songwriting—Preparing for the Marketplace; Advanced Songwriter Seminar and Workshop—Ready for the Marketplace. Cost of 8 week workshops: $175-185. Cost of at-home songwriter workshop: $25/lyric; $35/song. Private song and career consultation sessions: $45/hour. Top 40 single stressed. Collaboration opportunities available. No housing provided. Interviews/auditions held for songwriters and singer/songwriters to determine which workshop would be most helpful. Call for free brochure and/or to set up interview.

THE SONGWRITERS ADVOCATE (TSA), 47 Maplehurst Rd., Rochester NY 14617. (716)266-0679. Director: Jerry Englerth. "TSA is a non-profit educational organization that is striving to fulfill the needs of the songwriter. We offer opportunities for songwriters including: song evaluation workshops that afford songwriters the opportunty to bounce their songs off other songwriters and receive an objective critique and improve their craft. TSA evaluates tapes and lyric sheets via the mail. We do not measure success on a monetary scale, ever. It is the craft of songwriting that is the primary objective. If a songwriter can arm himself with knowledge about the craft and the business, it will increase his confidence and effectiveness in all his dealings. However, we feel that the songwriter should be willing to pay for professional help that will ultimately improve his craft and attitude. And by all means, join and strongly support a songwriting organization. In addition, for those of you who wish to have a demo made, TSA will also be able to accommodate you." Price list is available upon request. Membership dues are $10/year. Must be member to receive discounts or services.

THE SONGWRITERS GUILD OF AMERICA, 276 Fifth Ave., New York NY 10001. (212)686-6820. National Projects Director: George Wurzbach. Estab. 1931.

Ask-A-Pro: "2-hour bi-weekly music business forum to which all writers are welcome. It features industry professionals—publishers, producers, A&R people, record company executives, entertainment lawyers, artists—fielding questions from new songwriters." Offered year-round except summer. Charge: free to members, $2 for nonmembers.

Song Critique: "New York's oldest ongoing song critique. Guild songwriters are invited to either perform their song live or present a cassette demo for feedback. A Guild moderator is on hand to direct comments. Non-members may attend and offer comments. Free to members, $2 charge for nonmembers.

The Practical Songwriter: This is a ten week nuts and bolts seminar dealing with song re-writing, demo production, industry networking, song marketing, contracts, and publishing. Sessions are highlighted by visits from industry professionals. Instructor is songwriter/musician George Wurzbach. Fee: $130 for SGA members, $175 for non-members.

Pro-Shop: For each of 6 sessions an active publisher, producer, or A&R person is invited to personally screen material from professional Guild writers. Participation is limited to 10 writers. Audition of material is required. Coordinator is producer/musician/award winning singer, Ann Johns Ruckert. Fee; $75 (SGA members only).

Writing For The Nashville Market: An important 4 session workshop for any writer considering writing for the expanding market of Country/Pop music. Developed to give writers a realistic approach to breaking into this market. Instructor is Hit songwriter, author of *How To Pitch and Promote Your Songs* (Writer's Digest Books), Fred Koller. Fee; $60 for SGA members, $80 for non-members.
Other Courses And Workshops Will Include:
MUSIC THEORY FOR SONGWRITERS
POP MUSIC WORKSHOP
UNDERSTANDING MIDI
LYRIC WRITING
SATURDAY AFTERNOON LIVE (one day, selected topics)
ARTIST/SONGWRITER CAREER DEVELOPMENT
Other workshops presented in Nashville (615)329-1782 and Los Angeles (213)462-1108.

THE SONGWRITERS GUILD OF AMERICA, Suite 317, 6430 Sunset Blvd., Hollywood CA 90028. (213)462-1108. West Coast Director: B. Aaron Meza. Estab. 1931.
ASK-A-PRO: "2-hour music business rap session to which all writers are welcome, held on the first Thursday of each month at 7:00 pm. Features industry professionals fielding questions from songwriters." Each session lasts 2 hours. Free to all Guild members, $2 for non-members. Reservations necessary. Phone for more information.
Jack Segal's Songwriters Guild Supershop "Creating Your Career Song, Your Market Breakthrough": This very successful workshop focuses on working a song through to perfection, including, Title, Idea, Re-writes, and Pitching your songs. Please call for more information regarding this very informative workshop. Dates to be announced.
Song Critique Sessions: Held on the last Thursday of the month at 7:00 pm, SGA members are given the opportunity to present their songs and receive constructive feedback from industry professionals and peers. There is a limit on the number of songs critiqued, and reservations are required. Call the SGA office for more information.
Supershop: SGA professional writers explore the marketing aspects of songwriting. Over 7 sessions, the group meets with music industry professionals. Supershop is a unique experience in networking.

*SUMMER FESTIVAL OF PERFORMING ARTS, City Celebration, Inc., Fort Mason Bldg. A, San Francisco CA 94123. (415)474-3914. Festival Director: Courtney Bullock. A free weekly outdoor concert series featuring a variety of music and dance in Golden Gate Park. Musicians include soloists to big bands and orchestras. The Summer Festival also provides paid opportunities for artists to perform in Senior Centers and Convalescent Hospitals. Musicians can apply by sending a demo tape to City Celebration Summer Festival (photos are not necessary).

*SUMMER LIGHTS FESTIVAL, Greater Nashville Arts Foundation, 111 Fourth Ave. S., Nashville TN 37201. (615)259-6374. Program Coordinator: Steve Carson. Estab. 1981. To present the arts of Nashville to the world. Featured music is the music of Nashville: jazz, bluegrass, country, rock and gospel. Nashville Songwriters Association International always has a featured segment of the festival. The festival features Nashville music. Offers programs year-round. GNAF does music programs all year; festival is 4 days. Summer Lights 1990 May 31-June 3 in downtown Nashville. Approximately 2,000 songwriters/musicians participate in festival. Participants are amateur and professional individual vocalists, bands, ensembles, vocal groups, composers, individual instrumentalists, orchestras and opera/musical theater writers. Performers selected by invitation only. Take name and number and present before Programming Committee which issues invites. Performers work outside on stages and in the street of the city; those from out of town stay in hotels and motels.

UTAH ARTS FESTIVAL, Utah Arts Festival Foundation, Inc., 168 W 500 N, Salt Lake City UT 84103. (801)322-2428. Assistant Director: Robyn Nelson. Estab. 1977. "We promote the arts in Utah—visual, performing, and literary. All types of music are presented—emphasis on new music." Programs offered summer only. Performances last 5 days and take place at Triad Center, Downtown Salt Lake City during the third week in June. Participants are amateur and professional songwriters, individual vocalists, bands, ensembles, vocal groups, composers, individual instrumentalists and orchestras. Participants are selected by demo tape submissions. Send for application. Closing date for application is February. Musicians and performers are paid. Artists stay in local hotels. Festival will negotiate with national artists re: lodging for performance.

Contests and Awards

Songwriting and musician competitions can be great ways of gaining exposure for your songs and talents. Winners stand to walk away with money, merchandise, a recording deal or some other award, but all of the participants have the opportunity to make valuable contacts. Some contests are judged by music publishers and other music industry professionals, which guarantees that your song will be heard by at least one specialist. Sometimes music professionals will personally request to hear more material after the contest is over. Beneficial business relationships can result.

When participating in a competition, you are "selling" yourself and your work. Marketing techniques and professionalism should not be forgotten. Each contest you enter should be studied so you can best prepare your material for each award you seek.

Be aware that not all songwriting contests are legitimate, above-board competitions. Based on the information given us, we have confidence in the legitimacy of the contests that made it into this year's *Songwriter's Market*, but if you are considering entering an unlisted contest from another source, there are a few things to watch out for. First, read all the rules thoroughly before signing or sending anything. Be sure you understand what the prize is and what will happen to your song if you win. If the prize is a publishing contract, your entry fee often amounts to little more than paying to have your song published. If your song is a good song to begin with, then it could very likely be picked up by a legitimate publisher without charge and without the need for such a "contest." Never agree, either as part of the entry requirements or as a condition attached to winning a prize, to give up the songwriter's share of future earnings from the song. Some contests have even required entrants to transfer copyright of the entered songs to the contest sponsor. This is clearly not in the songwriter's best interest.

In evaluating any contest, you must weigh what you stand to gain against what you are being asked to give up. Just remember that it is almost always a bad idea to give away rights for the unrestricted use of your songs. Once you've given those rights away, there is not much hope of ever getting them back.

Contests listed here encompass all types of music and all levels of composition expertise. Most of them are annual, but some organizations sponsor different events throughout the year. Read each listing carefully and write a letter to any that interest you, asking to be put on their list to receive information about upcoming competitions. When you receive the information, read the rules carefully and be sure you understand them before entering the contest.

*ARTISTS' FELLOWSHIPS, New York Foundation for the Arts, Suite 600, Beekman St., New York NY 10038. (212)233-3900. For composers. Annual award.
Purpose: "Artists' Fellowships are $7,000 grants awarded by the New York Foundation for the Arts to individual originating artists. The Foundation is committed to supporting artists from all over New York State at all stages of their professional careers. Fellows may use the grant according to their own needs; it should not be confused with project support."
Requirements: Must be 18 years of age or older; resident in New York State for 2 years prior to application; and cannot be enrolled in any graduate or undergraduate degree program. Deadline: Sept. 17. Samples of work are required with application. 1 or 2 original compositions on separate audiotapes and at least 2 copies of corresponding scores or fully harmonized lead sheets.

Awards: All Artists' Fellowships awards are for $7,000. Payment of $6,500 upon verification of NY State residency, and remainder upon completion of a mutually agreed upon public service activity. Nonrenewable. "Fellowships are awarded on the basis of the quality of work submitted and the evolving professional accomplishments of the applicant. Applications are reviewed by a panel of five composers representing the aesthetic, ethnic, sexual and geographic diversity within New York State. The panelists change each year and review all allowable material submitted."
Tips: "Be sure to mark the scores clearly where tapes are cued-up."

*BALTIMORE OPERA COMPETITION FOR AMERICAN OPERATIC ARTISTS, 527 N. Charles St., Baltimore MD 21201. (301)727-0592. Competition Coordinator: James Harp. For performing artists. Annual award.
Purpose: "Prizes are awarded to talented operatic artists in order to further their development in the study of languages, voice and acting."
Requirements: Singers must be between the ages of 20 and 35, inclusive and must be citizens of the United States. They must present two letters of recommendation from recognized musical authorities." Deadline: May 18. Send for application. Singers must audition in person.
Awards: 1st Prize: $10,000; 2nd Prize $8,000; 3rd Prize $5,000; Steber Award $2,500; Puccini Award $2,000; Janowski Award $1,000; Collinge Memorial Award $1,000; $150 stipends to all semifinalists. Prize may be renewed upon audition. Singers are judged by a panel of internationally recognized judges eminent in the field of opera.
Tips: "The purpose of the competition is to encourage young operatic talent on the verge of a career. Singers must demonstrate potential in singing, fluency in languages and histrionic capability."

THE BUNTING INSTITUTE OF RADCLIFFE COLLEGE FELLOWSHIP PROGRAM, 34 Concord Ave., Cambridge MA 02138. (617)495-8212. Contact: Fellowship Coordinator. For songwriters, composers, performing artists and musical playwrights among others. Annual award. Estab. 1960.
Purpose: Fellowship program is designed to support women who wish to pursue independent study in the creative arts and performing arts, as well as other scholarly fields.
Requirements: Ph.D. or equivalent professional experience. Deadline: October 1. Send for application. Samples of work required with application. "Send 1 or 2 samples of recent compositions or performances on a single cassette tape; tape should be accompanied by written scores when appropriate."
Awards: The Bunting Fellowship Program: $20,500 for a one-year appointment. Applications are judged "on the significance and quality of the project proposal and on the difference the fellowship might make in the applicant's career."

BUSH ARTIST FELLOWSHIPS, E-900 First National Bank Bldg., 332 Minnesota St., St. Paul MN 55101. (612)227-5222. Director, Bush Artist Fellowships: Sally Dixon. For composers, musical playwrights, visual artists, writers and choreographers. Annual award. Applications in music composition and choreography are accepted in alternate years.
Purpose: "To provide uninterrupted time (6-18 months) for artist to pursue their creative development — do their own work."
Requirements: Applicant must be a Minnesota, North Dakota or South Dakota or western Wisconsin resident for 12 of preceeding 36 months, 25 years or older, not a student. Deadline: October-November. Send for application. Samples of work on cassette required with application.
Awards: Bush Artist Fellowships: $26,000 stipend and $7,000 additional for production and travel. Award is good for 6-18 months. "5 years after competition of preceeding fellowship, one may apply again." Applications are judged by peer review panels.

*CINTAS FELLOWSHIP, I.I.E 809 UN Plaza, New York NY 10017. (212)984-5564. Program Officer: Rebecca A. Sayles. For songwriters, composers and musical playwrights. Annual award. Estab. 1964.
Purpose: "Fellowships awarded to persons of Cuban citizenship or lineage for achievement in music composition (architecture, painting, sculpture, printmaking, photography and literature); students wishing to pursue academic programs are not eligible, nor are performing artists. Applicants must be creative artists of Cuban descent who have completed their academic and technical training." Deadline: March 1. Send for application. Samples of work required with application. "Send complete score and a cassette tape. Compositions submitted must be serious classical works. Popular songs and ballads will not be accepted."
Awards: Cintas Fellowship: $10,000 per grantee. Fellowship is good for 12 months. Applicant may apply no more than twice. Selection committee reviews applications.

*COLUMBIA ENTERTAINMENT COMPANY'S NATIONAL CHILDREN'S PLAYWRITING CONTEST, 309 Parkade Blvd., Columbia MO 65202. (314)874-5628. Chairperson, CEC Contest: Betsy Phillips. For musical playwrights. Annual award.

Purpose: "We are looking for top-notch scripts for theater school use, to challenge and expand the talents of our students, ages 10-15. We want good plays with large casts (20-30 characters) suitable for use with our theater school students. Full production of the winning script will be done by the students. A portion of travel expenses, room and board offered to winner for production of show."

Requirements: "Must be large cast plays, original story lines and cannot have been previously published. Please write for complete rules." Deadline: June 30. Send for application; then send scripts to address above. Full-length play, neatly typed. No name on title page, but name, address and name of play on a 3 × 5″ index card. Cassette tape of musical numbers required."

Awards: $250 first prize and partial travel expenses to see play produced. Second place winner gets no prize money but receives production of the play by the theater school plus partial travel expenses. This is a one-time cash award, given after any revisions required are completed. "The judging committee is taken from members of Columbia Entertainment Company's Executive and Advisory boards. At least eight members, with at least three readings of all entries, and winning entries being read by entire committee. We are looking for plays that will work with our theater school students."

Tips: "Remember the play we are looking for will be performed by 10-15 year old students with normal talents — difficult vocal ranges, a lot of expert dancing and so forth will eliminate the play. We especially like plays that deal with current day problems and concerns. However, if the play is good enough, any suitable subject matter is fine. It should be fun for the audience to watch."

*COMPOSERS GUILD, 40 N. 100 W., Box 586, Farmington UT 84025. (801)451-2275. President: Ruth Gatrell. For composers and songwriters. "We are a nonprofit organization working to help the composer/songwriter. Each year we sponsor classes, workshops, seminars, showcases/concerts, and a composition contest, with winning numbers eligible for performance in Composers Guild Spectacular." Estab. 1963.

Requirements: "Annual dues of $25 entitles members to reduced entry fee for contest ($5 members, $15 non-members), and classes, seminars, activities, critiques, musical showcases, and the opportunity to associate with other composers and learn from them." Annual composition contest deadline: August 31. Send for application. Scores and/or cassettes for entry are acceptable.

Awards: $1,900 distributed among 8 categories: keyboard, popular, choral, vocal solo, arrangements, instrumental, jazz and children's music. The best-of-the-show (can be from any music category) is awarded $500. "Applicants judged by professional, usually head of university music department or firmly established producer of performed music."

Tips: "Be as professional as possible — clear, neat manuscript. Have music taped on cassette. Sloppy manuscripts will not be accepted by Composers Guild. Do not send only copy of score or tape."

DELIUS COMPOSITION CONTEST, Jacksonville University, Jacksonville FL 32211. (904)744-3950, Ext. 3370. Chairman: William McNeiland. For composers. Annual award.

Requirements: Send for application.

Awards: First Prize: $500. Three Best-of-Category Prizes: $100 each.

*DIVERSE VISIONS REGIONAL GRANTS PROGRAM, Intermedia Arts, 425 Ontario SE, Minneapolis MN 55414. (612)627-4444. Director of Artist Programs: Al Kosters. For composers, performing artists and artists in all disciplines and genres. Annual award.

Purpose: Intermedia Arts encourages artists to investigate diverse issues/concerns in their work while challenging traditional, conventional and widely accepted contemporary approaches when creating, producing and presenting that work. *Diverse Visions*, formerly the Grants Program for Interdisciplinary Artists, is a regional grants program administered by Intermedia Arts which was developed to respond to those artists who attempting to explore new definitions of, or the boundaries between cultures, art disciplines and/or traditions in their work.

Requirements: Grants are available to artists working individually or collaboratively for personally-conceived productions. Only noncommercial projects over which the applicant has creative control and responsibility will be considered. Applicants must be a resident of Iowa, Kansas, Minnesota, Nebraska, North Dakota, South Dakota or Wisconsin, and must have physically resided in one of these states for at least 12 of the 24 months preceding the application deadline, and intend to remain a resident in that state during the grant period. Students who will be attending school full-time during the grant period (August 1, 1990-December 31, 1991) are not eligible. Projects associated with degree programs will not be considered. Deadline: April 27, 1990. Send for application. Applications received by the deadline are reviewed by staff for eligibility and completeness. Late or incomplete applications will not be considered. Too apply, all written materials must by typed. Do not reduce the size, staple or bind application materials. Do not submit additional pages and/or support materials that are not listed as required or optional. Place your name in the top righthand corner of each page of submitted material. The application form, a one-page projected description, a current resume and work samples. Write *Divers Visions* for more information.

Awards: 2 year period from date of award. "Extensions granted—but no additional money available."
Tips: "Submit quality work samples (of previous work) and be certain to respond with *all* that is required.

EAST & WEST ARTISTS INTERNATIONAL AUDITIONS, 310 Riverside Dr., #313, New York NY 10025. (212)222-2433. Executive Director/Founder: Miss Adolovni Acosta. For performing artists. Annual award.
Requirements: "Open to all classical instrumentalists, singers and ensembles of any nationality who were born after January 1, 1954 and have not given a New York recital debut." Deadline: January 24, 1990. Send SASE for information and application forms.
Awards: "A fully subsidized solo debut at Weill Recital Hall at Carnegie Hall; cash awards."

---

*FORT BEND SONGWRITERS ASSOC. SONGWRITING AND VOCAL PERFORMANCE CONTEST, P.O. Box 117, Richmond TX 77469. Coordinator: Terry Miller. For songwriters and performing artists; "amateurs only." Annual award.
Purpose: Objective is to promote the growth of the songwriting and vocal performance industries by providing an arena of competition for amateur writers and singers.
Requirements: Applicants must be of amateur status, must not have ever received royalties from ASCAP, BMI or SESAC and must not have ever been or currently be signed to a *national* record label. Deadline: April 30. Send for application. Samples of work required with application. "One song on a cassette with neatly printed or typed copy of the lyrics. Label lyric sheet and tape with name of song, songwriter or singer, address and phone number. Cue tape before sending."
Awards: Songwriting category: Grand prize $100 plus recording time and/or merchandise from sponsor as made available, 1st prize $75, 2nd prize $50, 3rd prize $25. Vocal performance category: 1st prize $75, 2nd prize $50, 3rd prize $25. Recording time must be used within 1 year of award. Judged by impartial personnel from the music industry.
Tips: "Read 'The Craft of Lyric Writing' by Sheila Davis and 'The Craft and Business of Songwriting' by John Braheny, have your songs critiqued by other writers and performers. While simple demo tapes are allowed, studio demos will probably get the most attention and have the best chance of winning. Each year the FBSA will try to have publishers, agents and record company people act as judges in our contest. This contest may be your foot in the door to a new career. Therefore, be honest with yourself. Send only your *best* material. Don't accept the opinion of friends and relatives, try to participate in some songwriters group that will give you a valid critique of your entry before you enter."

FULBRIGHT SCHOLAR PROGRAM, COUNCIL FOR INTERNATIONAL EXCHANGE OF SCHOLARS, Suite M-500, 3400 International Dr., NW, Washington DC 20008-3097. (202)686-7877. Estab. 1946. Director, Academic & University Liaison: M. Carlota Baca. For songwriters, composers, performing artists, musical playwrights and scholars/artists in all disciplines. Annual award.
Purpose: "Awards are offered annually in virtually all academic disciplines including musical composition."
Requirements: "U.S. citizenship at time of application; M.F.A., Ph.D. or equivalent professional qualifications; for lecturing awards, university teaching experience." Application materials for the competition become available in March each year, for grants to be taken up 1½ years later. Application deadlines: June 15—Australia, USSR, India, Latin America, except lecturing awards to Mexico, Venezuela, and the Caribbean. August 15—Africa, Asia, Western Europe, East Europe, the Middle East and lecturing awards to Mexico, Venezuela, and the Caribbean. Send for application. Samples of work are required with application. Applicant should refer to checklist in application packet.
Awards: "Benefits vary by country, but generally include round-trip travel for the grantee and for most full academic-year awards, one dependent; stipend in U.S. dollars and/or local currency; in many countries, tuition allowance for school age children; and book and baggage allowance. Grant duration ranges from 3 months-1 academic year. Applications undergo a two-stage peer review by CIES advisory committees; first by subject matter specialists and then by an interdisciplinary group of geographic area specialists. After nomination, applications are sent to the Board of Foreign Scholarships and the host countries for final review."
Tips: "The Applicant's Handbook, which is included in the application packet, provides suggestions on preparing a competitive application, as well as in-depth information about the review committee structure, etc."

---

*HARVEY GAUL COMPOSITION CONTEST, The Pittsburgh New Music Ensemble, Inc., Duquesne University School of Music, Pittsburgh PA 15282. (412)261-0554. Conductor/Executive Director: David Stock/Eva Tumiel-Kozak. For composers. Biennial.

Purpose: Objective is to encourage composition of new music. Winning piece to be premiered by the PNME.

Requirements: "Must be unpublished and unperformed compositions—new works scored for 6 to 16 instruments drawn from the following: flute, oboe, 2 clarinets, bassoon, horn, trumpet, trombone, tuba, 2 violins, cello, bass, 2 percussion, piano, harp, electronic tape." Deadline: April 30. Send for application. Samples of work are required with application. "Real name must not appear on score—must be signed with a "nom de plume." Entry fee: $10.

Awards: Harvey Gaul Composition Contest: $1,500. Judges review scores submitted."

HEMPHILL-WELLS SORANTIN YOUNG ARTIST AWARD, P.O. Box 5922, San Angelo TX 76902. (915)658-5877. For performing artists. Annual award.

Purpose: "There are 3 divisions of competition: Vocal, Instrumental and Piano. All candidates will be judged by the highest artistic standards, in regard to technical proficiency, musicianship, rhythm, selection of repertoire and stage presence. Objective: to further the career of the young artist."

Requirements: Piano/instrumental: not reached their 28th birthday by competition. Vocal: not reached their 31st birthday by competition. All contestants will perform all repertoire from memory. Deadline: October 19. Send for application. Judged on performance contest weekend.

Awards: A winner and runner-up will be declared in each division. The division winner will receive a cash award of $500; the runner-up will receive $250. An overall winner will be selected to appear with the San Angelo Symphony Orchestra on February 2, 1991, and will receive an additional $1,500 cash award. $500 to be paid at time of selection and $1,000 on February 2, 1991. Title held as winner of that year. Printed on all future information. Contest held every year. Can only win once. No limit on number of times you may enter. This is a competition for the young artist; highest priority will be placed on artistry, communication and stage presence.

INDIE BULLET MAGAZINE SONGWRITER/ARTIST CONTESTS, Rt. 14, Box 272, Tyler TX 75707. Estab. 1987. Send SASE for further information and entry blanks. Contest held each year.

Songwriter Contest: For songwriters of country music. Annual award. Four different deadlines for finalist selection each year: March 31, May 31, July 31 and September 30.

Requirements: Submit 1 country song in demo form on cassette with lyric sheet. Song must not have been nationally charted in *Indie Bullet* or prior to entry or during contest. Enclose SASE for acknowledgment of entry. Entry fee of $25 with entry. Entries will be judged on lyric, tune and commercial value by *Indie Bullet* staff to determine 24 finalists. The 24 finalists' demos will be copied on a master cassette (alphabetically by song title) and lyric sheets copied. The master cassette will be sent to all paid *Indie Bullet* subscribers for voting on top songwriter song. Winner will be notified by *Indie Bullet Magazine* via certified mail within 30 days following voting deadline.

Awards: 24-track studio recording of song with artist of songwriter's choosing and a national release of song with *Indie Bullet* advertising and subcontracted telephone promotion. "Prize value approximately $10,000."

INTERMOUNTAIN SONGWRITING COMPETITION, P.O. Box 71325, Salt Lake City UT 84107. (801)292-1609 or (801)964-1227. Contest Director: C. Boone-Smith. Estab. 1987. For songwriters. Annual award by Utah Songwriters Association.

Purpose: First place winner receives an all-expense paid trip to Nashville, Tennessee to attend Nashville Songwriters Association International Spring Symposium in March or to LASS in Los Angeles in October.

Requirements: All amateur songwriters may enter. Deadline: December 31. Send for application to enter. Send cassette tape and lyric sheet. Entry fee: $10 for first song, $5 each additional song.

Awards: First prize is a trip to Nashville, approximate value of $750.

Tips: "Submit a well-written song on a quality demo tape. Studio demos are not required but they usually get the most attention. Lyric sheets should be typed or legibly hand written. Noisy cassettes should be avoided. Radio deejays are among the judges, so they listen for commerciality."

KENNEDY CENTER FRIEDHEIM AWARDS, Kennedy Center for the Performing Arts, Washington DC 20566. (202)416-8031. Coordinator: Marilyn Cotter. Estab. 1978. For American composers. Annual award. For symphonic instrumental compositions in even-numbered years; for instrumental compositions for 1-13 instruments (chamber music) in odd-numbered years.

Market conditions are constantly changing! If you're still using this book and it is 1992 or later, buy the newest edition of Songwriter's Market at your favorite bookstore or order directly from Writer's Digest Books.

Purpose: Annual award for new music by an American. "Our goal is to bring high level public recognition and honor to contemporary American composers. Award may be used as composer wishes."

Requirements: Requirements for application: American citizenship or permanent residency status; composition must have had American premiere performance within 2 year period, July 1-June 30 in year of composition. May not include voices unless used as an instrument-must be without words. Deadline: July 15th. Send or call for application. 3 tapes and 1 score with application plus $20 fee.

Awards: 1st prize: $5,000; 2nd prize: $2,500; 3rd prize: $1,000; 4th prize: $500. Applications are judged by a 3-person jury: 1) each receives copy of taped performance without name of composer; 2) jury gathers to listen collectively to all compositions and examine score. They then nominate 10 semi-finalists; 3) jury members individually study scores (of 10) with tape, then confer by phone to select finalists; 4) these works are performed for final ranking. Prizes awarded at the conclusion of performance. This year's concert date: October 28 at 3:00 P.M. in the Concert Hall of the Kennedy Center. Admission is free to the public, but tickets are required.

Tips: "Get a top quality recording by a fine chamber group if possible."

*KATE NEAL KINLEY MEMORIAL FELLOWSHIP, College of Fine & Applied Arts, 110 Architecture Bldg., 608 E. Lorado Taft Dr., Champaign IL 61820. (217)333-1661. Contact: Dean — College of Fine & Applied Arts. For graduates of College of Fine & Applied Arts of the U of I or to graduates of similar institutions of equal educational standing whose major studies havebeen inart, architecture or music. Annual award.

Purpose: "Award is to be used toward defraying the expenses of advanced study of the Fine Arts in America or abroad."

Requirements: "Submit of application with purpose, 3 letters of reference, copies of transcripts and examples of work." Deadline: March 15. Send for application or call. In October send for application by writing or calling us. Samples of work are required with application. "Slides, musical compositions, tapes, films, essays or publications which the applicant wishes to exhibit as evidence of artistic ability or attainment. Applicants in musical performance may audition in person.

Awards: Judged by "high attainment in the applicant's major field of study as witnessed by academic marks and quality of work submitted or performed; high attainment in related cultural fields as witnessed by academic marks; the character, merit and suitability of the progam proposed by the applicant; excellence of personality, seriousness of purpose and good moral character. Also preference will be given to applicants who have not reached their twenty-fifth birthday." "You need a Bachelors in Fine Arts, Architecture or Music." "We are updating our application form and the amount and we will not have the new forms ready until October so do not write or call for an application or information until October please."

*MARIMOLIN COMPOSITION CONTEST, 44 Lorraine St., Roslindale MA 02131. (617)325-6477. For composers. Annual award.

Purpose: To encourage the creation of works for the combination of marimba and violin, or violin and marimba with tape accompaniment.

Requirements: Open to all composers. $20 entry fee. Deadline: early July. Send for application. A completed new work for violin and marimba. 2 scores, or 1 score and parts.

Awards: "Up to 3 winners will be selected. A total of $600 will be awarded at the judges discretion. The winning work(s) will be premiered during the following season. Works are judged anonymously by Marimolin, and the opinion of a reputable composer is sought in the final selection."

MID-SOUTH PLAYWRIGHTS CONTEST, 51 S. Cooper, Memphis TN 38104. (901)725-0776. Executive Director: Jackie Nichols. For musical playwrights. Annual award. Estab. 1983.

Requirements: Send script, tape, SASE. "Playwrights from the South will be given preference." Open to full-length, unproduced plays. Musicals must be fully arranged for the piano when received. Deadline: April 1.

Awards: Grants may be renewed. Applications judged by three readers.

MIXED BLOOD VERSUS AMERICA PLAYWRITING CONTEST, 1501 S. 4th St., Minneapolis MN 55454. (612)338-0937. Script Czar: Dave Kunz. For musical playwrights. Annual award. Estab. 1983.

Purpose: To encourage emerging playwrights (musical playwrights).

Requirements: "Send previously unproduced play (musical) resume, cover letter stipulating contest entry." Deadline April 15. Send SASE for copy of contest guidelines. Samples are not required.

Awards: Winner: $2,000 and full-production of winning play/musical. Review/reading by local theatre professionals.

Tips: "Professionalism is always a plus. Surprise us."

*MONTREAL INTERNATIONAL MUSIC COMPETITION/CONCOURS INTERNATIONAL DE MUS-IQUE DE MONTRÉAL, Place des Arts Montréal, Quebec H2X 1Z9 **Canada.** (514)285-4380. FAX:(514)285-4266. General Director: Mme. Monique Marcil, C.M.

Purpose: "The Montreal International Music Competition, operating on a four year cycle, is devoted to violin, piano and voice. The schedule for the coming years will be as follows: 1990 - recess year; 1991 - violin; 1992 - piano; 1993 - voice. There will be three tests open to the public and judged by an International Jury.

Requirements: "Musicians in the violin and piano competitions must be 16 to 30 years old; in the voice competition, musicians must be 20 to 35 years old." Registration fee: $35 (Canadian). Deadline: February 1, each year.

Awards: Nine prizes totalling $38,300 (Canadian).

*MUSEUM IN THE COMMUNITY COMPOSER'S AWARD FOR STRING QUARTET, P.O. Box 251, Scott Depot WV 25560. (304)757-2509. Contest Administrator: Trish Fisher. For composers. Biennial.

Purpose: The Composer's Competition is to promote the writing of new works for string quartet (two violins, viola and cello).

Requirements: Work must not have won any previous awards nor have been published or publicly performed or used commercially. Requires 3 copies of the original score, clearly legible and bound. Title to appear at the top of each composition, but the composer's name must not appear. Entry forms must be filled out and a SASE of the proper size enclosed for return of entry. Send for application.

Awards: Museum in the Community Composer's Award First place: $2,500. Up to 3 honorable mentions will be awarded at the discretion of the judges. Jurors will be three nationally known musicologists.

Tips: There is a non-returnable entry fee of $25 per entry. Winning composer will be awarded $2,500 prize and a premiere concert of the composition by the Montani String Quartet at the Teays Valley School for the Arts. Transportation to the premiere from anywhere in the continental United States will be provided by the Museum.

*MUSIC CITY SONG FESTIVAL, Box 17999-SW, Nashville TN 37217. (615)834-0027. Founder and Executive Director: Roy E. Sinkovich. Estab. 1979. "Prizes in 1989 totaled over $250,000. Sponsors for the 1989 competition included Atari Computer, Magnavox, Peavey, Shure, Smith Corona, TAS-CAM and Technics. The Music City Song Festival has eight divisions: Professional Song, Amateur Song, Novice Song, Vocal Performance, Professional Lyric, Amateur Lyric, Novice Lyric and Lyric Poem. Musical categories available are: Pop/Rock, Country, MOR/Adult Contemporary, R&B/Soul/Blues, Gospel/Contemporary Christian, Novelty/Miscellaneous (except for Vocal) and Musical Theater/Standards (Vocal only). Entrants submit cassette tapes to be judged by active music industry professionals (publishers, recording artists, producers, record company executives, radio personalities, managers, promoters, etc.) Entry fee varies, depending on level of competition (Professional, Amateur or Novice). All entries must be accompanied by an official MCSF entry form."

Awards: "433 prizes of cash, merchandise and cash plus merchandise are awarded to First through Tenth place in *each* musical category of each division. The Top Six Lyric Poem entries are published in *SoundMakers,* MCSF's free educational magazine distributed annually in conjunction with the competition. Finalist Certificates are awarded to the top 25 finalists in each musical category of each division. Honorable Mention Certificates are awarded to the top 10 percent in each musical category of each division. *SoundMakers* magazine is distributed free of charge to everyone on the MCSF mailing list regardless of whether they enter the competition. To be added to MCSF's mailing list for free entry information and *SoundMakers* magazine, contact the MCSF offices. NOTE: Entering the Music City Song Festival does not tie up your material in any way. You are free to continue pitching your songs throughout the competition. Entering the competition or winning an award does not give the MCSF any publishing or promotional rights to your song."

Tips: "Read the MCSF entry information very carefully. All tapes should present your songs so that words, music and vocals can be clearly heard and understood. Be sure to include a typed or neatly printed lyric sheet with tapes of original songs. Listen to the tape to be sure it is a good copy, then rewind it to the beginning of the song. For the purposes of the MCSF competition, each song must be submitted on a separate cassette labeled with song title only. Lyric sheets should be printed on 8½ × 11 *white* paper (so they can be photocopied for judging) and labeled with song title only. For more details, write to MCSF at the above address or call between 9:00 a.m. and 5:00 p.m. Central time."

"How to Use Your Songwriter's Market" (at the front of this book) contains comments and suggestions to help you understand and use the information in these listings.

*NACUSA YOUNG COMPOSER'S COMPETITION, NACUSA, Box 49652 Barrington Station, Los Angeles CA 90049. (213)541-8213. President, NACUSA: Marshall Bialosky. For NACUSA members 18-30 years of age. Annual award.
Purpose: Goal is "to encourage the writing and performance of new American concert hall music."
Requirements: Must have NACUSA membership and meet age restrictions. Samples are not required.
Awards: Judged by a committee of composers.

*NATIONAL MUSIC FAIR, 36 West Third Ave., Denver CO 80223. (303)722-9653. Producer of the Event: Original Projects Unlimited. For songwriters. Annual award.
Purpose: "Songwriters Association of America is a nonprofit organization geared towards launching the careers of amateur songwriters."
Requirements: "Send song on cassette for entries. $10 per song." Deadline: May. Send for application or call. Samples of work are required with application (entry).
Awards: "Judged by lyrics, arrangements, melody line, marketabiliby."

NATIONAL MUSIC THEATER NETWORK, INC., Suite 1111, 1457 Broadway, New York NY 10036. (212)382-0984. President: Timothy Jerome.
Purpose: "The objective of the award is to seek out the future creators of musicals/operas for Regional/Broadway development, as well as to focus attention via the award on the materials available today, that otherwise might not be visible. The goal of the incentive grant monies that are part of the award is to encourage a producer to take on the work and bring it to full presentation. A $30 evaluation fee and a completed musical theater or opera work, with book and score is required, as well as a completed submission form, provided by the Network." Send for application. Submit completed works.
Awards: Gala staged readings of the best new musical and opera.

*NATIONAL YOUNG ARTIST COMPETITION, Midland-Odessa Symphony & Chorale, Inc., P.O. Box 60658, Midland TX 79711. (915)563-0921. For student musicians under 26 years (30 yrs. — voice) who are not launched on a professional career under management. Annual competition the last Friday and Saturday of January (January 25 and 26, 1991).
Purpose: To encourage and promote young musicians' careers.
Requirements: Applicant must be a student musician under age 26 studying with music teacher, completed application forms, $25 entry, 5×7 glossy portrait-type photo (for publicity). Application deadline: December 30. Send for application. Samples are not required.
Awards: Lara Hoggard performance medallion. Up to $10,000 distributed among finalists and performing winners. Up to four winners perform with Midland-Odessa Symphony & Chorale, Inc., at regular classical subscription concerts. Contestants are judged by a panel of five judges.
Tips: Categories are for: piano, winds, strings and voice. Includes all categories but voice in secondary division. At least one of performing winners is from secondary division.

*NEW FOLK CONCERTS FOR EMERGING SONGWRITERS, Box 1466, Kerrville TX 78029. (512)257-3600. Attn: Kerrville Festivals Office. For songwriters and composers. Annual award.
Purpose: "Our objective is to provide an outlet for unknown songwriters to be heard."
Requirements: Songwriter enters 2 previously unpublished songs on same side of cassette tape — $5 entry fee per tape; more than one tape may be entered; 6-8 min. total for 2 songs. No written application necessary; no lyric sheets or press material needed. Deadline: April 20, 1990. Call or write for detailed information.
Awards: New Folk Award Winner. 40 writers invited to sing the 2 songs entered during The Kerrville Folk Festival. 6 writers are chosen as award winners. Each of the 6 receives a cash award of $150 and performs at a winner's concert during the Kerrville Folk Festival. Initial round of entries judged by the Festival Producer. 40 semifinalists judged by panel of 3 performer/songwriters.
Tips: "Keep in mind that the quality of the original song is more important than the singer, group or presentation of the song on the entry tape. Persons interested should contact our office for printed information."

*NEW MUSIC FOR YOUNG ENSEMBLES, Suite 9E, 12 W. 72nd St., New York NY 10023. (212)601-0085. Executive Director: Clair Rosengarten. For composers. Annual award.
Purpose: "To create a repertory of contemporary chamber music of intermediate difficulty, to make the music of living composers more accessible and to interest a new and ever-increasing advance in the music of today."
Requirements: American citizenship or resident of the US. Deadline: varies; send for application. Samples of work are required with application form. Samples should be copies of the original work.
Award: $500 first prize. Applications are judges by a "panel of professional composers."

*PULITZER PRIZE IN MUSIC, 702 Journalism, Columbia University, New York NY 10027. (212)854-3841. Administrator: Robert C. Christopher. For composers and musical playwrights. Annual award.
Requirements: "The piece must have its American premiere between March 15 and March 14 of year it is submitted for consideration." Deadline: March 14. Samples of work are required with application and $20 entry fee. "Send tape and score."
Awards: "1 award: $3,000. Applications are judged first by a nominating jury, then by the Pulitzer Prize Board."

*THE QUINTO MAGANINI AWARD IN COMPOSITION, % Norwalk Symphony Society, Inc., P.O. Box 550, Norwalk CT 06852. (203)454-2011. Contact: Dr. Richard Epstein. For composers.
Requirements: The competition is open to all American composers. Entries should be submitted anonymously, with Social Security Number as identity and appropriate return envelope and return postage. In an accompanying sealed envelope, composer should give name, address, social security number, and brief resume. The composition is to be scored for standard symphonic orchestra, and should not exceed 15 minutes in length; no soloists or concerti. Write for more information.
Awards: The recipient will receive a cash award ($2,500) and will have the composition performed in world premiere by the Norwalk Symphony Orchestra under the direction of Jesse Levine, Musical Director, during the 1990-91 season.

RICHARD RODGERS PRODUCTION AWARD, American Academy and Institute of Arts and Letters, 633 W. 155th St., New York NY 10032. (212)368-5900. Assistant to the Executive Director: Jeanie Kim. Estab. 1978. "The Richard Rodgers Production Award subsidizes a production by a nonprofit theater group in New York City of a work by composers and writers who are not already established in the field of musical theater. Development grants for staged readings may be given in lieu of the Production Award or in addition to it. The award is only for musicals—songs by themselves are not eligible." (Guidelines for this award may be obtained by sending an SASE to above address.)

*ROME PRIZE FELLOWSHIP, 41 East 65th St., New York NY 10021. (212)517-4200. Contact: Fellowships Coordinator. For composers. Annual award.
Purpose: "A center for independent study and advanced research, the academy provides living and working space for artists and scholars in the arts and humanities in a 50 room building on top of the Janiculum Hill overlooking Rome."
Requirements: "U.S. citizens only may apply. B.A. in field of application." Deadline: Nov. 15. Send or call for application. Samples of work are required with application. Tapes and scores.
Awards: "Rome Prize Fellowships—2 available in musical composition: $7,000 stipend, $500 European travel, $800 travel allowance, room, board, studio. One year in Rome. Judged by independent juries of professionals in the field."
Tips: "Write a good proposal explaining why a year in Rome would be invaluable to your development as a composer. Explain what you would do in Rome."

*LOIS AND RICHARD ROSENTHAL NEW PLAY PRIZE, % Cincinnati Playhouse, P.O. Box 6537, Cincinnati OH 45206. (513)421-5440. Contact: Literary Manager. For musical playwrights. Annual award.
Purpose: The Rosenthal Prize was established to encourage the production of new work in the theater and to give playwrights the opportunity to see their work through all stages of production.
Requirements: A work of any style or scale constituting a full evening of theater, musicals, collaborations or adaptations. Must not have received a full-scale professional production and must be unpublished at time of submission. Deadline: Jan. 15, 1991. Samples of work are required with application. Format should be complete, neatly typed, securely bound script.
Awards: Lois and Richard Rosenthal New Play Prize—$1,500 stipend, residency expenses and appropriate royalties. The prize is awarded by May; production of the show in winter or spring of following season. Each submission is read and evaluated by a member of the Playhouse Literary staff; finalists are judged by Artistic Director Worth Gardner.
Tips: "Follow submission guidelines carefully, make sure script is securely bound. Works of timely interest and a theatrical nature are encouraged. Works with previous readings or workshop productions are helpful. No submissions accepted before October 15, 1990."

*SANTA FE SYMPHONY COMMISSIONING PROGRAM, P.O. Box 9692, Santa Fe NM 87504-9692. (505)983-3530. General Manager: Lynn Case. For composers. Annual award.
Purpose: "Work to be commissioned for premiere during season either for orchestra chorus or chamber music or any combination of above. Submit scores and/or tapes of other classically-oriented works for chamber, chorus and/or orchestra.
Requirements: Submit resume, other scores and tapes. "Send legible scores and cassette tapes."
Awards: By panel of composers/musicians including Music Director.

SONGWRITERS ASSOCIATION OF WASHINGTON MID-ATLANTIC SONG CONTEST, Suite 632, 1377 K St. NW, Washington DC 20005. (703)768-4688. Contact: Director. Estab. 1979. Gives awards to songwriters and/or composers annually. "Contest is designed to afford *amateurs* the opportunity of receiving awards/exposure/feedback of critical nature in an environment of peer competition. Deadline is usually in the autumn of the year. Applicants must send for application; rules and regulations explained—amateur status is most important requirement. Samples of work are required with application: cassette, entry form and 3 copies of lyrics.
Awards: "Awards usually include free recording time/tapes for First Prizes; Grand Prize has been recording time/air fare. Awards change each year." Awards must be used within one calendar year. "Applications are judged by a panel of three judges per category, for five levels. First level is Pass/Fail; 2nd is point-judged to determine Honorable Mention; 3rd is for top twenty entries; 4th is for top ten and determines First Place Winner; 5th is for the top winners in each category, arriving at the grand prize winner. Reduced entry fees are offered for SAW members. Membership also entitles one to a newsletter and reduced rates for special events/seminars."

STANLEY DRAMA AWARD, Wagner College, 631 Howard Ave., Staten Island NY 10301. Estab. 1957. Director: Bill Bly. For musical playwrights. Annual award.
Purpose: "Our purpose is to encourage the writing of original plays and musicals."
Requirements: Deadline: September 1. Send for application. Samples of work and written recommendation are required with application. "Send firmly bound, typed script with cassette."
Awards: $2,000 one time award. "We're simply looking for the best play or musical submitted in a given year."
Tips: "Make sure submission materials are complete; do the best work you possibly can."

*THE JULIUS STULBERG AUDITIONS, INC., P.O. Box 107, Kalamazoo MI 49005. (616)375-2808. Business Manager: Mrs. Zoe Forsleff. For performing artists. Annual award.
Purpose: "To encourage continued excellence in musical education and accomplishment for young string players studying violin, viola, cello and string bass."
Requirements: Must be 19 year of age or younger. There is a $20 application fee. Send for application with samples of work. Prefers cassette tape, not to exceed 10 minutes in length. "Music on tape must be from standard concerto repertoire, and accompanied."
Awards: 1st place: $2,000 and solo performance with Kalamazoo Junior Symphony; 2nd place: $1,000 and recital performance with Fontana Concert Society; 3rd place: $500.
Tips: The cassette tapes are screened by a local panel of judges, from which 12 finalists are selected to compete in live competition. An outstanding panel of three judges are engaged to choose the winners. The 1990 judges were Sir Yehudi Menuhin, Maestro Catherine Comet and internationally-known violist, Csaba Erdelyi. The 1991 live competition will be March 2, 1991.

TALENT SEARCH AMERICA, 96 McGregor Downs, W. Columbia SC 29169. For songwriters, composers and lyricists. Awards given quarterly.
Purpose: "To discover and award new songwriters and lyricists." Deadlines are February 1, May 2, August 3, and November 4. Send SASE for entry forms and information. Samples of work on cassette and lyric sheet are required for entry with entry form. "All inquiries must be by mail. No phone calls, please. Many entrants have gained contracts and other interests with many music and creative writing companies. Winners lists are sent to winners only. Talent Search America is co-sponsored by selected companies in the music and creative writing businesses. Talent Search America is a national nonprofit contests partnership. Entrant information will not be returned or disclosed without written permission from winning entrants. Proper postage must be sent to gain entry forms."
Awards: Six awards given every quarter: 3 for songwriters, 3 for lyricists; $1,000 in all. Entries are judged on creativity, commercial appeal and originality.

MARVIN TAYLOR PLAYWRITING AWARD, P.O. Box 3030, Sonora CA 95370. (209)532-3120. Estab. 1980. For musical playwrights.
Purpose: To encourage new voices in American theater.
Requirements: Mail script w/SASE. We accept phone calls or written inquiry. No application form or fee. Submissions must be full-length, typewritten. SASE if manuscript is to be returned. Prefers cassette to written score w/original submissions. No more than 2 prior productions of script. Deadline: May 15.
Awards: Marvin Taylor Playwriting Award: $500 and full staging. Applications are judged by a committee of the theater's artistic staff.

*SIGVALD THOMPSON COMPOSITION AWARD COMPETITION, Fargo-Moorhead Symphony Orchestra, Box 1753, Fargo ND 58107-1753. (218)233-8397. Executive Director: Mark D. Madson. For "American citizens." Biennial award.

Purpose: "To select an orchestral composition by an American composer to be premiered by the Fargo-Moorhead Symphony. The objective of this award is to stimulate and encourage the writing and performance of works by American composers."
Requirements: "Manuscript must be of medium length. Only manuscripts written or completed during the past 2 years and which have not been performed publicly will be considered. Scoring should be for standard symphonic or chamber orchestra instrumentation and should not include soloist." Deadline:September 30, 1990. Send manuscript with composer's name, address, telephone number and date of composition on cover sheet. Samples are not required.
Awards: Sigvald Thompson Composition Award Competition-one award of $2,500 will be made, plus the premiere performance of the winning entry by the Fargo-Moorhead Symphony Orchestra. "Composition will be screened by a local panel, and the finalists will be submitted to national judges for review and recommendation."
Tips: "Only manuscripts written or completed during the past 2 years and which have not been performed publicly will be considered. Date of composition must be included on cover sheet."

*VOCAL SONGWRITER'S CONTEST, P.O. Box 2438, Petersburg VA 23804. (804)733-5908 or (804)541-3333. President: Robert (Cham) Laughlin. For songwriters and composers. Annual award.
Purpose: Objective is "to recognize good songs and lyrics as well as the writers of same."
Requirements: "Original songs, lyrics, compositions only!" Deadline: March 31. Send for application. Samples of work are required with application. "Send cassette tape for songs; lyrics should be typed or neatly printed."
Award: Grand prize $100. 1st, 2nd and 3rd place entries in each category receive certificates.
Tips: "Prepare your song correctly for entry into the contest!"

WYOMING COUNTRY MUSIC FOUNDATION ANNUAL SONGWRITING CONTEST, WCMF Sussex Route, Kaycee WY 82639. (307)738-2303 or 836-2939. Estab. 1983. Executive and Promotional Director: Helen Ullery or Floyd Haynes. For songwriters, composers and performers. Annual award.
Purpose: "To promote and encourage upcoming talent both in songwriting and the performing arts."
Requirements: Applicants can be from any geographical area. Deadline: May 15. Send for application (include SASE). Samples are not required. Annual membership fee: $25; entry fee per song: $10. For gospel song entries and information, contact Helen D. Ullery, Sussex Rt., Kaycee, WY 82639; for country songs and information, contact Floyd Haynes, P.O. Box 132, Guensey, WY 82214.
Awards: "Top 10 country and Top 5 gospel songs are sent to Nashville for review; 50% of entry fees go back to the top winners. Contestants cannot have been in the top 50 in national charts in the last 10 years."

*YOUNG ARTIST AWARDS COMPETITION, Ventura County Symphony, P.O. Box 1088, Ventura CA 93002. (803)643-8646. Operations Manager: Lynda Collum. For performing artists. Annual award.
Purpose: "Goal is to recognize exceptional pre-professional artists, under the age of 31 and residing in the state of California."
Requirements: "Must be under the age of 31 as of the preliminary competition date and residing in the State of California." Deadline: early March. Send for application. Samples are not required.
Awards: $1,000 to winner in each category (categorized by instrument, including voice); $100 to finalists in each category; $500 best performance award. One time cash award given at conclusion of competition. Selection based solely on competition performance of required repertoire.

*YWCA STUDIO CLUB COMPETITION, 610 Lexington Ave., New York NY 10022. (212)735-9763. Auditions Coordinator: Mrs. Cora Ette Brown. For young opera singers age 17-35. Annual award.
Purpose: First prize $1,500; second prize $1,000, awarded to the winner from the final competition.
Requirements: Write or call for application; "you must sing opera, one song must be in English, one aria or an art song. We have auditions from September through March. The annual competition is always in May."

Glossary

A&R Director. Record company executive in charge of the Artists and Repertoire Department who is responsible for finding and developing new artists and matching songs with artists.

A/C. Adult Contemporary music.

ACM. Academy of Country Music.

Advance. Money paid to the songwriter or recording artist before regular royalty payment begins. Sometimes called "up front" money, advances are deducted from royalties.

AFM. American Federation of Musicians. A union for musicians and arrangers.

AFTRA. American Federation of Television and Radio Artists. A union for performers.

AIMP. Association of Independent Music Publishers.

Air play. The radio broadcast of a recording.

AOR. Album-Oriented Rock. A radio format which primarily plays selections from rock albums as opposed to hit singles.

Arrangement. An adaptation of a composition for a performance or recording, with consideration for the melody, harmony, instrumentation, tempo, style, etc.

ASCAP. American Society of Composers, Authors and Publishers. A performing rights organization.

A-side. The side of a single which is considered to have "hit" potential and is promoted as such by the record company.

Assignment. Transfer of rights to a song from writer to publisher.

Audiovisual. Refers to presentations which use audio backup for visual material.

Bed. Prerecorded music used as background material in commercials.

Beta. ½" videocassette format. The Beta System uses a smaller cassette than that used with the VHS system.

BMA. Black Music Association.

BMI. Broadcast Music, Inc. A performing rights organization.

B-side. The flip side of a single promoted by a record company. Sometimes the B-side contains the same song as the A-side so there will be no confusion as to which song should receive airplay.

Booking agent. Person who solicits work and schedules performances for entertainers.

Business manager. Person who handles the financial aspects of artistic careers.

b/w. Backed with. Usually refers to the B-side of a single.

C&W. Country and western.

CAPAC. Composers, Authors & Publishers Association of Canada, Ltd. A performing rights organization.

Capo. A movable bar which clamps onto the fingerboard of a guitar to uniformly raise the pitch of the strings.

CARAS. Canadian Academy of Recording Arts and Sciences. An association of individuals involved in the Canadian music and recording industry.

Catalog. The collected songs of one writer, or all songs handled by one publisher.

CD. Compact Disc (see below).

Chart. The written arrangement of a song.

Charts. The weekly trade magazines' lists of the bestselling records.

CHR. Comtemporary Hit Radio. Top 40 pop music.

CIRPA. Canadian Independent Record Producers Association.

CMA. Country Music Association.

CMPA. Church Music Publishers Association.

CMRRA. Canadian Musical Reproduction Rights Association. A mechanical rights agency.

Collaborator. Person who works with another in a creative endeavor.

Compact disc. A small disc (about 4.7 inches in diameter) holding digitally encoded music that is read by a laser beam in a CD player.

Co-publish. Two or more parties own publishing rights to the same song.

Copyright. The exclusive legal right giving the creator of a work the power to control the publishing, reproduction and selling of the work.

Cover record. A new version of a previously recorded song.

CRIA. Canadian Recording Industry Association.

Crossover. A song that becomes popular in two or more musical categories (i.e. country and pop).

Cut. Any finished recording; a selection from an LP. Also to record.

DAT. Digital Audio Tape. A professional and consumer audio cassette format for recording and playing back digitally-encoded material. DAT cassettes are approximately one-third smaller than conventional audio cassettes.

Demo. A recording of a song submitted as a demonstration of writer's or artist's skills.

Disc. A record.

Distributor. Marketing agent responsible for getting records from manufacturers to retailers.

Donut. A jingle with singing at the beginning and end and instrumental background in the middle. Ad copy is recorded over the middle section.

Engineer. A specially trained individual who operates all recording studio equipment.

EP. Extended play record (usually 12″) containing more selections than a standard single, but fewer than a standard LP.

Evergreen. Any song that remains popular year after year.

Exploit. To seek legitimate uses of a song for income.

Folio. A softcover collection of printed music prepared for sale.

GMA. Gospel Music Association.

Harry Fox Agency. Organization that collects mechanical royalties.

Hit. A song or record that achieves top 40 status.

Hook. A memorable "catch" phrase or melody line which is repeated in a song.

IMU. International Musicians Union.

Indie. An independent record label.

ips. Inches per second; a speed designation for tape recording.

IRC. International reply coupon, necessary for the return of materials sent out of the country. Available at most post offices.

Jingle. Usually a short verse set to music designed as a commercial message.

Label. Record company, or the "brand" name of the records it produces.

LASS. Los Angeles Songwriters Showcase.

Lead sheet. Written version (melody, chord symbols and lyric) of a song.

Leader. Plastic (non-recordable) tape at the beginning and between songs for ease in selection.

LP. Designation for long-playing record played at 33⅓ rpm.

Lyric sheet. A typed or written copy of a song's lyrics.

Market. A potential song or music buyer; also a demographic division of the record-buying public.

Master. Edited and mixed tape used in the production of records; a very high-quality recording; the best or original copy of a recording from which copies are made.

Maxi-single. The cassette equivalent of a 12″ single. Also called Maxi-cassettes or Maxi-plays. (See 12″ Single.)

Mechanical right. The right to profit from the physical reproduction of a song.

Mechanical royalty. Money earned from record and tape sales.

Mix. To blend a multi-track recording into the desired balance of sound.

MOR. Middle of the road. Easy-listening popular music.

Ms. Manuscript.

Music jobber. A wholesale distributor of printed music.

Music publisher. A company that evaluates songs for commercial potential, finds artists to record them, finds other uses (such as TV or film) for the songs, collects income generated by the songs and protects copyrights from infringement.

NAIRD. National Association of Independent Record Distributors.

NARAS. National Academy of Recording Arts and Sciences.

NARM. National Association of Record Merchandisers.

NAS. National Academy of Songwriters, formerly Songwriters Resources and Services (SRS).

Needle-drop. Use of a prerecorded cut from a stock music house in an audiovisual soundtrack.

NMPA. National Music Publishers Association.

NSAI. Nashville Songwriters Association International.

One-stop. A wholesale distributor of records (and sometimes videocassettes, blank tapes and record accessories), representing several manufacturers to record stores, retailers and jukebox operators.

Overdub. To record an additional part (vocal or instrumental) onto a basic multi-track recording. To sweeten.

Payola. Dishonest payment to broadcasters in exchange for airplay.

Performing rights. A specific right granted by US copyright law that protects a composition from being publicly performed without the owner's permission.

Performing rights organization. An organization that collects income from the public performance of songs written by its members and then proportionally distributes this income to the individual copyright holder based on the number of performances of each song.

Personal manager. A person who represents artists, in numerous and varying ways, to develop and enhance their careers. Personal managers may negotiate contracts, hire and dismiss other agencies and personnel relating to the artist's career, screen offers and consult with prospective employers, review possible material, help with artist promotions and perform many services.

Piracy. The unauthorized reproduction and selling of printed or recorded music.

Pitch. To attempt to sell a song by audition; the sales talk.

Playlist. List of songs that a radio station will play.

Plug. A favorable mention, broadcast or performance of a song; to pitch a song.

Points. A negotiable percentage paid to producers and artists for records sold.

Press. To manufacture a record.

PROCAN. Performing Rights Organization of Canada Ltd.

Producer. Person who supervises every aspect of recording a song or album.

Product. Records, CDs and tapes available for sale.

Production company. Company that specializes in producing jingle packages for advertising agencies. May also refer to companies that specialize in audiovisual programs.

Professional manager. Member of a music publisher's staff who screens submitted material and tries to get the company's catalog of songs recorded.

Program director. Radio station employee who screens records and develops a playlist of songs that station will broadcast.

PRS. Performing Rights Society of England.

PSA. Public Service Announcement: a free broadcast "advertisement" for a non-profit service organization.

Public domain. Any composition with an expired, lapsed or invalid copyright.

Publish. To reproduce music in a saleable form and distribute to the public by sale or other transfer of ownership (rent, lease or lending).

Purchase license. Fee paid for music used from a stock music library.

Query. A letter of inquiry to a potential song buyer soliciting his interest.

R&B. Rhythm and blues.

Rack jobber. A wholesaler of records, tapes and accessories to retailers and mass-merchandisers not primarily in the record business (e.g. department stores).

Rate. The percentage of royalty as specified by contract.

Release. Any record issued by a record company.

Residuals. In advertising or television, payments to singers and musicians for subsequent use of a performance.

RIAA. Recording Industry Associations of America.

Royalty. Percentage of money earned from the sale of records or use of a song.

RPM. Revolutions per minute. Refers to phonograph turntable speed.

SAE. Self-addressed envelope (with no postage attached).

SASE. Self-addressed stamped envelope.

Self-contained. A band or recording act that writes all their own material.

SESAC. A performing rights organization.

SFX. Sound effects.

Shop. To pitch songs to a number of companies or publishers.

Showcase. A presentation of new artists or songs.

Single. 45 rpm record with only one song per side. A 12″ single refers to a long version of one song on a 12″ disc, usually used for dance music.

Solicited. Songs or materials that have been requested.

Song shark. Person who deals with songwriters deceptively for his own profit.

The Songwriters Guild of America. Organization for songwriters, formerly called AGAC.

Soundtrack. The audio, including music and narration, of a film, videotape or audiovisual program.

Split publishing. To divide publishing rights between two or more publishers.

Staff writer. A salaried songwriter who writes exclusively for one publishing firm.

Standard. A song popular year after year; an evergreen.

Statutory royalty rate. The maximum payment for mechanical rights guaranteed by law that a record company may pay the songwriter and his publisher for each record or tape sold.

Stiff. The first recording of a song that commercially fails.

Subpublishing. Certain rights granted by a US publisher to a foreign publisher in exchange for promoting the US catalog in his territory.

Sweeten. See Overdub.

Synchronization. Technique of timing a musical soundtrack to action on film or video.

Synchronization rights. Rights to use a composition in film or video.

Take. Either an attempt to record a vocal or instrumental part, or an acceptable recording of a performance.

Top 40. The first forty songs on the pop music charts at any given time. Also refers to a style of music which emulates that heard on the current top 40.

Track. Divisions of a recording tape (e.g., 24-track tape) that can be individually recorded in the studio, then mixed into a finished master.

Trades. Publications that cover the music industry.

12″ Single. A twelve inch record containing one or more remixes of a song, originally intended for dance club play.

U/C. Urban contemporary music.

U-matic. ¾″ professional videocassette format.

Unsolicited. Songs or materials that were not requested and are not expected.

VHS. ½″ videocassette format. The VHS system uses a larger cassette than that used with the Beta system.

Videocassette. Tape manufactured for video cassette recorder (VCR) that records and reproduces audiovisual programs.

Work. To pitch or shop a song.

Index

Can't find a listing? Check the end of each market section for the '90-'91 Changes lists. These lists include any market listings from the 1990 edition which were either not verified or deleted in this edition.

Can't find a listing? Check the end of each market section for the '90-'91 Changes lists. These lists include any market listings from the 1990 edition which were either not verified or deleted in this edition.

Can't find a listing? Check the end of each market section for the '90-'91 Changes lists. These lists include any market listings from the 1990 edition which were either not verified or deleted in this edition.

Can't find a listing? Check the end of each market section for the '90-'91 Changes lists. These lists include any market listings from the 1990 edition which were either not verified or deleted in this edition.

Can't find a listing? Check the end of each market section for the '90–'91 Changes lists. These lists include any market listings from the 1990 edition which were either not verified or deleted in this edition.

Can't find a listing? Check the end of each market section for the '90-'91 Changes lists. These lists include any market listings from the 1990 edition which were either not verified or deleted in this edition.

Can't find a listing? Check the end of each market section for the '90-'91 Changes lists. These lists include any market listings from the 1990 edition which were either not verified or deleted in this edition.

Can't find a listing? Check the end of each market section for the '90-'91 Changes lists. These lists include any market listings from the 1990 edition which were either not verified or deleted in this edition.

OTHER BOOKS TO HELP YOU MAKE
MONEY AND THE MOST OF
YOUR MUSIC TALENT

Jingles: How to Write, Produce, & Sell Commercial Music, by Al Stone 144 pages/$18.95, paperback

Music Publishing: A Songwriter's Guide, by Randy Poe 144 pages/$18.95, paperback

Making Money Making Music (No Matter Where You Live), by James Dearing 192 pages/ $17.95, paperback

Beginning Songwriter's Answer Book, by Paul Zollo 128 pages/$16.95, paperback

Playing for Pay: How To Be A Working Musician, by James Gibson 160 pages/$17.95, paperback

You Can Write Great Lyrics, by Pamela Phillips Oland 192 pages/$17.95, paperback

Protecting Your Songs & Yourself, by Kent J. Klavens 112 pages/$15.95, paperback

Gigging: The Musician's Underground Touring Directory, by Michael Dorf & Robert Appel 224 pages/$14.95, paperback

The Craft & Business of Songwriting, by John Braheny 322 pages/$19.95, hardcover

The Craft of Lyric Writing, by Sheila Davis 350 pages/$19.95, hardcover

Successful Lyric Writing: A Step-by-Step Course & Workbook, by Sheila Davis 292 pages/ $18.95, paperback

Getting Noticed: A Musician's Guide to Publicity & Self-Promotion, by James Gibson 240 pages/$12.95, paperback

The Performing Artist's Handbook, by Janice Papolos 219 pages/$12.95, paperback

The Songwriter's Guide to Making Great Demos, by Harvey Rachlin 192 pages/$12.95, paperback

Writing Music for Hit Songs, by Jai Josefs 256 pages/$17.95, hardcover

Making It in the New Music Business, by James Riordan 352 pages/$18.95

The Songwriter's Guide to Collaboration, by Walter Carter 178 pages/$12.95, paperback

How to Pitch & Promote Your Songs, by Fred Koller 144 pages/$12.95, paperback

A complete catalog of all Writer's Digest Books is available FREE by writing to the address shown below. To order books directly from the publisher, include $3.00 postage and handling for one book, $1.00 for each additional book. Ohio residents add 5½% sales tax. Allow 30 days for delivery.

Writer's Digest Books
1507 Dana Avenue
Cincinnati, Ohio 45207

Credit card orders call TOLL-FREE
1-800-289-0963

Prices subject to change without notice

Demo Materials Checklist _____

Does your demo package include

- ✔ a quality cassette with a clean recording of your best songs?

- ✔ a sturdy but easy-to-open mailer that will get your demo to its destination securely?

- ✔ a brief, neat cover letter of introduction?

- ✔ typed or clearly printed lyric sheets?